Organic Chemistry
Principles and Mechanisms

Organic Chemistry
Principles and Mechanisms

Volume 2

★ ★ ★ ★ ★

Joel M. Karty, Ph.D.
Elon University

W. W. Norton & Company
New York • London

W. W. Norton & Company has been independent since its founding in 1923, when William Warder Norton and Mary D. Herter Norton first published lectures delivered at the People's Institute, the adult education division of New York City's Cooper Union. The Nortons soon expanded their programs beyond the Institute, publishing books by celebrated academics from America and abroad. By mid-century, the two major pillars of Norton's publishing program—trade books and college texts—were firmly established. In the 1950s, the Norton family transferred control of the company to its employees, and today—with a staff of four hundred and a comparable number of trade, college, and professional titles published each year—W. W. Norton & Company stands as the largest and oldest publishing house owned wholly by its employees.

Printed in the United States of America

ISBN: 978-0-393-13684-5

W. W. Norton & Company, Inc., 500 Fifth Avenue, New York, N.Y. 10110
www.wwnorton.com

W. W. Norton & Company Ltd., Castle House, 75/76 Wells Street, London W1T 3QT

Chapter 15. Nucleophilic Addition to Polar π Bonds. 1: Addition of Strong Nucleophiles 1

Chapter 16. Nucleophilic Addition to Polar π Bonds. 2: Addition of Weak Nucleophiles; Acid and Base Catalysis 55

Chapter 18. Nucleophilic Addition-Elimination Reactions. 1: The General Mechanism Involving Strong Nucleophiles 170

Chapter 19. Nucleophilic Addition-Elimination Reactions. 2: Weak Nucleophiles 219

Chapter 21. Electrophilic Addition to Nonpolar π Bonds 2: Reactions Involving Cyclic Transition States 347

Chapter 22. Electrophilic Aromatic Substitution. 1: Substitution on Benzene and Symmetric Benzene Rings 400

Chapter 23. Electrophilic Aromatic Substitution. 2: Substitution Involving Mono- and Disubstituted Benzene and Other Aromatic Rings 448

Chapter 24. The Diels-Alder Reaction and Other Pericyclic Reactions 506

Chapter 25. Reactions Involving Free Radicals 560

Interchapter 2: Fragmentation Pathways in Mass Spectrometry 620

Chapter 26. Polymers 634

Credits for spectra

All NMR and IR spectra were obtained with permission from
- **Aldrich Spectral Libraries**, Sigma-Aldrich
- **Spectral Database for Organic Compounds, SDBS, AIST Japan**, *T.Yamaji, T.Saito, K.Hayamizu, M.Yanagisawa and O.Yamamoto, S.Kinugasa, K.Tanabe and T.Tamura*

All mass spectra were obtained with permission from
- **NIST Chemistry WebBook, NIST Standard Reference Database Number 69**, Eds. P.J. Linstrom and W.G. Mallard, National Institute of Standards and Technology, Gaithersburg MD, 20899, http://webbook.nist.gov

Chapter 15. Nucleophilic Addition to Polar π Bonds. 1: Addition of Strong Nucleophiles

Introduction

Species that have double or triple bonds, and therefore possess at least one π bond, take part in some of the most important reactions in organic chemistry. How such a species reacts depends largely upon whether or not its π bond is polar. In this chapter we will examine reactions involving *polar* π bonds—that is, π bonds joining atoms of significantly different electronegativity. In Chapter 20, we will examine reactions involving *nonpolar* π bonds.

Far and away the most common polar π bond is the one in the carbonyl (C=O) group. This group is present in ketones and aldehydes ($R_2C{=}O$ and RCH=O), carboxylic acids (RCO_2H), esters (RCO_2R), amides ($RCONR_2$), acid halides (RCO_2X) and acid anhydrides (RCO_2COR). Of these, we will focus primarily on ketones and aldehydes in this chapter because the remaining carbonyl-containing functional groups behave somewhat differently—we will study those in Chapters 18 and 19. Although less common, other polar π bonds encountered in organic molecules include those in imine (C=N) and nitrile (C≡N) functional groups, which we will also study in this chapter.

Both strong and weak nucleophiles can add to polar π bonds, and the mechanisms of such reactions are quite similar. As we will see, however, the addition of a weak nucleophile often requires either acid catalysis or base catalysis. Therefore, in this chapter we focus primarily on the addition of strong nucleophiles, which in general bear a full negative charge and can thus be represented by Nu^-. In Chapter 16, we will see how the reaction differs when the nucleophile being added is weak.

CHAPTER OBJECTIVES
Upon Completing This Chapter You Should Be Able To:

- Draw the general mechanism for the addition of a strong nucleophile to a polar π bond.
- Account for the difference between aldehydes and ketones in their relative susceptibility to nucleophilic addition.
- Draw the general mechanism for both *direct addition (1,2-addition)* and *conjugate addition (1,4-addition)* to an *α,β-unsaturated polar π bond.*
- Determine whether nucleophilic addition to an α,β-unsaturated carbonyl favors the direct-addition product or the conjugate-addition product, and explain the role of *reversibility* in such an outcome.
- Specify which solvents are compatible with hydride reagents such as $NaBH_4$ and $LiAlH_4$, and with organometallic reagents such as R-MgBr and R-Li.
- Determine whether the existence of a proposed Grignard or alkyllithium reagent is feasible, based on functional group compatibility.
- Account for the behavior of *lithium dialkylcuprates (R_2CuLi)* with regard to direct vs. conjugate addition.
- Predict the major organic product of a *Wittig reaction*, and draw its complete, detailed mechanism.
- Show how to synthesize a *Wittig reagent* from an alkyl halide precursor.
- Provide the mechanism for the *sulfonium ylide epoxidation* of a ketone or aldehyde, and predict the major organic product.

15.1. A REVIEW OF THE GENERAL MECHANISM: ADDITION OF STRONG NUCLEOPHILES

As we saw in Chapter 8, a nucleophile tends to form a bond with the atom at the positive end of a polar π bond. Whereas the nucleophile is relatively electron-rich, the partially positive atom of the π bond is relatively electron-poor. An example with a generic strong, negatively charged nucleophile is shown in Equation 15-1a.

General Mechanism for Nucleophilic Addition to a Polar π Bond

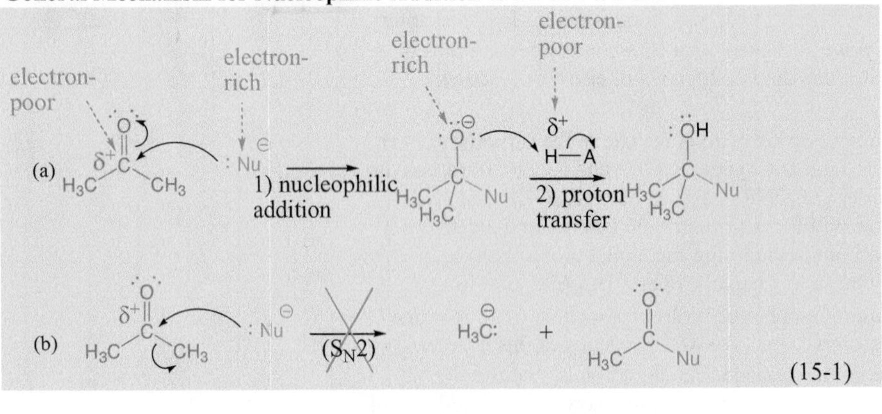

(15-1)

To avoid exceeding the octet on the atom attacked by the nucleophile, the π bond is broken and the pair of electrons from the π bond becomes a lone pair on the more electronegative atom of the π bond. Although we can instead envision a single bond being broken in an S_N2 step (Equation 15-1b), breaking of the π bond is typically favored, primarily because it is the weaker bond.

As shown in Equation 15-1a, the immediate product of nucleophilic addition (step 1) is often a strong base because it possesses a relatively unstable negative charge. Sometimes, species already present in the reaction mixture, such as the solvent, are acidic enough to protonate that product (step 2). Otherwise, an acid can be added in a subsequent step to bring about this protonation—a procedure called an acid work-up (Section 11.8).

Your Turn 15.1. The reaction below is similar to that in Equation 15-1a. In each step, label each species as either "electron-rich" or "electron-poor," draw in the appropriate curved arrows, and under each reaction arrow name the type of elementary step involved.

O + :Nu⊖ ⟶ ⊖O Nu ⟶(H—A) HO Nu

Solved Problem 15.1. For the reaction below, draw the complete, detailed mechanism and predict the product.

O, H ⟶(KCN / H_2O) ?

Think. What nucleophile is generated when KCN dissolves in water? Which atom will it attack? Which bond is most easily broken in the process? What is the role of water?

Solve. KCN is ionic, consisting of K^+ and NC^- ions. Therefore, in water KCN dissolves as K^+ and NC^-, the latter being a strong nucleophile. NC^- will subsequently attack the electron-poor carbonyl carbon, breaking the π bond from the double bond. The resulting O^- is protonated by the weakly acidic H_2O.

O, H + ⊖:CN ⟶ ⊖:O:, H, CN ⟶(H—OH) :O—H, H, CN + ⊖:OH

Problem 15.1. Draw the complete, detailed mechanism for the following reaction and draw the product.

O, CH_3 ⟶($NaSCH_3$ / CH_3CH_2OH) ?

Stereoselectivity is a concern for nucleophilic addition when the carbon atom that is attacked becomes a stereocenter in the product. An example is shown in Equation 15-2.

nucleophile can attack from either side of the carbon's plane

racemic mixture of enantiomers

H_3C CH_3 NH + :Nu⊖ ⟶ H_3C CH_3 ⊖:NH, Nu + H_3C CH_3 Nu, NH⊖ (15-2)

Because the carbon atom of the polar π bond is planar, a nucleophile can attack from either side. Thus, as we learned in Chapter 9, the result is a mixture of *R* and *S* stereochemical configurations at the bond formation site. A *racemic mixture* of enantiomers is formed if the reactants are achiral and the reaction takes place in an achiral environment. Otherwise, an unequal mixture of the *R* and *S* configurations is formed.

Your Turn 15.2. Circle and label each stereocenter in Equation 15-2.

We also found in Chapter 8 that nucleophilic addition tends to be *reversible* unless charge stability overwhelmingly favors products. In other words,

Only very strong nucleophiles undergo irreversible nucleophilic addition.

As we can see in Table 15-1, these are nucleophiles in which a negative charge is found on either a carbon atom or a hydrogen atom and is not stabilized significantly by resonance or inductive effects. A Grignard reagent such as CH_3MgBr behaves much like CH_3^- and therefore adds irreversibly. Lithium aluminum hydride ($LiAlH_4$) is a strong donor of hydride (H^-), which also adds irreversibly.

Table 15-1. Reversibility in Nucleophilic Addition

Nucleophiles that add *reversibly*	**Nucleophiles that add *irreversibly***
HO^-, RO^-	R-MgBr (R^-)
H_2N^-, R_2N^-	R-Li (R^-)
Cl^-, Br^-, I^-	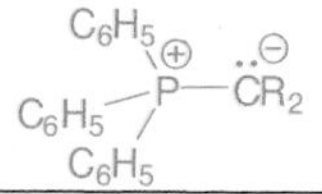 $(C_6H_5)_3\overset{\oplus}{P}–\overset{\ominus}{C}R_2$
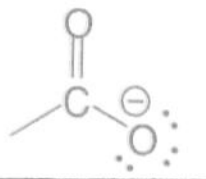 $CH_3C(=O)O^-$ (carboxylate)	$LiAlH_4$ (H^-)
$N{\equiv}C^-$	
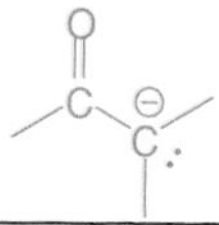 $C(=O)–\overset{\ominus}{C}$ (enolate)	
R_2CuLi (R^-)	

The cyanide anion ($N{\equiv}C^-$), however, adds reversibly despite the fact that the negative charge is localized on the carbon atom. This is in large part because the negative charge is stabilized considerably by the *effective electronegativity* of the *sp*-hybridization on C (Chapter 3). We have previously seen this effect of hybridization on the acidity of a terminal alkyne, RC≡CH, whose pK_a is about 25—some 25 orders of magnitude (10^{25} times) stronger than saturated alkanes. The NC^- anion is further stabilized by the electron-withdrawing effects of the electronegative nitrogen atom.

Enolate anions ($O{=}C{-}C^-$) also add reversibly despite, once again, a negative charge on carbon. In this case, the negative charge is stabilized not only by inductive effects of the oxygen atom but also by resonance with the carbonyl group.

Your Turn 15.3. In the structures below, draw the inductive arrow that shows how the negative charge on C is stabilized. Draw the missing resonance structure of the enolate anion that illustrates how its negative charge is further stabilized.

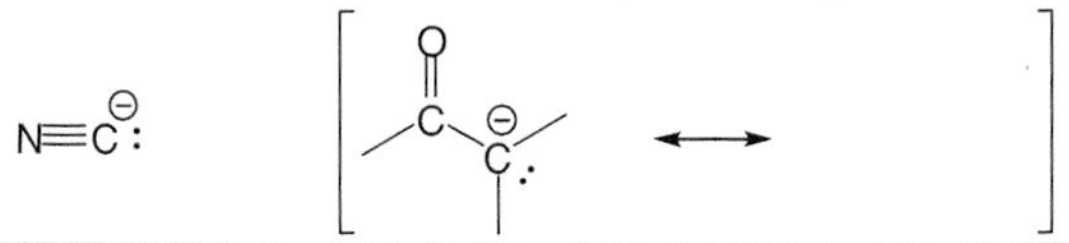

Solved Problem 15.2. Do you think that CH_3S^- will add *reversibly* or *irreversibly* to a carbonyl? Explain your answer.

Think. What formal charges would exist in the reactants and products, and on which atoms would they be located? Does charge stability strongly favor the products of nucleophilic addition? How might this affect reversibility?

Solve. An example of a nucleophilic addition step involving the nucleophile in question is shown below.

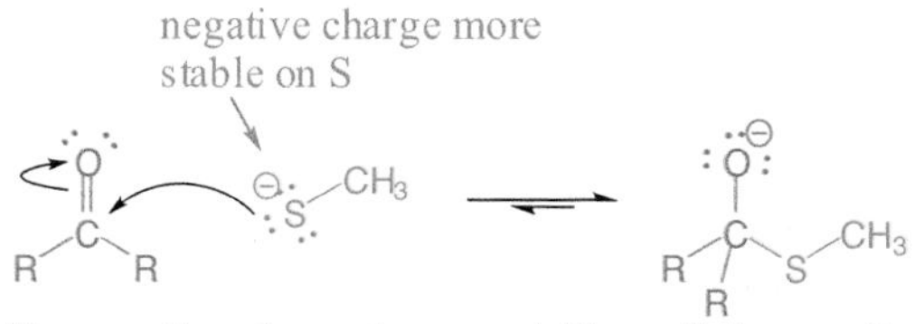

negative charge more stable on S

The negative charge is more stable on S than on O, so the reactants are favored. Because the reaction does not heavily favor products, it is reversible.

Problem 15.2. Do you think that F^- will add *reversibly* or *irreversibly* to a carbonyl? Explain.

15.2. LEAVING GROUPS ON THE POLAR π BOND

In this chapter, the polar π bonds we will consider are those in which the electron-deficient atom of the π bond (the carbon atom) is singly bonded only to alkyl groups and/or hydrogen atoms—that is, the π bonds of aldehydes, ketones, imines, and nitriles. As mentioned earlier, other compounds containing polar π bonds, such as amides, $RCONR_2$, and esters, RCO_2R, behave somewhat differently, so their reactions will be covered in Chapter 18. Nevertheless, it is helpful for the purposes of this chapter to understand the reason for this difference in reactivity.

Notice in Table 15-1 that a nucleophile such as CH_3O^- adds reversibly to a carbonyl group—the reverse step, in which CH_3O^- is *eliminated* and a C=O bond is regenerated, is also possible. Suppose, then, that a nucleophile were to attack an ester, as shown in Equation 15-3. If the nucleophilic addition is reversible, the nucleophile can later be eliminated to regenerate the initial ester (Equation 15-3a). However, a second reaction can also occur: The CH_3O group of the ester can be eliminated in the form of CH_3O^-. In other words, the CH_3O group of the ester can act as a *leaving group*. When this occurs, a C=O bond is indeed regenerated, but the overall product may be quite different from the initial ester.

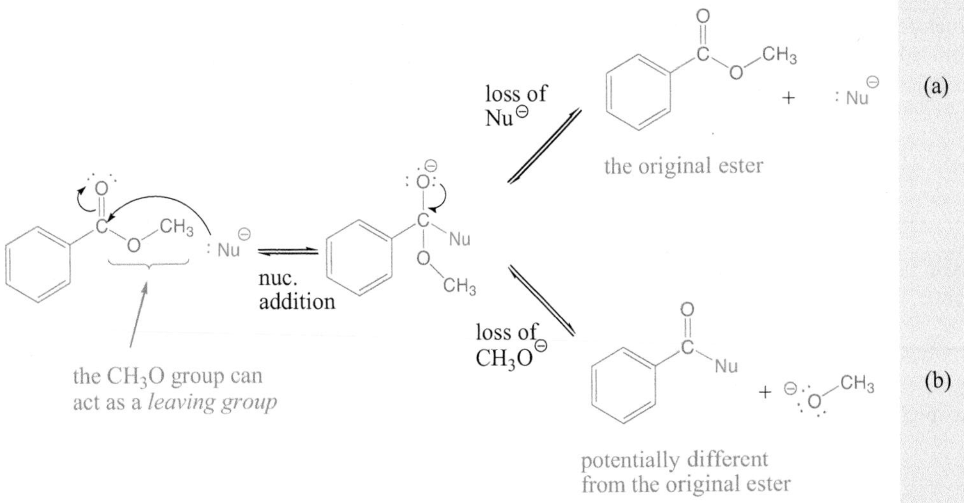

nuc. addition
loss of $Nu^{\ominus}$
the original ester
(a)
loss of $CH_3O^{\ominus}$
potentially different from the original ester
(b)
the CH_3O group can act as a *leaving group*

(15-3)

On the other hand, Table 15-1 illustrates that the *very* strong nucleophiles R^- and H^- add *irreversibly* to polar π bonds; once they add in, they are not subsequently eliminated. Therefore,

Hydrogen atoms and alkyl (R) groups normally do not act as leaving groups.

Consequently, as illustrated in Equation 15-4, if a nucleophile adds reversibly to a ketone or aldehyde, only that nucleophile can subsequently be eliminated. The same is true for an imine or nitrile. With this restriction, the only product we need to consider is that of nucleophilic addition.

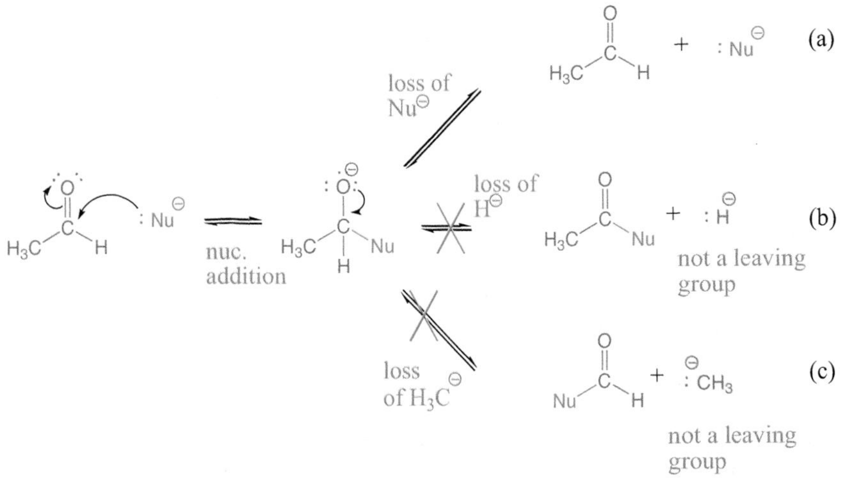

nuc. addition
loss of $Nu^{\ominus}$
(a)
loss of $H^{\ominus}$
not a leaving group
(b)
loss of $H_3C^{\ominus}$
not a leaving group
(c)

(15-4)

Your Turn 15.4. Each of the following compounds has a leaving group attached to the carbonyl carbon. Circle each leaving group.

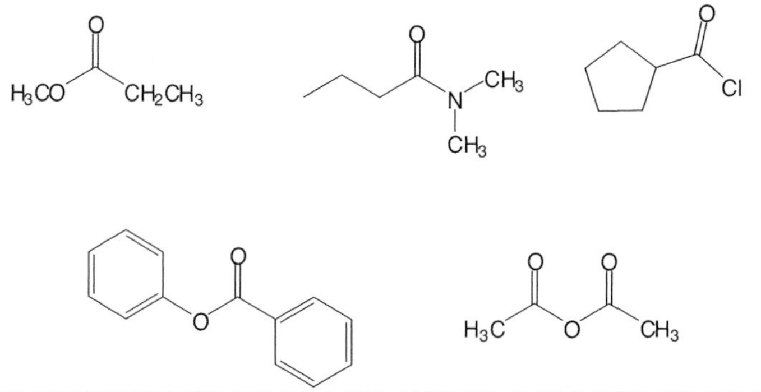

H_3CO CH_2CH_3 CH_3 N CH_3 Cl

H_3C O CH_3

15.3. RELATIVE REACTIVITY OF KETONES AND ALDEHYDES IN NUCLEOPHILIC ADDITION

Ketones and aldehydes exhibit very similar chemical behavior because they are quite similar structurally. However, the nucleophilic addition reactions they undergo differ noticeably in both thermodynamics and kinetics:

> Nucleophilic attack at a carbonyl carbon tends to be (1) more energetically favorable and (2) faster for an aldehyde than for a comparable ketone.

These points are exemplified in Table 15-2, which presents both equilibrium and rate data for *hydration* of three different carbonyl-containing compounds. (As we will see later, the key step in the mechanism of a hydration reaction is a nucleophilic addition.)

Table 15-2. Extent and Rate of Carbonyl Hydration in Ketones and Aldehydes

Reaction	Relative rate constants[a]	Percent hydration at equilibrium[b]
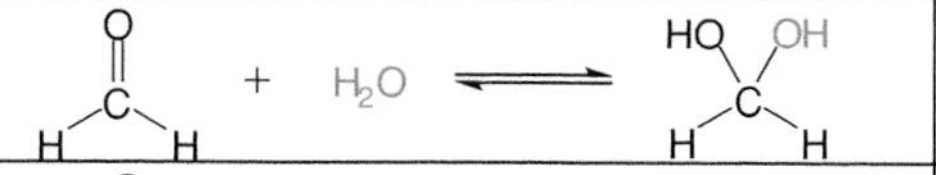 $H_2C{=}O + H_2O \rightleftharpoons H_2C(OH)_2$	5×10^5	> 99.9%
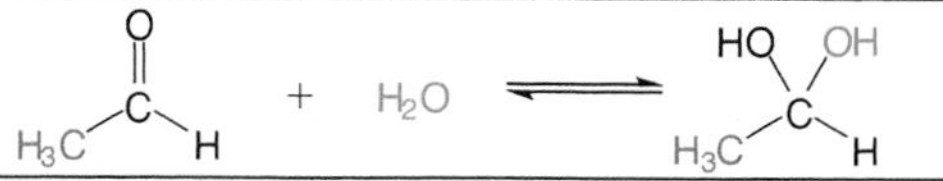 $H_3C{-}CHO + H_2O \rightleftharpoons H_3C{-}CH(OH)_2$	2×10^3	57%
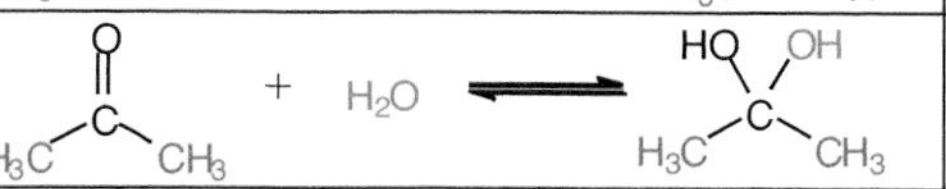 $(H_3C)_2C{=}O + H_2O \rightleftharpoons (H_3C)_2C(OH)_2$	1	< 1%

[a] Reactions take place in water. [b] Reactions take place in methanol.

Notice that both the rate of hydration and the extent of hydration at equilibrium are greater for the aldehydes than for the ketone. Both of these results can be explained by steric effects associated with the bulky alkyl groups of the ketone, as shown in Figure 15-1. In a ketone, the *steric repulsion* from the two alkyl groups on the carbonyl carbon (Figure 15-1a, left) make it difficult for the nucleophile to attack. Furthermore, each bulky alkyl group in the hydrate product (Figure 15-1a, right) crashes into the lone pairs on oxygen, generating *steric strain* and decreasing stability. On the other hand, as shown in Figure 15-1b, an aldehyde has at most one alkyl group bonded to the carbonyl carbon, so both of these steric effects are diminished.

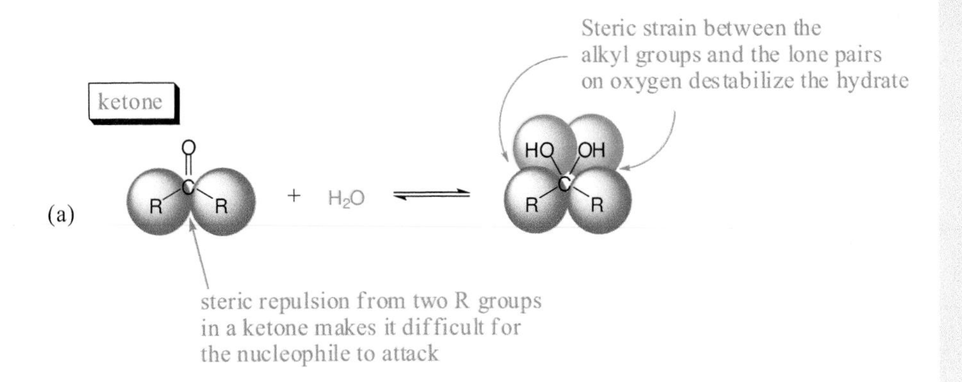

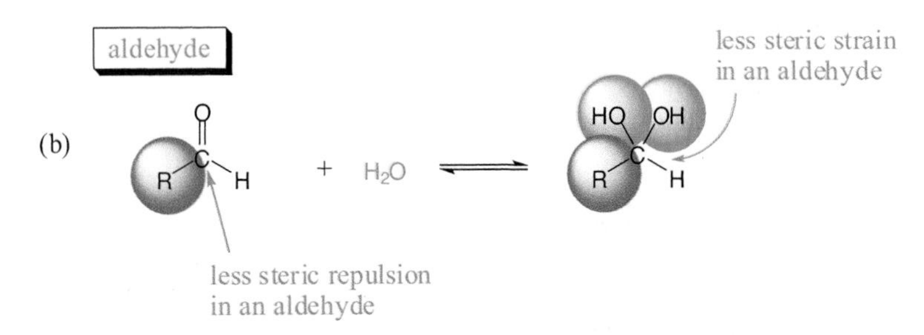

Figure 15-1. Steric Effects in Nucleophilic Addition **(a)** In a ketone, steric repulsion by each bulky alkyl group (left) makes it difficult for a nucleophile to attack. Steric strain in the hydrate product (right) decreases stability. **(b)** In an aldehyde, there is at most one bulky alkyl group, so steric effects are decreased.

Another reason for the greater reactivity of aldehydes compared to ketones is the greater stabilization of ketones by *inductive effects*, as illustrated in Figure 15-2. Recall from Section 7.6 that alkyl groups are electron-donating, so they decrease the concentration of positive charge at the carbonyl carbon. With less concentration of positive charge at that carbon, the carbonyl group is less susceptible to attack by a nucleophile bearing excess negative charge.

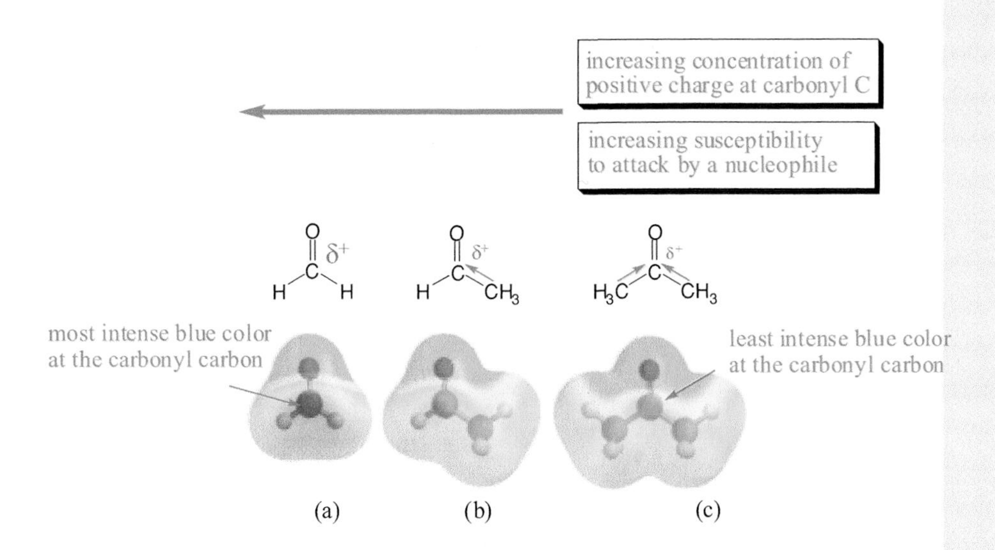

Figure 15-2. Inductive Effects in Nucleophilic Addition Electrostatic potential maps of **(a)** formaldehyde, **(b)** acetaldehyde, and **(c)** acetone. Additional alkyl groups bonded to the carbonyl carbon decrease its concentration of positive charge through induction, making it less reactive.

Your Turn 15.5. Label which of the following imines has the greatest concentration of positive charge at the C=N carbon, as well as which has the least concentration of positive charge. Which do you think is the more reactive imine? The least reactive?

Problem 15.3. Chloral, $Cl_3CCH{=}O$, forms a very stable hydrate called chloral hydrate. When dissolved in water, essentially 100% of chloral is hydrated. In contrast, the extent of hydration for ethanal (acetaldehyde) is much smaller (see Table 10-2). Explain why.

Problem 15.4. Which of the following would you expect to undergo hydration to a greater extent? Explain.

15.4. DIRECT ADDITION VERSUS CONJUGATE ADDITION

When a C=C double bond is conjugated to a polar π bond, as in propenal (Figure 15-3), two electron-deficient sites are present. Clearly, one of those sites is the carbonyl carbon, given that the highly electronegative oxygen atom is bonded to it. The other electrophilic site is the carbon atom *beta* to (two carbons away from) the carbonyl. We can see why this is so by examining one of its resonance contributors, which places a formal negative charge on the oxygen atom and a formal positive charge on the beta carbon (Figure 15-3a). Although this resonance contributor is somewhat weak due to the charges present, its contribution to the resonance hybrid does indeed place a small partial positive charge on the beta carbon, as indicated in the electrostatic potential map (Figure 15-3b).

(a)

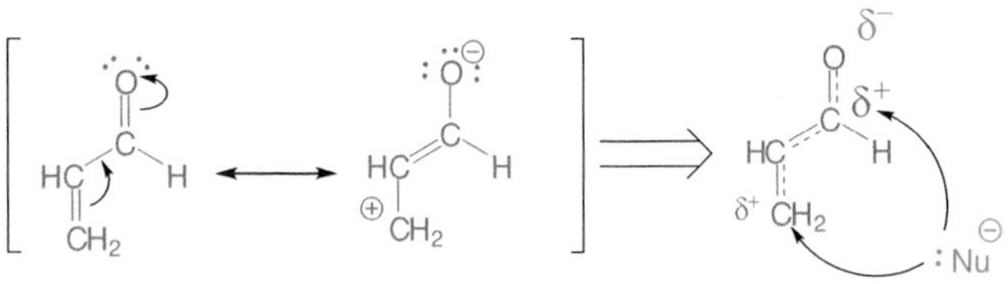

(b)

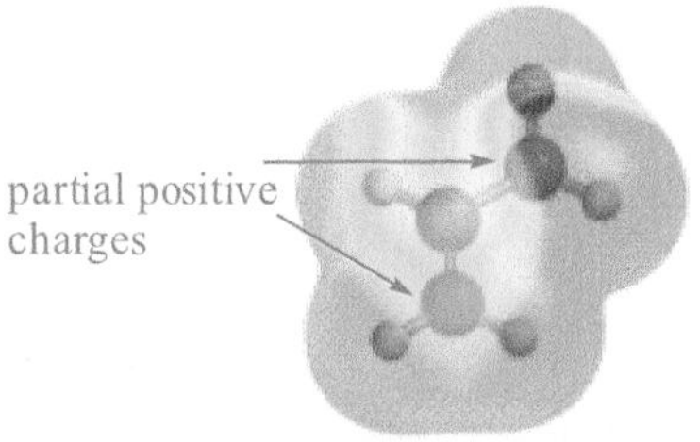

partial positive charges

Figure 15-3. Reactive Sites in an α,β-Unsaturated Carbonyl (a) Resonance structures of propenal are shown at left. The weak resonance contributor with separated charges generates a small partial positive charge on the β carbon in the resonance hybrid at right. Thus a nucleophile can attack at either the carbonyl carbon or the β carbon. **(b)** An electrostatic potential map of propenal, showing the partial positive charge (blue) on both the carbonyl carbon and the β carbon.

Your Turn 15.6. In the molecule below, circle and label the two electron-deficient sites.

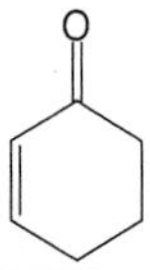

Given these *two electrophilic sites* in an **α,β-unsaturated carbonyl**, nucleophiles in general can attack at two positions—either at the carbonyl carbon itself (Equation 15-5), or at the beta carbon (Equation 15-6).

Mechanism for Direct Addition (1,2-addition) to an α,β-Unsaturated Carbonyl

attack at carbonyl C

1) nuc. additon

2) proton transfer

species add to adjacent atoms

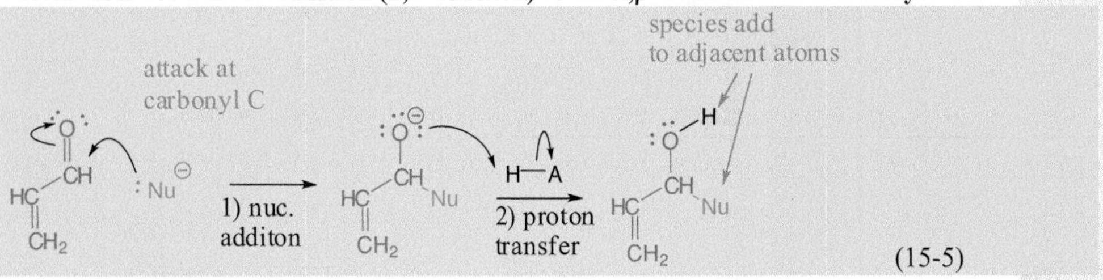

(15-5)

Mechanism for Conjugate Addition (1,4-addition) to an α,β-Unsaturated Carbonyl

species add to carbonyl oxygen and β carbon

attack at the β carbon

1) nuc. additon)

2) proton transfer

3 & 4) tautomerization

enol form

keto form

(15-6)

Attack of the nucleophile at the carbonyl carbon is called **1,2-addition**, or **direct addition**, because after protonation in the second step, species have added to adjacent atoms, which are said to be in a 1,2-positioning. Attack at the beta carbon, on the other hand, is called **1,4-addition**, or **conjugate addition**. After protonation in the second step, species have added to atoms separated by three bonds, which are said to be in a 1,4-positioning.

Notice in Equation 15-6 that the 1,4-addition product is an enol. As we saw in Sections 6.6c and 9.7e.1, this enol form will rapidly undergo *tautomerization* to generate the more stable keto form as the major product.

Your Turn 15.7. In the space provided here, draw the mechanism that converts the enol in Equation 15-6 into its keto form. (You may wish to review Section 9.7e.1.)

It is worth noting that if a carbon-nucleophile adds via conjugate addition, thereby forming a carbon-carbon bond, the process is called a **Michael reaction**, after the American chemist Arthur Michael. Over the years, however, the term *Michael reaction* has evolved into a generic description of conjugate additions involving any nucleophile.

Which of the two possible nucleophilic addition mechanisms dominates—i.e., direct addition or conjugate addition—depends in large part on the nature of the nucleophile. For example, CH_3O^- attacks propenal predominantly via conjugate addition (Equation 15-7), whereas $C_6H_{11}MgBr$ (in which $C_6H_{11}^-$ is the nucleophile) attacks largely via direct addition (Equation 15-8).

major product

CH_3ONa / CH_3OH

80%

(15-7)

major product

1) cyclohexyl-MgBr, reflux 1.5 hr

2) H_2O

71%

(15-8)

In general,

- Nucleophiles that add *reversibly* to the carbonyl group yield the *conjugate addition* product as the major product.
- Nucleophiles that add *irreversibly* to the carbonyl group yield the *direct addition* product as the major product.

Your Turn 15.8. Using Table 15-1, determine whether the nucleophilic addition reactions in Equations 15-7 and 15-8 are *reversible* or *irreversible.* Next to each reaction, write "reversible addition" or "irreversible addition."

Why does the major product depend upon the reversibility of the nucleophilic addition reaction? The answer stems from the fact that in general *the conjugate addition product is the thermodynamic product and the direct addition product is the kinetic product*. One reason why the conjugate addition product is the thermodynamic product—that is, the more stable product—is charge stability. Notice from Equation 15-6 that the immediate product of conjugate addition is an enolate anion, which, as shown below at left, has a resonance-stabilized negative charge. The direct addition product (Equation 10-5) shown at right, on the other hand, possesses an isolated negative charge, and is therefore less stable.

Comment [JMK1]: Margin note.
The conjugate addition product is the one that is most stable. The direct addition product is the one that is produced most rapidly.

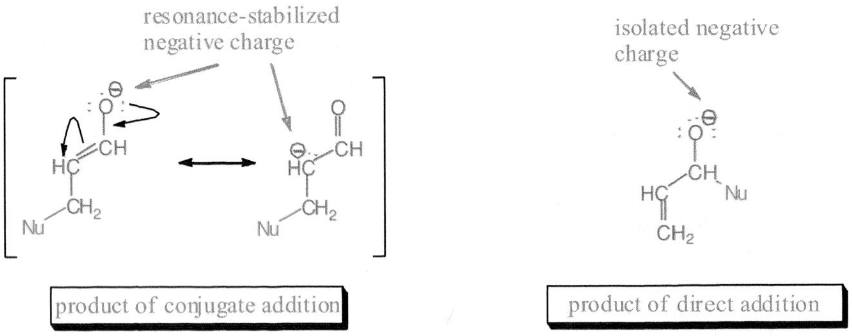

resonance-stabilized negative charge

isolated negative charge

product of conjugate addition

product of direct addition

A second reason that the conjugate addition product is the thermodynamic product involves the bond energies in the overall products. As shown below at left, the direct-addition product has a C=C double bond, whose average bond energy is 619 kJ/mol. On the other hand, the conjugate-addition product has a C=O bond, whose average bond energy is 720 kJ/mol. Thus, the conjugate-addition product is more stable.

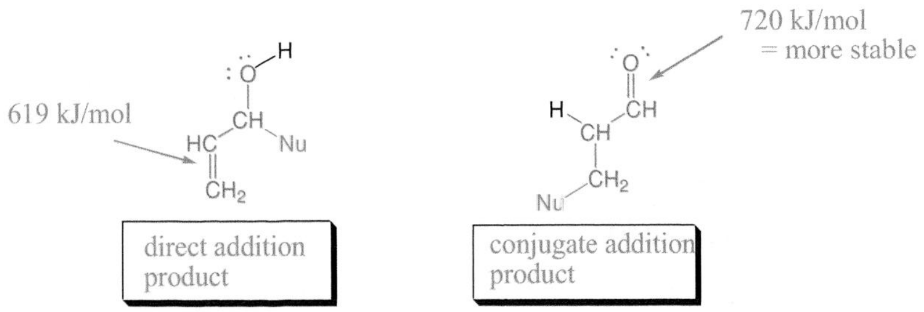

619 kJ/mol

720 kJ/mol = more stable

direct addition product

conjugate addition product

Saying that the direct addition product is generally the kinetic product means that it is formed faster, which implies that the path to form it has a lower activation energy (Figure 15-4). The activation energy of direct addition is lower because the concentration of positive charge is greater on the carbonyl carbon than on the beta carbon. Therefore, in the initial stages of nucleophilic attack, the nucleophile is better stabilized by its attraction to the carbonyl carbon than by its attraction to the beta carbon.

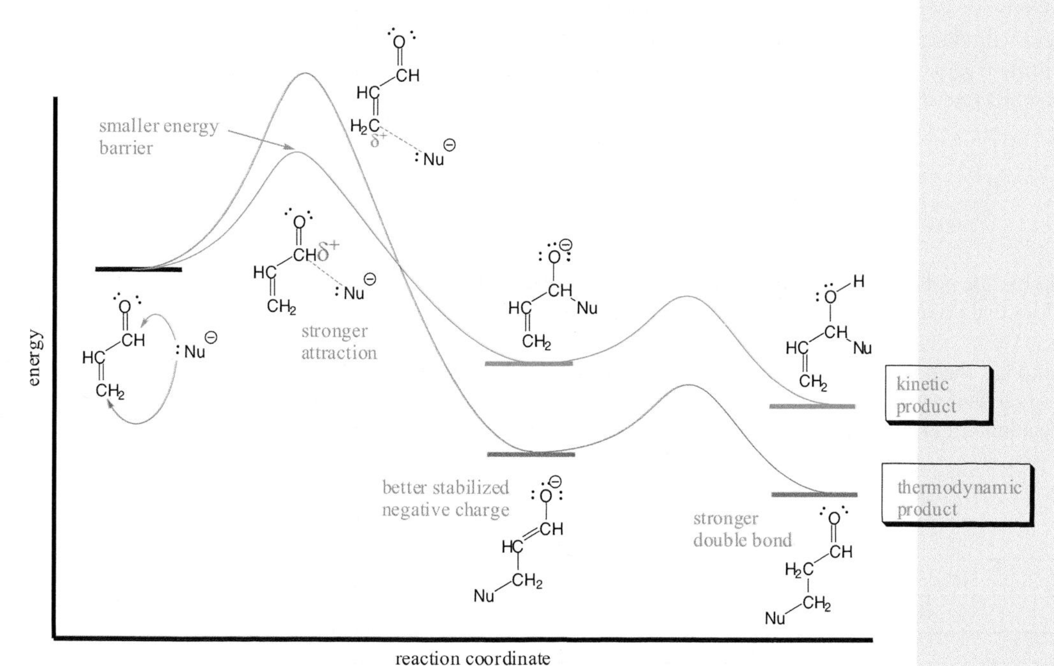

Figure 15-4. Direct vs. Conjugate Addition of a Generic Nucleophile to Propenal
The red curve represents direct addition (Equation 15-5); the blue curve, conjugate addition (Equation 15-6). The energy barrier is lower for direct addition because in the transition state, the nucleophile is attracted more strongly to the carbonyl carbon than to the beta carbon. Thus direct addition gives the kinetic product. The more stable product is from conjugate addition. Thus conjugate addition gives the thermodynamic product.

Your Turn 15.9. Label each product of nucleophilic addition as either the *thermodynamic product* or the *kinetic product.*

Ultimately, whether the major product is the kinetic or the thermodynamic product depends upon whether the reaction is under kinetic control or thermodynamic control. As we saw earlier, the nucleophile plays a major role in determining this—some nucleophiles add irreversibly to the carbonyl carbon whereas others add reversibly. If the nucleophile is one that adds reversibly, then the reaction takes place under thermodynamic control and the more stable conjugate-addition product is the major product. On the other hand, if the nucleophile is one that adds irreversibly, then the reaction takes place under kinetic control and the major product is the direct-addition product.

Solved Problem 15.3. Although we have examined conjugate addition thus far only as it pertains to carbonyl compounds, competition between direct addition and conjugate addition can also occur with other α,β-unsaturated polar π bonds. An example involving an α,β-unsaturated nitrile is shown below. Predict whether the reaction will take place via direct addition or conjugate addition, and draw the major product.

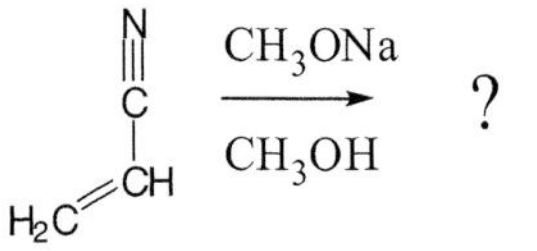

N≡C–CH=CH₂ $\xrightarrow[CH_3OH]{CH_3ONa}$?

Think. Which group has the polar π bond? Will the nucleophile add reversibly or irreversibly? How does that affect whether direct or conjugate addition takes place?

Solve. The C≡N group has the polar π bond. The nucleophile is CH_3O^-, which, as we know from Table 15-1, adds reversibly. Therefore, the thermodynamic product, which is formed via conjugate addition, is favored. The mechanism is essentially the same as that in Equation 15-6.

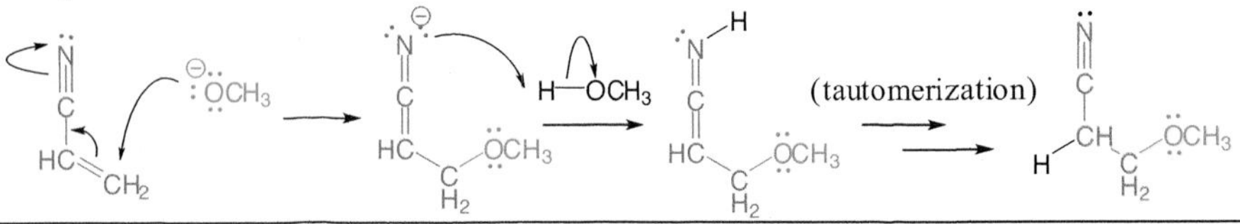

N≡C–CH=CH₂ + :ÖCH₃⁻ ⟶ ⁻N=C=CH–CH₂–OCH₃ + H–OCH₃ ⟶ H–N=C=CH–CH₂–OCH₃ ⟶(tautomerization)⟶ N≡C–CH₂–CH₂–OCH₃

Problem 15.5. Predict the major product of the following reaction.

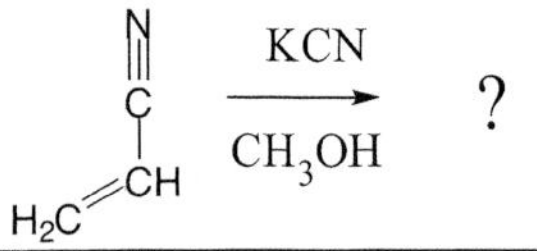

N≡C–CH=CH₂ $\xrightarrow[CH_3OH]{KCN}$?

Problem 15.6. For the reaction between cyclohex-2-en-1-one and a nucleophile, determine whether the major product will be that from *direct addition* or from *conjugate addition*. Explain.

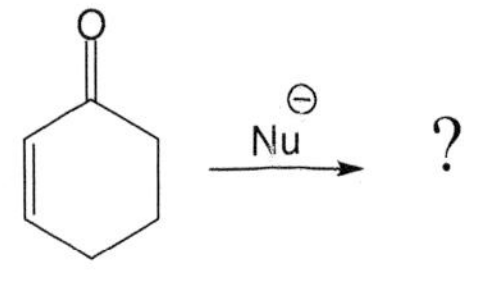

cyclohex-2-en-1-one $\xrightarrow{Nu^{\ominus}}$?

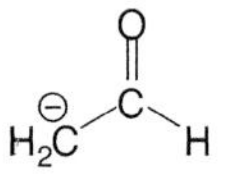

(a) CH_3SNa

(b) 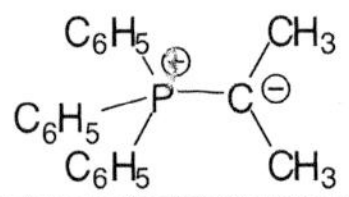 $(C_6H_5)_3P^{\oplus}$–$C^{\ominus}(CH_3)_2$

(c) $^{\ominus}H_2C$–C(=O)–H

(d) 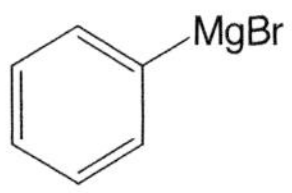 C_6H_5MgBr

(e) $LiAlH_4$

15.5. REACTIONS OF HYDRIDE AGENTS

The **hydride anion** is formally written as H:⁻, a hydrogen atom with an extra electron. However, unlike such species as Cl^- and HO^-, the hydride anion does not exist on its own at any appreciable concentration in solution. Solutions of the first two anions can be prepared by dissolving NaCl and KOH, respectively, in highly polar solvents, including water, ethanol, and DMSO. The hydride anion, on the other hand, is extremely reactive, both as a nucleophile and as a base, because its negative charge is not well stabilized. Consequently, it can react with those solvents in which it is soluble. To circumvent this problem, we often choose hydride sources in which the hydrogen is part of a covalent bond to a *less* electronegative atom. In these species, the hydrogen atom bears only a *partial* negative charge.

Two of the most common hydride sources in organic chemistry are **sodium borohydride** ($NaBH_4$) and **lithium aluminum hydride** ($LiAlH_4$, or LAH). Sodium borohydride is comprised of Na^+ and the polyatomic anion BH_4^-. Similarly, $LiAlH_4$ is comprised of Li^+ and AlH_4^-.

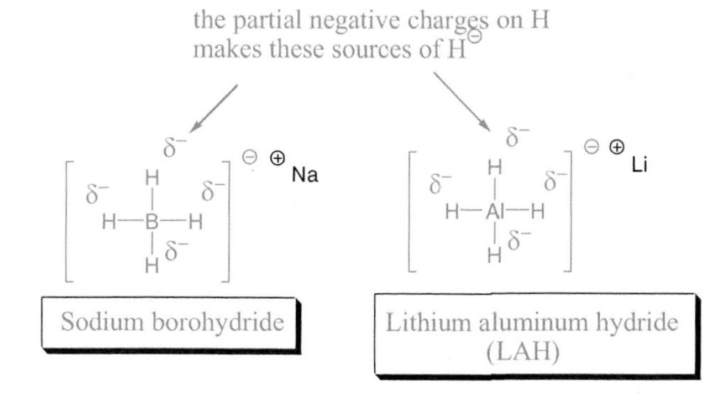

The most important role of these hydride sources is as reducing agents.

Both $NaBH_4$ and $LiAlH_4$ act as *reducing agents* in the presence of a compound containing a polar π bond.

For example, when 2-butanone is treated with a solution of $NaBH_4$ dissolved in water, racemic 2-butanol is formed (Equation 15-11). As we can see, reduction of the ketone is signified by the increase in the number of H atoms bonded to the carbonyl carbon, resulting in a decrease in that carbon's oxidation state. Similarly, treatment of 2-butanone with $LiAlH_4$ followed by aqueous acid reduces 2-butanone to the alcohol (Equation 15-12).

oxidation state = +2 oxidation state = 0

2-butanone $\xrightarrow[H_2O]{NaBH_4}$ 2-butanol (racemic) 83% (15-11)

2-butanone $\xrightarrow[\text{2) } H_3O^+]{\text{1) } LiAlH_4\text{, ether, reflux}}$ 2-butanol (racemic) 80% (15-12)

Although H^- does not physically exist on its own, Equations 15-11 and 15-12 suggest that we can *treat* both $NaBH_4$ and $LiAlH_4$ as simply H^-. As shown in Equation

15-13, we can envision H^- acting as a nucleophile attacking the carbonyl carbon in the first step of the mechanism. In the second step, a proton transfer occurs, converting the alkoxide anion into the final alcohol product. A racemic mixture of enantiomers is produced because the single stereocenter in the product is formed in the first step of the mechanism, in which the reactants and the reaction conditions are achiral.

Simplified Mechanism for Reactions in Equations 15-11 and 15-12

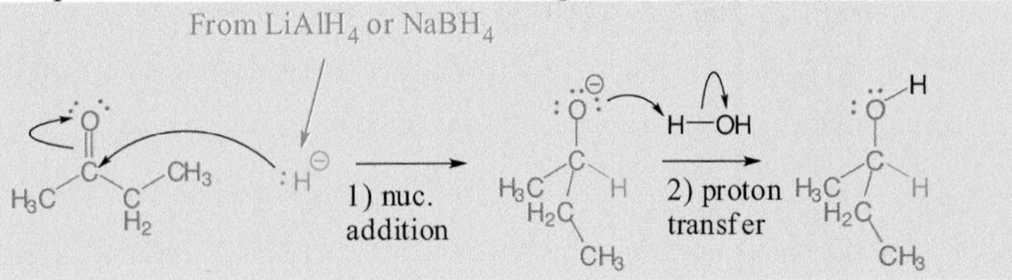

From $LiAlH_4$ or $NaBH_4$

1) nuc. addition

2) proton transfer

(15-13)

To take into account the fact that H^- cannot exist on its own, a rigorously formal mechanism must show the nucleophilic attack as a *hydride transfer*. That is, the hydrogen's bond to either B or Al is broken at the same time the carbon-hydrogen bond is formed. This is illustrated in Equation 15-14 for the sodium borohydride reduction of butanone. A similar mechanism occurs when $LiAlH_4$ is used as the reducing agent (see Your Turn 15.10). In the interest of simplicity, however, we will in general continue to work with the mechanism in Equation 15-13, unless otherwise necessary.

Complete Mechanism for Reaction in Equation 15-11

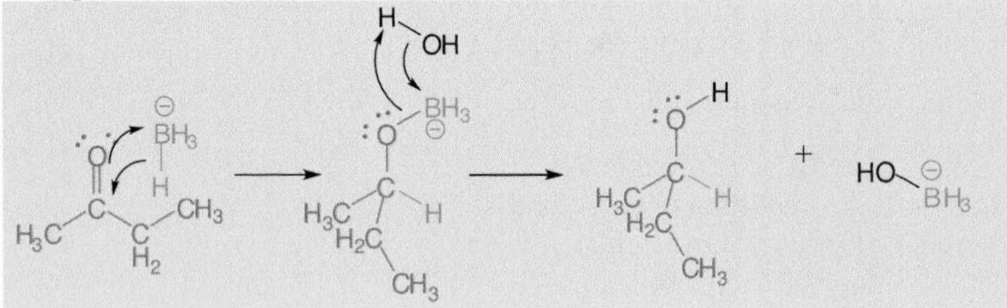

(15-14)

Your Turn 15.11. In the space provided below, draw the complete mechanism for the $LiAlH_4$ reduction of butanone (Equation 15-12) similar to that in Equation 15-14.

Notice that with $NaBH_4$ as the reducing agent, the reduction can take place in water (Equation 15-11). This is advantageous, because water is a weak acid, and therefore a source of protons, H^+. Therefore, both the addition of H^- to the carbonyl and the subsequent protonation can occur in the same reaction. On the other hand, reduction using $LiAlH_4$ requires two separate reactions (Equation 15-12). The first is the treatment of the carbonyl-containing species with $LiAlH_4$ dissolved in ether. The second is the treatment of the product from the first reaction with aqueous acid—an acid workup. The acid workup is necessary because the first reaction takes place in ether, whose acidity is too low to facilitate a proton transfer.

Why must reduction with $LiAlH_4$ take place in ether whereas reduction with $NaBH_4$ can take place in a weakly acidic solvent such as water or an alcohol? The answer is that *$LiAlH_4$ is much more reactive than $NaBH_4$*. The hydride from $LiAlH_4$ deprotonates the weakly acidic proton from water and alcohols very quickly (Equation 15-15), producing hydrogen gas—the exothermicity of the reaction can ignite the hydrogen, causing an explosion! Although $NaBH_4$ can also deprotonate water and alcohols, this proton transfer is quite slow, especially when the solution is slightly basic (Equation 15-16).

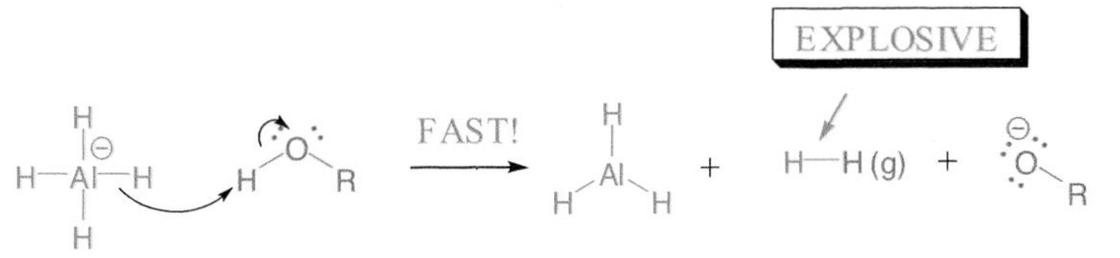

EXPLOSIVE

FAST!

(15-15)

VERY SLOW

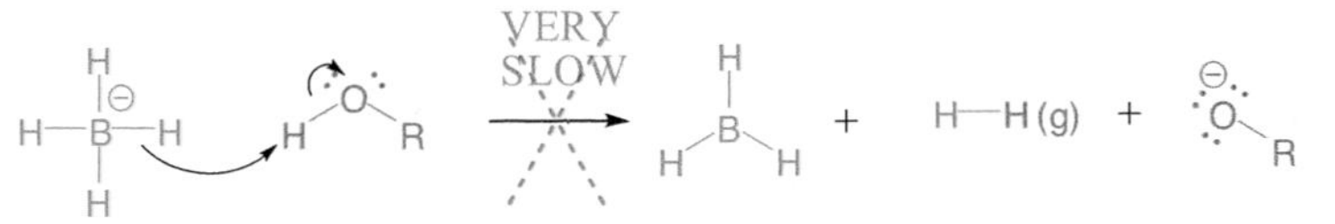

(15-16)

$LiAlH_4$ is more reactive than $NaBH_4$ because the electronegativity of aluminum (1.6) is substantially lower than that of boron (2.0). The electronegativity of H (2.1) is higher than that of either metal, giving H a partial negative charge in both the Al-H and the B-H bonds. However, the electronegativity *difference* is greater in the case of aluminum, giving H a higher concentration of negative charge in $LiAlH_4$ than in $NaBH_4$. As we learned in Chapter 7, the higher concentration of charge in $LiAlH_4$ makes it less stable, and thus more reactive.

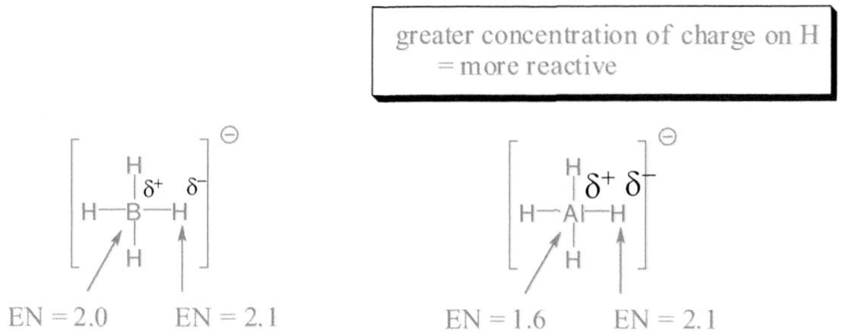

greater concentration of charge on H
= more reactive

EN = 2.0 EN = 2.1 EN = 1.6 EN = 2.1

Solved Problem 15.4. Predict the major organic product of the following reaction.

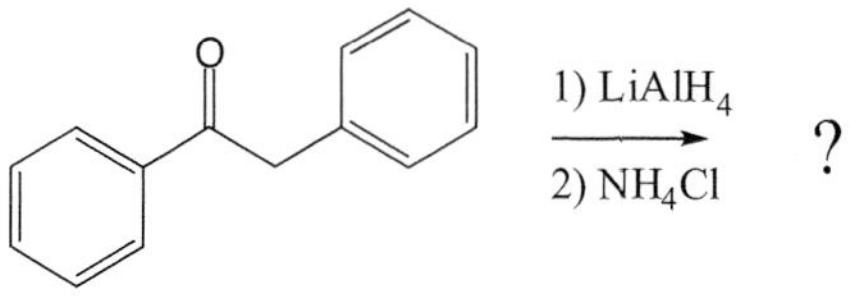

1) $LiAlH_4$
2) NH_4Cl
?

Think. To what nucleophile can $LiAlH_4$ be simplified? How does NH_4Cl behave in solution, and why must it not be added until reaction with $LiAlH_4$ is complete?

Solve. $LiAlH_4$ can be treated simply as H^-, which attacks the carbonyl carbon, as shown in the first step below.

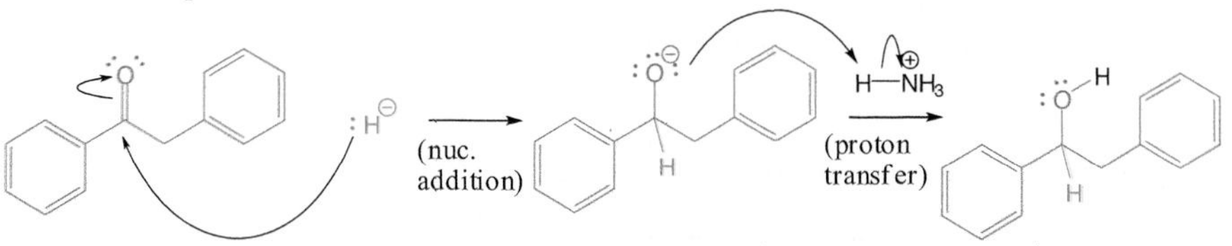

(nuc. addition) (proton transfer)

NH_4Cl is ionic, so in solution it dissociates into its NH_4^+ and Cl^- ions. NH_4^+ is weakly acidic, so to avoid destroying $LiAlH_4$, it is not added until the nucleophilic addition is complete. Instead, in the second step, NH_4^+ serves to protonate the strongly basic product from the first step.

Problem 15.7. Predict the major organic product in each of the following reactions.

(a) $NaBH_4$, CH_3CH_2OH → ?

(b) 1) $LiAlH_4$ 2) $H_3O^{\oplus}$

Functional groups with polar π bonds other than the carbonyl group react with hydride agents in much the same way. An imine, for example, is reduced with $LiAlH_4$ to an amine, as illustrated in Equation 15-17. As before, the nucleophilic addition of H^- takes place in an aprotic solvent such as ether and is followed by an aqueous acid workup. Similarly, $LiAlH_4$ reduces nitriles to primary amines (Equation 15-18). The first addition of H^- yields an intermediate that resembles a deprotonated imine. Because that intermediate also contains a polar π bond, and because $LiAlH_4$ is such a powerful hydride agent, a second addition of H^- occurs, effectively generating a dianion on the N atom. Subsequent acid workup protonates the nitrogen atom twice.

1) $LiAlH_4$/ether 2) H_3O^+ (15-17)

$LiAlH_4$/ether; H_3O^+ (15-18)

Problem 15.8. Draw a complete, detailed mechanism for the reaction in Equation 15-17.

Problem 15.9. Draw a complete, detailed mechanism for the reaction in Equation 15-18.

Problem 15.10. Predict the major organic product in each of the following reactions.

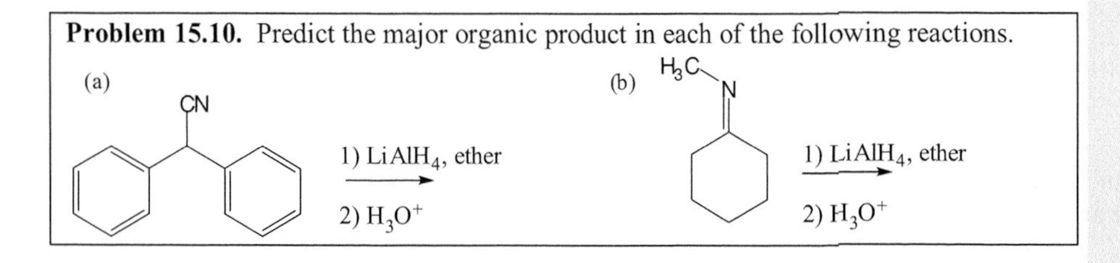

15.5a. Conjugate vs. Direct Addition of $NaBH_4$ and $LiAlH_4$

Recall from Table 15-1 that hydride reagents such as $NaBH_4$ and $LiAlH_4$ *irreversibly* add to polar π bonds. Therefore,

> $NaBH_4$ and $LiAlH_4$ add to an α,β-unsaturated carbonyl predominantly via *direct addition.*

We can see this in Table 15-3, which shows the outcomes of hydride reduction for a variety of unsaturated ketones and aldehydes.

Table 15-3. Relative Percentages of Direct vs. Conjugate Addition in Hydride Reductions:

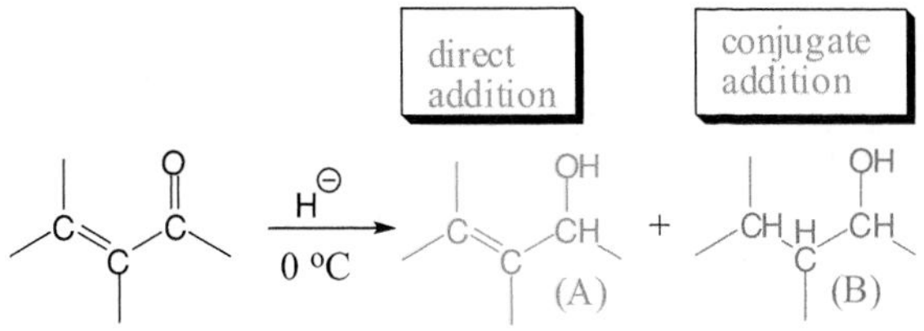

direct addition

conjugate addition

$$\text{C=C–C(=O)} \xrightarrow[0\ ^{\circ}\text{C}]{H^{\ominus}} \text{C=C–CH(OH)}\ (A) + \text{CH–CH}_2\text{–CH(OH)}\ (B)$$

	$NaBH_4$ reduction		*$LiAlH_4$ reduction*	
Carbonyl Compound	%A	%B	%A	%B
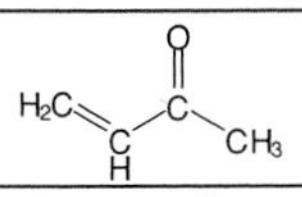 $H_2C=CH–C(=O)–CH_3$	57	43	83	17
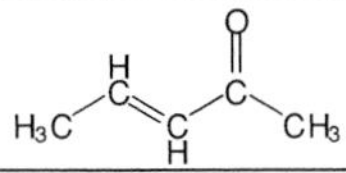 $H_3C–CH=CH–C(=O)–CH_3$	65	35	98	2
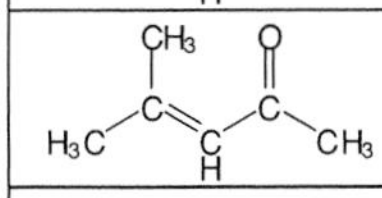 $(CH_3)(H_3C)C=CH–C(=O)–CH_3$	92	8	100	0
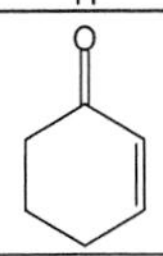 O (cyclohexenone)	55	45	98	2
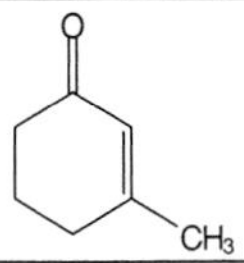 O, CH_3 (3-methylcyclohexenone)	70	30	100	0
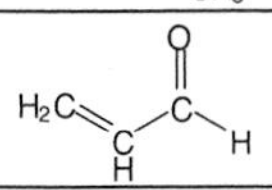 $H_2C=CH–C(=O)–H$	85	15	98	2
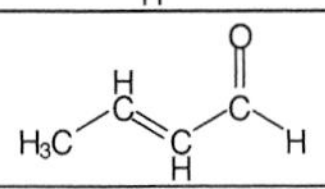 $H_3C–CH=CH–C(=O)–H$	92	8	100	0
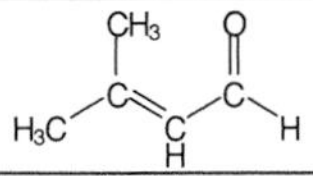 $(CH_3)(H_3C)C=CH–C(=O)–H$	>99	<1	100	0
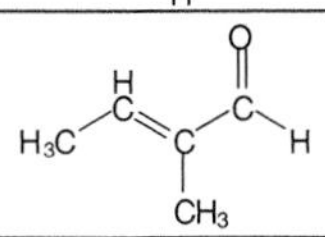 $H_3C–CH=C(CH_3)–C(=O)–H$	>99	<1	100	0

As we carefully examine Table 15-3, notice that the conjugate addition product is fully saturated—both double bonds are converted to single bonds. This is because nucleophilic addition occurs twice. The conjugate addition product is a ketone or aldehyde, which can subsequently be attacked by another equivalent of H^- (Equation 15-19). The direct addition product, on the other hand, yields an isolated C=C double bond, which is nonpolar and therefore inert to nucleophilic addition.

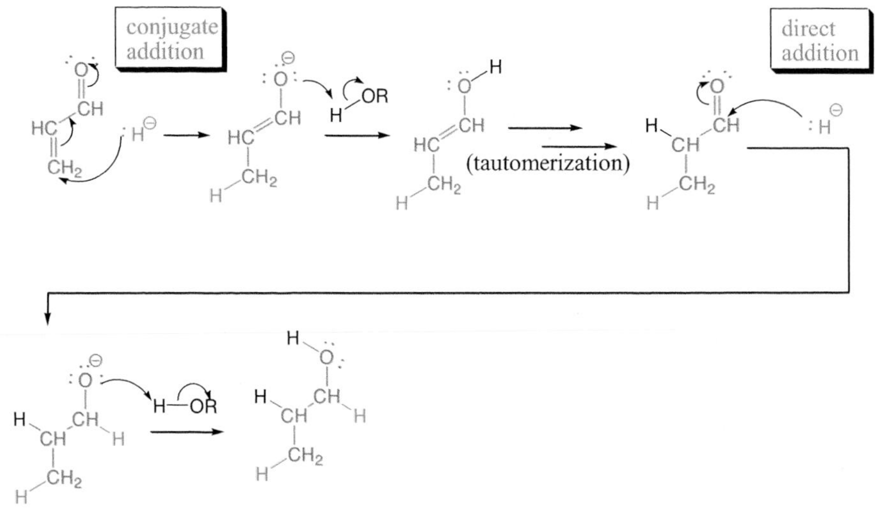

conjugate addition

direct addition

(tautomerization)

(15-19)

Although the direct-addition product is the major product of both $LiAlH_4$ and $NaBH_4$ reductions, notice in Table 15-3 that $NaBH_4$ tends to yield more conjugate-addition product than does $LiAlH_4$. In other words, the two reducing agents have *different selectivities*.

The different selectivity of $NaBH_4$ versus $LiAlH_4$ is a reflection of the greater concentration of negative charge on H in $LiAlH_4$. As a result, H^- from $LiAlH_4$ is more strongly attracted to the positively charged carbonyl carbon than is the H^- from $NaBH_4$. In other words, $LiAlH_4$ reacts faster with the C=O group than does $NaBH_4$. Because such reactions take place under kinetic control, $LiAlH_4$ tends to favor direct addition more than does $NaBH_4$.

Notice also in Table 15-3 that both $LiAlH_4$ and $NaBH_4$ undergo direct addition almost exclusively when the α,β-unsaturated carbonyl is an aldehyde. One reason for this is that the concentration of positive charge at the carbonyl carbon is greater in aldehydes than it is in ketones (see again Figure 15-2). Thus, reaction with an aldehyde tends to be faster than at a ketone, and, due to the kinetic control of such hydride additions, leads to more product.

Problem 15.11. Predict the products of each of the following reactions.

(a) 1) $LiAlH_4$ 2) $H_3O^{\oplus}$?

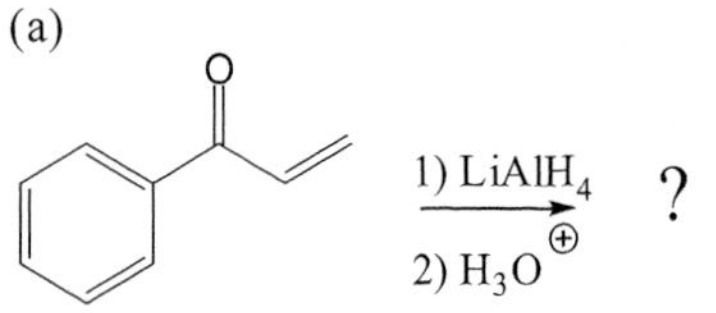

(b) $NaBH_4$, CH_3CH_2OH ?

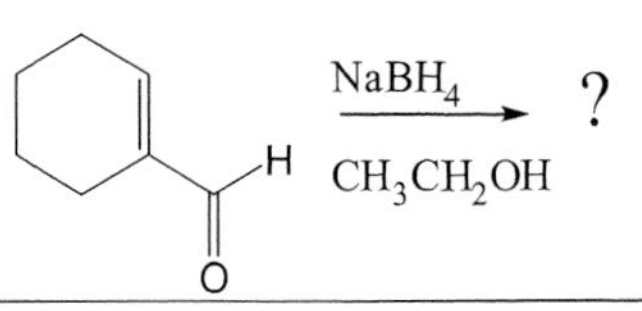

Problem 15.12. Suggest how to carry out the following transformation to obtain the greatest yield.

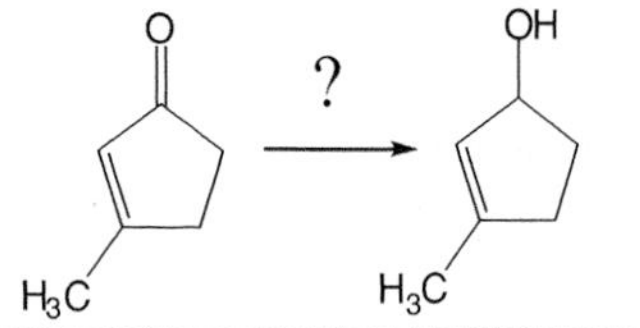

?

15.5b. Sodium Hydride

Sodium hydride, NaH, is another common hydride agent employed in organic chemistry. Its behavior, however, is somewhat different from that of $NaBH_4$ and $LiAlH_4$.

Sodium hydride, NaH, is a very strong base, but a poor nucleophile.

For example, treatment of acetone with NaH yields the acetone enolate anion *quantitatively* (i.e., with essentially 100% yield), as shown in Equation 15-20a. Reduction of the carbonyl (Equation 15-20b) does not occur.

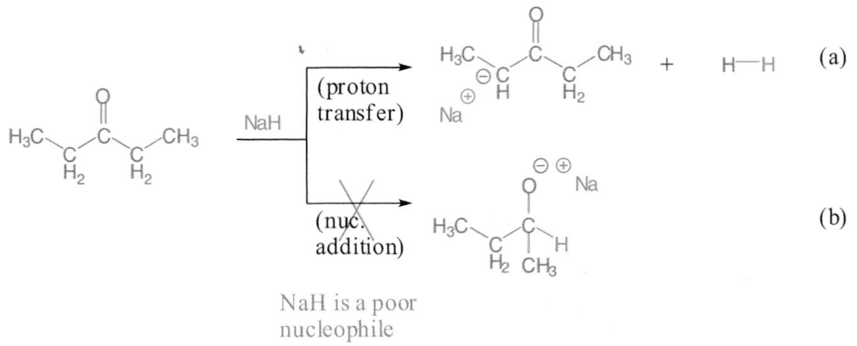

NaH
(proton transfer)
+ H—H (a)
(nuc. addition)
(b)
NaH is a poor nucleophile

(15-20)

Because of its nature as a base, NaH is often used to generate carbon-nucleophiles, as exemplified in Solved Problem 15.5.

Solved Problem 15.5. Predict the major organic product of the following sequence of reactions.

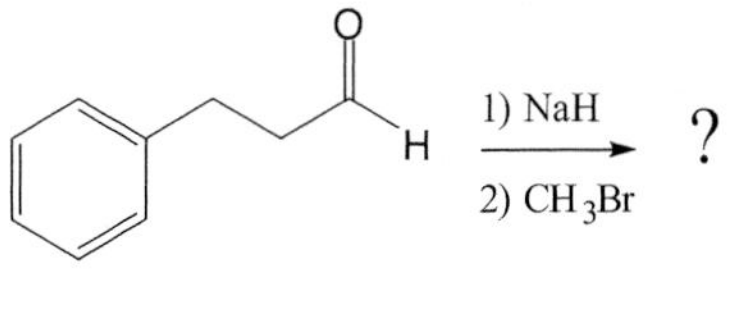

1) NaH
2) CH_3Br
?

Think. Will the hydride anion from NaH act as a base or a nucleophile? Which atom will it attack? How will the resulting species behave in the presence of CH_3Br?

Solve. NaH is a strong base but a poor nucleophile, so it will deprotonate at the alpha carbon. As we learned in Section 11.3, the resulting enolate anion is a strong nucleophile, and will displace Br from CH_3Br in an S_N2 reaction, yielding an alpha-alkylated ketone.

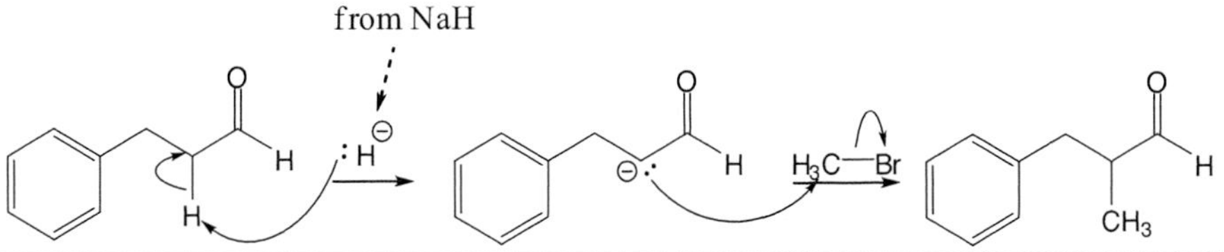

from NaH

Problem 15.13. Predict the major organic product in each of the following reactions.

(a) 1) NaH 2) CH_3Br ?

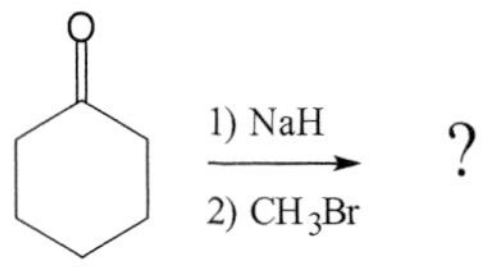

(b) 1) NaH 2) Cl ?

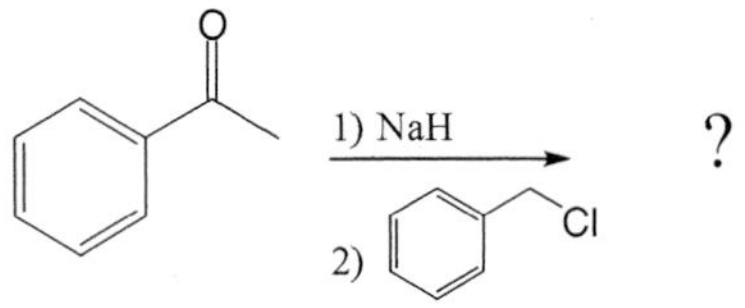

(c) H 1) NaH 2) Br ?

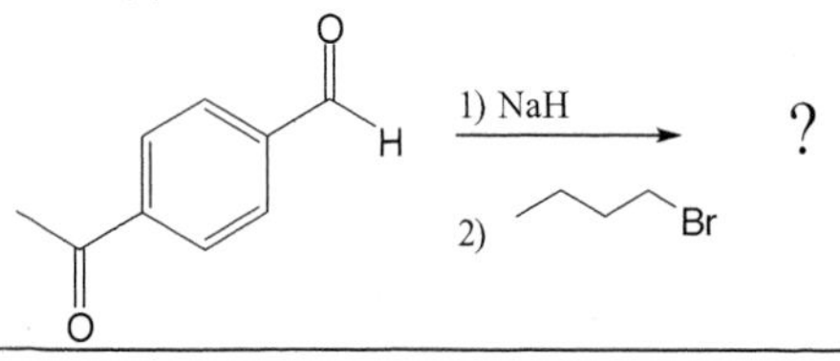

The reason that sodium hydride's behavior differs from that of $NaBH_4$ or $LiAlH_4$ is that NaH is an *ionic* hydride, consisting of Na^+ and H^- ions. In turn, its ionic character stems from the fact that the Na and H atoms have widely different electronegativities (0.9 vs. 2.1). Recall that the B-H and Al-H bonds in $NaBH_4$ and $LiAlH_4$ have more covalent character—the electronegativities of B (2.0) and Al (1.6) are closer to that of hydrogen.

Sodium hydride, because of its ionic character, is essentially insoluble in organic solvents—it remains a solid. It is therefore believed that reactions involving NaH take place at the NaH surface. Under these conditions, H^- *directly* participates in reactions, rather than through hydride transfers as we saw for $NaBH_4$ and $LiAlH_4$ (Equation 15-14). Therefore, the carbonyl oxygen is not involved in directing the H^- to the carbonyl C. Instead, H^- is free to deprotonate at the beta carbon, which, as we learned in Chapter 8, is a very fast reaction.

15.6. REACTIONS OF ORGANOMETALLIC COMPOUNDS: ALKYLLITHIUM REAGENTS AND GRIGNARD REAGENTS

In Section 6.2, we also learned that we can usually treat organometallic compounds like Grignard reagents (R-MgBr) and alkyllithium reagents (R-Li) as simply R^-.

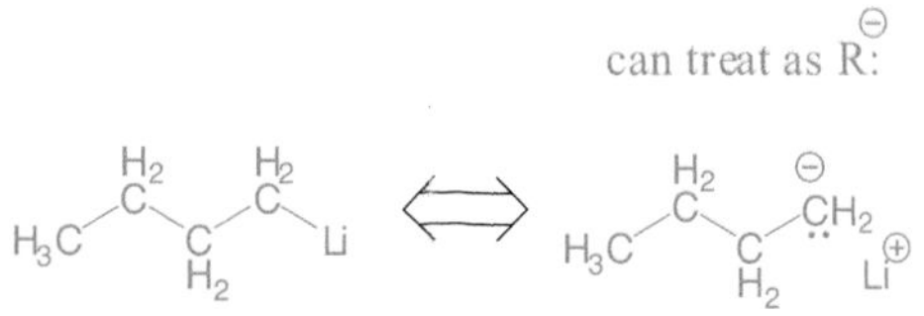

can treat as $R:^-$

H_3C H_2C H_2C CH_2 Li ⟺ H_3C H_2C CH_2 CH_2^- Li^+

butyllithium

can treat as $R:^-$

MgBr ⟺ $MgBr^+$

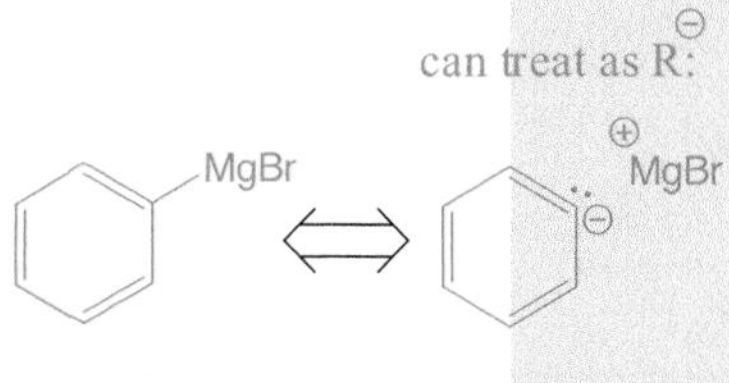

phenylmagnesium bromide

Because of the poorly stabilized charge on C, these types of reagents behave both as *strong bases* and as *strong nucleophiles*. For example, both alkyllithium reagents and Grignard reagents react rapidly with water in a substantially exothermic proton transfer (Equations 15-21 and 15-22) to produce an alkane and HO^-. The products are much more stable because the negative charge is transferred from a carbon atom to a more electronegative oxygen atom.

$$CH_3CH_2CH_2CH_2Li \xrightarrow{H_2O} CH_3CH_2CH_2CH_2H + {}^{\ominus}OH + Li^{\oplus} \quad (15\text{-}21)$$

$$C_6H_5MgBr \xrightarrow{H_2O} C_6H_5H + {}^{\ominus}OH + {}^{\oplus}MgBr \quad (15\text{-}22)$$

Although we can treat these organometallic reagents as R^-, we must recognize that they are not truly ionic. When dissolved in solution, free R^- does not exist. Instead, it is more correct to regard alkyllithium reagents and Grignard reagents as *R^- donors,* in much the same way that we view $LiAlH_4$ and $NaBH_4$ as H^- donors. The reaction that takes place is an R^- transfer from the metal atom to H^+, as shown for butyllithium in Equation 15-23.

Mechanism for the Reaction in Equation 15-21

$$CH_3CH_2CH_2CH_2Li \xrightarrow[\text{proton transfer}]{H-OH} CH_3CH_2CH_2CH_2H + {}^{\ominus}OH + Li^{\oplus} \quad (15\text{-}23)$$

Your Turn 15.12. In the space provided here, draw an R^- transfer mechanism for the reaction in Equation 15-22, similar to what is shown in Equation 15-23 for an alkyllithium reagent. Make sure to draw the products as well.

$$C_6H_5MgBr \xrightarrow{H-OH}$$

When an alkyllithium reagent or a Grignard reagent reacts with a functional group containing a polar π bond, R^- acts as a nucleophile. This behavior is exemplified with a ketone in Equation 15-24 and with a nitrile in Equation 15-25. When a Grignard reagent adds in as a nucleophile, it is called a **Grignard reaction**.

$$\text{cyclohexanone} \xrightarrow[2)\ H_3O^+]{1)\ CH_3(CH_2)_3\text{-Li/ether},\ -65\ ^\circ C,\ 3h} \text{1-butylcyclohexanol (HO, } (CH_2)_3CH_3\text{)} \quad 74\% \quad (15\text{-}24)$$

$$\underset{\text{benzonitrile}}{C_6H_5C{\equiv}N} \xrightarrow[2)\ CH_3OH]{1)\ C_6H_5MgBr,\ \text{ether, reflux 5 hrs}} \underset{70\%}{(C_6H_5)_2C{=}NH} \left(\xrightarrow[\text{(hydrolysis)}]{H_3O^{\oplus}} (C_6H_5)_2C{=}O \right) \quad (15\text{-}25)$$

Notice that in both cases, nucleophilic addition takes place in ether, followed by an acid work-up. It is vitally important to keep the first reaction free of any compounds with acidic protons, such as water or methanol. Otherwise, the alkyllithium or Grignard reagent will be destroyed via a proton transfer reaction like those shown in Equation 15-21 or 15-22.

Comment [JMK2]: Margin note.
Water or other acidic compounds must not be added until an alkyllithium or Grignard addition has come to completion.

Notice also that the acid work-up in Equation 15-25 is carried out with methanol. As we will see in Chapter 16, if it is carried out with H_3O^+ instead, the imine that is produced from nucleophilic addition is hydrolyzed to a ketone or aldehyde.

The mechanisms for these reactions are shown in Equations 15-26 and 15-27. Specifically, R^- adds to the electron-poor atom of the polar π bond. Once again, because free R^- does not exist in solution, each mechanism is more appropriately shown as a transfer of R^-.

Mechanism for Reaction in Equation 15-24

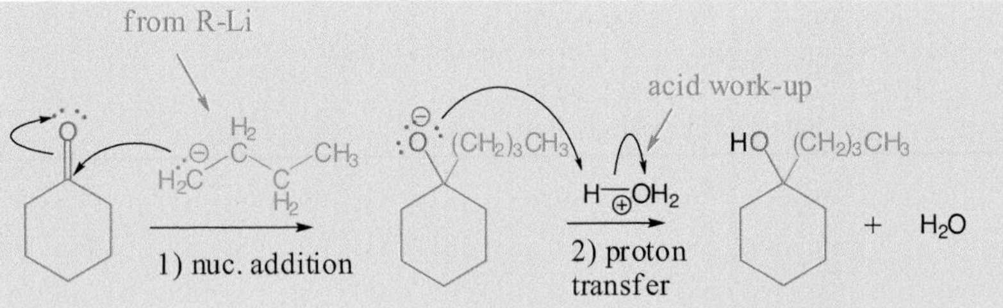

from R-Li

acid work-up

$(CH_2)_3CH_3$ · $H{-}OH_2^{\oplus}$ · HO $(CH_2)_3CH_3$ + H_2O

1) nuc. addition

2) proton transfer

(15-26)

Mechanism for Reaction in Equation 15-25

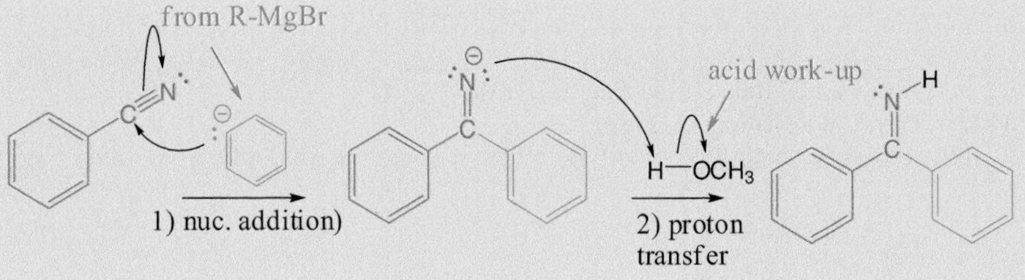

from R-MgBr

acid work-up

H—OCH_3

1) nuc. addition)

2) proton transfer

(15-27)

As we can see, the R^- nucleophiles from R-Li and R-MgBr add only once to a nitrile C. This is in contrast to what we saw with $LiAlH_4$ (Equation 15-18), in which H^- adds twice. In other words, these R^- nucleophiles are not strong enough to generate the -2 formal charge on N that is a necessary outcome of a second nucleophilic addition.

Solved Problem 15.6. Predict the major product of the following reaction.

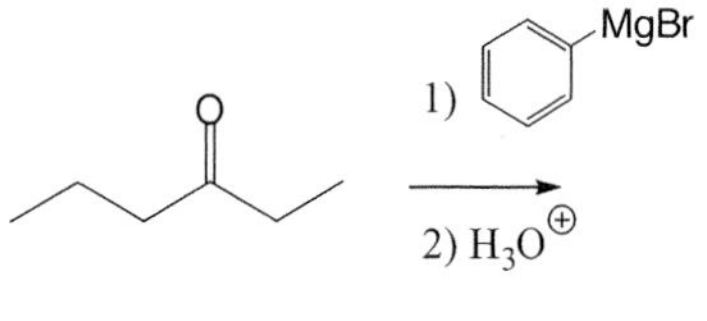

1) MgBr

2) $H_3O^{\oplus}$

Think. To what R^- nucleophile can the Grignard reagent be simplified? Which atom will it attack? What is the role of H_3O^+?

Solve. The C_6H_5MgBr Grignard reagent can be treated simply as $C_6H_5^-$, which will undergo nucleophilic addition at the carbonyl C. Once this is complete, H_3O^+ is added in an acid work-up to protonate the strongly basic O generated in the first step.

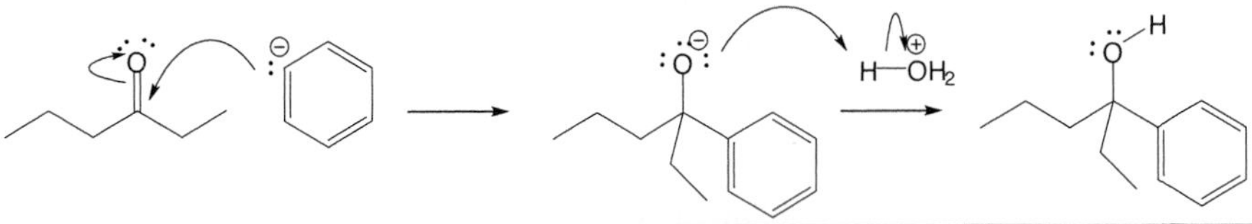

H—OH_2

Problem 15.14. Predict the major organic product in each of the following reactions.

(a) benzaldehyde; 1) PhMgBr, 2) H_3O^+ → ?

(b) cyclopentanone (with H_3C and CH_3 substituents); 1) CH_3Li, 2) H_3O^+ → ?

(c) alkenyl nitrile (CN); 1) CH_3Li, 2) CH_3OH → ?

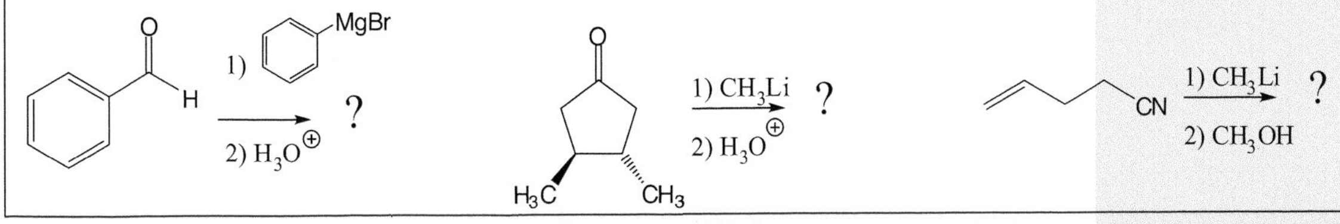

One interesting and quite useful reaction is the **carboxylation** of Grignard reagents, whereby a Grignard reagent adds to carbon dioxide (Equation 15-28). Although CO_2 is overall a nonpolar compound, each C=O bond is highly polar and the central carbon atom is quite susceptible to nucleophilic attack. The immediate product of this addition—a carboxylate anion—is subsequently protonated through an acid workup to yield a carboxylic acid. Because CO_2 is a gas at room temperature, carrying out this reaction requires either (1) bubbling CO_2 through an ether solution of the Grignard reagent, or (2) pouring the Grignard reagent over dry ice (which is solid CO_2).

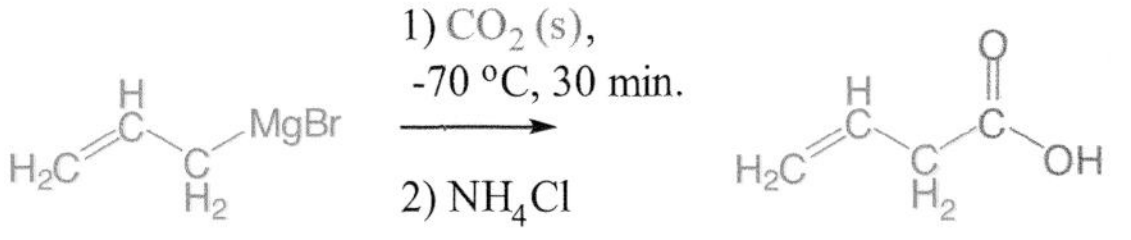

$$H_2C{=}CH{-}CH_2{-}MgBr \xrightarrow[\text{2) } NH_4Cl]{\text{1) } CO_2\text{ (s), } -70\ ^\circ C\text{, 30 min.}} H_2C{=}CH{-}CH_2{-}C(=O){-}OH \quad (15\text{-}28)$$

Problem 15.15. Draw the complete, detailed mechanism for the reaction in Equation 15-28.

Problem 15.16. Predict the major organic product in each of the following reactions.

(a) trimethylphenylmagnesium bromide (H_3C, H_3C, CH_3, MgBr); 1) CO_2 (s), 2) NH_4Cl → ?

(b) cyclopentyl-alkyl-MgBr; 1) CO_2 (s), 2) H_3O^+ → ?

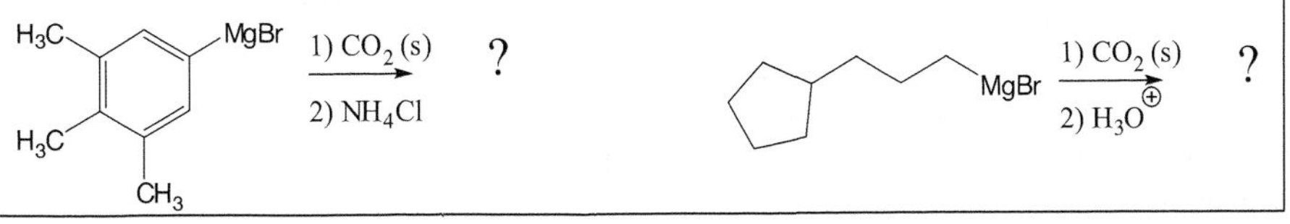

15.6a. Conjugate vs. Direct Addition of Alkyllithium and Grignard Reagents

As we saw in Table 15-1, compounds such as R-Li and R-MgBr behave as strong R^- nucleophiles that add *irreversibly* to polar π bonds. Therefore,

> Alkyllithium reagents and Grignard reagents both tend to strongly favor direct addition over conjugate addition.

For example, when CH_3MgBr reacts with *trans*-3-buten-2-one (Equation 15-29), 86% of the product is from direct addition, while the remaining 14% is from conjugate addition. Similarly, CH_3Li essentially yields only the direct addition product (Equation 15-30).

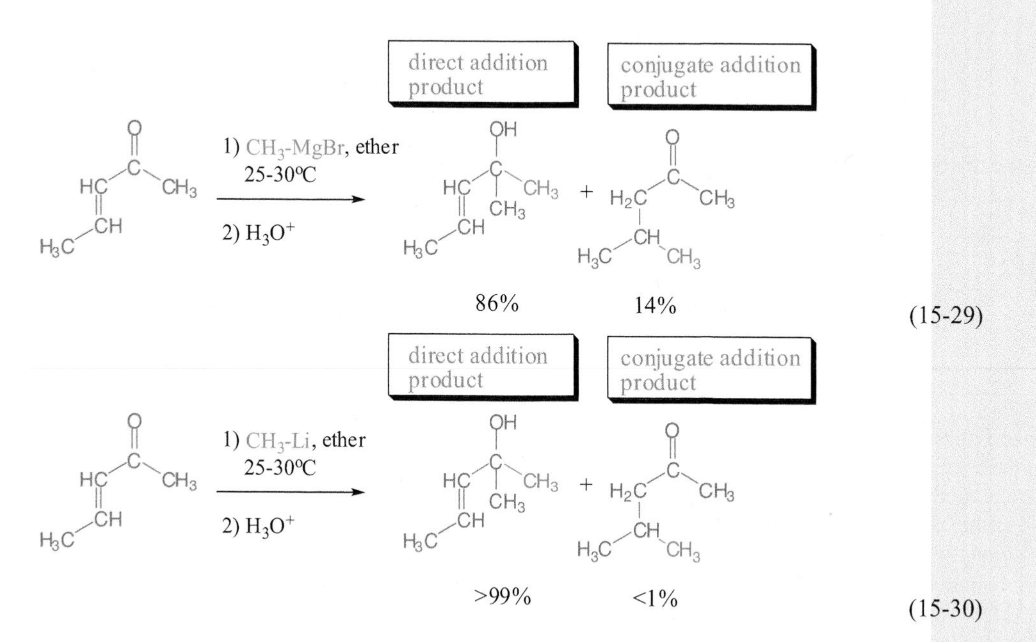

The tendency of each of these organometallic reagents to undergo direct addition can be explained by the nature of the R^- nucleophile to add *irreversibly* to the carbonyl carbon (recall Table 15-1). Each reaction is therefore under kinetic control. As we discussed previously, the R^- nucleophile reacts faster with the carbonyl carbon than with the beta carbon due to the greater concentration of positive charge at the carbonyl carbon.

Although alkyllithium reagents and Grignard reagents can often be used interchangeably, *alkyllithium reagents tend to be more reactive than Grignard reagents*. An ether solution of an alkyllithium reagent, for example, reacts violently with water when exposed to air. Although Grignard reagents do react with water, they do so much less violently. This difference in reactivity can be explained by the lower electronegativity of Li (1.0) compared to Mg (1.3), which places a greater concentration of negative charge on carbon in alkyllithium reagents.

Comment [JMK3]: **Margin note.** Alkyllithium reagents (R-Li) tend to be more reactive than Grignard reagents (R-MgBr).

As a reflection of this greater concentration of charge, alkyllithium reagents generally have a greater tendency toward direct addition to α,β-unsaturated carbonyls than do Grignard reagents. Notice in Equations 15-29 and 15-30, for example, that Grignard reagents yield a significant (although minor) amount of conjugate addition product, whereas alkyllithium reagents do not.

Problem 15.17. Predict the major product of each of the following reactions.

(a) 1) PhMgBr; 2) $H_3O^{\oplus}$ → ?

(b) 1) CH_3Li; 2) $H_3O^{\oplus}$ → ?

(c) CN; 1) CH_3Li; 2) CH_3OH → ?

15.6b. Limitations of Alkyllithium and Grignard Reagents

Both alkyllithium and Grignard reagents can be synthesized with a wide variety of R groups. Table 15-4 illustrates this with Grignard reagents specifically, but the same is typically true of alkyllithium reagents as well. The R group can be a saturated alkyl group, (including the CH_3, CH_2CH_3, and cyclohexyl groups), but it can also be unsaturated. Common unsaturated Grignard reagents, for example, include phenylmagnesium bromide, C_6H_5MgBr, and vinylmagnesium bromide, $H_2C{=}CH\text{-}MgBr$.

These strong organometallic reagents, however, must not contain functional groups that are susceptible to deprotonation or to nucleophilic attack. For example, the hypothetical Grignard reagent shown at left in Equation 15-31 is not feasible. The OH group is weakly acidic and can be deprotonated by a carbon atom bonded to Mg, a strongly basic carbon. As shown in Equation 15-31, such a reaction effectively destroys the Grignard reagent, so we say that the alkylmagnesium bromide functional group is *not compatible* with the OH group.

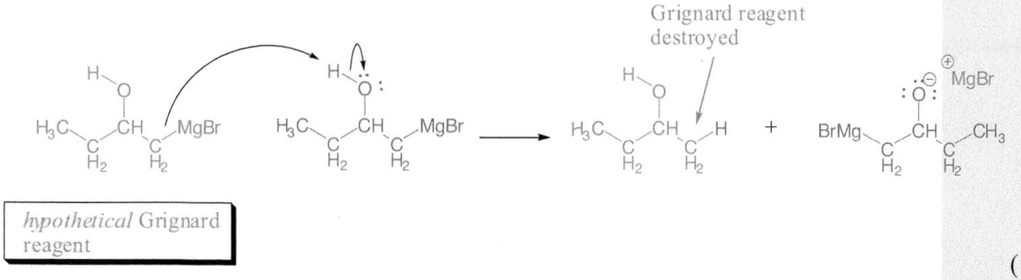

Grignard reagent destroyed

hypothetical Grignard reagent

(15-31)

Other groups that are not compatible with Grignard reagents or alkyllithium reagents are polar π bonds such as C=O, C=N, and C≡N, because the alkanide anion, R^-, will add to the electrophilic carbon. Furthermore, saturated alkyl halides are not compatible because they are prone to elimination or nucleophilic substitution reactions, with the R^- species behaving as a strong base or nucleophile, respectively.

Table 15-4. Limitations of Grignard reagents

Feasible Grignard reagents	Unfeasible Grignard reagents
H_3C—MgBr	H_3C–CH_2–CH(OH)–CH_2–MgBr — $R^{\ominus}$ will deprotonate
H_2CH_3C—MgBr	H–C(=O)– on a benzene ring bearing MgBr — $R^{\ominus}$ will add in as a nucleophile
$(H_3C)_2$CH–MgBr	Br–CH_2–CH(H)–CH_2–MgBr — $R^{\ominus}$ will eliminate HBr in an E2
cyclohexyl–MgBr	epoxide ring–CH_2–MgBr — $R^{\ominus}$ will open the ring in an S_N2
H_2C=CH–MgBr	
phenyl–MgBr	
H_3C–O–phenyl–MgBr	
Cl–phenyl–MgBr	

Problem 15.18. For each of the Grignard reagents that Table 15-4 suggests are *not* allowed, draw the complete mechanism of the reaction that would take place. The first is shown in Equation 15-31.

15.7. NUCLEOPHILIC ADDITION OF ORGANOMETALLIC COMPOUNDS: LITHIUM DIALKYL CUPRATES

Organocopper reagents, also called organocuprates, constitute another important class of organometallic compounds. Among the most common organocuprates are **lithium dialkylcuprates**, R_2CuLi, sometimes referred to as **Gilman reagents** (after the American chemist Henry Gilman). As with other organometallic reagents, lithium dialkylcuprates possess carbon atoms that are electron-rich, due to the fact that carbon has a higher electronegativity than copper. Therefore, these reagents, too, can be treated as simply R^-.

Lithium dialkylcuprates are much less reactive than either alkyllithium reagents (R-Li) or Grignard reagents (R-Mg-Br). Largely, this is because the C-Cu bond is significantly less polar than either the R-Mg bond or the R-Li bond. Because the electronegativity of Cu (1.9) is greater than that of Mg (1.3) or Li (1.0), R_2CuLi has the smallest concentration of negative charge on C.

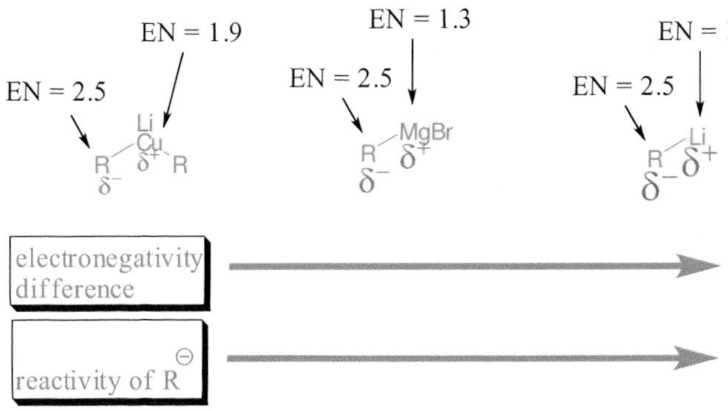

EN = 1.9 EN = 1.3 EN = 1.0

EN = 2.5 EN = 2.5 EN = 2.5

electronegativity difference →

reactivity of $R^{\ominus}$ →

Unlike alkyllithium and Grignard reagents, lithium dialkyl cuprates tend *not* to undergo direct addition at a polar π bond.

> When an α,β-unsaturated carbonyl compound is treated with R_2CuLi, R^- adds almost exclusively at the beta carbon via conjugate addition.

An example is shown in Equation 15-32.

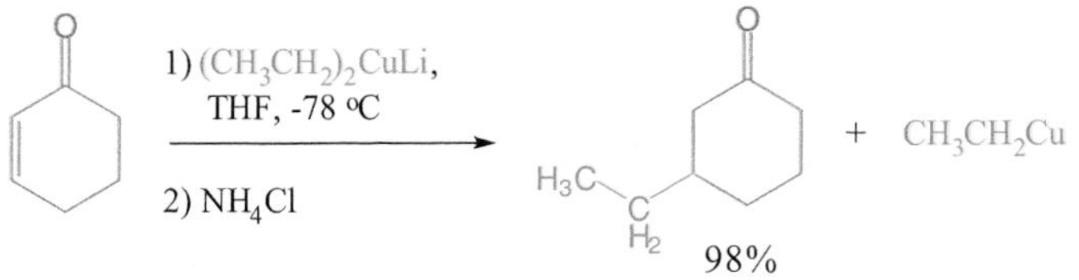

1) $(CH_3CH_2)_2CuLi$, THF, -78 °C
2) NH_4Cl

H_3C–CH_2 + CH_3CH_2Cu

98% (15-32)

The reason for this regioselectivity is not precisely known because the specific mechanism for the reaction of lithium dialkyl cuprates is not fully understood. However, chemists generally believe that the species that initially attacks as a nucleophile is *not* R^-. Instead, many believe that a key step is the reversible binding of R_2Cu^- to the C=C double bond, followed by the transfer of the alkyl group. As we have seen previously with nucleophiles that add reversibly to the carbonyl carbon, the reversible nature of the initial binding may explain the tendency of organocopper reagents to react via conjugate addition instead of direct addition.

Solved Problem 15.7. Predict the major organic product of the following reaction.

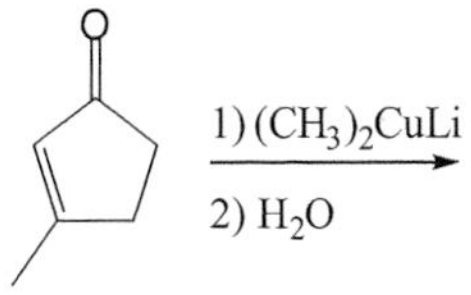

1) $(CH_3)_2CuLi$
2) H_2O

Think. To what R^- nucleophile can this lithium dialkyl cuprate be simplified? Will it add predominantly via direct addition or conjugate addition? What role does H_2O play after addition of R^- is complete?

Solve. This lithium dialkyl cuprate is a source of H_3C^-, which will add to the α,β-unsaturated carbonyl via conjugate addition. The resulting enolate anion is protonated by H_2O.

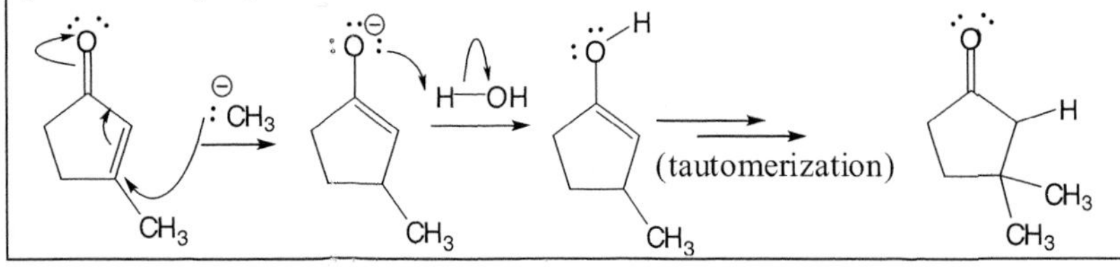

(tautomerization)

Problem 15.19. Predict the major product of each of the following reactions.

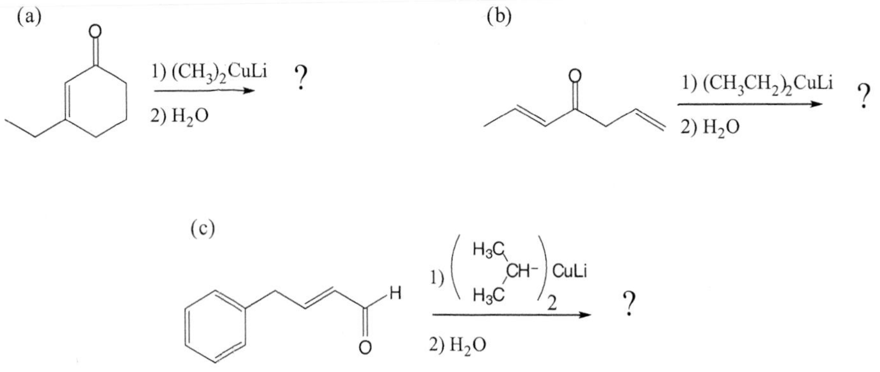

(a) 1) $(CH_3)_2CuLi$ 2) H_2O ?

(b) 1) $(CH_3CH_2)_2CuLi$ 2) H_2O ?

(c) 1) $((H_3C)_2CH-)_2CuLi$ 2) H_2O ?

Although in most other reactions it is difficult to predict the stereochemistry, it appears that steric hindrance is the dominant factor in the conjugate addition of a lithium dialkylcuprate. For example, in the reaction of lithium dimethylcuprate with 4-methylcyclohex-2-enone (Equation 15-33), the major product is the *trans* diastereomer instead of the *cis*. The bulky R_2Cu^- species encounters less steric repulsion when it approaches the ring from the side opposite the alkyl group already attached.

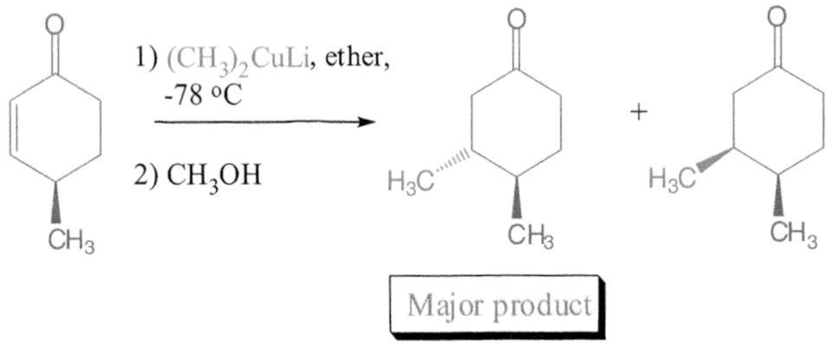

1) $(CH_3)_2CuLi$, ether, -78 °C
2) CH_3OH

Major product

(15-33)

15.8. WITTIG REAGENTS AND THE WITTIG REACTION: SYNTHESIS OF ALKENES

Wittig reagents (pronounced *vittig*), named after the German chemist Georg Wittig, comprise an important class of compounds used to synthesize alkenes. As shown below, a Wittig reagent is characterized by a C-P bond in which the C atom bears a -1 formal charge and the P atom bears a +1 formal charge. Because the charged P and C atoms are adjacent to each other, each with an octet of electrons, a Wittig reagent is also termed a **phosphonium ylide** (pronounced *ilid*). As indicated, the -1 charge on C makes a Wittig reagent highly nucleophilic at the C atom.

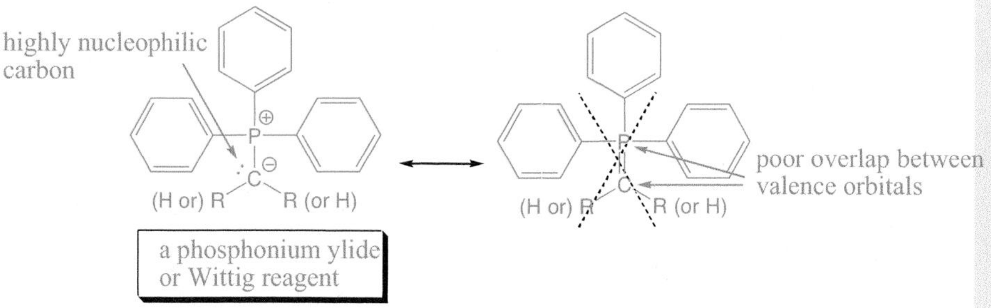

highly nucleophilic carbon

(H or) R R (or H)

a phosphonium ylide or Wittig reagent

(H or) R R (or H)

poor overlap between valence orbitals

Normally, such a structure with adjacent positive and negative charges is the weaker contributor of two resonance structures—the stronger contributor being that in which such atoms are connected by a double bond and each atom has a zero formal charge. In the case of a Wittig reagent, however, the latter resonance structure is the *weaker* contributor, as indicated at right above. This is because the π bond of a C=P bond would require the interaction of orbitals from different valence shells—the second shell on carbon and the third shell on phosphorus. Not only is there poor spatial overlap between such atomic orbitals, but they are also substantially different in energy (recall Chapter 3). Both factors lead to a weak interaction and, consequently, little stabilization relative to the atomic orbital energies—in other words, a weak bond. Thus, the structure above at left—with separated charges—is the more accurate representation.

The primary importance of Wittig reagents is in their reaction with ketones and aldehydes—so-called **Wittig reactions**. An example is shown in Equation 15-34. As we can see from this example, a Wittig reaction results in the joining of two carbon-containing groups by a C=C double bond—one group from the Wittig reagent, and the second from the ketone or aldehyde.

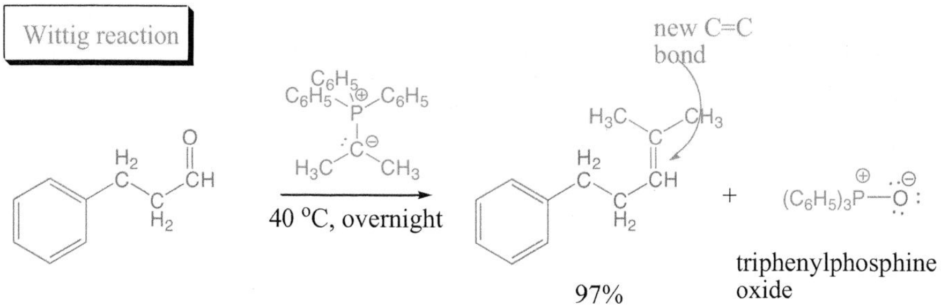

Wittig reaction

new C=C bond

40 °C, overnight

97%

$(C_6H_5)_3P—O$ triphenylphosphine oxide

(15-34)

Notice, in particular, that the newly-formed C=C bond is between the carbonyl carbon and the P-C carbon. In other words,

In a Wittig reaction, the C=O bond of a ketone or aldehyde is converted into a C=C bond.

The mechanism for this reaction is shown in Equation 15-35. In step 1, the highly nucleophilic C atom of the Wittig reagent attacks the carbonyl carbon, yielding a **betaine** (pronounced *beta-ene*)—that is, a species in which a positive and a negative charge are separated by two neutral atoms. Step 2 is a coordination step, in which a bond is formed between the negatively charged oxygen atom and the positively charged phosphorus atom. This results in a 4-membered ring, which, due to the strain, falls apart into the alkene and triphenylphosphine oxide.

Mechanism for the Reaction in Equation 15-34

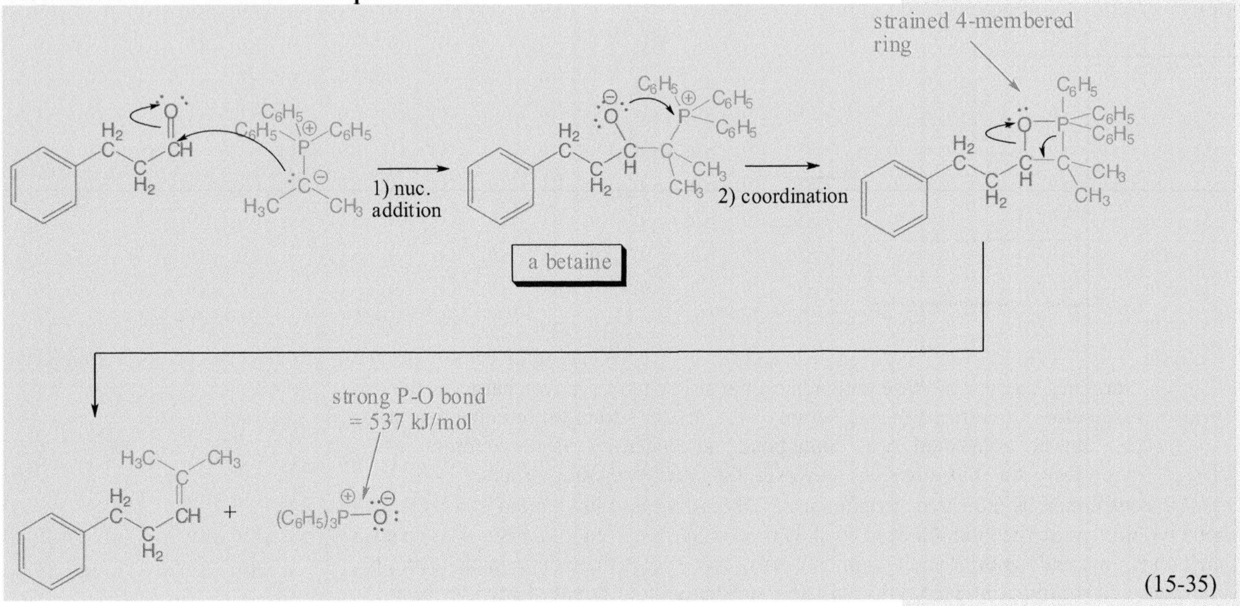

strained 4-membered ring

1) nuc. addition

2) coordination

a betaine

strong P-O bond = 537 kJ/mol

$$+ \; (C_6H_5)_3P^{\oplus}-O^{\ominus}$$

(15-35)

Clearly the first two steps of this reaction are driven by the principle of *electron-rich-to-electron-poor*. The last step, however, is driven primarily by the formation of the strong phosphorus-oxygen bond, whose bond energy is 537 kJ/mol.

Your Turn 15.13. In each of the first two steps of the mechanism in Equation 15-35, label the pertinent electron-rich and electron-poor sites.

If (E)/(Z) isomerism exists about the C=C double bond in the Wittig product, a mixture of the two isomers is produced, as shown in Equation 15-36. The reason for this can be seen from the first step of the mechanism, in which either face of the carbonyl-containing compound can be attacked. Generally one isomer is heavily favored over the other. However, we reserve discussion on making such predictions, because which isomer is favored depends upon the nature of the two reactants as well as on the composition of the solution.

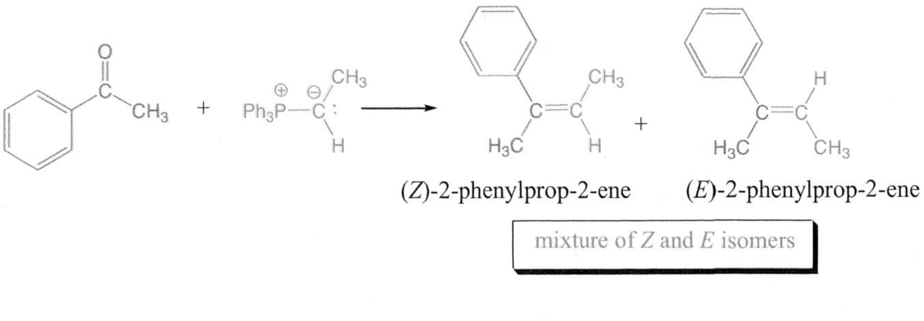

(*Z*)-2-phenylprop-2-ene (*E*)-2-phenylprop-2-ene

mixture of *Z* and *E* isomers

(15-36)

Problem 15.20. Draw the complete, detailed mechanism for the following reaction and predict the major organic product(s). Pay attention to stereochemistry.

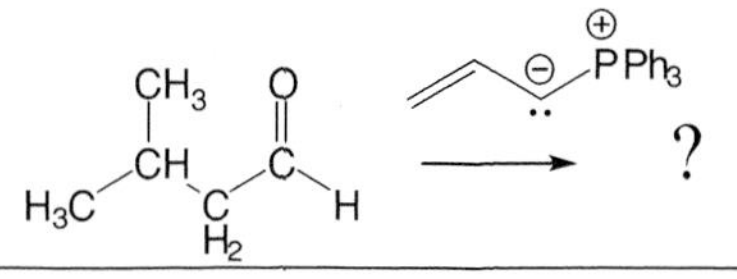

As was indicated previously in Table 15-1, Wittig reagents undergo *irreversible* addition to a carbonyl group, reflecting that they are very strong nucleophiles. Therefore, an α,β-unsaturated ketone or aldehyde that is treated with a Wittig reagent undergoes direct addition rather than conjugate addition. An example is shown in Equation 15-37.

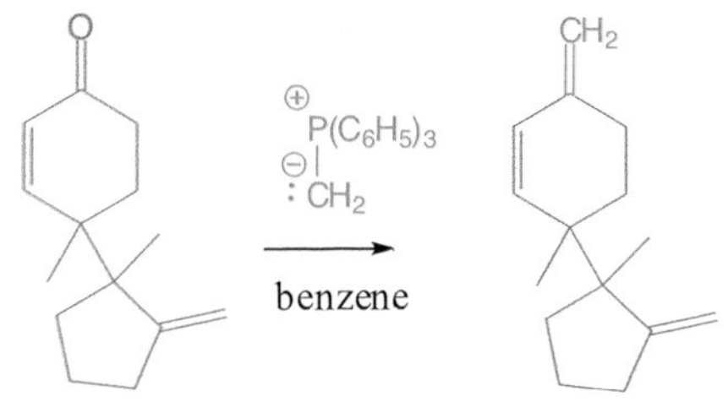

benzene

92%

(15-37)

15.8a. Generating Wittig Reagents

One of the reasons that Wittig reactions are so useful is that Wittig reagents can be generated from common precursors—alkyl halides. As shown in Equation 15-38, the Wittig reagent in Equation 15-34 can be synthesized from 2-bromopropane.

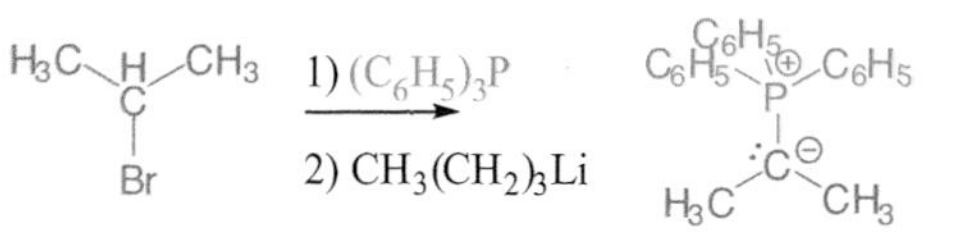

1) $(C_6H_5)_3P$

2) $CH_3(CH_2)_3Li$

2-bromopropane

56%

(15-38)

The alkyl halide is first treated with triphenyl phosphine, $P(C_6H_5)_3$, and the product of that reaction is treated with a strong base such as butyllithium.

The mechanism for this reaction is shown in Equation 15-39. Step 1 is an S_N2 reaction, in which the nucleophile is Ph_3P and the leaving group is the halide anion. The organic product possesses a positive charge on the phosphorus atom. Although Ph_3P is neutral, it is a rather good nucleophile because the phosphorus atom in the product can accommodate the positive charge due both to its large size (being in the third row of the periodic table) and its low electronegativity.

Your Turn 15.14. Verify that triphenylphosphine is a very good nucleophile by looking up its relative nucleophilicity and that of Br^- in Chapter 10. Write their relative nucleophilicities here.

$P(C_6H_5)$ _______ Br^- ________

Step 2 of Equation 15-39 is deprotonation by the alkyllithium species. A strong base like an alkyllithium is necessary because deprotonation occurs at a carbon atom. Carbon acids are in general extremely weak because a negatively charged carbon atom is normally very unstable. Here, however, deprotonation is facilitated by the fact that the negative charge that develops on C is stabilized by the adjacent positive charge on C—opposite charges attract.

Mechanism for Reaction in Equation 15-38

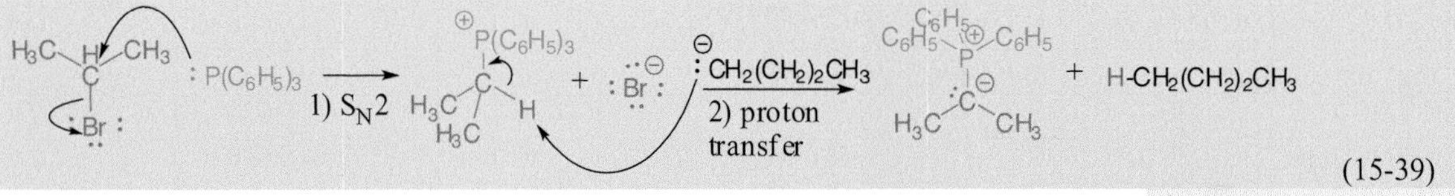

1) S_N2 2) proton transfer + $H{-}CH_2(CH_2)_2CH_3$ (15-39)

Problem 15.21. Draw the complete, detailed mechanism for the following reaction and provide structures for both the product and the intermediate that is not shown.

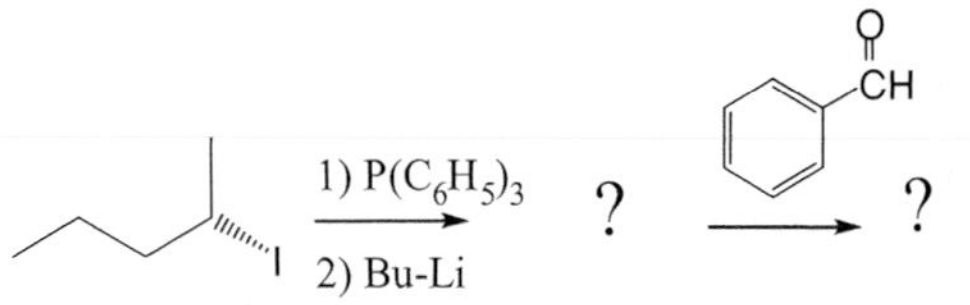

1) $P(C_6H_5)_3$ 2) Bu-Li → ? → ?

Problem 15.22. Draw an alkyl halide that could be used to synthesize the following Wittig reagent.

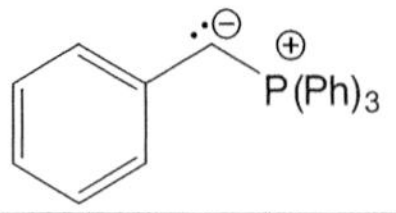

Notice that in the proton transfer step in Equation 15-39, the carbon atom that is deprotonated is the one originally bonded to the leaving group in the alkyl halide precursor. Therefore,

In order for an alkyl halide to be a suitable precursor for a Wittig reagent, the C atom bonded to the leaving group must possess at least one proton.

If that carbon atom does not possess any protons, the reaction will stop at the S_N2 product, as shown in Equation 15-40.

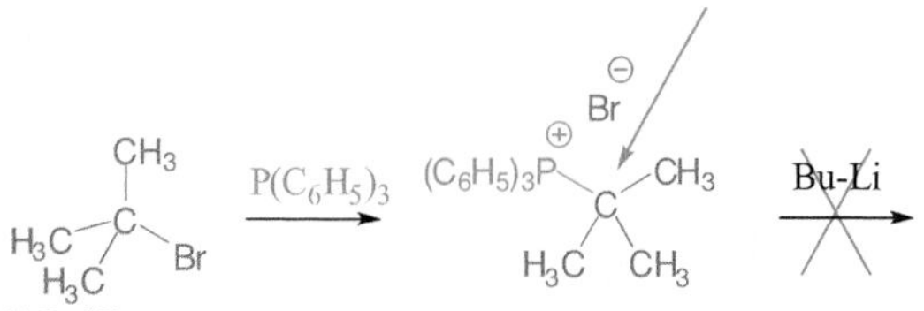

no protons on this carbon, so no deprotonation occurs

$P(C_6H_5)_3$ → Bu-Li (15-40)

Solved Problem 15.8. Show how you could synthesize 4-octene using butanal as your only source of carbon.

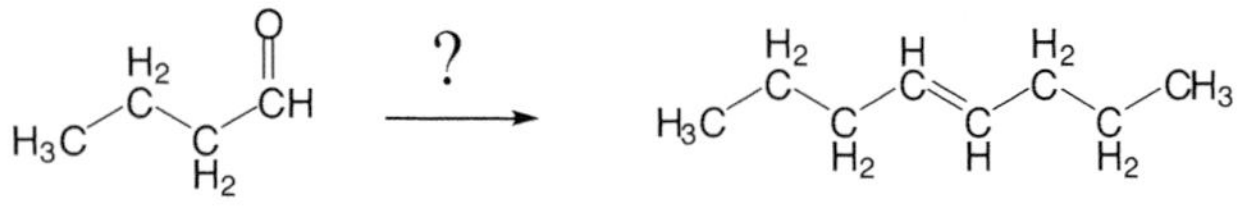

Think. What Wittig reagent would you need to carry out this reaction? What alkyl halide could serve as a precursor to that Wittig reagent? How can that alkyl halide be synthesized from butanal?

Solve. We can carry out a transform on the product, reversing a Wittig reaction.

$H_3C-CH_2-CH_2-CH{=}CH-CH_2-CH_2-CH_3$ $\xrightarrow{\text{reverse Wittig}}$ $H_3C-CH_2-CH_2-CH{=}O$ + $^{\ominus}HC(-P^{\oplus}(C_6H_5)_3)-CH_2-CH_2-CH_3$

Wittig reagent

The Wittig reagent can be synthesized from a four-carbon alkyl halide. The alkyl halide cannot be produced directly from butanal, but can be produced from 1-butanol, and 1-butanol can be synthesized by reducing butanal using a hydride agent.

$^{\ominus}HC(-P^{\oplus}(C_6H_5)_3)-CH_2-CH_2-CH_3$ $\Rightarrow$ $H_2C(Br)-CH_2-CH_2-CH_3$ $\Rightarrow$ $H_2C(OH)-CH_2-CH_2-CH_3$ $\Rightarrow$ $HC(=O)-CH_2-CH_2-CH_3$

In the forward direction, the synthesis might appear as follows.

$HC(=O)-CH_2-CH_2-CH_3$ $\xrightarrow[\text{EtOH}]{NaBH_4}$ $H_2C(OH)-CH_2-CH_2-CH_3$ $\xrightarrow{PBr_3}$ $H_2C(Br)-CH_2-CH_2-CH_3$ $\xrightarrow[\text{2) Bu-Li}]{\text{1) }P(C_6H_5)_3}$ $^{\ominus}HC(-P^{\oplus}(C_6H_5)_3)-CH_2-CH_2-CH_3$ $\xrightarrow{H_3C-CH_2-CH_2-CH=O}$ $H_3C-CH_2-CH_2-CH{=}CH-CH_2-CH_2-CH_3$

Problem 15.23. Show how you could carry out the following synthesis, beginning with benzaldehyde, and using any other reagents necessary.

?

15.9. SULFONIUM YLIDES: FORMATION OF EPOXIDES

Just like phosphonium ylides, **sulfonium ylides** are species with opposite charges on adjacent atoms, each with an octet of electrons. In this case, however, the positive charge is on a sulfur atom.

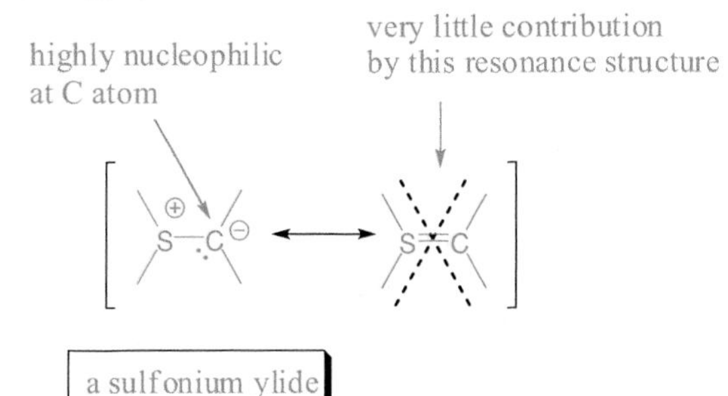

a sulfonium ylide

Phosphonium and sulfonium ylides are also similar in that they each have a resonance structure in which no atoms have a formal charge, as shown above at right. However, just as we saw with phosphonium ylides, that resonance structure for a sulfonium ylide has very little contribution to the resonance hybrid, because it requires a π bond between atomic orbitals in different shells—the second shell on C and the third shell on S. As a result, the structure above at left is a more accurate representation of the species, reflecting the strong nucleophilic character of the C atom.

Sulfonium ylides are synthesized in much the same way as phosphonium ylides, as shown in Equation 15-41. A dialkyl sulfide is treated with an alkyl halide, followed by treatment with a strong base.

$$(H_3C)_2S \xrightarrow[\text{2) NaH}]{\text{1) } CH_3I} (H_3C)_2S^{\oplus}-\ddot{C}H_2^{\ominus} \qquad (15\text{-}41)$$

The mechanism for this reaction, shown in Equation 15-42, is essentially identical to that for the synthesis of a Wittig reagent, shown previously in Equation 15-39. Step 1 is an S_N2 reaction in which the sulfide displaces the halide. In step 2, the carbon atom attached to S is deprotonated to produce the ylide.

Mechanism for the Reaction in Equation 15-41

$$(H_3C)_2\ddot{S}: \; + \; H_3C-\ddot{I}: \xrightarrow{\text{1) } S_N2} (H_3C)_2S^{\oplus}-CH_2-H \; + \; :H^{\ominus} \xrightarrow{\text{2) proton transfer}} (H_3C)_2S^{\oplus}-\ddot{C}H_2^{\ominus} \qquad (15\text{-}42)$$

Because of the negative charge on the carbon atom of the C–S bond, *sulfonium ylides are strong nucleophiles* and therefore add readily to carbonyls. However, as we can see in Equation 15-43, their overall reaction with ketones and aldehydes is somewhat different from the Wittig reaction. No C=C double bond is formed; instead, the product is an epoxide.

$$C_6H_5C(=O)CH_3 \xrightarrow[25\ ^{\circ}C,\ 1.5\ h]{(H_3C)_2S^{\oplus}-\ddot{C}H_2^{\ominus}} \underset{84\%}{C_6H_5C(CH_3)(-O-CH_2-)} + H_3C-S-CH_3 \qquad (15\text{-}43)$$

In particular,

> In the reaction between a sulfonium ylide and a ketone or aldehyde, the epoxide ring that forms involves the C and O atoms of the initial C=O bond, and the C atom of the C-S bond.

Your Turn 15.15. Circle the epoxide ring in Equation 15-43 and label it.

The mechanism for this epoxidation reaction is shown in Equation 15-44. Similar to the Wittig reaction, step 1 involves nucleophilic addition of the sulfonium ylide, resulting in a *betaine*—the positive charge on S and the negative charge on C are separated by two neutral atoms. Step 2 is simply an internal S_N2 reaction, where the dialkyl sulfide is the leaving group.

Mechanism for the Reaction in Equation 15-43

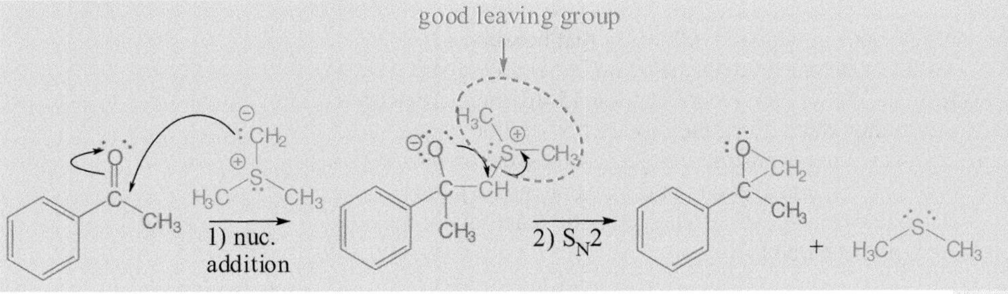

good leaving group

1) nuc. addition

2) S_N2

(15-44)

Why is the overall product of this reaction different from that of a Wittig reaction? In part it is because the S–O double bond is much weaker than the P=O double bond. In order to form an alkene product instead of an epoxide, dimethyl sulfoxide [$(CH_3)_2SO$] would also have to be produced. In dimethyl sulfoxide, the S–O bond energy is 436 kJ/mol, whereas that of the P–O bond in triphenylphosphine oxide is 537 kJ/mol—a difference of roughly 100 kJ/mol! Consequently there is much less of a driving force to form the S–O bond, and hence less of a driving force to form the alkene product.

Like Wittig reagents, sulfonium ylides are very strong nucleophiles and add *irreversibly* to a carbonyl group. Thus, upon attack of an α,β-unsaturated ketone or aldehyde, a sulfonium ylide undergoes direct addition rather than conjugate addition, as shown in Equation 15-45.

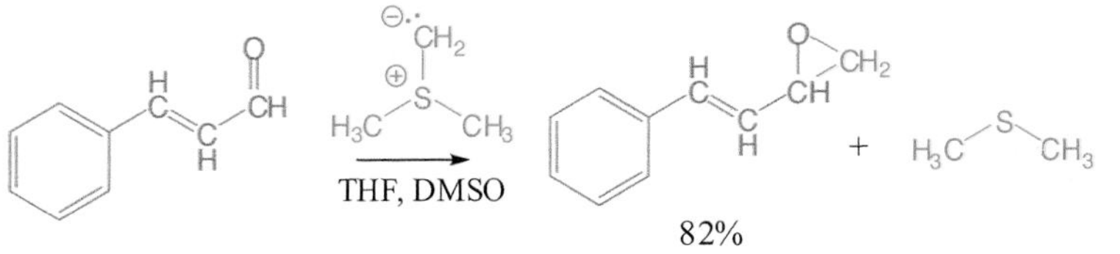

THF, DMSO

82%

(15-45)

Problem 15.24. For each of the following reactions, draw the complete mechanism and predict the major organic product.

(a)

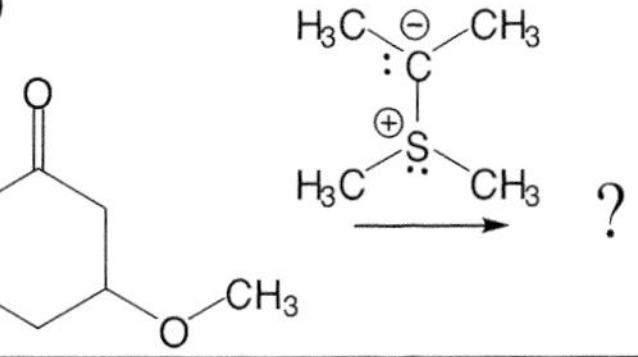

(b)

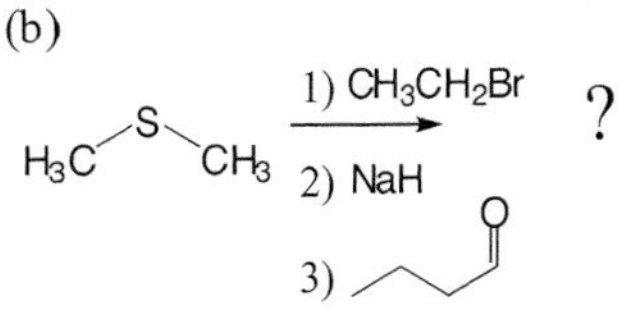

1) CH_3CH_2Br

2) NaH

3)

Problem 15.25. For each of the following epoxides, draw the sulfonium ylide and the ketone or aldehyde from which it can be synthesized.

(a) (b) 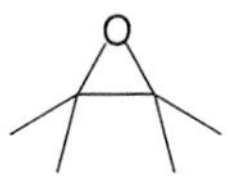 (c)

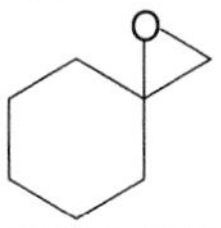

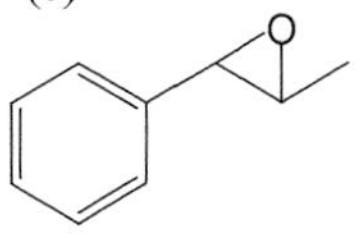

15.10. ORGANIC SYNTHESIS: GRIGNARD AND ALKYLLITHIUM REACTIONS IN SYNTHESIS

One of the most important reactions in organic synthesis is that between a carbonyl-containing compound—such as a ketone or aldehyde—and either a Grignard (R-MgBr) or alkyllithium (R-Li) reagent. As we can see in Equation 15-46, there are two main reasons why such reactions are so important. First, they are carbon-carbon bond-formation reactions, and so can play a key role in constructing the carbon skeleton of a target compound. Second, an OH group is generated at one of the carbon atoms joined by the new bond. Therefore, we can take advantage of the characteristic reactivity of the OH group to carry out further changes at that carbon.

further reactions can be carried out at the OH group

1) R-MgBr or R-Li

2) $H_3O^{\oplus}$

new C-C bond

(15-46)

For example, as we saw in Section 11.6, an alcohol can be converted into an ether via a *William synthesis*. One way to do so, as shown in Equation 15-47, is to add a strong base such as NaH, and treat the resulting alkoxide anion (RO^-) with an alkyl halide (R-Br).

1) H_3C-MgBr

2) $H_3O^{\oplus}$

1) NaH

2) $PhCH_2Br$

(15-47)

Alternatively, as shown in Equation 15-48, the product alcohol can be converted to an alkyl halide using PBr_3 (Section 11.1), and can then be treated with an alkoxide salt.

1) R-Li

2) $H_3O^{\oplus}$

PBr_3

$NaOCH_2CH_3$

OCH_2CH_3

(15-48)

Recall also from Sections 15.8 and 15.9 that alkyl halides are precursors to Wittig reagents and sulfonium ylides. Therefore, as shown in Equation 15-49, the alkyl halide generated in Equation 15-48 could instead be used to facilitate a Wittig reaction.

1) $P(C_6H_5)_3$
2) Bu-Li

$\oplus P(C_6H_5)_3$

(15-49)

In future chapters we will see how an alcohol can be converted into a Grignard or alkyllithium reagent (Chapter 17), or can be oxidized to a ketone or aldehyde (Chapter 19). In these ways, the alcohol product of a Grignard or alkyllithium reaction can be used to facilitate another such reaction.

Because of the utility of Grignard and alkyllithium reactions in synthesis, it is important to be able to reverse these reactions comfortably in your mind, in order to execute transforms efficiently in a retrosynthetic analysis. Such transforms can be carried out on essentially any alcohol, by disconnecting the bond between the alcohol carbon and an adjacent carbon, as shown in Equation 15-50. One precursor is a ketone or aldehyde, whose carbonyl group contains the alcohol carbon from the product. In the other precursor, the second carbon atom from the disconnected bond is bonded to the metal atom.

disconnect C-C bonds adjacent to OH group

C=O bond

C-metal bond

reverse Grignard

$H_2C=CH-CH(OH)-CH=CH_2 \Rightarrow H_2C=CH-CH=O + BrMg-CH=CH_2$

(15-50)

Notice in Equation 15-50, however, that the carbon-carbon bond on the left could have been disconnected instead. In this case, we would have arrived at the same precursors as in Equation 15-50, because of the symmetry of the alcohol. In general, however, disconnecting different C-C bonds will result in different precursors. An example is shown in Equation 15-51, in which the alcohol has three different C-C bonds adjacent to the OH group.

HO CH3

+ BrMg—CH3 (a)

CH3 + BrMg (b)

H3C + BrMg (c)

(15-51)

As we can see, disconnecting the C-C bond indicated by the red, blue, or green wavy line yields the precursors in Equation 15-51a, 15-51b, or 15-51c, respectively.

Having the choice of which C-C bond to disconnect may at first seem daunting. However, with practice, carrying out such transforms will become quite straightforward, and you will appreciate the options that the Grignard reaction affords.

Problem 15.26. Show how the molecule below can be synthesized from each of the Grignard reagents shown in Equation 15-51.

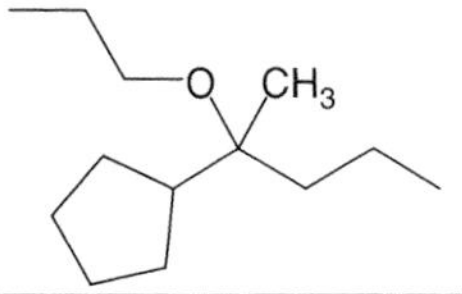

O CH3

Problem 15.26. Show how the following compound can be synthesized from two different alkyllithium reagents.

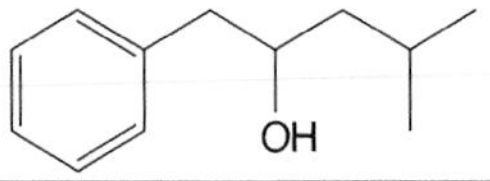

OH

15.11. ORGANIC SYNTHESIS: CONSIDERATIONS OF DIRECT ADDITION vs. CONJUGATE ADDITION

As we saw in Section 15.4, a nucleophile can attack an α,β-unsaturated carbonyl at either the carbonyl carbon, yielding the direct-addition product (Equation 15-52a), or the beta carbon, yielding the conjugate addition product (Equation 15-52b).

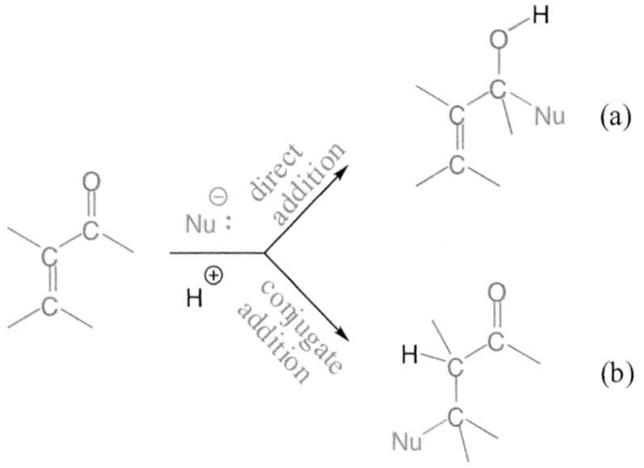

Nu : ⊖ H ⊕ direct addition (a) conjugate addition (b)

(15-52)

As we can see, direct addition converts the carbonyl group to an OH group, leaving the C=C double bond unaltered. By contrast, in conjugate addition, the double bond between the alpha and beta carbons is converted into a single bond, leaving the C=O bond unaltered.

When reversing one of these reactions in a retrosynthetic analysis, be sure to look for these clues. For example, in the molecule at left in Equation 15-53, notice that the cyano group is beta to the C=O bond. Thus, the target can be generated by conjugate addition, in which NC^- attacks the beta carbon.

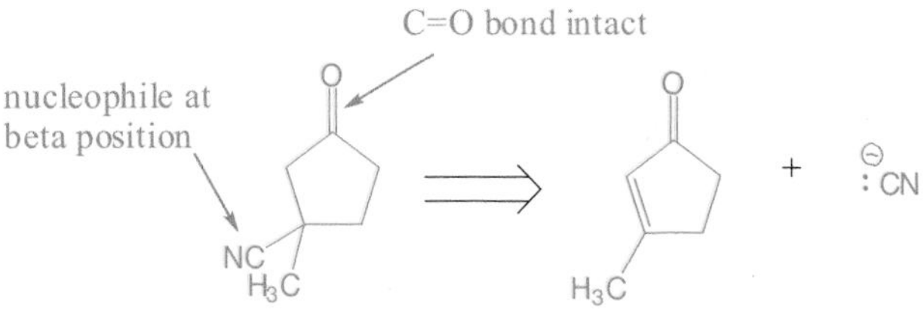

C=O bond intact

nucleophile at beta position

NC H3C ⟹ H3C + ⊖:CN

(15-53)

In the forward direction, the synthetic step might appear as in Equation 15-54.

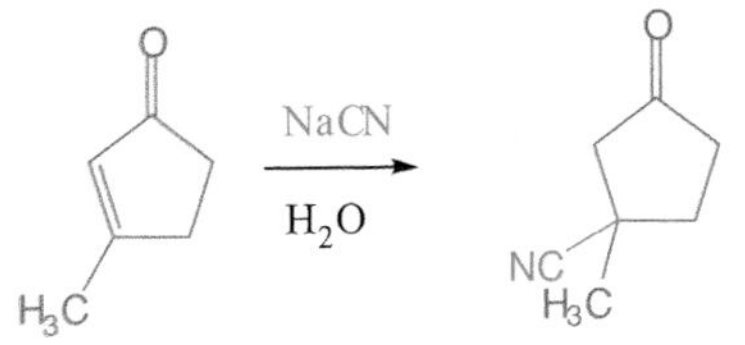

NaCN / H_2O

(15-54)

On the other hand, in the molecule at left in Equation 15-55, a C=C double bond is adjacent to an alcohol group. We can therefore envision it as the result of direct addition, with H^- as the nucleophile.

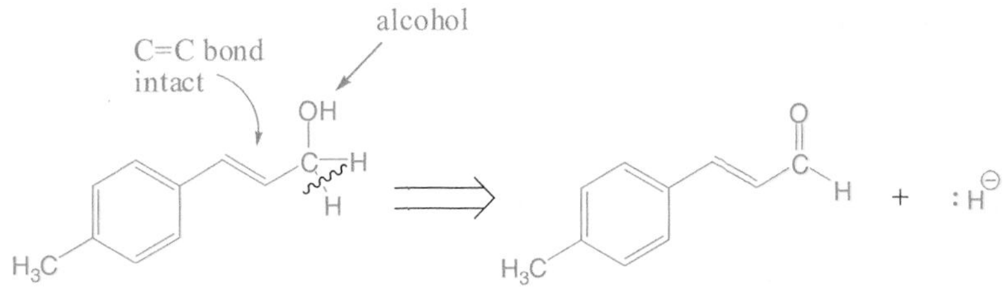

C=C bond intact; alcohol

(15-55)

Thus, the forward reaction might appear as in Equation 15-56.

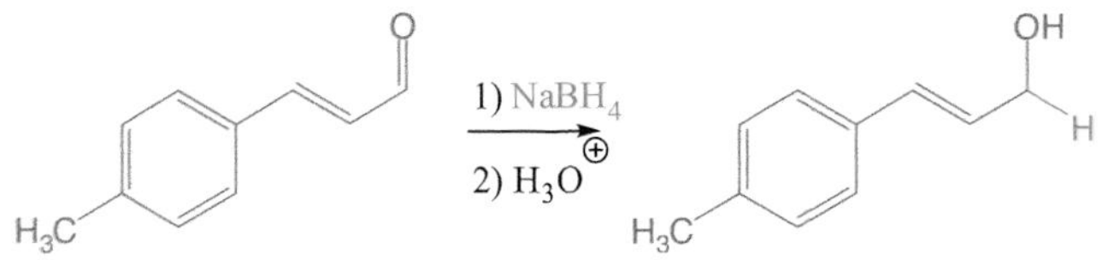

1) $NaBH_4$ 2) H_3O^+

(15-56)

If a particular retrosynthetic analysis suggests the use of an R^- nucleophile in the forward direction, then we must also consider *regioselectivity*. Suppose, for example, we carry out the transform in Equation 15-57, for which the precursors at right are an α,β-unsaturated ketone and an R^- nucleophile.

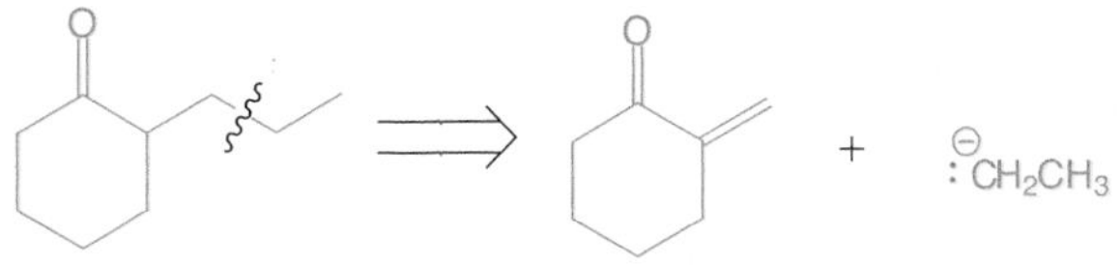

(15-57)

In the forward direction, there are a variety of forms the R^- nucleophile can take, such as an alkyllithium reagent (R-Li), a Grignard reagent (R-MgBr), or a lithium dialkyl cuprate (R_2CuLi). Recognizing that we wish the nucleophile to attack at the beta carbon, we should choose the form of a lithium dialkyl cuprate, which we know leads almost exclusively to the conjugate addition product. Thus, the forward reaction would appear as in Equation 15-58.

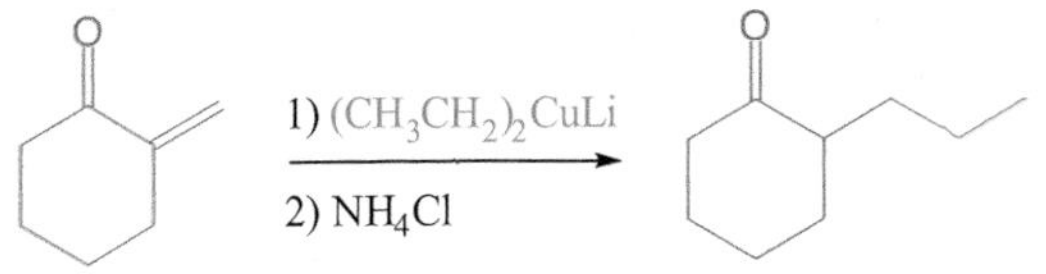

1) $(CH_3CH_2)_2CuLi$ 2) NH_4Cl

(15-58)

Problem 15.27. Show how you would synthesize each of the following from 4-hexen-3-one.

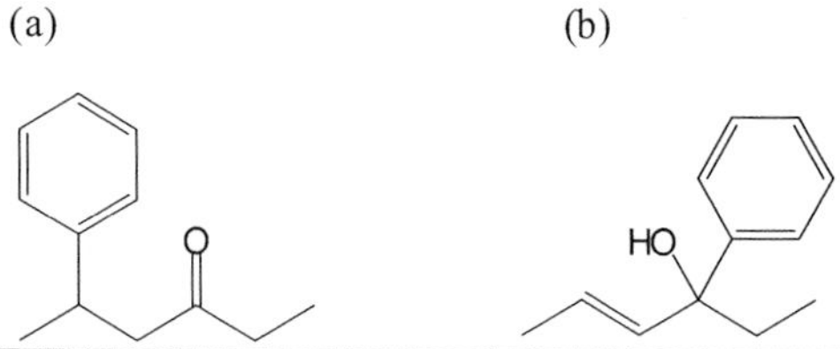

(a) (b)

HO

15.12. ORGANIC SYNTHESIS: CONSIDERATIONS OF REGIOSELECTIVITY IN THE FORMATION OF ALKENES

In Section 15.8, we learned that alkenes can be synthesized via the Wittig reaction. In Chapters 8–10, we also saw examples of alkene formation via E1 and E2 reactions. However, the Wittig reaction is generally regarded as the more synthetically useful reaction, due to its *regiospecificity*. In a Wittig reaction, a C=C double bond forms precisely at the location of the initial C=O bond in the ketone or aldehyde. On the other hand, E1 and E2 reactions typically result in a mixture of alkene isomers, and occasionally the desired isomer is the minor product.

Suppose, for example, that we wish to synthesize 1-cyclopentyl-1-pentene. As shown in Equation 15-59, this can be accomplished straightforwardly using the Wittig reaction.

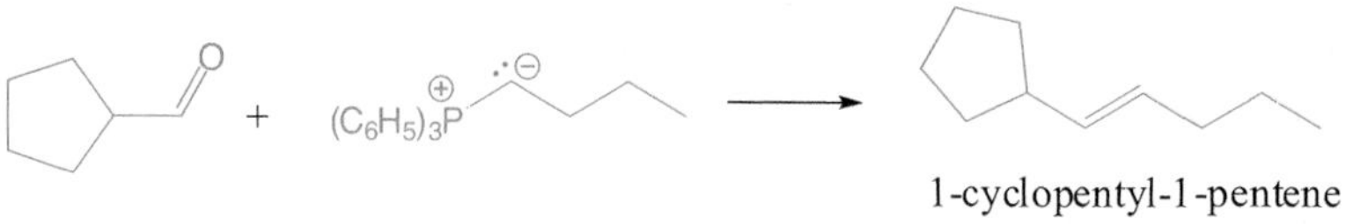

O + $(C_6H_5)_3\overset{\oplus}{P}$ ⊖ ⟶

1-cyclopentyl-1-pentene (15-59)

However, attempting to synthesize this compound using an elimination reaction is problematic. One possible precursor is 1-bromo-1-cyclopentylpentane, as shown in Equation 15-60, but the major product is an undesired isomer—a trisubstituted alkene. Recall that according to Zaitsev's rule (Section 8.3d), elimination favors the more highly substituted alkene. In this case, the desired product is the less highly substituted alkene—a disubstituted alkene.

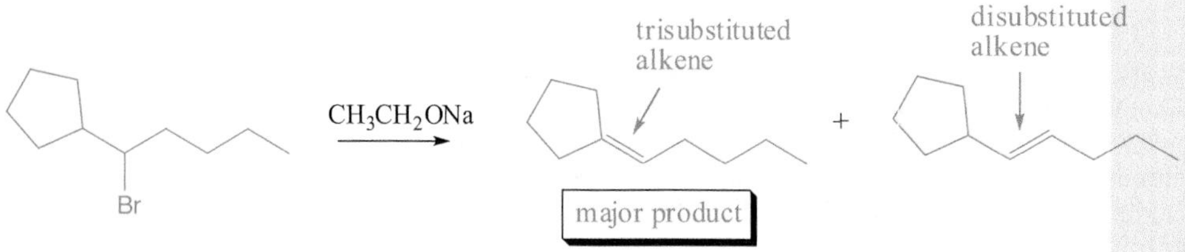

trisubstituted alkene

disubstituted alkene

Br $\xrightarrow{CH_3CH_2ONa}$ +

major product

(15-60)

A similar problem arises if 2-bromo-1-cyclopentylpentane is used as the precursor. As shown in Equation 15-61, both possible elimination products are disubstituted alkenes, so a significant amount of each will be produced.

disubstituted alkene disubstituted alkene

CH_3CH_2ONa, heat (15-61)

The main lesson from these examples is that, when given the option of using either a Wittig reaction or an elimination reaction to synthesize an alkene, a Wittig reaction is usually the better choice.

15.13. WRAPPING UP AND LOOKING AHEAD

This chapter began by introducing the fundamental mechanism by which a strong nucleophile adds to a polar π bond, called *direct addition*, or *1,2-addition*. In that mechanism, nucleophilic attack takes place at the electron-poor atom of a polar π bond, followed by protonation of that bond's electron-rich atom. If the polar π bond is α,β-unsaturated, a second nucleophilic addition mechanism is also available: *conjugate addition*, or *1,4-addition*. Which of these mechanisms dominates depends on the reversibility of the direct addition mechanism. Nucleophiles that add *irreversibly* to the polar π bond favor the direct addition product. These include H^- from either $LiAlH_4$ or $NaBH_4$, R^- from either R-MgBr or R-Li, and both Wittig reagents and sulfonium ylides. Other nucleophiles that add *reversibly* favor conjugate addition.

Throughout the remainder of this chapter, we examined the utility of a variety of nucleophiles that undergo nucleophilic addition. $LiAlH_4$ and $NaBH_4$ serve to reduce polar π bonds—most notably, ketones and aldehydes are reduced to alcohols. Grignard and alkyllithium reagents are used to form a new C-C single bond to the electron-poor carbon atom of the polar π bond, whereas lithium dialkyl cuprates are used to form a new C-C bond to the polar π bond's beta carbon. Wittig reagents are used to synthesize alkenes, and sulfonium ylides are used to synthesize epoxides.

In Chapter 16, we will examine nucleophilic addition reactions involving relatively weak nucleophiles, often requiring acid- or base-catalysis. Among those are some of the most useful reactions in organic synthesis, such as the *aldol reaction*. The aldol reaction is an important carbon-carbon bond-formation reaction that allows us to join together two separate carbon backbones, each of which can be quite elaborate. Other reactions we will encounter in Chapter 16 are more specifically aimed at altering particular functional groups.

Table 15-5. Functional Group Transformations

	Starting Functional Group	Typical Reagents and Reaction Conditions	Functional Group Formed	Key Electron-Rich Species	Key Electron-Poor Species	Type of Mechanism	Discussed in Section(s)
(1)	$R(or\ H)-C(=O)-R(or\ H)$ Ketone or aldehyde	1) $NaBH_4$ or $LiAlH_4$ 2) $H_3O^{\oplus}$	$R(or\ H)-C(OH)(H)-R(or\ H)$ alcohol	$H^{\ominus}$ Hydride anion	$C=O$ (δ^+ on C)	Nucleophilic addition	15.5
(2)	$R(or\ H)-C(=N-R(or\ H))-R(or\ H)$ imine	1) $LiAlH_4$ 2) $H_3O^{\oplus}$	$R(or\ H)-C(H)(NH-R(or\ H))-R(or\ H)$ amine	$H^{\ominus}$ Hydride anion	$C=N$ (δ^+ on C)	Nucleophilic addition	15.5
(3)	$R-C\equiv N$ Nitrile	1) $LiAlH_4$ 2) $H_3O^{\oplus}$	$R-CH_2-NH_2$ 1° amine	$H^{\ominus}$ Hydride anion	$-C\equiv N$ (δ^+ on C)	Sequential nucleophilic additions	15.5
(4)	$C=CH-C(=O)-R(or\ H)$ α,β-unsaturated	1) $NaBH_4$ or $LiAlH_4$ 2) $H_3O^{\oplus}$	$C=CH-C(OH)(H)-R(or\ H)$ Alcohol	$H^{\ominus}$ Hydride anion	$C=O$ (δ^+ on C)	Nucleophilic addition	15.5a
(5)	$(H\ or)\ R-C(=O)-CH_2-R$ Ketone or aldehyde	NaH	$(H\ or)\ R-C(=O)-\ddot{C}^{\ominus}H-R$ Enolate anion	$H^{\ominus}$ Hydride anion	$C(=O)-C-H$ ($H\delta^+$)	Proton transfer	15.5b
(6)	$(H\ or)\ R-C(H)(Br)-R(or\ R)$ Alkyl halide	1) $P(C_6H_5)_3$ 2) R-Li	$(H\ or)\ R-\ddot{C}^{\ominus}-R(or\ H)$ with $P(C_6H_5)_3$ Wittig reagent	δ^- $:P(C_6H_5)_3$ Triphenyl phosphine	C (δ^+)	S_N2	15.8a
(7)	$(H\ or)\ R-C(H)(Br)-R(or\ R)$ Alkyl halide	1) $S(CH_3)_2$ 2) NaH	$(H\ or)\ R-\ddot{C}^{\ominus}-R(or\ H)$ with $^{\oplus}S(CH_3)_2$ (H_3C, CH_3) Sulfonium ylide	δ^- $:S(CH_3)_2$	C (δ^+)	S_N2	15.9

Table 15-6. Reactions that Alter the Carbon Skeleton

	Reactant	Typical Reagent and Reaction Conditions	Product Formed	Key Electron-Rich Species	Key Electron-Poor Species	Type of Reaction	Discussed in Section(s)
(1)	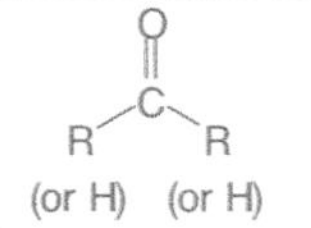 O=C(R)R (or H) (or H) Ketone or aldehyde	1) R-Li or R-MgBr 2) $H_3O^{\oplus}$	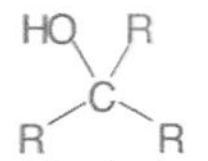 HO, R, C, R, R Alcohol	$R^{\ominus}$	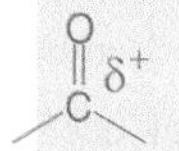 O, C, δ+	Nucleophilic addition	15.6
(2)	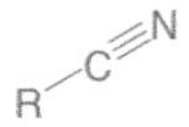 R–C≡N Nitrile	1) R-MgBr 2) CH_3OH	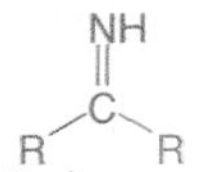 NH=C(R)R Imine	$R^{\ominus}$	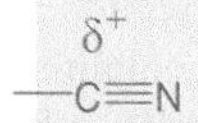 δ+ —C≡N	Nucleophilic addition	15.6
(3)	 R–MgBr Grignard reagent	1) CO_2 (s) 2) NH_4Cl	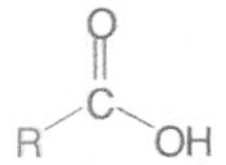 O=C(R)OH Carboxylic acid	$R^{\ominus}$	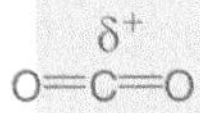 δ+ O=C=O	Nucleophilic addition	15.6
(4)	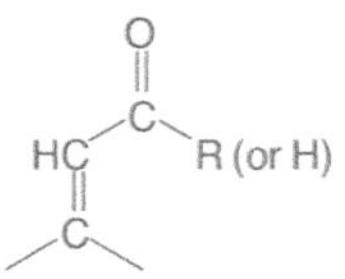 O, C, HC, R (or H), C α,β-unsaturated	1) R_2CuLi, THF 2) NH_4Cl	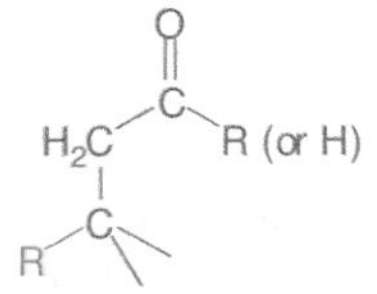 O, C, H_2C, R (or H), C, R Ketone or aldehyde	$R^{\ominus}$	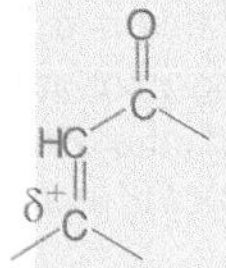 O, C, HC, δ+, C	Conjugate nucleophilic addition	15.7
(5)	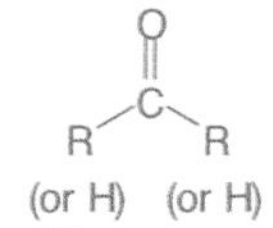 O=C(R)R (or H) (or H) Ketone or aldehyde	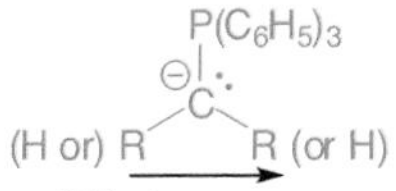 $P(C_6H_5)_3$, ⊖, C, (H or) R, R (or H) Wittig reagent	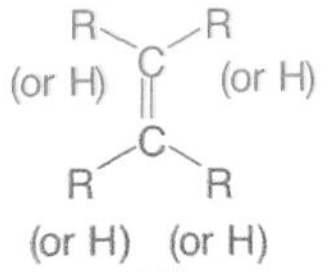 R, R (or H), C, (or H), C, R, R (or H) (or H) Alkene	$R^{\ominus}$	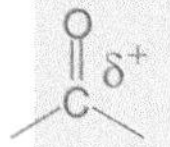 O, C, δ+	Wittig reaction	15.8
(6)	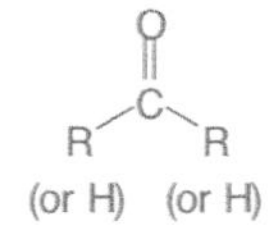 O=C(R)R (or H) (or H) Ketone or aldehyde	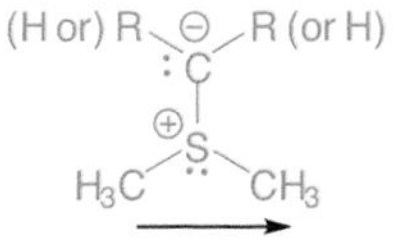 (H or) R, ⊖, R (or H), C, ⊕, S, H_3C, CH_3 Sulfonium ylide	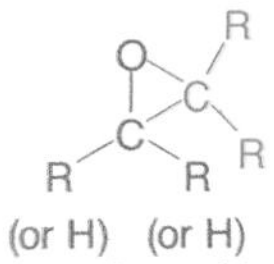 O, C, R, C, R, R, R (or H) (or H) Epoxide	$R^{\ominus}$	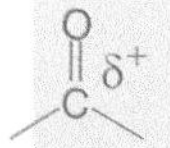 O, C, δ+	Epoxidation	15.9

CHAPTER SUMMARY AND KEY TERMS

- The general mechanism for the addition of a strong, negatively charged nucleophile (Nu^-) to a **polar π bond** consists of two steps:

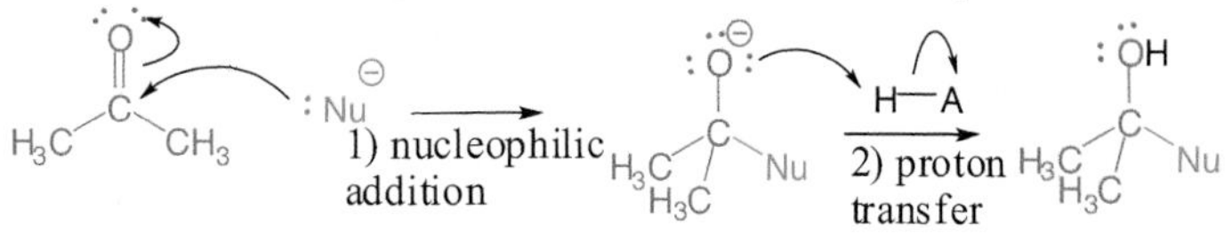

  Nucleophilic attack occurs in the first step, followed by protonation. (Section 15.1)
- Most nucleophiles add to a polar π bond reversibly. Nucleophiles that add irreversibly include H^- from either $NaBH_4$ or $LiAlH_4$ and R^- from either R-MgBr or R-Li. (Section 15.1)
- Some carbonyl-containing functional groups—including carboxylic acids (RCO_2H), esters (RCO_2R), amides ($RCONR_2$), acid chlorides (RCO_2Cl), and acid anhydrides (RCO_2COR)—have a *leaving group* attached to the carbonyl carbon. These functional groups have reactivities that differ from those of ketones and aldehydes; they will be discussed in Chapter 18. (Section 15.2)
- Nucleophilic addition to the carbonyl group of an aldehyde tends to be more energetically favorable and faster than addition to the carbonyl group of a ketone. (Section 15.3)
- A polar π bond that is **α,β-unsaturated** is susceptible to nucleophilic attack at both the electron-poor atom of the polar π bond and the **beta carbon**. Attack at the former yields the **direct addition** (or **1,2-addition**) product; attack at the latter yields the **conjugate addition** (or **1,4-addition**) product. (Section 15.4)

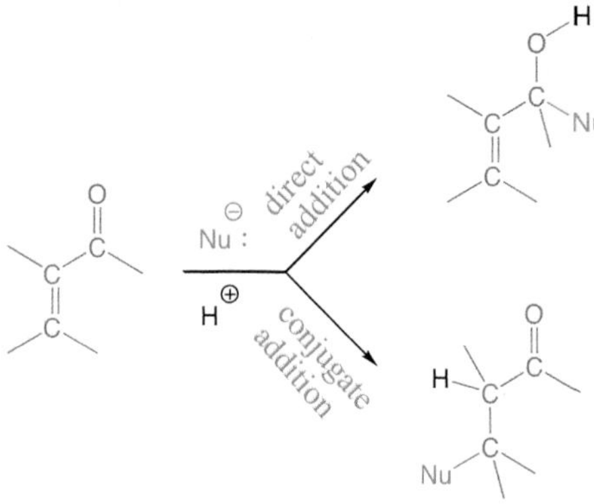

- Direct addition to an α,β-unsaturated polar π bond dominates if the nucleophile adds *irreversibly* to the polar π bond. Otherwise, conjugate addition is favored. (Section 15.4)
- **Lithium aluminum hydride ($LiAlH_4$)** and **sodium borohydride ($NaBH_4$)** are sources of H^- that behave as **reducing agents** in the presence of a polar π bond. Both reagents reduce ketones ($R_2C{=}O$) and aldehydes ($RCH{=}O$) to alcohols (R-OH). A nitrile (R-CN) can be reduced to a primary amine ($R\text{-}NH_2$) by $LiAlH_4$, but not by $NaBH_4$. (Section 15-5)
- $LiAlH_4$ is a very strong base, so it is not compatible with protic solvents like water and alcohols. (Section 15-5)
- **Sodium hydride** (NaH) is an ionic hydride, and thus a strong base, but is not nucleophilic. (Section 15.5b)
- **Grignard reagents (R-MgBr)** and **alkyllithium reagents (R-Li)** favor direct addition over conjugate addition. They are strong nucleophiles and strong bases that are not compatible with acidic functional groups or those that are prone to nucleophilic attack. (Section 15.6)

- **Lithium dialkyl cuprates (R_2CuLi)** are weak R^- nucleophiles that favor conjugate addition over direct addition. (Section 15.7)
- A **Wittig reagent**, also called a **phosphonium ylide**, is characterized by a $^+P{-}C{:}^-$ bond and is strongly nucleophilic at the negatively charged C atom. In a **Wittig reaction**, the phosphonium ylide undergoes nucleophilic addition to the C=O bond of a ketone or aldehyde, resulting in the formation of an alkene. (Section 15.8)
- A **sulfonium ylide** is characterized by a $^+S{-}C{:}^-$ bond, and is strongly nucleophilic at the negatively charged C atom. A sulfonium ylide will add to the C=O bond of a ketone or aldehyde, ultimately producing an epoxide. (Section 15.9)

PROBLEMS

28. For which of the following compounds will the nucleophile add *reversibly* to a polar π bond? Which will add *irreversibly*?

(a) Li (b) MgBr (c) ONa (d) ONa

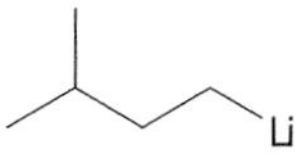

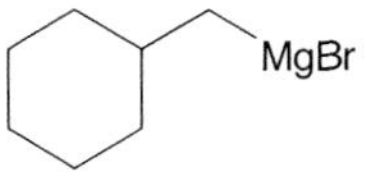

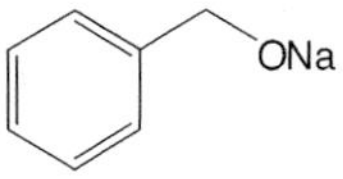

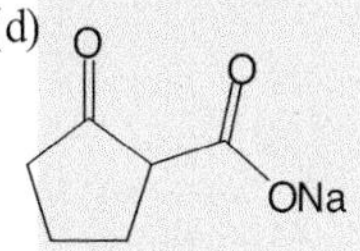

(e) $(H_3C{-}CH_2{-}CH_2)_2CuLi$ (f) N Li (g) H_2O (h) N H

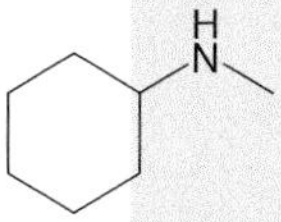

(i) O (j) SNa (k) SH

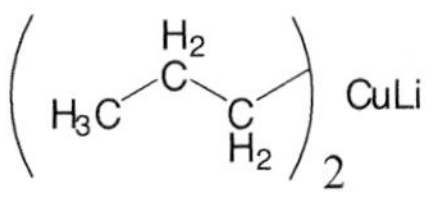

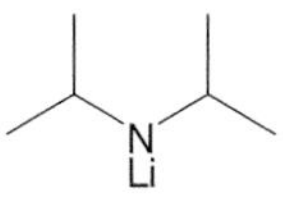

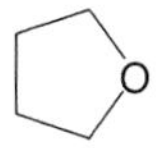

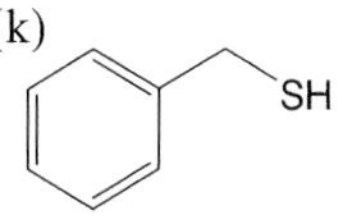

29. For each pair of compounds, which do you think has the polar π bond that will undergo nucleophilic addition more rapidly? Why?

(a) or 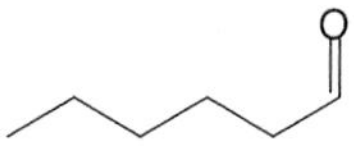 (b) CH_3 or CF_3

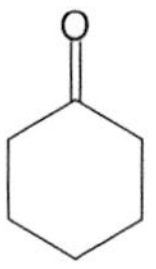

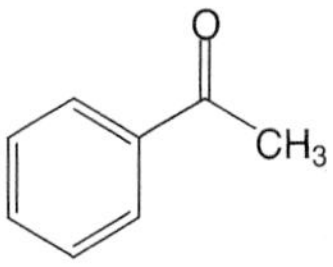

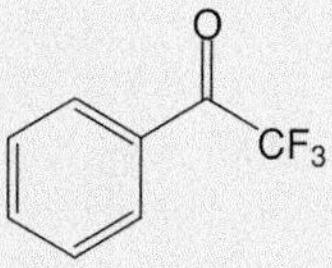

(c) Cl or Cl (d) $Cl_3C{-}C{\equiv}N$ or $H_3C{-}C{\equiv}N$

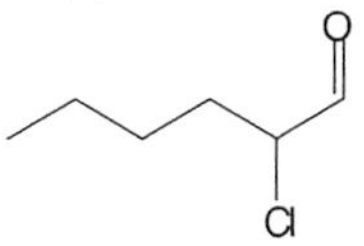

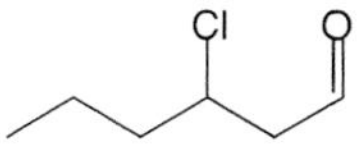

30. For each reaction below, draw the mechanism and predict the major product.

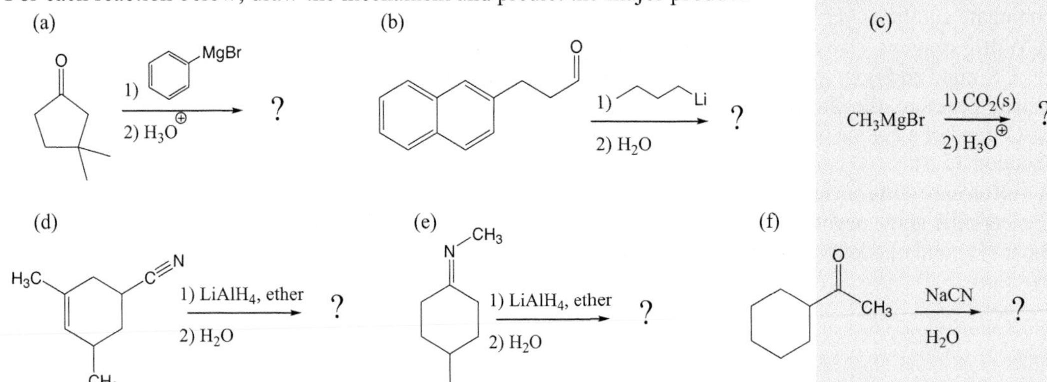

31. For each reaction below, draw the mechanism and predict the major products.

(a) KCN / H_2O ?

(b) KCN / H_2O ?

(c) 1) CH_3MgBr, ether; 2) H_2O ?

(d) 1) $(H_2C{=}C(CH_3))_2CuLi$; 2) H_2O ?

(e) CH_3CH_2SNa / ethanol ?

32. For each reaction below, predict the major organic product, and draw the complete, detailed mechanism.

(a) OH; 1) PBr_3; 2) $(C_6H_5)_3P$; 3) Bu-Li; 4) acetone ?

(b) 1) $(CH_3)_2SCH_2$; 2) CH_3SNa, H_2O ?

(c) 1) C_6H_5MgBr; 2) H_3O^+ ? 1) NaH; 2) CH_3CH_2Br ?

(d) 1) $NaBH_4$, EtOH; 2) PBr_3; 3) $(CH_3)_2S$; 4) NaH ? H_3C–CH(=O) ?

33. Show two different syntheses for the following compound, one using $(CH_3)CuLi$ as a reagent, and the other using $(CH_3CH_2)_2CuLi$.

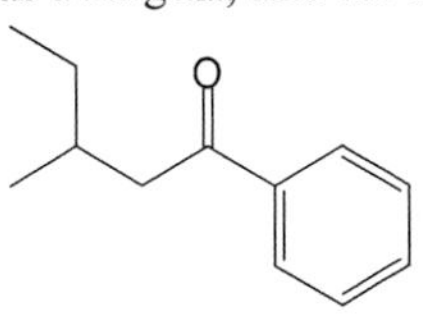

34. Show how you can synthesize the following alcohol from three different Grignard reagents.

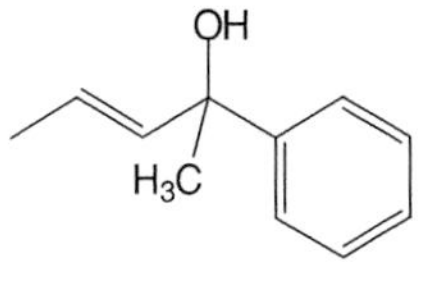

OH

H_3C

35. When propenal is treated with sodium acetylide, a product is formed, whose IR spectrum exhibits a broad absorption between 3,200 cm^{-1} and 3,600 cm^{-1}, and shows no absorption near 1,650 cm^{-1}. (a) Draw the structure of the product. (b) Argue whether the nucleophile adds *reversibly* or *irreversibly* to the carbonyl group.

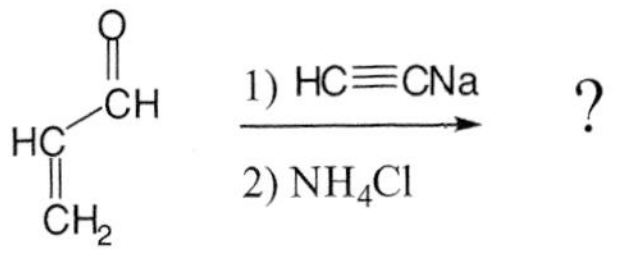

$H_2C{=}CH{-}CH{=}O$ → 1) $HC{\equiv}CNa$ 2) NH_4Cl → ?

36. Deuterium, a heavy isotope of hydrogen, contains 1 proton, 1 neutron, and 1 electron. The chemical behavior of deuterium is essentially identical to that of H. Therefore, D_2O behaves the same as H_2O; $LiAlD_4$ behaves the same as $LiAlH_4$; and CD_3Li behaves the same as CH_3Li. With this in mind, draw the detailed mechanism of each of the following reactions. Using the mechanism, predict the products.

(a) 1) $LiAlH_4$ 2) D_2O → ?

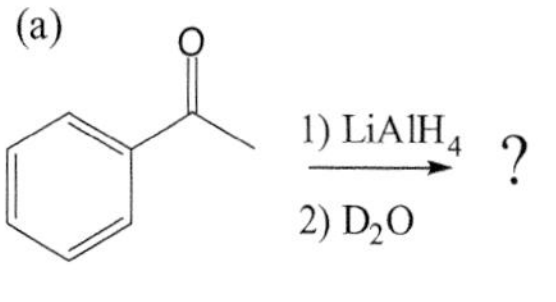

(b) 1) $LiAlD_4$ 2) H_2O → ?

(c) 1) $LiAlD_4$ 2) D_2O → ?

(d) 1) CH_3Li 2) D_2O → ?

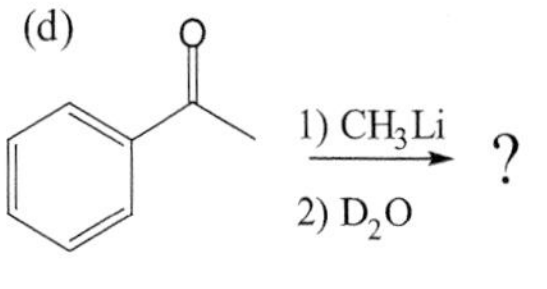

(e) 1) CD_3Li 2) H_2O → ?

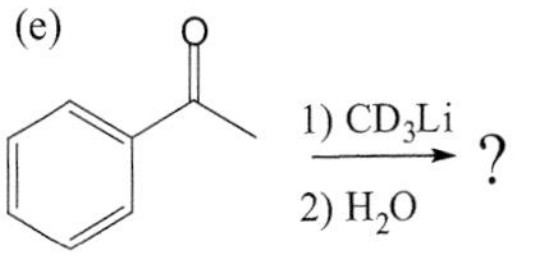

(f) 1) CD_3Li 2) D_2O → ?

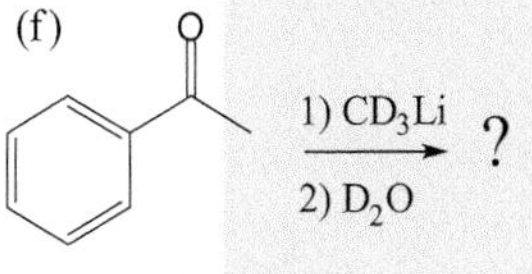

37. Consider the following reaction in which an epoxide is formed.

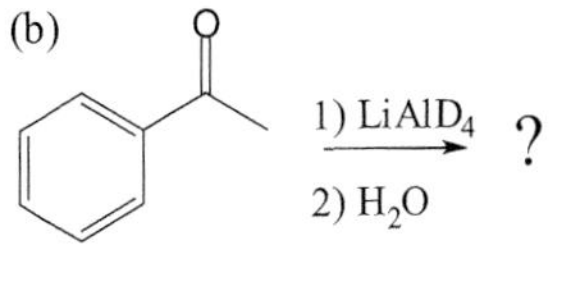

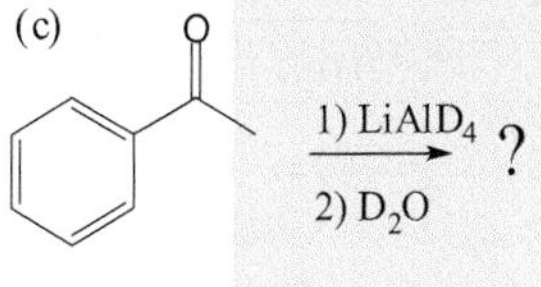

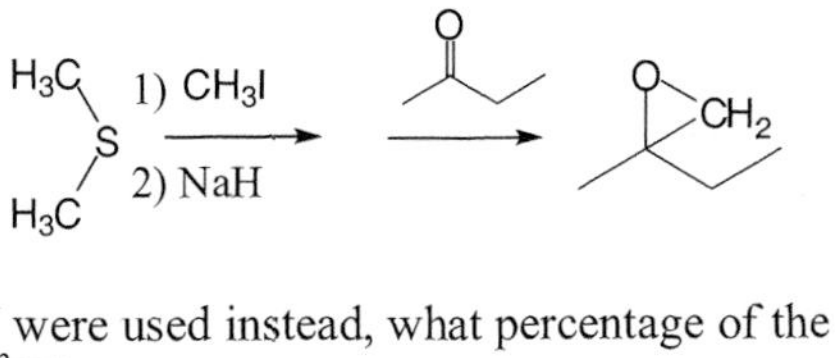

$(H_3C)_2S$ → 1) CH_3I 2) NaH → (+ ketone) → epoxide (CH_2)

If $^{13}CH_3I$ were used instead, what percentage of the epoxide product would contain ^{13}C?

38. Determine the structures of compounds A – J below.

Cl OH $\xrightarrow{PBr_3}$ A $\xrightarrow{KCN}$ B $\xrightarrow[2)\ H_2O]{1)\ LiAlH_4,\ ether}$ C $\xrightarrow[NaOH,\ heat]{CH_3Br\ (excess)}$ Cl

O O $\xrightarrow[2)\ CH_3CH_2Br]{1)\ NaH}$ D $\xrightarrow[CH_3CH_2OH]{NaBH_4}$ E $\xrightarrow[2)\ CH_3CH_2Br]{1)\ NaH}$ F

O $\xrightarrow[2)\ NH_4Cl]{1)\ (H_2C{=}CH{-}CH_2)_2CuLi}$ G $\xrightarrow[CH_3CH_2OH]{NaBH_4}$ H $\xrightarrow{PBr_3}$ I $\xrightarrow[heat]{(CH_3)_3CONa}$ J

39. Determine the structures of compounds A – O below.

A $\xrightarrow[2)\ CH_3OH]{1)\ C_6H_5MgBr}$ NH, O $\xrightarrow[2)\ H_2O]{1)\ LiAlH_4,\ ether}$ B $\xrightarrow[heat]{H_3O^{\oplus}}$ C $\xrightarrow[2)\ CH_3CH_2Br]{1)\ NaOH}$ D

O $\xrightarrow[2)\ H_2O]{1)\ LiAlH_4,\ ether}$ E $\xrightarrow{PBr_3}$ F $\xrightarrow[2)\ Bu\text{-}Li]{1)\ P(C_6H_5)_3}$ G $\xrightarrow{HCHO}$ H

OH $\xrightarrow{PBr_3}$ I $\xrightarrow{NaCN}$ J $\xrightarrow[2)\ CH_3OH]{1)\ CH_3MgBr,\ ether}$ K $\xrightarrow[2)\ H_2O]{1)\ LiAlH_4,\ ether}$ L $\xrightarrow[NaOH,\ heat]{CH_3Br\ (excess)}$

O $\xrightarrow[2)\ NH_4Cl]{1)\ (C_6H_{11})_2CuLi}$ M $\xrightarrow{(CH_3)_2C^{\ominus}{-}S^{\oplus}(CH_3)_2}$ N $\xrightarrow[CH_3CH_2OH]{NaOCH_2CH_3}$ O

40. In this chapter, we mentioned that alkyllithium and Grignard reagents are highly reactive with protic solvents like water and alcohols, and therefore require aprotic solvents like ethers. Recall that acetone is an aprotic solvent that can be employed in nucleophilic substitution and elimination reactions. However, acetone cannot be used as a solvent for reactions involving alkyllithium and Grignard reagents. Explain why.

41. Provide the reagents necessary to perform the following transformation.

42. In the chapter, we mentioned that conjugate addition of $NaBH_4$ to an α,β-unsaturated carbonyl results in two separate nucleophilic additions. Conjugate addition of a lithium dialkyl cuprate (R_2CuLi), on the other hand, results in only a single nucleophilic addition. Explain.

43. Unlike most hydrates, cyclopropanone's hydrate is stable and can be isolated. Explain why its hydrate is stable.

44. A Wittig reagent can be prepared from 5-bromo-1,3-cyclopentadiene in the usual way. However, that Wittig reagent is unreactive toward ketones or aldehydes. (a) Draw the complete mechanism showing the formation of the Wittig reagent. (b) Explain why that Wittig reagent does not undergo nucleophilic addition with ketones or aldehydes.

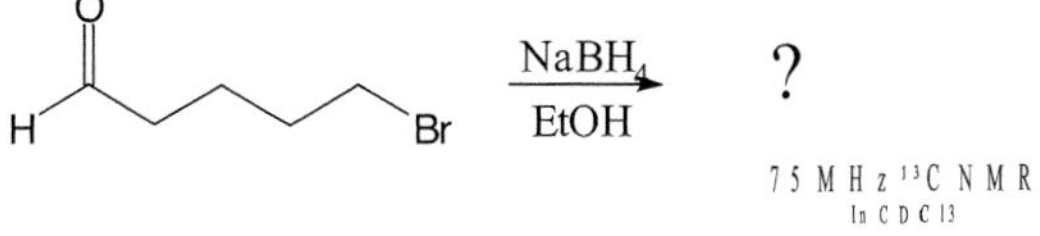

45. When 5-bromopentanal is treated with sodium borohydride, a compound is produced whose ^{13}C-NMR spectrum is shown below. In its IR spectrum, no absorption bands appear near 1,700 cm^{-1} or above 3,000 cm^{-1}. Propose a mechanism to account for the formation of that product.

$NaBH_4$, EtOH ?

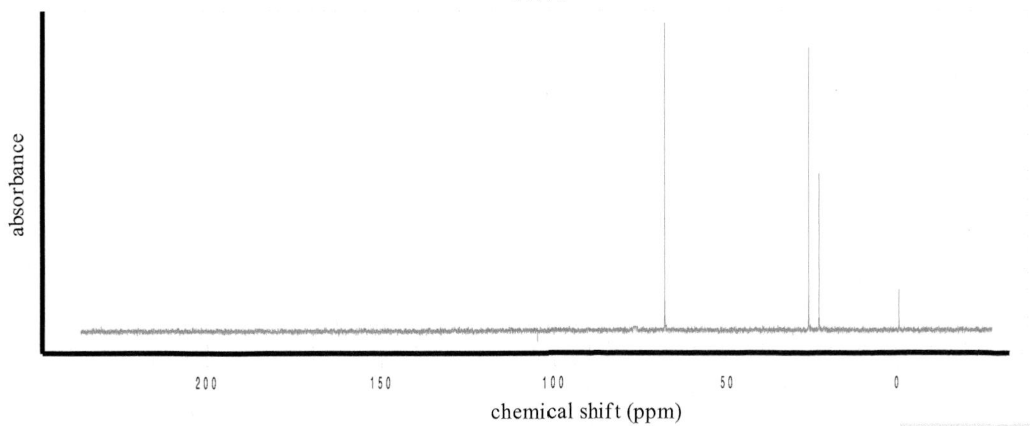

46. When carbon disulfide (CS_2) is treated with an alcohol in the presence of base, the product is a xanthate salt. If an alkyl halide is also present, a xanthate ester is formed. Propose a mechanism for each of these reactions.

S=C=S —(ROH, NaOH)→ R–O–C(=S)–SNa (a xanthate salt)

S=C=S —(ROH/R'Br, NaOH)→ R–O–C(=S)–S–R' (a xanthate ester)

47. Lithium dimethylcuprate reacts with the beta alkynyl carbonyl shown below.

H_3C–C≡C–C(=O)–CH_3 —$(CH_3)_2CuLi$→ ?

The IR spectrum of the product is shown below. The proton NMR spectrum exhibits four signals: 1.9 ppm, 3H; 2.1 ppm, 3H; 2.2 ppm, 3H; 6.1 ppm, 1H. What is the structure of the product?

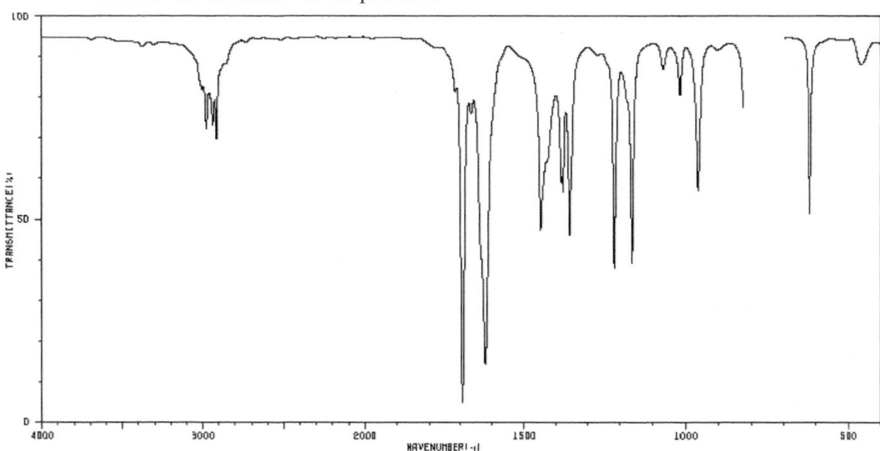

48. Treatment of a nitrile with cyanide yields an α-aminomalonitrile, as shown in the reaction below. Provide a detailed mechanism for this reaction.

(cyclopentyl)–CH₂–CH₂–C≡N —(NaCN, HCN)→ (cyclopentyl)–CH₂–CH₂–C(CN)₂–NH₂

49. Phenylmagnesium bromide reacts with sulfur dioxide to produce a reactive intermediate, which upon further reaction with CH_3Br produces methylphenylsulfone. Propose a mechanism for this reaction, and propose a structure for the reactive intermediate.

PhMgBr —(SO_2, THF, -78°)→ [?] —(CH_3Br)→ Ph–S(=O)₂–CH_3

50. When phenyl-5-bromopentanone is treated with triphenylphosphine, followed by base, a compound is produced whose formula is $C_{11}H_{12}$. Its ^{13}C-NMR spectrum exhibits nine signals—six signals appear between 120 ppm and 140 ppm, and the remaining three appear below 50 ppm. For this reaction, draw the complete, detailed mechanism, as well as the major organic product.

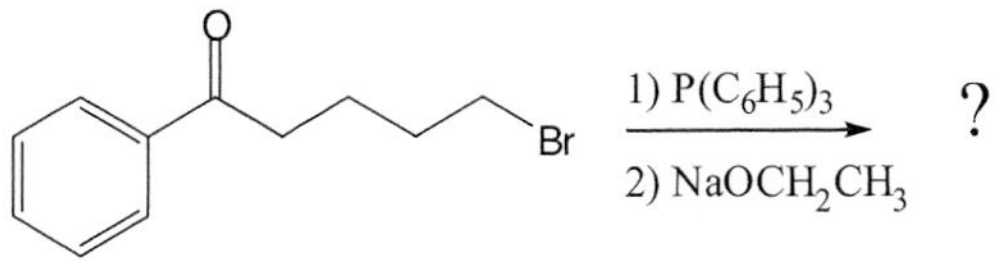

Br

1) $P(C_6H_5)_3$

2) $NaOCH_2CH_3$

?

51. In the following reaction, an α,β-unsaturated ketone reacts with a conjugated Wittig reagent to produce a relatively highly strained bicyclic compound. Draw the complete, detailed mechanism for this reaction. (A key intermediate has been provided.)

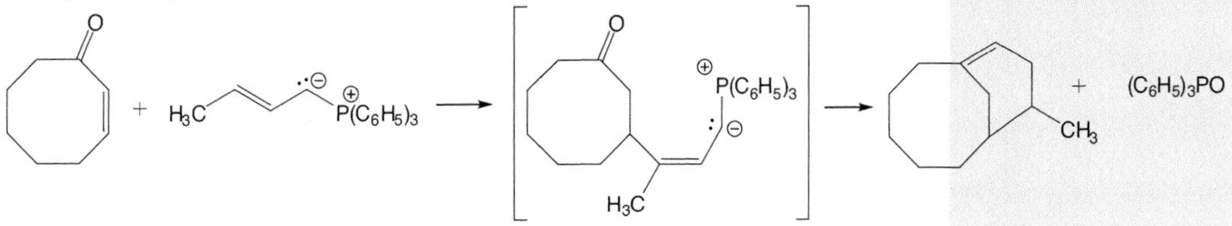

O + H_3C ⊕ $P(C_6H_5)_3$ → [O ⊕ $P(C_6H_5)_3$ H_3C] → CH_3 + $(C_6H_5)_3PO$

52. Suggest how you would synthesize each of the following from phenylethanone, using any reagents necessary. (Each synthesis may require more than one synthetic step.)

?

(a) Br (b) (c) O (d) O

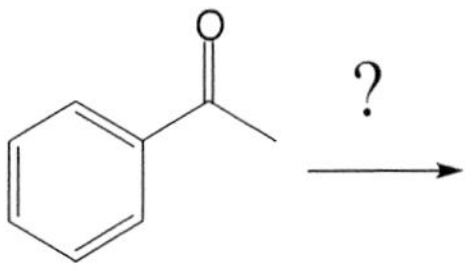

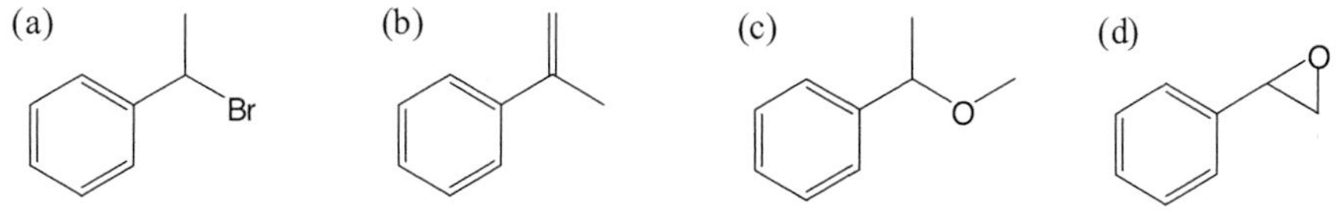

53. Suggest how you would carry out the following synthesis using any reagents necessary. (The synthesis may require more than one synthetic step.)

MgBr ?

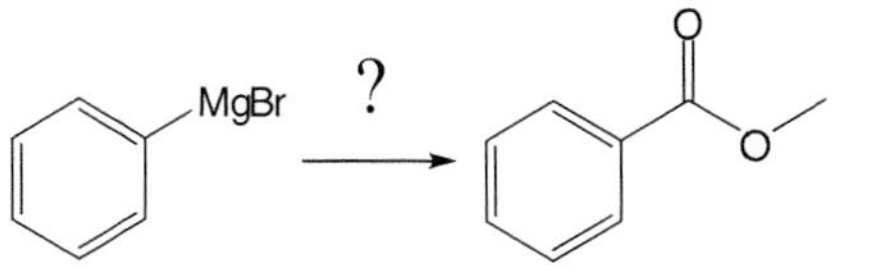

54. Suggest how you would carry out the following synthesis using any reagents necessary. (The synthesis may require more than one synthetic step.)

O ? OH

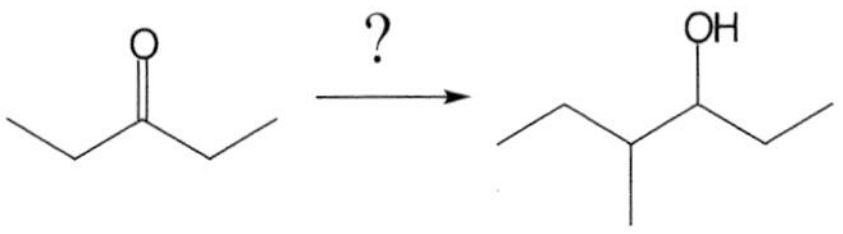

55. Show how you would carry out the following synthesis using any reagents necessary. (The synthesis may require more than one synthetic step.)

O

?

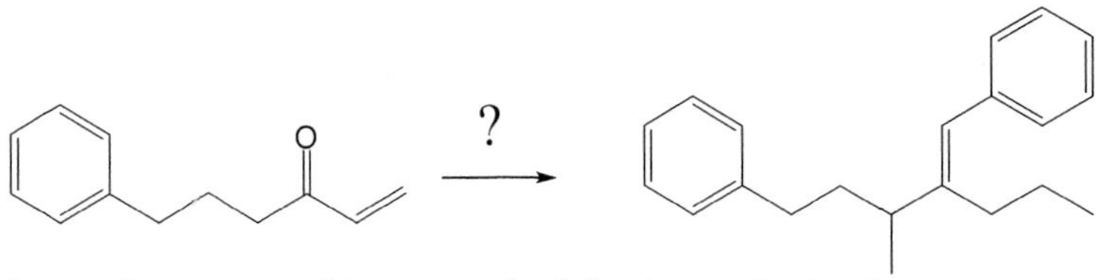

56. Suggest how you would carry out the following synthesis using any reagents necessary. (The synthesis may require more than one synthetic step.)

O

?

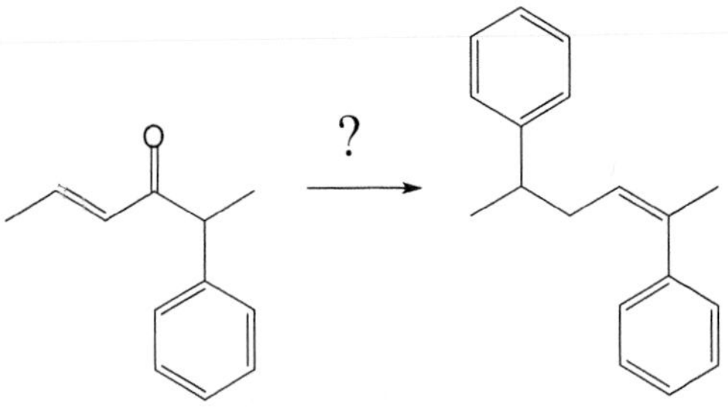

57. The following is an example of Corey-Chaykovsky aziridation reaction. Draw its complete, detailed mechanism.

1) CH_3I
2) NaH
3) R–C(=NH)–R'

H_3C–S–CH_3 → HN—CH_2, C, R, R'

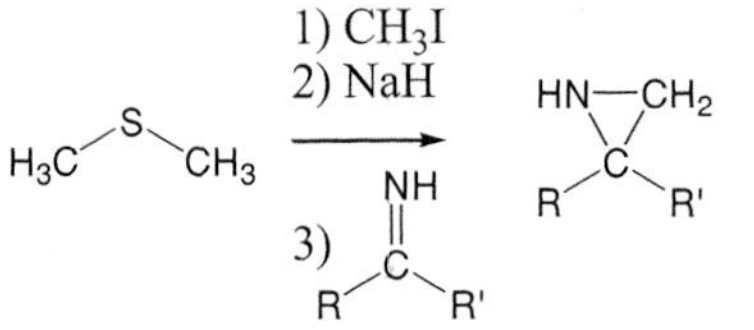

58. The following is an example of Corey-Chaykovsky cyclopropanation. Draw its complete, detailed mechanism.

1) CH_3I
2) NaH
3) R–C(=O)–CH=CH–R'

H_3C–S(=O)–CH_3 → R–C(=O)–CH, CH_2, HC–R' + H_3C–S(=O)–CH_3

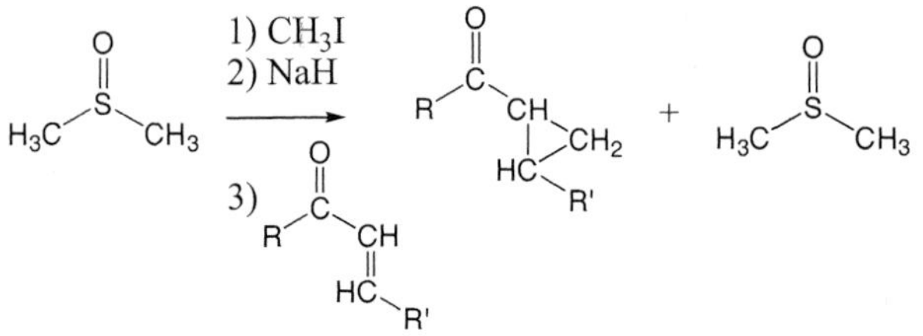

Chapter 16. Nucleophilic Addition to Polar π Bonds. 2: Addition of Weak Nucleophiles; Acid and Base Catalysis

Introduction

Chapter 15 began by introducing the principles governing the addition of strong nucleophiles to polar π bonds. Typically, a polar π bond undergoes *1,2-addition*, or *direct addition*, in which the nucleophile attacks the electron-poor carbon of the polar π bond. However, if the polar π bond is α,β-unsaturated, the nucleophile can also attack at the beta carbon via a *1,4-addition*, or *conjugate addition*. The competition between direct addition and conjugate addition is governed by the reversibility of nucleophilic addition to the polar π bond: only the very strong nucleophiles that add *irreversibly* to a polar π bond favor direct addition, whereas those that add *reversibly* favor conjugate addition.

Throughout the remainder of Chapter 15, we examined various reactions involving H^- and R^- nucleophiles. Polar π bonds can be reduced by $LiAlH_4$ or $NaBH_4$. Grignard reagents (R-MgBr) and alkyllithium reagents (R-Li) generate new C-C single bonds at the electron-poor C atom of the polar π bond, whereas lithium dialkyl cuprates (R_2CuLi) generate such a bond at the beta carbon. Wittig reagents ($(C_6H_5)_3P^+{-}^-CR_2$) convert a ketone or aldehyde into an alkene, and sulfonium ylides ($(CH_3)_2S^+{-}^-CR_2$) convert a ketone or aldehyde into an epoxide.

In this chapter, we will maintain our focus on nucleophilic addition, examining reactions that involve weak nucleophiles. As we will see, such reactions can frequently be catalyzed by a strong acid or strong base. Under such conditions, the nucleophilic addition mechanism is altered slightly, providing a lower-energy route to forming products. Of these reactions, we will spend the greatest amount of time on the *aldol reaction*, as it is one of the most important and versatile reactions in synthesis.

CHAPTER OBJECTIVES

Upon Completion of This Chapter You Should Be Able to...

- Draw the fundamental mechanism for the addition of a weak nucleophile to a polar π bond under neutral, basic, and acidic conditions.
- Explain why the addition of weak nucleophiles tends to be catalyzed by strong acids or strong bases.
- Predict the major product when a weak nucleophile adds to an α,β-unsaturated polar π bond.
- Show how to convert a ketone or aldehyde into an acetal, thioacetal, imine, or enamine, and draw the corresponding mechanisms for these reactions.
- Predict the hydrolysis products of an acetal, imine, or nitrile, and draw the corresponding mechanisms.
- Explain the utility of a Woff-Kishner reduction, and draw its mechanism.
- Draw the mechanisms for aldol addition and aldol condensation reactions under basic and acidic conditions.
- Incorporate synthetically useful crossed aldol reactions in a synthesis scheme.
- Recognize when an intramolecular aldol reaction is favorable, and predict the major products.
- Specify the types of reactants that can be used for a Robinson annulation, and predict the major products.
- Draw the mechanism for the benzoin condensation reaction.

16.1. ADDITION OF WEAK NUCLEOPHILES: ACID AND BASE CATALYSIS

Thus far we have dealt mainly with the addition of strong nucleophiles to polar π bonds. In general, those nucleophiles bear a full negative charge or (in the case of hydride reagents and organometallic reagents) can be treated *as if* they bore a full negative charge. However, as we saw in Chapters 8–10, a variety of *neutral* species can act as nucleophiles, including water, alcohols (ROH), amines (RNH_2), thiols (RSH), and phosphines (RPH_2). These nucleophiles can also add to polar π bonds.

Equation 16-1, for example, shows that ethanol, a weak nucleophile, can add to the C=O bond of butanone to produce a **hemiacetal**, a compound in which a carbon atom is bonded to both an OH group and an OR group.

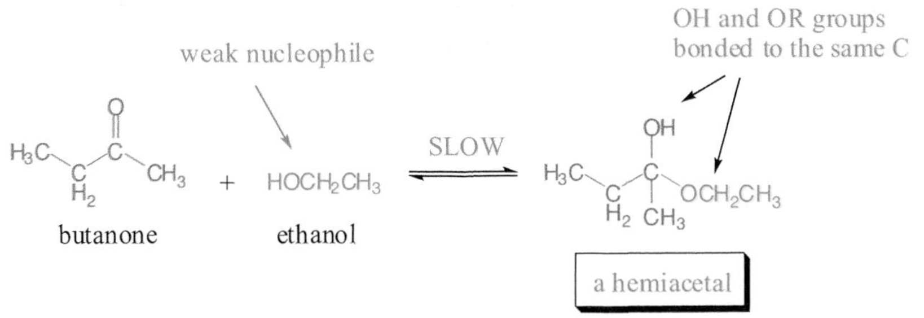

(16-1)

However, as indicated, this reaction tends to be quite slow. We can understand why from the mechanism, which is shown in Equation 16-2.

Mechanism of the Reaction in Equation 16-1

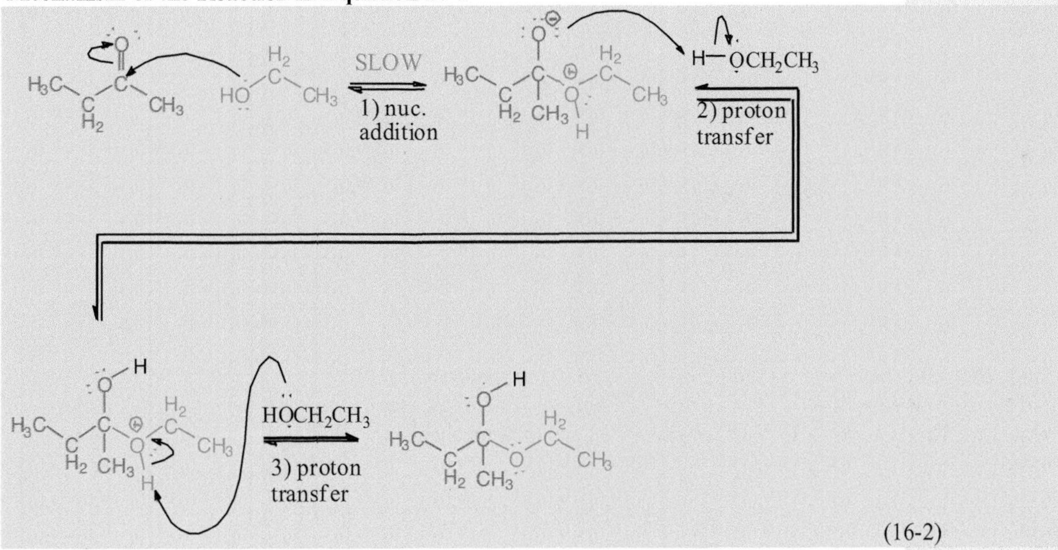

(16-2)

The first two steps of the mechanism are essentially the same as the mechanism for the addition of a strong nucleophile to a carbonyl—nucleophilic attack on the carbonyl C, followed by protonation. Notice that because the nucleophile is originally neutral, it develops a positive charge upon addition to the π bond. Therefore, deprotonation is necessary in the final step in order to yield an overall neutral product.

The sluggishness of the reaction can be attributed to charge stability. Notice that neither of the reactants has a formal charge. The product of nucleophilic attack (the first step), on the other hand, does bear formal charges, making it significantly less stable. Thus, the nucleophilic addition step is quite unfavorable and slow.

> **Your Turn 16.1.** At each stage of the mechanism in Equation 16-2, count the total *number* of charges that exist (not the total charge) and write it at the upper left of each reaction arrow (for example, one positive charge and one negative charge should be counted as two charges).

Frequently, the addition of a weak nucleophile can be sped up dramatically in the presence of either a strong base or a strong acid, as shown in Equations 16-3 and 16-4.

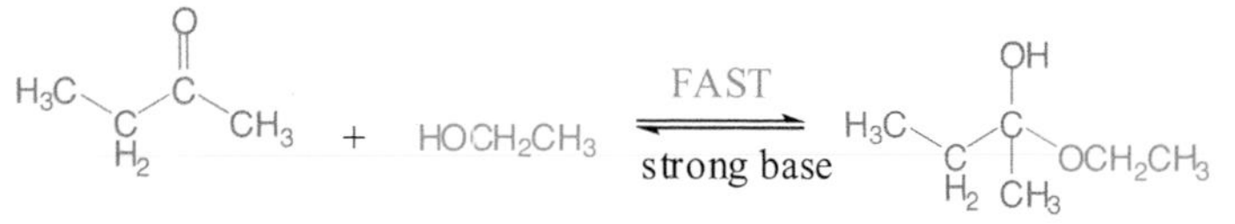

$H_3C{-}CH_2{-}C(=O){-}CH_3 + HOCH_2CH_3 \xrightleftharpoons[\text{strong base}]{\text{FAST}} H_3C{-}CH_2{-}C(OH)(CH_3){-}OCH_2CH_3$ (16-3)

$H_3C{-}CH_2{-}C(=O){-}CH_3 + HOCH_2CH_3 \xrightleftharpoons[\text{strong acid}]{\text{FAST}} H_3C{-}CH_2{-}C(OH)(CH_3){-}OCH_2CH_3$ 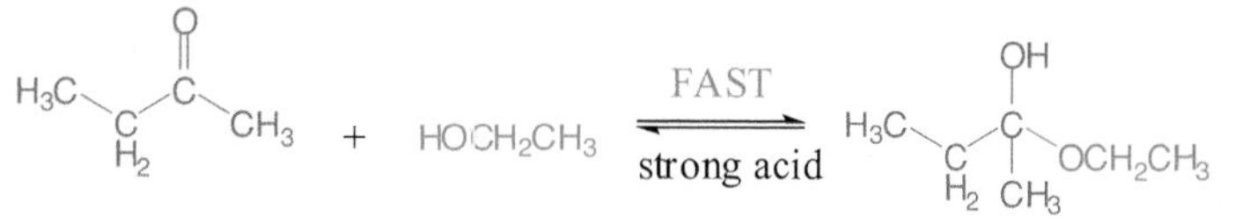 (16-4)

The reasons for these increased reaction rates can be understood by considering the respective mechanisms. Under basic conditions (Equation 16-5), the strong base deprotonates the weak ROH nucleophile in the first step, generating RO^-, a strong nucleophile. In the second step, RO^- adds to the C=O bond, and the resulting species is protonated by ROH in the final step.

Mechanism of the Reaction in Equation 16-3

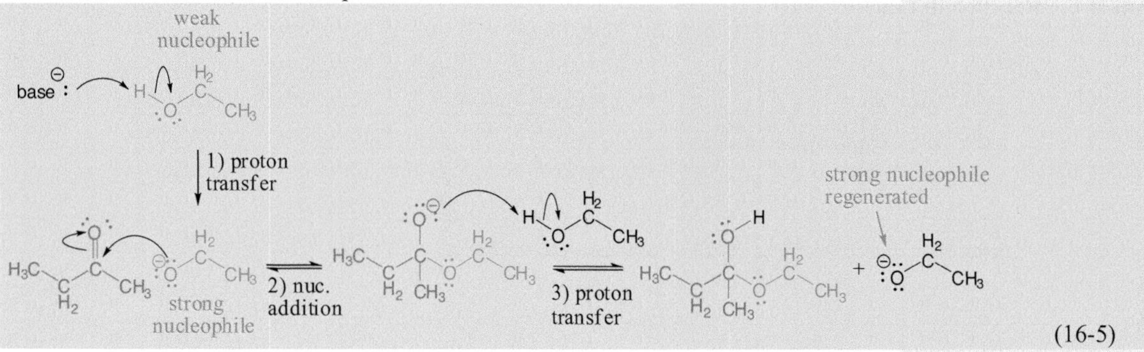

weak nucleophile

base: + H–O–CH2–CH3

1) proton transfer

strong nucleophile

2) nuc. addition

3) proton transfer

strong nucleophile regenerated

(16-5)

Notice that at each stage of the mechanism, the total number of formal charges remains unchanged, so none of the steps is significantly unfavorable. Therefore, none of the steps hinders the overall reaction. This is contrary to what we saw in the reaction mechanism under neutral conditions.

> **Your Turn 16.2.** At each stage of the mechanism in Equation 16-5, write the total *number* of charges that exist (not the total charge).

Notice also in Equation 16-5 that the nucleophile/base is regenerated in the last step, so it not consumed in the overall reaction. Thus, the reaction is **base-catalyzed**, and only a small amount—a *catalytic amount*—of base is required.

The mechanism of the reaction that takes place under acidic conditions (Equation 16-4) is shown in Equation 16-6.

Mechanism of the Reaction in Equation 16-4

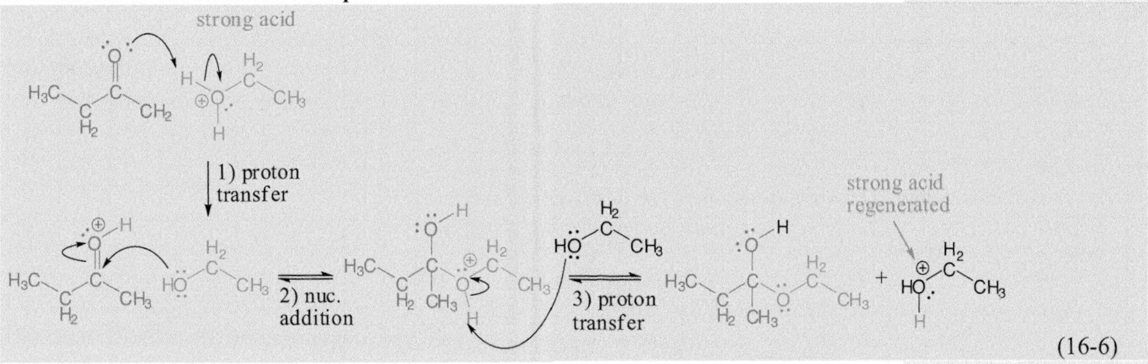

strong acid

1) proton transfer

2) nuc. addition

3) proton transfer

strong acid regenerated

(16-6)

In the first step, the strong acid protonates the O atom of the carbonyl group. In the second step, the weak ROH nucleophile adds to the carbonyl, and the resulting positively charged species is deprotonated by ROH in the final step.

Just as we saw in the base-catalyzed mechanism, the total number of charges remains the same throughout the mechanism under acidic conditions. Therefore, no single step is significantly unfavorable, so the overall reaction can proceed quickly.

Your Turn 16.3. At each stage of the mechanism in Equation 16-6, write the total *number* of charges that exist (not the total charge).

Notice in Equation 16-6 that the strong acid—the protonated alcohol—is regenerated in the final step. Because the acid increases the reaction rate and is not consumed overall, the reaction is said to be **acid-catalyzed**.

To better understand why the presence of an acid increases the reaction rate, it helps to compare the specific species involved in the nucleophilic addition step under neutral conditions (Equation 16-2) and acidic conditions (Equation 16-6). The attacking species is the same in each reaction—a weak ROH nucleophile. The difference is in the form of the ketone being attacked. Under neutral conditions, the ketone's carbonyl group is uncharged, as shown at left below. Under acidic conditions, the carbonyl group is protonated, giving the O atom a +1 charge, as shown at right below.

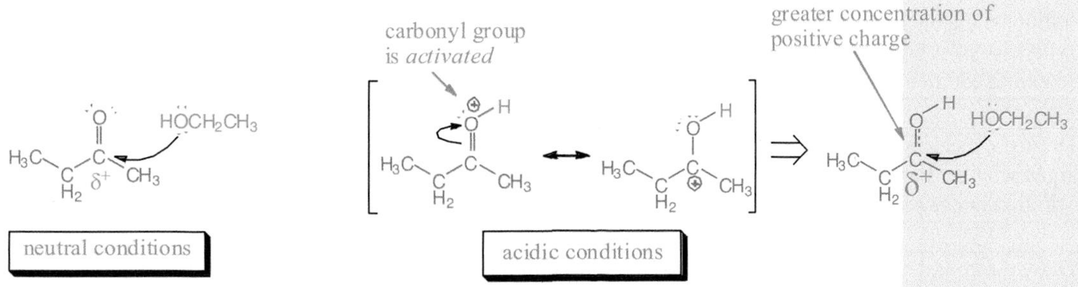

carbonyl group is *activated*

greater concentration of positive charge

neutral conditions

acidic conditions

As we can see, the protonated ketone has a moderately strong resonance contributor in which the formal positive charge is on the carbonyl carbon. Thus, the partial positive charge on the carbonyl carbon is greater in the protonated ketone than in the neutral ketone, as the resonance hybrid indicates. With a larger concentration of positive charge, the carbonyl carbon more strongly attracts a nucleophile. We say that the protonated carbonyl group is **activated** toward nucleophilic attack.

Your Turn 16.4. Indicate which of the following nitrile groups is activated toward nucleophilic attack.

Solved Problem 16.1. In Chapter 15, we saw that water can add to a ketone or aldehyde to form a *hydrate*, as shown below. Draw the mechanism for this reaction under (a) neutral and (b) basic conditions. Under which conditions do you think this hydration reaction will proceed faster? Why?

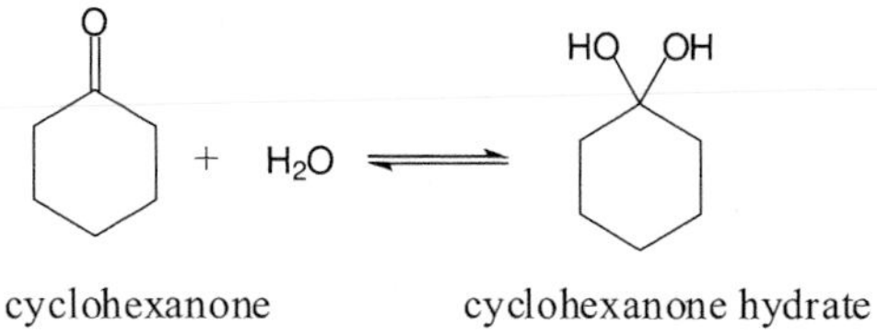

cyclohexanone cyclohexanone hydrate

Think. Under neutral conditions, what nucleophiles are present? Under basic conditions, what nucleophiles are present? What is the total number of charges before and after the nucleophilic addition step in each mechanism?

Solve. Under neutral conditions, water acts as the nucleophile.

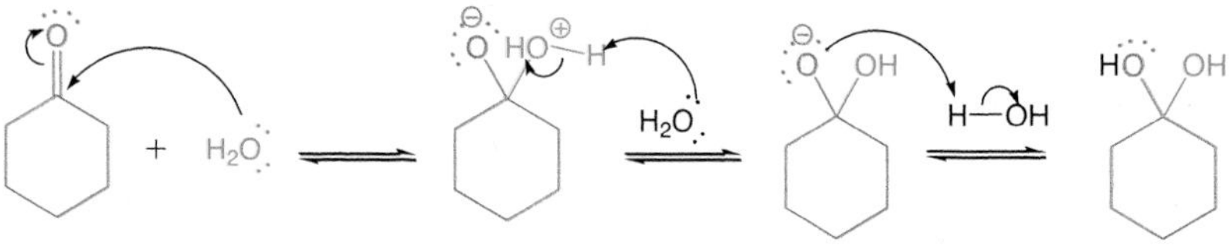

Under basic conditions, HO^- is present in a significant concentration and can thus act as the nucleophile.

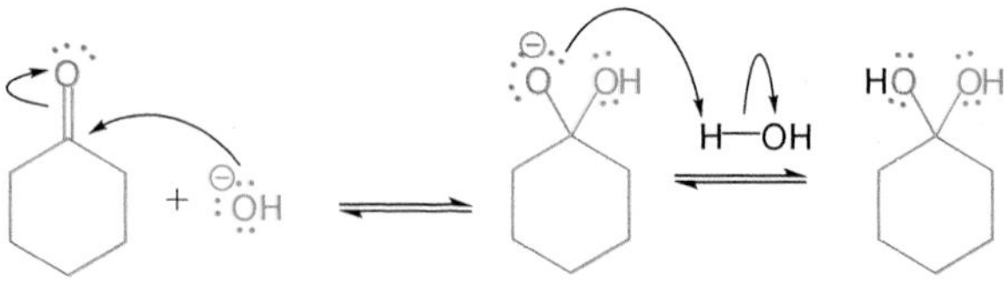

Under neutral conditions, the nucleophilic addition step increases the total number of charges by two, whereas under basic conditions, the total number of charges remains the same. Thus nucleophilic addition is more favorable and faster under basic conditions.

Problem 16.1. Draw the mechanism for the hydration of cyclohexanone under acidic conditions, and argue whether this reaction should be faster or slower than the corresponding hydration under neutral conditions.

Problem 16.2. Draw the complete, detailed mechanism for the following reaction under (a) basic and (b) acidic conditions.

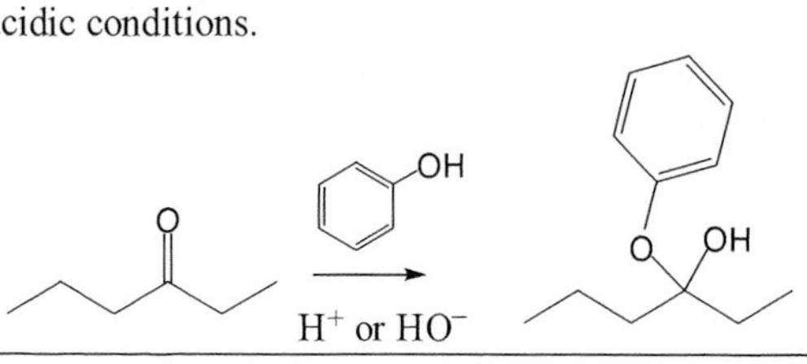

H^+ or HO^-

16.1a. Addition of HCN: Formation of Cyanohydrins

When a ketone or aldehyde is treated with aqueous HCN, the product is a **cyanohydrin**, in which an OH group and a cyano (CN) group are bonded to the same carbon atom. Examples are shown in Equations 16-7 and 16-8.

a cyanohydrin
an α-hydroxy acid
HCN
H_2O, 0 °C
SLOW
hydrolysis (several steps)
methanal (formaldehyde)
75%
glycolic acid

(16-7)

a cyanohydrin
an α-hydroxy acid
HCN
H_2O, 20 °C
SLOW
hydrolysis (several steps)
cyclohexanone
70%

(16-8)

This reaction is important for two reasons. First, it is another valuable *carbon-carbon bond-formation reaction*, giving us an additional means of constructing carbon backbones. Second, as we will learn in greater detail in Chapter 18, the C≡N functional group is readily transformed into a carboxylic acid via a *hydrolysis* reaction. The overall product is an alpha-hydroxyacid. Not only are these compounds useful in synthesis, but some alpha-hydroxyacids, such as glycolic acid, have applications in the treatment of a variety of skin ailments.

In the overall reaction of HCN with the carbonyl group, the cyano group adds to the carbonyl carbon and a hydrogen adds to the carbonyl oxygen. This reaction occurs in three steps, as shown in Equation 16-9. In the first step, NC^- is generated by an equilibrium proton transfer from the weakly acidic HCN to water. In the second step, NC^- attacks the carbonyl group, generating a negative charge on the carbonyl's oxygen. The third step is protonation of that oxygen.

Mechanism of the Reaction in Equation 16-8

very small amount generated
nucleophile regenerated
1) proton transfer
2) nuc. addition
3) proton transfer

(16-9)

Under normal conditions, HCN reacts quite slowly with the carbonyl carbon despite the fact that NC^- is a very good nucleophile. The reason is that the equilibrium proton transfer between HCN and water heavily favors reactants, so only a small amount of NC^- is generated (only about 0.001% of HCN molecules dissociate into NC^- and H_3O^+).

Your Turn 16.5. To verify that the first step of Equation 16-9 heavily favors the reactants, write the appropriate pK_a value below each acid in the equilibrium. (You may wish to consult Table 6-1.)

On the other hand, the reaction can be sped up dramatically by the addition of a small amount of either KCN (Equation 16-10) or a strong base such as NaOH (Equation 16-11).

FAST

$$R_2C{=}O \xrightleftharpoons[\text{KCN, } H_2O]{\text{HCN}} R_2C(OH)CN \quad (16\text{-}10)$$

catalytic amount

FAST

$$R_2C{=}O \xrightleftharpoons[\text{NaOH, } H_2O]{\text{HCN}} R_2C(OH)CN \quad (16\text{-}11)$$

catalytic amount

The reason for this acceleration is that the addition of either KCN or NaOH increases the amount of NC^- present in solution. KCN is an ionic compound that dissociates into K^+ and NC^- in water, while HO^- from KOH deprotonates HCN quantitatively to produce NC^-. Notice in Equation 16-9 that the NC^- generated in either of these fashions is not consumed during the course of the reaction, because the NC^- that is used in the second step is regenerated in the final step. Hence, both KCN and NaOH are *catalysts* for the nucleophilic addition of HCN.

Your Turn 16.6. Verify that HO^- quantitatively deprotonates HCN by (a) drawing the products of the reaction below, and (b) writing the appropriate pK_a below each acid involved.

$$HCN + HO^{-} \rightleftharpoons$$

Problem 16.3. For each reaction, draw the complete, detailed mechanism and predict the products.

(a) benzophenone $\xrightarrow[\text{KCN, } H_2O]{\text{HCN}}$?

(b) aldehyde $\xrightarrow[\text{NaOH, } H_2O]{\text{HCN}}$?

16.1b. Direct vs. Conjugate Addition of Weak Nucleophiles and HCN

Like negatively charged nucleophiles, neutral nucleophiles can attack α,β-unsaturated carbonyls at two locations—at the carbonyl carbon to give the direct addition product and at the beta carbon to give the conjugate addition product. In general:

Neutral nucleophiles heavily favor conjugate addition.

An example with ethanethiol (CH_3CH_2SH) as the nucleophile is shown in Equation 16-12.

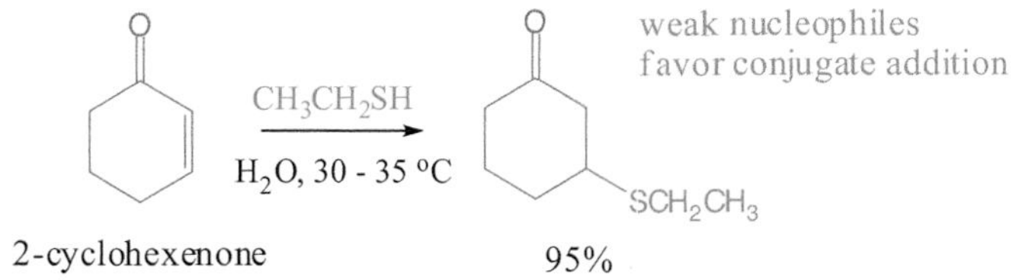

CH_3CH_2SH, H_2O, 30 - 35 °C

weak nucleophiles favor conjugate addition

SCH_2CH_3

2-cyclohexenone 95% (16-12)

The mechanism for this reaction is shown in Equation 16-13. Neutral nucleophiles favor conjugate addition because the nucleophilic addition step is reversible and therefore takes place under thermodynamic control. As we saw in Section 15.4, the conjugate-addition product is the thermodynamic product. Conjugate addition not only leads to a resonance-stabilized enolate anion, but also allows the strong C=O bond to remain intact.

Mechanism of the Reaction in Equation 16-12

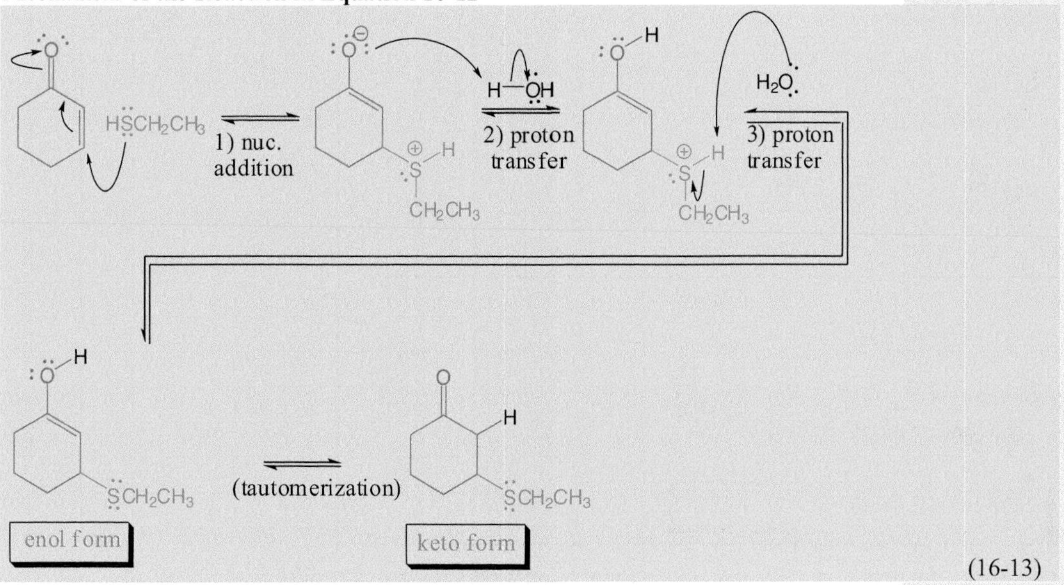

$HSCH_2CH_3$ 1) nuc. addition

$H-OH$ 2) proton transfer

H_2O 3) proton transfer

CH_2CH_3 CH_2CH_3

SCH_2CH_3 (tautomerization) SCH_2CH_3

enol form keto form

(16-13)

Frequently, the addition of neutral nucleophiles to α,β-unsaturated carbonyls does not require acidic conditions. Unlike straight addition, conjugate addition of neutral nucleophiles can proceed at a reasonable rate, in large part because of resonance stabilization in the enolate anion produced in the first step.

Similarly, HCN adds to α,β-unsaturated carbonyls via conjugate addition. This is because the addition of NC^- to the carbonyl group is reversible (Table 15-1). An example of such a reaction is shown in Equation 16-14.

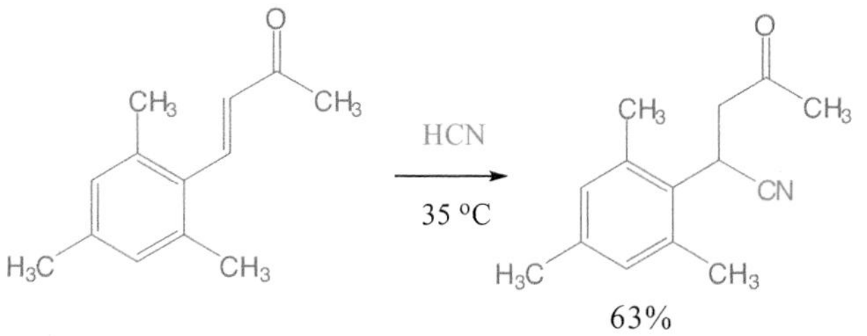

CH_3 CH_3 HCN, 35 °C CH_3 CH_3 CN

H_3C CH_3 H_3C CH_3

63% (16-14)

Solved Problem 16.2. Predict the product of the following reaction and draw its complete, detailed mechanism.

CH_3NH_2 / HCl, acetone/H_2O → ?

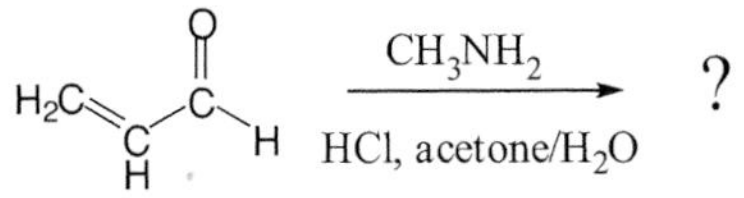

Think. Does CH_3NH_2 add to the carbonyl group reversibly or irreversibly? Will this result in straight addition or conjugate addition?

Solve. Being a weak nucleophile, CH_3NH_2 adds reversibly to a carbonyl group, so upon attacking an α,β-unsaturated carbonyl, CH_3NH_2 will undergo conjugate addition. Notice that the HCl below the reaction arrow indicates acidic conditions, so no strongly basic species should appear in the mechanism. Therefore, we do not show the nucleophile attacking in the first step, because it would generate a strongly basic O^-. Instead, the O atom is protonated, generating an activated carbonyl.

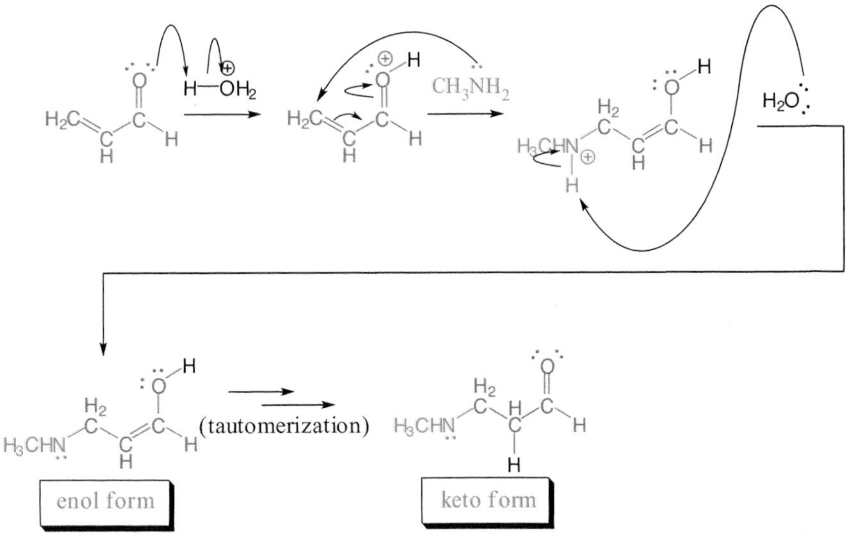

(tautomerization)

enol form

keto form

Problem 16.4. For each reaction below, predict the major product and draw the complete, detailed mechanism.

(a) HCN / KOH, H_2O → ?

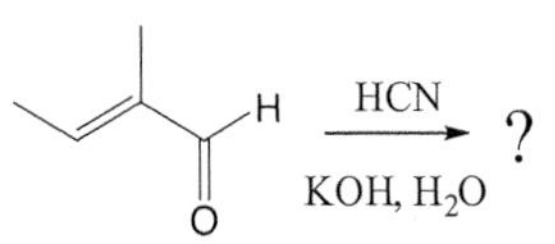

(b) → ?

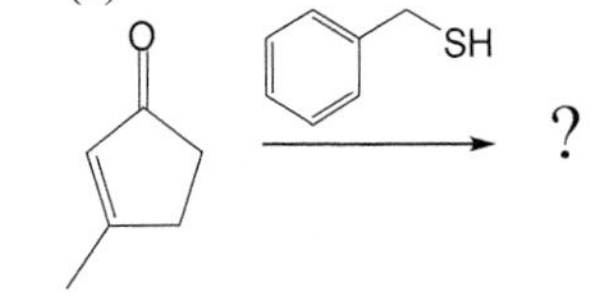

(c) THF → ?

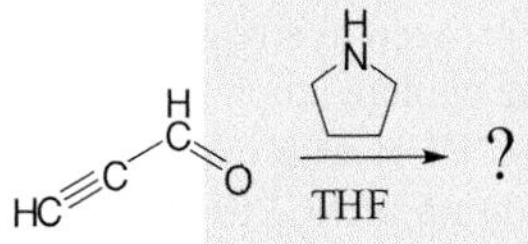

16.2. FORMATION AND HYDROLYSIS REACTIONS INVOLVING ACETALS, THIOACETALS, IMINES, ENAMINES, AND NITRILES

In Section 16.1, we saw that weak nucleophiles can add to polar π bonds. Frequently, the immediate product of such a reaction can react further under the conditions required for nucleophilic addition. In this section, we will examine some of those reactions—the formation of acetals, thioacetals, and imines from ketones or aldehydes. We will also examine the hydrolysis of acetals, imines, enamines, and nitriles. As we will see, the hydrolyses of the first three compounds are simply the reverse of their formation reactions.

16.2a. Formation and Hydrolysis of Acetals

In Equation 16-1, we saw that a *hemiacetal* forms when a ketone or aldehyde is treated with an alcohol, and in Equations 16-3 and 16-4, we saw that the reaction is catalyzed under either basic or acidic conditions (Equation 16-15).

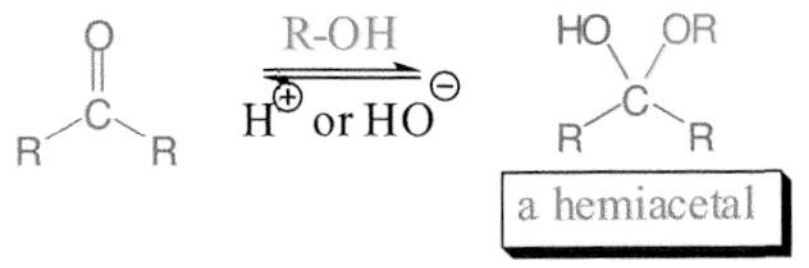

$$R_2C{=}O \underset{H^{\oplus} \text{ or } HO^{\ominus}}{\overset{R\text{-}OH}{\rightleftharpoons}} R_2C(OH)(OR)$$

a hemiacetal

(16-15)

If the aldehyde or ketone is treated with a *large excess* of the alcohol under *acidic* conditions, the hemiacetal reacts further to form an **acetal**, in which two alkoxy (RO) groups are bonded to the same carbon. As indicated in Equation 16-16, this overall reaction is reversible.

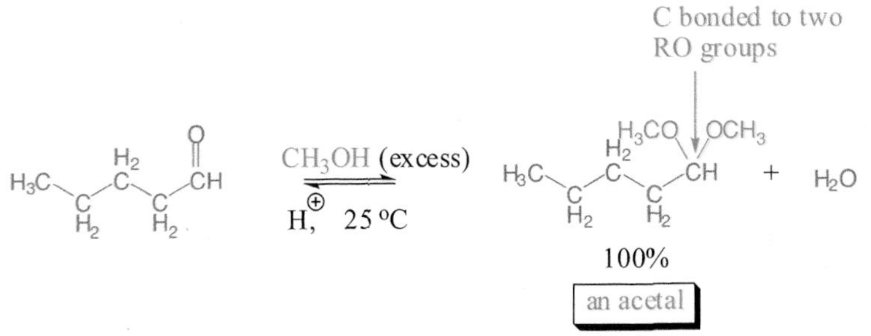

C bonded to two RO groups

$$H_3C{-}CH_2{-}CH_2{-}CH_2{-}CH{=}O \underset{H^{\oplus},\ 25\,^{\circ}C}{\overset{CH_3OH \text{ (excess)}}{\rightleftharpoons}} H_3C{-}CH_2{-}CH_2{-}CH_2{-}CH(OCH_3)_2 + H_2O$$

100%

an acetal

(16-16)

The complete mechanism for this acetal formation reaction is shown in Equation 16-17.

Mechanism of the Reaction in Equation 16-16

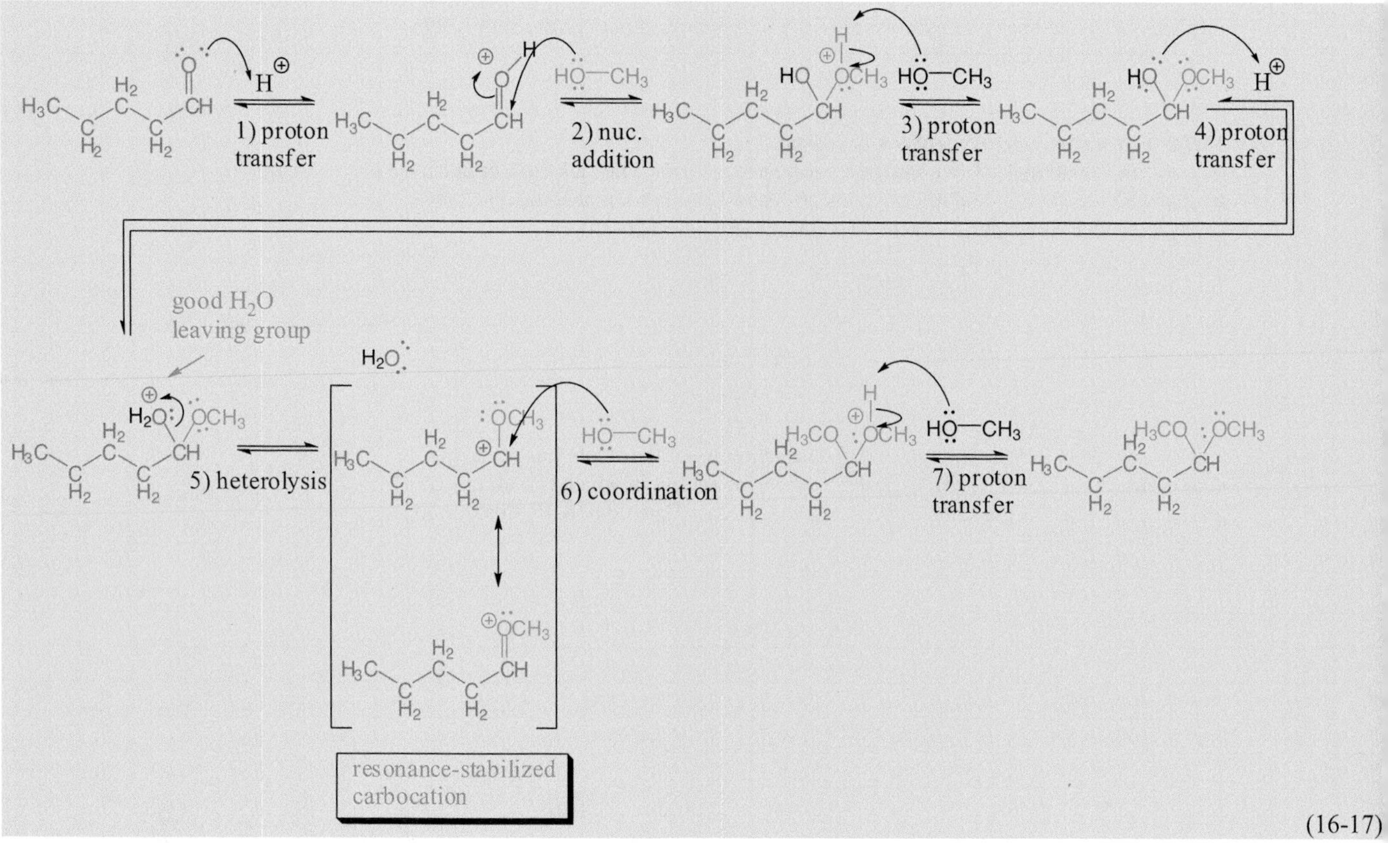

1) proton transfer — 2) nuc. addition — 3) proton transfer — 4) proton transfer

good H_2O leaving group

5) heterolysis — resonance-stabilized carbocation — 6) coordination — 7) proton transfer

(16-17)

Notice that the first three steps are identical to the acid-catalyzed nucleophilic addition in Equation 16-4. In the first step, the C=O bond is protonated, which *activates* it toward nucleophilic addition by the weak ROH nucleophile in the second step. The remaining steps essentially comprise an S_N1 reaction. In the fourth step, protonation of the OH group generates a good H_2O leaving group, which departs in the fifth step to produce a resonance-stabilized carbocation. That carbocation is subsequently attacked by another ROH nucleophile in step 6, and a final proton transfer results in the neutral acetal.

Your Turn 16.7. In the mechanism in Equation 16-17, circle the hemiacetal and the acetal and label them.

An important feature of acetal formation is the fact that the reaction takes place under equilibrium conditions. Therefore, the equilibrium can be shifted via Le Châtelier's principle. As we mentioned above, formation of the acetal product is favored by using excess alcohol, a reactant. By the same token, the reverse reaction is favored by using excess water, a product, under acidic condition. This is exemplified in Equation 16-18, whose mechanism is precisely the reverse of that in Equation 16-17.

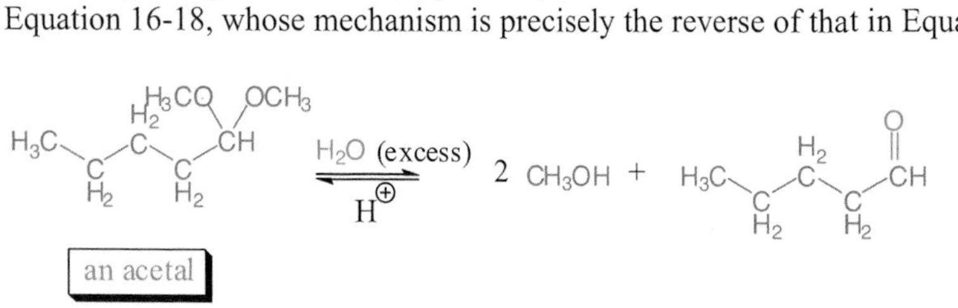

an acetal $\xrightleftharpoons[H^{\oplus}]{H_2O\text{ (excess)}}$ 2 CH_3OH + (aldehyde)

(16-18)

Note that Equation 16-18 is another example of *hydrolysis*, since the addition of water results in the breaking of the C-OCH_3 bonds.

Problem 16.5. Draw the complete, detailed mechanism for the reaction in Equation 16-18.

As we will see in greater detail in Chapter 17, the reversibility of acetal formation enables us to employ acetals as **protective groups** for ketones and aldehydes. Whereas ketones and aldehydes are susceptible to attack by nucleophiles (at the carbonyl carbon) and bases (at the alpha carbon), acetals are inert to both strong nucleophiles and strong bases.

The most popular alcohol used to protect ketones and aldehydes is 1,2-ethanediol (ethylene glycol), as shown in Equation 16-19. This compound has two alcohol functional groups per molecule, so only one equivalent is needed. Also, it forms a highly favored 5-membered ring, which helps in acetal formation.

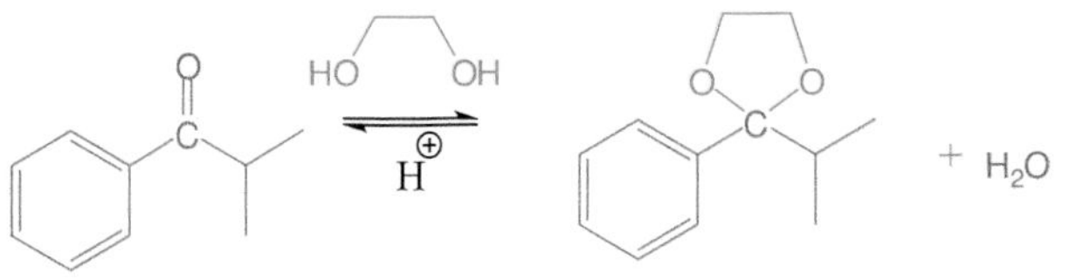

HO OH
$H^{\oplus}$
$+ H_2O$

(16-19)

Problem 16.6. Draw a complete, detailed mechanism for the reaction in Equation 16-19.

Note that although a hemiacetal can form under either basic or acidic conditions, only acidic conditions promote the formation of the acetal from the hemiacetal. In other words,

A ketone or aldehyde does not readily form an acetal under basic conditions.

The reason for this limitation is that the nucleophilic substitution that would be required is unfavorable. As we can see in Equation 16-20, the leaving group would have to be HO^-, which, as we learned in Chapter 10, is a very poor leaving group for an S_N1 or S_N2 reaction.

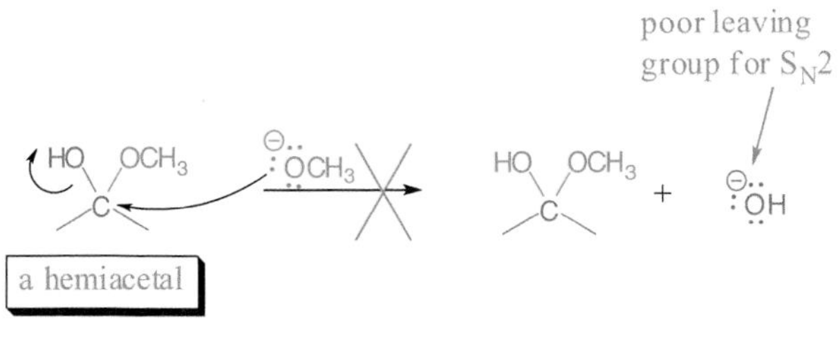

poor leaving group for S_N2

a hemiacetal

(16-20)

16.2b. Formation of Thioacetals

As we should expect, 1,3-propanedithiol ($HS\text{-}CH_2CH_2CH_2\text{-}SH$) reacts with a ketone or aldehyde under acidic conditions (Equation 16-21) in much the same way as 1,2-ethanediol does (Equation 16-19). The product is a cyclic **thioacetal** ("thio" indicates sulfur in place of oxygen), also called a **1,3-dithiane**. Like the five-membered ring in the cyclic acetal made from 1,2-ethandiol, the six-membered ring in this thioacetal product is highly favored.

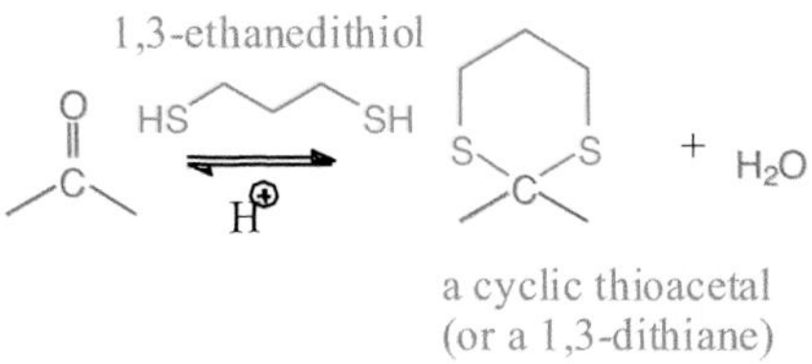

1,3-ethanedithiol
HS SH
$H^{\oplus}$
+ H_2O
a cyclic thioacetal
(or a 1,3-dithiane)

(16-21)

In Chapter 17, we will learn two major uses of 1,3-dithianes. One is in the conversion of aldehydes to ketones, as shown in Equation 16-22a. The other is in the reduction of a carbonyl group to a **methylene** (CH_2) group, as shown in Equation 16-22b.

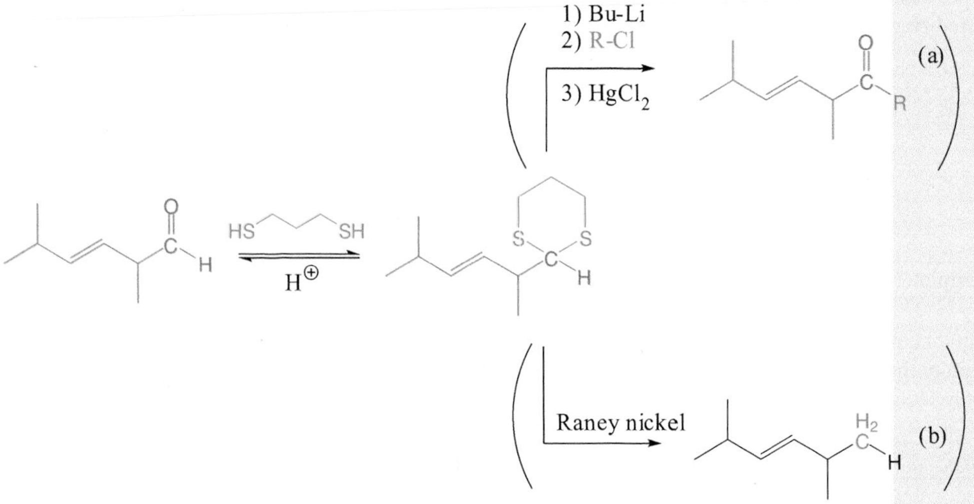

1) Bu-Li
2) R-Cl
3) $HgCl_2$
(a)

HS SH
$H^{\oplus}$

Raney nickel
(b)

(16-22)

16.2c. Formation and Hydrolysis of Imines and Enamines

Ammonia (NH_3) and amines ($R\text{-}NH_2$) are also weak nucleophiles that can add reversibly to carbonyl groups under mildly acidic conditions, as shown in Equations 16-23 and 16-24. The product is an **imine**, which has a characteristic C=N double bond.

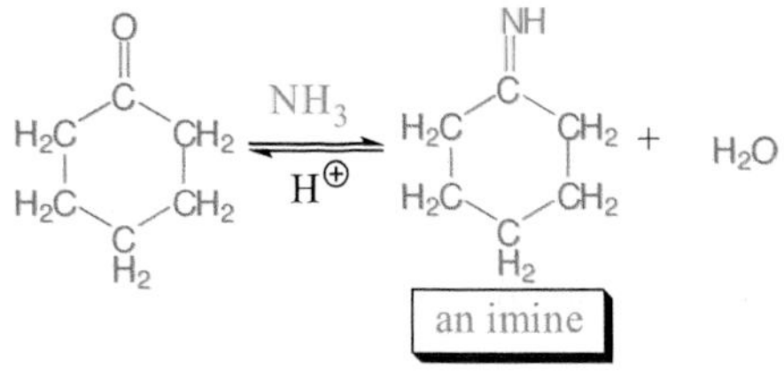

NH_3
$H^{\oplus}$
+ H_2O
an imine

(16-23)

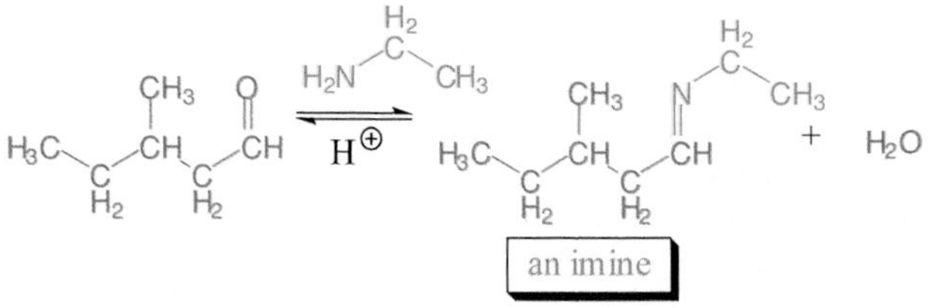

$H^{\oplus}$
+ H_2O
an imine

(16-24)

The complete mechanism for this imine formation is shown in Equation 16-25.

Mechanism of the Reaction in Equation 16-23

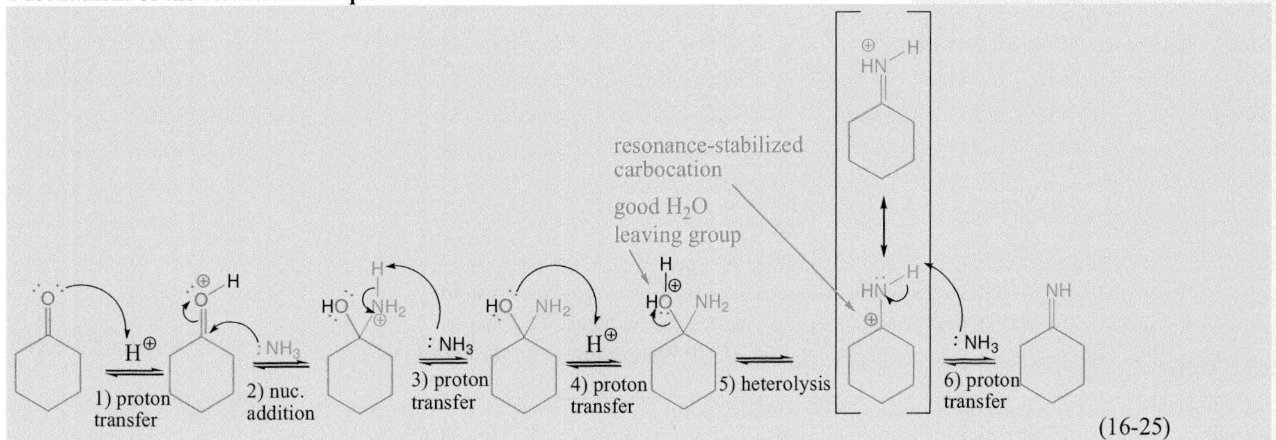

(16-25)

Notice that the first five steps of the mechanism for imine formation (Equation 16-25) are identical to the first five steps of the mechanism for acetal formation (Equation 16-17). The first three steps comprise an acid-catalyzed nucleophilic addition of NH_3. In the fourth step, the OH group is protonated to make a good water leaving group, which departs in the fifth step.

The difference between the acetal-formation and the imine-formation mechanisms is in the sixth step. In imine formation, the amino group is deprotonated, thus completing the second step of an E1 mechanism (Chapter 9). In acetal formation, such a deprotonation is not available, because the oxygen atom adjacent to the carbocation is not bonded to any hydrogen atoms.

Problem 16.7. Draw the complete, detailed mechanism for the reaction in Equation 16-24.

Just as with acetal formation, the reversibility of imine formation allows us to drive the reaction in the reverse direction via Le Châtelier's principle. Thus, as shown in Equation 16-26, an imine can be *hydrolyzed* by treating it with excess water under acidic conditions.

NH $\underset{H^{\oplus}}{\overset{H_2O}{\rightleftharpoons}}$ O + NH_3

(16-26)

Problem 16.8. Draw the complete, detailed mechanism for the reaction in Equation 16-26.

Solved Problem 16.3. Do you think that imine formation, such as the one below, can take place under *basic* conditions?

O $\underset{NaOH,\ H_2O}{\overset{NH_3}{\rightleftharpoons}}$ NH

Think. Under basic conditions, what types of species should not appear in the mechanism? In the mechanism that would be necessary for imine formation under these conditions, are all the steps reasonable?

Solve. Under basic conditions, no strong acids can appear in the mechanism. Thus, the mechanism would appear as follows.

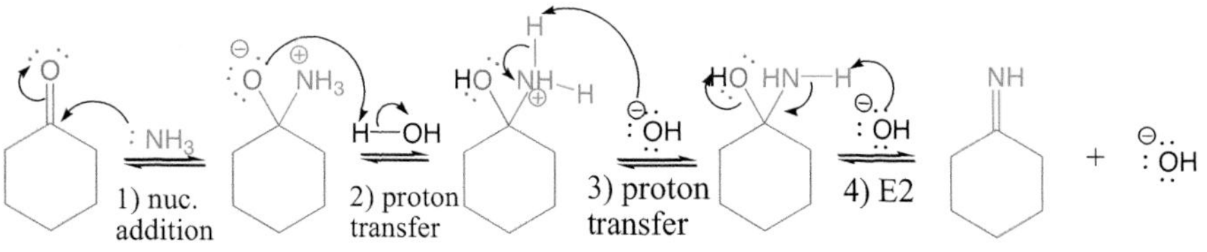

The first three steps are plausible. The appearance of a positive charge on N is reasonable under basic conditions because species like H_4N^+ are only weakly acidic. However, the fourth step is not plausible. As we learned in Chapter 9, HO^- is not a sufficiently good leaving group for an E2 reaction. Therefore, *imine formation does not take place under basic conditions*.

Problem 16.9. Do you think that imine hydrolysis, such as the one below, can take place under *basic* conditions? Explain.

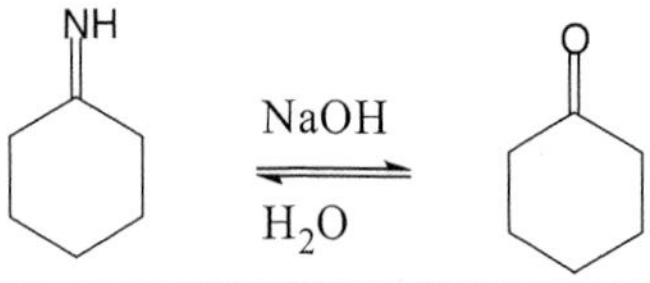

As we can see from the overall reactions in Equations 16-23 and 16-24, *imine formation requires at least two protons on the nucleophilic N atom*. One of those protons is removed in the third step of the mechanism (Equation 16-25), and the other is removed in the sixth step. Thus

> Only NH_3 and primary amines ($R\text{-}NH_2$) can form imines upon reaction with ketones or aldehydes.

Although a secondary amine (R_2NH) has only one hydrogen on N and thus cannot form an imine, it can react with a ketone or aldehyde to produce an **enamine**, in which an amino group is attached to an alkene carbon (Equation 16-27).

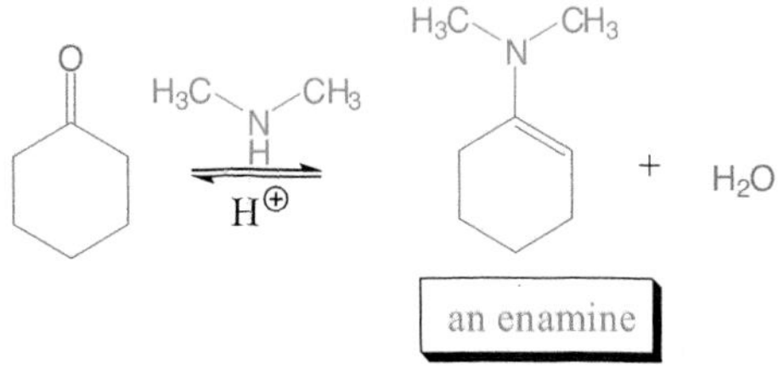

(16-27)

Given that there is a single hydrogen on the amino N, the mechanism for this reaction (Equation 16-28) is identical to that for imine formation (Equation 16-25) through the first five steps. The only difference is in the last step. In imine formation (Equation 16-25), the second of two hydrogens on N is removed. In enamine formation, no such H exists, so a slightly less acidic H is removed from the adjacent C.

Mechanism of the Reaction in Equation 16-27

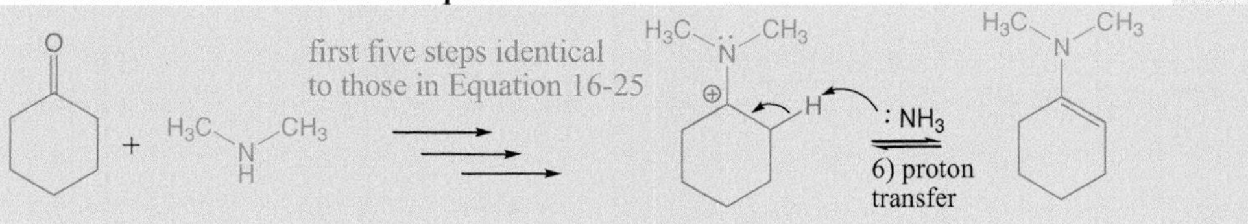

first five steps identical to those in Equation 16-25

6) proton transfer

(16-28)

Problem 16.10. For each reaction below, draw the complete mechanism and the major products that are formed.

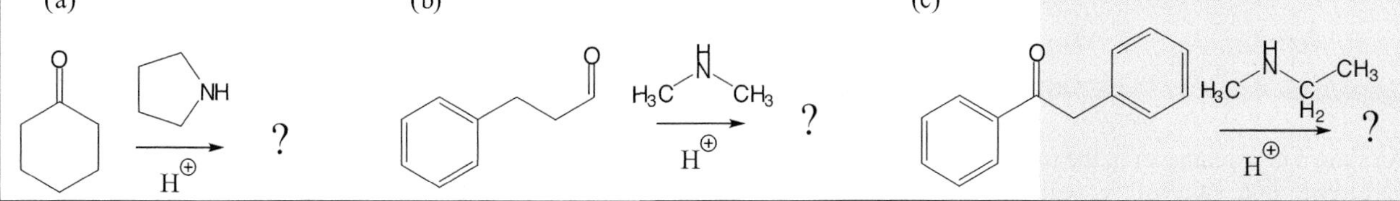

Solved Problem 16.4. The following reaction does *not* form an imine or enamine. Explain why.

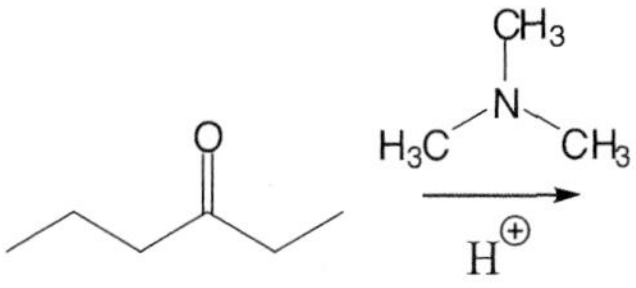

Think. Which of the steps in Equations 16-25 or 16-28 can the reaction include? Are there any steps that are not possible?

Solve. Only the first two steps of Equation 16-25 can take place. The acid that is present can protonate the carbonyl O in the first step, and amine N can attack the carbonyl C. The third step would normally require a deprotonation of the N atom, but no such proton exists. Thus, the only product that can be formed cannot be isolated, because it is too unstable.

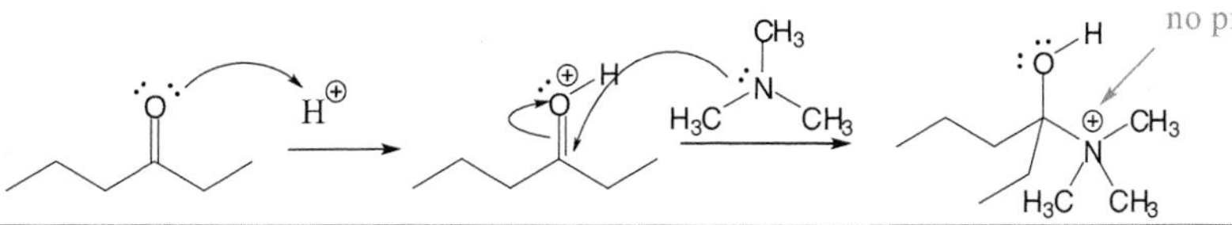

no proton on N

Problem 16.11. The following reaction does *not* form an imine or enamine. Explain why.

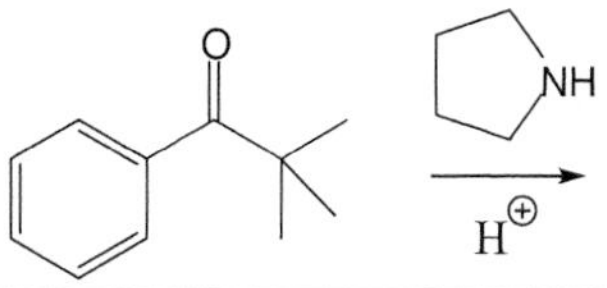

16.2d. Hydrolysis of Nitriles

Closely related to the hydrolysis of acetals and imines is the hydrolysis of nitriles (R–C≡N). As shown in Equations 16-29 and 16-30, treatment of a nitrile with water under either acidic or basic conditions produces a primary amide (R–CO–NH_2).

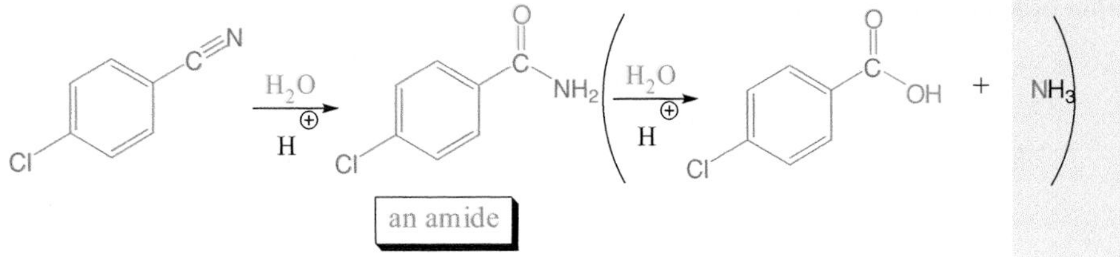

an amide

(16-29)

an amide

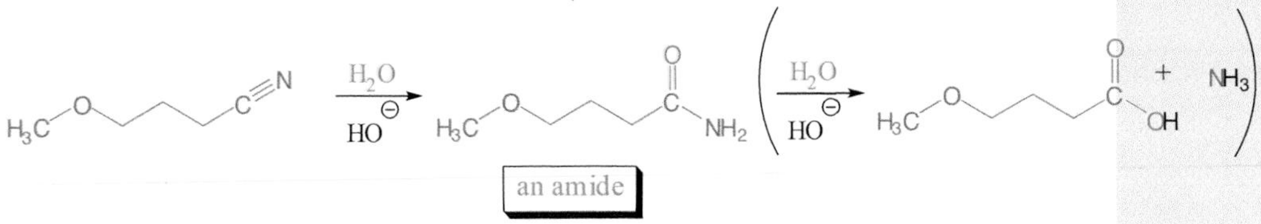

(16-30)

As shown in parentheses in the two equations, further hydrolysis converts the amide to a carboxylic acid. We will study those reactions in detail in Chapter 18.

The mechanism for the hydrolysis of a nitrile under acidic conditions is shown in Equation 16-31.

Mechanism of the Reaction in Equation 16-29

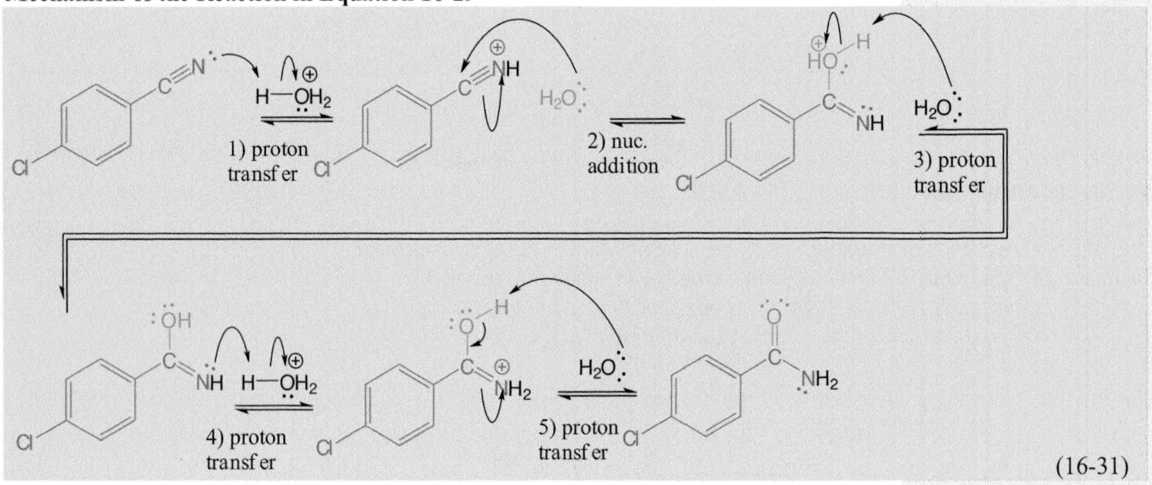

1) proton transfer

2) nuc. addition

3) proton transfer

4) proton transfer

5) proton transfer

(16-31)

Although this mechanism consists of five elementary steps, notice that the only step that is *not* a proton transfer is the nucleophilic addition step—the second step. The four proton transfer steps make it possible to avoid generating strongly basic species in the mechanism, as the reaction takes place under acidic conditions. Moreover, the proton transfer steps are responsible for both adding H atoms to N and removing them from O.

The mechanism for the hydrolysis of a nitrile under basic conditions is shown in Equation 16-32.

Mechanism for the Reaction in Equation 16-30

1) nuc. addition
2) proton transfer
3) proton transfer
4) proton transfer

(16-32)

As in hydrolysis under acidic conditions, the only non-proton-transfer step is the nucleophilic addition step—in this case, it is the first step. Because the reaction takes place under basic conditions, the proton transfer steps in its mechanism prevent the generation of strongly acidic species. Furthermore, similar to the acid-catalyzed mechanism, the proton transfer steps serve to add H atoms to N and remove one from O.

Problem 16.12. For each reaction below, draw the complete, detailed mechanism and predict the major organic product.

(a) H_2O, HO^- → ?

(b) H_2O, H^+ → ?

16.3. THE WOLFF-KISHNER REDUCTION

When a ketone or aldehyde is treated with hydrazine, $H_2N\text{-}NH_2$, followed by heating in the presence of base, the carbonyl group, C=O, is reduced to a methylene group, CH_2. This is known as a **Wolff-Kishner reduction**. An example is shown in Equation 16-33, in which 1-phenyl-1-butanone is reduced to butylbenzene.

Comment [JMK4]: Margin note. Wolff-Kishner reduction converts C=O to CH_2 in basic conditions.

Wolff-Kishner reduction

the carbonyl group is reduced to a CH_2 group

1-phenyl-1-butanone —($H_2N\text{-}NH_2$, KOH; H_2O/triethylene glycol (heat))→ butylbenzene (82%) + $N_2(g)$ + H_2O

(16-33)

The Wolff-Kishner reduction is one of three commonly used reactions that reduce a carbonyl group to CH_2. As we can see from Equation 16-33, the reaction takes place under basic conditions. The other two reactions, which we will encounter in Chapter 17, take place under neutral and acidic conditions, respectively.

Your Turn 16.8. Verify that the reaction in Equation 16-33 is a reduction by computing the oxidation state of the carbonyl carbon in the reactant and the corresponding atom in the product. Label each of those carbon atoms with its oxidation state.

The mechanism for the Wolff-Kishner reduction is shown in Equation 16-34. Because each N atom of hydrazine possesses two H atoms, the first six steps are identical to the imine-formation mechanism in Equation 16-25. The result is a **hydrazone**, characterized by the C=N-NR$_2$ group.

Mechanism of the Reaction in Equation 16-33

the anion is stabilized by both resonance and inductive effects

six steps in Equation 16-25

$H_2N—NH_2$

7) proton transfer

a hydrozone

8) proton transfer

9) E2

10) proton transfer

+ $N_2(g)$

the stability of N_2 heavily drives this reaction

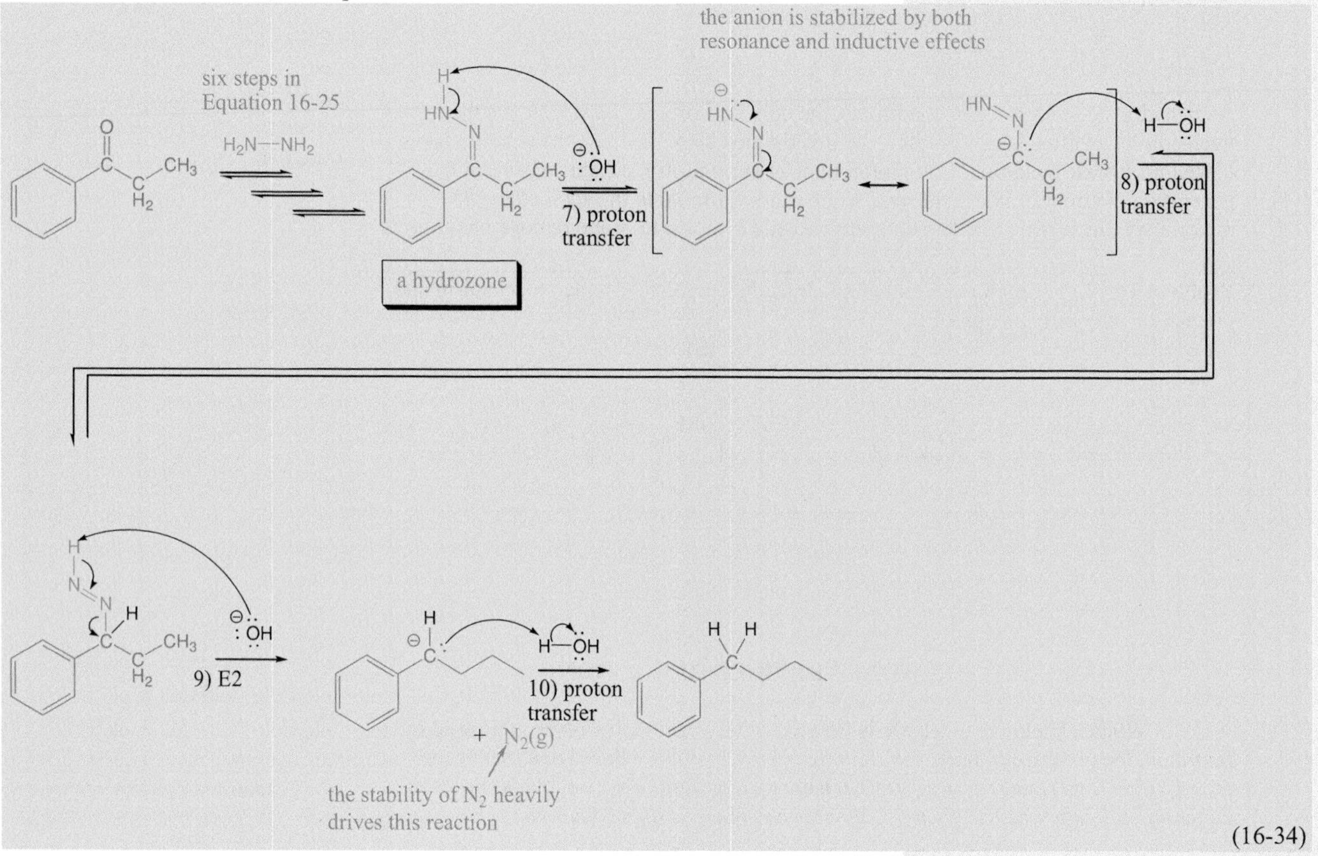

(16-34)

The role of the final four steps is to remove two hydrogens from the NH$_2$ group, and add two hydrogens to what was originally the carbonyl C.

Notice that in step 7 HO$^-$ deprotonates a nitrogen atom. Normally, HO$^-$ is not a strong enough base to do so, but in this case the conjugate base is stabilized by resonance involving the adjacent double bond, and by inductive effects involving the adjacent electron-withdrawing N atom.

Moreover, there are two peculiarities of the E2 step. First, the proton and the leaving group that are removed are on adjacent N atoms—usually we see them on adjacent C atoms. Second, the leaving group is quite poor—a negative charge becomes localized on a C atom. Normally this would prevent an E2 reaction from occurring, but the formation of N$_2$(g) is a substantial driving force. Not only is N$_2$(g) very stable, but, being a gas, it physically leaves the reaction system once it is formed. This makes the overall reaction *irreversible*, and, by Le Châtelier's principle, helps the formation of additional products.

Problem 16.13. For each reaction below, draw the complete, detailed mechanism and predict the product.

(a) 1) H_2NNH_2, H^+ 2) NaOH/H_2O, heat ?

(b) 1) H_2NNH_2, H^+ 2) NaOH/H_2O, heat ?

Problem 16.14. What carbonyl-containing compound could be used as a reactant in the following reaction?

? 1) H_2NNH_2, H^+ 2) NaOH/H_2O, heat

16.4. ENOLATE AND ENOL NUCLEOPHILES: ALDOL AND ALDOL-TYPE ADDITIONS

Nearly all of the acid- and base-catalyzed nucleophilic addition reactions we have encountered in the chapter thus far are ones in which the nucleophilic atom is *not* carbon. However, such reactions that involve carbon-nucleophiles are among the most important reactions in organic synthesis. These include aldol and aldol-type reactions, which we will examine throughout the rest of this chapter.

16.4a. Base-Catalyzed Aldol Addition

When ethanal (acetaldehyde, $CH_3CH{=}O$) is treated with sodium hydroxide (Equation 16-35), the product is 3-hydroxybutanal, a compound containing a 4-carbon chain.

a β-hydroxycarbonyl
(an aldol)

HC(=O)CH₃ —NaOH→ HC(=O)CH₂CH(OH)CH₃

acetaldehyde

3-hydroxybutanal (16-35)

Because the product contains both an aldehyde functional group and an alcohol functional group, it is called an **aldol**, and the reaction that forms it is termed an **aldol addition**. Notice that the carbonyl and the hydroxyl groups in the product are separated by a single carbon atom; the molecule is therefore classified as a **β-hydroxycarbonyl**, which is the general form of any aldol addition product.

Every aldol addition produces a β-hydroxycarbonyl.

Your Turn 16.9. In the aldol product in Equation 16-35, circle and label the aldehyde group and the alcohol group. Also label the α and β carbons.

Problem 16.15. Which of the following compounds could be the product of an aldol reaction? Explain.

(a) (b) (c)

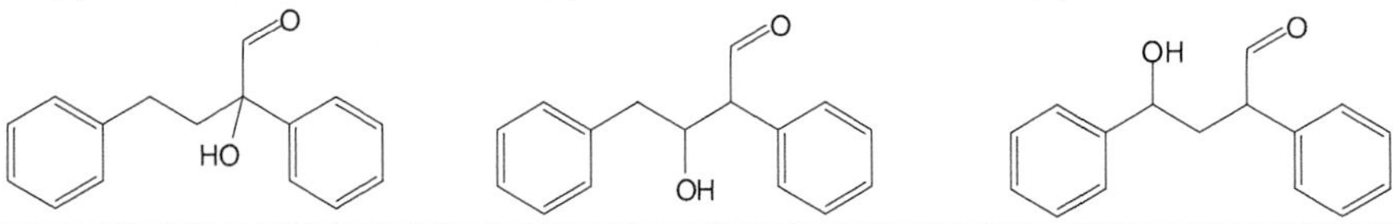

HO OH OH

Clearly the reaction in Equation 16-35 must form a carbon-carbon bond. As we have seen in previous chapters, a carbon-carbon bond can form between an electron-rich carbon and an electron-poor carbon. In acetaldehyde, the carbonyl carbon is clearly electron-poor, as it bears a significant partial positive charge, but neither carbon atom appears to be electron-rich.

Treatment with HO^-, however, *reversibly* deprotonates the alpha carbon to yield an enolate anion, as shown in step 1 in Equation 16-36. An enolate anion is electron-rich at the alpha carbon and can act as a nucleophile. (Recall that in Chapter 11 we saw enolate anions act as nucleophiles in S_N2 reactions, attacking alkyl halides and molecular halogens to yield alkylated and halogenated carbonyls, respectively.) In step 2, the newly formed enolate anion enters into a nucleophilic addition reaction with a second molecule of acetaldehyde that still has its proton (and hence is neutral overall). The immediate product is an alkoxide anion (RO^-), which is subsequently protonated in step 3.

Comment [JMK5]: Margin note.
An enolate anion is nucleophilic at the alpha carbon.

Mechanism of the Reaction in Equation 16-35

a second molecule of the aldehyde

base is regenerated

1) proton transfer

2) nuc. addition

3) proton transfer

enolate anion nucleophilic at C

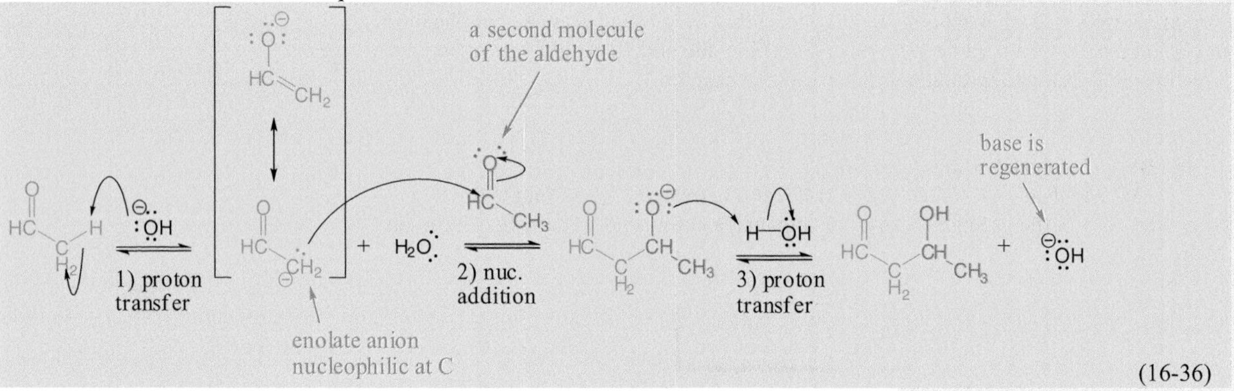

(16-36)

Notice that this nucleophilic addition step is *reversible* (recall Table 15-1). This is because the enolate anion is stabilized by resonance and so is substantially more stable than the R^- nucleophiles comprising alkyllithium and Grignard reagents (Section 15.6).

Solved Problem 16.5. Draw the complete, detailed mechanism for the following reaction and use the mechanism to predict the products.

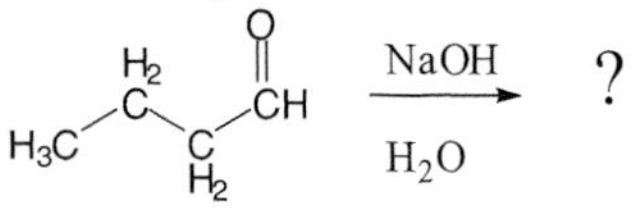

$$H_3C-CH_2-CH_2-CHO \xrightarrow[H_2O]{NaOH} ?$$

Think. How is this reaction similar to that in Equation 16-35 (and 16-36)? How is it different? What is the role of NaOH?

Solve. Just as in Equation 16-35, an aldehyde is treated with hydroxide. The only difference is the carbon backbone—in this case, we have a 4-carbon aldehyde, whereas in Equation 16-35 there is a 2-carbon aldehyde. The mechanisms are therefore essentially identical. In the first step, HO^- acts as a base to generate an enolate anion. (Note that HO^- could also act as a nucleophile, but as we saw in Chapter 9, proton transfer reactions are very fast, so the dominant reaction is deprotonation of the aldehyde.) In the second step, the enolate anion acts as a nucleophile, attacking a second molecule of butanal that still has its proton. That step forms a C-C bond between the two species. Finally, the O^- is protonated to yield the β-hydroxycarbonyl.

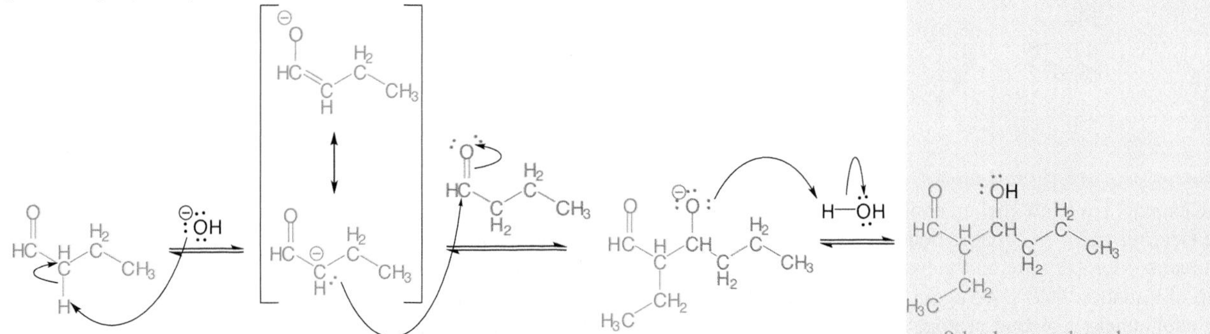

a β-hydroxycarbonyl

Problem 16.16. Draw the complete, detailed mechanism for the following reaction and predict the product.

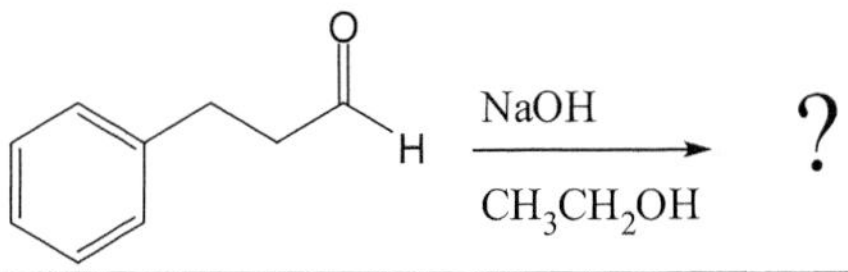

NaOH
CH_3CH_2OH
?

16.4b. Acid-Catalyzed Aldol Addition

The formation of an aldol can also be catalyzed by acid. As shown in Equation 16-37, for example, treatment of propanal with a strong acid yields 3-hydroxy-2-methylpentanal—a β-hydroxycarbonyl.

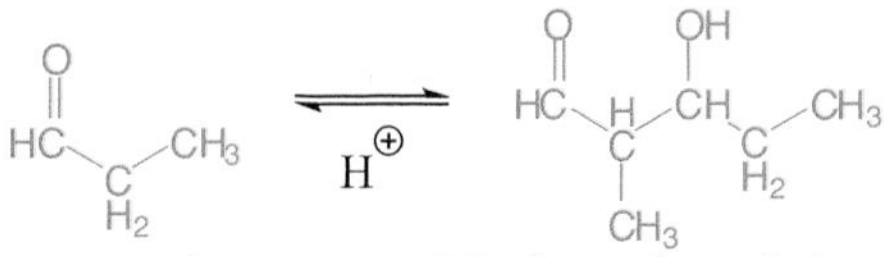

propanal $\xrightleftharpoons[H^{\oplus}]{}$ 3-hydroxy-2-methylpentanal (16-37)

Once again, however, we are faced with the question of what acts as a nucleophile under these reaction conditions. Unlike what we saw under basic conditions, the nucleophile cannot be an enolate anion, given that a strong base is necessary to generate it. As we learned in Chapter 9, no significant concentration of a strong base can exist in acidic conditions.

The nucleophile, instead, must be the *enol* form of the aldehyde, the formation of which takes place in two proton transfer steps and is catalyzed by the presence of the acid (Equation 16-38).

Comment [JMK6]: **Margin note.** Under acidic conditions, the enol form of an aldehyde can behave as a nucleophile.

Mechanism for the Reaction in Equation 16-37

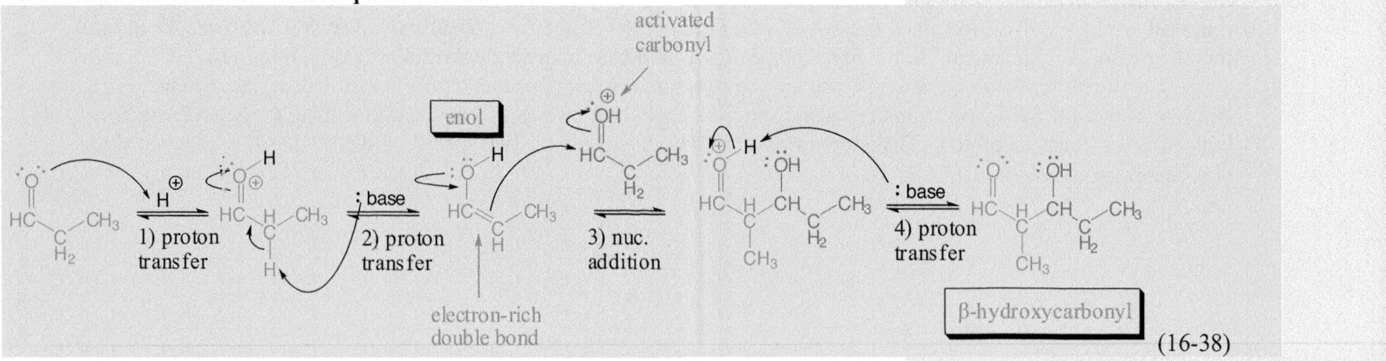

(16-38)

In Chapter 11 we saw that an enol can act as a nucleophile at the alpha carbon because of the electron-rich C=C double bond. There we saw enols act as nucleophiles in S_N2 reactions—for example, in the halogenation of the carbonyl's alpha carbon. In the third step of Equation 16-38, we again see this nucleophilic character as the alpha carbon of the enol attacks a second protonated aldehyde. In the final step of the mechanism, a proton transfer produces the neutral aldol, or β-hydroxycarbonyl.

Notice in Equation 16-38 that the enol attacks the *protonated* form of the carbonyl. This is because enols are neutral and are therefore *weak nucleophiles*. As we saw before, the protonated form of the carbonyl generates a much more electron-deficient carbonyl carbon, thereby *activating* it toward nucleophilic attack.

Problem 16.17. For the reaction below, predict the major organic product and draw the complete, detailed mechanism.

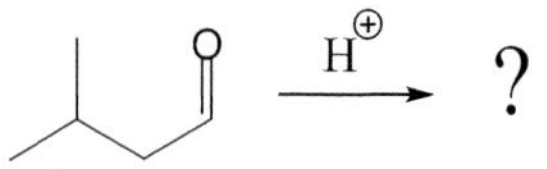

Solved Problem 16.6. Show how to synthesize the molecule below using an aldol reaction.

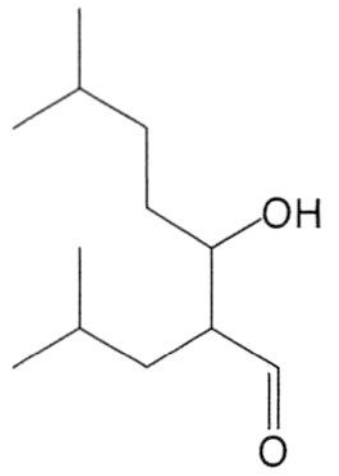

Think. Can you identify the portion of the molecule that characterizes it as a β-hydroxycarbonyl? Which carbons of the β-hydroxycarbonyl will have been joined together in an aldol addition? Upon disconnection of that C-C bond, what carbon backbones are produced?

Solve. The alpha and beta carbons of the C=O group are labeled below. As we can see, an OH group is attached to the beta carbon, so the molecule is indeed a β-hydroxycarbonyl. To reverse the aldol reaction, we disconnect the bond between the alpha and beta carbons, as indicated. In the precursor, the C-OH bond is a C=O group.

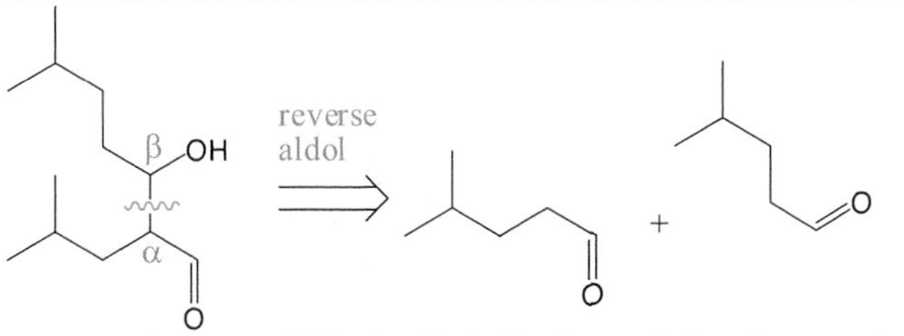

reverse aldol

β OH

α

The two precursors are the same aldehyde. So in the forward direction, we simply treat that aldehyde with either NaOH or a strong acid.

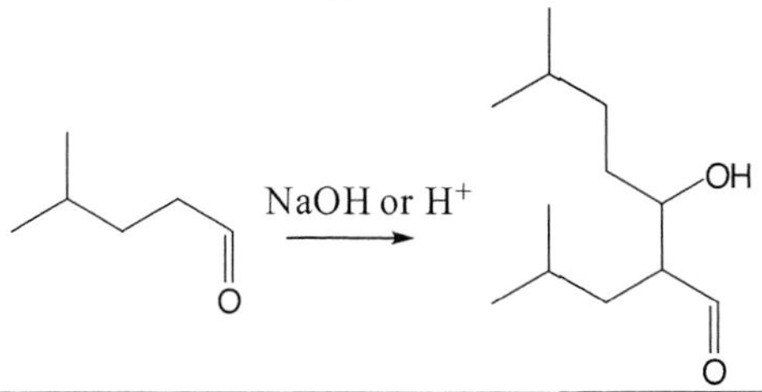

NaOH or H^+

OH

Problem 16.18. Show how to synthesize the molecule below using an aldol reaction.

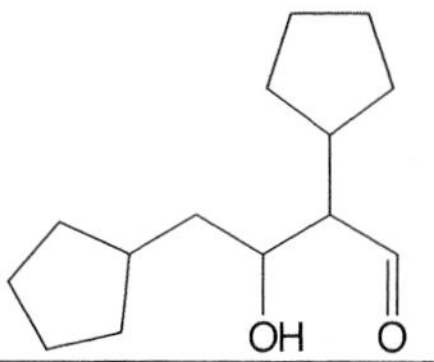

OH O

16.5. ALDOL CONDENSATIONS

As we saw in Section 16.4, a *β-hydroxycarbonyl* is the immediate product of an aldol addition. If heat is added during the reaction, water is eliminated from the β-hydroxycarbonyl, giving the overall product a C=C double bond. An example is shown in Equation 16-39, which takes place under basic conditions.

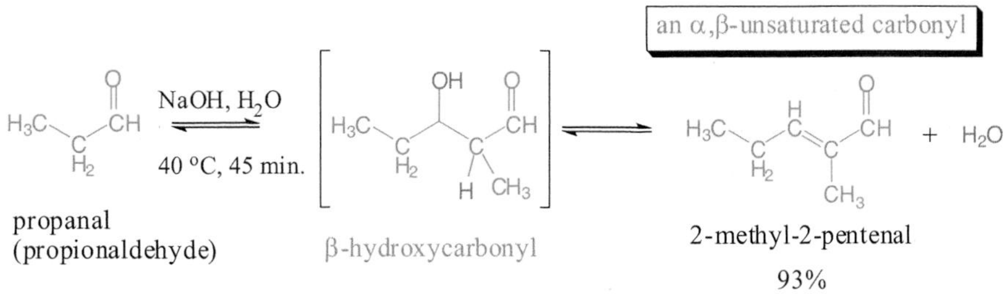

an α,β-unsaturated carbonyl

H_3C–CH_2–CH(=O) propanal (propionaldehyde) —NaOH, H_2O, 40 °C, 45 min.⇌ [β-hydroxycarbonyl] ⇌ 2-methyl-2-pentenal 93% + H_2O (16-39)

This overall reaction, in which an aldol addition is followed by dehydration, is called an **aldol condensation**. In general, a *condensation* reaction is one in which two larger molecules bond together with the elimination of a smaller molecule; in this case, that smaller molecule is H_2O.

Comment [JMK7]: Margin note. An aldol condensation is an aldol addition followed by dehydration.

Notice in Equation 16-39 that the newly-formed C=C double bond appears between the alpha and beta carbons of the aldehyde. The product is thus called an **α,β-unsaturated carbonyl**. In general,

The product of an aldol condensation is an α,β-unsaturated carbonyl.

The reason heat promotes the condensation reaction has to do with *entropy*. Recall from Section 10.2f that *heat favors an increase in entropy*. And, as we can see in Equation 16-39, the dehydration step results in an increase in the number of independent species, and thus an increase in entropy.

Under basic conditions, dehydration of a β-hydroxycarbonyl takes place via an **E1cb mechanism**, which stands for *conjugate base unimolecular elimination* (Equation 16-40).

Mechanism of Dehydration of an Aldol Addition Product Under Basic Conditions: An E1cb Mechanism

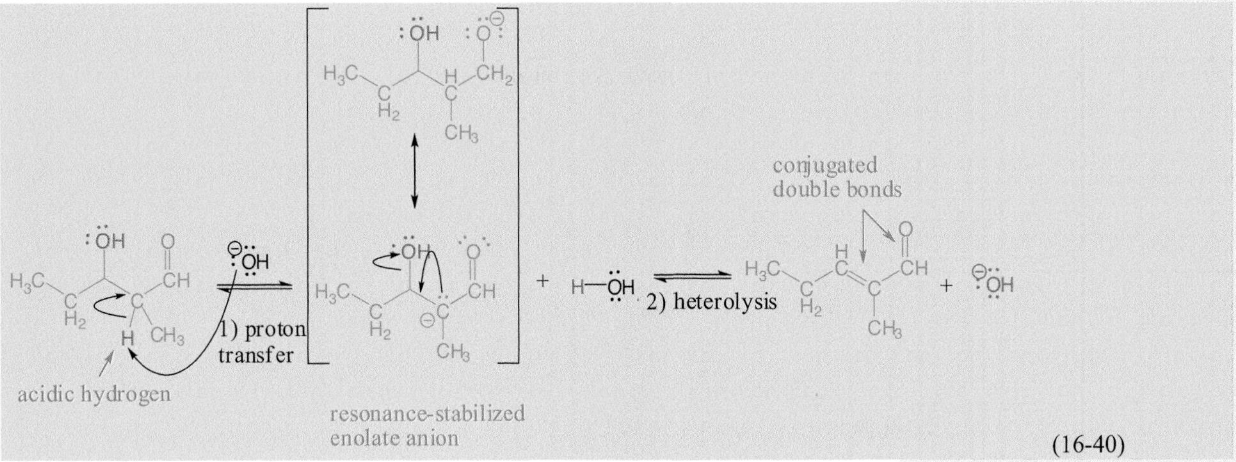

(16-40)

Because of the enhanced acidity at the alpha carbon, the first step is a fast proton transfer, generating a resonance-stabilized enolate anion. In the second step, the HO^- leaving group departs to yield the overall product.

This elimination may seem to contradict a general rule we encountered in Section 10.3, which states that an HO^- leaving group is in general not suitable for elimination reactions. In this case, however, elimination is favored, in part, by the stability that arises from the conjugation between the C=C and C=O double bonds. Furthermore, although we will not discuss it in detail, the available proton transfer in the first step allows the E1cb mechanism to have a lower overall energy barrier than either the E1 or E2 mechanisms.

Comment [JMK8]: **Margin note.** Conjugation of the double bonds in the α,β-unsaturated carbonyl favors dehydration.

Problem 16.19. As shown below, if 3-hydroxybutanal is heated under basic conditions, dehydration occurs. However, no dehydration occurs when pent-4-en-2-ol is subjected to the same conditions. Explain.

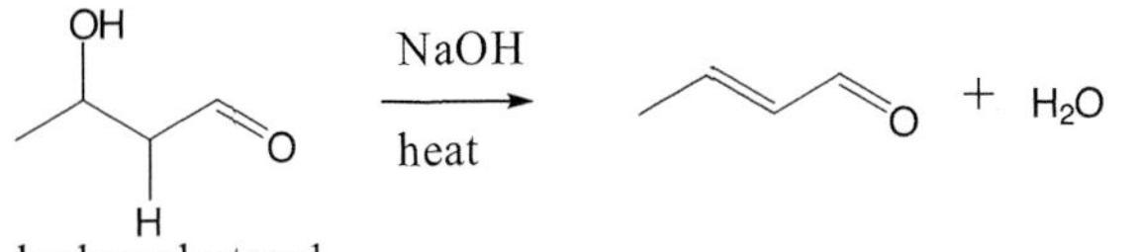

OH
NaOH
heat
+ H_2O
H
3-hydroxybutanal

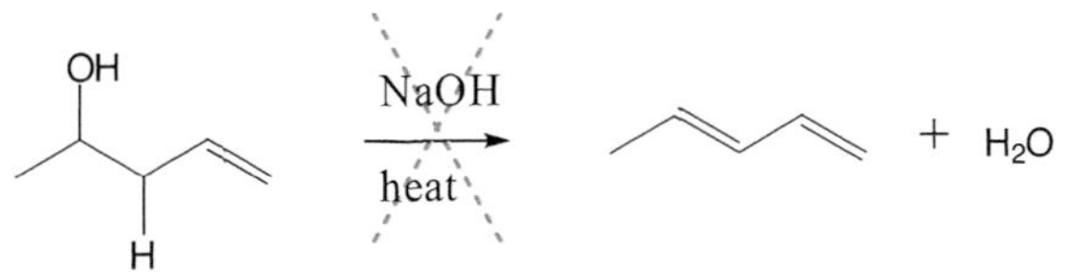

OH
NaOH
heat
+ H_2O
H
pent-4-en-2-ol

Aldol condensations can also take place under acidic conditions, once again producing an α,β-unsaturated carbonyl (Equation 16-41).

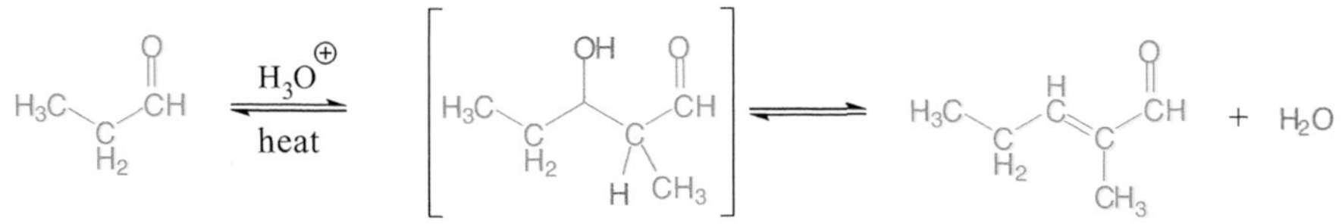

$H_3O^{\oplus}$
heat
+ H_2O

(16-41)

The mechanism for this reaction is essentially an E1 mechanism, shown in Equation 16-42. In the first step, protonation of the OH group generates a very good water leaving group. The leaving group departs in the second step, and a final deprotonation yields the overall product.

Mechanism of Dehydration of an Aldol Addition Product Under Acidic Conditions

1) proton transfer
2) heterolysis
3) proton transfer

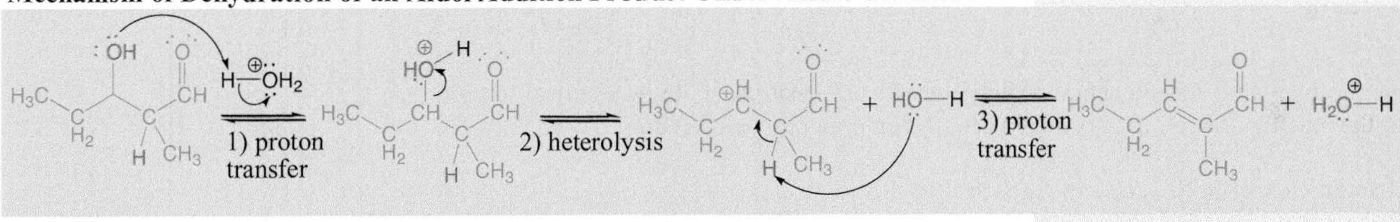

(16-42)

Notice that in the final step of Equation 16-42, the alpha proton is not the only one that can be detached in a dehydration reaction. As shown in Equation 16-43b, a gamma proton can also be removed, yielding a β,γ-unsaturated carbonyl. However, essentially none of this product is formed. The α,β-unsaturated carbonyl product (Equation 16-43a) possesses *conjugated double bonds*, and is thus more stable than the β,γ-unsaturated carbonyl.

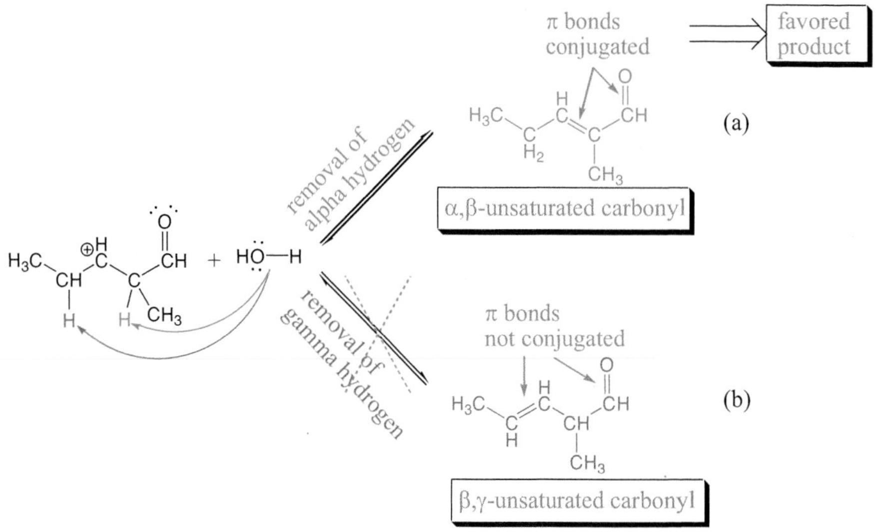

π bonds conjugated → favored product

(a) α,β-unsaturated carbonyl

removal of alpha hydrogen

removal of gamma hydrogen

π bonds not conjugated

(b) β,γ-unsaturated carbonyl

(16-43)

16.6. ALDOL REACTIONS INVOLVING KETONES

Ketones with alpha hydrogens can participate in aldol additions in the same way that aldehydes do. Equation 16-44 illustrates such a reaction with acetone.

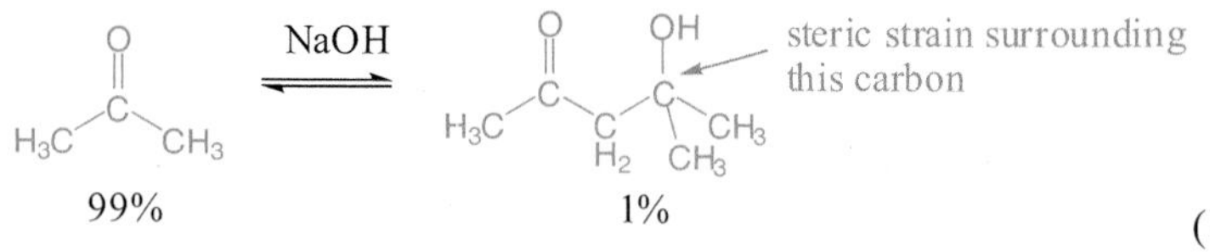

NaOH

99%

1%

steric strain surrounding this carbon

(16-44)

The mechanism for this reaction, which is shown in Equation 16-45, is identical to that for the reaction involving only aldehydes, shown previously in Equation 16-36.

Mechanism of the Reaction in Equation 16-44

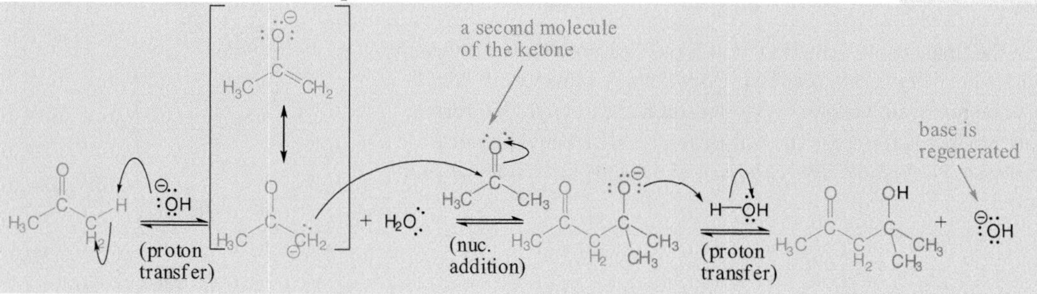

(proton transfer)

a second molecule of the ketone

(nuc. addition)

(proton transfer)

base is regenerated

(16-45)

As we can see from Equation 16-44, however, a complication arises with percent yield—at equilibrium, very little product is formed. This is a reflection of the fact that nucleophilic addition to a ketone yields a product with considerable steric strain, and is therefore less favorable than addition to an aldehyde. Recall from Section 15.3 that a similar phenomenon occurs with the hydration of ketones and aldehydes.

Comment [JMK9]: **Margin note.** Aldol reactions involving ketones favor reactants.

Because aldol additions involving ketones generally favor reactants, chemists must manipulate the equilibrium using Le Châtelier's principle in order to achieve a reasonable yield. Although we will not discuss the details, one way to do so is to remove the aldol product as it is formed.

16.7. CROSSED ALDOL REACTIONS

The aldol additions we have examined thus far have involved only a single aldehyde or a single ketone; the nucleophilic species (either the enolate anion or the enol) is derived from the same aldehyde or ketone it attacks. However, we can imagine a scenario in which the nucleophilic species is generated from a *different* aldehyde or ketone. Equation 16-46, for example, illustrates the enolate anion of propanal attacking a molecule of ethanal (acetaldehyde), yielding 3-hydroxy-2-methylbutanal. Such a reaction is called a **crossed aldol addition**.

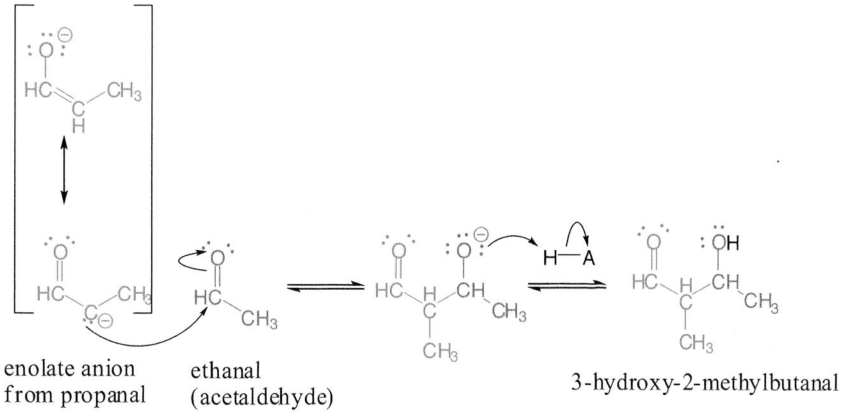

enolate anion from propanal — ethanal (acetaldehyde) — 3-hydroxy-2-methylbutanal

(16-46)

To carry out such a reaction, we might imagine treating propanal with NaOH and ethanal (acetaldehyde), as shown in Equation 16-47. The hope is that the base will deprotonate propanal, and the resulting enolate anion will react with ethanal to produce 3-hydroxy-2-methylbutanal. Indeed, as shown in the equation, the desired product is formed, but so are three other aldol products. Not only does this compromise the reaction yield, but the four products are difficult to separate due to their similar physical properties. Consequently, such a reaction is *not* synthetically useful.

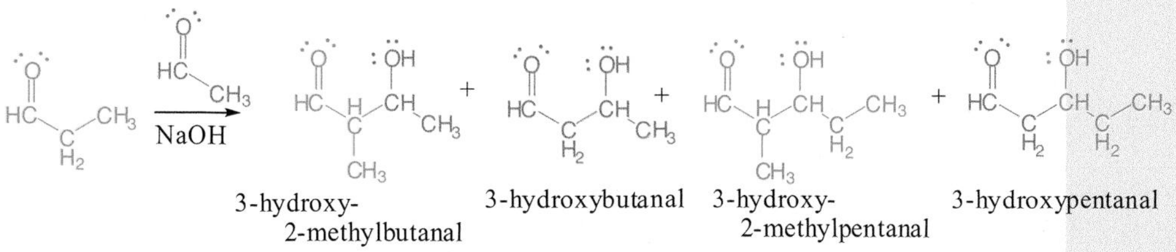

NaOH

3-hydroxy-2-methylbutanal + 3-hydroxybutanal + 3-hydroxy-2-methylpentanal + 3-hydroxypentanal

(16-47)

The problem stems from the fact that deprotonation of an alpha hydrogen by NaOH is slightly unfavorable. Thus, at any given time throughout the reaction, a significant concentration of HO^- exists, and both aldehydes are deprotonated to a small extent. In other words, the enolate anions from *both* aldehydes are present at the same time, and each enolate anion can attack one of two different neutral aldehydes. Consequently, as shown in Equation 16-48, there are four different pairings of an enolate anion with a neutral aldehyde, and each gives rise to a different aldol product.

(a)

(b)

(c)

(d)

(16-48)

Problem 16.20. Draw the complete, detailed mechanism for the reaction in Equation 16-48c.

One way around this complication is to use an aldehyde that has no alpha hydrogens, such as methanal, benzaldehyde, or dimethylpropanal.

Comment [JMK10]: **Margin note.** HO^- can be used as the base in crossed aldol reactions if one aldehyde has no alpha protons.

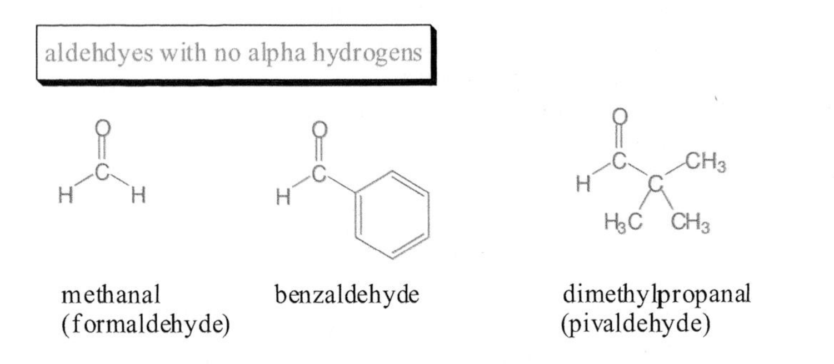

If an aldehyde *with* alpha hydrogens is added slowly to a basic solution of an aldehyde *without* alpha hydrogens, primarily one aldol product is formed.

An example is shown in Equation 16-49.

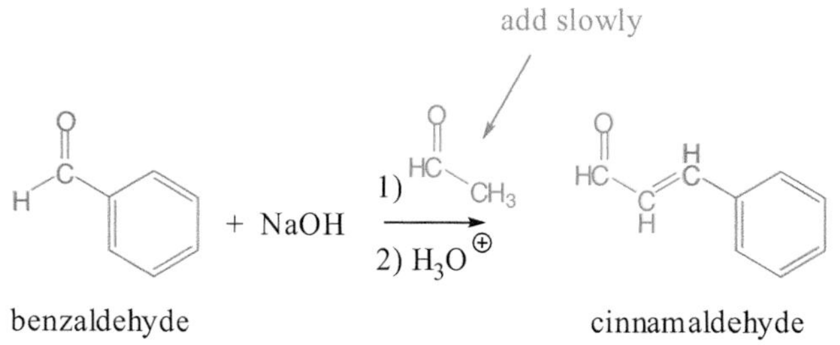

add slowly

benzaldehyde + NaOH → 1) acetaldehyde; 2) $H_3O^{\oplus}$ → cinnamaldehyde 67% (16-49)

Because benzaldehyde has no alpha hydrogens, it is not deprotonated by NaOH, so it does not form an enolate anion. Thus, in contrast to Equation 16-47, only one enolate anion is present at any given time. Moreover, if acetaldehyde (which has alpha hydrogens) is added slowly, we avoid a buildup of the neutral aldehyde, and thus minimize the amount of product from the aldol reaction between acetaldehyde and its own enolate anion—a self-reaction.

Your Turn 16.10. Indicate which ketone or aldehyde below would be the best choice to use for a crossed aldol reaction with butanal.

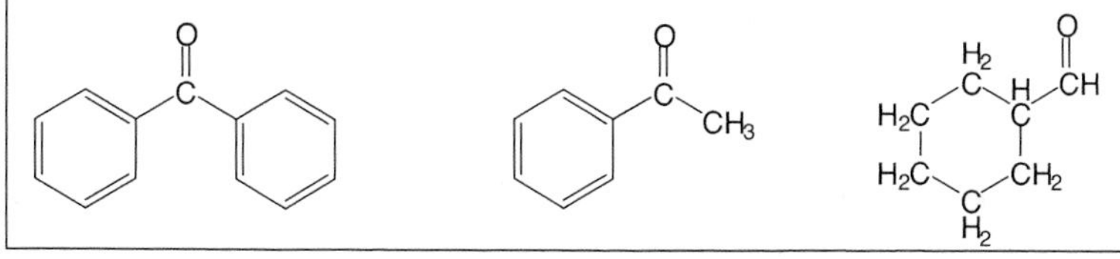

Solved Problem 16.7. Predict the product of the following reaction, in which propanal is added slowly to a basic solution of formaldehyde.

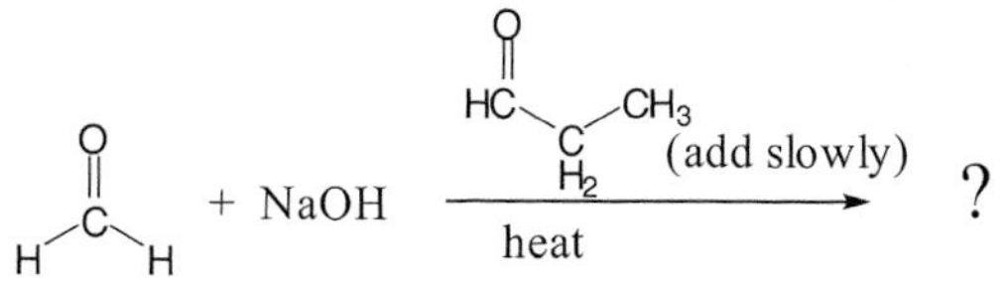

formaldehyde + NaOH → propanal (add slowly), heat → ?

Think. Which aldehyde can form an enolate anion and which cannot? Which neutral aldehyde is present in only small concentrations in the reaction mixture?

Solve. Formaldehyde has no alpha hydrogens, so it cannot form an enolate anion. Thus, the only enolate nucleophile that is present is derived from propanal.

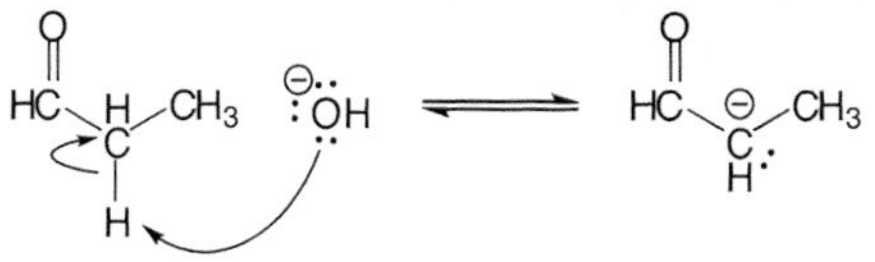

Furthermore, because propanal is added slowly, there is never a substantial concentration of it in its neutral form. So the major reaction is that between the propanal enolate anion and formaldehyde, as outlined below.

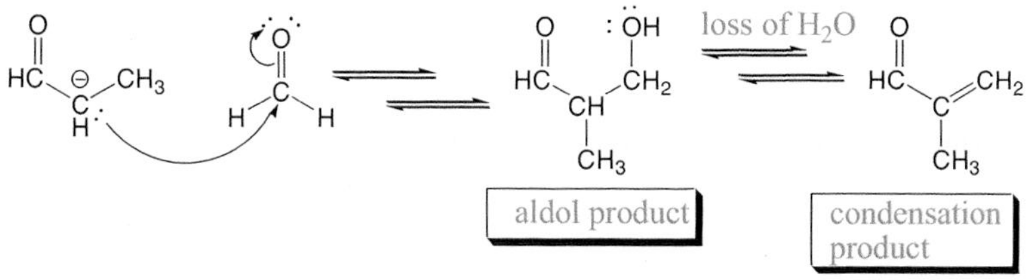

loss of H_2O

aldol product

condensation product

Notice that because the reaction is heated, dehydration leads to the condensation product.

Problem 16.21. Predict the product of the following reaction, in which phenylethanal is added slowly to a basic solution of dimethylpropanal.

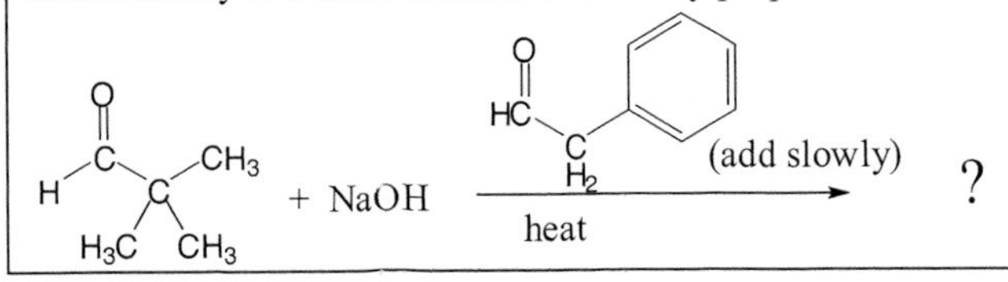

O, H, C, CH3, H3C, CH3, + NaOH, O, HC, C, H2, (add slowly), heat, ?

Solved Problem 16.8. Show how to synthesize the following molecule using an aldol condensation.

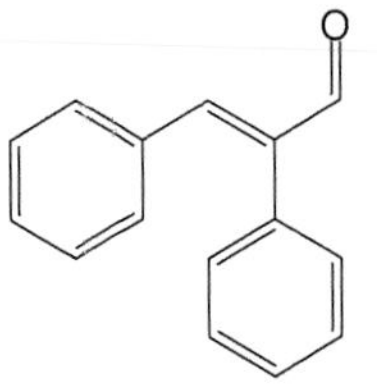

Think. Can you identify the portion of the molecule that characterizes it as an α,β-unsaturated carbonyl? From what β-hydroxycarbonyl could it have been generated? Upon applying a transform to that β-hydroxycarbonyl to reverse an aldol addition, which C-C bond should be disconnected?

Solve. The alpha and beta carbons of the C=O group are labeled below. As we can see, the target is an α,β-unsaturated carbonyl, so it can be the product of dehydrating the β-hydroxycarbonyl shown. To apply a transform that reverses an aldol addition, we must disconnect the bond between the alpha and beta carbons, as indicated.

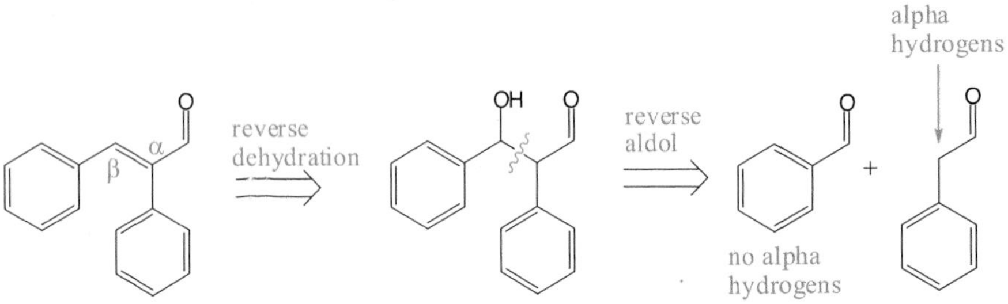

O, α, β, reverse dehydration, OH, O, reverse aldol, O, +, no alpha hydrogens, alpha hydrogens, O

Because these aldehyde precursors are different from each other, more than one aldol product is possible in the forward direction. To produce only the desired product, we should slowly add the aldehyde *with* alpha hydrogens to a basic solution of the aldehyde *without* alpha hydrogens.

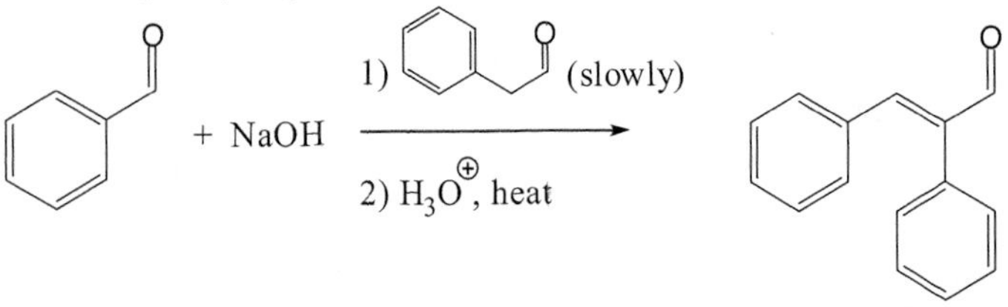

O, + NaOH, 1) (slowly), 2) $H_3O^{\oplus}$, heat, O

Problem 16.22. Show how to synthesize the following molecule using an aldol reaction.

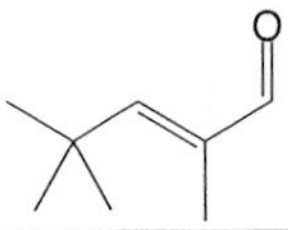

O

A second way to carry out a crossed aldol reaction is to use a very strong base such as lithium diisopropylamide (LDA) to generate the enolate anion, as shown in Equation 16-50.

cyclohexanone 1) LDA, THF 2) HC(=O)–CH₂–CH₂–CH=CH–(CH₂)₄–CH₃ → 70%

(16-50)

LDA is a very strong base, and deprotonates an alpha carbon both quantitatively and rapidly. Therefore, essentially 100% of cyclohexanone is converted to its enolate anion prior to the addition of the second carbonyl-containing compound. In this way, only one enolate anion is available to react in the second step of the synthesis.

In an aldol reaction involving ketones, a complication arises from the fact that ketones often have two chemically distinct alpha carbons. Deprotonation of such a ketone at one alpha carbon will produce an enolate anion that is different from that produced by deprotonation at the other. Thus, two different aldol products are possible. Certainly this is not an issue with a symmetric ketone like cyclohexanone (Equation 16-50), where both alpha carbons are chemically equivalent. It becomes an issue, however, with asymmetric ketones such as methylbutanone, as shown in Equations 16-51a and 16-51b.

-H⊕ (a) (b)

Two different enolate anions can be formed

different aldol products

(16-51)

Fortunately, we can choose the base wisely to determine which alpha proton is predominantly the one removed in the first step. For example, as shown in Equation 16-52, if NaOH is used as the base, the major aldol product is of the form that appears in Equation 16-51a. On the other hand, if lithium diisopropylamide (LDA) is used as the base (Equation 16-53), the major aldol product is of the form in Equation 16-51b.

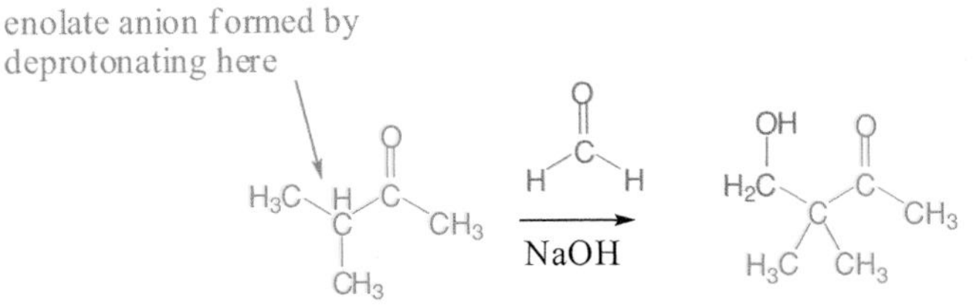

enolate anion formed by deprotonating here

methylbutanone → (NaOH, $H_2C{=}O$) 4-hydroxy-3,3-dimethylbutanone 72% (16-52)

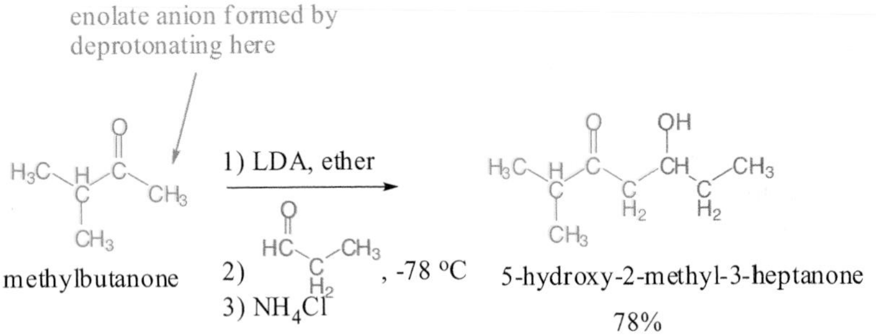

enolate anion formed by deprotonating here

methylbutanone → 1) LDA, ether; 2) propanal, -78 °C; 3) NH_4Cl → 5-hydroxy-2-methyl-3-heptanone 78% (16-53)

Recall from Section 11.3 that when NaOH is used as the base, the favored product is the thermodynamic enolate anion, which is formed by deprotonating the more highly substituted alpha carbon. On the other hand, when LDA is used as the base, the favored product is the kinetic enolate anion, which is formed by deprotonating the less highly substituted alpha carbon.

Your Turn 16.11. In each box below, write the base that would accomplish the respective aldol reactions.

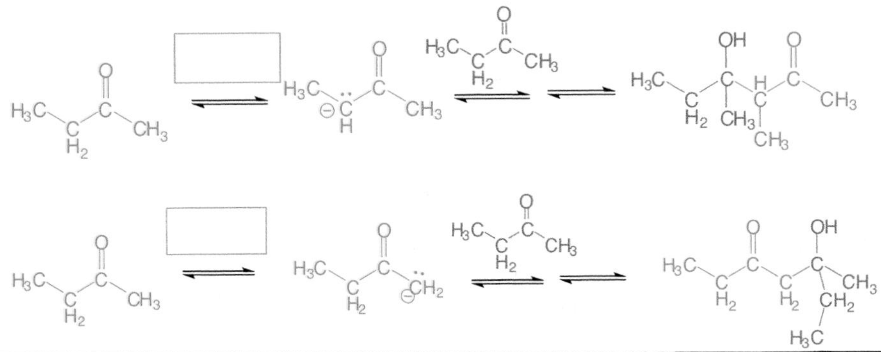

16.8. INTRAMOLECULAR ALDOL REACTIONS

If a molecule includes two carbonyl-containing functional groups, then an *intramolecular* aldol reaction (that is, one between different parts of the same molecule) is possible. The result is the formation of a bond between two carbon atoms on the molecule's backbone, and, consequently, a *ring*. An example is shown with hexanedial (Equation 16-54).

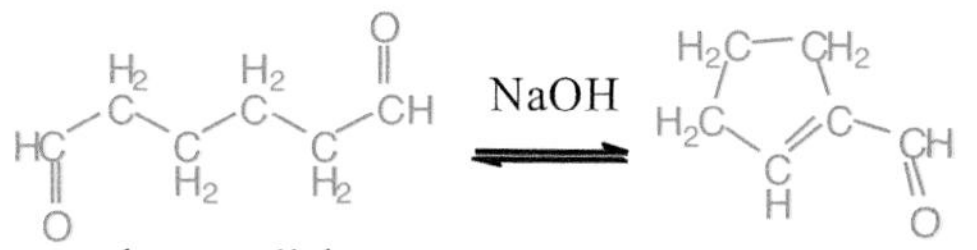

hexanedial —NaOH→ 71%

(16-54)

Your Turn 16.12. In the product of Equation 16-54, circle the structural features that characterize it as the product of an aldol condensation.

The mechanism for this reaction, which is shown in Equation 16-55, is identical to aldol condensations that occur between two separate aldehyde molecules (Equation 16-40).

Mechanism of the Reaction in Equation 16-54

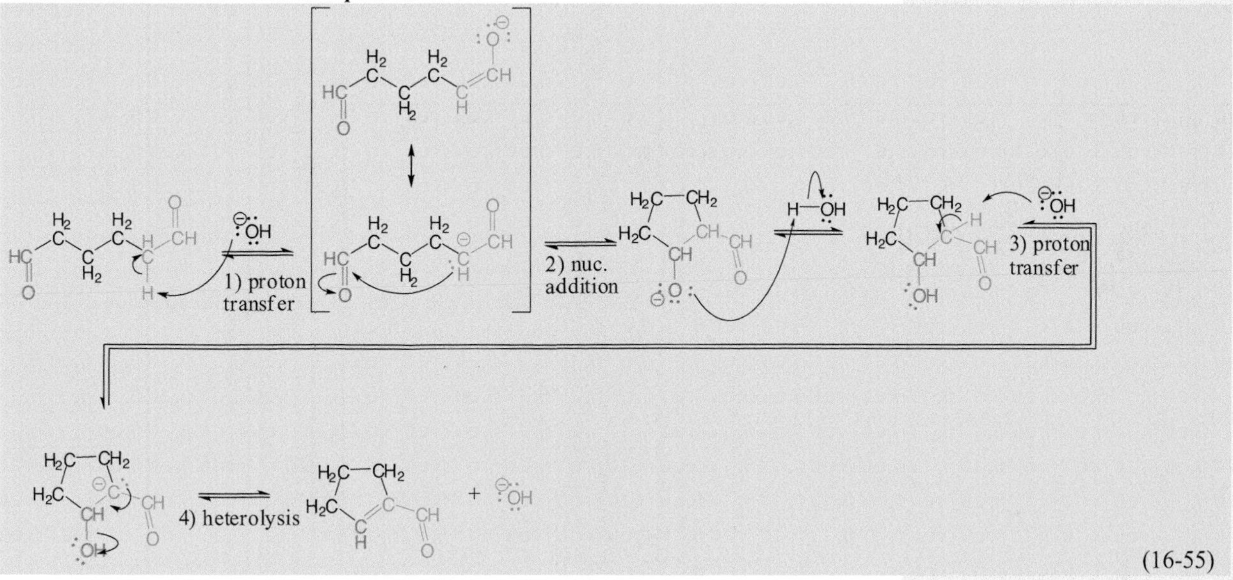

1) proton transfer

2) nuc. addition

3) proton transfer

4) heterolysis

(16-55)

In Chapter 9 we learned that cyclization reactions, in general, are favored over their corresponding intermolecular reactions when the product is a 5- or 6-membered ring. Indeed, in Equation 16-54 the product is a 5-membered ring. By contrast, dialdehydes such as pentanedial (Equation 16-56) and octanedial (Equation 16-57) do not favor intramolecular aldol reactions because their aldol products would possess 4-membered and 7-membered rings, respectively. The former is not favored because of the large amount of ring strain in a 4-membered ring. That latter possesses some ring strain, but is also disfavored because, with so many conformations available to the open-chain form, an excessive decrease in entropy is required to close the ring (Section 9.7f).

Comment [JMK11]: **Margin note.** Intramolecular aldol reactions are favored when 5- or 6-membered rings are formed.

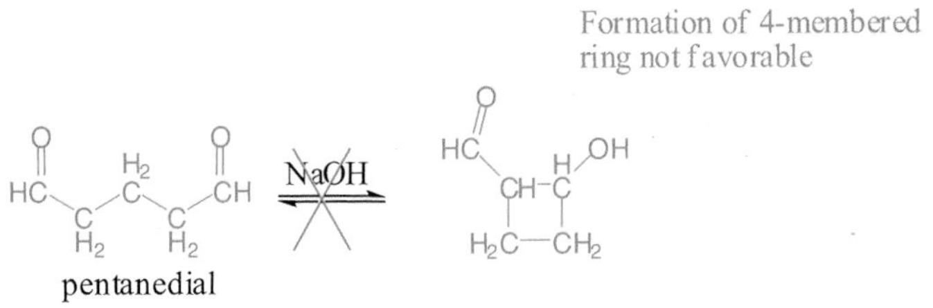

Formation of 4-membered ring not favorable

pentanedial

(16-56)

Formation of 7-membered ring not favorable

octanedial

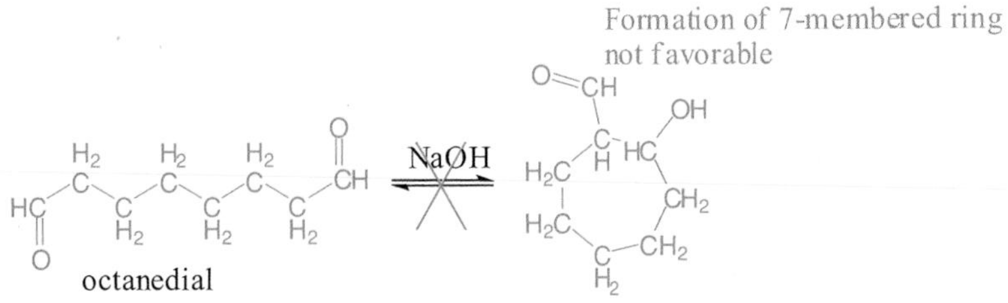

(16-57)

Problem 16.23. The intramolecular aldol reaction involving heptanedial is favorable. Draw the mechanism for this reaction, along with the major product that is formed. Explain why the reaction is favorable.

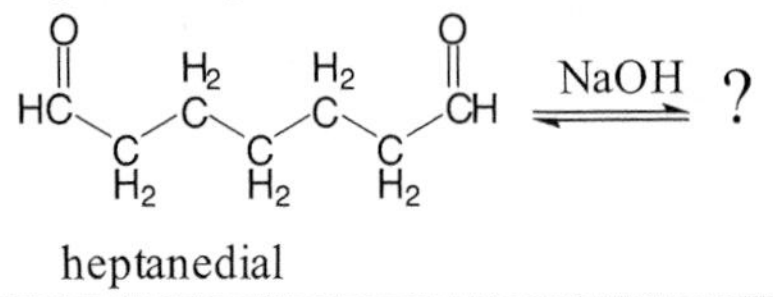

heptanedial

Equation 16-58 provides an example of a di-carbonyl compound that can form three different enolate anions, and can thus form three different cyclic aldol products.

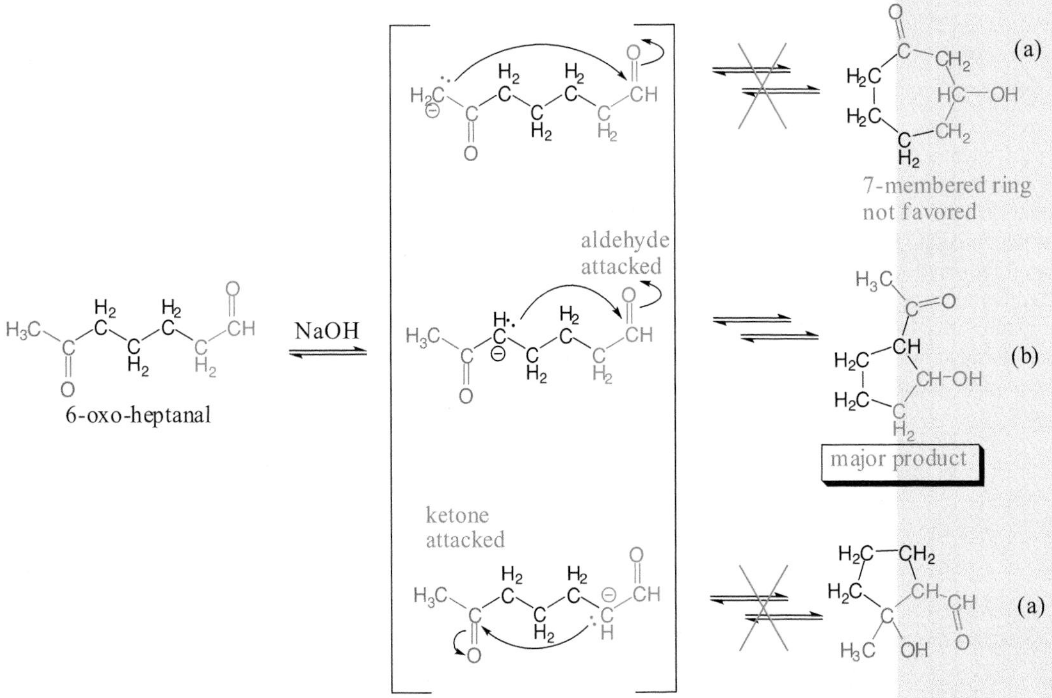

6-oxo-heptanal

(a) 7-membered ring not favored

aldehyde attacked

(b) major product

ketone attacked

(a)

(16-58)

In this case, the product in Equation 16-58b is heavily favored over the others. As we have seen previously, the aldol product in Equation 16-58a is not favored because it forms a 7-membered ring. On the other hand, the reactions in Equations 16-58b and 16-58c both form 5-membered rings. The major difference between the two reactions is in the functional group that is attacked—in Equation 16-58b it is an aldehyde, whereas in Equation 16-58c, it is a ketone. Recall from Section 16.6 that addition to a ketone gives rise to greater steric strain, and is thus less favorable than addition to an aldehyde.

Solved Problem 16.9. Draw the complete, detailed mechanism for the following reaction and predict the major product. (You may assume that Le Châtelier's principle is exploited to drive the reaction toward products.)

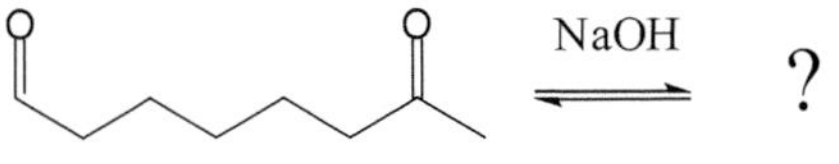

NaOH

?

Think. What enolate anions can be formed? Which of those can attack a carbonyl group to form a 5- or 6-membered ring? In those nucleophilic additions, what kind of carbonyl group is attacked—a ketone or aldehyde?

Solve. There are three possible enolate anions resulting from deprotonation of an alpha proton, as shown below. The possible aldol products are also shown.

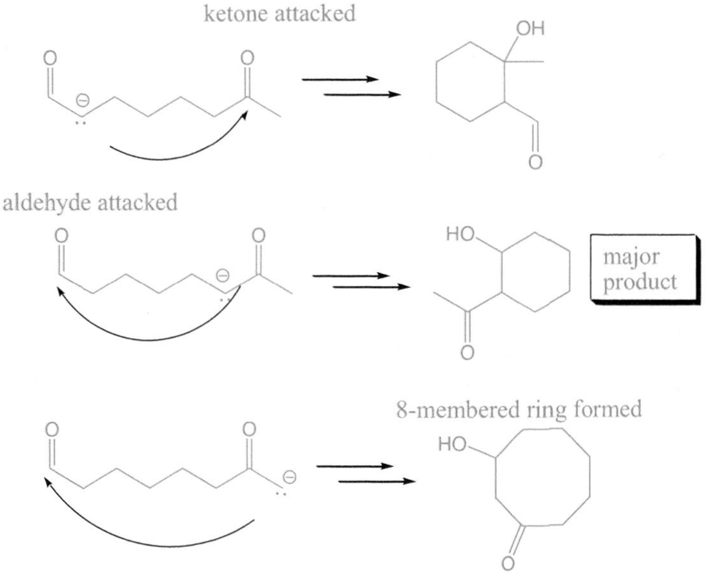

ketone attacked

aldehyde attacked

major product

8-membered ring formed

The first and second products are favored over the third because of the sizes of the rings that are formed—six-membered rings in the first two products, and an eight-membered ring in the third. Moreover, because nucleophilic is favored at an aldehyde over a ketone, the second product is favored over the first. Thus the second product is the major product.

Problem 16.24. Predict the major product of the following reaction.

NaOH

?

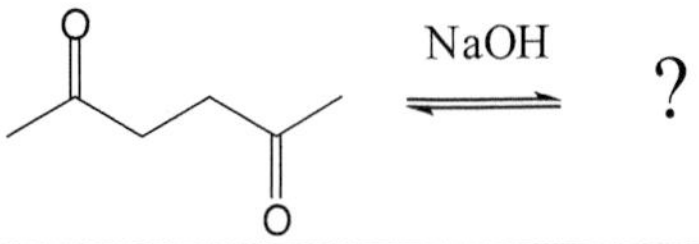

16.9. ALDOL ADDITIONS INVOLVING NITRILES AND NITROALKANES

Aldol additions are not limited to just ketones and aldehydes. Other functional groups containing a polar π bond have acidic alpha hydrogens as well. When deprotonated, their resulting enolate anions can act as nucleophiles just as the enolate anions of ketones and aldehydes.

In compounds containing nitrile (C≡N) and nitro (NO_2) groups, for example, the alpha hydrogens are somewhat acidic. As we can see below, the pK_a of a nitrile's alpha hydrogen is about 25, and that of a nitro group's alpha hydrogen is around 10.

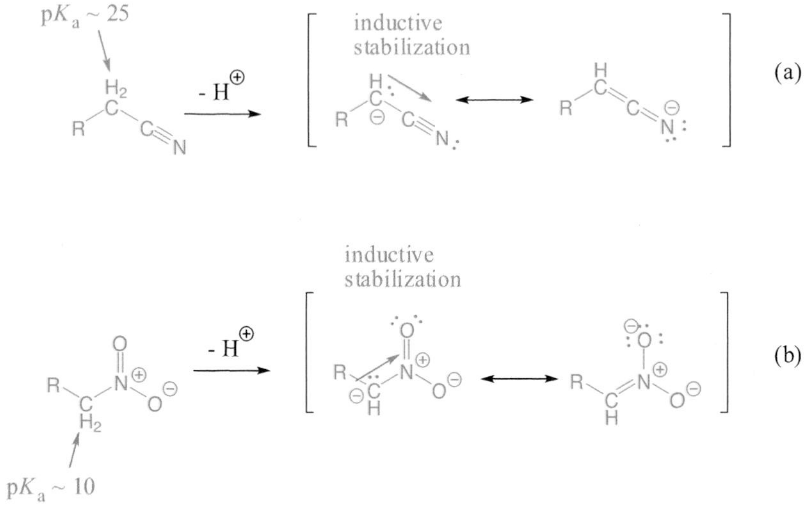

pKa ~ 25

- H⊕

inductive stabilization

(a)

inductive stabilization

- H⊕

(b)

pKa ~ 10

(16-59)

The acidity of a hydrogen alpha to a nitrile or nitro group, like that of a ketone or aldehyde hydrogen, derives from both resonance and inductive stabilization in the conjugate base. As we can see in Equation 15-59a and 15-59b, the CN and NO_2 groups, respectively, are electron-withdrawing which helps to reduce the concentration of negative charge on C. The negative charge is further dispersed by resonance delocalization over two separate atoms—C and N in Equation 15-59a, and C and O in Equation 15-59b.

Equations 16-60 and 16-61 provide examples of aldol reactions involving a nitrile and nitroalkane, respectively.

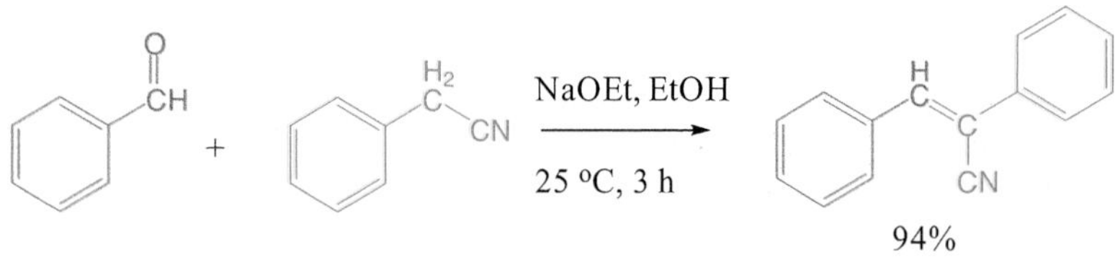

NaOEt, EtOH

25 °C, 3 h

94%

(16-60)

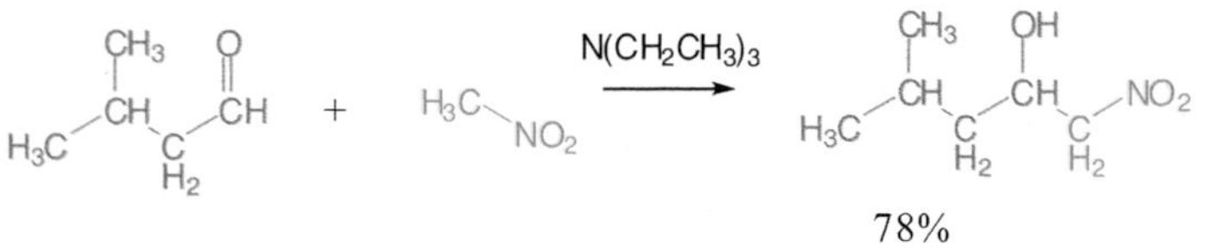

$N(CH_2CH_3)_3$

78%

(16-61)

The mechanisms of these reactions are identical to those of aldol reactions involving only ketones or aldehydes (see Solved Problem 16.9 and Problem 16.24). Interestingly, however, the aldol reaction involving a nitroalkane can be carried out using a weak base such as an amine. This is because the nitroalkane's alpha hydrogen is moderately acidic (pK_a ~10).

Solved Problem 16.10. Draw the complete, detailed mechanism for the reaction in Equation 16-60.

Think. Which protons are the most acidic? After deprotonation, which polar π bond undergoes nucleophilic addition? How is the C=C double bond formed in an aldol reaction?

Solve. The hydrogen alpha to the CN group is the most acidic, and is removed by the base in the first step. The resulting enolate anion attacks the aldehyde group, and the O^- generated in that step is subsequently protonated. The C=C bond is then formed by dehydration, which takes place by the E1cb mechanism.

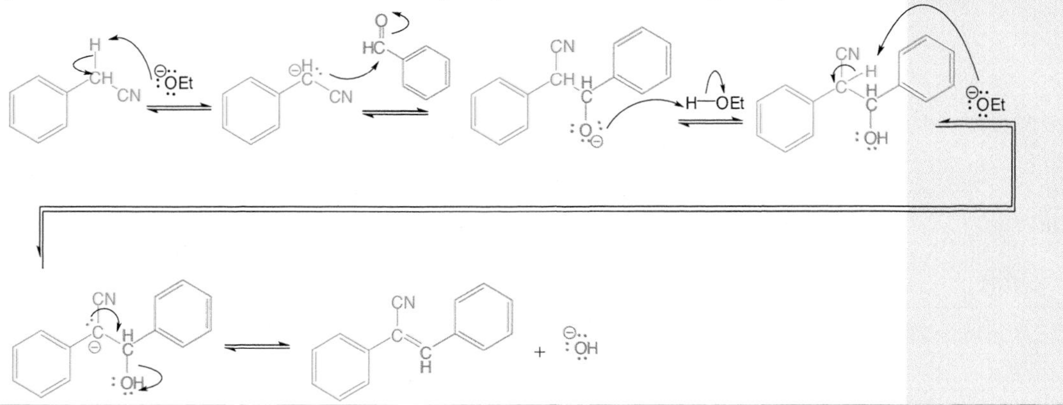

Problem 16.25. Draw the complete, detailed mechanism for the reaction in Equation 16-61.

Problem 16.26. For the reaction below, draw the complete, detailed mechanism, and predict the major organic product.

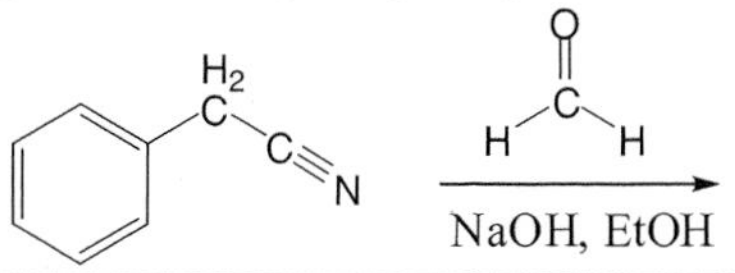

NaOH, EtOH

16.10. THE ROBINSON ANNULATION

As we learned in Chapter 4, six-membered rings are the most abundant in nature due to their relative stability. The ability to synthesize such rings is therefore quite attractive to organic chemists. Sir Robert Robinson, an English chemist, developed such a reaction; it has since become known as the **Robinson annulation** (*annulation* means "ring formation"). An example is shown in Equation 16-29.

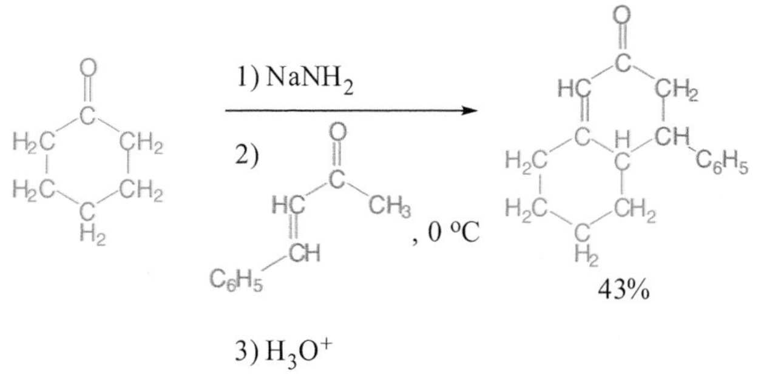

1) $NaNH_2$

2) , 0 °C

3) H_3O^+

43%

(16-62)

The mechanism for this reaction is shown in Equation 16-63. It is essentially the conjugate addition of an enolate anion (also called a *Michael reaction*, Section 15.4) followed by an intramolecular aldol condensation.

Mechanism of the Robinson Annulation Reaction in Equation 16-62

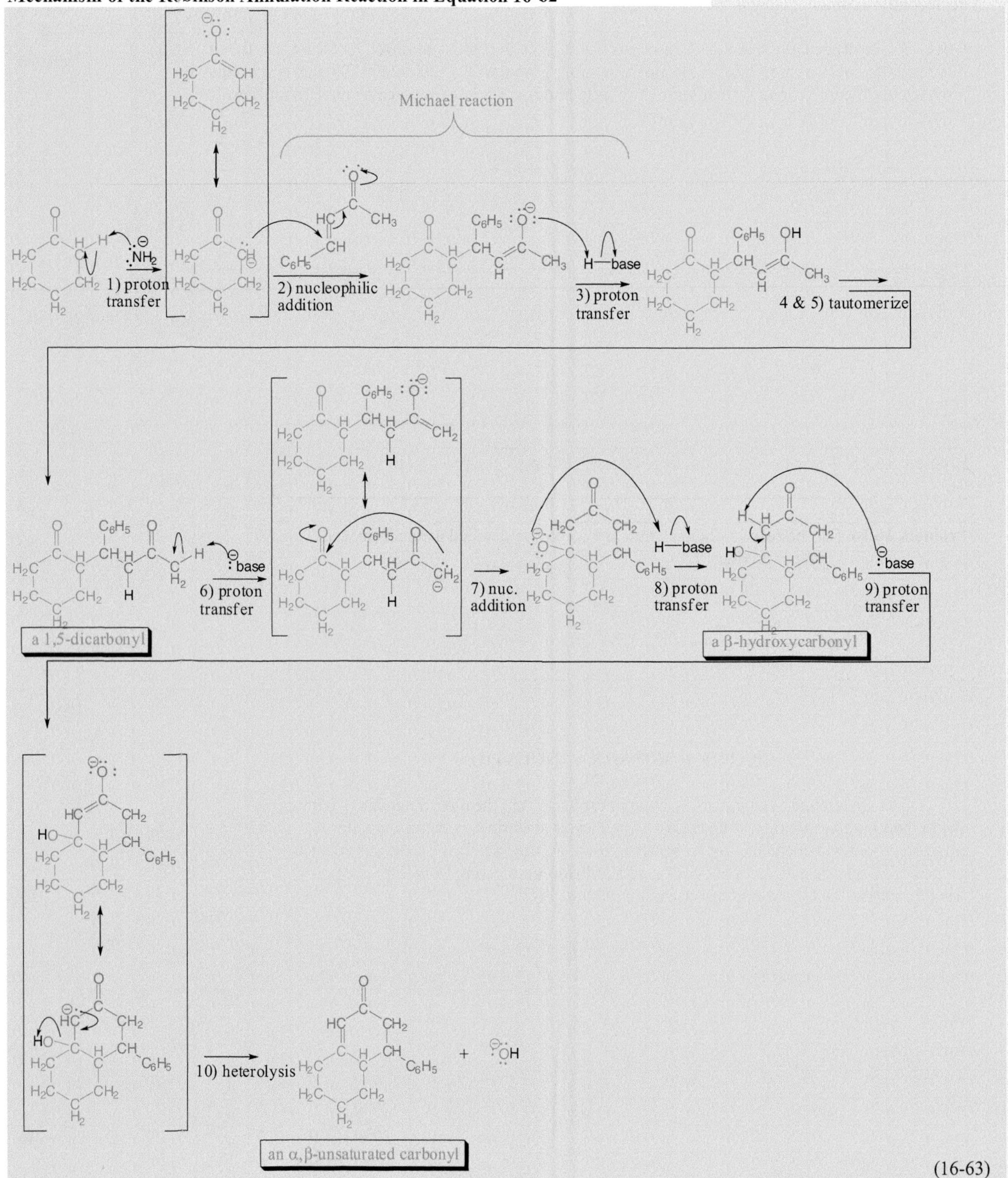

(16-63)

The first step deprotonates the alpha carbon of cyclohexanone to produce an enolate nucleophile, which undergoes conjugate addition to the α,β-unsaturated carbonyl in the second step. Conjugate addition is favored over direct addition because the addition of an enolate anion to a carbonyl group is *reversible* and thus under thermodynamic control (Section 15.4). After protonation in the third step, the enol undergoes tautomerization, yielding a 1,5-dicarbonyl. The methyl group is then deprotonated to generate another enolate nucleophile, which subsequently enters an internal aldol reaction to produce a β-hydroxycarbonyl. Notice that in that aldol reaction, the new 6-membered ring is formed. Finally, dehydration takes place in an E1cb mechanism—deprotonation followed by the departure of HO^-—to produce an α,β-unsaturated carbonyl.

From this mechanism, we can see that the reactants of a Robinson annulation must have the general form in Equation 16-64.

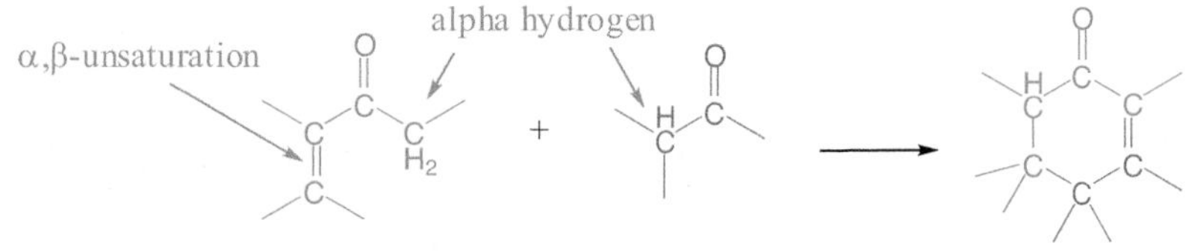

α,β-unsaturation   alpha hydrogen

(16-64)

In particular,

1. One of the reactants of a Robinson annulation must be an α,β-unsaturated carbonyl and the second must simply be a carbonyl-containing compound with an acidic alpha hydrogen.
2. The α,β-unsaturated carbonyl must have two acidic alpha hydrogens on the side of the carbonyl opposite the C=C double bond.

The first of these requirements ensures that an enolate nucleophile can be formed and conjugate addition can take place. The second requirement ensures that the intramolecular aldol condensation can take place—deprotonation of the first alpha hydrogen generates the enolate nucleophile that leads to the formation of a six-membered ring, while the second alpha hydrogen is removed in the dehydration steps.

Problem 16.27. Based on the above restrictions, which of the following pairs of reactants are suitable for a Robinson annulation? For each pair that is suitable, draw the complete, detailed mechanism of the Robinson annulation that could occur.

(a)

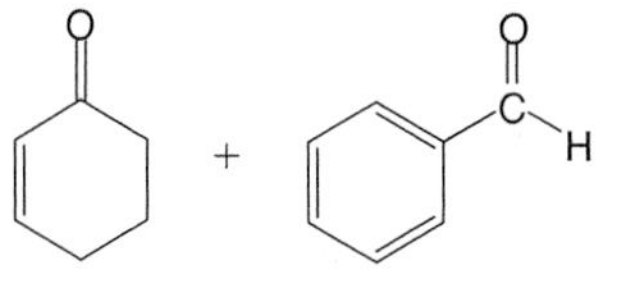

(b)

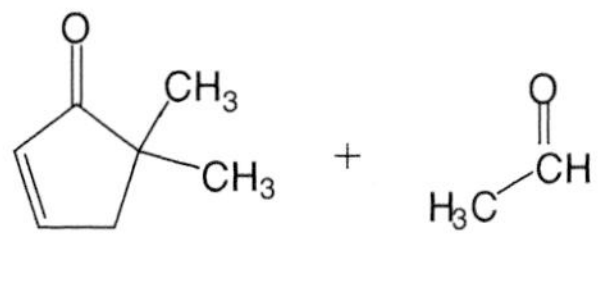

(c)

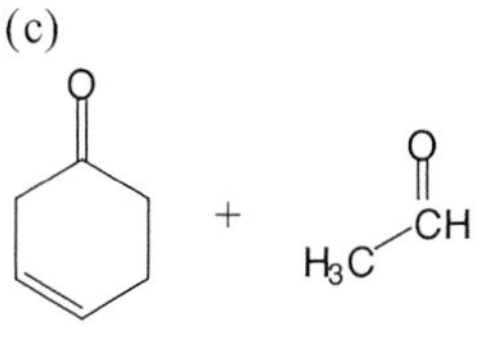

(d)

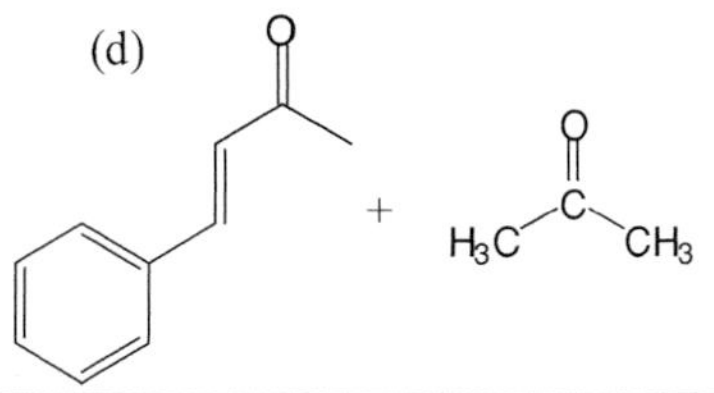

16.11. THE BENZOIN CONDENSATION: SYNTHESIS OF AN α-HYDROXY CARBONYL

When benzaldehyde is treated with a catalytic amount of KCN under basic conditions, benzoin is produced (Equation 16-65). This reaction, called the **benzoin condensation**, is strikingly similar to the overall reaction of an aldol addition in that two aldehyde molecules are coupled together to yield a hydroxycarbonyl. The major difference is that in the benzoin condensation the product is an α-hydroxycarbonyl whereas in an aldol addition the product is a β-hydroxycarbonyl.

an α-hydroxycarbonyl

KCN

$HO^{\ominus}$/ H_2O, EtOH

benzaldehyde

2-hydroxy-1,2-diphenylethanone (benzoin)

88%

(16-65)

If we think backwards, we see that benzoin must be generated from the formation of a bond between the two carbonyl carbons of benzaldehyde. For this to happen, one of the carbonyl carbons must be electron-rich and the other electron-poor. How does a carbonyl carbon become electron-rich?

The answer has to do with the presence of NC^-. In the first two steps of the mechanism (Equation 16-66), NC^- participates in a *reversible* nucleophilic addition to one molecule of benzaldehyde to yield a *cyanohydrin* (Section 16.1a). Thus the initial aldehyde hydrogen becomes acidic and is deprotonated in the third step, leaving a negative charge on the aldehyde carbon. This step is favorable largely because the negative charge on the conjugate base is resonance-stabilized by both the benzene ring and the CN group.

Mechanism of the Benzoin Condensation Reaction in Equation 16-65

resonance stabilized by both the CN and the benzene ring

H has become acidic

1) nuc. addition

2) proton transfer

3) proton transfer

4) nuc. addition

5) proton transfer

6) E2

catalyst regenerated

a β-hydroxy nitrile

(16-66)

Your Turn 16.13. It is stated above that the aldehyde hydrogen in benzaldehyde becomes acidic because of the resonance stabilization of the negative charge in the species below. Draw four additional resonance structures of this species in the space provided.

OH ⊖ C: C≡N ⟷

Once the negatively charged C is generated, it attacks a second molecule of the aldehyde in the fourth step. In the fifth step, the newly-formed O^- is protonated, and in the final step, an E2 reaction regenerates a C=O bond and eliminates NC^-.

Notice that steps 3 through 5 in the mechanism constitute an *aldol addition*, essentially identical to the mechanism of the reaction shown previously in Equation 16-60. In step 3, the carbon alpha to the cyano group is deprotonated, making an enolate nucleophile. Next, that nucleophilic carbon attacks the carbonyl carbon of a second molecule of benzaldehyde. Finally, the resulting negatively charged oxygen atom is protonated. Whereas aldol additions involving only carbonyl groups yield β-hydroxy carbonyls, the result here is a β-hydroxy nitrile.

Your Turn 16.14. Confirm that the indicated species in the mechanism is indeed a β-hydroxynitrile by circling and labeling the OH group that is beta to the CN group.

Notice also that NC^- is not consumed overall in the mechanism because it is regenerated in the final step. Thus, it behaves as a catalyst in this reaction.

Problem 16.28. Draw the products of the reaction in Equation 16-66 if (a) KCN is replaced by $K^{13}CN$ and (b) H_2O is replaced by D_2O.

16.12. ORGANIC SYNTHESIS: ALDOL REACTIONS IN SYNTHESIS

Aldol reactions are invaluable tools in organic synthesis, not only because they are carbon-carbon bond formation reactions, but also because the functional groups they involve—ketones and aldehydes—are very common in nature. Thus aldol reactions can be used to produce compounds with a wide variety of structures. Earlier in this chapter, for example, we saw that aldol reactions can form rings. Perhaps more impressively, aldol reactions can be used to link together two compounds with elaborate carbon frameworks, such as in the reaction below—a reaction that comprises one of the steps in a synthesis of Epothilone B, an anticancer agent.

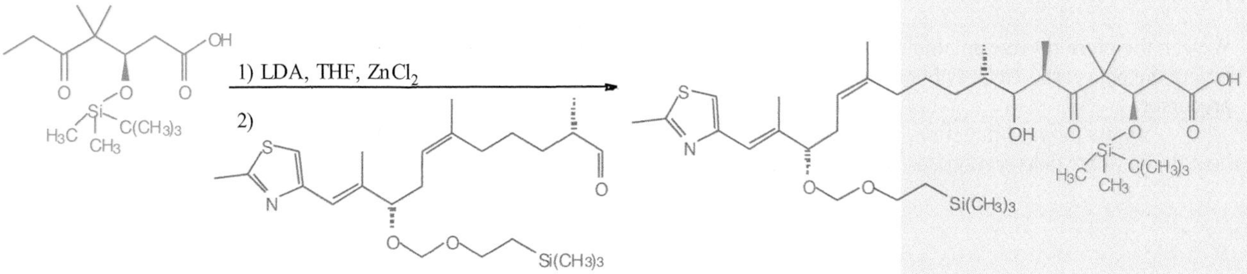

OH O O O H3C Si C(CH3)3 CH3

1) LDA, THF, $ZnCl_2$

2) S N O O O Si(CH3)3 O

S N O O Si(CH3)3 OH O O O OH H3C Si C(CH3)3 CH3

Because of the utility of aldol reactions in synthesis, it is important to be able to efficiently carry out transforms that reverse aldol reactions as part of a retrosynthetic analysis. To do so, it is helpful to consider the following guidelines.

- The product of an aldol addition is a β-hydroxycarbonyl, and the product of an aldol condensation is an α,β-unsaturated carbonyl.
- The new C-C bond that is formed in an aldol reaction appears between the alpha and beta carbons in the product, so reversing an aldol reaction involves disconnecting that bond.
- In constructing the precursors to an aldol reaction, the beta carbon from the aldol product receives a C=O bond.

These guidelines are illustrated in the following two generic transforms.

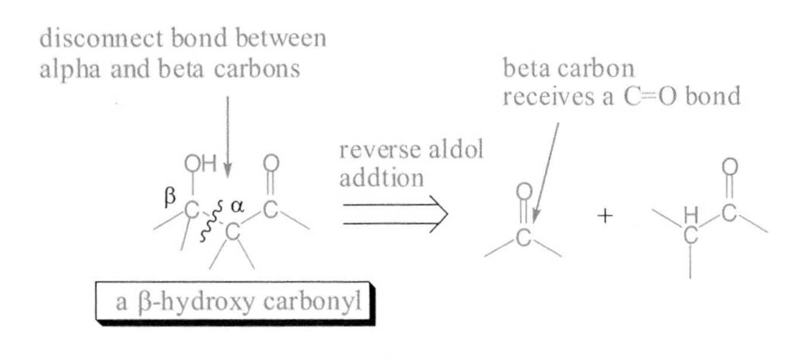

disconnect bond between
alpha and beta carbons

reverse aldol
condensation

an α,β-unsaturated carbonyl

Suppose, for example, that our target compound is 5,5-dimethylcyclohex-2-enone, which we recognize as an α,β-unsaturated ketone.

alpha carbon
in target

beta carbon
in target

5,5-dimethylcyclohex-2-enone 3,3-dimethyl-5-oxohexanal

We can therefore reverse an aldol condensation by disconnecting the bond shown, and giving the beta carbon a C=O bond. Thus, 3,3-dimethyl-5-oxohexanal is a suitable precursor.

In the forward direction, we can simply treat the precursor with NaOH and apply heat (to facilitate dehydration), as shown below.

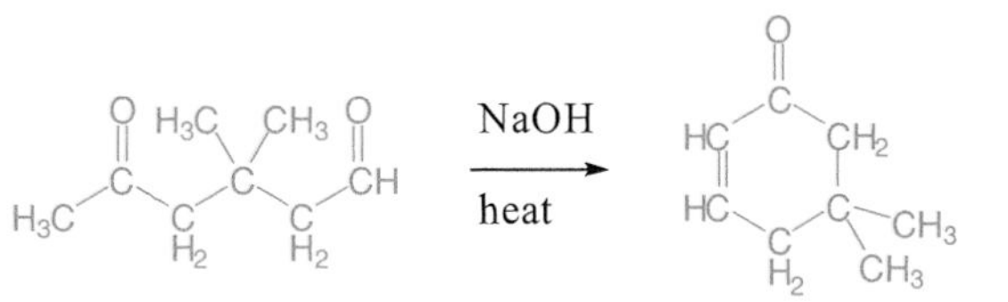

NaOH

heat

Problem 16.29. Show how to synthesize the following compound from either an aldol addition or aldol condensation.

(a) (b)

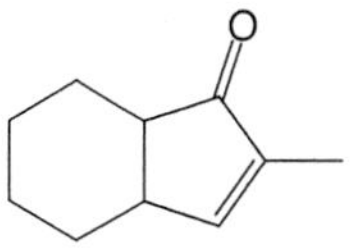

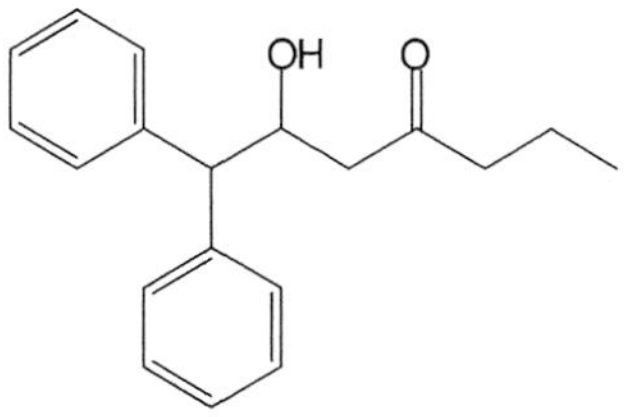

16.13. ORGANIC SYNTHESIS: IMAGINING AN ALTERNATE TARGET MOLECULE IN A RETROSYNTHETIC ANALYSIS

When a target molecule has conspicuous structural characteristics, it is often clear as to which reactions should be used in a synthesis. For example, as we saw in the previous section, if a portion of the target molecule is a β-hydroxycarbonyl or an α,β-unsaturated carbonyl, we should consider employing an aldol reaction. However, further reactions on an aldol product, such as those in Equation 16-67, would disguise these characteristics. In Equation 16-67a, the OH group of a β-hydroxycarbonyl is converted to Br using PBr_3 (Section 11.1). In Equation 16-67b, the C=O group is reduced to an OH group using $NaBH_4$ (Section 15.5).

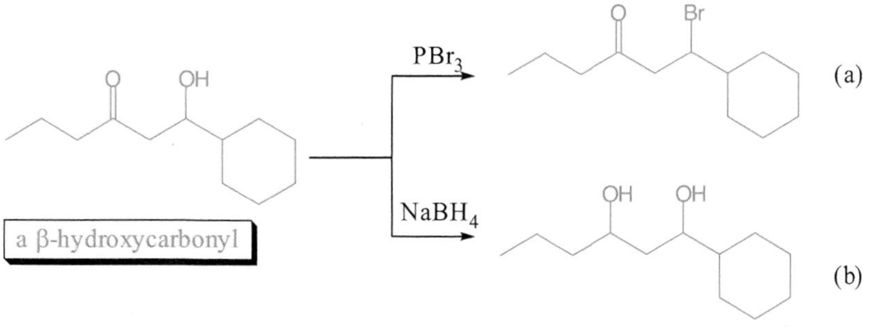

a β-hydroxycarbonyl

PBr_3 (a)

$NaBH_4$ (b)

(16-67)

Therefore, when given a particular target molecule, we should be prepared to imagine a new target molecule with alternate functional groups, which more closely resembles the immediate product of a reaction we wish to use. If we can subsequently determine which reactions will convert the altered molecule into the real target molecule, then the synthesis can be completed.

Suppose, for example, we are to synthesize the target below, and we wish to use, as our starting material, ketones and aldehydes of four or fewer carbons.

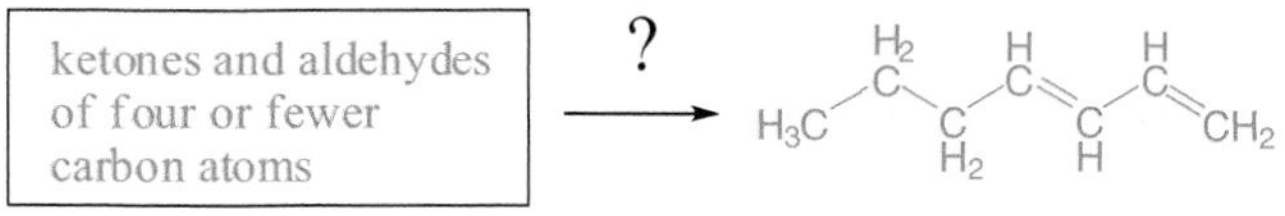

ketones and aldehydes of four or fewer carbon atoms → ?

Because the target contains seven carbon atoms, we must employ a carbon-carbon bond formation reaction. An aldol reaction can form such a bond, but the target is not a β-hydroxycarbonyl or an α,β-unsaturated carbonyl. However, as shown below, we can imagine, as an alternate target, an aldol product that can be formed from a four-carbon aldehyde and a three-carbon ketone.

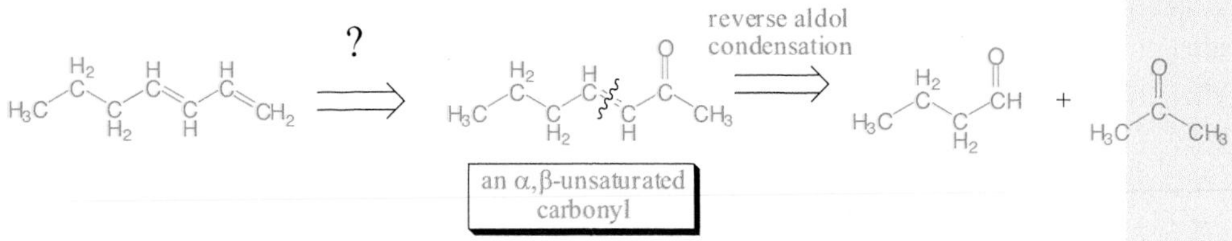

? reverse aldol condensation

an α,β-unsaturated carbonyl

Thus, the task is to determine how the aldol product can be converted into the target. Because a C–C single bond must be converted to a C=C double bond, we can envision using an E2 reaction on the appropriate alkyl halide.

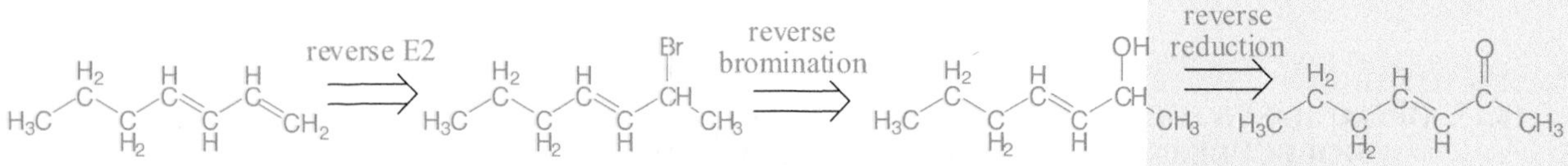

reverse E2 reverse bromination reverse reduction

The alkyl halide can be produced from the corresponding alcohol using PBr_3, and the alcohol can be generated by reducing the target molecule using $LiAlH_4$.

Having completed the retrosynthetic analysis, the synthesis in the forward direction might appear as follows.

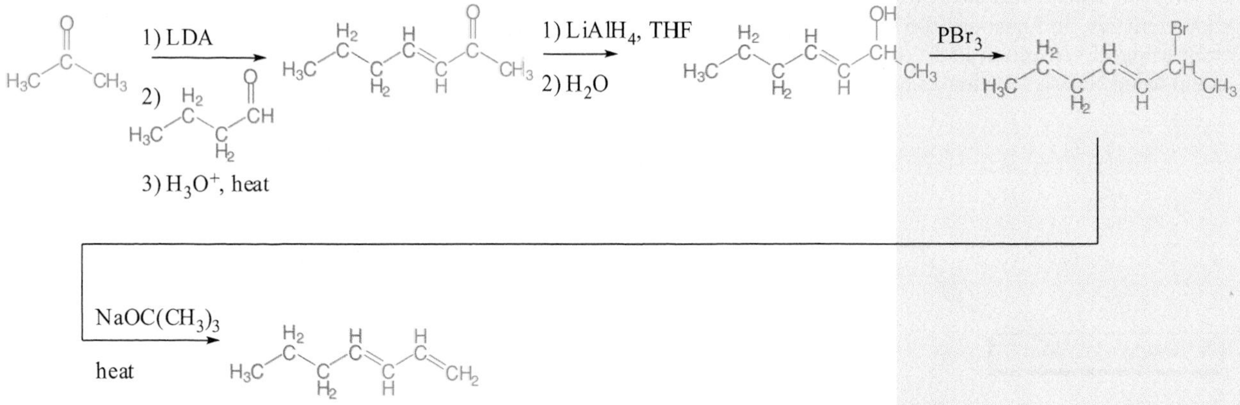

1) LDA
2) (butanal)
3) H_3O^+, heat

1) $LiAlH_4$, THF
2) H_2O

PBr_3

$NaOC(CH_3)_3$
heat

Problem 16.30. Show how to synthesize the compound below from any acyclic compound.

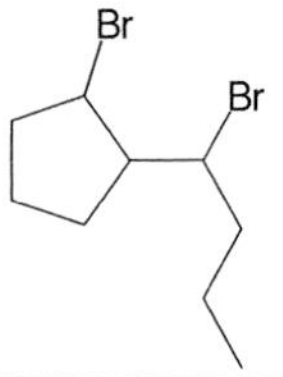

Although the example in this section focuses on the use of an aldol reaction, be prepared to employ the same general strategy with other reactions that alter the carbon skeleton as well.

16.14. FUNCTIONAL GROUP CHEMISTRY

In Section 10.10, we stressed the importance of being familiar with reactivity from a big-picture point of view, as well as from the microscopic (i.e., mechanistic) point of view. Thus, we began to highlight the major aspects of reactivity of various functional groups in sections entitled "Functional Group Chemistry." Here we continue with such an approach, addressing functional group chemistry as it pertains to the nucleophilic addition reactions we encountered in Chapters 15 and 16.

Although a variety of functional groups can undergo nucleophilic addition, the bulk of such reactions involve ketones and aldehydes. Thus, these are the only two functional groups we shall discuss here.

You will notice that in each figure outlining a functional group's reactivity, major aspects of reactivity from previous chapters are included along with the new ones from Chapters 15 and 16. However, they are distinguished by color; the new aspects of reactivity appear in green, whereas the ones from previous chapters are gray.

16.14a. Ketones

Probably the most important aspect of a ketone's reactivity we encountered in Chapters 15 and 16 is its susceptibility to nucleophilic attack at the carbonyl carbon. That carbon is highly electron-poor, and nucleophiles tend to be electron-rich. When a nucleophile attacks that carbon, a pair of electrons from the C=O double bond ends up on O, so the C=O double bond becomes a C−O single bond. As indicated below, if the nucleophile is H^-, the ketone is reduced to an alcohol (Section 15.5). If it is an R^- nucleophile, a new carbon-carbon bond is formed (Section 15.6).

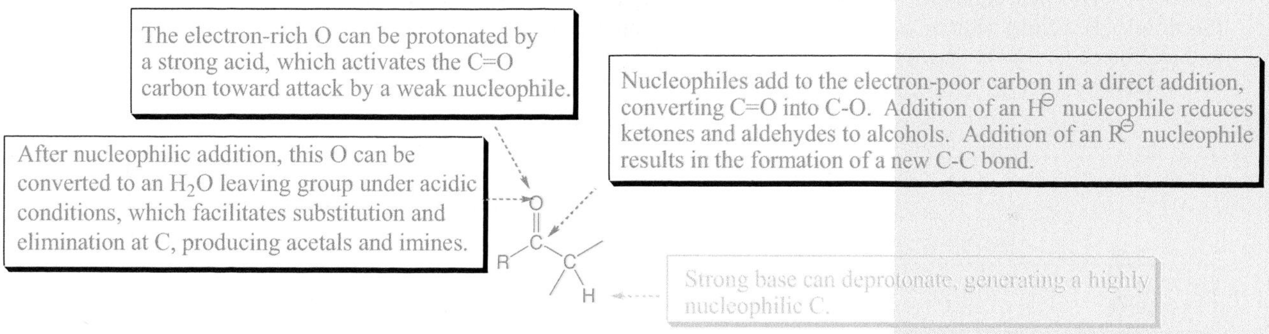

The electron-rich O can be protonated by a strong acid, which activates the C=O carbon toward attack by a weak nucleophile.

Nucleophiles add to the electron-poor carbon in a direct addition, converting C=O into C-O. Addition of an $H^⊖$ nucleophile reduces ketones and aldehydes to alcohols. Addition of an $R^⊖$ nucleophile results in the formation of a new C-C bond.

After nucleophilic addition, this O can be converted to an H_2O leaving group under acidic conditions, which facilitates substitution and elimination at C, producing acetals and imines.

O
C
R
C
H

Strong base can deprotonate, generating a highly nucleophilic C.

The carbonyl's O atom is electron-rich, and therefore reacts with electron-poor species such as H^+ from an acid. When that O atom is protonated, the carbonyl C atom becomes more electron-poor, and thus becomes activated toward nucleophilic attack (Section 16.1). This facilitates the addition of weak nucleophiles such as water and alcohols (ROH).

Finally, the OH group that is formed upon nucleophilic addition can be protonated further under acidic conditions, generating a very good H_2O leaving group. This facilitates substitution and elimination at the carbonyl C, producing compounds such as acetals (Section 16.2a) and imines (Section 16.2c), respectively.

16.14b. Aldehydes

As indicated below, aldehydes behave quite similarly to ketones under conditions for nucleophilic addition. The carbonyl C is susceptible to nucleophilic attack; the carbonyl O can be protonated to activate the carbonyl C; and under acidic conditions, substitution or elimination can take place at the carbonyl C after nucleophilic addition.

The electron-rich O can be protonated by a strong acid to activate the C=O carbon toward attack by a weak nucleophile.

Nucleophiles add to the electron-poor carbon in a direct addition, converting C=O into C-O. Addition of an $H^{\ominus}$ nucleophile reduces ketones and aldehydes to alcohols. Addition of an $R^{\ominus}$ nucleophile results in the formation of a new C-C bond.

After nucleophilic addition, this O can be converted to an H_2O leaving group under acidic conditions, which facilitates substitution and elimination at C, producing acetals and imines.

Strong base can deprotonate, generating a highly nucleophilic C.

Aldehyde H is not acidic.

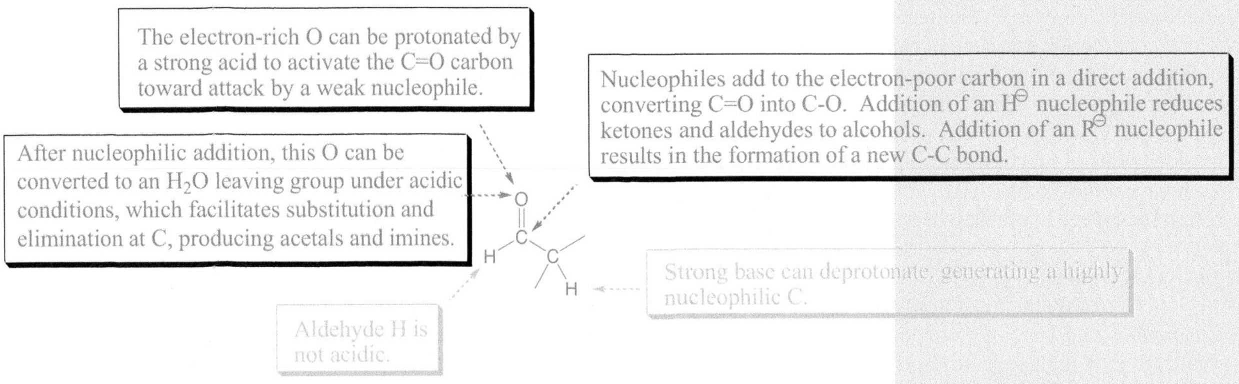

16.14c. α,β-Unsaturated Ketones and Aldehydes

A special case arises when a ketone or aldehyde is α,β-unsaturated. The β carbon of such a compound is electron-poor, so a nucleophile can add not only to the carbonyl C (via direct addition), but to the β carbon (via conjugate addition) as well (Section 15.4). Direct addition tends to be favored by nucleophiles that add irreversibly to the carbonyl C, whereas conjugate addition tends to be favored by nucleophiles that add reversibly.

direct addition favored by nucleophiles that add irreversibly to the C=O group

conjugate addition favored by nucleophiles that add reversibly to the C=O group

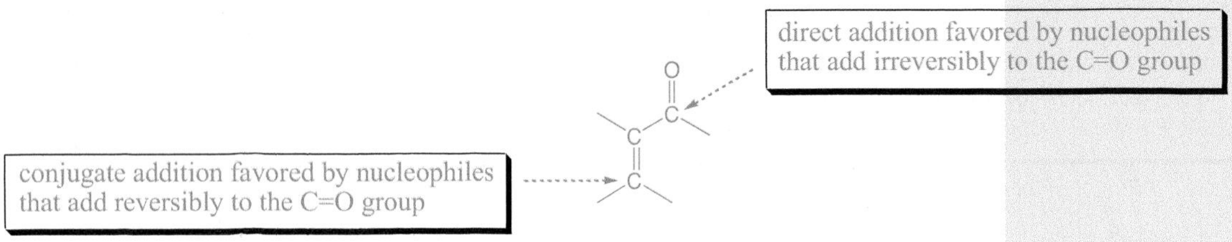

16.15. WRAPPING UP AND LOOKING AHEAD

This chapter is the second of two chapters devoted to nucleophilic addition to polar π bonds. In Chapter 15, the focus was primarily on the addition of strong nucleophiles. Here, the emphasis has been on the addition of weaker nucleophiles that typically require acid or base catalysis. Whereas base catalysis speeds up nucleophilic addition by converting a weak nucleophile into a strong nucleophile, acid catalysis functions by *activating* the polar π bond. In both types of catalysis, the catalyst is not consumed—it reacts in one step, but is regenerated in another.

In contrast to most of the reactions in Chapter 15, the nucleophilic addition reactions presented in this chapter are reversible. Thus, their equilibria can generally be driven either toward products or toward reactants by exploiting Le Châtelier's principle. Most notable is the acid-catalyzed formation and hydrolysis of an acetal. Excess alcohol favors the acetal formation, whereas excess water favors hydrolysis back to the ketone or aldehyde. As we will see in Chapter 17, this reversibility is a key to protecting certain functional groups throughout the course of a synthesis.

The latter part of this chapter focused primarily on aldol and aldol-type reactions. These reactions not only form carbon-carbon bonds, but also are quite versatile because they involve very common functional groups—ketones and aldehydes. Aldol reactions can be used to link together two separate carbon frameworks, and can also be used to form new rings.

In the chapters to come, we will apply much of what we have learned about nucleophilic addition reactions. We will see, for example, that nucleophilic addition reactions have many important applications in organic synthesis, the topic of Chapter 17. Frequently, nucleophilic addition reactions that form carbon-carbon bonds are instrumental in constructing a carbon backbone, and the functional group transformations we learned in this and the previous chapter can be extremely useful when a synthesis calls for altering the reactivity at specific locations within a molecule. In Chapter 18, we will begin to study the *nucleophilic addition-elimination* mechanism, which, as the name suggests, involves aspects of nucleophilic addition. As we will see, the nucleophilic addition-elimination is the basis for a variety of reactions involving carbonyl-containing compounds such as carboxylic acids, esters, and amides.

APPLICATIONS TO BIOLOGY AND BIOCHEMISTRY

16.16. RING OPENING AND CLOSING OF MONOSACCHARIDES; MUTAROTATION

In Section 1.12b, we showed that a monosaccharide can have both open-chain and cyclic forms. In water, the various forms equilibrate, as shown below for D-glucose and D-ribose.

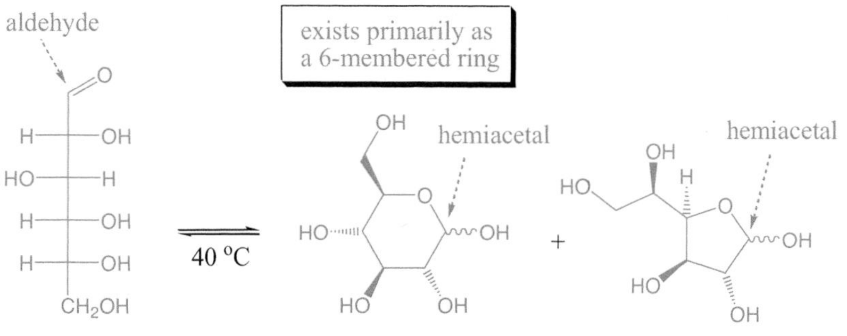

aldehyde — exists primarily as a 6-membered ring — hemiacetal — hemiacetal

40 °C

D-glucose 0.003% ⇌ D-glucopyranose >99.8% + D-glucofuranose <0.2% (16-68)

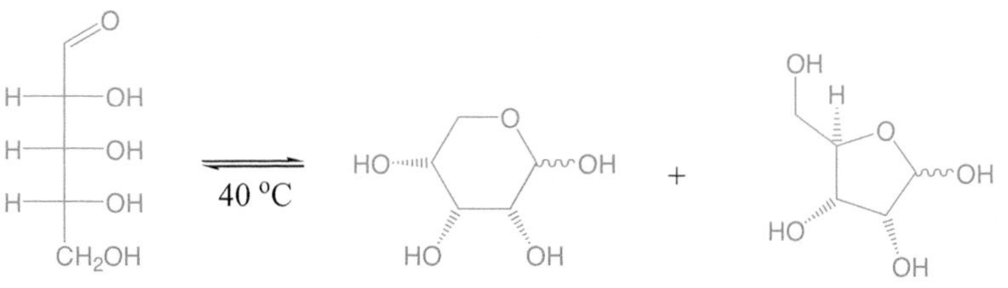

40 °C

D-ribose 0.02% ⇌ D-ribopyranose 76% + D-ribofuranose 24% (16-69)

The mechanisms showing how D-glucose cyclizes to its 6- and 5-membered rings are shown in Equations 16-70a and 16-70b, respectively. Step 1 is the nucleophilic addition of an alcohol to the carbonyl group, and steps 2 and 3 are both proton transfers.

Mechanisms Showing the Cyclization of D-Glucose to its 6- and 5-Membered Ring Forms

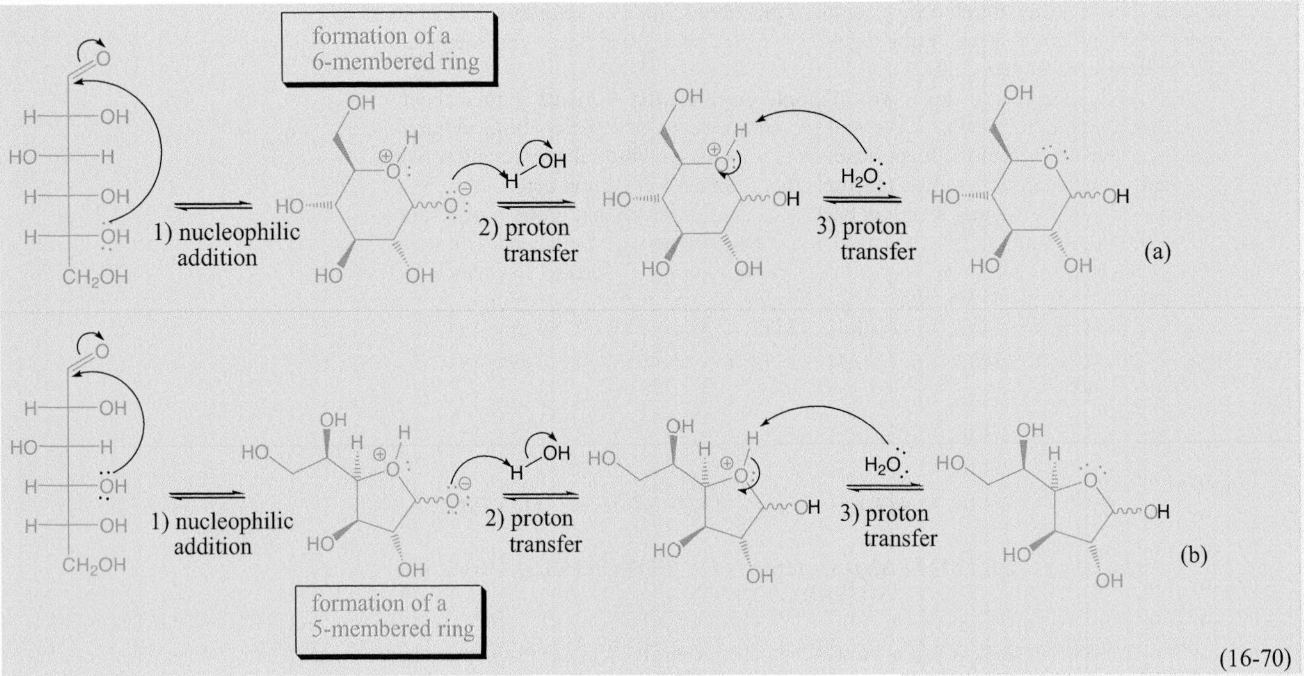

formation of a 6-membered ring

1) nucleophilic addition 2) proton transfer 3) proton transfer (a)

formation of a 5-membered ring

1) nucleophilic addition 2) proton transfer 3) proton transfer (b)

(16-70)

These mechanisms are essentially the same as the one shown previously in Equation 16-2. This is not surprising, because in each case, the carbonyl group of a ketone or aldehyde reacts with an alcohol to produce a hemiacetal. The main difference, however, is that in the mechanism in Equation 16-2, the reaction is *intermolecular*, whereas in Equation 16-70, it is *intramolecular*.

Recall from Section 8.6b that cyclization reactions are favored when a 5- or 6-membered ring is formed, and that the formation of a 6-membered ring is usually favored over a 5-membered ring. As we can see in Equations 16-68 and 16-69, this is no different for the cyclization of monosaccharides. Specifically,

- At equilibrium, monosaccharides typically favor their 5- and 6-membered ring forms over their open-chain forms.
- The 6-membered ring form is generally favored over the 5-membered ring form.

Because of the importance of the 5- and 6-membered ring forms of monosaccharides, specific nomenclature has been developed to distinguish the two forms from each other, as well as from the open-chain form. Under this system, the monosaccharide's name is modified by inserting "pyran" or "furan" prior to the "ose" suffix, depending upon ring size.

- A monosaccharide that has cyclized to a 6-membered ring is designated as a **pyranose**.
- One that has cyclized to a 5-membered ring is designated as a **furanose.**

Thus, as indicated in Equation 16-68 above, the cyclic form of D-glucose that has a 6-membered ring is called D-glucopyranose, and the one that has a 5-membered ring is called D-glucofuranose. The corresponding cyclic forms of D-ribose are D-ribopyranose and D-ribofuranose.

Looking back at the reactions in Equations 16-68 and 16-69, notice that during the cyclization of a monosaccharide, the carbonyl carbon becomes a *new stereocenter*.

As with any reaction in which a new stereocenter is generated, a mixture of both the *R* and *S* stereochemical configurations is produced. This is why the stereochemical configuration at that carbon is not specified by dash-wedge notation, but rather the C–O bond is denoted as a squiggly line (∿∿).

As we can see in Equation 16-70a, the nucleophilic addition step is the step in which the new stereocenter is produced. In this step, the alcohol group can attack the carbonyl carbon from either side of the carbon's plane, shown in Equations 16-71a and 16-71b for the formation of D-glucopyranose.

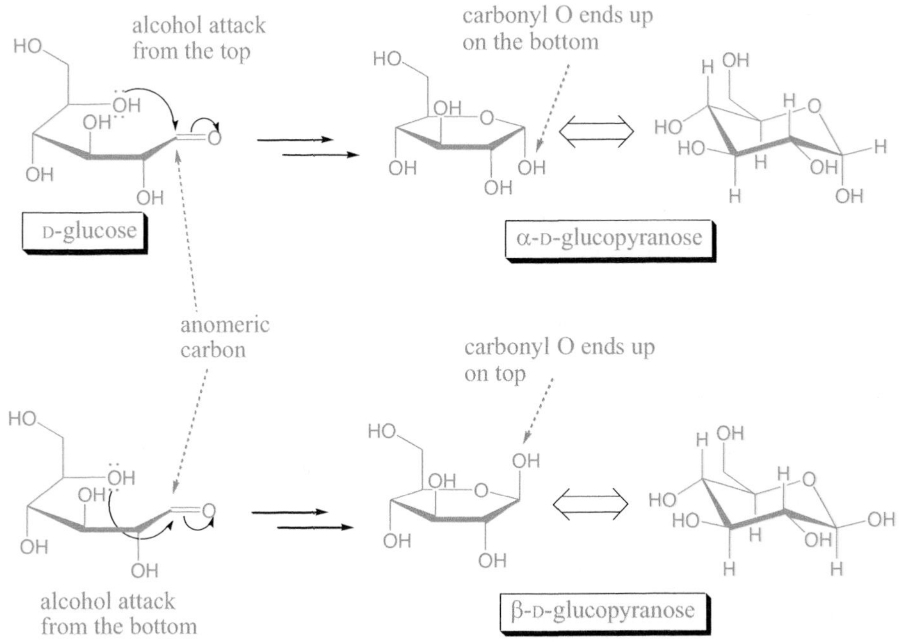

alcohol attack from the top

carbonyl O ends up on the bottom

D-glucose

α-D-glucopyranose

(a)

anomeric carbon

carbonyl O ends up on top

alcohol attack from the bottom

β-D-glucopyranose

(b)

(16-71)

The two stereoisomers differ in configuration at just one of the stereocenters, and thus are *diastereomers* of each other. In carbohydrate chemistry, they are more specifically designated as **anomers** of each other, and the carbon atom that differs in stereochemical configuration—the one that is part of the carbonyl group in the open-chain form—is called the **anomeric carbon**. One anomer is called the α-anomer, and the other the β-anomer.

Comment [JMK12]: Margin note.
Anomers are diastereomers that are produced upon cyclization of a monosaccharide, and differ in stereochemical configuration only at the carbon atom that is part of the carbonyl group in the open-chain form.

- In the **α-anomer** of a cyclic monosaccharide, the anomeric OH and the CH_2OH substituents are located on opposite sides of the ring.
- In the **β-anomer**, the two substituents are located on the same side of the ring.

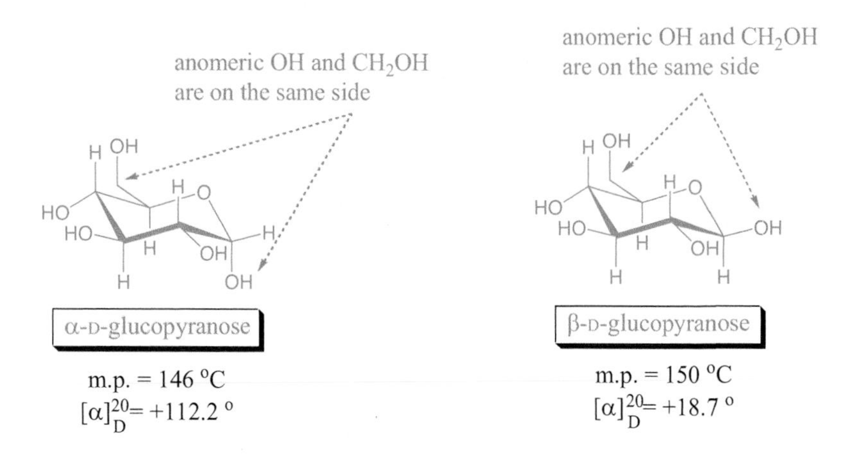

Problem 16.31. (a) Draw the Haworth and chair conformations of α-D-ribofuranose and β-D-ribofuranose. (b) Draw the mechanisms that show how each of these anomers is produced from the acyclic form of the monosaccharide.

Problem 16.32. Name each of the following monosaccharides.

(a) (b)

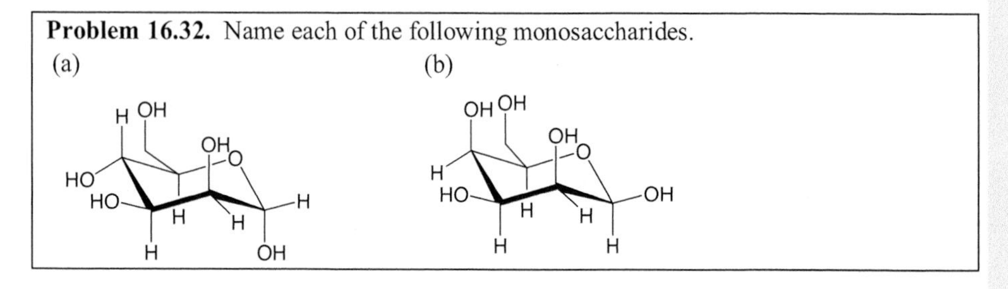

Being diastereomers, α- and β-anomers have different physical properties. For example, the melting point of α-D-glucopyranose is 146 °C, and that of β-D-glucopyranose is 150 °C. Additionally, the two have different optical properties. Whereas the specific rotation of α-D-glucopyranose in water is +112.2°, that of β-D-glucopyranose is +18.7°.

Quite interestingly, if pure crystalline α-D-glucopyranose is dissolved in water, the specific rotation changes over time, from +112.2° to 52.5°. Likewise, the specific rotation of β-D-glucopyranose changes over time, from +18.7° to 52.5°. This phenomenon is called **mutarotation**, and stems from the fact that in water, each anomer equilibrates with the open-chain form, and thus the two anomers equilibrate with each other (Equation 16-72).

α-D-glucopyranose ⇌ (open-chain D-glucose) ⇌ β-D-glucopyranose

36% 64%

Using the specific rotation of an equilibrium mixture of two anomers, we can calculate the relative amounts of the two anomers. For D-glucose, for example, let x be the equilibrium amounts of the α-anomers, and let the remaining amount in the mixture,

1-x, be the equilibrium amount of the β-anomer. The specific rotation of the mixture is the weighted average of their individual specific rotations, according to Equation 16-72.

$$[\alpha]^{20}_{\text{D, mixture}} = x\,(112.2^\circ) + (1-x)(18.7^\circ) = 52.5^\circ \qquad (16\text{-}72)$$

Solving for x, we find that the equilibrium amount of the α-anomer is 36%, and that of the β-anomer is 64%.

Problem 16.33. The specific rotation of α-D-mannopyranose is +29.3°, and that of β-D-mannopyranose is -16.3°. When either anomer is dissolved in water, the specific rotation slowly changes to +14.5°. Calculate the relative amounts of the two anomers at equilibrium.

CHAPTER SUMMARY AND KEY TERMS

- Nucleophilic addition of a weak nucleophile to a polar π bond is typically slow. If the nucleophilic atom has a weakly acidic proton, **base catalysis** can increase the rate of the reaction by converting the weak nucleophile into a strong one. Alternatively, **acid catalysis** can increase the reaction rate by **activating** the polar π bond. (Section 16.1)
- A **cyanohydrin** can be formed via the addition of HCN to the carbonyl group of a ketone or aldehyde, and the reaction can be catalyzed by the addition of a strong base or NC^-. (Section 16.1a)
- When a weak nucleophile adds to an α,β-unsaturated polar π bond, conjugate addition is generally favored over direct addition. (Section 16.1b)
- Acetals, thioacetals, imines, and enamines can be formed reversibly from ketones or aldehydes under acidic conditions. Formation of each of these products is favored (via Le Châtelier's principle) if there is an excess of the respective nucleophiles. (Section 16.2a – 162c)
- Acetals, imines, and enamines can be hydrolyzed to ketones or aldehydes under acidic conditions using an excess of water. Nitriles can be hydrolyzed to amides. (Sections 16-2a, 16.2c, and 16.2d)
- The C=O group of a ketone or aldehyde can be reduced to a methylene (CH_2) group via the **Wolff-Kishner reduction**, in which the ketone or aldehyde is first treated with hydrazine (H_2NNH_2), followed by heating under basic conditions. (Section 16.3)
- When treated with a strong acid or base, a ketone or aldehyde can react via an **aldol addition**, resulting in a **β-hydroxy carbonyl**. Under basic conditions, an enolate anion acts as a nucleophile, whereas under acidic conditions, an enol does. (Sections 16.4 and 16.6)
- Heating an aldol reaction facilitates an **aldol condensation**, in which the β-hydroxy carbonyl product undergoes dehydration to yield an **α,β-unsaturated carbonyl**. (Section 16.5)
- Aldol reactions involving ketones tend to be unfavorable, and thus require exploiting Le Châtelier's principle to drive the reaction toward products. (Section 16.6)
- An aldol reaction that forms a carbon-carbon bond between two different carbonyl-containing compounds is a **crossed aldol reaction**. Such reactions are not synthetically useful if they form a mixture of aldol products. (Section 16.7)
- A crossed aldol reaction can be synthetically useful if one of the carbonyl-containing reactants possesses no alpha hydrogens. Alternatively, an aldol reaction can be synthetically useful if it involves a ketone that is first deprotonated quantitatively by a very strong base like LDA. (Section 16.7)

- An intramolecular aldol reaction is favored if it forms a five- or six-membered ring. Such reactions involving the attack of an aldehyde are favored over ones involving the attack of a ketone. (Section 16.8)
- A nitrile or nitroalkane that possesses an acidic alpha hydrogen can participate in an aldol reaction. (Section 16.9)
- The **Robinson annulation** produces a six-membered ring from two separate carbonyl-containing compounds, one of which is an α,β-unsaturated carbonyl. Such a reaction consists of a conjugate addition to the α,β-unsaturated carbonyl, followed by an intramolecular aldol condensation. (Section 16.10)
- The **benzoin condensation** produces an α-hydroxy carbonyl. NC^- is used as a catalyst to increase the acidity of the aldehyde H on benzaldehyde. (Section 16.11)

REACTION TABLES

Table 16-1. Functional Group Transformations

	Starting Functional Group	Typical Reagents and Reaction Conditions	Functional Group Formed	Key Electron-Rich Species	Key Electron-Poor Species	Type of Mechanism	Discussed in Section(s)
(1)	O ‖ C, R R (or H) (or H) Ketone or aldehyde	H-Nu → strong base; Nu = OR, RS, NR_2	HO Nu, C, R R (or H) (or H)	$Nu^{\ominus}$	O ‖ C δ^+	Base-catalyzed nucleophilic addition	16.1
(2)	O ‖ C, R R (or H) (or H) Ketone or aldehyde	H-Nu → strong acid; Nu = OR, RS, NR_2	HO Nu, C, R R (or H) (or H)	δ^- H—Nu :	$^{\oplus}$OH ‖ C	Acid-catalyzed nucleophilic addition	16.1
(3)	O ‖ C, HC ‖ C; α,β-unsaturated ketone or aldehyde	H-Nu →; Nu = OR, RS, NR_2	H, H–C–C(=O), Nu–C	δ^- H—Nu :	O ‖ C, HC ‖ C δ^+	Conjugate nucleophilic addition	16.1b
(4)	O ‖ C, R R (or H) (or H) Ketone or aldehyde	ROH (excess) → $H^{\oplus}$	RO OR, C, R R (or H) (or H) Acetal	δ^- R—ÖH	$^{\oplus}$OH ‖ C	Nucleophilic addition, then S_N1	16.2a
(5)	O ‖ C, R R (or H) (or H) Ketone or aldehyde	RSH (excess) → $H^{\oplus}$	HS SH, C, R R (or H) (or H) Thioacetal	δ^- R—S̈H	$^{\oplus}$OH ‖ C	Nucleophilic addition, then S_N1	16.2b
(6)	O ‖ C, R R (or H) (or H) Ketone or aldehyde	NH_3 or RNH_2 (excess) → $H^{\oplus}$; Ammonia or 1° amine	N–R ‖ C, R R (or H) (or H) Imine	δ^- R—N̈H_2	$^{\oplus}$OH ‖ C	Nucleophilic addition, then E1	16.2c

(7)	$RC(=O)CHR_2$ (or H) Ketone or aldehyde	R_2NH (excess), $H^{\oplus}$ 2° amine	$RC(NH_2)=CHR_2$ (or H) Enamine	δ^- $R_2\ddot{N}H$	$C=\overset{\oplus}{O}H$	Nucleophilic addition, then E1	16.2c
(8)	$R_2C(OR)(OR)$ (or H) (or H) Acetal	H_2O (excess), $H^{\oplus}$	$R_2C=O$ (or H) (or H) Ketone or aldehyde	δ^- $H_2\ddot{O}:$	$C=\overset{\oplus}{O}R$	S_N1, then E1	16.2a
(9)	$R_2C=NR$ (or H) (or H) Imine	H_2O (excess), $H^{\oplus}$	$R_2C=O$ (or H) (or H) Ketone or aldehyde	δ^- $H_2\ddot{O}:$	$C=\overset{\oplus}{N}HR$	Nucleophilic addition, then E1	16.2c
(10)	$R-C\equiv N$ Nitrile	H_2O (1 eq.), $H^{\oplus}$ or $HO^{\ominus}$	$RC(=O)NH_2$ (or H) Amide	δ^- $H_2\ddot{O}:$ or $:\ddot{O}H^{\ominus}$	δ^+ $-C\equiv N$ or $-C\equiv\overset{\oplus}{N}H$	Nucleophilic addition	16.2d
(11)	$R_2C=O$ (or H) (or H) Ketone or aldehyde	1) $H_2N\text{-}NH_2$, H^+ 2) KOH / H_2O, heat	R_2CH_2	δ^- $H_2\ddot{N}NH_2$	$C=\overset{\oplus}{O}H$	Nucleophilic addition, then E1, then E2	16.3

Table 16-2. Reactions that Alter the Carbon Skeleton

	Reactant	Typical Reagent and Reaction Conditions	Product Formed	Key Electron-Rich Species	Key Electron-Poor Species	Type of Reaction	Discussed in Section(s)
(1)	$R_2C=O$ (or H) (or H) Ketone or aldehyde	H-CN NaOH or KCN	$R_2C(OH)CN$ (or H) (or H) Cyanohydrin	$NC^{\ominus}$	$C=O$ δ^+	Nucleophilic addition	16.1a
(2)	$HC(=O)CHR_2$ Aldehyde	NaOH	$HC(=O)CR_2C(OH)HCR_2$ β-hydroxycarbonyl	$C(=O)\ddot{C}^{\ominus}$ Enolate anion	$C=O$ δ^+	Nucleophilic addition	16.4a
(3)	$HC(=O)CHR_2$ Aldehyde	H^+	$HC(=O)CR_2C(OH)HCR_2$ β-hydroxycarbonyl	$C(OH)=C$ Enol	$C=\overset{\oplus}{O}H$	Nucleophilic addition	16.4b
(4)	$HC(=O)C(R)HCH(OH)R$ β-hydroxycarbonyl	$H^{\oplus}$ or $HO^{\ominus}$ heat	$HC(=O)C(R)=CHR$ α,β-unsaturated carbonyl			E1 or E1cb	16.5

(5)	R–C(=O)–CHR₂ Ketone	NaOH →	R–C(=O)–CR₂–C(OH)(R)–CHR₂ β-hydroxycarbonyl	–C(=O)–C̈⊖– Enolate anion	O=C (δ+)	Nucleophilic addition	16.6
(6)	R–C(=O)–H (or H) Aldehyde	1) NaOH → 2) H–C(=O)–CHR₂	H–C(=O)–CR₂–C(OH)(R)–H β-hydroxycarbonyl	–C(=O)–C̈⊖– Enolate anion	O=C (δ+)	Nucleophilic addition	16.7
(7)	R–C(=O)–CHR₂ Ketone	1) LDA → 2) R–C(=O)–R	R–C(=O)–CR₂–C(OH)(R)–R β-hydroxycarbonyl	–C(=O)–C̈⊖– Enolate anion	O=C (δ+)	Nucleophilic addition	16.7
(8)	R–CH₂–CN (or NO₂) Nitrile or nitroalkane	R–C(=O)–R → NaOH	R–CH(CN)–C(OH)(R)–R CN (or NO₂)	⊖C̈H–CN (or NO₂)	O=C (δ+)	Nucleophilic addition	16.9
(9)	R–C(=O)–CHR₂ Ketone	1) NaNH₂ → 2) R–CH=CH–C(=O)–CH₂–R 3) H_3O^+	H₂C–C(=O)–C(R)–C(R)–CR₂–CH(R) (ring) R, R	–C(=O)–C̈⊖– Enolate anion	O=C–CH=C (δ+)	Conjugate addition, then another nucleophilic addition	16.10
(10)	C_6H_5–C(=O)–H	KCN ⇌ $HO^{\ominus}$/ H_2O, EtOH	C_6H_5–C(=O)–CH(OH)–C_6H_5	C_6H_5–C⊖(OH)–C≡N	C_6H_5–C(=O)(δ+)–H	Two nucleophilic additions, then an E2	16.11

PROBLEMS

34. For each reaction below, predict the major organic product and draw the complete, detailed mechanism.

(a) CH_3CH_2OH (excess), $H^{\oplus}$?

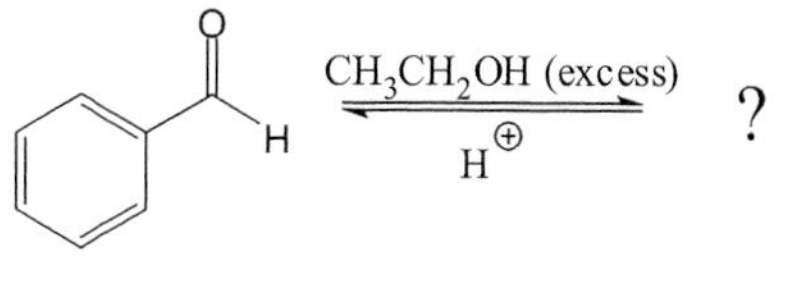

(b) HO OH, $H^{\oplus}$?

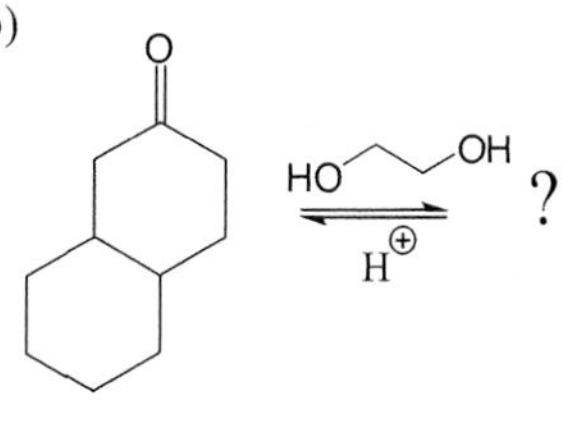

(c) CH_3OH (excess), $H^{\oplus}$

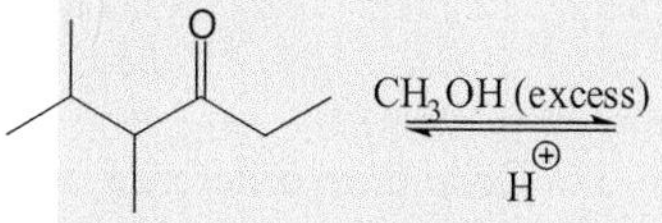

(d) HO SH, $H^{\oplus}$?

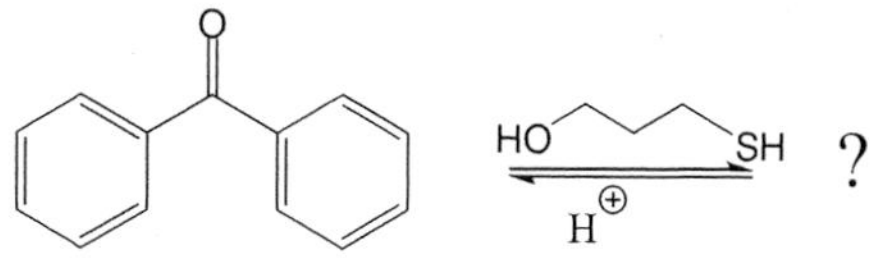

(e) HO OH, $H^{\oplus}$?

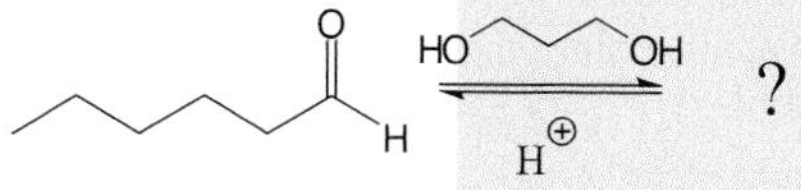

35. For each reaction below, predict the major organic product and draw the complete, detailed mechanism.

(a) CH_3; NH_3 (excess), $H^{\oplus}$?

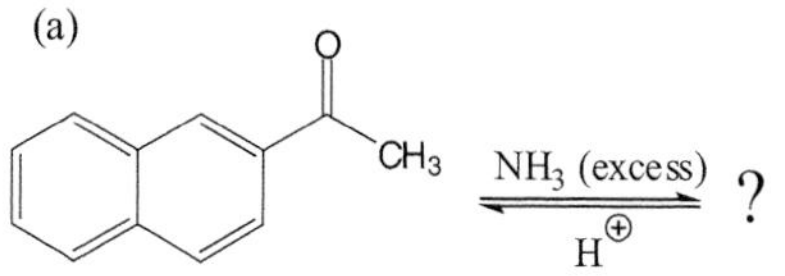

(b) CH_3NH_2 (excess), $H^{\oplus}$?

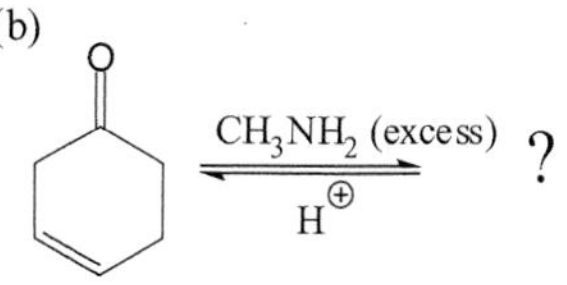

(c) N, CH_3; H_2O (excess), $H^{\oplus}$?

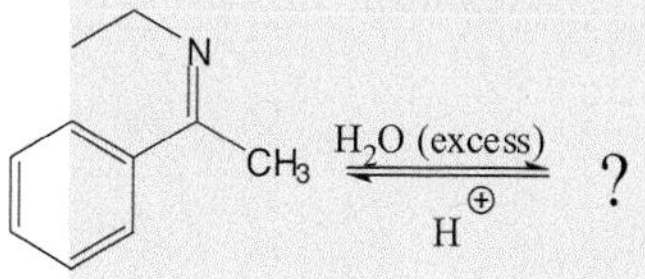

(d) H_3C, H_3C; H_3C–NH–CH_3 (excess), $H^{\oplus}$?

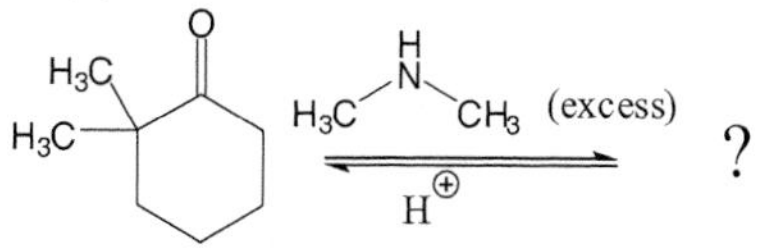

(e) N; H_2O (excess), $H^{\oplus}$?

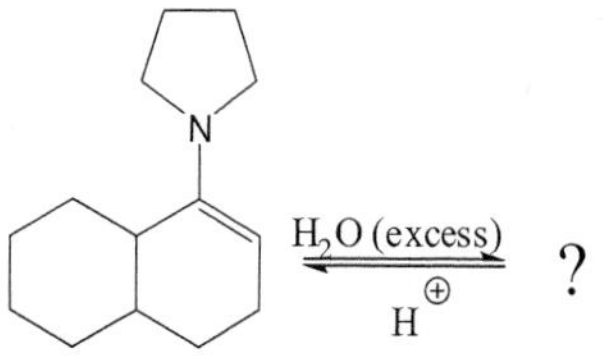

36. For each reaction below, predict the major organic product and draw the complete, detailed mechanism.

(a) O O, CH_3; H_2O (excess), $H^{\oplus}$?

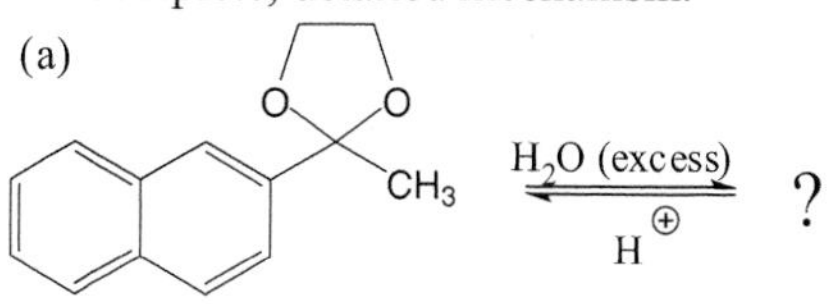

(b) H_3C, O; H_2O (excess), $H^{\oplus}$?

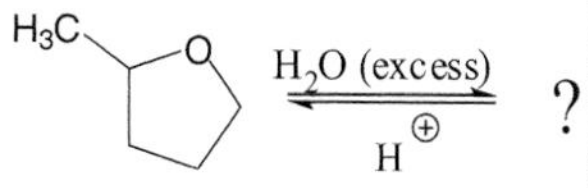

(c) HO, CN; H_2O, $H^{\oplus}$?

(d) H_3CH_2CO OCH_2CH_3; H_2O (excess), $H^{\oplus}$?

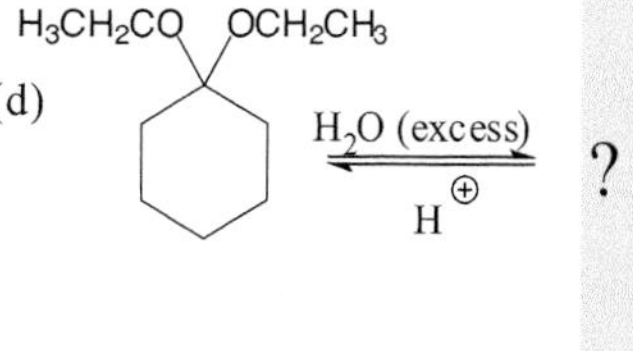

37. For each reaction below, predict the major organic product and draw the complete, detailed mechanism.

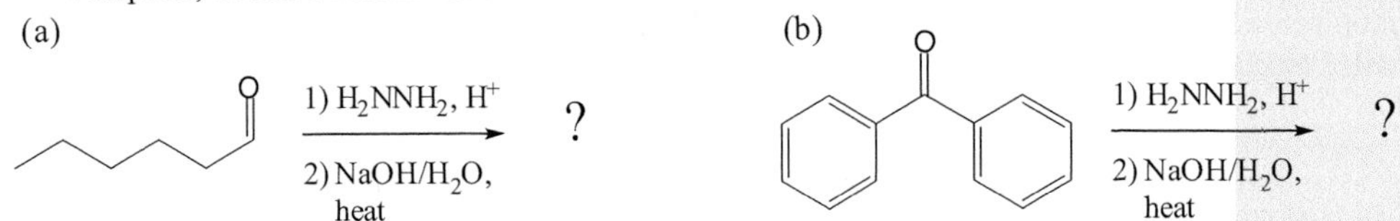

38. Draw three different ketone or aldehyde precursors that could be used to produce hexane via a Wolff-Kishner reduction.

39. When acetone is dissolved in either a slightly basic or a slightly acidic solution of oxygen-18 labeled water, $H_2{}^{18}O$, oxygen-18 labeled acetone, $(CH_3)_2C{=}{}^{18}O$, is produced. This is a form of an isotopic exchange reaction between acetone and water. Provide a mechanism to account for this reaction in (a) basic solution and (b) acidic solution. (Hint: is the addition of the nucleophile reversible or irreversible?)

$$H_3C{-}C({=}O){-}CH_3 + H_2{}^{18}O \xrightarrow{\text{acid or base}} H_3C{-}C({=}{}^{18}O){-}CH_3 + H_2O$$

40. For each reaction, draw the complete, detailed mechanism and predict the major organic product.

(a) NaOH, heat → ?

(b) $H^\oplus$, heat → ?

(c) NaOH → ?

(d) NaOH, heat → ?

41. For each reaction, draw a complete, detailed mechanism and predict the major product.

(a) 1) LDA; 2) (benzaldehyde) → ?

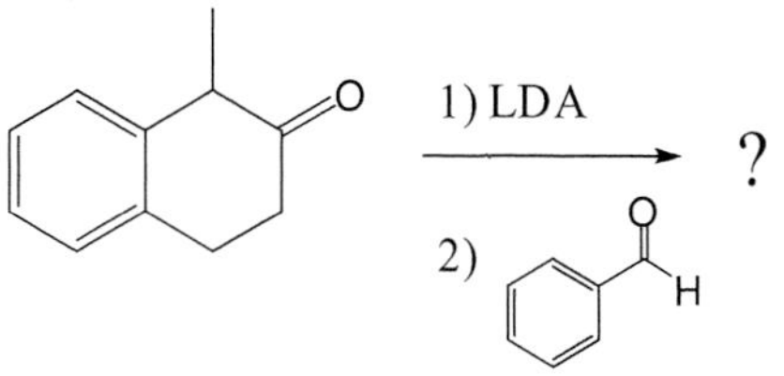

(b) 1) NaOH; 2) → ?

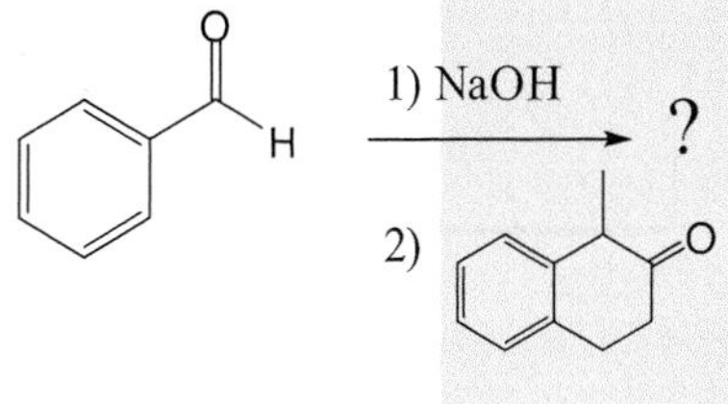

(c) NaOH, heat → ?

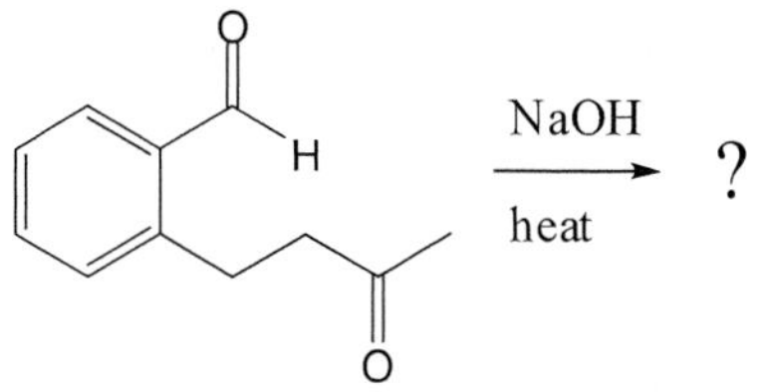

(d) 1) LDA; 2) → ?

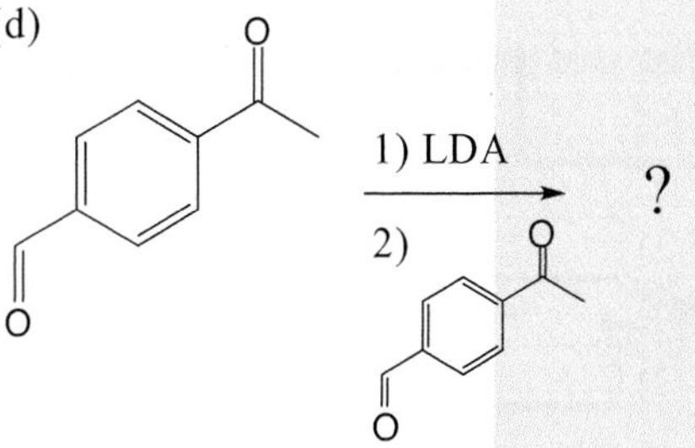

42. Which of the following do you think will produce more aldol product at equilibrium? Why?

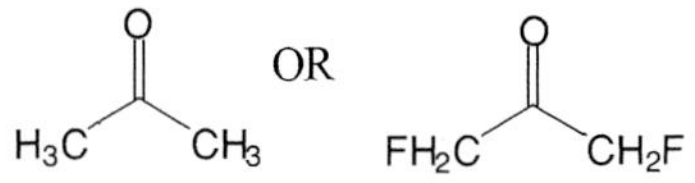

H_3C–C(=O)–CH_3 OR FH_2C–C(=O)–CH_2F

43. Predict the major product(s) of each of the following reactions.

(a) 1) $(CH_3)_2CuLi$; 2) H_2NNH_2, $HO^{\ominus}$, heat

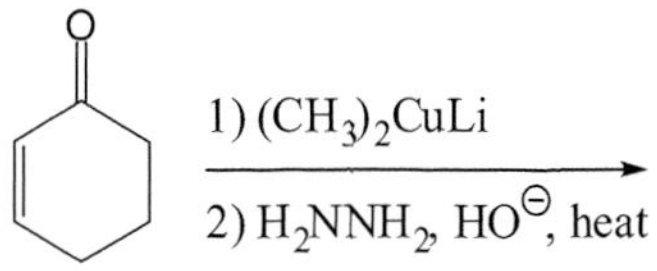

(b) 1) NaOH; 2) $NaBH_4$, EtOH

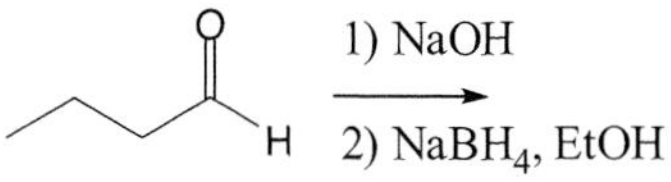

44. Provide the reagent(s) missing from each of the following reactions.

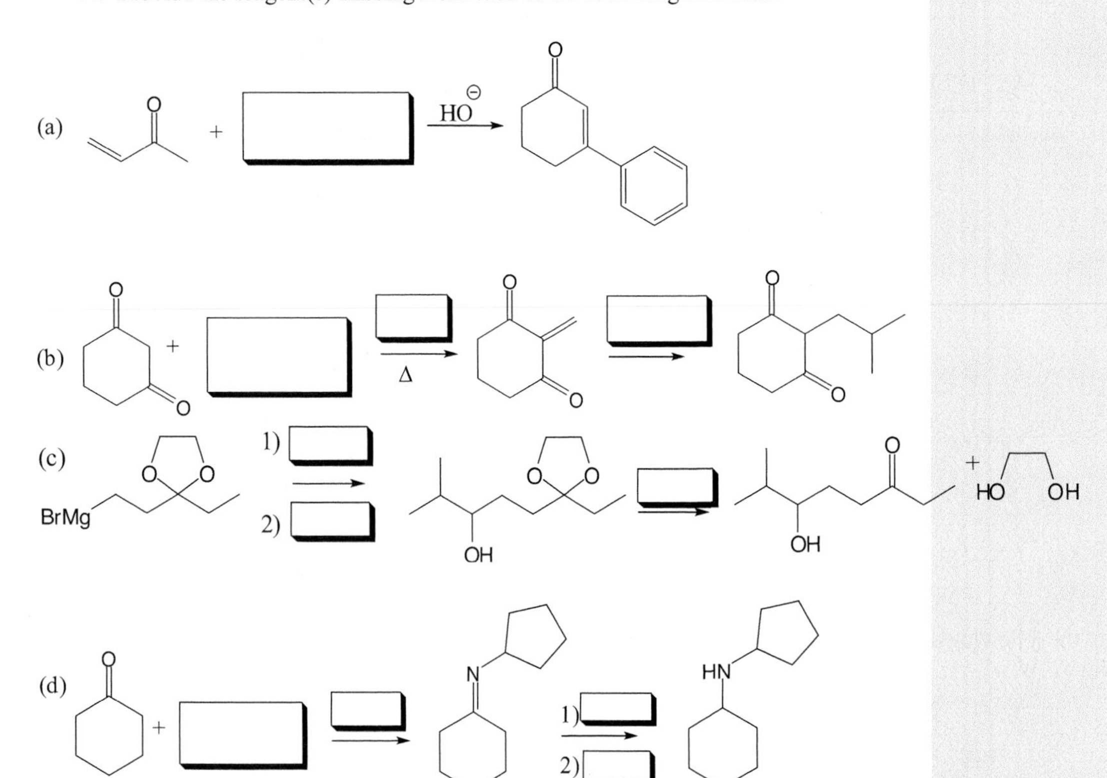

45. Suggest how you would synthesize each of the following, using cyclopentanone as one of the reagents.

(a)

(b)

(c)

(d)

CN

(e)

46. Suggest how you would synthesize the following compound. As your starting material, you may use any organic reagents that contain exactly two carbon atoms, and any inorganic reagents.

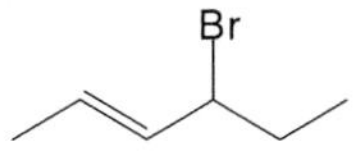

Br

47. Suggest how you would synthesize the following compound using phenylethanal as your only source of carbon atoms.

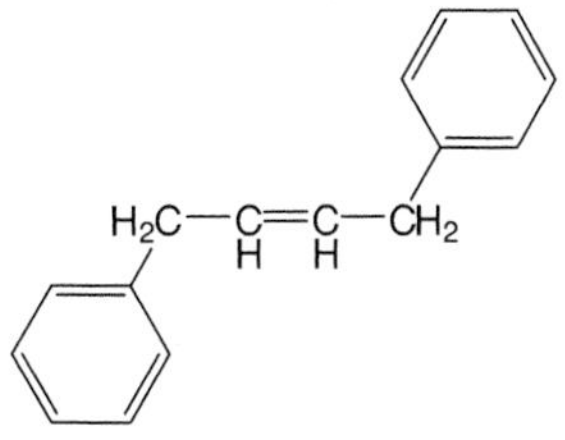

$H_2C-\underset{H}{C}=\underset{H}{C}-CH_2$

48. Suggest how you would synthesize 2-methylhexane from hex-4-en-3-one and any other reagents necessary.

49. An enamine, $R_2C{=}C\text{-}NR_2$, behaves as a nucleophile in much the same way that an enolate anion does, with nucleophilic character at the carbon alpha to that bonded to the amine. This is because an enamine has resonance structures similar to those observed for an enolate anion (see below).

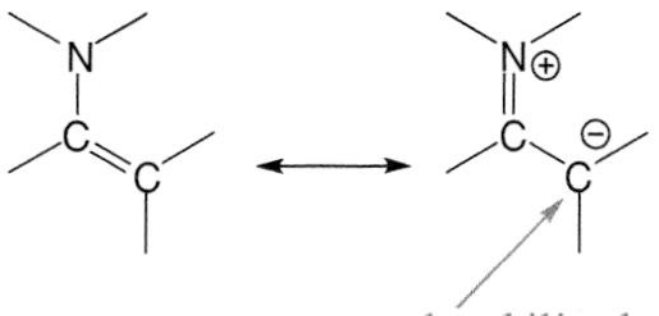

nucleophilic character

With this understanding, draw the complete mechanism for the following reaction, and provide the structure of the missing product.

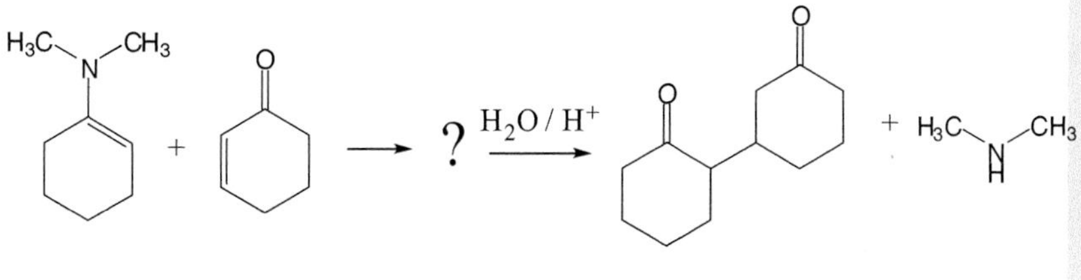

H_3C CH_3 N + → ? $\xrightarrow{H_2O / H^+}$ + H_3C N CH_3 H

50. Draw the complete, detailed mechanism for the following reaction and, using the mechanism, predict the major product. Note that TsOH is a relatively acidic compound.

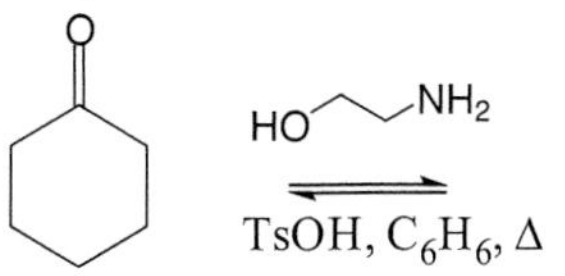

HO NH_2

TsOH, C_6H_6, Δ

51. As shown in the reaction below, a secondary nitro compound can be hydrolyzed to a ketone upon treatment with aqueous sulfuric acid. Propose a mechanism for this reaction.

H_2O
H_2SO_4

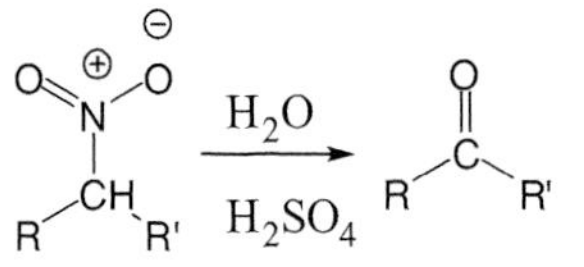

52. Draw a complete, detailed mechanism for the following reaction.

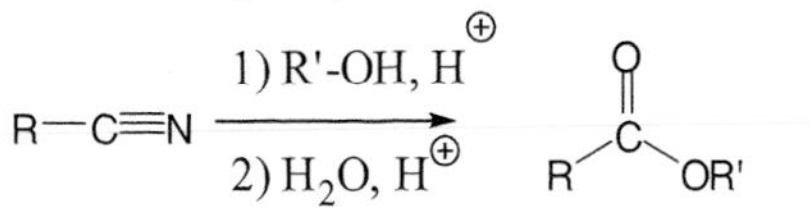

R—C≡N
1) R'-OH, $H^{\oplus}$
2) H_2O, $H^{\oplus}$

53. An aldol-type reaction can be performed with an immine enolate as the nucleophile, as shown below. Upon hydrolysis, the product is the normal β-hydroxycarbonyl. Notice that LDA is used as the base instead of HO^-. (a) Explain why HO^- cannot be used as a base for this reaction. (b) Provide a detailed mechanism for this reaction, including the structure of the intermediate species not shown.

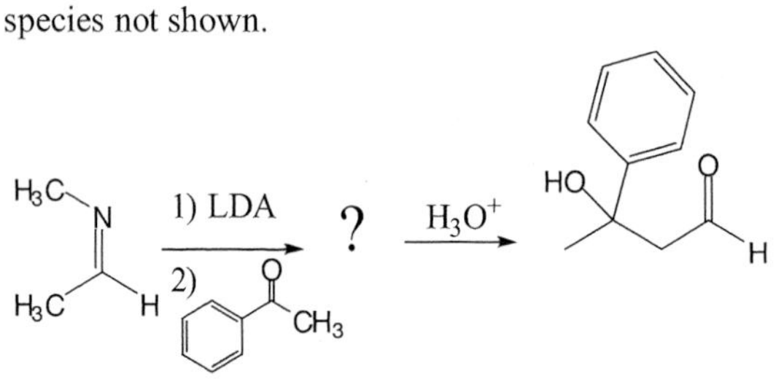

1) LDA
2)
?
H_3O^+

54. An aldehyde or a ketone can condense with an α-haloester under basic conditions to give an α,β-epoxy ester, also called a *glycidic ester*. An example is shown below. Provide a detailed mechanism for this reaction.

NaOEt

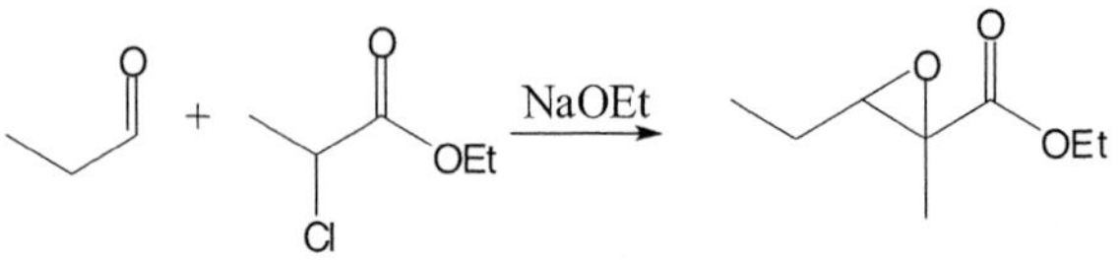

55. Treatment of a nitrile with base, followed by acid hydrolysis, yields a β-keto nitrile, as shown below. Provide a detailed mechanism for this reaction.

1) NaOEt
2) $H_3O^{\oplus}$

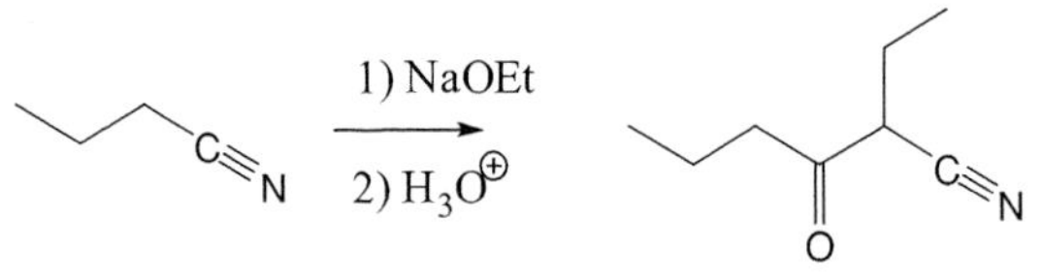

56. An isonitrile is an unusual species that has the form $R{-}\overset{\oplus}{N}{\equiv}\overset{\ominus}{C}$. When an isonitrile is reacted with water, an N-alkylformamide is formed, as shown below. Propose a mechanism for this reaction.

H_2O
$H^{\oplus}$

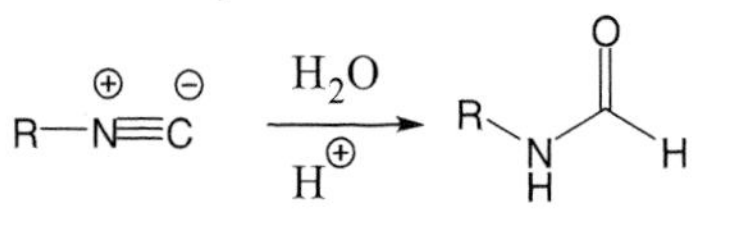

57. In this chapter we illustrated that the formation of an acetal from a ketone or aldehyde has a very similar mechanism to the formation of an imine. Both require acidic conditions in order to generate a water leaving group. At very acidic pH, however, the rate of imine formation slows down (shown below), whereas the rate of acetal formation does not. Explain this pH dependence of imine formation.

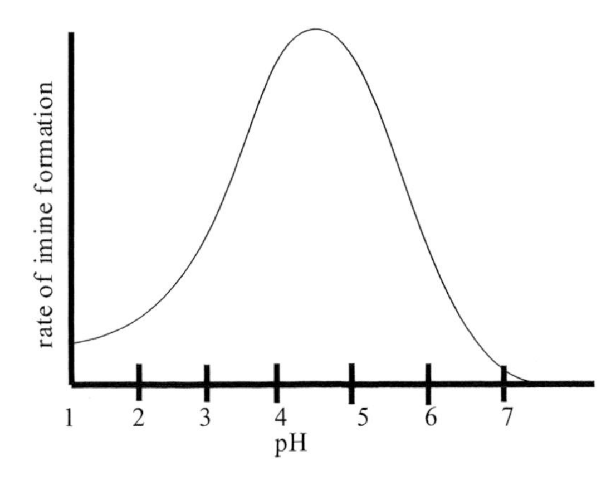

58. Hydroxylamine, H_2NOH, has both an alcohol functional group and an amine functional group. Therefore, it can feasibly undergo reaction with a ketone or aldehyde to produce either an acetal or an imine. (a) Draw each of these mechanisms for the reaction of hydroxylamine with acetone. (b) Which is the major product? (Hint: which step decides the outcome?)

59. When benzaldehyde and propopenenitrile are combined, no reaction occurs. In the presence of a catalytic amount of NaCN, however, the following reaction takes place. Draw a complete, detailed mechanism to account for these results.

O, H + CN —NaCN→ O, CN

60. A compound with formula $C_{10}H_{14}O$ has the following IR, ^{1}H-NMR, and ^{13}C-NMR spectra. The DEPT spectra reveal that the seven carbon signals farthest upfield are produced from CH_2 carbons. The compound can be synthesized using an aldol condensation reaction, simply by heating a compound C_5H_8O in the presence of NaOH. (a) Provide the structure of this compound and (b) provide the mechanism for the reaction that is described.

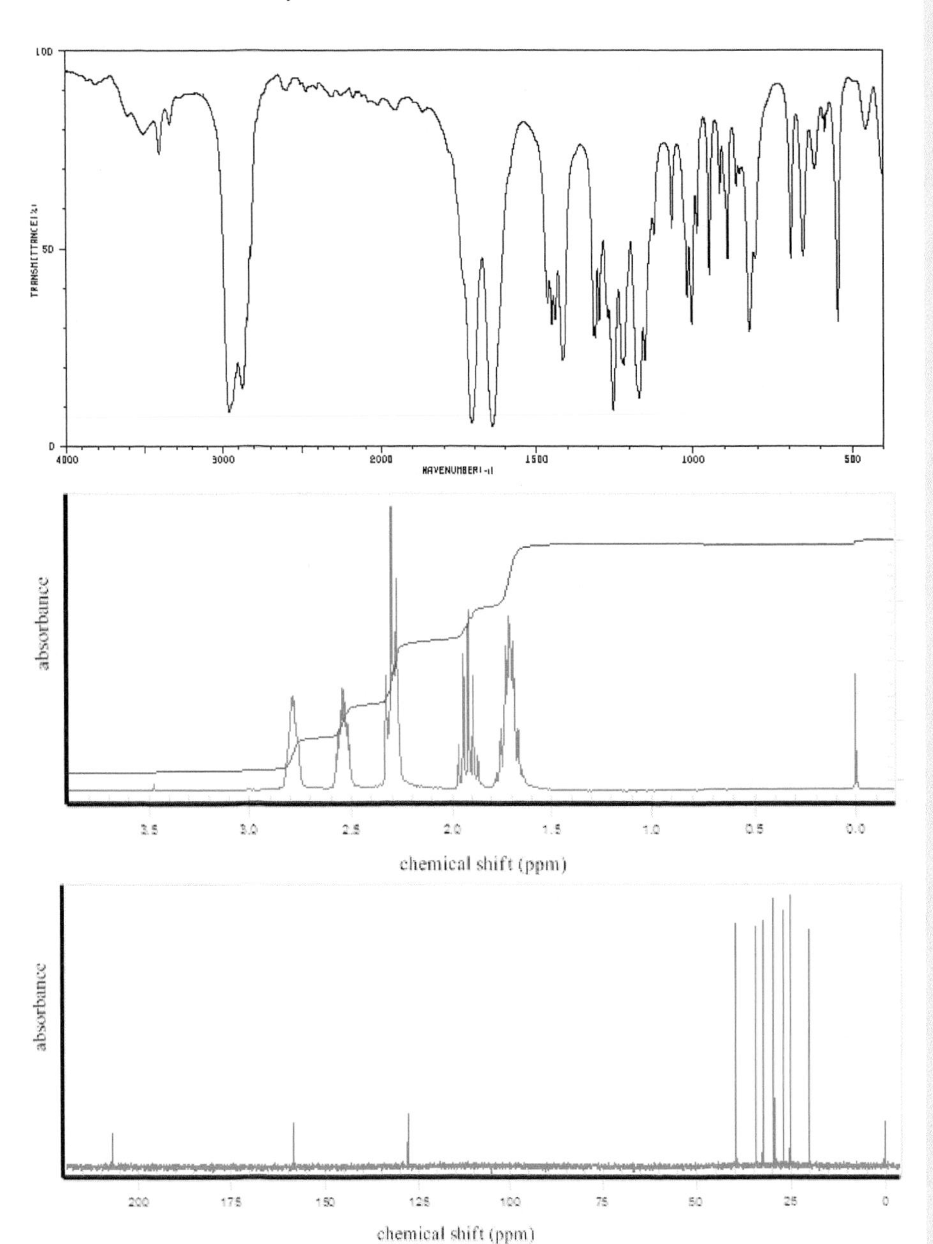

61. When 2-butenal is treated with 3-phenylpropenal in the presence of a strong base, a compound is formed whose formula is $C_{13}H_{12}O$. In its proton NMR spectrum, 1 signal has a chemical shift around 10 ppm, several signals have a chemical shift between 7 and 9, and several signals have a chemical shift between 5 and 6. Integration of those signals gives a 1:5:6 ratio. (a) Provide the structure of the product and (b) draw a complete, detailed mechanism that accounts for the formation of that product.

62. The following crossed aldol reaction can be carried out using a weak base such as pyridine. (a) Draw the complete, detailed mechanism for this reaction, and (b) explain why a relatively weak base can be used.

diethyl malonate

63. The following reaction is believed to proceed through the intermediate shown. Draw the complete, detailed mechanism that leads to the formation of that intermediate.

heat

64. When a 1,5-diketone is treated with acid, a 2,6-dialkyl pyran is produced. Propose a mechanism for this reaction.

65. When treated with acid, 2,5-hexanedione forms a compound with the formula C_6H_8O. The proton NMR spectrum of the product is shown below. A key intermediate is shown. Propose a mechanism for this reaction.

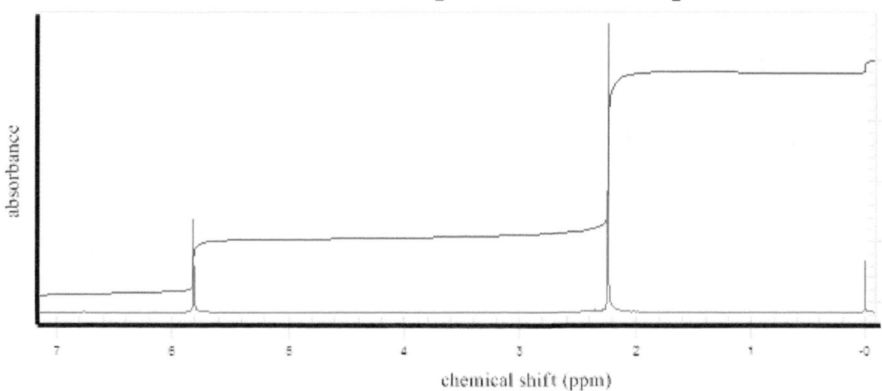

66. A carbamate can be prepared by treating an isocyanate with an alcohol, as shown. As we will see in Chapter 27, this type of reaction is employed in synthesizing polyurethanes. Propose a mechanism for this transformation.

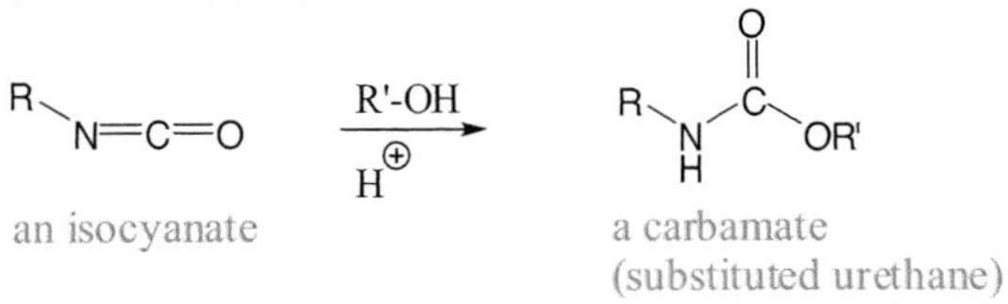

R–N=C=O —(R'-OH, $H^{\oplus}$)→ R–NH–C(=O)–OR'

an isocyanate

a carbamate (substituted urethane)

67. As shown below, an imino ester is formed when a nitrile is treated with an alcohol in the presence of *dry* HCl, followed by treatment of a weak base such as sodium bicarbonate. Propose a mechanism for this reaction.

R–C≡N —(1) R'-OH, *dry* HCl; 2) $NaHCO_3$)→ R–C(=NH)–OR'

an imino ester

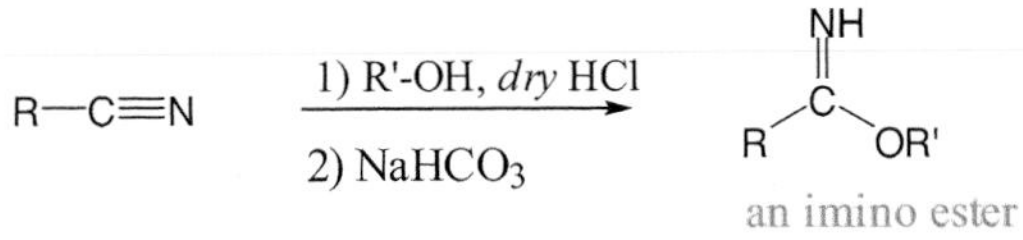

68. Pentanedinitrile undergoes a cyclization reaction when treated with ammonia under weakly acidic conditions. The product is an imidine. Propose a mechanism for this reaction.

N≡C–CH$_2$CH$_2$CH$_2$–C≡N + NH_3 —(NH_4Cl)→ cyclic imidine (NH, NH, NH)

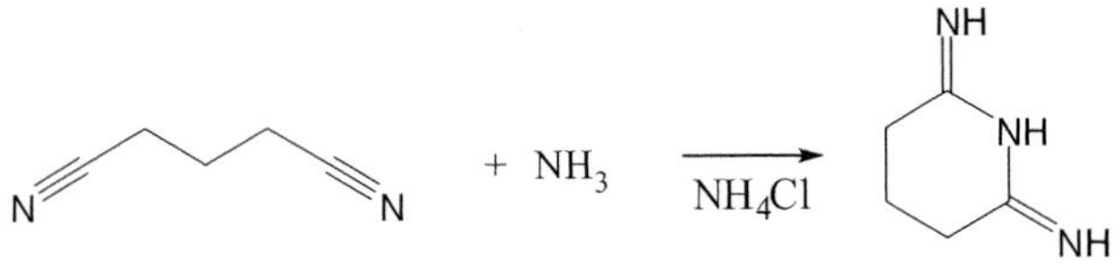

69. Draw the complete, detailed mechanism for the following reaction, which produces an amidine—a nitrogen analog to an ester.

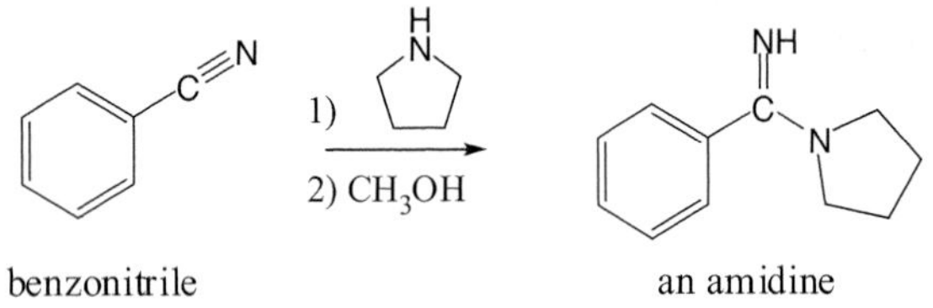

benzonitrile —(1) pyrrolidine (H–N); 2) CH_3OH)→ an amidine (Ph–C(=NH)–N-pyrrolidine)

70. After consulting the previous problem, suggest how the following amidine can be synthesized from benzonitrile, $C_6H_5C≡N$. (More than one synthetic step may be necessary.)

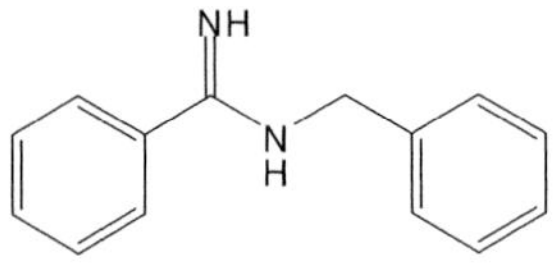

Ph–C(=NH)–NH–CH$_2$–Ph

an amidine

71. When an α,β-unsaturated carbonyl is treated with H_2O_2 under basic conditions, the C=C double bond is epoxidized as shown below. Propose a mechanism for this reaction.

cyclohexenone —(H_2O_2, $HO^{\ominus}$)→ epoxy cyclohexanone (O)

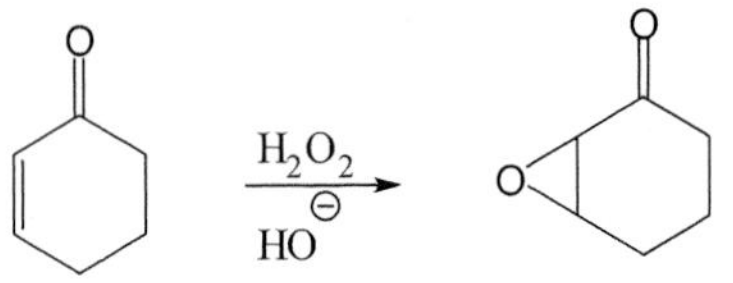

72. When acetonitrile is treated with concentrated sulfuric acid, followed by water, a product is formed, whose proton NMR spectrum exhibits three signals: singlet, 1.3 ppm, 9H; singlet, 3H, 2.0 ppm; broad singlet, 8.2 ppm, 1H. Its IR spectrum exhibits one broad absorption of medium intensity between 3,300 cm^{-1} and 3,500 cm^{-1}, and a narrow, intense absorption near 1,650 cm^{-1}. A key intermediate is shown. Draw the structure of the product, and draw the complete, detailed mechanism for the reaction.

$H_3C{-}C{\equiv}N$ + $(H_3C)_3C{-}OH$ $\xrightarrow{H_2SO_4\text{ (conc.)}}$ $[H_3C{-}C{\equiv}N^{\oplus}{-}C(CH_3)_3]$ $\xrightarrow{H_2O}$?

73. In mildly acidic conditions, 3-(2-aminophenyl)-propenal reacts to form a compound whose molecular weight is 129 g/mol. The proton NMR spectrum for the product is shown below. Its ^{13}C-NMR spectrum contains nine peaks, between 120 and 150 ppm. Propose a mechanism for this reaction and draw the product.

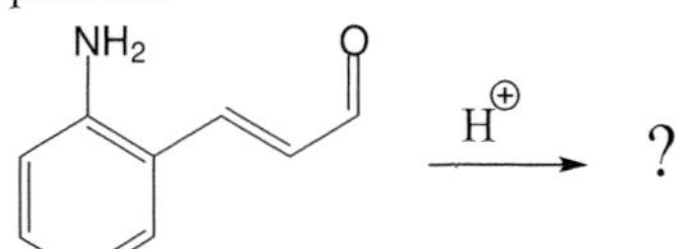

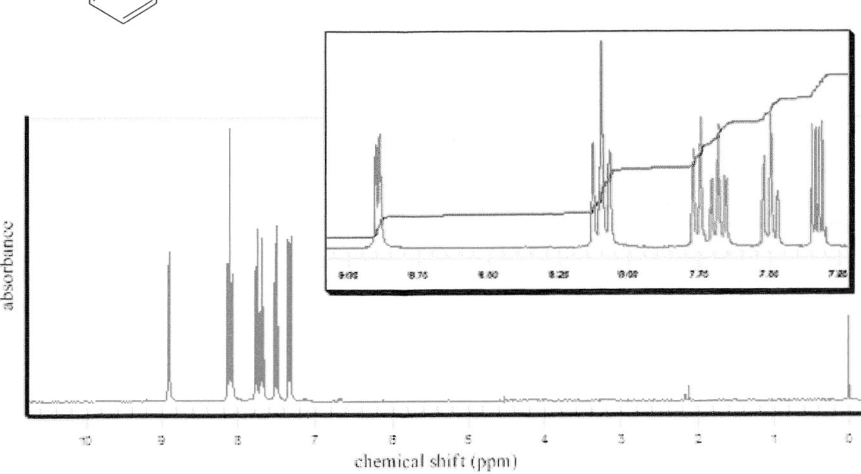

74. The following is an example of a Darzens reaction. Draw its complete, detailed mechanism.

$ClCH_2CO_2CH_2CH_3$ + CH_3CH_2CHO $\xrightarrow[HOC(CH_3)_3]{KOC(CH_3)_3}$ epoxide ester (OCH_2CH_3)

75. The following is an example of a Wittig-Horner reaction. Draw its complete, detailed mechanism. (A key intermediate is provided.)

$(EtO)_2P(O)CH_2C(O)OR$ $\xrightarrow[2)\ R'CHO]{1)\ CH_3(CH_2)_3Li}$ [oxaphosphetane intermediate: EtO, EtO, $O^{\ominus}$, OR, R'] ⟶ $R'CH{=}CHC(O)OR$ + $(EtO)_2P(O)O^{\ominus}$

76. In a Nef reaction, a nitroalkane is deprotonated to make a *nitronate salt*, which is subsequently hydrolyzed in acid to product a ketone. Draw the complete, detailed mechanism for this reaction.

NO_2 (R, R') $\xrightarrow{KH}$ nitronate (R, R') $\xrightarrow{H_2SO_4}$ ketone (R, R')

77. Reaction of 2,5-hexanedione with ammonia produces a compound whose ^{1}H-NMR spectrum is shown below. Its ^{13}C-NMR spectrum exhibits three signals. Draw the complete, detailed mechanism leading the formation of that product.

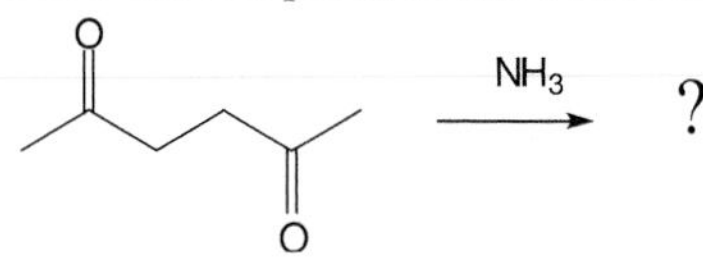

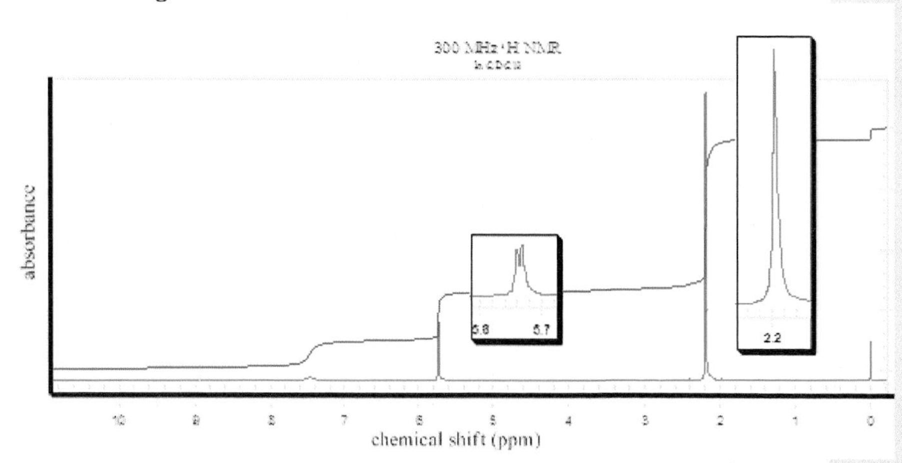

Chapter 17. Organic Synthesis. 2: Intermediate Topics

Introduction

In Chapter 11, we were introduced to the basics of organic synthesis, focusing mainly on how to construct a molecule with the appropriate carbon skeleton, as well as how to convert one functional group into another. In this chapter, we will continue with organic synthesis, focusing on some higher-level topics that enable us to synthesize more elaborate target molecules.

Much of our focus here will be geared toward the formation of new carbon-carbon bonds. Recognizing that carbon-carbon bonds typically form between oppositely charged carbon atoms, we will begin with a strategy of forming such bonds between carbon atoms of like charge. Next, we will focus on clues in a target molecule that help us determine the types of carbon-carbon bond-formation reactions that should be considered in a synthesis. We will also learn one way to tackle a synthesis in which such clues do not exist.

Another focus of this chapter will be on ways to circumvent *synthetic traps*. (Recall from Section 11.4 that a synthetic trap arises when the conditions necessary for a desired reaction at one site within a molecule will cause an undesired reaction at another site.) Specifically, we will discuss the use of selective reactions that target one functional group over another. We will also discuss strategies for protecting the functional group we wish to remain intact.

Finally, we will introduce a new reaction that is quite useful in organic synthesis—catalytic hydrogenation. As we will see, in addition to being a useful reaction for functional group conversions, it allows us to apply some of the strategies mentioned above.

CHAPTER OBJECTIVES
Upon Completing This Chapter You Should Be Able To:

- Identify reactions that reverse the charge (polarity) at a carbon atom, and incorporate such reactions in organic syntheses.
- Analyze the relative positioning of functional groups in a target molecule to determine which carbon-carbon bond-formation reactions should be considered in a synthesis.
- Devise a synthesis that utilizes reactions in which specific functional groups, such as aldehydes, ketones, and alkenes, are removed entirely from a molecule.
- Specify situations in which a *selective reaction* is called for, and incorporate such reactions in a synthesis.
- Explain the basic principles behind the use of a *protecting group*, and demonstrate the protection and deprotection of ketones, aldehydes, and alcohols in syntheses.
- Describe the basic mechanism of catalytic hydrogenation, and predict the products of catalytic hydrogenation of alkenes, alkynes, aldehydes, and ketones.

17.1. UMPOLUNG IN ORGANIC SYNTHESIS: FORMING CARBON-CARBON BONDS BETWEEN CARBON ATOMS BEARING LIKE CHARGES

In Section 7.1, we learned that in order for a bond to form between two atoms, the atoms are generally of opposite charge—one atom tends to bear a partial or full negative charge (and thus is electron-rich) and the other tends to bear a partial or full positive charge (making it electron-poor). This general idea is applicable to a wide variety of bond-formation reactions, including those that form carbon-carbon bonds. Consider, for example, the reaction in Equation 17-1.

electron-rich carbon

electron-poor carbon

carbon-carbon bond tends to form between an electron-rich and an electron-poor carbon

(17-1)

As we can see, the bond that is formed involves the carbon atom from NC^- and the carbon atom attached to Cl in the alkyl halide. The former carbon bears a full negative charge, whereas the latter one bears a partial positive charge.

Because carbon-carbon bond-formation reactions tend to involve oppositely charged carbon atoms, a problem arises when we wish to bring about the formation of a bond between two carbon atoms bearing like charges. For example, as indicated in Equation 17-2, no bond readily forms between the carbonyl carbon of a ketone and the carbon atom attached to Br in an alkyl bromide. This is because both carbons are

Comment [JMK13]: Margin note
Carbon atoms bearing like charges do not readily join together to form a bond.

attached to atoms with relatively high electronegativities (bromine and oxygen, respectively) and thus bear partial positive charges.

both carbon atoms are relatively electron-poor

no reaction

(17-2)

One way to bring about the formation of a bond between two such carbons is to carry out a separate reaction that first reverses the charge (or *polarity*) at one of the carbons. Thus, one carbon atom would become electron-rich while the other would remain electron-poor. This general idea of reversing a charge at a particular atom, called **umpolung** (a German term meaning "polarity reversal"), is common practice in organic synthesis. In fact, we have already encountered reactions that utilize umpolung in the formation of a carbon-carbon bond. One is in the synthesis of a Wittig reagent (Section 15.8a), shown in Equation 17-3. In the alkyl halide reactant, the carbon atom bonded to the halogen atom bears a partial positive charge and is relatively electron-poor. By contrast, in the Wittig reagent that is produced, that carbon atom has become electron-rich.

electron-poor carbon atom

1) $(C_6H_5)_3P$

2) $CH_3(CH_2)_3Li$

electron-rich carbon atom

2-bromopropane

56%

(17-3)

Another example involves the benzoin condensation (Section 16.11), part of whose mechanism is shown in Equation 17-4. Benzaldehyde's carbonyl carbon begins electron-poor, bearing a strong partial positive charge. In a key intermediate in the mechanism (shown in square brackets), however, that carbon atom has become electron-rich.

electron-poor carbon atom

electron-rich carbon atom

KCN

$HO^{\ominus}$ / H_2O, EtOH

benzaldehyde

2-hydroxy-1,2-diphenylethanone (benzoin)

88%

(17-4)

The sections that follow present two other reactions that take advantage of umpolung at a carbon atom, and thus can be quite helpful when designing a synthesis that requires carbon-carbon bond-formation. One reaction, discussed in Section 17.1a, is the formation of *organometallic reagents*, such as Grignard (R-MgX) and alkyllithium (R-Li) reagents, from an alkyl halide. The second, discussed in Section 17.1b, involves *acyl anion equivalents*.

17.1a. Making Organometallic Reagents: Reversing the Polarity at an Alkyl Halide Carbon

As indicated previously in Equation 17-2, bond formation does not occur readily between a carbonyl carbon and an alkyl halide carbon, the reason being that both such carbon atoms bear partial positive charges. To circumvent this problem, we can reverse the polarity at the alkyl halide carbon, giving that carbon atom a partial negative charge. Two reactions that accomplish this are shown below, both of which produce *organometallic reagents*. Equation 17-5 illustrates that an alkyl halide can be converted into a *Grignard reagent* (R-MgX) simply by treatment with solid magnesium in an ether such as tetrahydrofuran (THF). Similarly, as shown in Equation 17-6, an *alkyllithium reagent* (R-Li) can be synthesized from an alkyl halide by treatment with solid lithium.

electron-poor carbon atom (could also be Cl or I)
δ^+ Br —Mg(s), THF→ δ^- MgBr electron-rich carbon atom
a Grignard reagent
(7-5)

electron-poor carbon atom (could also be Cl)
$H_3C-CH_2-CH_2-CH_2-Br$ (δ^+) —Li(s), diethyl ether→ $H_3C-CH_2-CH_2-CH_2-Li$ (δ^-) electron-rich carbon atom
an alkyllithium reagent
(7-6)

Notice that in both cases the partial positive charge of the alkyl halide carbon becomes a partial negative charge in the organometallic reagent. Thus, umpolung has taken place, which facilitates the formation of a bond with an electron-poor carbon, such as in an epoxide ring-opening reaction (Section 10.7) or a Grignard reaction (Section 15.6).

Comment [JMK14]: **Margin note.** When an alkyl halide is converted into an organometallic reagent, the charge on the carbon atom bonded to the halogen is reversed, going from partially positive to partially negative.

Your Turn 17.1. Write either δ^+ or δ^- next to the carbon atom bonded to the halogen in the reactant and the carbon atom bonded to Li in the product.

Br —Li(s), ether→ Li

A related reaction is the synthesis of a *lithium dialkylcuprate* (R_2CuLi), an example of which is shown in Equation 17-7. As we can see, a lithium dialkylcuprate is synthesized from the corresponding alkyllithium reagent by treatment with copper iodide (CuI). Because the metal-containing carbon atom bears a partial negative charge in both the alkyllithium reagent and the lithium dialkylcuprate, umpolung technically does *not* occur in such a reaction. However, as shown below, synthesizing a lithium dialkylcuprate from an alkyl halide does involve the reversal of polarity at carbon. Once again, this facilitates the formation of a carbon-carbon bond with an electron-poor carbon, as we have seen previously in conjugate addition to an α,β-unsaturated carbonyl (Section 15.7).

$$\left(H_3C{-}\overset{\delta^+}{C}H(CH_3){-}Br \xrightarrow[\text{diethyl ether}]{Li(s)} \right) H_3C{-}\overset{\delta^-}{C}H(CH_3){-}Li \xrightarrow[\text{THF}]{CuI} [(CH_3)_2\overset{\delta^-}{C}H]_2CuLi \qquad (17\text{-}7)$$

a lithium dialkylcuprate

Although each of the above reactions that forms an organometallic reagent may appear to be rather simple, their mechanisms are quite complex—they involve free radicals (Chapter 25), so we will not discuss them here. Suffice it to say that the synthesis of Grignard reagents and alkyllithium reagents from alkyl halides (Equations 17-5 and 17-6, respectively) are examples of reduction reactions. Notice that in each of these reactions, transforming a carbon-halogen bond into a carbon-metal bond lowers the oxidation state of carbon by two.

Problem 17.1. Predict the product of each of the following reactions.

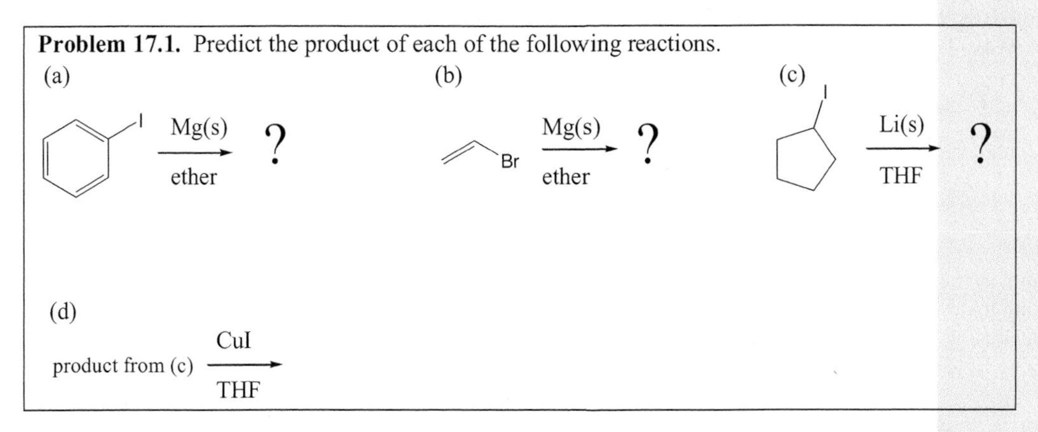

Problem 17.2. Show how to synthesize each of the following organometallic compounds from an alkyl halide.

(a) Li (b) MgCl (c) MgBr (d) Li Cu

Solved Problem 17.1. Using formaldehyde ($H_2C{=}O$) as your only source of carbon, show how you would synthesize 1-propanol.

$$H_2C{=}O \xrightarrow{?} H_3C{-}CH_2{-}CH_2{-}OH$$

Think. Must carbon-carbon bonds be formed in the synthesis? If so, what should the electron-rich species be? What should the electron-poor species be? Can the synthesis take place in a single reaction? If not, what precursor should we choose?

Solve. Since our only source of carbon contains a single carbon atom and the product contains a chain of three carbon atoms, it is clear that carbon-carbon bonds must be formed. Realize, however, that a carbon-carbon bond-formation reaction would be difficult to carry out directly between two molecules of formaldehyde, because such a reaction would entail the formation of a bond between two carbon atoms bearing the same partial positive charge. We must therefore consider a precursor which has a carbon atom bearing a significant negative charge. A Grignard reagent would suffice, especially realizing that the target is an alcohol, the product of a Grignard reaction.

In our retrosynthetic analysis, we perform a "reverse Grignard reaction" as our first transform, disconnecting the carbon-carbon bond involving the carbon that bears the OH group. This shows that the final product can be made from an ethyl Grignard reagent (CH_3CH_2MgBr) and formaldehyde. Formaldehyde is an available starting material, but the ethyl Grignard is not. We must therefore devise a synthesis for it.

an alcohol is the product of a Grignard reaction

$H_3C-CH_2-CH_2-OH$ ⟹ (reverse Grignard) H_3C-CH_2-MgBr (new target) + $H_2C{=}O$

As we just learned, the ethyl Grignard can be generated from CH_3CH_2Br. Once again, CH_3CH_2Br is not an available starting material, but it can be made from ethanol using PBr_3.

H_3C-CH_2-MgBr ⟹ (reverse Grignard formation) H_3C-CH_2-Br ⟹ (reverse bromination) H_3C-CH_2-OH

We now recognize ethanol as the possible product of a Grignard reaction between CH_3MgBr and our starting material, $H_2C{=}O$. CH_3MgBr is generated from CH_3Br, which can be made from CH_3OH using PBr_3. Finally, CH_3OH can be made by reducing our starting material using a hydride reagent such as $NaBH_4$.

H_3C-CH_2-OH ⟹ (reverse Grignard) $H_3C-MgBr$ + $H_2C{=}O$ ⟹ (reverse Grignard formation) H_3C-Br ⟹ (reverse bromination) H_3C-OH ⟹ (reverse reduction) $H_2C{=}O$

The synthesis is therefore reported as follows:

$H_2C{=}O$ —($NaBH_4$, EtOH)→ H_3C-OH —(PBr_3)→ H_3C-Br —(Mg)→ $H_3C-MgBr$ —(1) $H_2C{=}O$; 2) $H^\oplus$)→ H_3C-CH_2-OH

—(PBr_3)→ H_3C-CH_2-Br —(Mg)→ H_3C-CH_2-MgBr —(1) $H_2C{=}O$; 2) $H^\oplus$)→ $H_3C-CH_2-CH_2-OH$

Problem 17.3. Using acetaldehyde ($CH_3CH{=}O$) as your only source of carbon, show how to synthesize 3-methylpentan-3-ol.

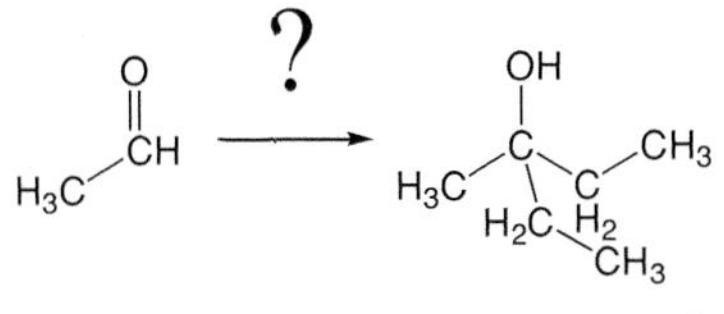

3-methylpentan-3-ol

Problem 17.4. Show how you would synthesize 4-phenylbutan-1-ol from bromobenzene, using oxirane, as your only other source of carbon.

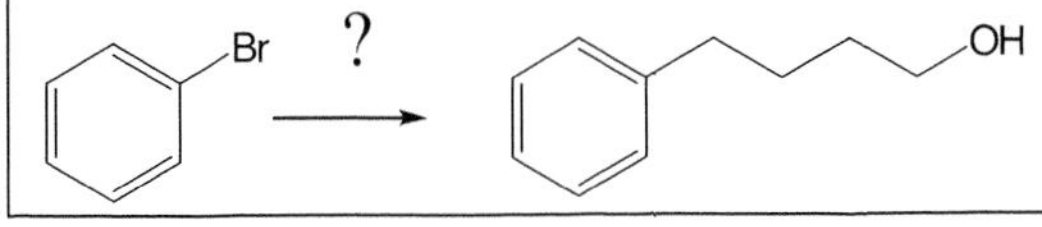

17.1b. Acyl Anion Equivalents: Reversing the Polarity at an Aldehyde Carbon

In the previous section, we saw that the difficulty in forming a bond between an alkyl halide carbon and a carbonyl carbon can be circumvented by first converting the alkyl halide into an organometallic compound. This reverses the polarity of the alkyl halide carbon, changing it from electron-poor to electron-rich. Another way to circumvent the problem is to reverse the polarity of the carbonyl carbon instead. An example of how to do so is shown in Equation 17-8.

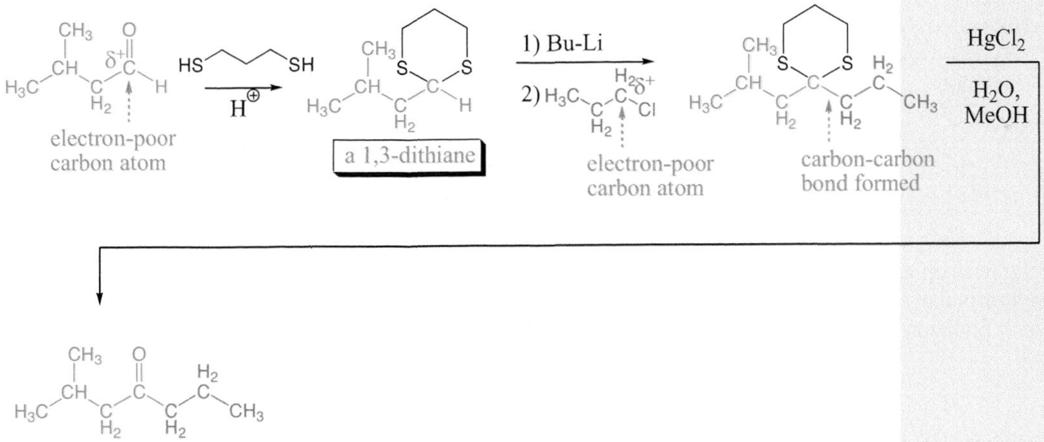

electron-poor carbon atom — $H^{\oplus}$ — a 1,3-dithiane — 1) Bu-Li 2) H_3C-CH_2-CH_2-Cl — electron-poor carbon atom — carbon-carbon bond formed — $HgCl_2$, H_2O, MeOH

(17-8)

In the first reaction in this sequence, 1,3-propanedithiol converts the aldehyde into a 1,3-dithiane, which is a specific example of a thioacetal (Section 16.2b). Next, butyllithium ($CH_3CH_2CH_2CH_2$-Li) is added, followed by the alkyl halide, resulting in the formation of a carbon-carbon bond. Finally, the 1,3-dithiane is converted back to a carbonyl group upon hydrolysis with aqueous $HgCl_2$. (This hydrolysis step is similar to hydrolysis of a regular acetal, discussed in Section 16.2a, but is catalyzed by Hg^{2+} instead of H^+.)

Your Turn 17.2. In the space provided below, draw the complete mechanism for the formation of the 1,3-dithane in Equation 17-8. (You may wish to review Section 16.2b.)

The key to carbon-carbon bond formation is the increase in acidity of the aldehyde hydrogen when the C=O group is converted into the 1,3-dithiane. Under normal conditions, an aldehyde hydrogen is not sufficiently acidic to be deprotonated by butyllithium, a base that is among the strongest known. When it is part of a 1,3-dithiane, however, that proton's pK_a is approximately 31, which is much more acidic than butyllithium's conjugate acid ($pK_a \sim 50$). Therefore, as shown in the mechanism below, the ensuing deprotonation by butyllithium produces a negatively-charged carbon atom that is highly nucleophilic. Effectively, then, the aldehyde carbon's polarity has been reversed—i.e., umpolung has taken place—and subsequent treatment with the alkyl halide allows the carbon-carbon bond to be formed via an S_N2 reaction.

Comment [JMK15]: **Margin note**
Converting an aldehyde to a 1,3-dithiane makes an aldehyde hydrogen acidic enough to be deprotonated by Bu-Li.

Mechanism for Carbon-Carbon Bond Formation in Equation 17-8

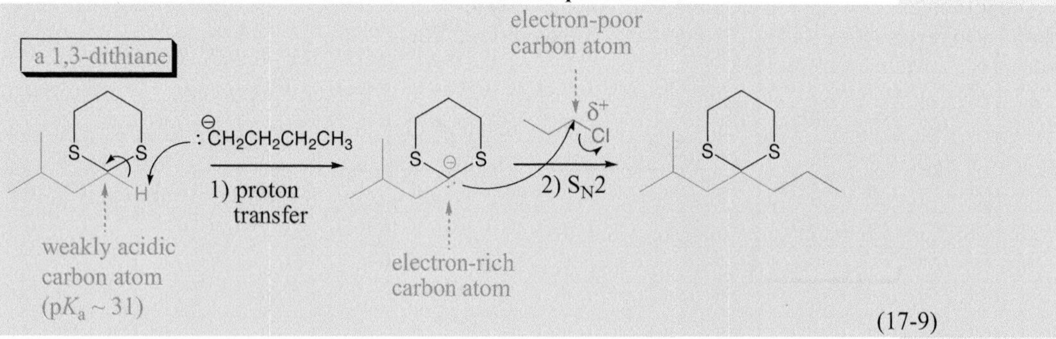

a 1,3-dithiane
electron-poor carbon atom
δ^+
Cl
$:\overset{\ominus}{C}H_2CH_2CH_2CH_3$
1) proton transfer
2) S_N2
weakly acidic carbon atom ($pK_a \sim 31$)
electron-rich carbon atom

(17-9)

Being a strong nucleophile, a deprotonated 1,3-dithiane can also attack the electron-poor carbonyl carbon of a ketone or aldehyde in a nucleophilic addition reaction. An example is shown in Equation 17-10.

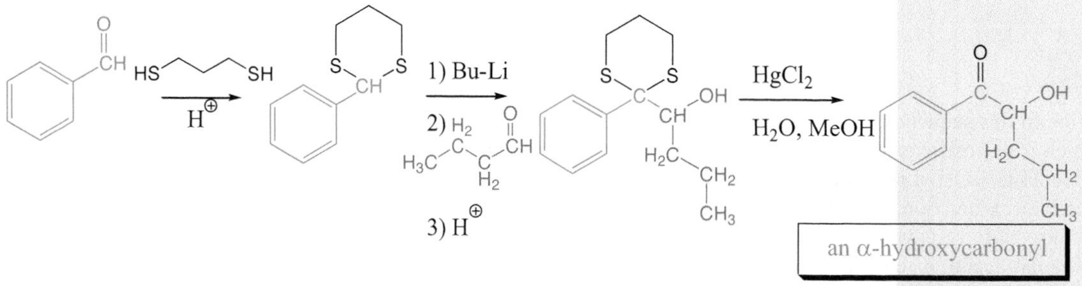

HS~~SH, $H^{\oplus}$
1) Bu-Li
2) $H_3C-C(H_2)-C(H_2)-CH=O$
3) $H^{\oplus}$
$HgCl_2$
H_2O, MeOH
an α-hydroxycarbonyl

(17-10)

This reaction is particularly interesting because the product is an α-hydroxycarbonyl, and thus resembles the product of an aldol reaction, a β-hydroxycarbonyl (Section 16.4). The difference is in the location of the OH group relative to the C=O group.

Your Turn 17.3. Draw the mechanism that shows how the second structure (the 1,3-dithiane) in Equation 17-10 is converted into the third structure.

Problem 17.5. Draw the complete, detailed mechanism for the following sequence of reactions, and draw the product.

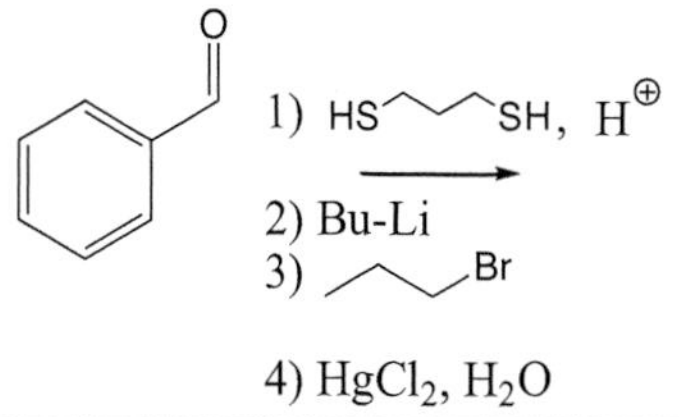

1) HS⁀⁀SH, $H^{\oplus}$
2) Bu-Li
3) ⁀⁀Br
4) $HgCl_2$, H_2O

Problem 17.6. Show how to carry out each of the following syntheses.

(a) ? (b) ?

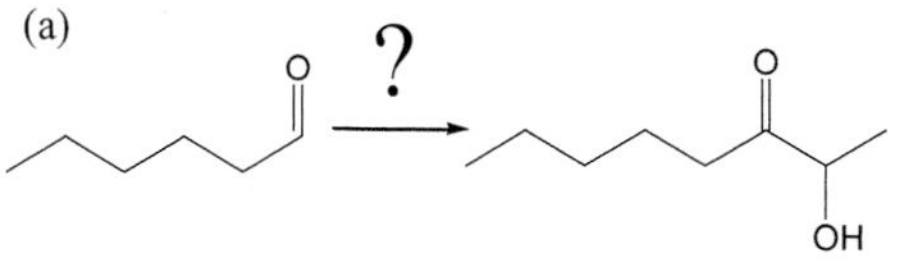

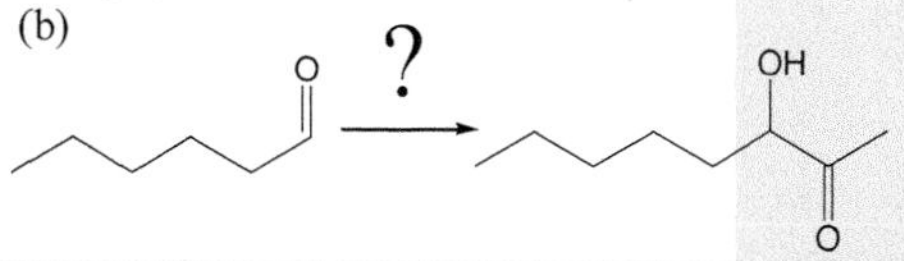

It is helpful to realize that the overall products of the reactions in Equations 17-8 and 17-10 are the same as the ones that would be produced if the nucleophile were an **acyl anion** (a *hypothetical* species in which a carbonyl carbon bears a -1 formal charge) instead of a deprotonated 1,3-dithiane. Thus, deprotonated 1,3-dithianes are often called **acyl anion equivalents**. This point is illustrated in Equations 17-11a and 17-11b.

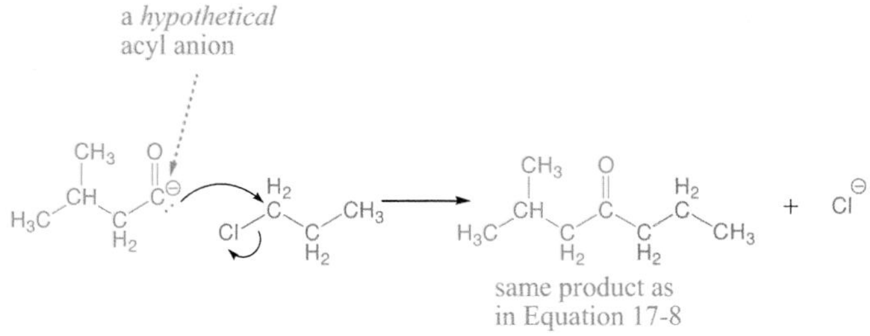

a *hypothetical* acyl anion

same product as in Equation 17-8 (a)

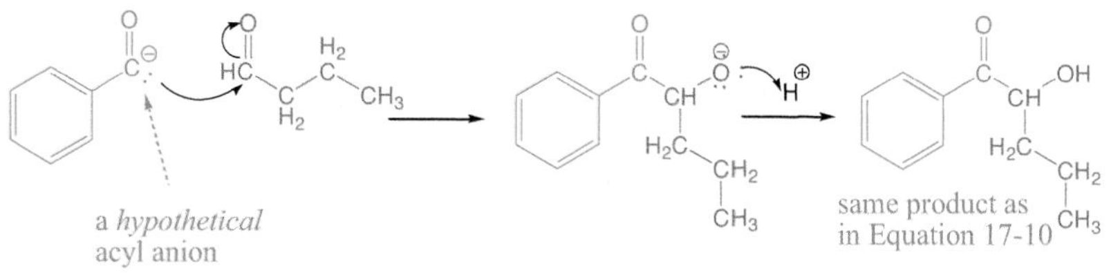

a *hypothetical* acyl anion

same product as in Equation 17-10 (b)

(17-11)

With this understanding, we can see that the appearance of an acyl anion in a retrosynthetic analysis is a clear indication that a 1,3-dithiane should be considered as part of a synthesis. Solved Problem 17.2 provides an example.

Solved Problem 17.2. Outline a synthesis of 1-hydroxy-3-methyl-1-phenyl-2-butanone using 2-methylpropanal and any other necessary reagents.

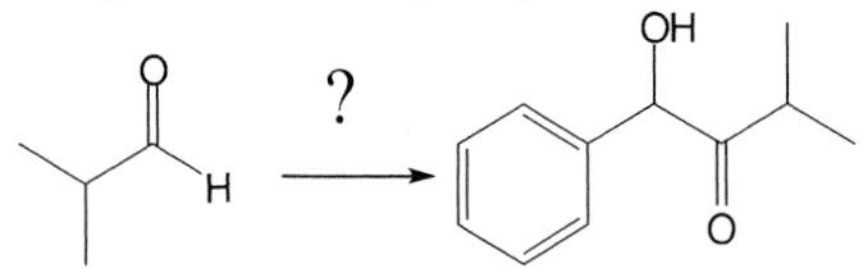

?

OH

H

O

Think. Which carbon-carbon bond is the one that must be formed? What hypothetical acyl anion appears to be the nucleophile required to form that bond? How can that bond actually be formed using a 1,3-dithiane?

Solve. The carbon-carbon bond that is formed is attached to an alcohol group in the product. In a retrosynthetic analysis, we can therefore disconnect that carbon-carbon bond in a reverse nucleophilic addition to arrive back at benzaldehyde and the *acyl anion* of 2-methylpropanal (i.e., the acyl anion of the starting material).

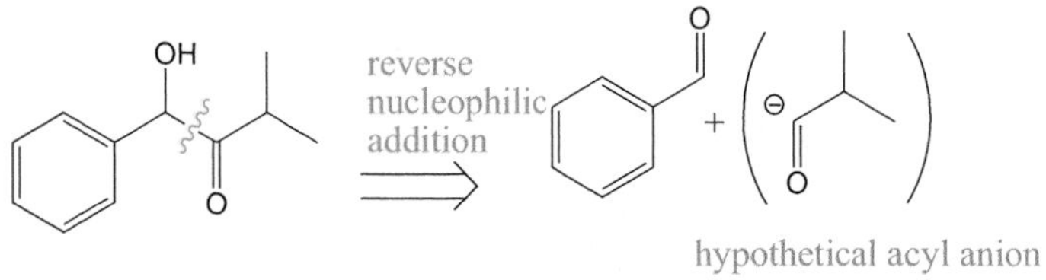

OH

reverse nucleophilic addition

O

+

hypothetical acyl anion

Because the acyl anion doesn't exist, we must consider using a 1,3-dithiane as an *acyl anion equivalent*; the synthesis would thus appear as follows.

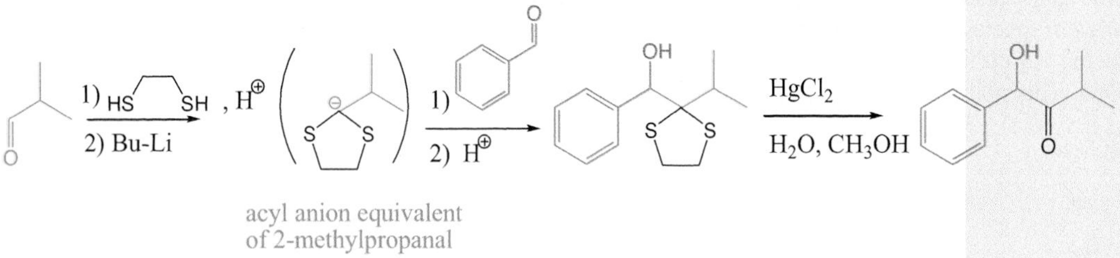

1) HS⁄⁀SH , $H^{\oplus}$
2) Bu-Li

acyl anion equivalent of 2-methylpropanal

1) benzaldehyde
2) $H^{\oplus}$

$HgCl_2$
H_2O, CH_3OH

OH

O

Problem 17.7. Outline a synthesis of 2-hydroxy-3-methyl-1-phenyl-1-butanone from 2-methylpropanal.

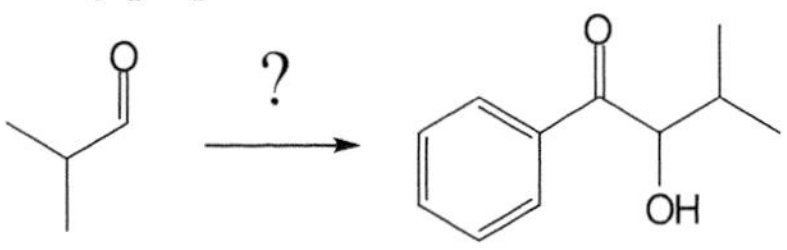

?

O

OH

17.2. RELATIVE POSITIONING OF FUNCTIONAL GROUPS IN CARBON-CARBON BOND FORMATION REACTIONS

In Chapter 11, we learned that carbon-carbon bond-formation reactions are important in organic synthesis because they allow us to alter the carbon framework of a particular molecule. In many of those reactions, two functional groups are left with very specific relative locations along the carbon skeleton. That relative positioning can be critical to a synthesis because, as we have seen many times before, those functional groups govern the sites at which subsequent reactions can take place.

Consider, for example, the formation of a *cyanohydrin*, shown in Equation 17-12. A carbon-carbon bond is formed between the cyanide carbon and the carbonyl carbon, yielding an α-hydroxynitrile. Notice, in particular, that the two functional groups that remain in the product—a nitrile group (C≡N) and an alcohol group (C−OH)—are *adjacent* to each other. In other words, the carbon atoms involved in these functional groups have a **1,2-positioning** relative to each other.

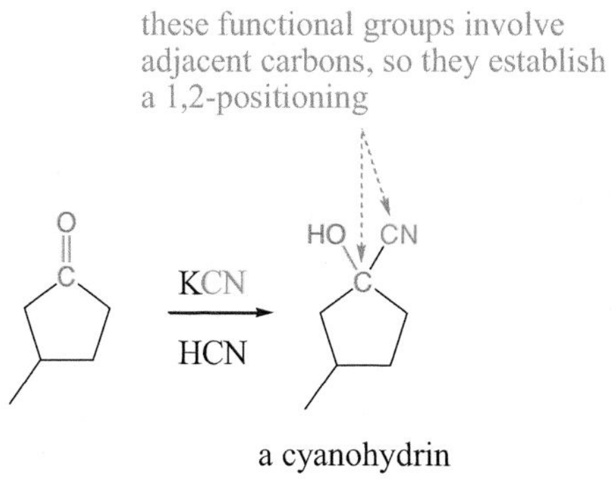

these functional groups involve adjacent carbons, so they establish a 1,2-positioning

KCN / HCN

a cyanohydrin

(17-12)

Knowing that this reaction produces a compound with 1,2-positioning of the resulting functional groups is particularly useful when our target molecule is *not* a cyanohydrin, but still has functional groups with 1,2-positioning. Suppose, for example, we wish to synthesize the following α-hydroxy acid starting from the ketone given.

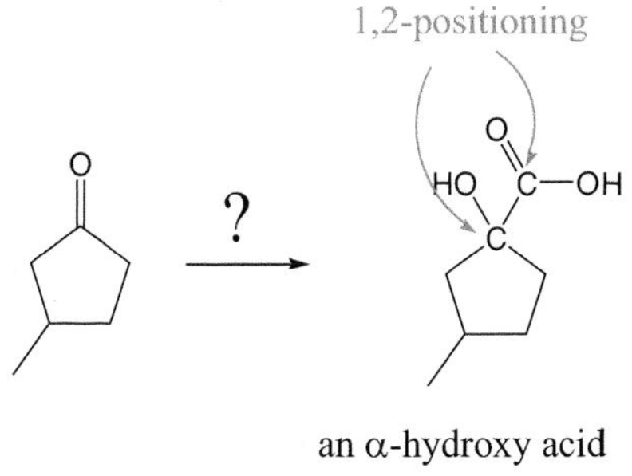

1,2-positioning

?

an α-hydroxy acid

We can see that the carboxylic acid and alcohol functional groups in the target are in a 1,2-positioning, so we could consider a cyanohydrin as a synthetic intermediate. As shown in the retrosynthetic analysis below, such an intermediate is obtained by applying a transform that reverses a nitrile hydrolysis.

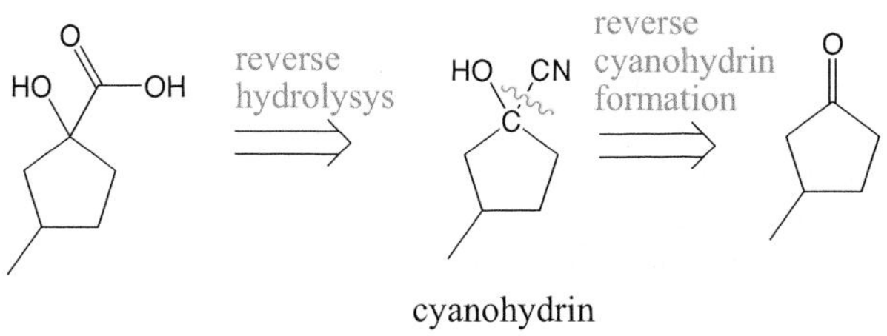

reverse hydrolysys

reverse cyanohydrin formation

cyanohydrin

In the forward direction, the synthesis would appear as follows.

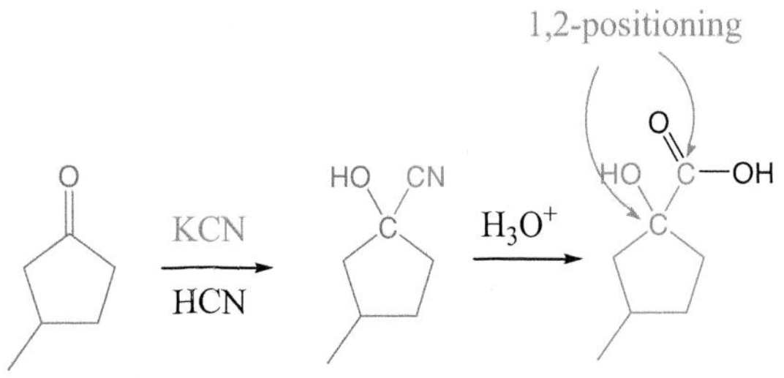

1,2-positioning

KCN / HCN → HO CN C (a cyanohydrin) → H_3O^+ → HO C—OH (O) C (an alpha hydroxy acid)

a cyanohydrin   an alpha hydroxy acid

Solved Problem 17.3. Show how to synthesize the α-hydroxyl acid below, using compounds with three or fewer carbon atoms.

O OH OH

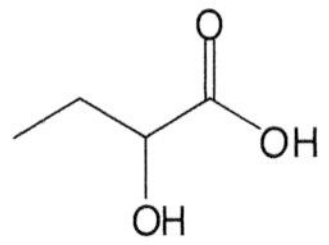

Think. From what cyanohydrin could this target be synthesized? How could that cyanohydrin be synthesized from compounds containing three or fewer carbons?

Solve. The appropriate cyanohydrin precursor is shown in the retrosynthetic analysis below, and is obtained by applying a transform that reverses a nitrile hydrolysis.

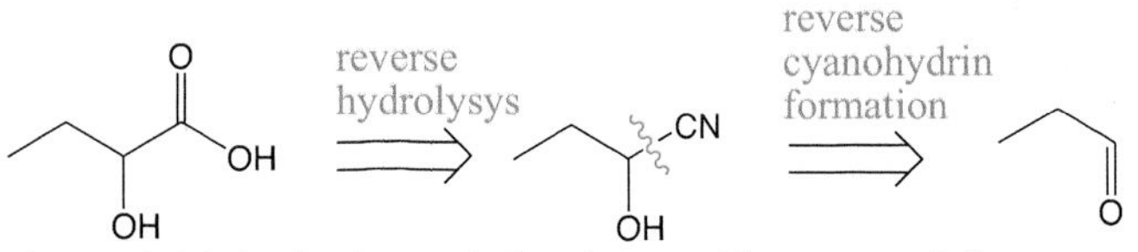

O OH OH ⟹ (reverse hydrolysys) CN OH ⟹ (reverse cyanohydrin formation) O

The synthesis in the forward direction would appear as follows.

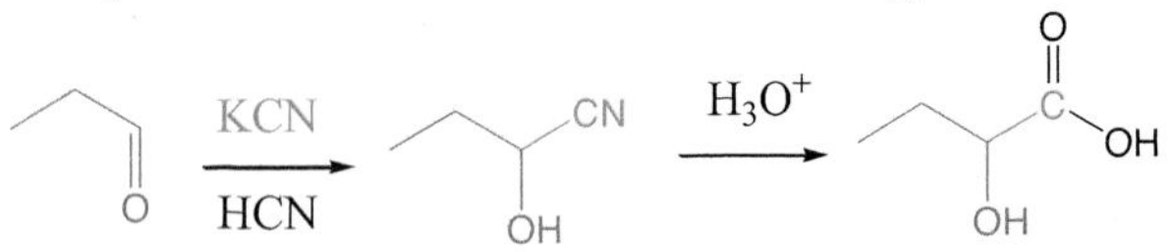

O → KCN / HCN → CN OH → H_3O^+ → O C OH OH

a cyanohydrin   an alpha hydroxy acid

Problem 17.8. Show how to synthesize the α-hydroxyl acid below, using compounds with three or fewer carbon atoms.

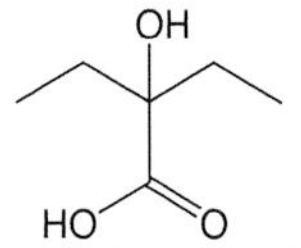

OH HO O

Cyanohydrin formation is not the only carbon-carbon bond-formation reaction that produces functional groups with specific relative positioning along the carbon backbone. Other such reactions we have previously encountered are shown in Table 17-1.

Table 17-1. Reactions that Form Carbon-Carbon Bonds

Relative Positioning	Product Formed	Electron-Rich Reactant	Electron-Poor Reactant	Discussed in Section
1,2-	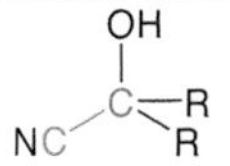 Cyanohydrin	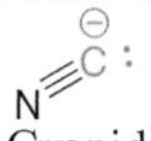 Cyanide anion	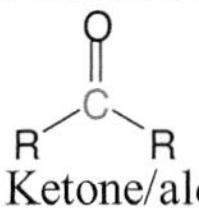 Ketone/aldehyde	16.1
1,2-	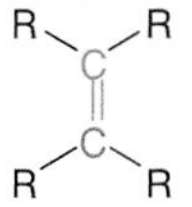	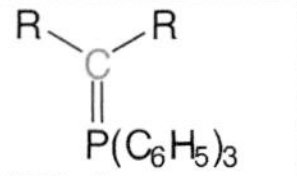 Wittig reagent	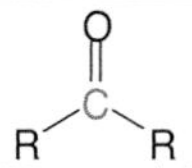 Ketone/aldehyde	15.8
1,2-	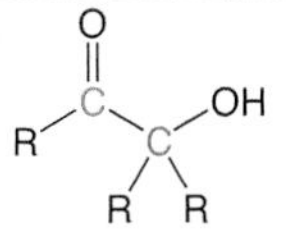 α-hydroxy carbonyl	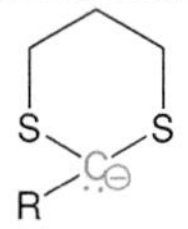 Deprotonated 1,3-dithiane	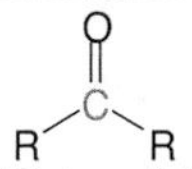 Ketone/aldehyde	17.1b
1,3-	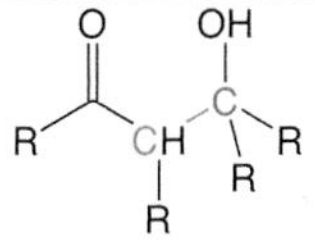 β-hydroxy carbonyl	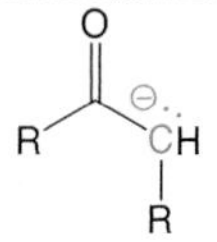 Enolate anion	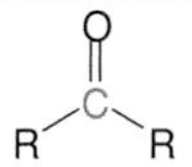 Ketone/aldehyde	16.4
1,4-	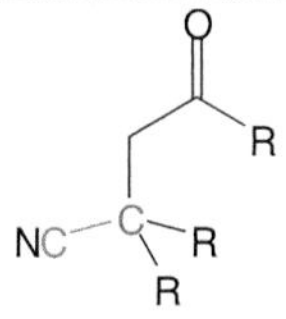 β-cyano ketone/aldehyde	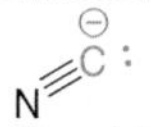 Cyanide anion	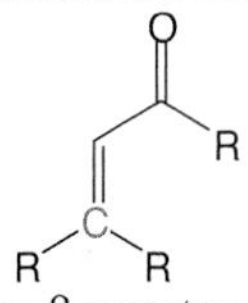 α,β-unsaturated ketone/aldehyde	16.1
1,5-	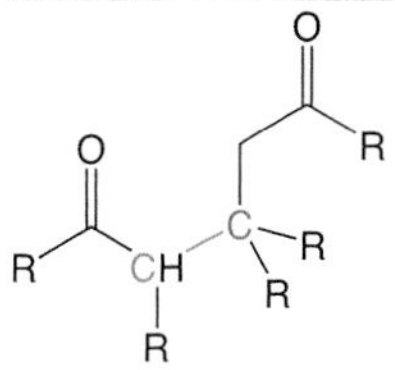 1,5-dicarbonyl	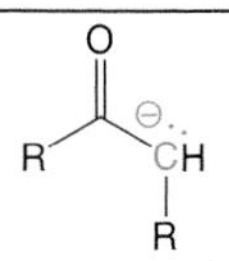 Enolate anion	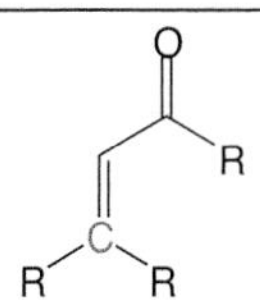 α,β-unsaturated ketone/aldehyde	16.4

Your Turn 17.4. For each entry in Table 17-1, circle the appropriate carbon atoms in the respective products that are indicated by the relative positioning of the functional groups. (Hint: they are not necessarily the atoms colored red and blue.)

As you can see, these reactions can be used to strategically give products with 1,2-, 1,3-, 1,4-, and 1,5-positioning of the functional groups that remain. Therefore, if a target has functional groups with one of these relative positionings and the synthesis calls for a carbon-carbon bond-formation reaction, you should consider employing one of the reactions from Table 17-1. An example is shown in Solved Problem 17.4.

Comment [JMK16]: Margin note
If a synthesis requires a carbon-carbon bond-formation and the target exhibits functional groups in a 1,2-, 1,3-, 1,4-, or 1,5-positioning, consider incorporating a reaction from Table 17-1.

Solved Problem 17.4. Show how you can synthesize 2-methyl-1,3-pentanediol from compounds containing 5 or fewer carbons.

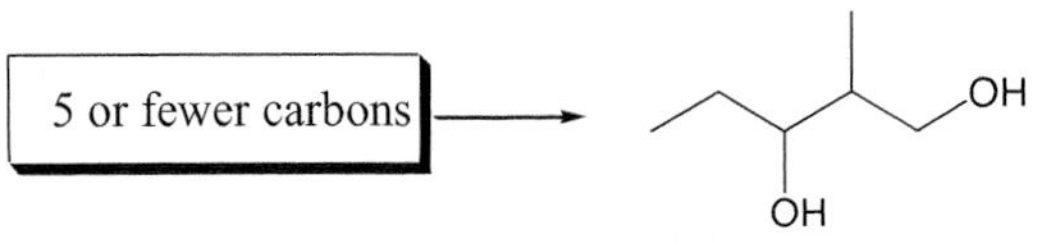

5 or fewer carbons → [2-methyl-1,3-pentanediol: OH, OH]

Think. Will a carbon-carbon bond-formation reaction be necessary? What is the relative positioning of the functional groups in the target? Does the appropriate carbon-carbon bond formation reaction in Table 17-1 leave us with the correct functional groups, or will we need to carry out an additional functional group conversion?

Solve. Clearly we will have to employ a carbon-carbon bond-formation reaction, given that the target's carbon skeleton contains 6 carbons bonded together. The 1,3-positioning of the two hydroxyl groups in the product suggests that we should employ an aldol reaction, which yields a β-hydroxycarbonyl. Therefore, our task becomes simply to apply a transform that takes our target molecule back to a β-hydroxycarbonyl. This is a reverse hydride reduction, and it can be performed on either of the two OH groups. Below we show this transform applied to the OH group on C3. From there, we disconnect the appropriate C-C bond to take us back to the aldol reactants, 2-pentanone and formaldehyde.

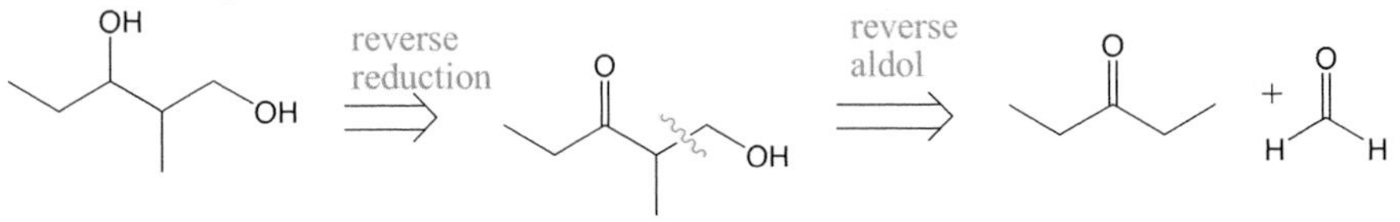

OH, OH ⇒ (reverse reduction) O, OH ⇒ (reverse aldol) O + O, H, H

In the forward direction, the synthesis would appear as follows:

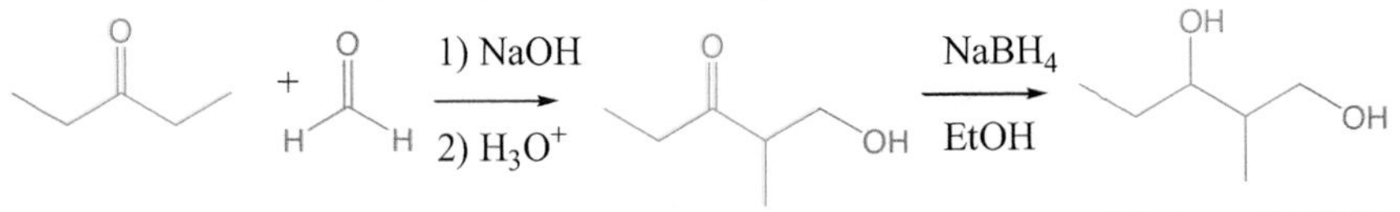

O + O, H, H → (1) NaOH; 2) H_3O^+) O, OH → ($NaBH_4$, EtOH) OH, OH

Problem 17.9. Show how you can synthesize 2-methyl-1,3-pentanediol from compounds containing 3 or fewer carbons.

17.3. REACTIONS THAT REMOVE A FUNCTIONAL GROUP ENTIRELY FROM A MOLECULE: REDUCTIONS OF C=O TO CH_2

When we design a synthesis, we typically begin by looking for structural features in the target that might indicate the need to employ certain reactions. For example, in the previous section we saw that if a target calls for a carbon-carbon bond-formation reaction and exhibits a specific relative positioning of functional groups, we should consider employing a reaction from Table 17-1. Frequently, however, a synthesis will call for a carbon-carbon bond-formation reaction, but no functional groups in the target provide a clear indication of what that reaction should be.

For cases like this, we can sometimes invoke reactions that remove a functional group entirely. Thus, a retrosynthetic analysis might require us to *imagine* a functional group in a precursor at a location where no functional group exists in the target. The presence of that functional group in the intermediate might then facilitate a particular carbon-carbon bond-formation reaction, and the functional group that remains could subsequently be removed.

In this context, we will discuss the use of three reactions that convert the C=O group of a ketone or aldehyde into a CH_2 group. Thus, the ketone or aldehyde is effectively removed entirely. Section 17.2a will discuss the Wolff-Kishner reduction, Section 17.2b will discuss the Clemmensen reduction, and Section 17.2c will discuss the Raney-nickel reduction.

17.3a. The Wolff-Kishner Reduction

The Wolff-Kishner reduction, first discussed in Section 16.3, converts the carbonyl (C=O) group of a ketone or aldehyde into a methylene (CH_2) group. An example is shown in Equation 17-13.

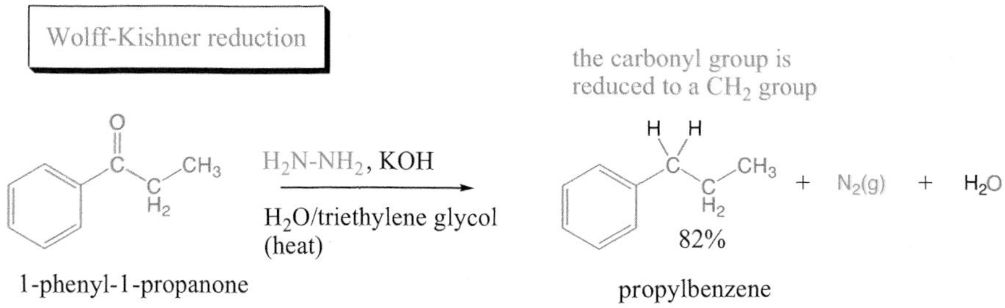

Wolff-Kishner reduction

the carbonyl group is reduced to a CH_2 group

1-phenyl-1-propanone $\xrightarrow[\text{H}_2\text{O/triethylene glycol (heat)}]{\text{H}_2\text{N-NH}_2\text{, KOH}}$ propylbenzene (82%) + $N_2(g)$ + H_2O

(17-13)

Thus, as we can see, a Wolff-Kishner reaction effectively removes a ketone or aldehyde functional group from the molecule.

Prior to doing so, however, the presence of the ketone or aldehyde group can facilitate the formation of a new carbon-carbon bond. For example, as shown in Equation 17-14, alkylation can take place at the alpha carbon via an S_N2 reaction (Section 10.3). Alternatively, Equation 17-15 shows that conjugate addition to an α,β-unsaturated ketone or aldehyde results in the formation of a new carbon-carbon bond at the beta carbon (Section 15.7).

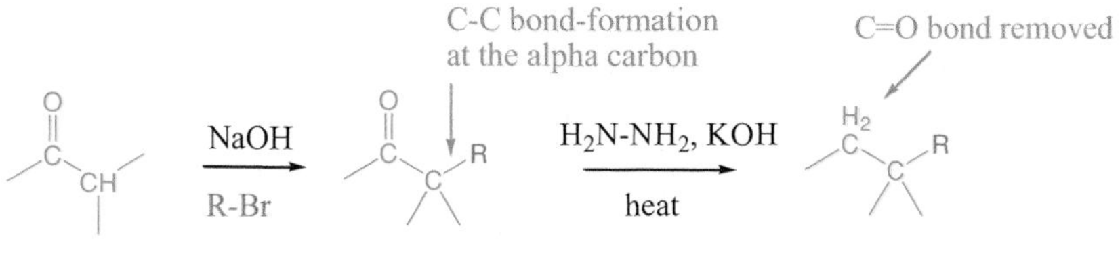

C-C bond-formation at the alpha carbon

C=O bond removed

$\xrightarrow[\text{R-Br}]{\text{NaOH}}$ $\xrightarrow[\text{heat}]{\text{H}_2\text{N-NH}_2\text{, KOH}}$

(17-14)

C-C bond-formation at the beta carbon

C=O bond removed

$\xrightarrow[\text{NH}_4\text{Cl}]{\text{R}_2\text{CuLi, THF}}$ $\xrightarrow[\text{heat}]{\text{H}_2\text{N-NH}_2\text{, KOH}}$

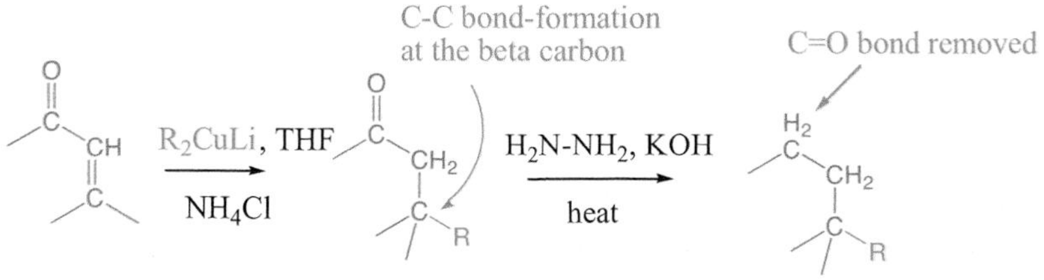

(17-15)

With this in mind, suppose that we wish to synthesize propylbenzene from starting materials containing eight or fewer carbon atoms, as shown below.

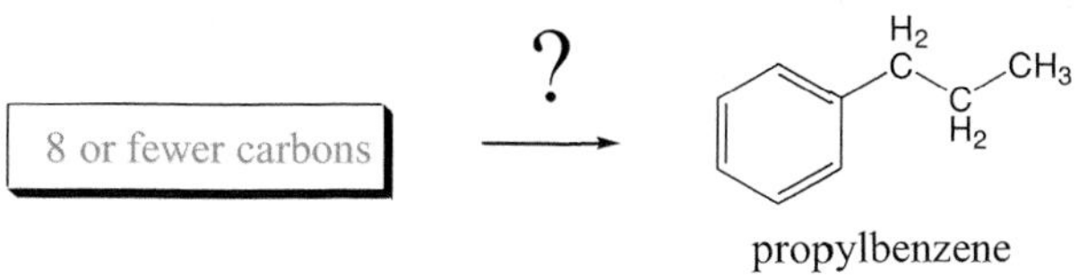

8 or fewer carbons $\xrightarrow{?}$ propylbenzene

Given that the target contains nine carbon atoms, it is clear that we must use a carbon-carbon bond-formation reaction. That reaction could be an alpha-alkylation if we imagine one of the CH_2 groups being produced from a carbonyl group in a precursor, as shown in the retrosynthetic analysis below.

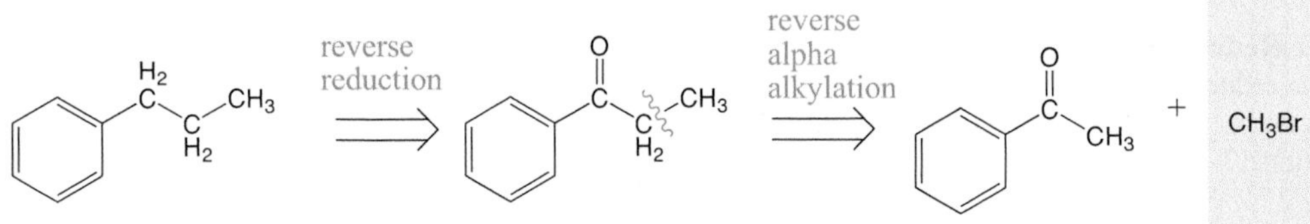

reverse reduction

reverse alpha alkylation

+ CH_3Br

In the forward direction, the synthesis would appear as follows.

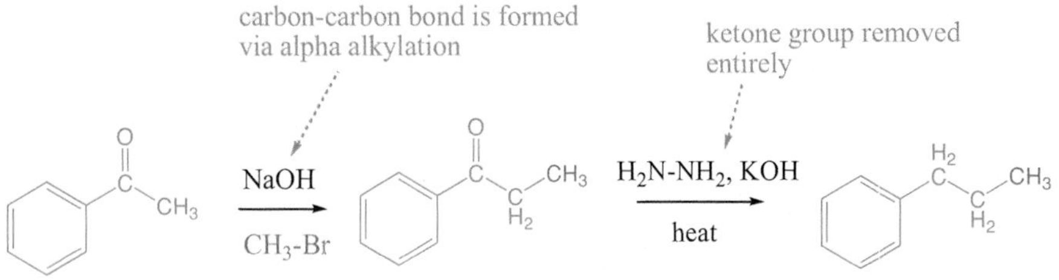

carbon-carbon bond is formed via alpha alkylation

ketone group removed entirely

NaOH / CH_3-Br

H_2N-NH_2, KOH / heat

Problem 17.10. Show how to synthesize propylbenzene from starting materials containing seven or fewer carbon atoms.

7 or fewer carbons ? → propylbenzene

As shown in Solved Problem 17.5, a similar strategy can be applied when the carbon-carbon bond-formation reaction is conjugate addition involving a lithium dialkyl cuprate.

Solve Problem 17.5. Show how to synthesize the compound below beginning with an α,β-unsaturated ketone or aldehyde.

α,β-unstaturated ketone or aldehyde ? →

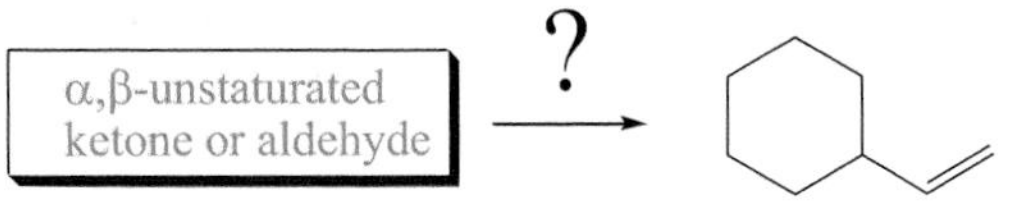

Think. What carbon-carbon bond could you disconnect in a transform? If that bond is the result of conjugate addition to an α,β-unsaturated ketone or aldehyde, which CH_2 group could we imagine coming from a C=O group?

Solve. The C-C single bond that is not part of the ring could have come from conjugate addition to an α,β-unsaturated ketone, as shown below. Recognizing that such bond-formation takes place at the beta carbon of an α,β-unsaturated carbonyl, we can envision the top-most CH_2 group on the ring to have come from a C=O group.

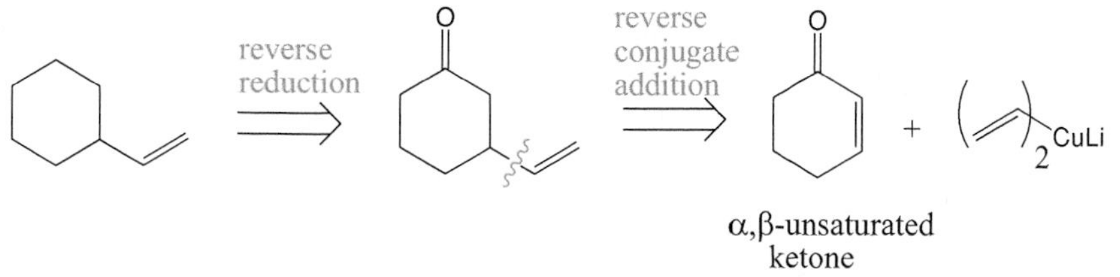

reverse reduction ⟹ reverse conjugate addition ⟹ + CuLi

α,β-unsaturated ketone

Therefore, the synthesis in the forward direction might appear as follows.

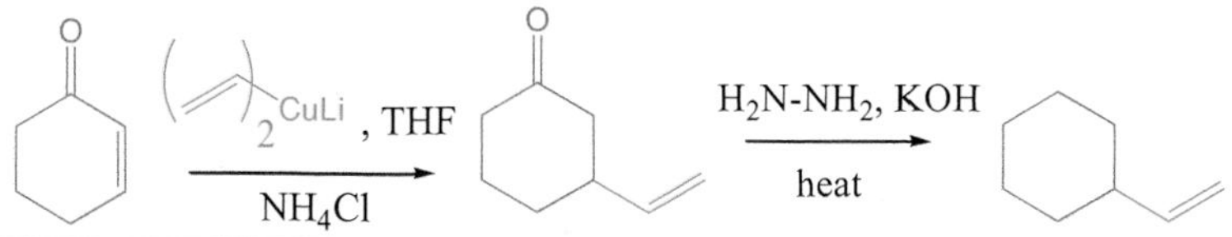

CuLi, THF; NH_4Cl → H_2N-NH_2, KOH; heat →

Problem 17.11. Show how the compound below can be synthesized from four different α,β-unsaturated ketones.

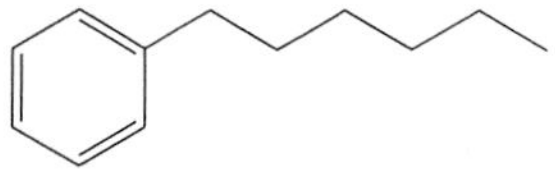

17.3b. The Clemmensen Reduction

Although the discussion in this section thus far has focused on the use of the Wolff-Kishner reaction, you should be aware of two other reactions that also serve to reduce the C=O group of a ketone or aldehyde to a CH_2 group. One is the **Clemmensen reduction**, named after Erik Christian Clemmensen, a Danish chemist. (The other is the Raney-nickel reduction, discussed in Section 17.3c.) An example is shown in Equation 17-16.

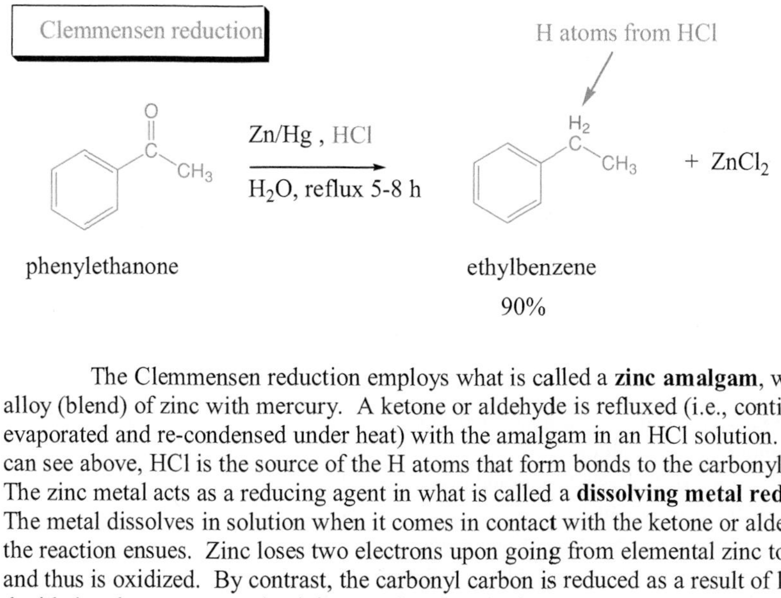

Clemmensen reduction

H atoms from HCl

phenylethanone → Zn/Hg, HCl; H_2O, reflux 5-8 h → ethylbenzene 90% + $ZnCl_2$ (17-16)

The Clemmensen reduction employs what is called a **zinc amalgam**, which is an alloy (blend) of zinc with mercury. A ketone or aldehyde is refluxed (i.e., continuously evaporated and re-condensed under heat) with the amalgam in an HCl solution. As we can see above, HCl is the source of the H atoms that form bonds to the carbonyl carbon. The zinc metal acts as a reducing agent in what is called a **dissolving metal reduction**. The metal dissolves in solution when it comes in contact with the ketone or aldehyde and the reaction ensues. Zinc loses two electrons upon going from elemental zinc to $ZnCl_2$, and thus is oxidized. By contrast, the carbonyl carbon is reduced as a result of losing the double bond to oxygen and gaining two bonds to hydrogen.

17.3c. The Raney-Nickel Reduction

As mentioned in the previous section, a third reaction that reduces the carbonyl group of a ketone or aldehyde to a methylene group is the **Raney-nickel reduction**, developed by Murray Raney, an American chemist. An example is shown in Equation 17-17.

Raney-nickel reduction

formation of thioacetal

C=O group replaced by CH_2 group

$HSCH_2CH_2SH$, $H^{\oplus}$

Raney-Ni (H_2)

82%

(17-17)

In a Raney-nickel reduction, the ketone or aldehyde is first converted to a *thioacetal* by treatment with a thiol under acidic conditions (Section 16.2b). Subsequent treatment with **Raney nickel** converts the thioacetal group into a methylene group.

Raney nickel has two roles in this reaction. First, it is the source of hydrogen. Raney nickel is obtained by treatment of a 50:50 alloy of aluminum and nickel with hot NaOH, which serves to etch the metal. The spongy network that remains is then treated with hydrogen gas, which adsorbs (accumulates via chemical interactions) to the metal in part because of the metal's excellent surface area. Raney nickel also serves as a *catalyst* for the H_2 reduction, a process that will be described in greater detail in Section 17.5. (As a cautionary note, Raney nickel is so reactive that it must be kept under an inert liquid or an inert gas, for it will ignite spontaneously on contact with atmospheric O_2.)

17.3d. Limitations of the Wolff-Kishner, Clemmensen, and Raney-Nickel Reductions

As we have said, the Wolff-Kishner, Clemmensen, and Raney-nickel reactions reduce the carbonyl group of a ketone or aldehyde to a methylene group. However, looking back at Equations 17-13, 17-16, and 17-17, notice that the three reactions take place under different conditions. The Wolff-Kishner reduction takes place under strongly basic conditions, the Clemmensen reduction takes place under strongly acidic conditions, and the Raney-nickel reaction takes place under mild conditions in the presence of a metal catalyst. Thus, if there are functional groups present other than the ketone or aldehyde we wish to reduce, we must take care in deciding upon which of these reduction reactions to use.

Comment [JMK17]: Margin note
The Wolff-Kishner, Clemmensen, and Raney-nickel reductions take place under basic, acidic, and catalytic hydrogenation conditions, respectively.

- The Wolff-Kishner reduction should be avoided if there is a functional group present that is susceptible to reaction under basic conditions.
- The Clemmensen reduction should be avoided if there is a functional group present that is susceptible to reaction under acidic conditions.
- The Raney-nickel reduction should be avoided if there is a functional group present that is susceptible to reaction in the presence of H_2 and a metal catalyst.

Although we have not yet discussed the third of these conditions, we will see in Section 17.5 that alkenes ($R_2C{=}CR_2$), alkynes ($RC{\equiv}CR$), and aldehydes $RCH{=}O$) are reactive in the presence of H_2 and a metal catalyst.

These ideas are explored further in Solved Problem 17.6.

Solved Problem 17.6. Which reduction reaction(s)—the Wolff-Kishner, Raney nickel, or Clemmensen—can be used to carry out the following transformation?

O

Br ? Br

Think. Are there any functional groups, aside from the carbonyl group, that are susceptible to reaction in the presence of HO^-? HCl? H_2 gas and a metal catalyst?

Solve. The alkyl halide that is present is susceptible to nucleophilic substitution with HO^-, a strong nucleophile, so the Wolff-Kishner reaction should be avoided. The aromatic and alkyl halide functional groups are not susceptible to reaction with HCl, so the Clemmensen reduction could be used. And no alkene, alkyne, or aldehyde groups are present, so the Raney-nickel reduction could also be used.

Problem 17.12. Which reduction reaction(s)—the Wolff-Kishner, Raney nickel, or Clemmensen—can be used for each of the following?

(a) 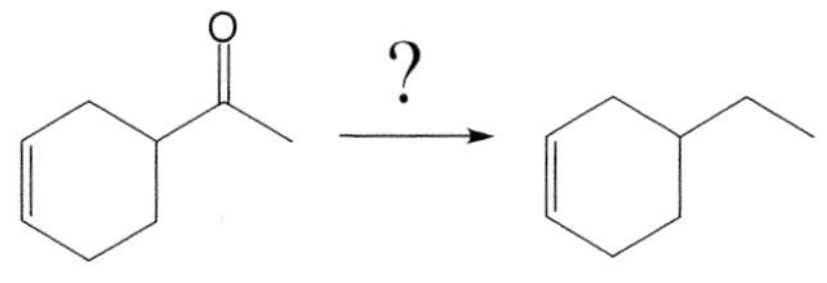 O ?

(b)  O O ? O

(c) 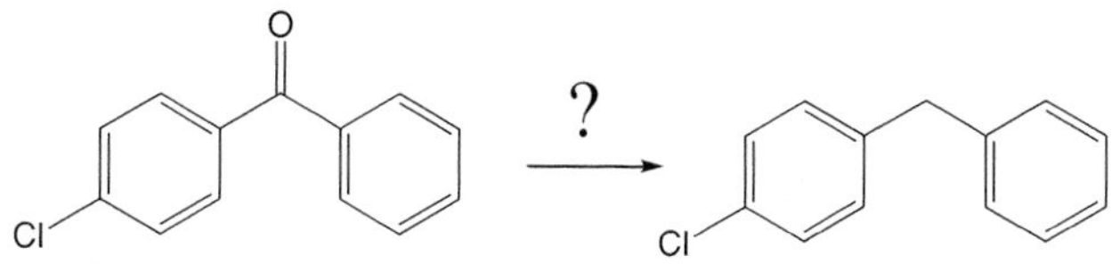 O Cl ? Cl

17.4. AVOIDING SYNTHETIC TRAPS: SELECTIVE REAGENTS AND PROTECTING GROUPS

As we saw in Section 11.4, a **synthetic trap** arises when a specific transform in a retrosynthesis would lead to an undesired reaction in the *forward* direction. Generally, this is because a functional group we wish to leave alone would in fact be **labile** under the reaction conditions—that is, the functional group is reactive and readily undergoes a change.

Many of the difficulties presented by synthetic traps can be surmounted in one of two ways: (1) By employing a **selective reagent** (Section 17.4a) or (2) by using a **protecting group** (Section 17.4b). As we will see in the following sections, both of these strategies exploit differences in reactivity among functional groups.

17.4a. Selective Reactions

When two or more outcomes are possible for a given reaction, we often find that the actual result depends upon the specific reagents that are used and the specific reaction conditions. In many cases, we can exploit this specificity in designing a synthesis. When we can, the reaction is called a **selective reaction** and the reagent that causes such selectivity is called a **selective reagent**.

We first encountered an example of a selective reaction in Chapter 9, in the context of the competition among nucleophilic substitution and elimination reactions. Namely, S_N2 and E2 reactions tend to compete with each other, given that strong nucleophiles are typically strong bases, but we can choose specific reagents to favor selectively one reaction over another. For example, Cl^- favors the S_N2 reaction (Equation 17-18a), whereas the *t*-butoxide anion selectively favors the E2 reaction (Equation 17-18b).

selective reagent for substitution

NaCl

OTs

Cl + $TsO^{\ominus}$ (a)

$NaOC(CH_3)_3$

+ $TsO^{\ominus}$ + $NaOC(CH_3)_3$ (b)

selective reagent for elimination

(17-18)

We saw another example of selective reagents in Section 10.3a, in the context of alkylations at the alpha carbons of ketones and aldehydes. As discussed in Section 10.3a and as shown in Equation 17-19, lithium diisopropylamide (LDA) is bulky and irreversibly deprotonates ketones and aldehydes, so it is selective for alkylation at the least highly substituted alpha carbon. By contrast, NaOH deprotonates ketones and aldehydes reversibly, so it is selective for alkylation at the most highly substituted alpha carbon.

lithium diisopropylamide (LDA) is selective for alkylation at the less highly substituted alpha carbon

1) $(C_3H_7)_2N^- Li^+$

2) CH_3Br

O, CH_3

O, H_3C, CH_3 (a)

1) NaOH

2) CH_3Br

O, CH_3, CH_3 (b)

sodium hydroxide is selective for alkylation at the more highly substituted alpha carbon

(17-19)

Nucleophilic addition to α,β-unsaturated carbonyls presents us with another case of selectivity in reactions. As we saw in Section 15.4, very strong nucleophiles like Grignard reagents (R-MgBr) selectively add to the carbonyl carbon in a *direct addition*

(Equation 17-20a). Weaker nucleophiles like lithium dialkylcuprates (R_2CuLi), on the other hand, selectively add to the beta carbon in a *conjugate addition* (Equation 17-20b).

selective for direct addition

1) CH_3MgBr
2) H^+

HO CH3 (a)

1) $(CH_3)_2CuLi$
2) NH_4Cl

CH3 O (b)

selective for conjugate addition

(17-20)

The discussion that has been presented in this section regarding selective reactions is far from exhaustive; rather, it is intended simply to be an introduction to the concept and to demonstrate how selective reactions can be used in synthesis. As we continue to learn more reactions, we will find several more opportunities for designing syntheses that take advantage of selectivity. For example, in Section 17.5, we will see that catalytic hydrogenation allows for the selective reductions involving C≡C triple bonds, C=C and C=O double bonds. And as foreshadowing to what we will see in Chapters 18 and 19, the reduction of a compound that contains both a ketone and an ester functional group can be carried out selectively with $NaBH_4$ (Equation 17-21a) but not with $LiAlH_4$ (Equation 17-21b)

reduces both groups containing C=O

1) $LiAlH_4$
2) H^+

OH OH (a)

$NaBH_4$
CH_3OH

OH O (b)

selectively reduces the ketone

(17-21)

Solved Problem 17.7. Show how you would carry out the following synthesis using any reagents necessary.

O ?

Think. What reaction could be used to remove the ketone functional group from the molecule? What precursor would be necessary prior to that reaction? To make that precursor, is a selective reaction necessary?

Solve. In Section 17.2, we saw that the C=O groups of a ketone or aldehyde can be removed using a Wolff-Kishner, Clemmensen, or Raney-nickel reduction. We can therefore imagine a precursor in which a C=O group is attached to the ring at the position indicated below. This yields a precursor that could be the product of a conjugate addition involving a lithium dialkylcuprate. Applying a transform that reverses such a conjugate addition, we arrive back at the α,β-unsaturated ketone starting material.

reverse carbonyl reduction ⟹ reverse conjugate addition ⟹ + $(\text{vinyl})_2CuLi$

In the forward direction, realize that the lithium dialkyl cuprate is used to selectively react at the carbonyl carbon rather than at the beta carbon. Also, we must be careful when reducing the C=O group because an alkene group is present. Alkenes are not susceptible to reaction under basic conditions, so a Wolff-Kishner reduction could be used.

1) $(\text{vinyl})_2CuLi$ 2) NH_4Cl → ; $H_2N\text{-}NH_2$, KOH, heat →

Problem 17.13. Show how you would carry out the following synthesis using any reagents necessary.

? →

17.4b. Protecting Groups

An understanding of selective reactions, as described in the previous section, allows us to exploit differences in the reactivity of functional groups (or sites on a functional group) when we wish to react one group in a molecule but leave another alone. However, there are times when this is not feasible; a step in a synthesis may require the use of a reagent that would react with two or more functional groups. In situations like these, we may be able to use a **protecting group** to temporarily make one or more functional groups unreactive under the specific conditions our desired reaction calls for. After making the desired change in the molecule, we remove the protecting group and restore the original functional group.

Comment [JMK18]: Margin note
Some functional groups can be protected to make them temporarily unreactive under a particular set of conditions.

In this section, we will focus primarily on the protection of the carbonyl group in ketones and aldehydes, as well as the protection of alcohols. Realize, however, that the use of protecting groups has become a mature subdiscipline of organic synthesis, and several authors have published books in this area. Suffice it to say that protection of other functional groups will be revisited in future chapters as we learn the mechanisms of the reactions responsible for protection and deprotection steps.

The general idea of using a protecting group is outlined in Figure 17-1. Suppose we have a molecule with a functional group "A"—we wish to convert the "A" group to another functional group "B," but there is a labile (i.e., reactive) group that would also be changed. Direct conversion of A to B is therefore not possible without affecting the labile group. We work around this problem by selectively changing the labile group to another functional group that will not react under the conditions that convert "A" to "B."

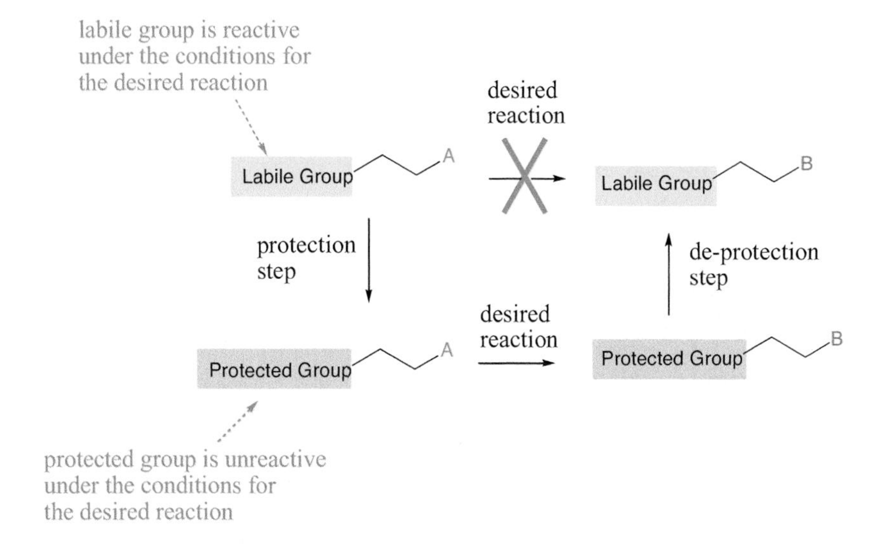

Figure 17-1. The general strategy for using a protecting group.
The starting material (top left) cannot be converted to the target (top right) directly because the labile group would also react under those conditions. A separate reaction, called a *protection step*, is carried out to convert the labile group into a different group (bottom left) that is unreactive under the conditions that convert A to B. Next, the desired reaction is carried out to convert A to B (bottom right), and a final *deprotection step* converts the protected group back into the original labile group (top right).

Reversibility is important here.

> A good protecting group must be unreactive under one set of conditions, but *must be able to be removed* under another set of mild conditions to restore the original functional group (or perhaps another group which does not interfere with later steps in a synthesis) at the same location.

It would be a poor choice, for example, to protect the carbonyl group of a ketone by converting it into a methylene (CH_2) group using the Clemmensen reduction (Equation 17-22). The reactivity at that carbon would be diminished too much; we do not know of a reaction that would allow us to selectively convert that CH_2 group back into a carbonyl group.

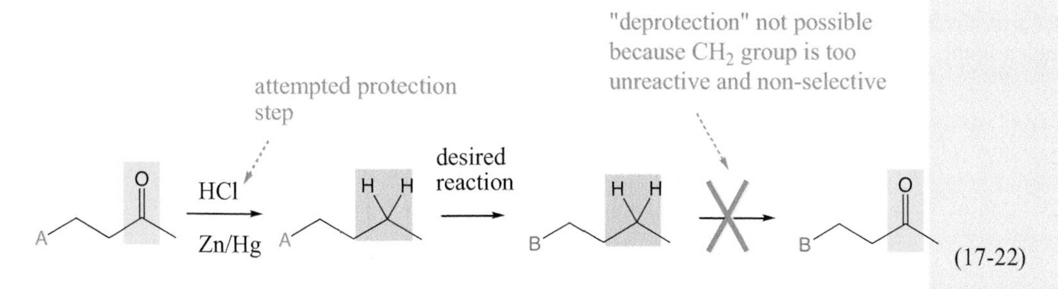

(17-22)

17.4b.1. Protection of ketones and aldehydes Ketones and aldehydes are most often protected by converting them to **acetals**, as shown in Equation 17-23. An acetal consists of two ether functional groups on the same carbon, and ethers are resistant to strong bases, strong nucleophiles, oxidizing agents, and reducing agents. As we saw in Section 16.2a, an acetal can be formed by reacting a ketone or aldehyde with excess alcohol under acidic conditions. Fortunately, the ketone or aldehyde functional groups can be recovered by hydrolysis under mildly acidic conditions, also discussed in Section 16.2a.

protection
an acetal is a protected carbonyl
deprotection
excess ROH
$H^{\oplus}$
desired reaction
excess H_2O
$H^{\oplus}$

(17-23)

The most commonly used alcohol in protecting ketones and aldehydes is ethane-1,2-diol (or, **ethylene glycol**), which is $HOCH_2CH_2OH$ (Equation 17-24). Its popularity is due in part to the fact that it contains two alcohol groups on the same molecule, so only one molar equivalent is needed to protect a carbonyl (rather than the two molar equivalents that would be required if a mono-alcohol were used). Additionally, the acetal that it produces is in the form of a 5-membered ring, which favors the formation of the acetal.

formation of a stable 5-membered ring helps acetal formation
ethane-1,2-diol contains two alcohol functional groups
$H^{\oplus}$
protection
desired reaction
H_2O
$H^{\oplus}$
deprotection

(17-24)

To see how such a protecting group might be employed, let's propose a way in which to carry out the synthesis in Equation 17-25.

?

(17-25)

Seeing that the product is an alcohol, it may at first appear that we can arrive back at the starting material through a simple reverse-Grignard transform, as shown in Equation 17-26.

reverse Grignard reaction
MgBr
+

(17-26)

However, notice that the Grignard reagent that is called for has a carbonyl group on it. As we learned in Section 15.6b, such groups are incompatible with Grignard reagents. To work around this, we can instead envision using a Grignard reagent in which that carbonyl group is protected, as shown in Equation 17-27.

a protected C=O

desired Grignard reaction

deprotection step

1) (butanone) 2) H^+ ; $H_3O^{\oplus}$

(17-27)

A natural question to ask is: How do we synthesize that protected Grignard reagent? We know that the cyclic acetal is produced from a C=O group, and we know from Section 17.1a that a Grignard reagent is produced from an analogous alkyl halide. To avoid the presence of a C=O group on the Grignard reagent, the C=O must already be protected prior to the addition of Mg, so the retrosynthetic analysis would appear as follows.

C=O group must already be protected before the formation of the Grignard reagent

reverse Grignard formation

reverse acetal formation

(17-28)

The synthesis is then reported by reversing the arrows and adding the appropriate reagents. The aldehyde is protected by treatment with ethylene glycol ($HOCH_2CH_2OH$) under acidic conditions, and the Grignard reagent is produced by treatment with solid Mg in ether.

protection step

HO–CH₂CH₂–OH, $H^{\oplus}$; Mg(s), ether

(17-29)

Problem 17.14. Propose a synthesis of 2,5-hexanedione using acetone as your only source of carbon. (Hint: consider how you might use a protecting group.)

17.4b.2. Protection of alcohols Alcohols are weakly acidic, are prone to elimination under acidic conditions, and, as we will see in Chapter 19, are also prone to oxidation. Depending upon the specific step in a synthesis, we may wish to suppress the reactivity of an alcohol by temporarily converting it to a less reactive functional group.

Just as we were able to protect ketones and aldehydes, we can protect an alcohol in the form of an *ether*. Ethers are unreactive toward strong bases and strong nucleophiles and are more difficult to oxidize than alcohols. To convert an alcohol into an ether, we can utilize the Williamson synthesis (Chapter 10), an S_N2 reaction in which an alkoxide anion (a deprotonated alcohol) displaces a halogen on a substrate (Equation 17-30).

strong nucleophile

ethers are generally unreactive under basic, oxidizing, and reducing conditions

NaH

(17-30)

Using a cleverly designed substrate, methyl chloromethyl ether (Equation 17-31), the product is an *acetal*, the same as the protected ketones and aldehydes we saw in the previous section. More specifically, the protected alcohol is called a **methoxymethyl (MOM) ether**. Being an acetal, the MOM ether is an easily removed protecting group via hydrolysis; it will decompose to formaldehyde, methanol, and the original alcohol when treated with *dilute aqueous acid*.

protection with methyl chloromethyl ether

de-protection

NaOH

10% H_2SO_4

a methoxymethyl (MOM) ether

(17-31)

Your Turn 17.5. Circle and label the acetal functional group in Equation 17-31.

Your Turn 17.6. In the space provided here, draw the complete, detailed mechanism for both the protection step and the deprotection step in Equation 17-31.

Another method of protecting alcohols employs ether functional groups of a different sort—those that involve silicon. If an alcohol is treated with *tert*-butyldimethylsilyl chloride (TBDMS-Cl), an S_N2 reaction on the Si center leads to the formation of a **silyl ether**, where the ether group is of the form C-O-Si (Equation 17-32) instead of C-O-C. Like traditional ether groups, silyl ethers are resistant to many reactions that take place under basic conditions.

protection of alochol with *tert*-butyldimethylsilyl chloride (TBDMS-Cl)

a silyl ether is a protected alcohol

deprotection using $F^{\ominus}$

reactive alcohol group

$Bu_4N^{\oplus}\ F^{\ominus}$

THF

(17-32)

The TBDMS protecting group differs from the MOM ether protecting group in the conditions necessary for deprotection. Whereas the MOM ether protecting group is removed under mildly acidic conditions, the TBDMS protecting group is removed by F^- in an S_N2 reaction on the Si center. Even though RO^- is a terrible leaving group for most S_N2 reactions, the Si-F bond that is formed is very strong and thus compensates—its bond energy is 553 kJ/mol, making it about 50% stronger than a C-C single bond!

Your Turn 18.7. In the space provided here, draw the complete, detailed mechanism for the reaction in Equation 17-32 based on the description in the text.

Solved Problem 17.8. Show how to carry out the following synthesis, using any reagents necessary.

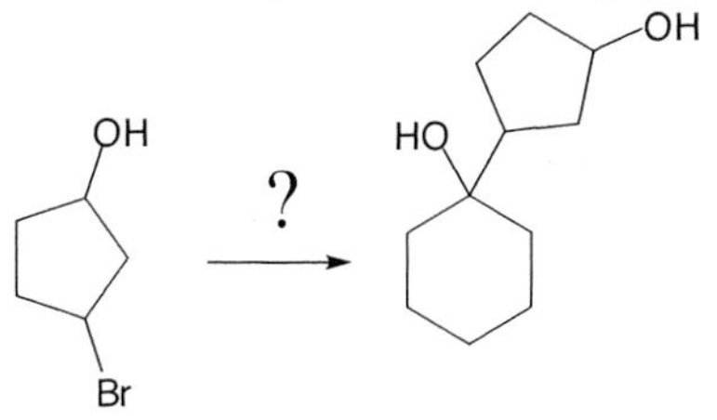

OH ? HO OH

Br

Think. What reaction can be reversed in a transform that disconnects a carbon-carbon bond involving an alcohol? What would be the precursors of that reaction? In the forward direction, would the intended reaction take place? If not, do we need to incorporate a protecting group?

Solve. It appears that a carbon-carbon bond must be formed between the two rings, leaving an alcohol on one of those carbons involved in that newly formed bond. This suggests a Grignard reaction. We can therefore begin our retrosynthesis with a transform that disconnects that carbon-carbon bond in a reverse Grignard. We can then envision the necessary Grignard reagent being formed from the corresponding alkyl bromide.

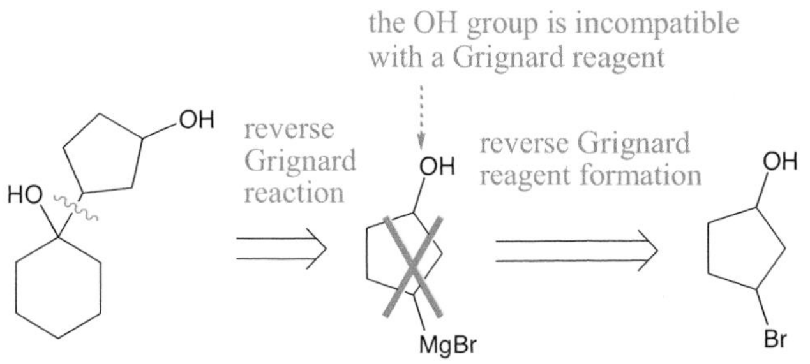

the OH group is incompatible with a Grignard reagent

OH HO reverse Grignard reaction OH reverse Grignard reagent formation OH

MgBr Br

However, a *synthetic trap* arises, because the desired Grignard reagent has an alcohol group, which, as we learned in Section 15.6b, introduces an incompatibility. To work around this problem, we can still begin with the bromoalcohol, but simply protect the alcohol part of it before adding Mg(s) to carry out the dissolved metal reduction. The synthesis is shown below:

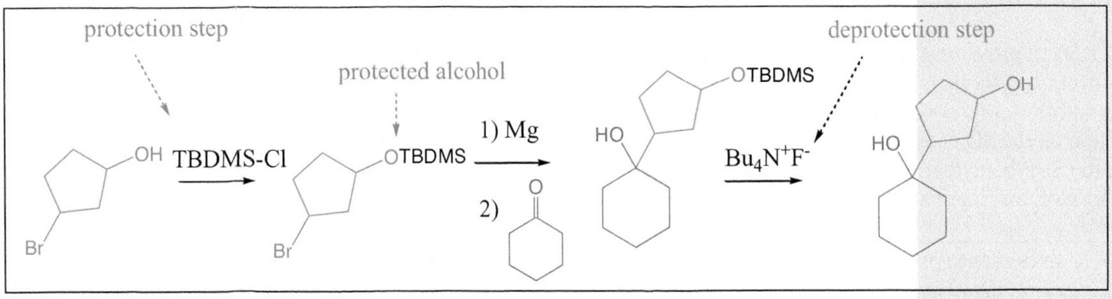

protection step

protected alcohol

OH TBDMS-Cl

OTBDMS 1) Mg 2)

HO OTBDMS

deprotection step

$Bu_4N^+F^-$

HO OH

Br Br

Problem 17.15. Could the synthesis in the previous Solved Problem be carried out if the alcohol were protected using methyl chloromethyl ether, as shown below? Why or why not?

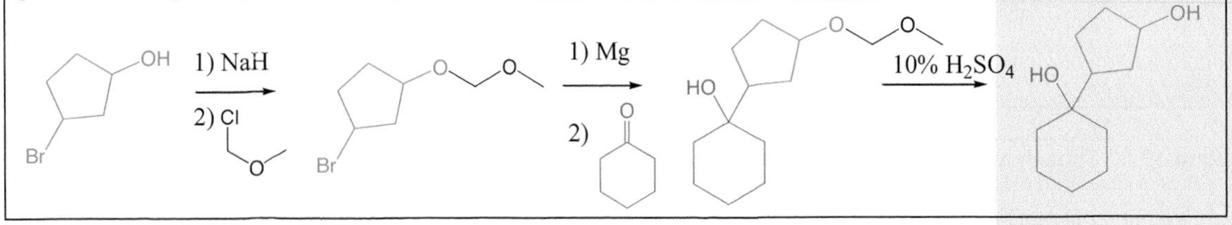

OH 1) NaH 2) Cl O

1) Mg 2) O

HO

10% H_2SO_4 HO OH

Br Br

Problem 17.16. Show how you would carry out the following synthesis.

O OH ? HO OH

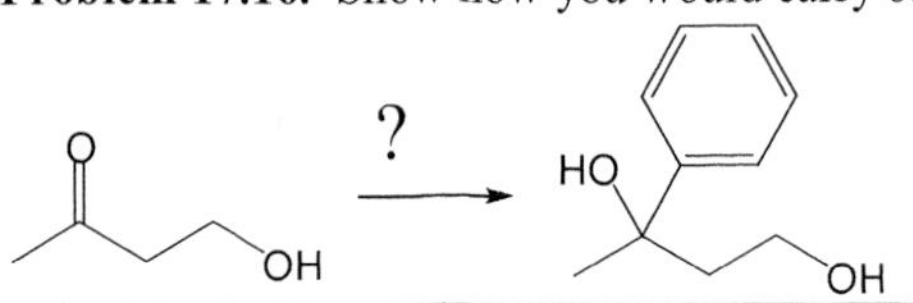

Problem 17.17. Propose how you would carry out the following synthesis using a TBDMS protecting group.

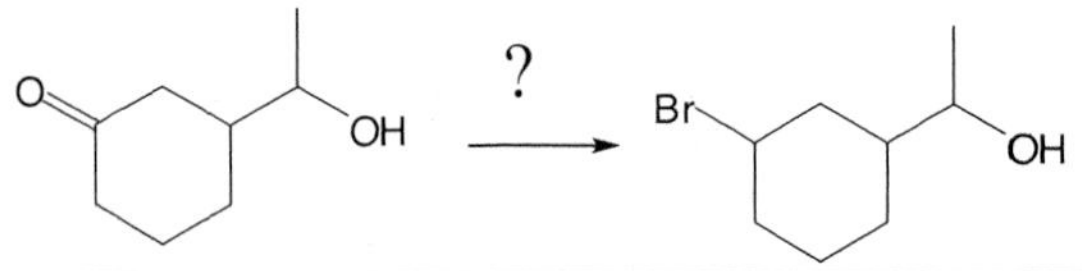

O OH ? Br OH

Both 1,2-diols and 1,3-diols can be protected using formaldehyde ($H_2C{=}O$), as shown in Equations 17-33 and 17-34. The protected forms are 5- and 6-membered ring acetals, respectively. This method of protection is in fact the same one we encountered in Section 17.4b.1, where a diol was used to protect a ketone or aldehyde. Deprotection, as we saw previously, simply requires dilute aqueous acid.

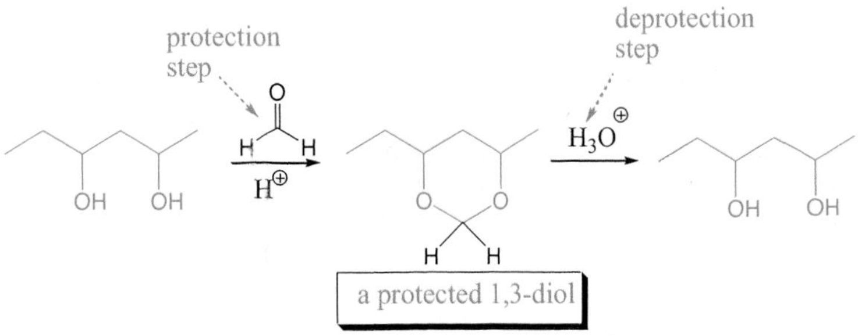

protection step

deprotection step

OH OH $\xrightarrow[H^{\oplus}]{H_2C=O}$ O O H H $\xrightarrow{H_3O^{\oplus}}$ OH OH

a protected 1,3-diol

(17-33)

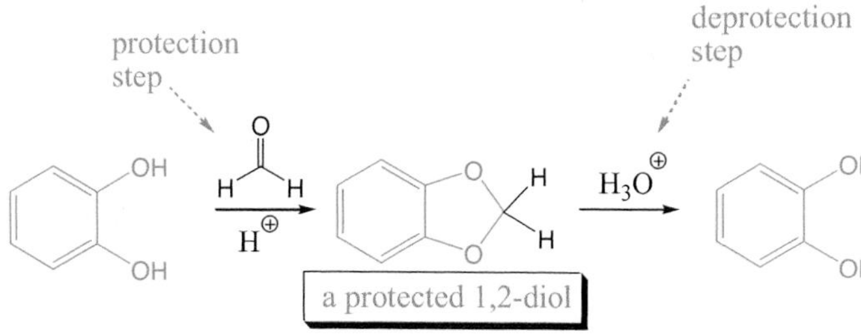

protection step
deprotection step
$H^{\oplus}$
$H_3O^{\oplus}$
a protected 1,2-diol

(17-34)

Problem 17.18. Show how you would synthesize each of the following from 1,2,5-pentanetriol.

(a) H_3CO ... OH ... OH

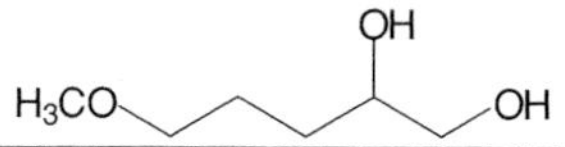

(b) OH ... OH ... OH

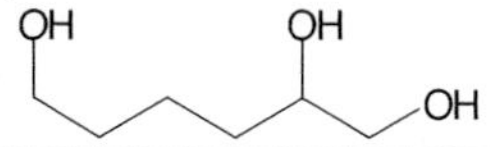

Finally, there is yet another common method for protecting alcohols, which uses dihydropyran (DHP). As shown in Equation 17-35, the protected form is an acetal. De-protection therefore requires only mildly acidic conditions. The protection step, however, involves a reaction whose mechanism we have not yet encountered—it will be covered in detail in Chapter 20.

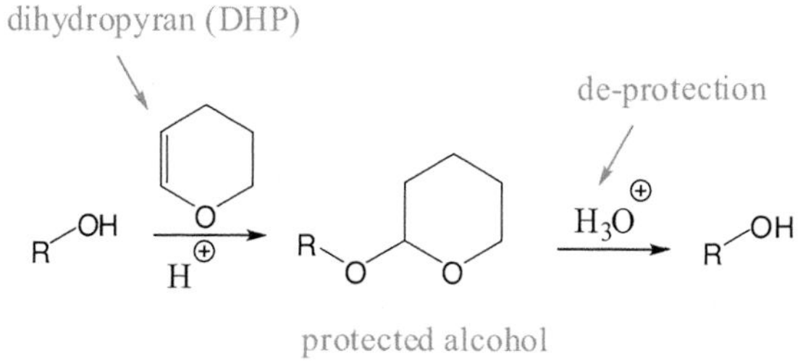

dihydropyran (DHP)
de-protection
$H^{\oplus}$
$H_3O^{\oplus}$
protected alcohol

(17-35)

17.5. CATALYTIC HYDROGENATION

In Section 17.3, we saw how a functional group can be removed entirely from a molecule, via the reduction of a ketone's or aldehyde's C=O group to a CH_2 group. In Section 17.4, we discussed how reactions we have encountered previously can be used to selectively target one functional group over another. In this section, we introduce a new reaction, called **catalytic hydrogenation**, which can accomplish similar tasks. Namely, we will see that catalytic hydrogenation can be used to remove an alkene functional group entirely from a molecule. Additionally, it is a selective reaction, involving alkenes, alkynes, and carbonyl-containing groups such as ketones and aldehydes.

There are two main reasons why catalytic hydrogenation is introduced in this chapter. First, it is a reaction that is quite useful in synthesis, for reasons mentioned above. Second, its mechanism, as we will see, is substantially different from essentially every other reaction in this book.

17.5a. Catalytic Hydrogenation of Alkenes

In the presence of a solid metal catalyst such as Pd, Pt, or Ni (all elements in the same column of the periodic table), an alkene will readily undergo addition of H_2 gas to convert the C=C double bond into a C–C single bond. An example is shown in Equation 17-36.

Comment [JMK19]: Margin note
Catalytic hydrogenation converts an alkene into an alkane.

catalytic hydrogenation

$H_3C-CH_2-CH_2-CH=CH_2$ $\xrightarrow[\text{Pd(s), 25 °C, } H_2O]{H_2 \text{ (1 atm)}}$ $H_3C-CH_2-CH_2-CH_2-CH_3$

82%

double bond converted to a single bond

solid catalyst

(17-36)

In such reactions, the metal is called a **heterogeneous catalyst** because it exists in a different physical phase than the rest of the reaction mixture. The catalyst used during catalytic hydrogenation is *an insoluble solid*, suspended (by stirring) in the solution that contains both hydrogen and the organic substance to be hydrogenated (dissolved in an unreactive solvent such as water or acetic acid).

The detailed mechanism for catalytic hydrogenation is relatively complex. A simplified picture, however, is shown in Figure 17-2.

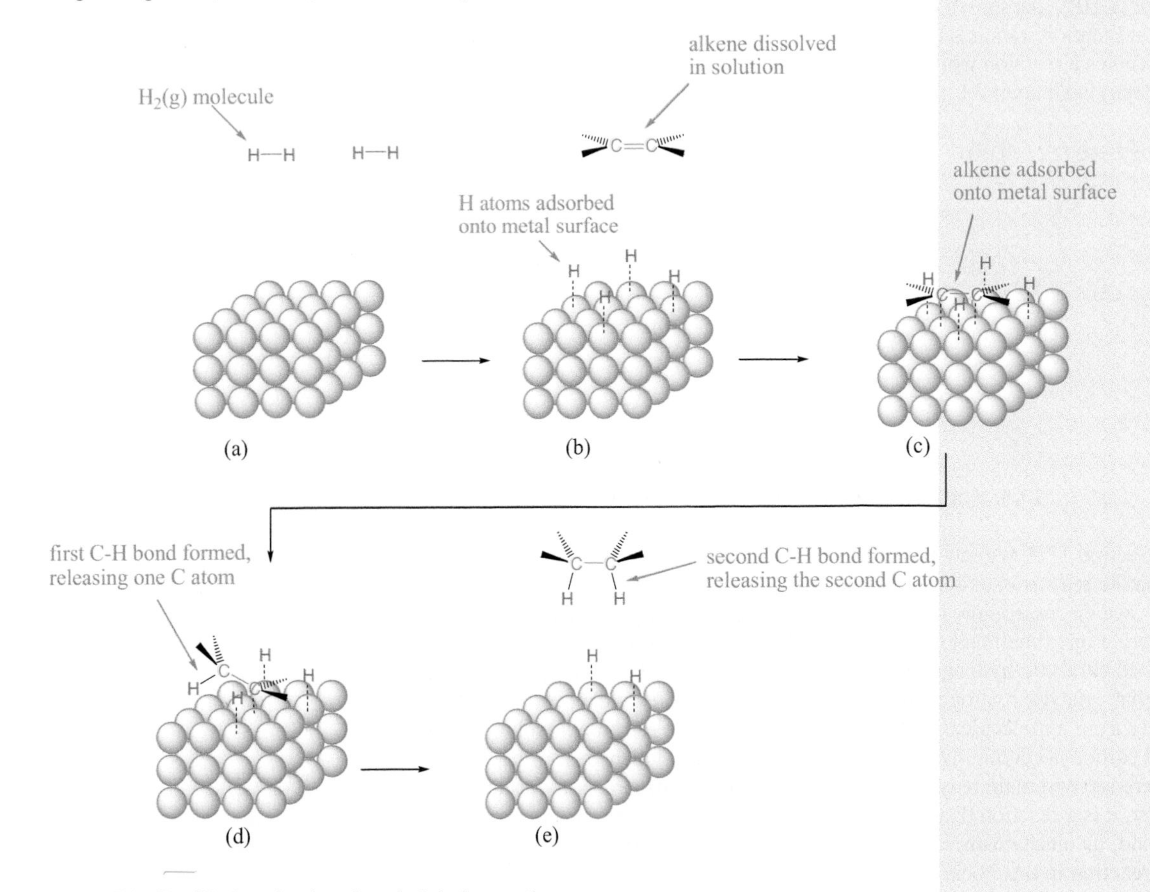

Figure 17-2. Simplified mechanism of catalytic hydrogenation.
(a to b) Hydrogen gas adsorbs to the surface of the metal catalyst, breaking the H-H bonds. (b to c) A molecule of the alkene adsorbs to the surface of the metal catalyst. (c to d) A carbon-hydrogen bond is formed, liberating a carbon atom from the catalyst. (d to e) The second carbon atom forms a bond to H, liberating the entire alkane from the the catalyst surface.

Initially, the hydrogen and the alkene adsorb onto the surface of the catalyst, as shown in Figure 17-2a through 17-2c. As that occurs, the H–H single bonds are effectively broken, producing individual H atoms that reside on the metal surface. Similarly, adsorption of the alkene effectively breaks the π bond of the C=C double bond. Eventually, an adsorbed H atom encounters an adsorbed alkene, and the first of two C–H bonds is formed (Figure 17-2d). Shortly thereafter, the second C–H bond is formed through a similar process (Figure 17-2e). Notice that as each C–H bond is formed, the corresponding carbon atom is released from the metal surface.

We can take advantage of such alkene reductions in a synthesis that calls for the formation of a new C–C single bond, by first incorporating a reaction that forms a new C=C double bond. Suppose, for example, we wish to carry out the following synthesis, beginning with starting materials having six or fewer carbon atoms.

six or fewer carbon atoms ?⟶

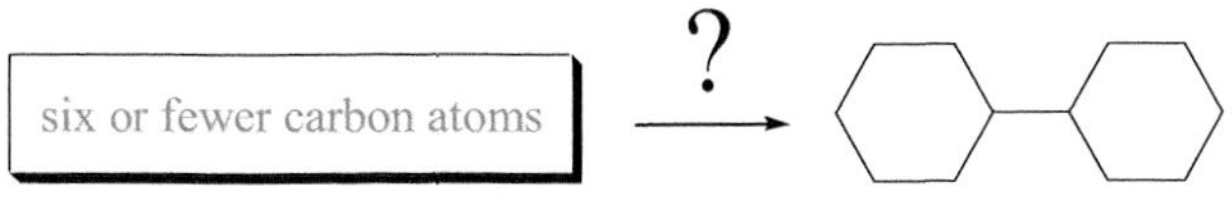

Notice that no functional groups appear in the target, so there is no relative positioning of functional groups to provide a clear indication of which carbon-carbon bond formation should be used. However, as shown in the retrosynthetic analysis below, the target can be produced from an alkene intermediate in which the two rings are joined by a C=C double bond—catalytic hydrogenation could reduce the C=C double bond to a C–C single bond. That C=C double bond, in turn, could be produced using a Wittig reaction (Section 15.8), which requires the ketone and Wittig reagent shown. And the Wittig reagent could be produced from bromocyclohexane (Section 15.8a).

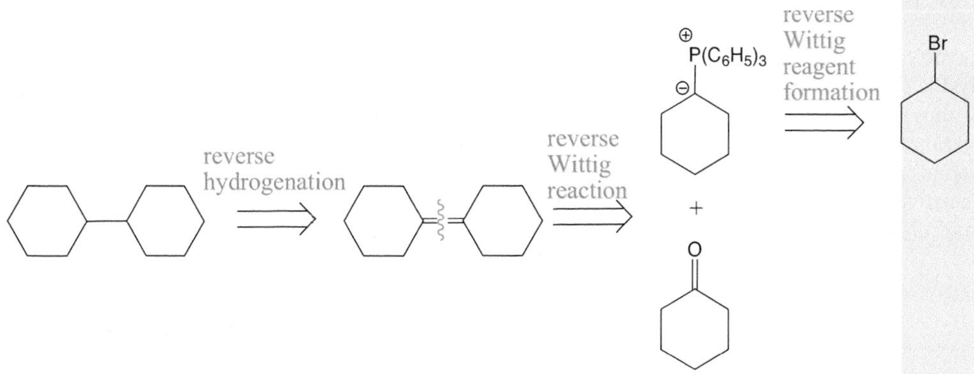

reverse hydrogenation ⟹ reverse Wittig reaction ⟹ $\oplus P(C_6H_5)_3$ $\ominus$ + O — reverse Wittig reagent formation ⟹ Br

The synthesis in the forward direction would then appear as follows.

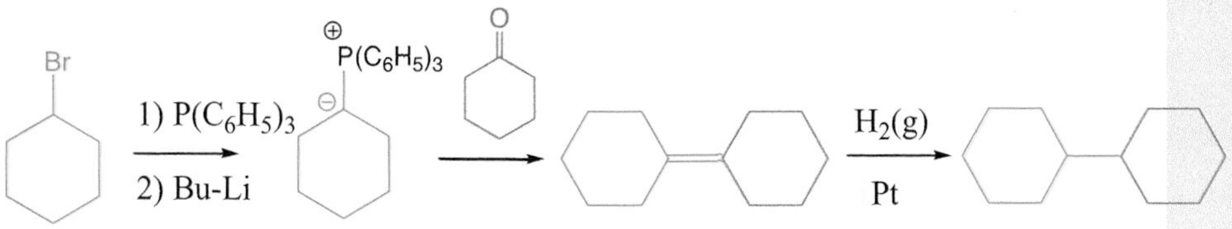

Br — 1) $P(C_6H_5)_3$, 2) Bu-Li ⟶ $\oplus P(C_6H_5)_3$ $\ominus$ — O ⟶ — $H_2(g)$, Pt ⟶

Problem 17.19. Show how you would carry out the following synthesis using a Wittig reaction.

O ?⟶

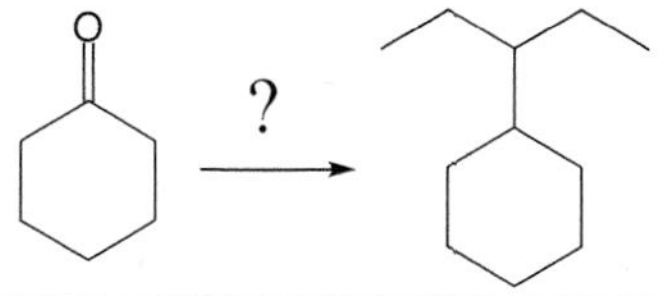

17.5b. Catalytic Hydrogenation of Alkynes: Poisoned Catalysts

Not surprisingly, the C≡C triple bond of an alkyne can undergo catalytic hydrogenation, because it, too, contains carbon-carbon π bonds. Similar to what we saw in the catalytic hydrogenation of an alkene, the addition of H_2 removes a π bond and causes the total number of bonds between the alkyne carbons to decrease by one. Thus, as shown in Equation 17-37, an alkyne is reduced to an alkene.

one addition of H_2 reduces an alkyne to an alkene

a second addition of H_2 reduces the alkene to an alkane

1-hexyne $\xrightarrow[\text{Ni, } CH_3OH]{H_2 \text{ (excess)}}$ [alkene] $\longrightarrow$ hexane 85%

(17-37)

The alkene that is produced is susceptible to catalytic hydrogenation, as indicated in Equation 17-37 and as we saw in the previous section. Therefore, with equimolar amounts of H_2 and the alkyne under normal conditions, we run the risk of producing a mixture of the alkene and alkane products—a generally undesirable result. On the other hand, with *excess* H_2, the alkene intermediate will be reduced completely, producing only the alkane.

Reduction of an alkyne can be stopped at the alkene stage by using a *poisoned catalyst*. A **poisoned catalyst** is simply a metal catalyst that has been specially treated to decrease its catalytic ability, thus making possible a slower and more controlled reaction. One example is **Lindlar's catalyst**—palladium treated with calcium carbonate ($CaCO_3$) and a small amount of quinoline. Barium sulfate ($BaSO_4$) can also be used instead of calcium carbonate. Representative hydrogenation reactions with such catalysts are shown in Equations 17-38 and 17-39.

Comment [JMK20]: Margin note
Catalytic hydrogenation with excess H_2 converts an alkyne into an alkane. Using a poisoned catalyst, however, the reduction stops at the alkene.

Comment [JMK21]: Margin note

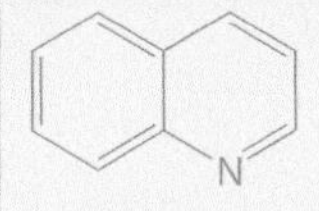

quinoline

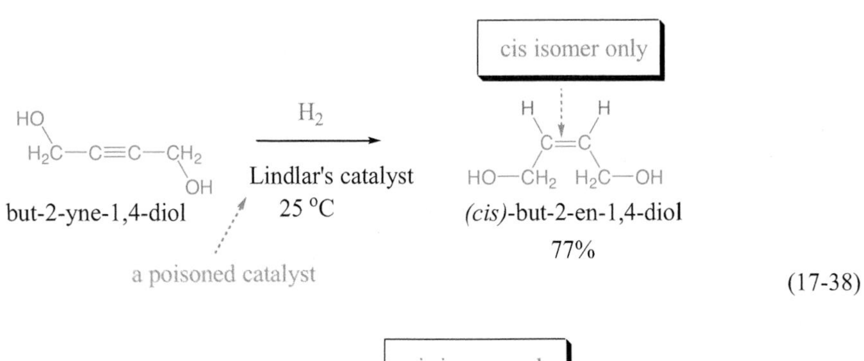

(17-38)

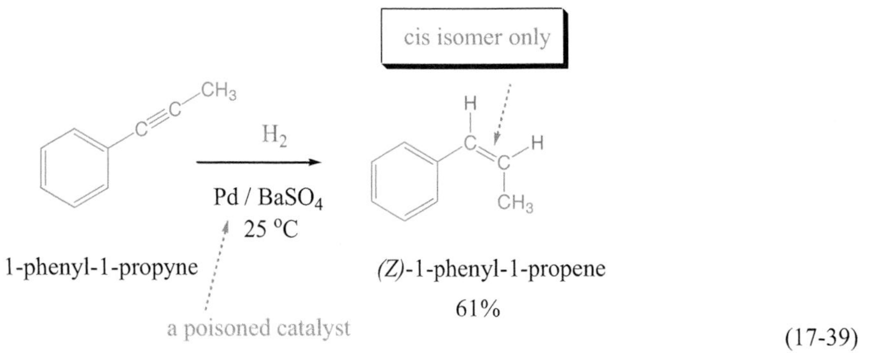

(17-39)

Notice especially from the above reactions that catalytic hydrogenation takes place *stereoselectively*. More specifically,

> The reduction of an alkyne to an alkene via catalytic hydrogenation favors the *cis* isomer over the *trans*.

The reason for this stereoselectivity can be understood from the simplified picture of the mechanism we saw previously in Figure 17-2. Namely, after the first H atom adds to one carbon of the multiple bond (Figure 17-2d), the second H atom adds to the other carbon (Figure 17-2e) before any significant changes occur in orientation of the molecule. Thus, the individual H atoms end up on the same side of the newly formed C=C double bond; the H atoms are said to add in a *syn* fashion.

Problem 17.20. In Equation 17-39, notice that the double bonds in the starting material are unaffected. Explain why.

Solved Problem 17.9. Outline a synthesis of *(Z)*-1-phenylhept-2-ene from bromophenylmethane.

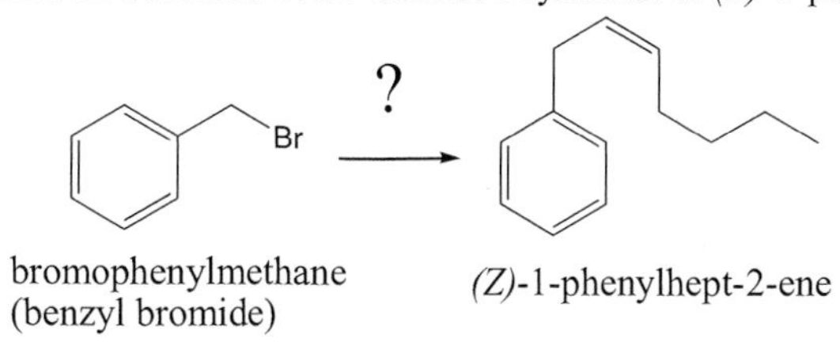

Br

?

bromophenylmethane
(benzyl bromide)

(Z)-1-phenylhept-2-ene

Think. Does this synthesis require a carbon-carbon bond formation reaction? If so, what species possessing an electron-rich carbon could be used? What species containing an electron-poor carbon could be used? Are there any stereochemical issues that must be considered? Can the product be formed in a single reaction, or should we consider making it from a precursor?

Solve. Clearly the carbon skeleton is different in the products than in the reactants; a carbon-carbon bond-formation reaction is necessary. Unfortunately, we do not have at our disposal a way to form a carbon-carbon bond between an alkene carbon and an alkyl halide in a single reaction. We must therefore perform *retrosynthetic analysis*, seeking a precursor from which we can readily make the product. As we have seen previously in this section, a *cis*-alkene can be made by hydrogenating an alkyne, suggesting the possibility of an alkyne precursor, as shown below. That alkyne, in turn, can be the result of an S_N2 reaction that forms the necessary carbon-carbon bond. Overall, our retrosynthetic analysis appears as follows:

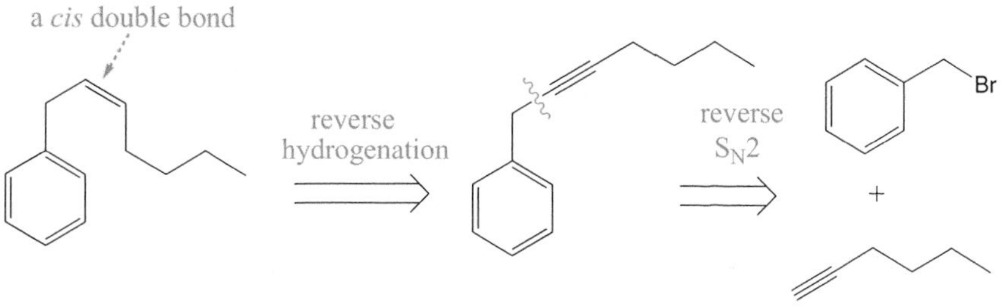

a *cis* double bond

reverse
hydrogenation

reverse
S_N2

Br

+

The synthesis would then appear as follows. A strong base deprotonates the terminal alkyne, thus converting it into a strong nucleophile. Addition of bromophenylmethane results in an S_N2 reaction to generate the new carbon-carbon bond. Subsequent treatment with hydrogen gas in the presence of a poisoned catalyst allows the reduction of the triple bond to stop at the double bond.

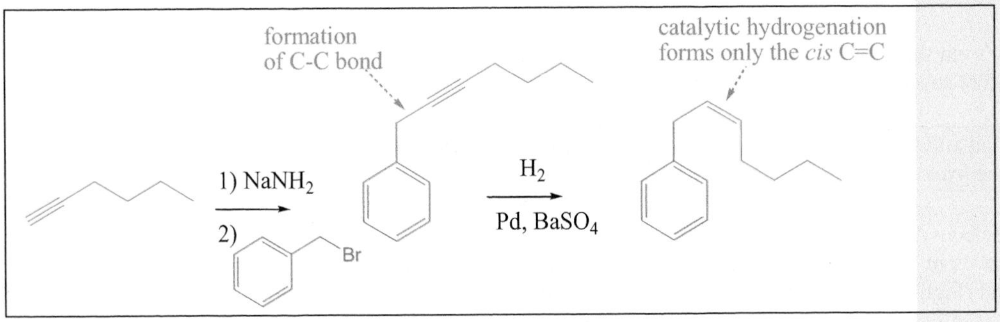

formation of C-C bond

catalytic hydrogenation forms only the *cis* C=C

1) $NaNH_2$

2) (benzyl bromide) Br

H_2

Pd, $BaSO_4$

Problem 17.21. Show how you would carry out the following synthesis.

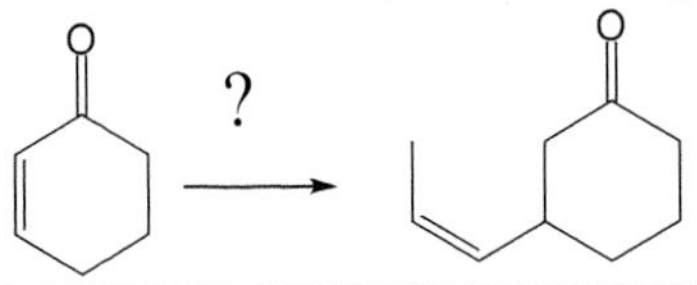

?

17.5c. Addition of H_2 to Other Functional Groups

Catalytic hydrogenation is not limited only to carbon-carbon multiple bonds; the addition of hydrogen to the π bonds of other systems is feasible as well. As Table 17-2 illustrates, a variety of functional group conversions can be performed using catalytic hydrogenation, though not with equal ease. Pay particular attention to the typical experimental conditions required.

Notice that the reduction of an aldehyde is essentially as easy as reduction of an alkene or alkyne. Other functional groups are more difficult to reduce and their reactions generally proceed with poorer yields. This is particularly true for the reduction of amides to amines, because one of the products is an amine, which serves to poison (i.e., deactivate) the metal catalyst. If one attempts to force the reaction by increasing the temperature and/or pressure of H_2, the risk of unwanted side reactions increases. Fortunately, $LiAlH_4$ reduces amides to amines in good yield, as we will see in Chapter 18.

Comment [JMK22]: Margin note
Aldehydes are relatively easy to reduce via catalytic hydrogenation

Table 17-2: Reduction of Various Functional Groups via Catalytic Hydrogenation

Reactant	Reaction Conditions	Product
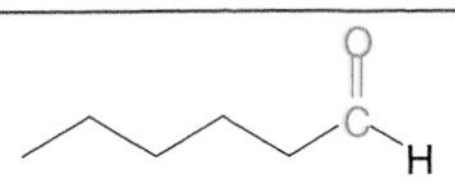 aldehyde	H_2, Pt, 20 °C, 1 atm	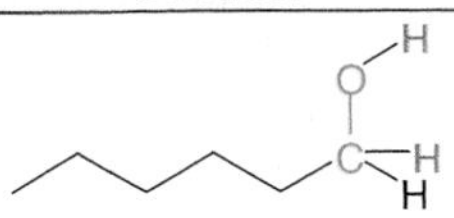 1° alcohol
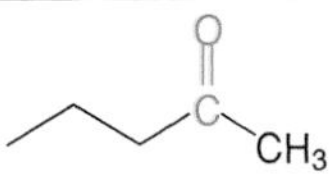 ketone	H_2, Rh, 50 °C, 3 atm	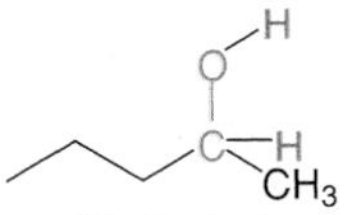 2° alcohol
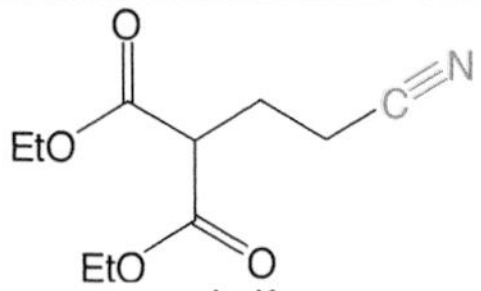 nitrile	H_2, Raney Ni, 80 °C, 75 atm	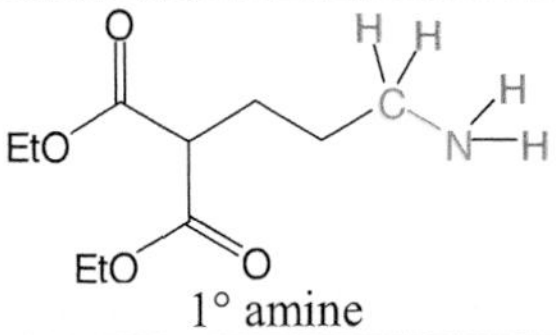 1° amine
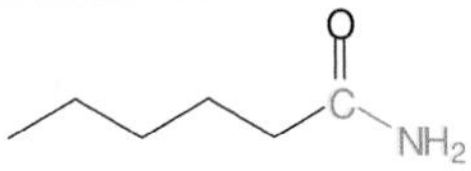 1° amide	1 equiv. H_2, Pt, 250 °C, 200 atm (< 50% yield)	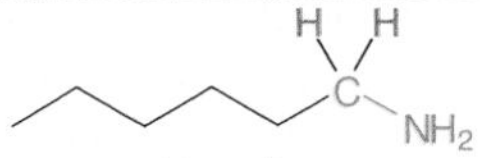 1° amine

17.5d. Selectivity in Catalytic Hydrogenation

We have seen that catalytic hydrogenation can reduce a variety of different functional groups, including alkenes, alkynes, aldehydes, ketones, esters, and amides. As we alluded to earlier, catalytic hydrogenation can take place selectively, so if two or more of such functional groups appear in a particular molecule, it is often possible to carry out the reduction of just one of them. For example, as shown in Equation 17-40, when limonene is treated with one equivalent of H_2, only the terminal C=C double bond is reduced.

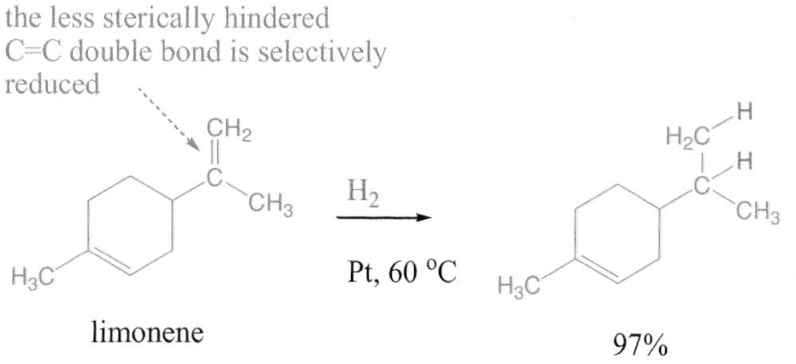

the less sterically hindered C=C double bond is selectively reduced

limonene $\xrightarrow[\text{Pt, 60 °C}]{H_2}$ 97% (17-40)

The reason is that the terminal alkene is less highly substituted, so its double bond is less sterically hindered. In general,

> Catalytic hydrogenation is more favored at a less sterically hindered multiple bond than at a more sterically hindered one.

The reason is that with more steric bulk surrounding the double bond, it is more difficult for the alkene to adsorb to the surface of the metal catalyst—a critical step in catalytic hydrogenation that we saw previously in Figure 17-2c.

Problem 17.22. There are two possible *syn*-addition products in the catalytic hydrogenation of α-pinene, as indicated, but one of them is formed exclusively. Which one? Why?

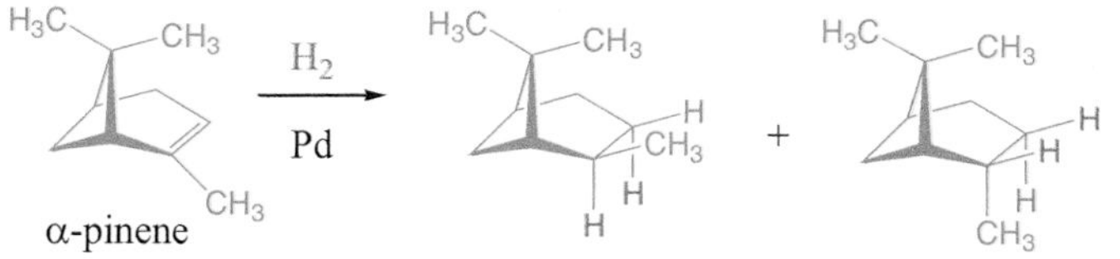

α-pinene $\xrightarrow[\text{Pd}]{H_2}$ +

Another example of selectivity in catalytic hydrogenation is seen in Equation 17-41, in which the compound that is subjected to catalytic hydrogenation has both a C=C double bond and a C≡C triple bond. As we can see, the latter is the one that is selectively reduced.

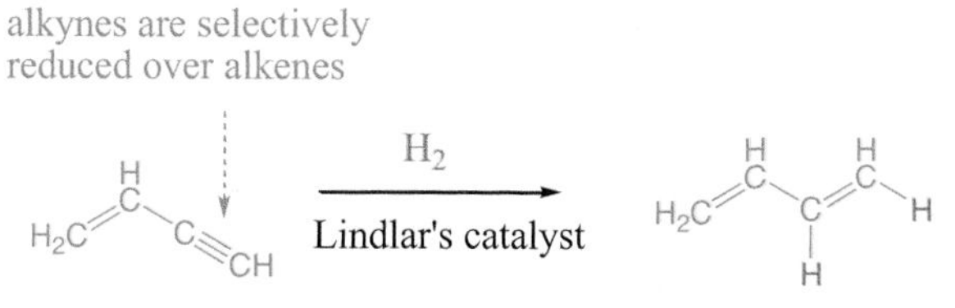

alkynes are selectively reduced over alkenes

$H_2C{=}CH{-}C{\equiv}CH \xrightarrow[\text{Lindlar's catalyst}]{H_2} H_2C{=}CH{-}CH{=}CH_2$ (17-41)

In general,

> Catalytic hydrogenation selectively reduces alkynes over alkenes.

In part, this is attributed to the fact that alkynes are usually less sterically hindered than alkenes are, given that alkyne carbons can bond to only one alkyl group, but alkene carbons can bond to two. Thus, alkynes can typically adsorb to the surface of the metal catalyst more easily than alkenes can.

Problem 17.23. The following reaction is one step in a process that can be used to make vitamin A. Draw its product.

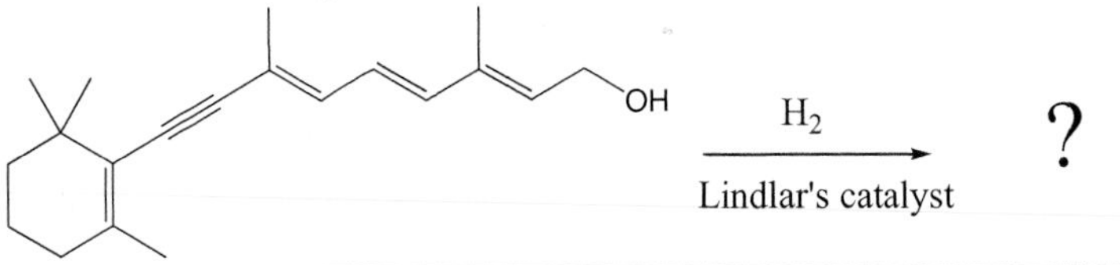

OH $\xrightarrow[\text{Lindlar's catalyst}]{H_2}$?

A final example of selectivity in catalytic hydrogenation involves the functional groups from Table 17-2. Of the groups in that table, only aldehydes are reduced under mild conditions, similar to those under which alkenes and alkynes are reduced. Therefore, alkenes, alkynes, and aldehydes can be selectively reduced over functional groups such as ketones, nitriles, and amides. An example is shown in Equation 17-42.

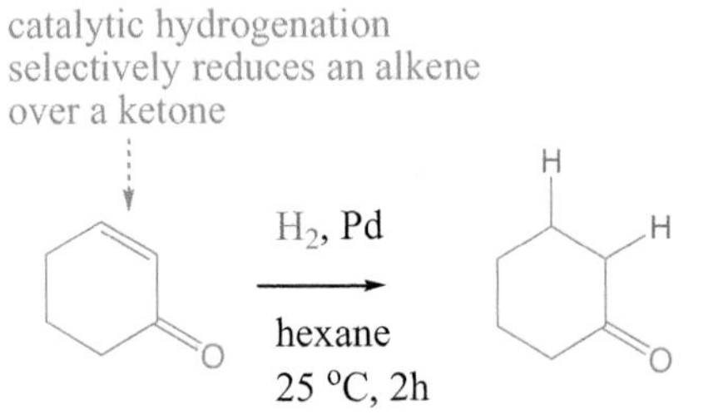

catalytic hydrogenation selectively reduces an alkene over a ketone

cyclohex-2-enone $\xrightarrow[\text{hexane, 25 °C, 2h}]{H_2, Pd}$ cyclohexanone 99% (17-42)

Problem 17.24. Show how you would carry out the following synthesis.

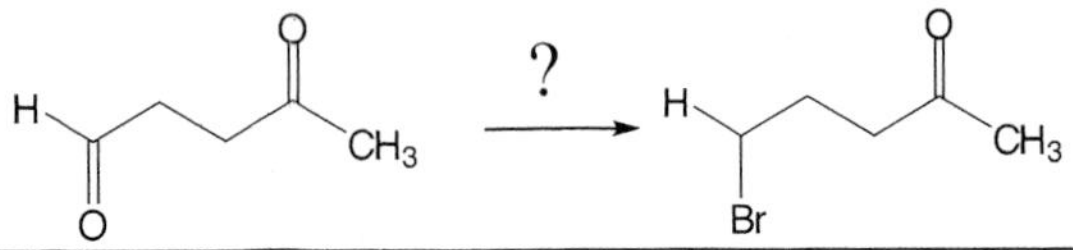

?

17.6. FUNCTIONAL GROUP CHEMISTRY

Although this chapter's main focus is on synthesis strategies, we did indeed encounter new reactions that affect our "big picture" understanding of the chemical behavior of certain functional groups. Those functional groups include haloalkanes, ketones, aldehydes, alkenes, and alkynes. As usual, the new aspects of functional group chemistry appear in green, whereas the ones introduced in previous chapters appear gray.

17.6a. Haloalkanes

Previously we have seen that haloalkanes are susceptible to nucleophilic substitution and elimination reactions, owing to the fact that the haloalkane carbon is electron-poor. In Section 17.1a, however, we learned that haloalkanes can be converted to organometallic compounds such as Grignard (R-MgX) or alkyllithium (R-Li) reagents, by treatment with solid Mg or Li, respectively. Thus, the haloalkane carbon becomes electron-rich, making it both nucleophilic and basic.

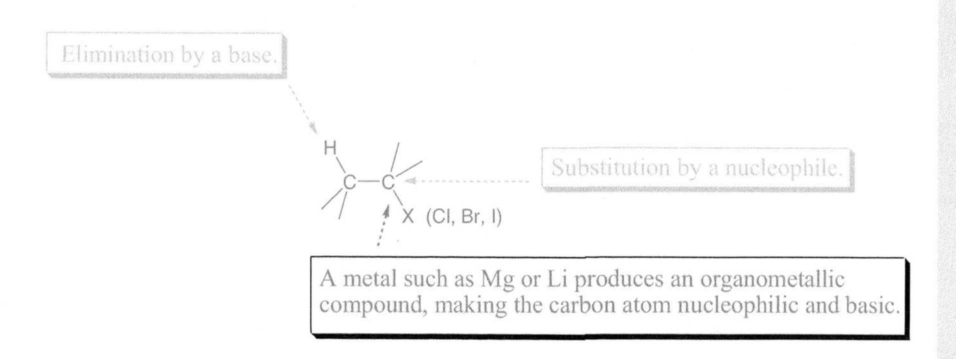

17.6b. Ketones

The new aspect of a ketone's chemical reactivity we encountered in this chapter is its susceptibility to reduction via catalytic hydrogenation (Section 17.5c). In the presence of a catalyst such as Pt, Pd, or Ni, H_2 will add to the carbonyl group, reducing the ketone to an alcohol.

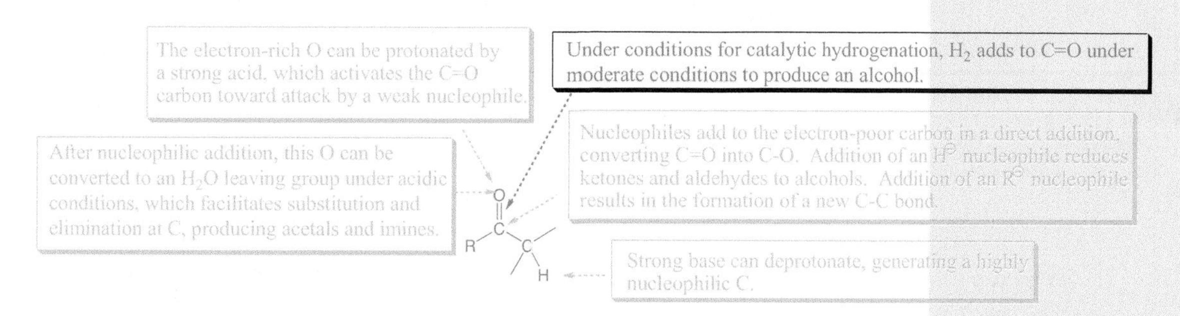

17.6c. Aldehydes

Similar to ketones, aldehydes can be reduced to alcohols via catalytic hydrogenation (Section 17.5c). Additionally, the aldehyde hydrogen, which is normally not acidic, can be made acidic by converting the C=O group to a 1,3-dithiane (Section 17.1b). Thus, the carbonyl carbon can be made nucleophilic.

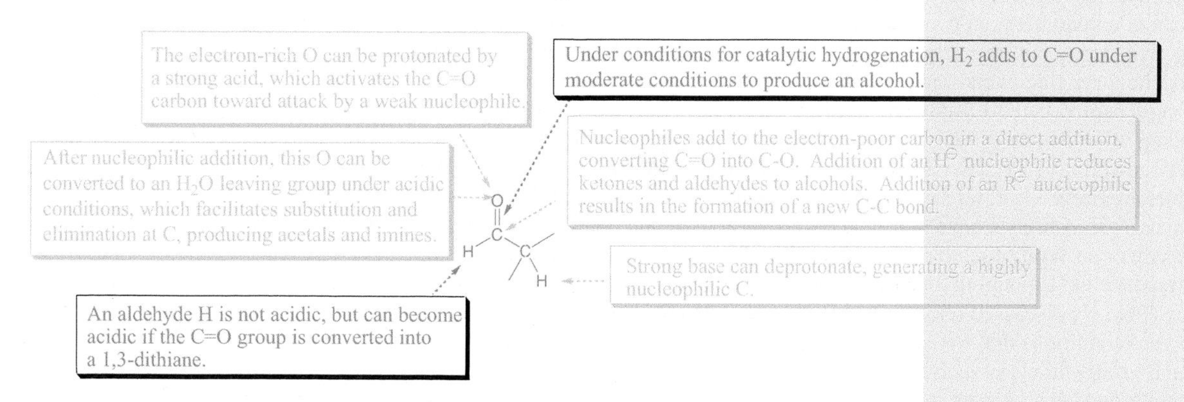

17.6d. Alkenes

In Section 17.5a, we saw that alkenes are susceptible to catalytic hydrogenation. In the presence of a catalyst such as Pd, Pt, or Ni, H_2 will add to an alkene, thus reducing it to an alkane.

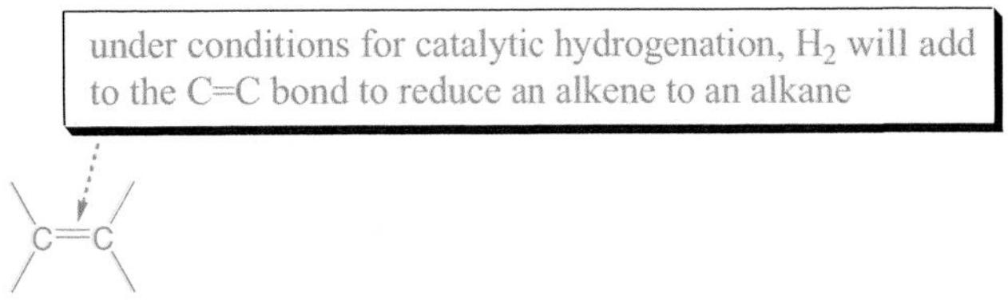

under conditions for catalytic hydrogenation, H_2 will add to the C=C bond to reduce an alkene to an alkane

C=C

17.6e. Alkynes

Similar to alkenes, alkynes will readily undergo catalytic hydrogenation. If the catalyst is poisoned, addition of H_2 takes place in a controlled fashion, producing a *cis* alkene. Otherwise, the alkene that is initially produced can be reduced a second time, yielding an alkane.

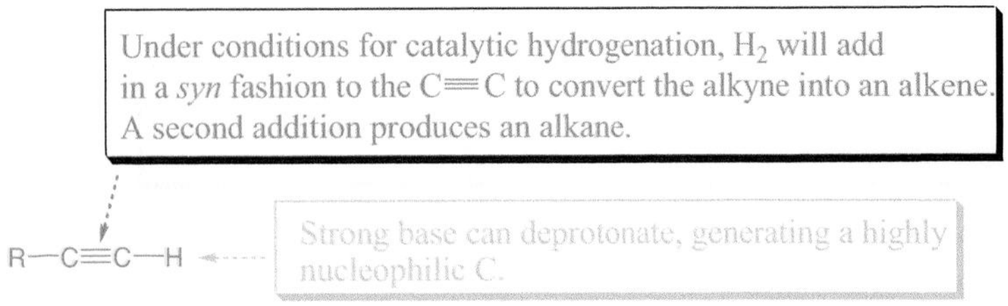

Under conditions for catalytic hydrogenation, H_2 will add in a *syn* fashion to the C≡C to convert the alkyne into an alkene. A second addition produces an alkane.

R—C≡C—H

Strong base can deprotonate, generating a highly nucleophilic C.

17.7. WRAPPING UP AND LOOKING AHEAD

We began our discussion of synthesis in Chapter 11, introducing some basic thinking that goes into designing organic syntheses. In this chapter, we extended that knowledge, discussing some higher-level concepts that can be applied toward designing more complex syntheses.

The first few sections dealt with aspects of incorporating carbon-carbon bond-formation reactions in a synthesis. We discussed ways in which to facilitate the formation of a bond between two carbon atoms with like charge, by incorporating a reaction that carries out *umpolung* (polarity reversal) at one of the carbons. Examples included the formation of an organometallic compound from an alkyl halide, and producing a deprotonated 1,3-dithiane from an aldehyde. Then, we saw how the relative positioning of functional groups within a target provides clues as to the type of carbon-carbon bond-formation reaction we should consider incorporating in a synthesis. When such clues are not present, we saw that we can sometimes utilize reactions that remove a functional group entirely from a molecule once a carbon-carbon bond has been formed. Our focus was on Wolff-Kishner, Clemmensen, and Raney-nickel reductions, which serve to reduce the C=O group of a ketone or aldehyde to a CH_2 group.

Next, we discussed selective reactions and protecting groups. A desired reaction may require conditions that would result in an undesired reaction at a particular functional group. In many such cases, we can employ a selective reagent to target one functional group (or site) over another. When this is not possible, we can seek to protect a functional group by temporarily converting it into one that is unreactive under the conditions necessary for the desired reaction. After the desired reaction is complete, the original functional group can be restored via a deprotection step. In this context, we learned how to protect ketones and aldehydes, as well as alcohols.

Finally, we introduced a new reaction, catalytic hydrogenation, which serves to reduce a variety of functional groups, including alkenes, alkynes, aldehydes, ketones, nitriles, and amides. Catalytic hydrogenation is not only useful for carrying out specific functional group conversions, but is useful for two other important reasons as well. First, it provides a means by which to remove a functional group entirely from a molecule, as it converts an alkene to an alkane. Second, it is a selective reaction, favoring the reductions of alkenes, alkynes, and aldehydes.

As new reactions are discussed in the chapters to come, you will see opportunities to apply the concepts from this chapter even more extensively. In Chapters 18 and 19, for example, you will see that nucleophilic addition-elimination reactions exhibit selectivity with carbonyl-containing functional groups such as amides, esters, carboxylic acids, acid anhydrides, and acid halides. And in Chapter 25, we will see how free-radical reactions are selective toward specific types of carbon atoms. Moreover, in Chapter 20, we will learn how alcohols can be protected using a reaction that proceeds via an electrophilic addition mechanism.

CHAPTER SUMMARY AND KEY TERMS

- The formation of a bond between two carbon atoms is problematic when the atoms are of like charge. To circumvent such a problem, we can first carry out a reaction that reverses the charge (polarity) of one atom, via a process termed **umpolung**. (Section 17.1)
- Umpolung takes place at a haloalkane carbon upon treatment with a metal such as Mg or Li, producing a Grignard or alkyllithium reagent, respectively. Alternatively, umpolung can take place at an aldehyde carbon by first converting the aldehyde to a 1,3-dithiane, followed by treatment with a very strong base like an alkyllithium. (Sections 17.1a and 17.1b)
- Many carbon-carbon bond-formation reactions leave functional groups with a very specific relative positioning. Thus, target molecules that exhibit one such relative positioning provide clues as to which of those reactions should be considered in a synthesis. (Section 17.2)
- If a synthesis requires the formation of a new carbon-carbon bond but the target does not exhibit a specific relative positioning of functional groups, the synthesis may call for a reaction that removes a functional group entirely from a molecule. (Section 17.3)
    - Reactions that remove a ketone or aldehyde functional group include the **Wolff-Kishner reduction**, the **Clemmensen reduction**, and the **Raney-nickel reduction**. These reactions take place under acidic, basic, and catalytic hydrogenation conditions, respectively, so care must be taken to avoid unwanted side reactions at other functional groups in the molecule. (Section 17.3)
    - An alkene or alkyne functional group can be removed via catalytic hydrogenation. (Section 17.5)
- If two or more reactive functional groups appear in a molecule, we can often carry out a reaction at just one of those groups by employing either a *selective reagent* or a *protecting group*. (Section 17.4)
    - A **selective reagent** favors reaction with one functional group over another. (Section 17.4a)
    - A **protecting group** temporarily converts one functional group into one that is unreactive under the conditions necessary for a step that a synthesis calls for. Ketones, aldehydes, and ethers can often be protected in the form of an acetal or ether. (Section 17.4b)
- **Catalytic hydrogenation** is a reaction in which H_2 adds to a molecule in the presence of a metal catalyst such as Pt, Pd, or Ni. Such a reaction readily reduces an alkane to an alkene. (Section 17.5a)
- Using a **poisoned catalyst**, catalytic hydrogenation reduces an alkyne to a *cis* alkene. (Section 17.5b)

- Catalytic hydrogenation will readily reduce an aldehyde to an alcohol. Under moderate conditions, a ketone can also be reduced to an alcohol, and under more extreme conditions, other functional groups such as nitriles and amides can be reduced. (Section 17.5c)
- Catalytic hydrogenation is selective toward alkenes, alkynes, and aldehydes. (Section 17.5d)

REACTION TABLES

Table 17-3. Functional Group Transformations

	Starting Functional Group	Typical Reagents and Reaction Conditions	Functional Group Formed	Key Electron-Rich Species	Key Electron-Poor Species	Type of Mechanism	Discussed in Section(s)
(1)	R–X Haloalkane	Mg → ether	R–MgX Grignard reagent	N/A	N/A	Dissolving metal reduction	17.1a
(2)	R–X Haloalkane	Li → ether	R–Li Alkyllithium reagent	N/A	N/A	Dissolving metal reduction	17.1a
(3)	R–Li Alkyllithium reagent	CuI → ether	Li / R–Cu–R Lithium dialkyl cuprate	N/A	N/A	N/A	17.1a
(4)	R–C(=O)–R or H Ketone or aldehyde	Zn/Hg , HCl → H_2O, reflux	R–CH₂–R or H Alkane	N/A	N/A	Clemmensen reduction	17.3b
(5)	R–C(=O)–R or H Ketone or aldehyde	1) $HSCH_2CH_2SH$, H^+ → 2) Raney-nickel	R–CH₂–R or H Alkane	N/A	N/A	Raney-nickel reduction	17.3c
(6)	R₂C=CR₂ Alkene	H_2 → Pt, Pd, or Ni	R₂CH–CHR₂ Alkane	N/A	N/A	Catalytic hydrogenation	17.5a
(7)	R—C≡C—R Alkyne	H_2 → poisoned catalyst	RHC=CHR *cis*-alkene	N/A	N/A	Catalytic hydrogenation	17.5b
(8)	R–C(=O)–R or H Ketone or aldehyde	H_2 → Pt, Pd, or Ni	R–CH(OH)–R or H Alcohol	N/A	N/A	Catalytic hydrogenation	17.5c

Table 17-4. Reactions that Alter the Carbon Skeleton

	Reactant	Typical Reagent and Reaction Conditions	Product Formed	Key Electron-Rich Species	Key Electron-Poor Species	Type of Reaction	Discussed in Section(s)
(1)	Aldehyde	1) HS~~SH, H^+ 2) BuLi, R–X 3) $HgCl_2$, H_2O	Ketone	Deprotonated 1,3-dithiane	δ^+ R–X	Nucleophilic substitution	17.1b
(2)	Aldehyde	1) HS~~SH, H^+ 2) BuLi, R(C=O)R 3) $HgCl_2$, H_2O	α-hydroxycarbonyl	Deprotonated 1,3-dithiane	C=O δ^+	Nucleophilic addition	17.1b

PROBLEMS

25. Show how each of the following organometallic compounds can be synthesized from an alkyl halide.

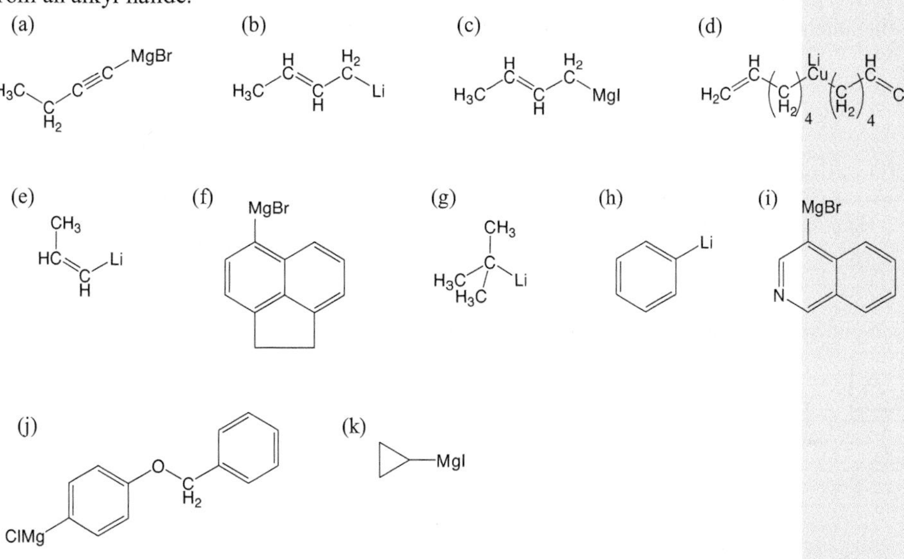

26. Draw the organometallic compound that would be produced by each of the following reactions.

(a) Br; Li, ether → ?

(b) $H_2C{=}C{=}CH$–Br; Mg, THF → ?

(c) CH_3, H_3C–N, MgBr; Mg, THF → ?

(d) Cl; Mg, ether → ?

(e) H_3C–CH_2–CH_2–CH_2–Br; 1) Li, THF 2) CuI → ?

(f) N, Br; Li, THF → ?

(g) Cl; 1) Li, THF 2) CuI → ?

27. Using acetone, any alcohol with six or fewer carbons, and any inorganic reagents necessary, show how to synthesize each of the compounds below.

(a) OH (b) OH (c) HO (d) OH

28. Supply the missing intermediates and reagents in the following synthesis.

O, CH; 1) $LiAlH_4$ 2) H_3O^+ → A; Mg, ether → B; 1) C 2) H_3O^+ → OH; 1) NaH 2) D → O

29. Supply the missing intermediates and reagents in the following synthesis.

OH; A → B; Mg, ether → C

O; 1 LDA 2) D 3) H_3O^+, Δ → O; 1) E 2) NH_4Cl → O; 1) C 2) H_3O^+ → HO

30. Show how to synthesize each of the following compounds, using propanal and any other ketone or aldehyde as your only starting materials containing carbon.

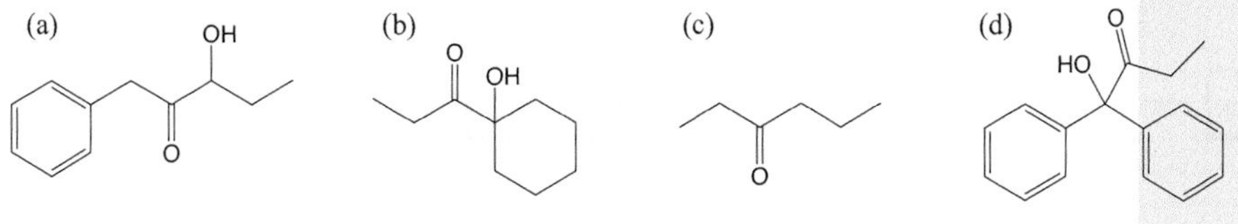

(a) OH O
(b) O OH
(c) O
(d) HO O

31. Provide the missing intermediates and reagents in the following synthesis.

O CH, H_3C CH_3; HS SH, $H^{\oplus}$ → A; 1) Bu-Li, 2) B, 3) $H^{\oplus}$ → S S, H_3C CH_3; $HgCl_2$, H_2O, MeOH → C

D; Li, THF → E; 1) C, 2) H_3O^+ → HO, H_3C CH_3

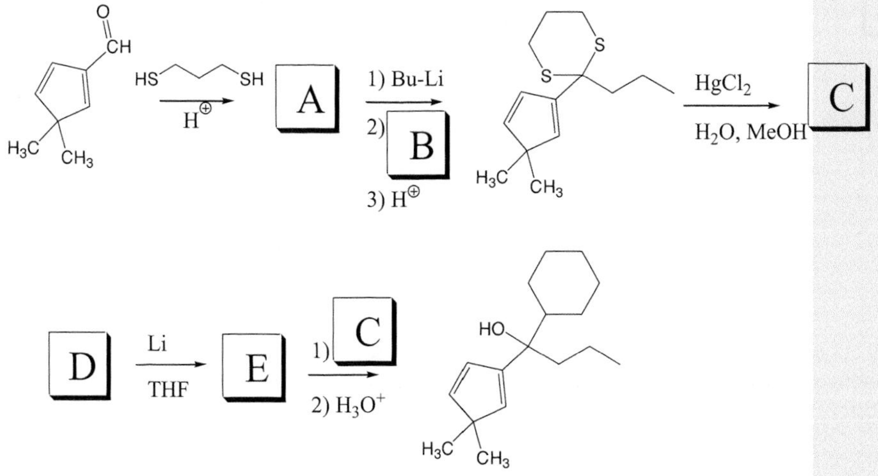

32. Supply the missing reagents and intermediates in the following synthesis.

O O O; A → O O O; 1) B, 2) H_3O^+ → O O OH; C

TBDMS O, O O; H_3O^+ → D; 1) E, 2) H_3O^+ → TBDMS O, HO; $Bu_4N^+F^-$ → F

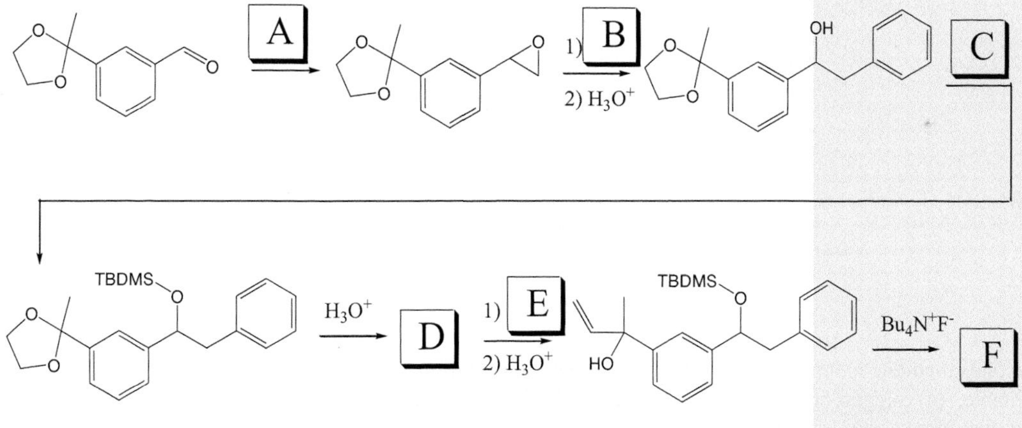

33. Show how to synthesize each of the following compounds, given the respective restraints on the starting materials.

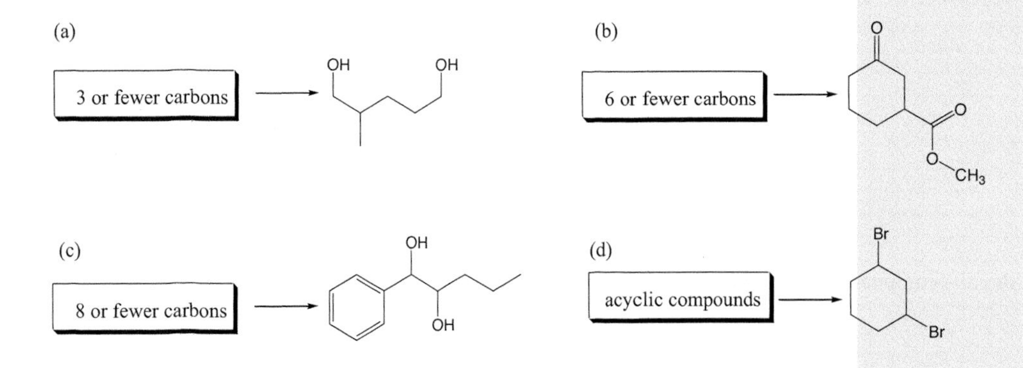

34. Show how to carry out each of the following syntheses, using any reagents necessary. (Hint: notice that in each case a ketone or aldehyde functional group is entirely removed.)

(a)

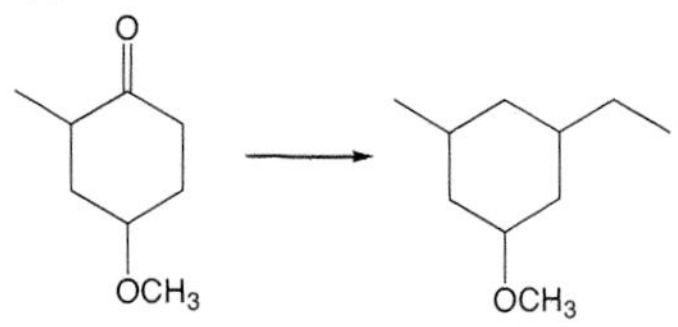

O

OCH_3 → OCH_3

(b)

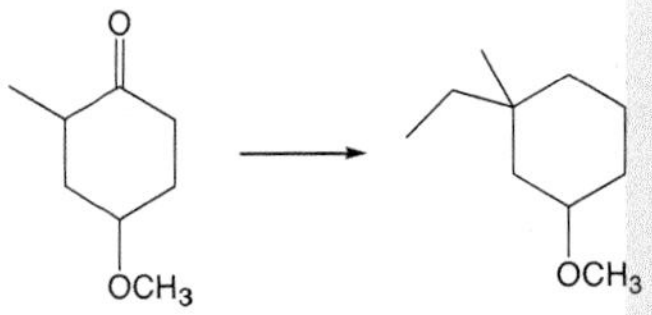

O

OCH_3 → OCH_3

(c)

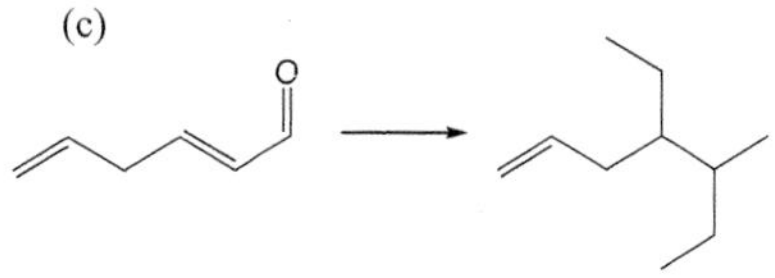

O

(d)

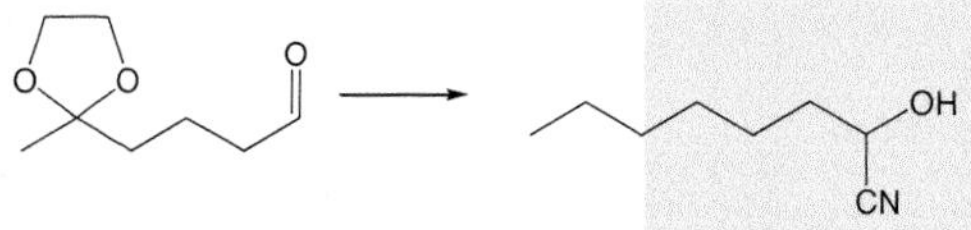

O O O → OH CN

35. Cyclohexanedione monoethylene acetal (shown below) is commercially available. (a) Suggest how you would synthesize 4-ethylidenecyclohexanone from that monoacetal. (b) What problems would arise if you tried to synthesize the same target from 1,4-cyclohexanedione?

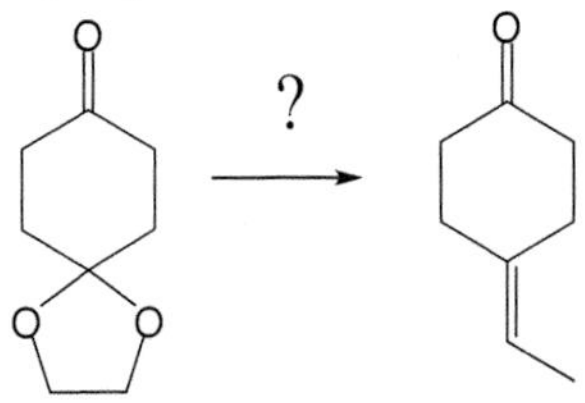

O ? O

O O

1,4-cyclohexanedione monoethylene acetal → 4-ethylidenecyclohexanone

36. In the chapter, we learned that converting a ketone or aldehyde to an ether is a good way to protect the carbonyl group. In Chapter 15, we saw that a ketone or

aldehyde can be converted into an epoxide, which is a cyclic ether. Why would this be a poor choice as a protecting group?

37. A student wishes to carry out the following reaction. Explain the problem(s) associated with this synthesis scheme, and suggest a means by which to carry out the transformation efficiently.

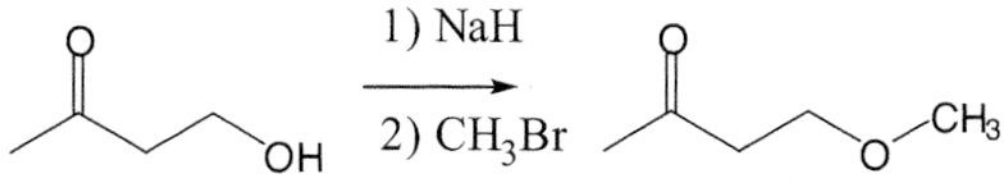

1) NaH

2) CH_3Br

38. Suppose we wish to carry out the following functional group conversion in which "A" is converted to "B." However, under the reaction conditions that carry out this transformation, the alcohol group is reactive, so protecting the alcohol would be necessary. In the chapter, we learned that there is more than one way in which to protect alcohols. Which do you think will be effective? Which ones will not? Why?

(a)

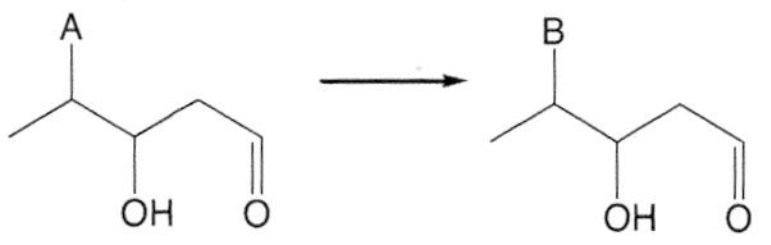

(b)

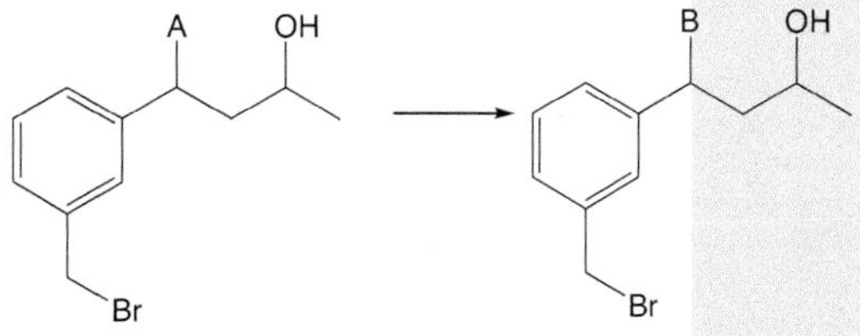

39. Propose how you would carry out each of the following syntheses.

(a) ?

(b) ?

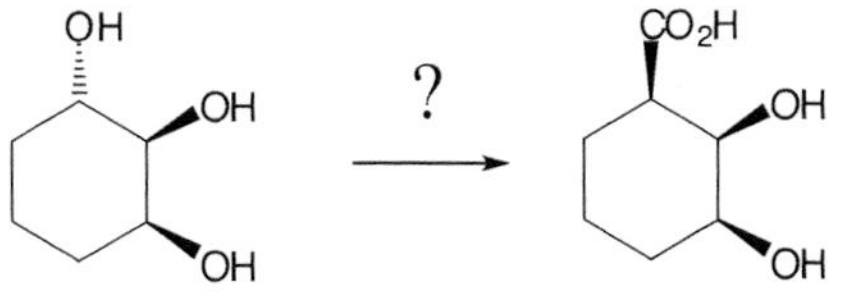

40. Suggest how you would synthesize each of the following compounds beginning with 2-pentanone.

a. 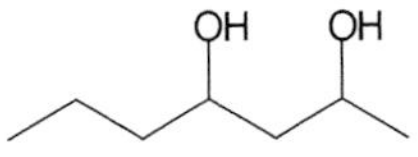 OH OH

b. 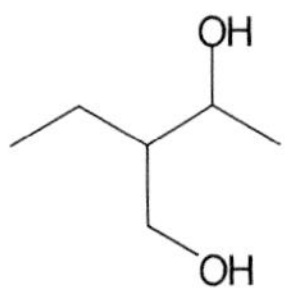 OH OH

c. 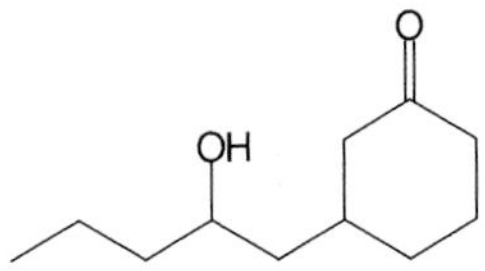 OH O

d. 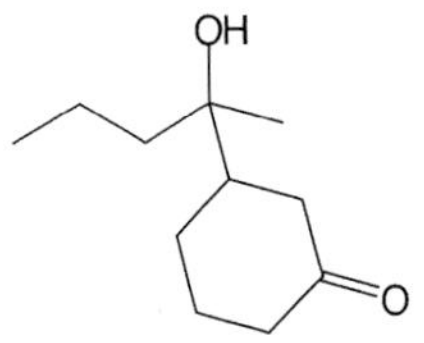 OH O

41. Show how you would synthesize 3,4-hexanediol using propanal as your only source of carbon atoms.

42. Show how you would carry out each of the following syntheses.

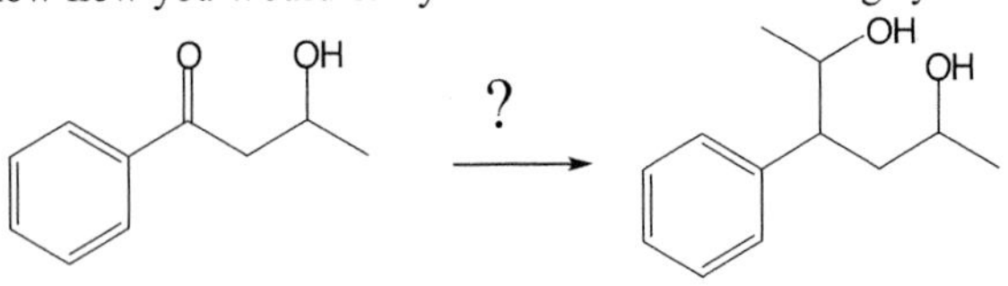

a. O OH ? → OH OH

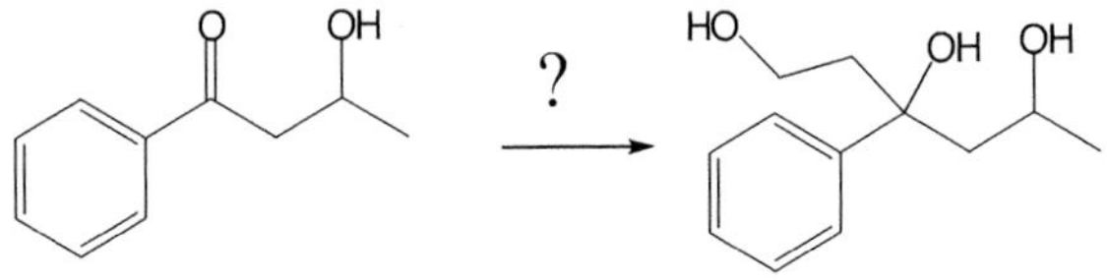

b. O OH ? → HO OH OH

43. Show how you would carry out the following synthesis? (Hint: what rearrangement occurs when an enol is formed?)

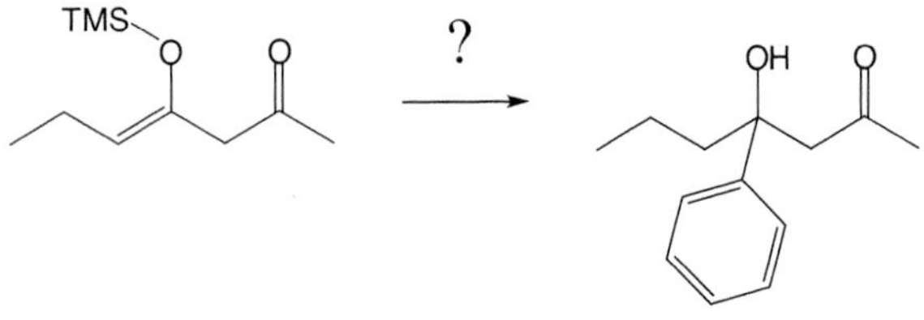

TMS O O ? → OH O

44. Show how you would synthesize the following compound using propanal as your only carbon source.

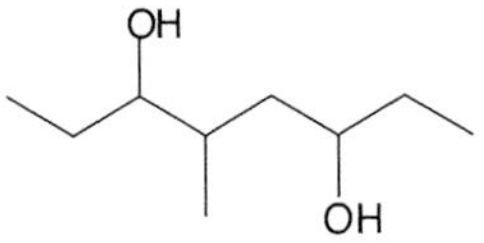

OH OH

45. Predict the product for each of the following reactions. Unless otherwise indicated, you may assume that one molar equivalent of H_2 reacts.

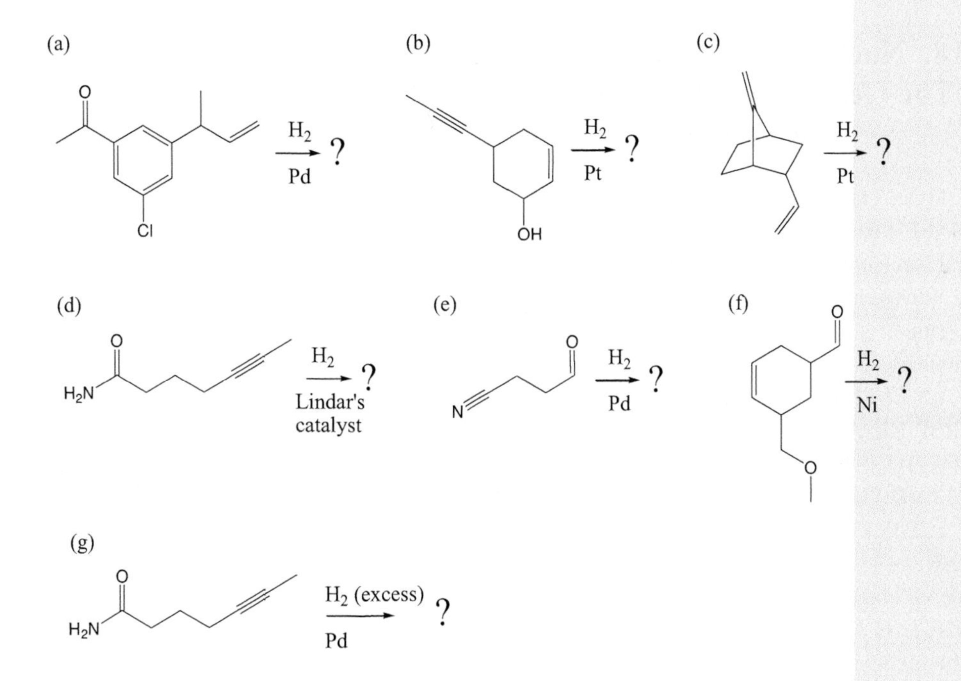

46. Show how to carry out each of the following syntheses. (Hint: consider how you might incorporate selective reagents or protecting groups.)

(a)

(b)

(c)

(d)

(e)

Chapter 18. Nucleophilic Addition-Elimination Reactions. 1: The General Mechanism Involving Strong Nucleophiles

Introduction

In Chapters 15 and 16 we discussed reactions in which nucleophiles add to functional groups containing polar π bonds, such as ketones, aldehydes, imines, and nitriles. Those nucleophilic addition reactions are driven, in large part, by the flow of electrons from the electron-rich nucleophile to the electron-poor atom of the polar π bond.

A variety of other functional groups contain polar π bonds as well, and are therefore susceptible to nucleophilic attack. For example, carboxylic acids have the polar carbonyl group (shown in blue below). So do esters, amides, acid anhydrides, and acid halides (collectively known as **carboxylic acid derivatives**). Sulfinic acids, sulfonic acids, sulfonate esters, sulfonamides, and sulfonyl halides all have a polar S=O double bond (also shown in blue). And H_2CrO_4, a potent oxidizing agent (discussed in Chapter 19), contains a polar metal-oxygen double bond.

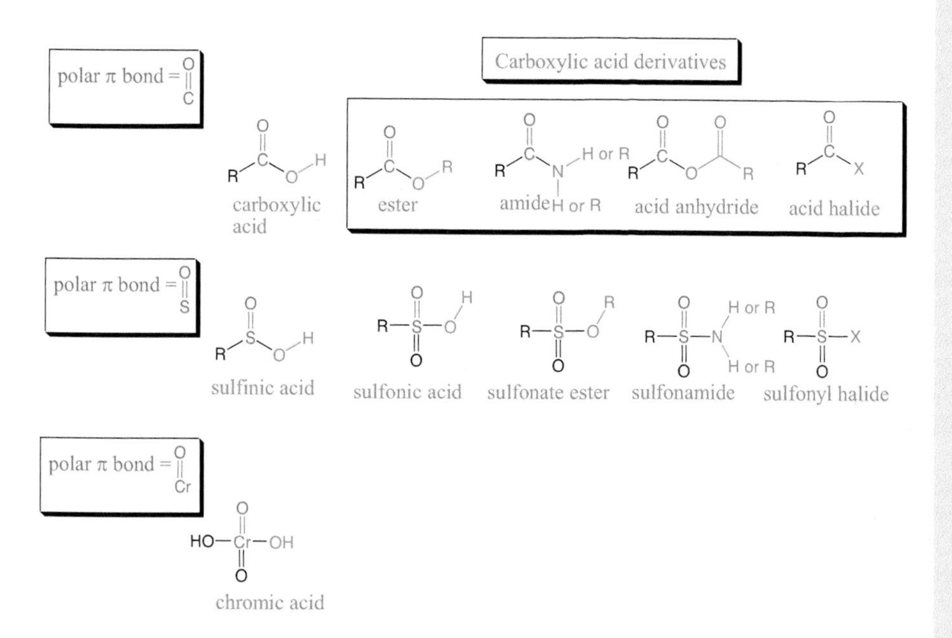

Although these functional groups are susceptible to nucleophilic attack, they participate in different *overall* reactions than we saw in Chapters 15 and 16. Whereas the functional groups in Chapters 15 and 16 primarily undergo nucleophilic addition, these functional groups tend to undergo what is called a *nucleophilic addition-elimination* mechanism. This is because they each contain a *leaving group* (shown above in red) bonded to the electron-deficient atom of the polar π bond. By contrast, ketones, aldehydes, imines, and nitriles do not possess a suitable leaving group; the electron deficient carbon is bonded to H and/or alkyl groups only, so any leaving group would have to depart as H^- or R^-, which are very unstable anions.

Comment [JMK23]: Margin note
A compound can undergo a nucleophilic addition-elimination reaction if it possesses a leaving group bonded to an atom of a polar π bond.

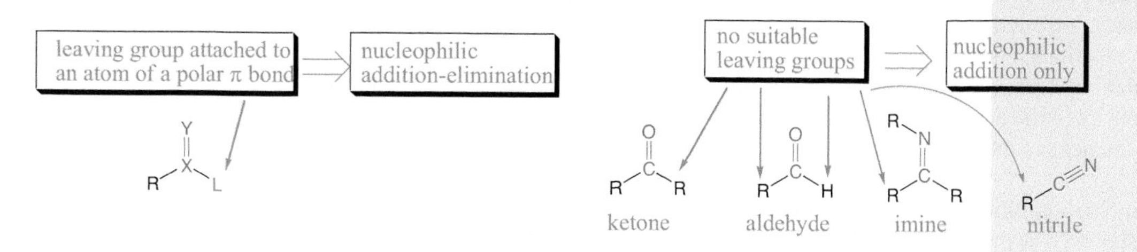

As we will see throughout this chapter and Chapter 19, there are a wide variety of reactions that proceed via a nucleophilic addition-elimination mechanism. In this chapter, we will focus just on nucleophilic addition-elimination reactions that involve strong nucleophiles bearing a negative charge. These include alkoxide anions (RO^-), hydride anions (H^-) from various reducing agents, and alkyl anions (R^-) from various organometallic reagents. In Chapter 19, we will shift our focus to reactions involving weak nucleophiles.

CHAPTER OBJECTIVES
Upon Completion of This Chapter You Should Be Able to:

- Identify the types of compounds capable of undergoing nucleophilic addition-elimination reactions, and draw the general mechanism involving such compounds.
- Draw an energy diagram for a general nucleophilic addition-elimination mechanism and identify the rate-determining step.
- Predict the products of an acyl substitution reaction and determine whether or not such a reaction is energetically favorable.
- Draw the mechanism for saponification, and explain why it is irreversible.
- Describe how an amide can be converted to a carboxylic acid under basic conditions, and show how to use such reactions to synthesize a primary amine in a Gabriel synthesis.
- Explain why methyl ketones can undergo acyl substitution in a haloform reaction to produce a carboxylic acid.
- Predict the outcomes of treating various acid derivatives with reducing agents, including $NaBH_4$, $LiAlH_4$, diisobutylaluminum hydride (DIBAH), and lithium tri-*tert*-butoxyaluminum hydride.
- Predict the outcomes of treating various acid derivatives with organometallic reagents such as alkyllithium reagents (R-Li), Grignard reagents (R-MgBr), and lithium dialkylcuprates (R_2CuLi).

18.1. AN INTRODUCTION TO NUCLEOPHILIC ADDITION-ELIMINATION REACTIONS: BASE-PROMOTED TRANSESTERIFICATION

We begin our discussion of nucleophilic addition-elimination reactions with *base-promoted transesterification*, in which an ester is treated with an alkoxide anion (RO^-). Base-promoted transesterifications are among the simplest of nucleophilic addition-elimination reactions, but they provide us insight into many of the principles that underlie more complex reactions. Thus, base-promoted transesterification acts as a prototype for other nucleophilic addition-elimination reactions we will encounter throughout this and the next chapter.

18.1a. The General Nucleophilic Addition-Elimination Mechanism

When an ester such as methyl benzoate is treated with potassium *t*-butoxide, a different ester, *t*-butyl benzoate, is produced.

methyl benzoate + $K^{\oplus}\,{}^{\ominus}O\text{–}C(CH_3)_3$ $\xrightleftharpoons{\text{ether}}$ *t*-butyl benzoate 85% + $K^{\oplus}\,{}^{\ominus}O\text{–}CH_3$ (18-1)

This reaction is an example of a **base-promoted transesterification**. It is a *transesterification* because one ester is converted into another, and it is *base-promoted* because one of the reactants, potassium *t*-butoxide, is a strong base.

The mechanism for such a transesterification, shown in Equation 18-2, is typical of reactions involving a nucleophile and an acid derivative. It is called a *nucleophilic addition-elimination* mechanism, which, as we can see, describes the two steps that take place. Step 1 is *nucleophilic addition*, in which a nucleophile attacks the electron-poor carbonyl carbon. This forces a pair of electrons from the initial C=O bond onto the O atom, which generates a negative charge on O. The product of that step is a **tetrahedral intermediate**, which, in step 2, undergoes *nucleophilic elimination*. A lone pair of electrons on the negatively charged oxygen atom is used to regenerate the C=O double bond, and the leaving group departs as CH_3O^-.

Mechanism for the Reaction in Equation 18-1

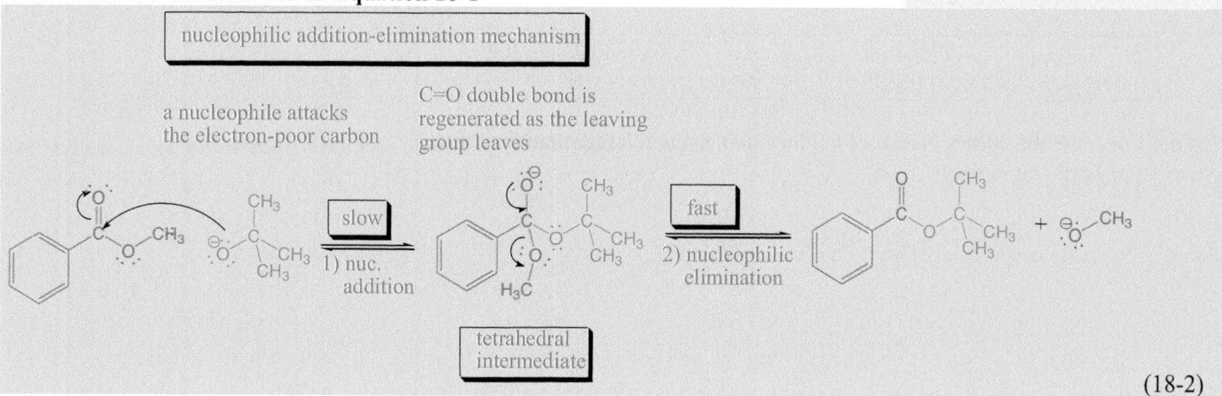

(18-2)

Your Turn 18.1. Below is the mechanism for another base-promoted transesterification reaction, but the curved arrow notation has been omitted. (a) Complete the mechanism by adding the curved arrow notation. (b) Circle and label the tetrahedral intermediate. (c) Below each reaction arrow, write the name of the elementary step that takes place.

Problem 18.1. For each of the following reactions, draw the complete, detailed mechanism and the major product(s).

(a) $\xrightarrow[CH_3CH_2OH]{NaOCH_2CH_3}$?

(b) $\xrightarrow[THF]{ONa}$?

Overall, nucleophilic addition-elimination results in a *substitution* at the carbonyl carbon that is part of an acyl group (RC=O). Specifically, the $-OCH_3$ group attached to the carbonyl carbon is replaced by an $-OC(CH_3)_3$ group. Thus, such reactions are often referred to as **nucleophilic acyl substitution**. Keep in mind, however, that this mechanism is quite different from the S_N2 and S_N1 mechanisms we encountered in Chapters 7 and 8. Recall that in an S_N2 mechanism, the leaving group departs at the same time the nucleophile attacks. In an S_N1 mechanism, the leaving group departs first, followed by attack of the nucleophile. Here, the nucleophile attacks first, followed by the departure of the leaving group.

Comment [JMK24]: Margin note. Nucleophilic acyl substitution proceeds through a nucleophilic addition-elimination mechanism.

Why do acyl substitutions not take place via the S_N1 or S_N2 mechanism? In part it is because the leaving group is on an sp^2-hybridized carbon. Recall from Chapter 7 that due to the increased *s*-character of its hybridized orbitals, an sp^2-hybridized carbon not only binds the leaving group more tightly, but would also form a relatively unstable carbocation if the leaving group were to depart on its own. Moreover, the nucleophilic addition-elimination mechanism is favored over the S_N2 mechanism because of the possible bonds that can be broken upon attack of the nucleophile, the π bond is the weakest.

Comment [JMK25]: **Margin note.** The sp^2-hybridization of the carbonyl carbon makes S_N2 and S_N1 reactions unfavorable.

18.1b. Kinetics of Nucleophilic Addition-Elimination: The Reaction Free Energy Diagram

Notice from Equation 18-2 that the first step of the nucleophilic addition-elimination mechanism is significantly slower than the second step. In other words,

> In a nucleophilic addition-elimination mechanism, the first step (i.e., nucleophilic addition) is generally the rate-determining step.

This indicates that the energy barrier of the first step is much larger than that of the second step, as shown in Figure 18-1.

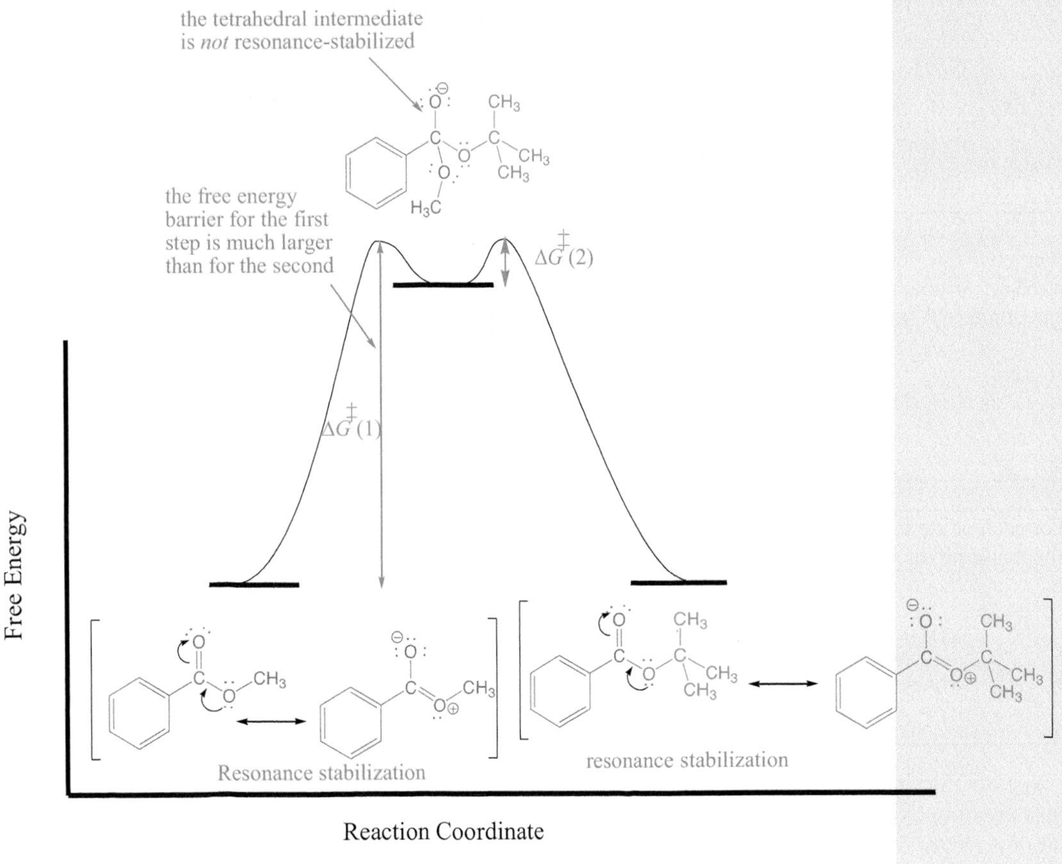

the tetrahedral intermediate is *not* resonance-stabilized

the free energy barrier for the first step is much larger than for the second

$\Delta G^\ddagger(1)$

$\Delta G^\ddagger(2)$

Free Energy

Resonance stabilization

resonance stabilization

Reaction Coordinate

Figure 18-1. Reaction free energy diagram for nucleophilic addition-elimination.
The first step, nucleophilic addition, is the rate determining step (i.e., the slow step) because it has a much greater energy barrier than the second step. Largely this is because resonance involving the lone pair of electrons on the leaving group does not exist in the tetrahedral intermediate.

Part of the reason for the relatively large energy barrier of the first step is the *resonance-stabilization* involving the π bond of the carbonyl group and a lone pair of electrons from the leaving group, as shown in Figure 18-1. By contrast, the tetrahedral intermediate is not resonance-stabilized (the π bond is absent), so it is significantly higher in energy. According to the Hammond postulate (Section 9.3a), the transition state closely resembles the tetrahedral intermediate, so the transition state's energy, too, is relatively high.

The reverse is true for the second step. When the leaving group departs to regenerate the C=O bond, resonance is reestablished, which serves to stabilize the overall product. Once again, according to the Hammond postulate, the transition state closely resembles the tetrahedral intermediate, so the energy barrier is relatively low.

Your Turn 18.2. Complete the reaction free energy diagram for the reaction in Your Turn 18.1 by drawing (a) the appropriate species in the boxes provided, and (b) vertical double-headed arrows to indicate the free energies of activation.

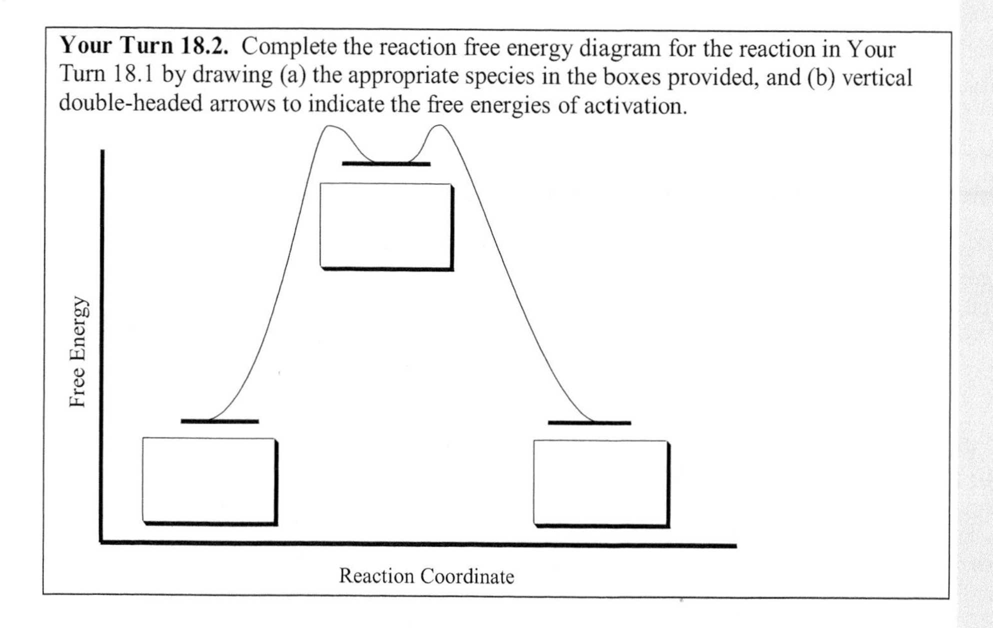

18.1c. Thermodynamics and Reversibility

Looking back at Equation 18-1, notice that the reactants and products are connected by an equilibrium reaction arrow ($\rightleftharpoons$). In other words,

Transesterification is a *reversible* reaction.

Thus, if *t*-butyl benzoate is treated with CH_3O^-, methyl benzoate will be produced via nucleophilic addition-elimination.

Your Turn 18.3. In the space provided below, draw the detailed mechanism for the reverse of the reaction in Equation 18-1.

The reversibility of such a reaction is consistent with the reaction's thermodynamics depicted previously in the free energy diagram in Figure 18-1. Namely, the overall reactants and products appear at roughly the same energy, so the overall energy barrier that must be traversed in the reverse direction is roughly the same as that in the forward direction. Recall from Section 9.12 that, by contrast, a reaction is generally irreversible if the overall products are much lower in energy (i.e., more stable) than the overall reactants.

The reason why base-promoted transesterification reactions are reversible has much to do with charge stability. As we can see, the charged species on the reactant and product sides are both alkoxide anions (RO^-). In both cases, the negative charge resides on O, there is no resonance delocalization of that charge, and an attached alkyl group weakly donates electrons inductively. Thus, both anions have similar stabilities, reflected by the similar pK_a values of their respective conjugate acids, which are 15.5 and 19.

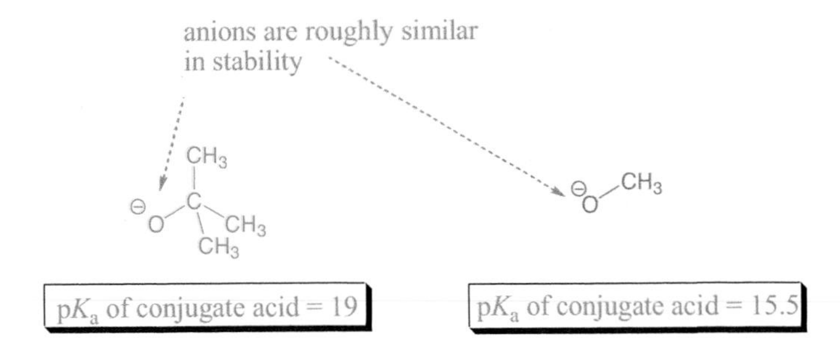

Although base-promoted transesterification reactions are reversible, this is *not* true of all nucleophilic addition-elimination reactions. As we will see, the relative stabilities of the nucleophile and leaving group play major roles.

18.2. REACTION OF AN ESTER WITH HYDROXIDE (SAPONIFICATION) AND ITS REVERSE REACTION

On several occasions throughout this book, we have seen examples in which the hydroxide anion (HO^-) behaves chemically very similar to alkoxide anions (RO^-). Not only do they have similar basicities, but they have similar nucleophilicities as well. Therefore, we should expect HO^- to react with an ester in a manner that is analogous to the base-promoted transesterification we saw in the previous section.

Indeed, as we can see in Equation 18-3, when ethyl acetate is treated with NaOH, followed by acid workup, nucleophilic acyl substitution appears to have taken place.

saponification

H_3C–C(=O)–O–CH_2–CH_3 → 1) KOH, CH_3OH, 60 min., 35 °C; 2) HCl → H_3C–C(=O)–OH

ethyl ethanoate (ethyl acetate) → ethanoic acid (acetic acid) 87% (18-3)

The first reaction in this sequence is known as **saponification**, which literally means "soap making" (*sapo* is the Latin root for "soap"). Ancient civilizations made crude soap by boiling animal fat (which is chiefly long-chain esters) together with wood ash, a source of HO^- ions. (See Problem 18.47 at the end of the chapter.)

Thus, in general,

> An ester can undergo *saponification* when treated with hydroxide (HO^-) to produce a carboxylic acid.

Although the overall reaction in Equation 18-3 is similar to the base-promoted transesterification in Equation 18-1, there are two key differences to note. First, as indicated by the one-directional arrow in Equation 18-3, saponification is *irreversible*, in

Comment [JMK26]: Margin note
Saponification is an irreversible reaction.

contrast to the reversible nature of transesterification. Second, whereas saponification requires acid workup, transesterification does not.

Both of these differences are explained by the mechanism of saponification, shown in Equation 18-4.

Mechanism for the Reaction in Equation 18-3

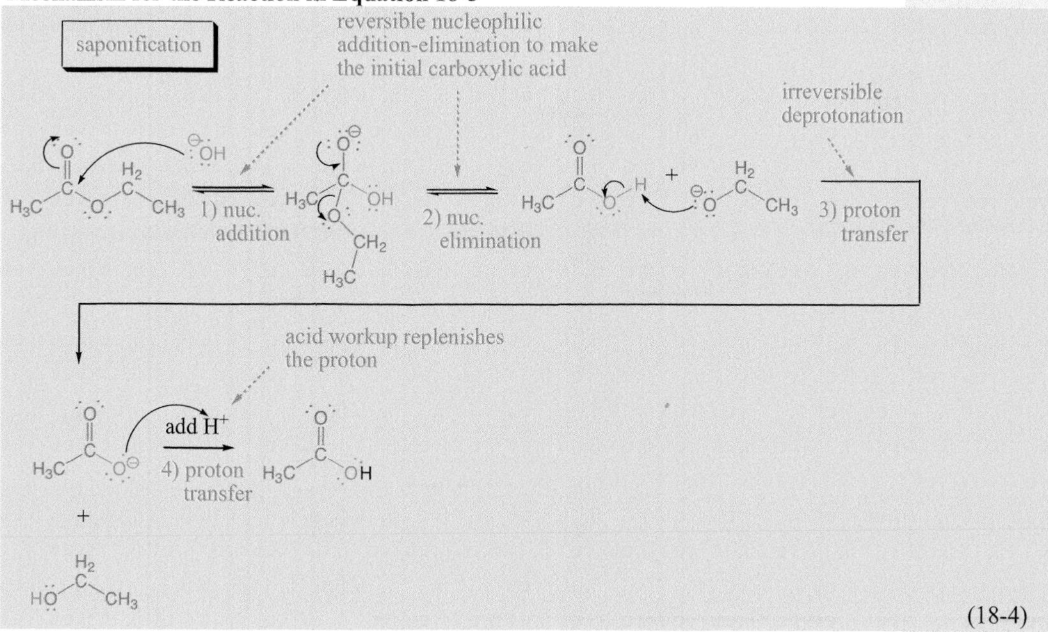

(18-4)

Steps 1 and 2 are identical to the nucleophilic addition and elimination steps we saw previously in Equation 18-2. The carboxylic acid that is produced is then *rapidly* and *irreversibly* deprotonated under the basic conditions of the reactions (see Your Turn 18.3), producing a carboxylate anion (RCO_2^-). That proton is then replenished upon addition of a strong acid.

Your Turn 18.4. To convince yourself that the proton transfer reaction in step 3 in Equation 18-4 is irreversible, use the appropriate pK_a values from Table 6-1 to compute the equilibrium constant, K_{eq}, of that step (see Section 6.2b). Which side of that proton transfer step is favored? To what extent?

K_{eq} =

The reason that the *overall* saponification reaction is irreversible is due entirely to the irreversible deprotonation in step 3. You will notice that the initial carboxylic acid is produced reversibly, and is in equilibrium with the starting ester. As that carboxylic acid is produced, it is continually removed from the equilibrium via step 3. According to Le Châtelier's principle, the equilibrium is thus continually shifted toward products, which helps drive the reaction to completion.

Comment [JMK27]: Margin note. The irreversible deprotonation that occurs in step 3 of saponification (Equation 18-4) makes the overall reaction irreversible.

The irreversible nature of a saponification reaction can be understood better from its reaction free energy diagram, shown in Figure 8-2. Notice that the immediate products of nucleophilic addition-elimination—the carboxylic acid and the alkoxide anion—appear at roughly the same energy as the overall reactants, just as we saw in Figure 8-1. By contrast, the products of the proton transfer in step 3—a carboxylate anion and an alcohol—are much lower in energy, due in large part to the resonance stabilization in the carboxylate anion. That additional stability gained in step 3 makes the overall reaction much more favorable energetically.

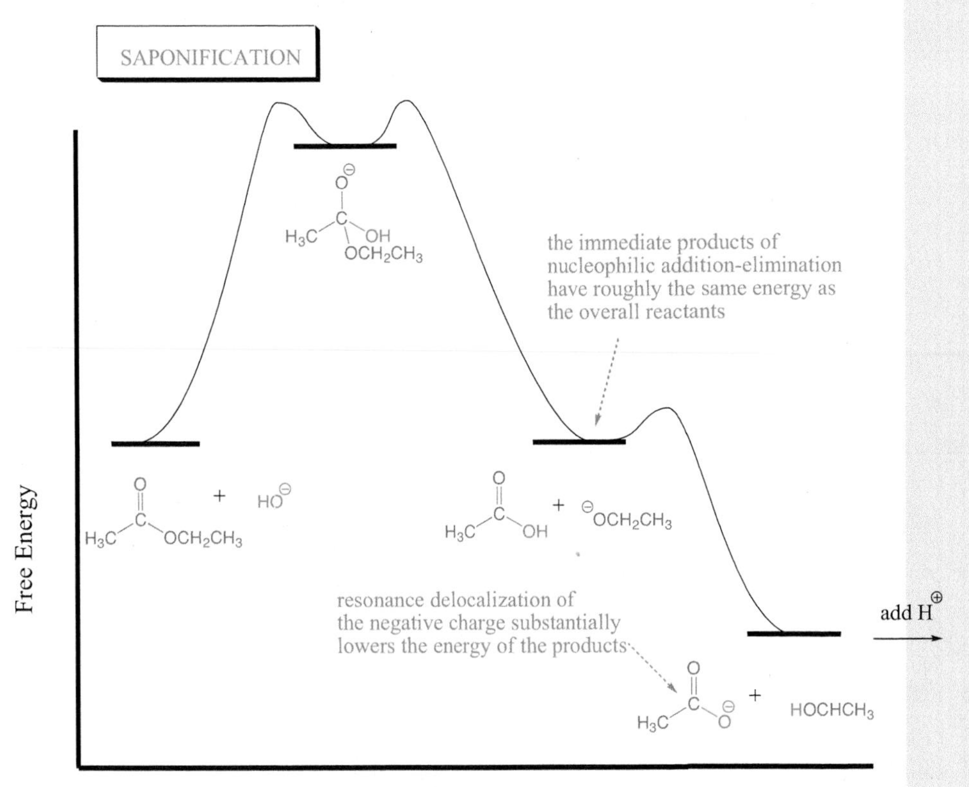

Figure 18-2. Free energy diagram of a saponification reaction
The direct products of nucleophilic addition-elimination, RCO_2H and RO^-, have roughly the same energy as the overall reactants. The products of the proton transfer in the third step, however, are substantially lower in energy, due largely to the resonance delocalization of the negative charge in the carboxylate anion.

A disadvantage of the irreversible proton transfer between a carboxylic acid and an alkoxide anion arises when we attempt to produce an ester from a carboxylic acid. As shown in Equation 18-5, an alkoxide anion simply deprotonates the carboxylic acid and no further reaction takes place.

Comment [JMK28]: **Margin note**
An ester cannot be produced by treating a carboxylic acid with an alkoxide anion.

irreversible proton transfer

no further reaction takes place

$$RCO_2H + RO^- \longrightarrow RCO_2^- + ROH \qquad (18\text{-}5)$$

You might imagine that a nucleophilic addition-elimination reaction can still take place involving the newly formed carboxylate anion and ROH, shown below at left, but such a reaction is not feasible. The carboxylate anion has two equivalent resonance structures, heavily stabilizing the carbonyl group's π electrons. The ROH nucleophile is a weak nucleophile, and thus cannot overcome such resonance stabilization.

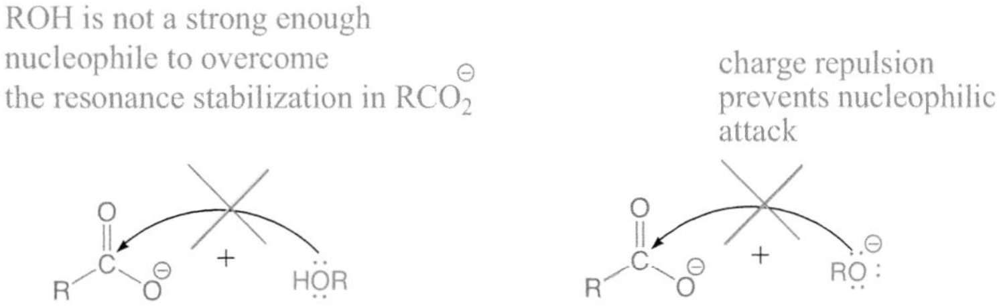

ROH is not a strong enough nucleophile to overcome the resonance stabilization in $RCO_2^{\ominus}$

charge repulsion prevents nucleophilic attack

Moreover, it is not feasible for any excess RO^- to attack the newly formed carboxylate anion (shown above at right). Not only is the carboxylate anion's resonance stabilization difficult to overcome, but nucleophilic attack is made even more difficult by the charge repulsion between the two negatively charged species.

Your Turn 18.5. To illustrate the stabilization of a carboxylate anion, draw the resonance structure and resonance hybrid in the spaces provided below.

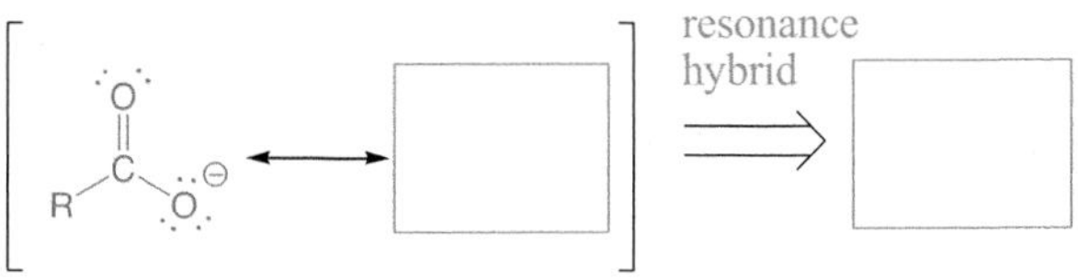

resonance hybrid

Even though carboxylic acids do not undergo nucleophilic addition-elimination under the conditions we have seen here, there are other conditions that make such reactions feasible. Later in this chapter, for example, we will see that carboxylic acids undergo nucleophilic addition-elimination with $LiAlH_4$. And in Chapter 19, we will in fact see that esters can be produced from carboxylic acids under acidic conditions.

Problem 18.2. For each reaction below, draw the complete, detailed mechanism and predict the overall products.

(a)

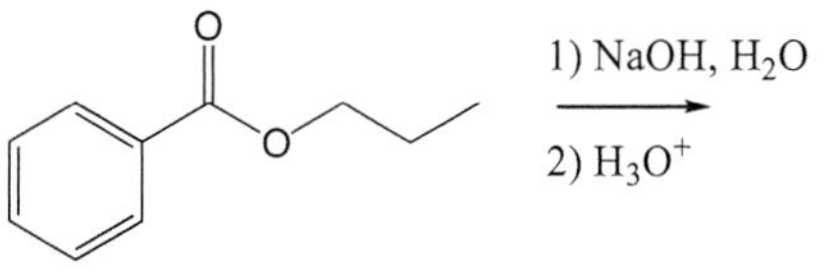

1) NaOH, H_2O
2) H_3O^+

(b)

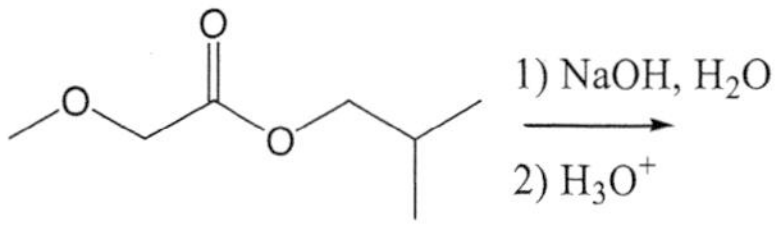

1) NaOH, H_2O
2) H_3O^+

18.3. ACYL SUBSTITUTIONS INVOLVING OTHER CARBOXYLIC ACID DERIVATIVES: THE THERMODYNAMICS OF ACYL SUBSTITUTION

The acyl substitution reactions we have examined thus far have been quite limited in scope, involving an ester as the acid derivative, and either RO^- or HO^- as the nucleophile. However, numerous other acyl substitutions can be carried out, simply by using different combinations of acid derivatives and nucleophiles. For example, as shown in Equation 18-6, CH_3O^- can displace Cl^- from an acid chloride to produce an ester.

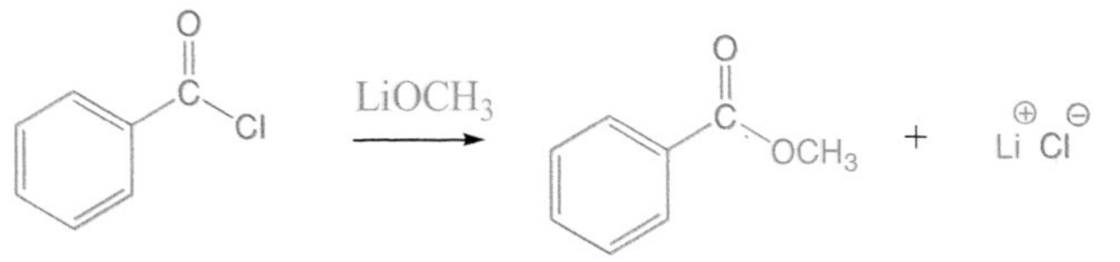

benzoyl chloride —$LiOCH_3$→ methyl benzoate 84% + $Li^{\oplus}$ $Cl^{\ominus}$

(18-6)

The mechanism for this reaction is shown in Equation 18-7. It consists of the usual nucleophilic addition and elimination steps, and proceeds through a tetrahedral intermediate.

Mechanism for the Reaction in Equation 18-6

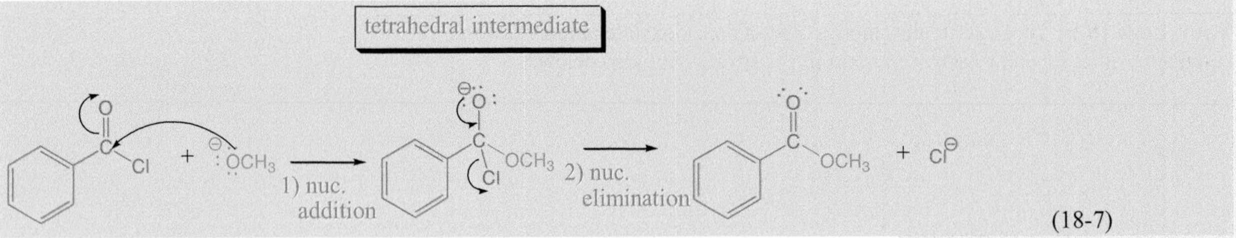

tetrahedral intermediate

1) nuc. addition

2) nuc. elimination

(18-7)

Your Turn 18.6. An ester such as methyl acetate can react with H_2N^- to produce an amide. The nucleophilic addition-elimination mechanism that describes this reaction is shown below. (a) Add the curved arrows to show the electron movement. (b) Under each reaction arrow, write the name of the elementary step taking place. (c) Label the tetrahedral intermediate.

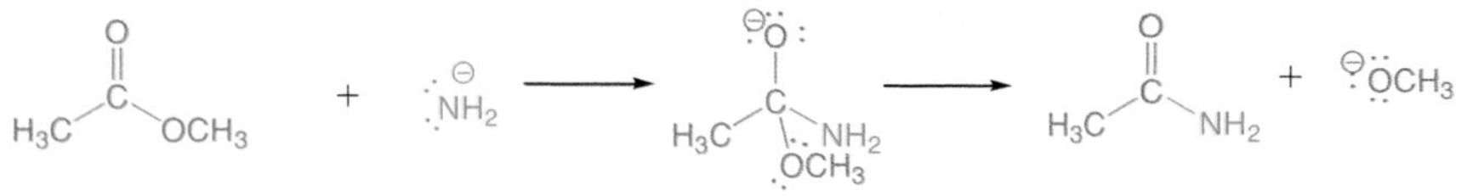

Not every combination of acid derivative and nucleophile, however, leads to an effective acyl substitution reaction. As shown below, for example, essentially no acyl substitution takes place when an ester is treated with chloride ion.

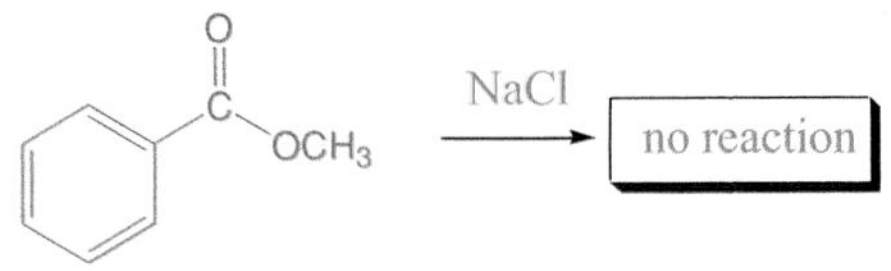

methyl benzoate —NaCl→ no reaction

(18-8)

We can understand why by examining the generic overall acyl substitution reaction in Equation 18-9. As we can see, the nucleophile (Nu^-) bears a negative charge on the reactant side, and the leaving group (L^-) bears the negative charge in the products.

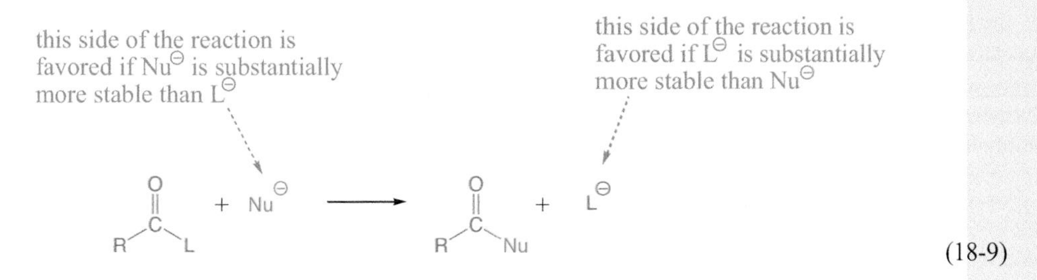

(18-9)

If L^- is more stable than Nu^-, the reaction is energetically favorable. This is the case with the reaction in Equation 18-6, as the leaving group, Cl^-, is more stable than the nucleophile, CH_3O^-. By contrast, if Nu^- is more stable than L^-, then the reaction is not energetically favorable, and thus does not proceed readily. This is the case with the reaction in Equation 18-8.

Such ideas pertaining to whether an acyl substitution reaction is energetically favorable can be summarized in a "stability ladder," shown in Figure 18-3.

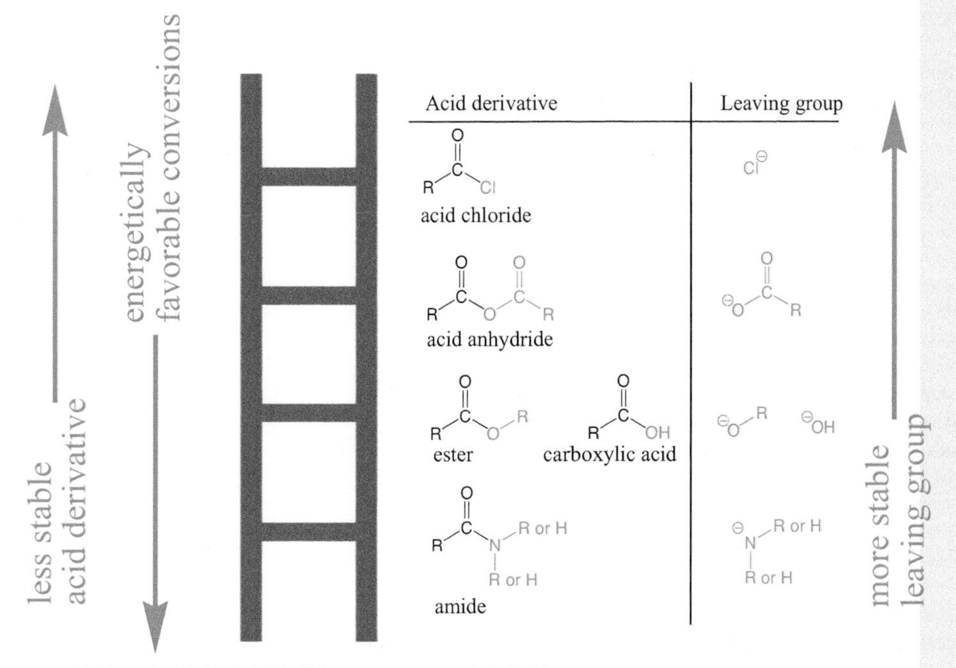

Figure 18-3. The "stability ladder" for carboxylic acid derivatives
A reaction that converts an acid derivative from a higher rung to a lower rung is energetically favorable and generally takes place readily. Going from a lower to a higher rung is not favorable, and is generally quite difficult to carry out.

As we know from experience, descending a real ladder is easier than ascending it. Similarly,

- An acyl substitution that converts an acid derivative from a higher rung on the stability ladder to one on a lower rung of the ladder is energetically favorable.
- An acyl substitution that converts an acid derivative from a lower rung on the stability ladder to one on a higher rung of the ladder is *not* energetically favorable.

For example, the conversion of an acid chloride (RCOCl) to an ester (RCO_2R) represents descending two rungs on the stability ladder, and thus is energetically favorable. This is consistent with what we concluded earlier, from the fact that the reaction in Equation

18-6 readily takes place. By the same token, the conversion of an ester to an acid chloride is *not* favorable, consistent with the lack of reaction in Equation 18-8.

Your Turn 18.7. Indicate whether each of the following conversions would be energetically favorable or unfavorable.

(a) O O O Cl

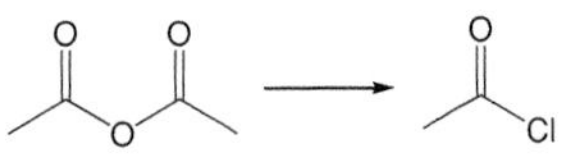

(b) O N H O O

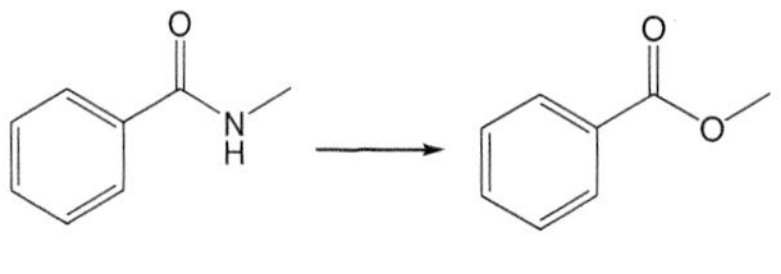

(c) O Cl O O

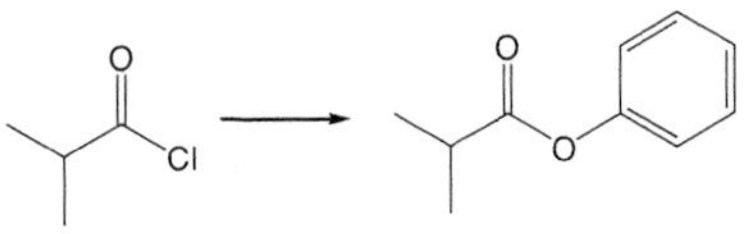

(d) O O O O HO OH O

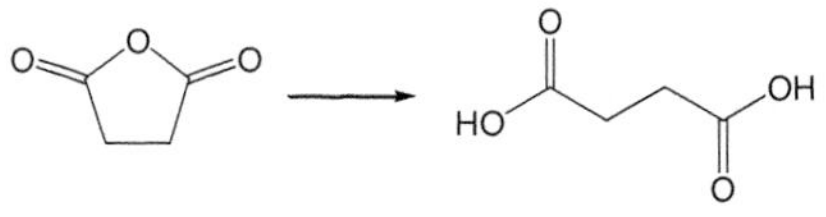

Solved Problem 18.1. Determine whether or not the following reaction will take place. If so, draw the complete, detailed mechanism and predict the major product(s).

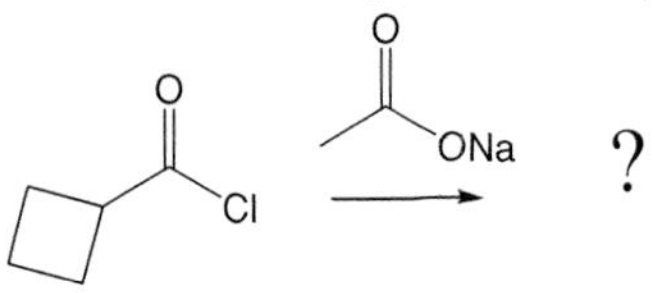

O Cl O ONa ?

Think. What is the nucleophile? What is the leaving group? Is the potential acyl substitution reaction energetically favorable?

Solve. The nucleophile is the acetate anion, $CH_3CO_2^-$, and the leaving group is Cl^-, part of the acid chloride. In an acyl substitution reaction between these species, $CH_3CO_2^-$ replaces Cl^- in a nucleophilic addition-elimination mechanism, as shown below.

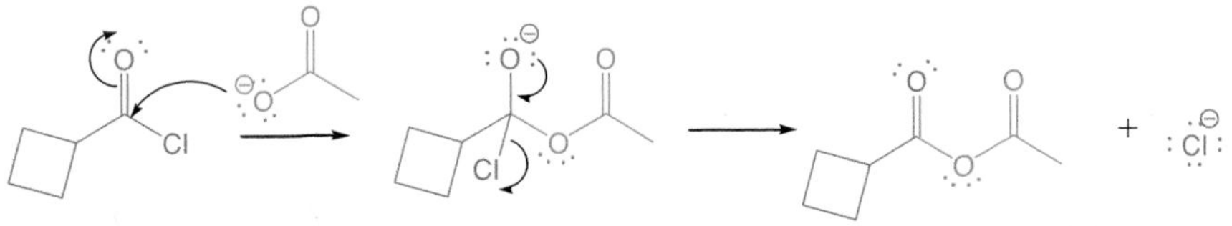

O Cl O O O O Cl O O O O O + Cl

Notice that in the stability ladder, the product acid derivative, an acid anhydride, is below the reactant acid derivative, an acid chloride. Therefore, this reaction is energetically favorable and will take place readily.

Problem 18.3. For each of the following reactions, draw the complete, detailed mechanism and predict the major product(s). If no reaction takes place, write "no reaction."

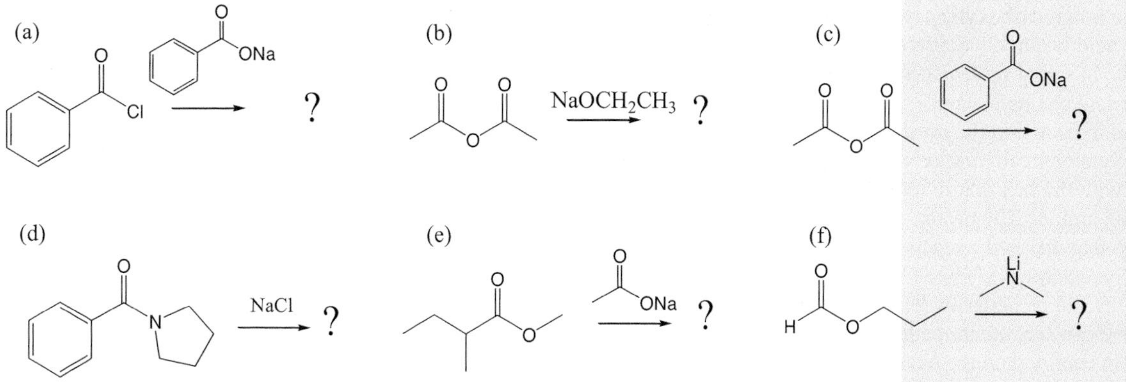

(a) ONa, Cl → ?

(b) $NaOCH_2CH_3$ → ?

(c) ONa → ?

(d) N, NaCl → ?

(e) ONa → ?

(f) H, O, Li, N → ?

18.4. CARBOXYLIC ACIDS FROM AMIDES: THE GABRIEL SYNTHESIS OF PRIMARY AMINES

In Section 18.3, we learned that the conversion of an amide ($RCONR_2$) to a carboxylic acid (RCO_2H) is energetically *unfavorable*, represented by the fact that an amide appears on a lower rung of the stability ladder (Figure 18-3) than does a carboxylic acid. However, as shown in Equation 18-10, we can carry out such a transformation by treating an amide with HO^-, followed by acid workup.

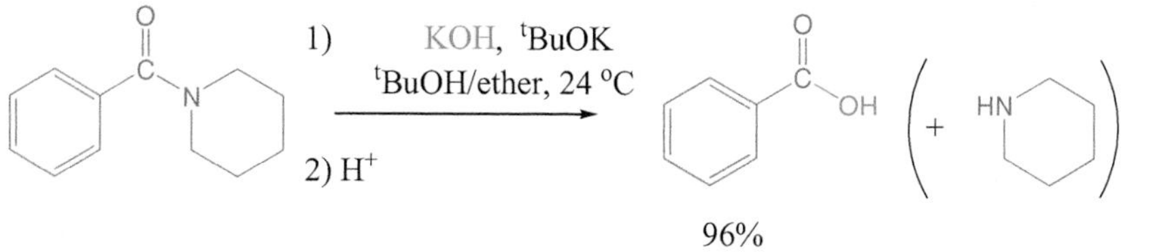

1) KOH, ^tBuOK, ^tBuOH/ether, 24 °C
2) H^+

OH + HN

96%

(18-10)

This apparent discrepancy can be reconciled by the mechanism for this reaction, which is shown in Equation 18-11.

Mechanism for the Reaction in Equation 18-10

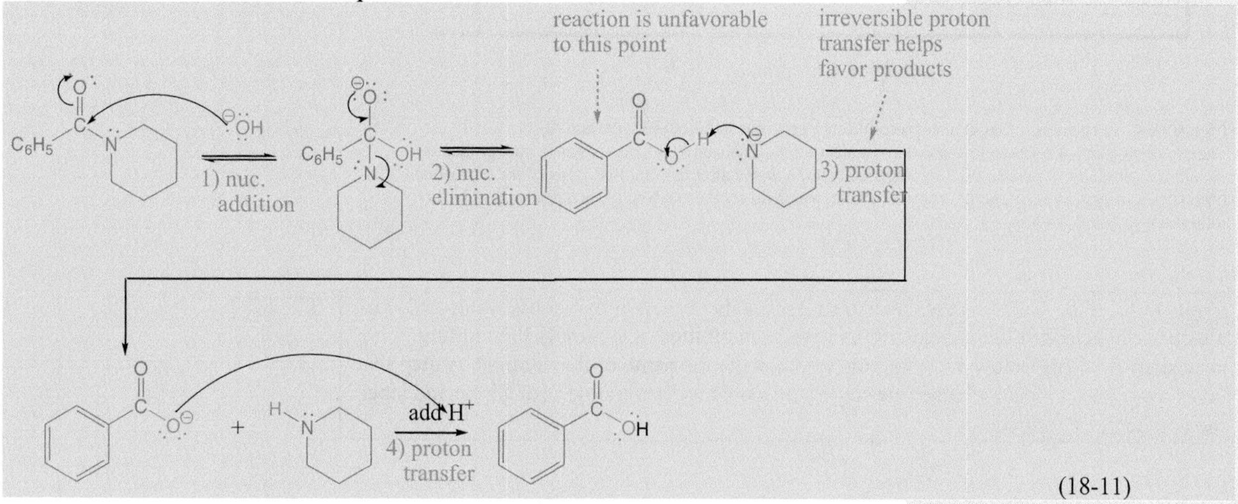

reaction is unfavorable to this point

irreversible proton transfer helps favor products

C_6H_5 C N O OH

1) nuc. addition

C_6H_5 C O OH N

2) nuc. elimination

C O H N

3) proton transfer

C O + H N

add H^+

4) proton transfer

C OH

(18-11)

The first two steps comprise the usual nucleophilic addition-elimination mechanism to produce the initial carboxylic acid. Under the basic conditions of the reaction, that carboxylic acid is quickly deprotonated in step 3, producing a carboxylate anion. Finally, acid workup in step 4 replenishes the proton on the carboxylate anion so that the carboxylic acid can be isolated.

As indicated in the mechanism, the direct formation of that carboxylic acid from an amide is energetically unfavorable, and the reaction is reversible to that point. This is consistent with the fact that in the stability ladder, a carboxylic acid appears on a higher rung than an amide. The proton transfer in step 3, however, is irreversible, and thus is the critical step that drives the reaction toward products—*without that step, no considerable amount of product would form*.

Comment [JMK29]: **Margin note.** The irreversible proton transfer in step 3 of Equation 18-11 makes feasible the conversion of an amide to a carboxylic acid.

This can be better understood from the reaction free energy diagram in Figure 18-4. As we can see, the immediate products from nucleophilic addition and elimination are higher in energy than the overall reactants. Thus, direct acyl substitution to form the carboxylic acid is energetically unfavorable. The irreversible proton transfer in the third step, however, is responsible for lowering the energy dramatically, which helps favor products.

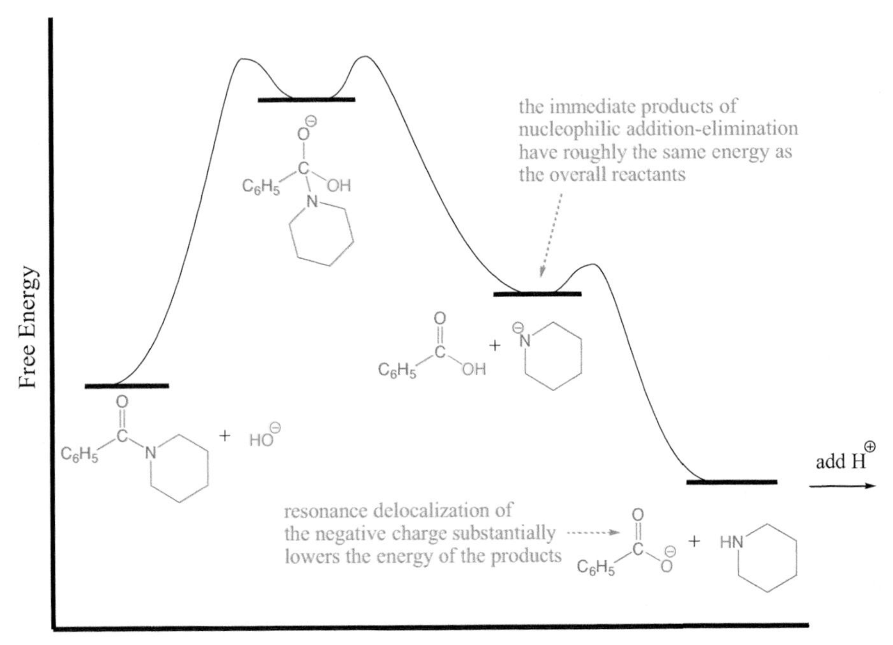

Figure 18-4. Free energy diagram corresponding to the mechanism in Equation 18-11
The direct products of nucleophilic addition-elimination, RCO_2H and R_2N^-, are higher in energy than the overall reactants. Thus the reaction is energetically unfavorable after the first two steps of the mechanism. The third step, however, is quite energetically favorable, which drives the reaction toward products. This is followed by an acid workup.

Your Turn 18.8. Below is the mechanism for another reaction that converts an amide to a carboxylic acid, but the curved arrows have been omitted. (a) Supply the missing curved arrows. (b) Below each reaction arrow, write the name of the elementary step that takes place and indicate whether the step is reversible or irreversible. (c) Circle and label the tetrahedral intermediate.

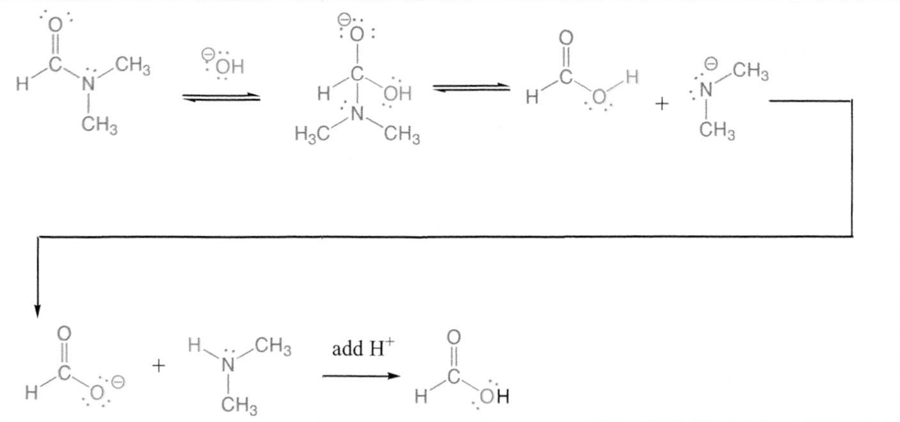

It is also helpful to consider the parallels between the mechanism in Equation 18-11 and the mechanism for saponification we saw previously in Equation 18-4. In both cases, the acyl substitution product is initially formed after the first two steps under equilibrium (i.e., reversible) conditions. And in both cases, an irreversible proton transfer in step 3 drives the reaction toward products, prior to a final acid workup.

Problem 18.4. For each of the following reactions, draw the complete, detailed mechanism and predict the major product(s).

(a) 1) NaOH, 2) H_3O^+ ?

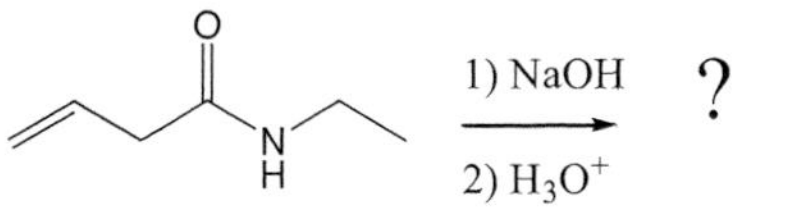

(b) 1) NaOH, 2) H_3O^+ ?

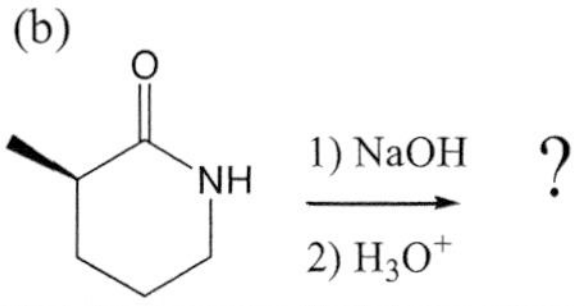

Although the carboxylic acid is usually the desired product of an acyl substitution such as that in Equation 18-10, there are instances where we wish to isolate the amine. One such reaction is the **Gabriel synthesis**, an example of which is shown in Equation 18-12.

The *Gabriel synthesis* is an effective way to synthesize a primary amine (RNH_2) from an alkyl halide.

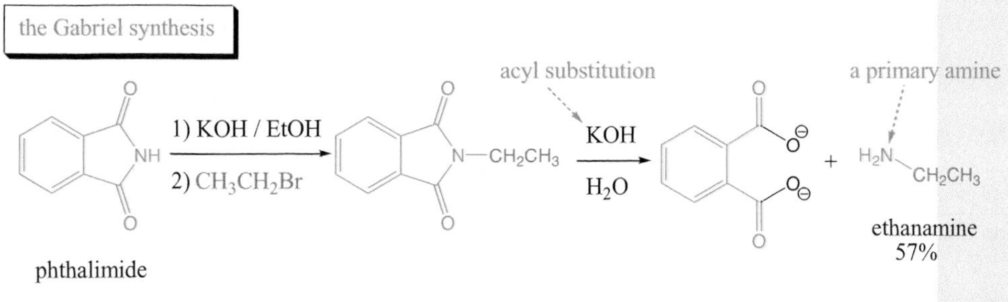

the Gabriel synthesis

phthalimide → 1) KOH / EtOH, 2) CH_3CH_2Br → (acyl substitution) KOH, H_2O → + (a primary amine) ethanamine 57%

(18-12)

In the Gabriel synthesis, phthalimide is first treated with a strong base such as potassium hydroxide, followed by an alkyl halide. Subsequent treatment with hydroxide then liberates the primary amine.

As we can see in the mechanism in Equation 18-13, step 1 is simply a proton transfer reaction in which hydroxide deprotonates phthalimide at the N atom. The resulting anion is strongly nucleophilic at N, so when an alkyl halide is added in step 2, an S_N2 reaction ensues. Steps 3 through 8 comprise two successive acyl substitutions, each one similar to the mechanism shown in Equation 18-11.

Mechanism for the Reaction in Equation 18-12

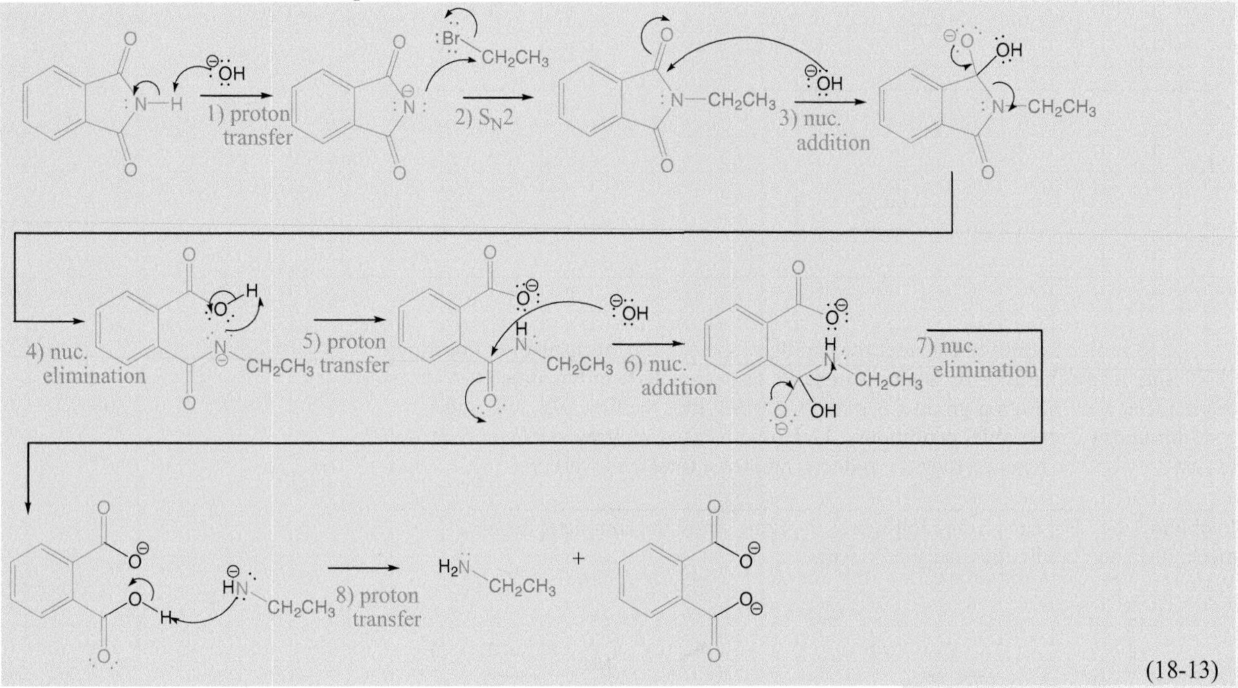

1) proton transfer
2) S_N2
3) nuc. addition
4) nuc. elimination
5) proton transfer
6) nuc. addition
7) nuc. elimination
8) proton transfer

(18-13)

The benefit to synthesizing a primary amine via the Gabriel synthesis can be seen when we consider the complications that arise when a primary amine is synthesized via alkylation of ammonia (Equation 18-14). As we saw in Section 10.2, the primary amine product is contaminated with the products from *polyalkylation*. By contrast, the Gabriel synthesis produces only the intended primary amine.

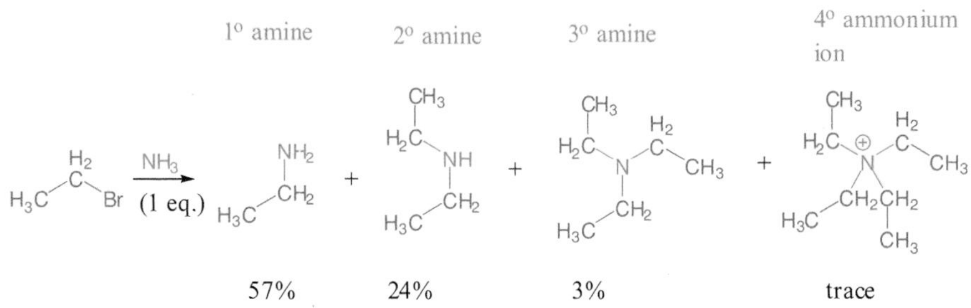

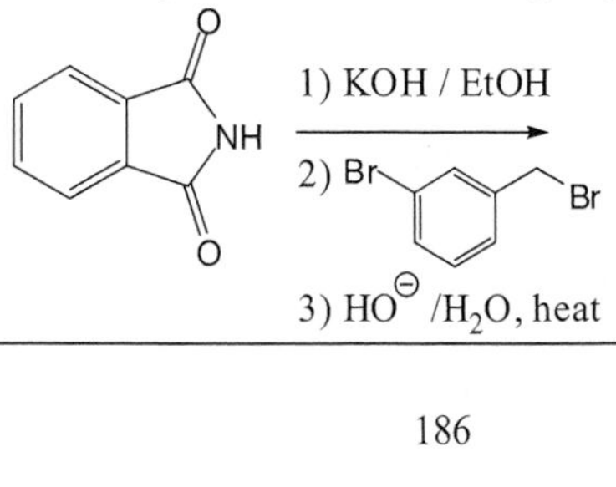

Comment [JMK30]: **Margin note.** The Gabriel synthesis produces primary amines only, whereas alkylation of ammonia produces a mixture of various amines.

$CH_3CH_2Br \xrightarrow[(1\ eq.)]{NH_3}$ 1° amine + 2° amine + 3° amine + 4° ammonium ion

1° amine	2° amine	3° amine	4° ammonium ion
57%	24%	3%	trace

(18-23)

Problem 18.5. Predict the product of the following sequence of reactions.

1) KOH / EtOH
2) Br–CH₂–C₆H₄–CH₂–Br (meta)
3) $HO^{\ominus}$ / H_2O, heat

Solved Problem 18.2. Suggest how to carry out the following synthesis.

O ? NH$_2$

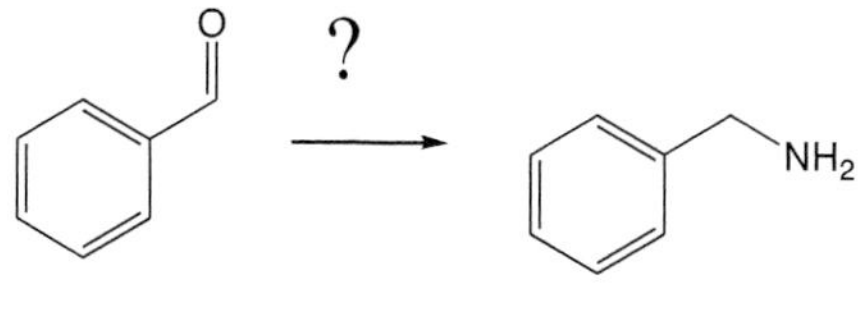

Think. What alkyl halide can be used as a precursor in a Gabriel synthesis of the target amine? How can that alkyl halide be produced from the starting material?

Solve. To produce the target amine in a Gabriel synthesis, a benzyl halide such as bromophenyl methane is required, as shown in the retrosynthetic analysis below. That halide can be synthesized from the corresponding primary alcohol, which, in turn can be produced by reducing the starting aldehyde.

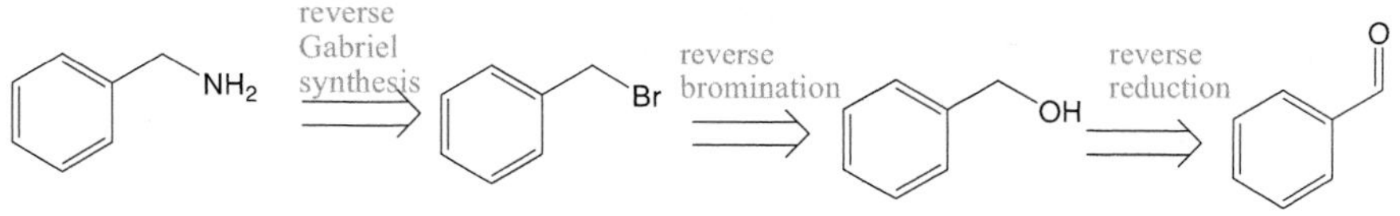

NH$_2$ reverse Gabriel synthesis ⟹ Br reverse bromination ⟹ OH reverse reduction ⟹ O

To write the synthesis, we reverse the arrows and add the appropriate reagents. First we show how to synthesize the alkyl bromide. Subsequently, that alkyl bromide is incorporated along with phthalimide in a Gabriel synthesis.

O NaBH$_4$ / ethanol → OH PBr$_3$ → Br

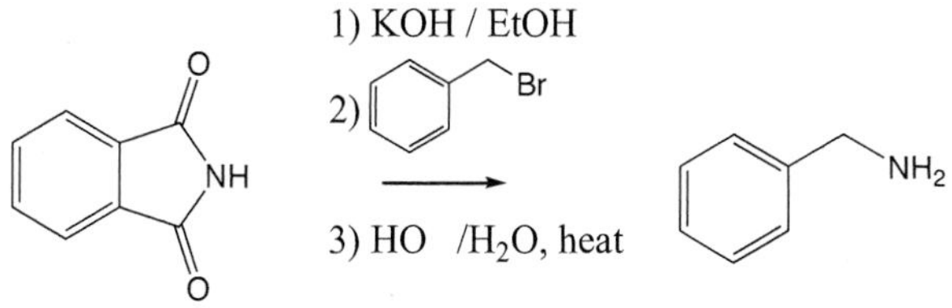

O NH O 1) KOH / EtOH 2) Br 3) HO /H$_2$O, heat → NH$_2$

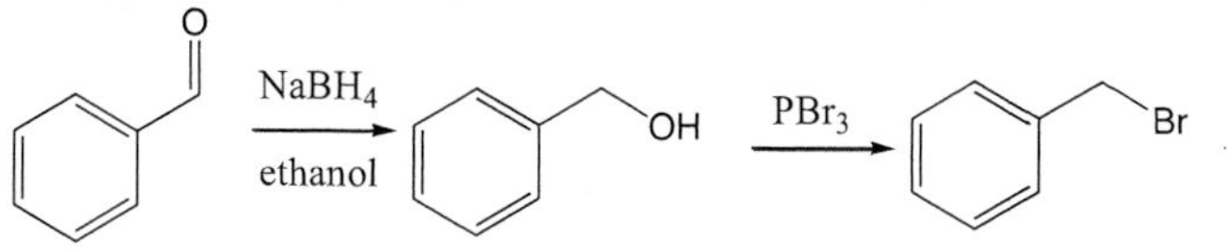

Problem 18.6. Suggest how you would carry out the following synthesis.

O ? → NH$_2$

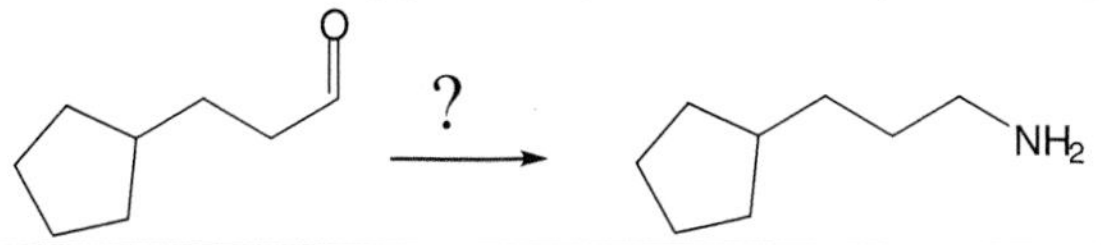

18.5. HALOFORM REACTIONS

In all of the acyl substitution reactions we have discussed so far, one reactant is an acid derivative, in which the carbonyl carbon is bonded to a leaving group. As we can see in Equation 18-24, however, a methyl ketone (RCOCH$_3$) can also undergo acyl substitution when treated with Br$_2$ in aqueous sodium hydroxide, followed by acid workup.

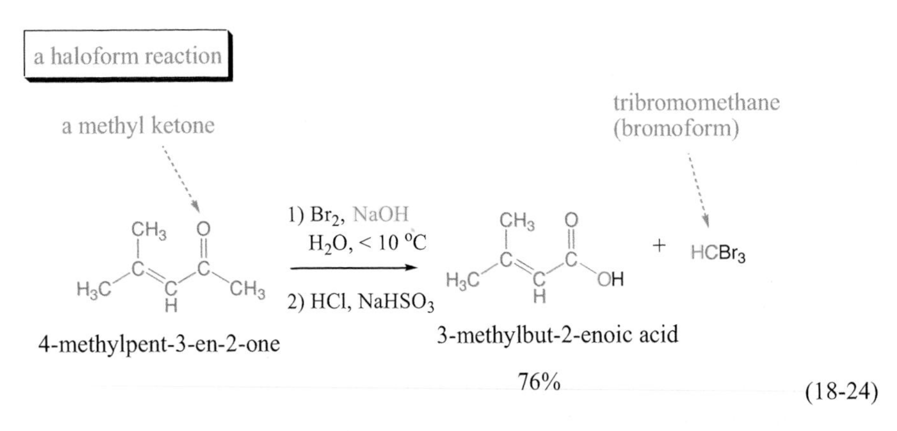

One of the products, bromoform ($HCBr_3$), is an example of a **haloform**, which has the general formula HCX_3 (X is a halogen atom). Thus, the reaction is called a **haloform reaction**. Other haloform reactions can take place when a methyl ketone is treated with Cl_2 or I_2, producing chloroform ($HCCl_3$) or iodoform (HCI_3), respectively. Thus,

> In general, a methyl ketone ($RCOCH_3$) can undergo a haloform reaction when treated with a molecular halogen (X_2) under basic condition, producing a carboxylic acid (RCO_2H) and a haloform (HCX_3) byproduct.

Your Turn 18.9. The reactions below differ from the one in Equation 18-24 only by the identity of the halogen molecule. Draw the products in the boxes provided.

(a) 4-methylpent-3-en-2-one $\xrightarrow[\text{2) HCl}]{\text{1) } Cl_2\text{, NaOH/}H_2O}$ [ ]

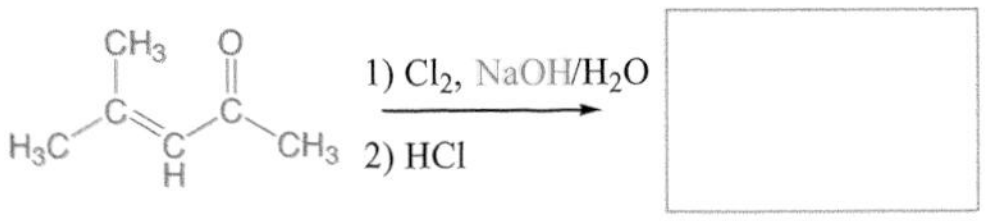

(b) 4-methylpent-3-en-2-one $\xrightarrow[\text{2) HCl}]{\text{1) } I_2\text{, NaOH/}H_2O}$ [ ]

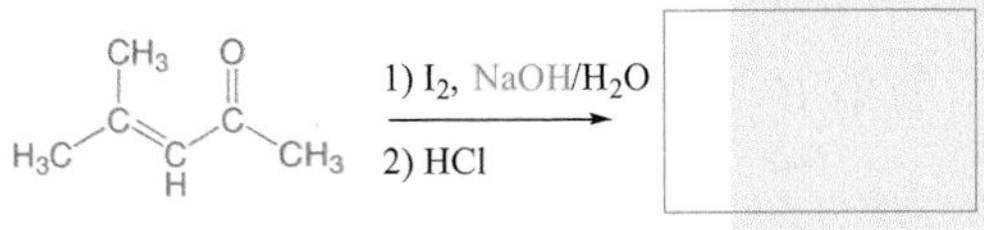

The fact that such an acyl substitution reaction takes place at all should at first seem peculiar, because it appears that HO^- replaces H_3C^-, a very poor leaving group. This peculiarity, however, is explained by the mechanism, shown in Equation 18-25.

Mechanism for the Reaction in Equation 18-24

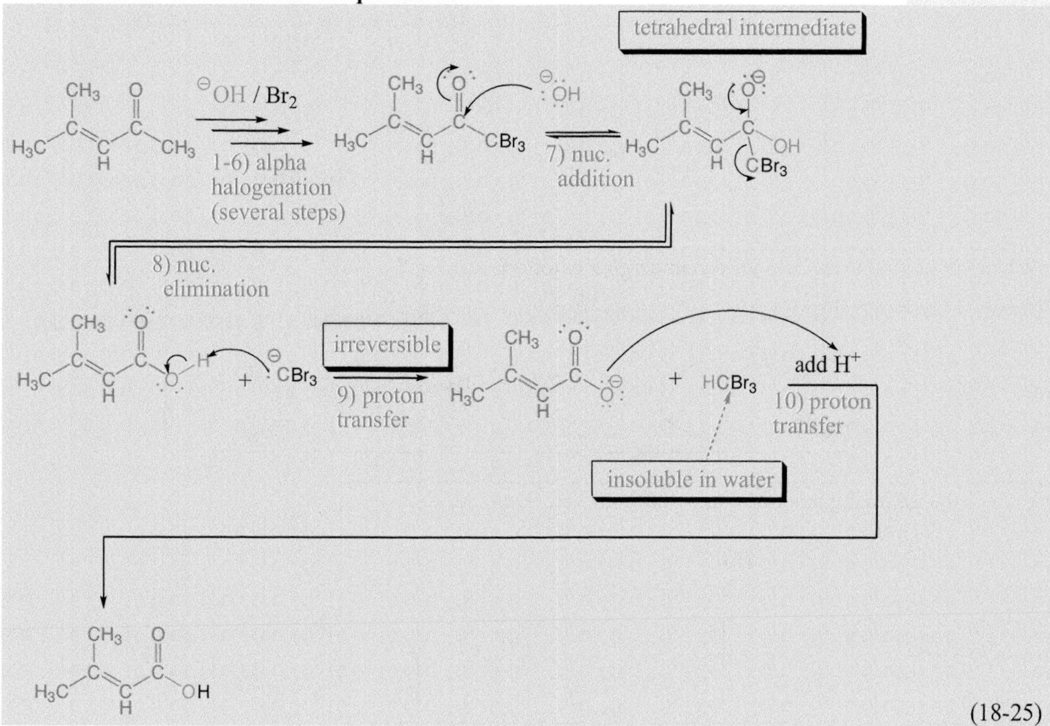

(18-25)

In the first six steps of this mechanism, the three alpha hydrogens on the methyl group are replaced by bromine atoms, according to the alpha halogenation mechanism discussed previously in Section 10.4. The resulting tribromomethyl ketone ($RCOCBr_3$) then undergoes attack by HO^- in step 7 to produce a tetrahedral intermediate, which subsequently eliminates Br_3C^- in step 8 to produce an initial carboxylic acid. In step 9, that carboxylic acid is deprotonated by Br_3C^-, yielding a relatively stable carboxylate anion. In the final acid workup in step 10, the proton is replenished on the carboxylate anion to produce the final carboxylic acid product.

Thus, as we can see, the leaving group in the nucleophilic addition-elimination mechanism is *not* H_3C^-, but instead is Br_3C^-. This is important, because H_3C^- is a very poor leaving group, which, as we learned in Section 9.5, is reflected by the fact that it is among the strongest bases known (pK_a of $CH_4 \sim 50$). By contrast, Br_3C^- is a much better leaving group, reflected by its much weaker basicity (pK_a of $Br_3CH \sim 20$). Notice, in fact, that the basicity of Br_3C^- is close to that of CH_3O^-, whose conjugate acid, CH_3OH, has a pK_a of 16. And as we saw in Section 18-1, CH_3O^- is a suitable leaving group for nucleophilic addition-elimination.

The reason for the relatively good leaving group ability of Br_3C^- has much to do with the inductive effects from the Br atoms. Each Br atom is electron-withdrawing, and thus stabilizes the negative charge that develops on carbon. The collective stabilization brought about by *three* Br atoms enables nucleophilic acyl substitution to take place. Interestingly, as shown below, an ethyl ketone cannot undergo acyl substitution because it has only two alpha hydrogens, so the halogenation product has only two alpha bromines. Without the third bromine atom on the alpha carbon, the leaving group is not sufficiently stable.

Comment [JMK31]: Margin note. The haloform reaction requires a CH_3 group attached to the C=O group in order to generate a relatively good CX_3 leaving group.

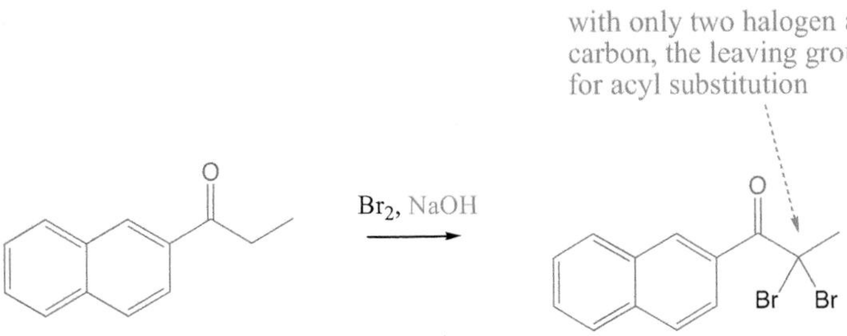

with only two halogen atoms on the alpha carbon, the leaving group is not sufficient for acyl substitution

Br_2, NaOH

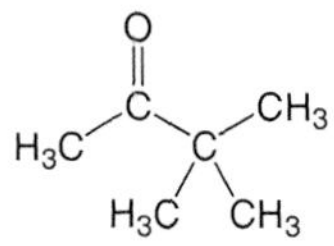

Br Br

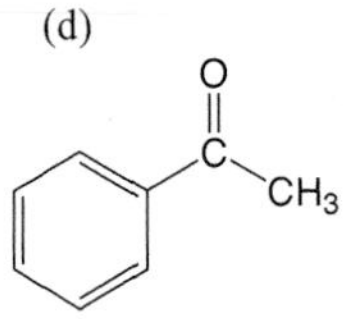

(18-26)

Your Turn 18.10. Which of the following ketones can undergo a haloform reaction?

(a) H_3C C(=O) CH_3 (b) H_3C C(=O) C(H_3C)(CH_3) CH_3 (c) 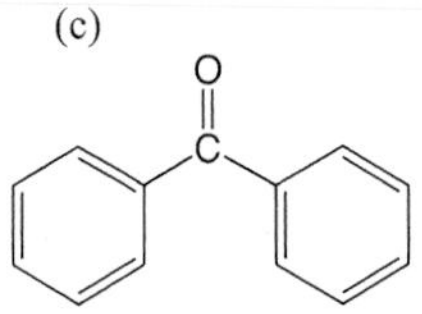 (d) C(=O) CH_3 (e) H_2C=CH–C(=O)–CH(CH_3)CH_3

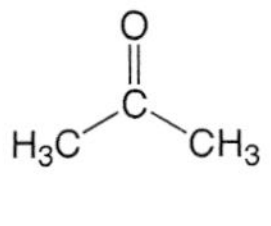

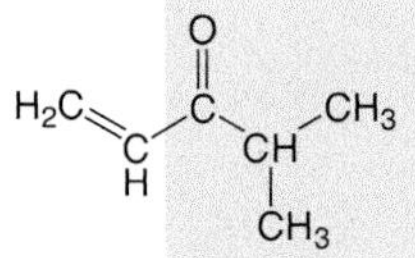

Problem 18.7. For each of the following reactions, draw the complete, detailed mechanism and the major product(s).

(a) Br — 1) Br_2, NaOH (aq) 2) H_3O^+ ?

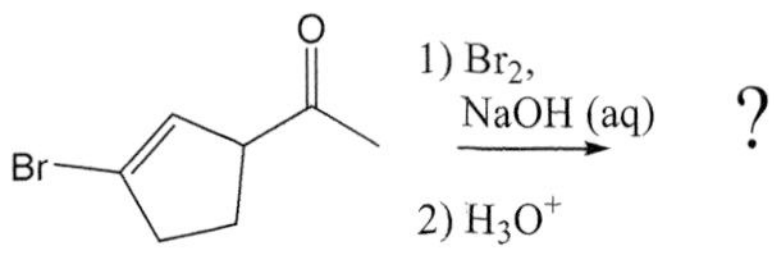

(b) 1) I_2, NaOH (aq) 2) H_3O^+ ?

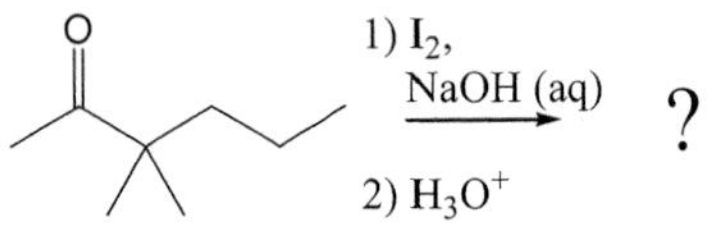

Solved Problem 18.3. Show how to carry out the following synthesis.

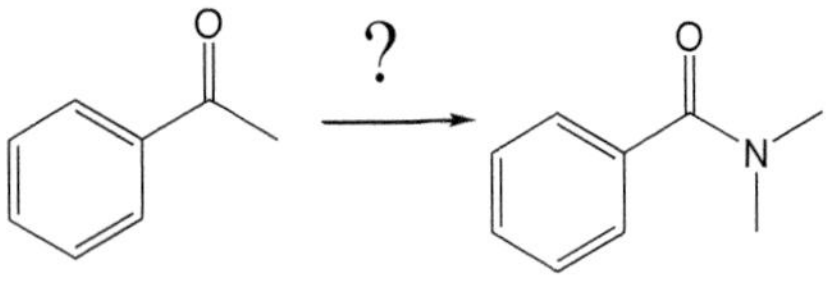

?

N

Think. What reaction can convert a methyl ketone into a compound with a leaving group on the carbonyl carbon? Can the product of that reaction be converted directly into the amide target, or must another precursor be used?

Solve. The starting compound is a methyl ketone, which does not have a suitable leaving group. However, a haloform reaction can be used to convert that methyl ketone into a carboxylic acid.

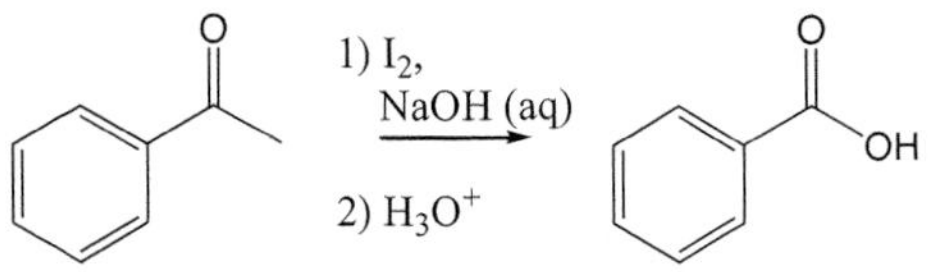

1) I_2, NaOH (aq) 2) H_3O^+ OH

We must now determine how to convert the carboxylic acid into the amide target. In a retrosynthetic analysis, we know that the amide can be produced from an ester via an acyl substitution. The ester, in turn, can be produced using diazomethane (Section 10.5).

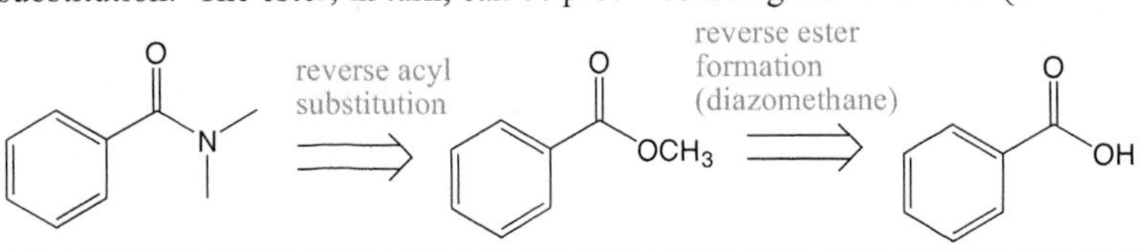

N — reverse acyl substitution ⟹ OCH_3 — reverse ester formation (diazomethane) ⟹ OH

To complete the synthesis, we must reverse the arrows and supply the appropriate reagents.

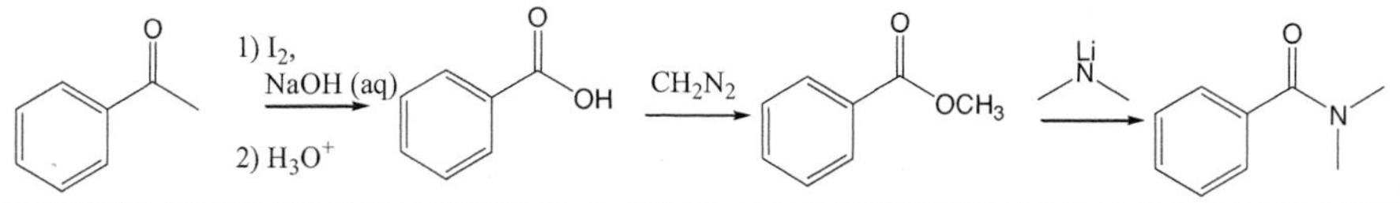

1) I_2, NaOH (aq) 2) H_3O^+ → CH_2N_2 → OCH3 → Li-N(CH3)2 →

Problem 18.8. Show how to carry out the following synthesis.

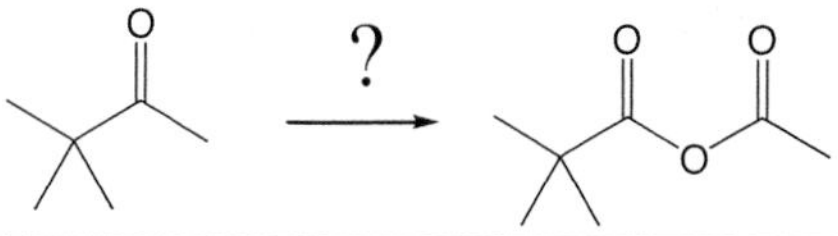

?

It is important to realize that Br_3C^-, despite its three Br atoms, is less stable than HO^-, reflected by its stronger basicity. Consequently, the acyl substitution that takes place (steps 7 and 8 in Equation 18-25) is somewhat unfavorable energetically, and thus is reversible. However, the proton transfer step that follows (step 9 in Equation 18-25) is energetically quite favorable, which helps drive the reaction toward products. Moreover, the haloform that is produced in that step is insoluble in water, so it is effectively removed from the reaction mixture. According to Le Châtelier's principle, this drives the acyl substitution reaction even further toward products.

Of historical interest, prior to the advent of spectroscopy, the iodoform (CHI_3) reaction was commonly used as a test for methyl ketones. Iodoform is a bright yellow solid at room temperature, and is insoluble in water. Therefore, if a bright yellow precipitate appears upon treating an organic compound with I_2 in basic solution, it is likely that the compound is a methyl ketone.

Problem 18.9. A compound whose molecular formula is $C_6H_{12}O$ produces a bright yellow solid when it is treated with iodine and a basic solution of water. The compound's IR spectrum shows a distinct peak at 1,708 cm^{-1} and its ^{1}H-NMR spectrum contains only two singlets: one at 1.2 ppm and one at 2.2 ppm. Integration shows that the upfield signal has three times the area of the downfield signal. (a) Draw the structure for this molecule. (b) Draw the products of the reaction that is described.

18.6. HYDRIDE REDUCING AGENTS

To this point in the chapter, all of the nucleophilic addition-elimination reactions we have examined are ones that form a carboxylic acid or acid derivative as a product. In such reactions, the nucleophile that attacks the polar π becomes a potential leaving group in the product.

However, not all nucleophiles that can attack a carbonyl group are capable of behaving as leaving groups. For example, hydride ions (H^-), from sources such as $NaBH_4$ and $LiAlH_4$, are excellent nucleophiles but very poor leaving groups. As we will see in this section, such nucleophiles can still react with acid derivatives in nucleophilic addition-elimination reactions, but some key differences exist.

We will begin by examining the reactions that acid derivatives and carboxylic acids undergo with the common hydride reagents $NaBH_4$ and $LiAlH_4$. Following these discussions, we will examine reactions involving the specialized hydride reagents diisobutylaluminum hydride and lithium tri-*tert*-butoxyaluminum hydride.

18.6a. Reactions Involving $NaBH_4$

As shown in Equations 18-27 and 18-28 below, $NaBH_4$ can readily reduce acid chlorides and acid anhydrides, the two least stable types of acid derivatives. More specifically,

> Treatment of an acid chloride (RCOCl) or acid anhydride (RCO_2COR) with $NaBH_4$, followed by acid workup, produces a primary alcohol (RCH_2OH).

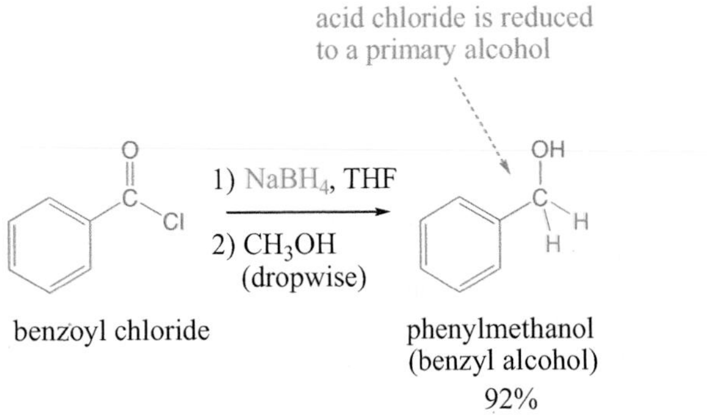

acid chloride is reduced to a primary alcohol

1) $NaBH_4$, THF
2) CH_3OH (dropwise)

benzoyl chloride → phenylmethanol (benzyl alcohol) 92%

(18-27)

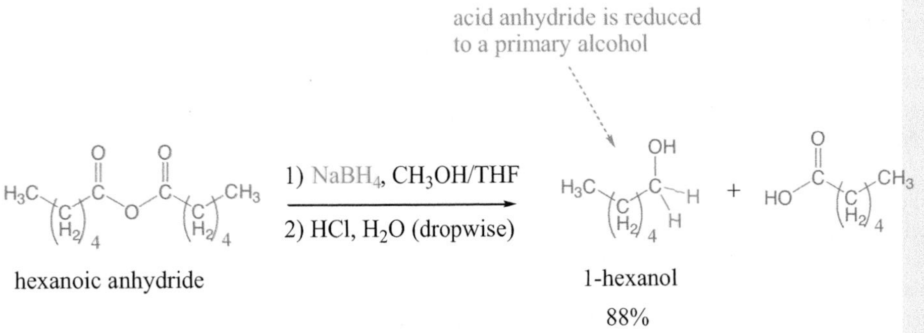

acid anhydride is reduced to a primary alcohol

1) $NaBH_4$, CH_3OH/THF
2) HCl, H_2O (dropwise)

hexanoic anhydride → 1-hexanol 88%

(18-28)

Notice that in the product containing the H^- nucleophile (in red in Equations 18-27 and 18-28), no carbonyl group is present. This is in contrast to the acyl substitution reactions we have seen previously, and is explained by the mechanism shown in Equation 18-29.

Mechanism for the Reaction in Equation 18-27

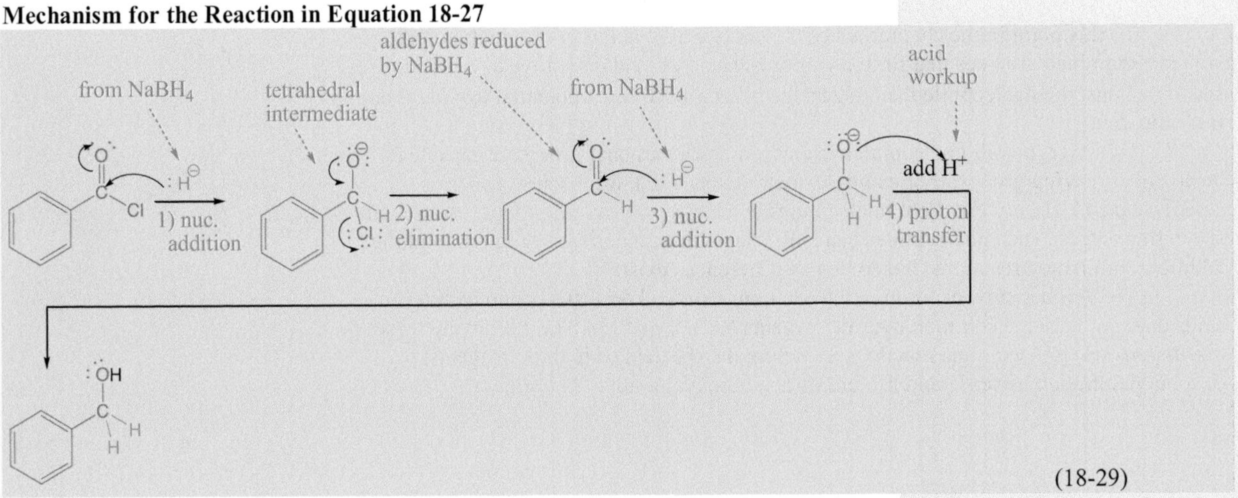

from $NaBH_4$; 1) nuc. addition; tetrahedral intermediate; 2) nuc. elimination; aldehydes reduced by $NaBH_4$; from $NaBH_4$; 3) nuc. addition; acid workup; add H^+; 4) proton transfer

(18-29)

As we can see, the first two steps comprise the usual nucleophilic addition-elimination mechanism, producing an aldehyde as an intermediate. Under these reduction conditions, however, that aldehyde reacts rapidly with another equivalent of hydride to produce an alkoxide anion (Section 15.5). Subsequent acid workup yields the alcohol.

Your Turn 18.11. Below is the mechanism for the $NaBH_4$ reduction of a different acid chloride, but the curved arrow notation has been omitted. (a) Supply the missing curved arrows. (b) Write the name of each elementary step underneath each reaction arrow. (c) Circle and label the tetrahedral intermediate.

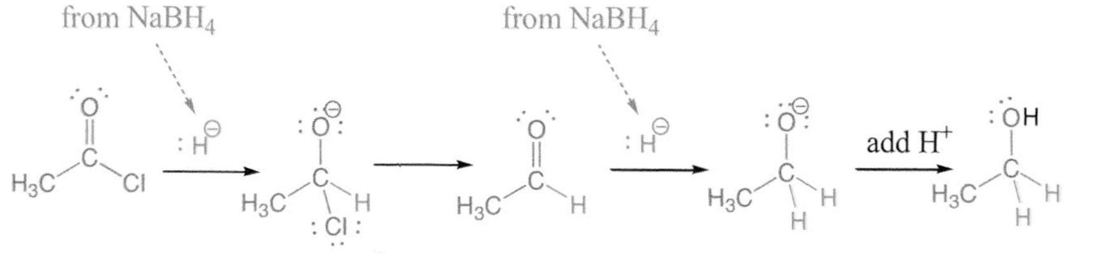

from $NaBH_4$ from $NaBH_4$

add H^+

Problem 18.10. Draw the complete, detailed mechanism for the reaction in Equation 18-28.

Problem 18.11. For each of the following reactions, predict the major product and draw the complete, detailed mechanism.

(a) 1) $NaBH_4$ 2) H_3O^+ ?

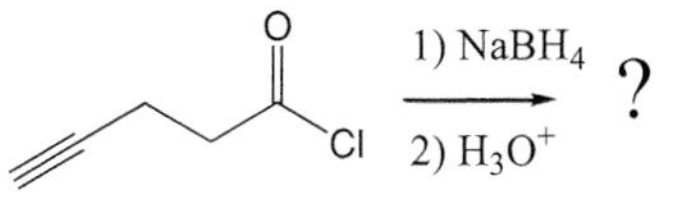

(b) 1) $NaBH_4$ 2) H_3O^+ ?

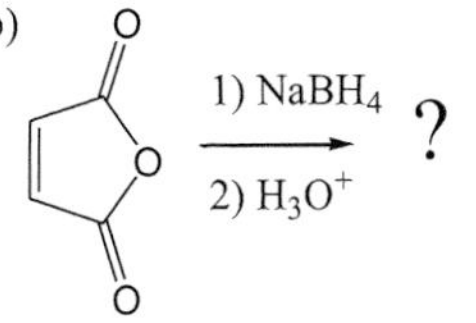

Esters, too, can be reduced by $NaBH_4$ (Equation 18-30) to a primary alcohol. However, as indicated, the reaction is *very* slow and is generally not practical for synthesis. The sluggishness of this reaction reflects the resonance stabilization involving the carbonyl group and the alkoxy leaving group, shown previously in Figure 18-1. (This will be discussed further in Chapter 19.)

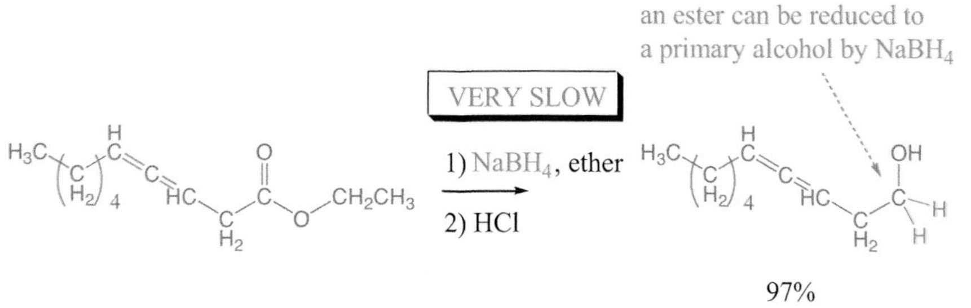

an ester can be reduced to a primary alcohol by $NaBH_4$

VERY SLOW

1) $NaBH_4$, ether
2) HCl

97%

(18-30)

We can take advantage of an ester's low reactivity to *selectively* reduce a more reactive carbonyl-containing functional group, such as an acid chloride, acid anhydride, aldehyde, or ketone. For example, in the β-ketoester in Equation 18-31, the ketone functional group is readily reduced to the alcohol, but the ester functional group is unaffected.

Comment [JMK32]: Margin note
$NaBH_4$ can be used to selectively reduce acid chlorides, acid anhydrides, ketones, and aldehydes over esters.

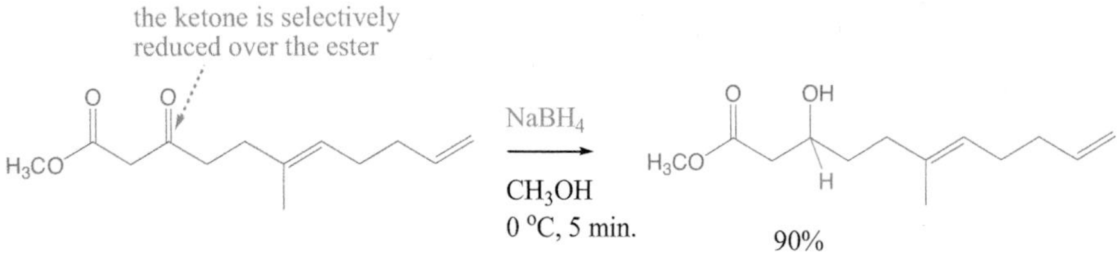

the ketone is selectively reduced over the ester

$NaBH_4$, CH_3OH, 0 °C, 5 min. — 90%

(18-31)

Given that $NaBH_4$ reduces esters relatively slowly, it should be no surprise that $NaBH_4$ is ineffective at reducing amides, as indicated in Equation 18-32. Recall from Figure 18-3 that amides are even more stable than esters.

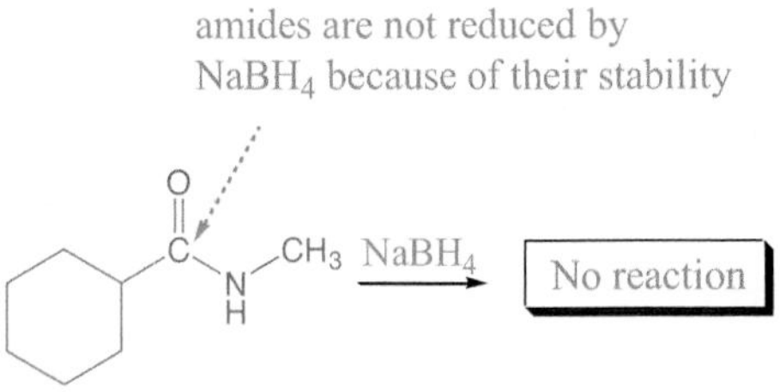

amides are not reduced by $NaBH_4$ because of their stability

$NaBH_4$ → No reaction

(18-32)

Perhaps somewhat surprisingly, however,

$NaBH_4$ cannot reduce carboxylic acids.

The reason this might be surprising is that carboxylic acids appear on the same rung of the stability ladder (Figure 18-3) as esters, and esters are in fact reduced by $NaBH_4$. Realize, however, that a carboxylic acid possesses a relatively *acidic proton*, whereas an ester does not. The H^- from $NaBH_4$ is basic, and therefore deprotonates the carboxylic acid (Equation 18-33) before nucleophilic addition occurs (recall from Chapter 8 that proton transfer reactions are very fast). The product is a carboxylate anion, RCO_2^-, which, owing to its large amount of resonance stabilization, does not react further with $NaBH_4$.

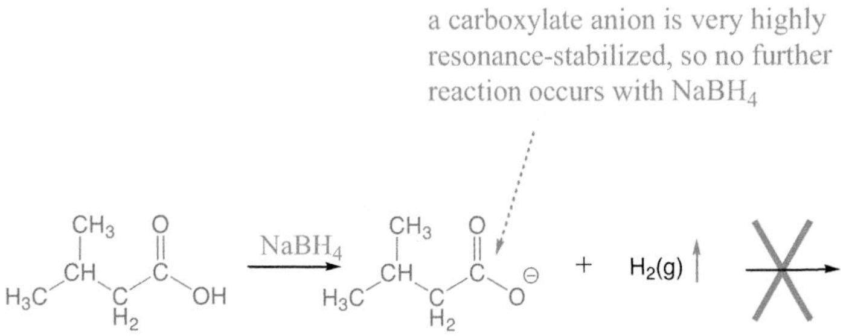

a carboxylate anion is very highly resonance-stabilized, so no further reaction occurs with $NaBH_4$

$NaBH_4$ → + $H_2(g)$↑

(18-33)

Your Turn 18.12. Draw the mechanism for the reaction in Equation 18-33. (You may wish to review Section 15.5.)

Solved Problem 18.4. For the following reaction, draw the complete, detailed mechanism and predict the major product.

OCH3 OCH3 O O Cl NaBH4 ethanol ?

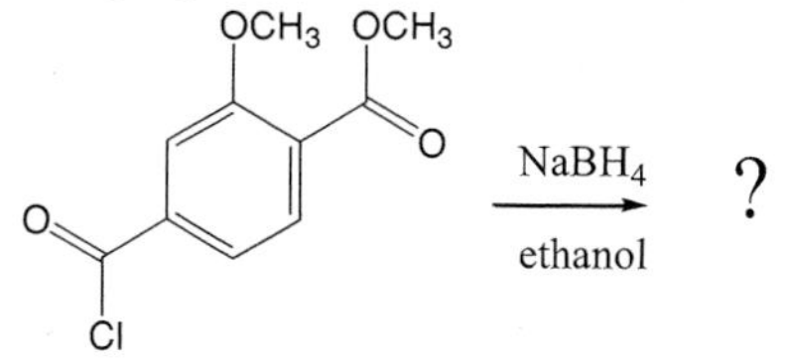

Think. Which functional groups in the reactant can be reduced by $NaBH_4$? Does the reduction of one of those groups take place more readily than the other(s)?

Solve. The acid chloride and ester groups can be reduced by $NaBH_4$ to produce primary alcohols. The ether group cannot be reduced by $NaBH_4$. Whereas $NaBH_4$ reduces an acid chloride readily, reduction of an ester by $NaBH_4$ is sluggish, so the acid chloride will be reduced selectively. The mechanism and major product for this reaction are shown below.

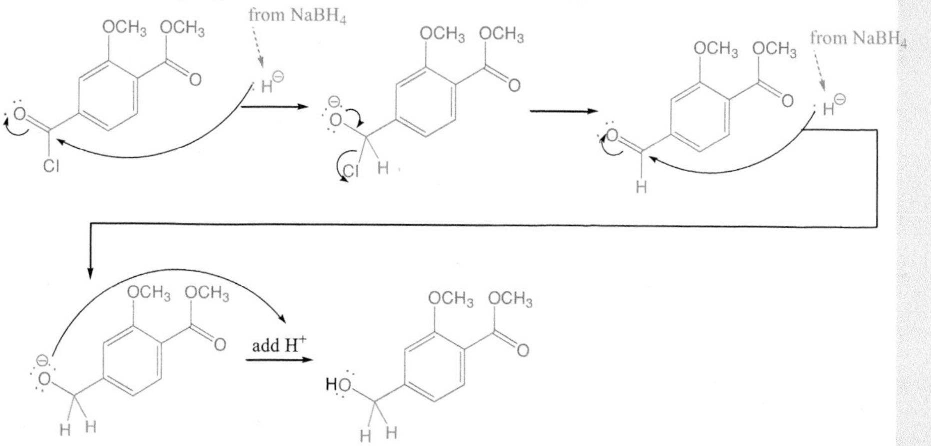

from $NaBH_4$ OCH3 OCH3 O H⊖ O Cl → OCH3 OCH3 O ⊖O Cl H → OCH3 OCH3 from $NaBH_4$ O H⊖ O H

OCH3 OCH3 O ⊖O H H add H^+ → OCH3 OCH3 O HO H H

Problem 18.12. For each of the following reactions, draw the complete, detailed mechanism and predict the major product.

(a) O O O $\xrightarrow[\text{EtOH}]{\text{NaBH}_4}$?

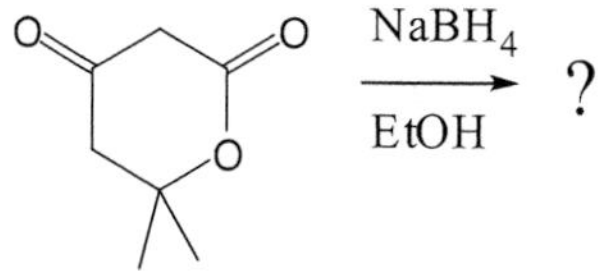

(b) H O O N H $\xrightarrow[\text{EtOH}]{\text{NaBH}_4}$?

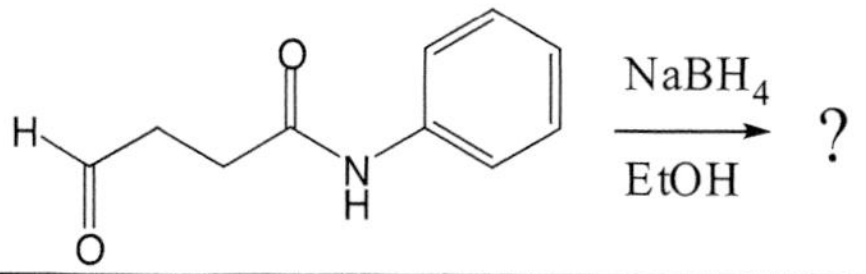

Problem 18.13. Show how the following carboxylic acid can be converted into the corresponding alcohol using $NaBH_4$ as the reducing agent. (Hint: can you convert the carboxylic acid into a different acid derivative first?)

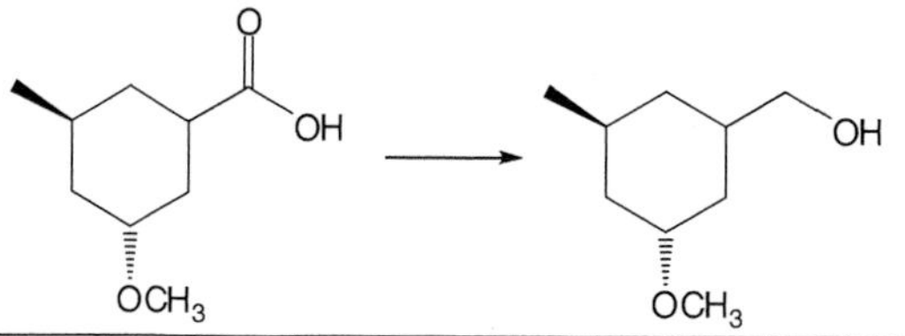

O OH OCH3 → OH OCH3

18.6b. Reactions involving $LiAlH_4$

Recall from Section 15.5 that in many respects, the chemical behavior of $LiAlH_4$ is similar to that of $NaBH_4$. Thus, it should be no surprise that $LiAlH_4$, like $NaBH_4$, will reduce acid chlorides (Equation 18-34) and acid anhydrides (Equation 18-35) to primary alcohols.

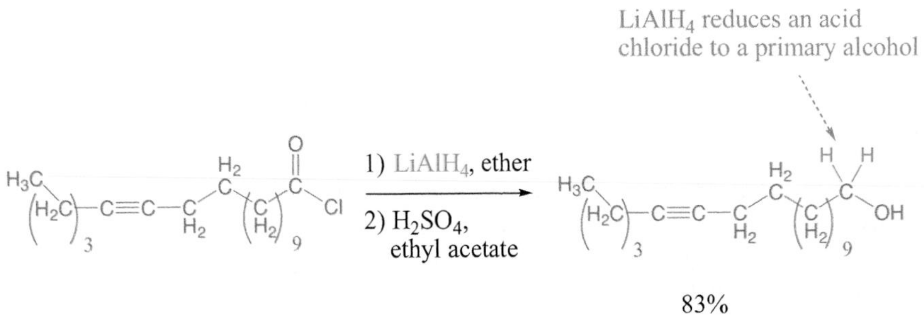

$LiAlH_4$ reduces an acid chloride to a primary alcohol

1) $LiAlH_4$, ether
2) H_2SO_4, ethyl acetate

83%

(18-34)

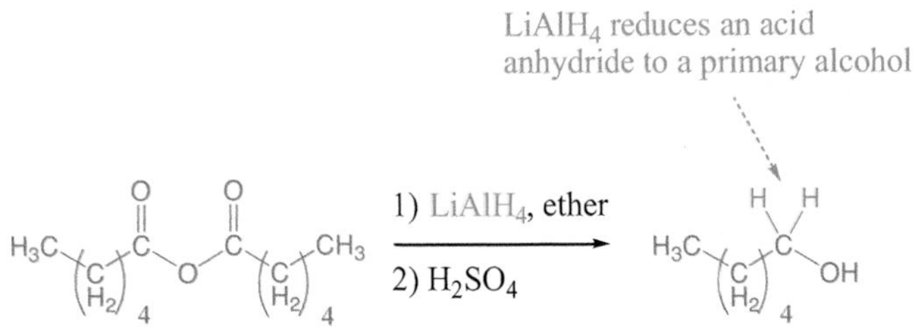

$LiAlH_4$ reduces an acid anhydride to a primary alcohol

1) $LiAlH_4$, ether
2) H_2SO_4

(18-35)

However, $LiAlH_4$ is much more reactive than $NaBH_4$ because aluminum has a lower electronegativity than does boron (Section 15.5). Therefore, when it is feasible, $NaBH_4$ is the preferred reducing agent—it is safer and easier to use.

The advantage of the higher reactivity of $LiAlH_4$ comes when we wish to reduce a less reactive carbonyl-containing functional group, such as an ester, carboxylic acid, or amide. As we can see in Equations 18-36 and 18-37, for example,

$LiAlH_4$ readily reduces esters and carboxylic acids to primary alcohols.

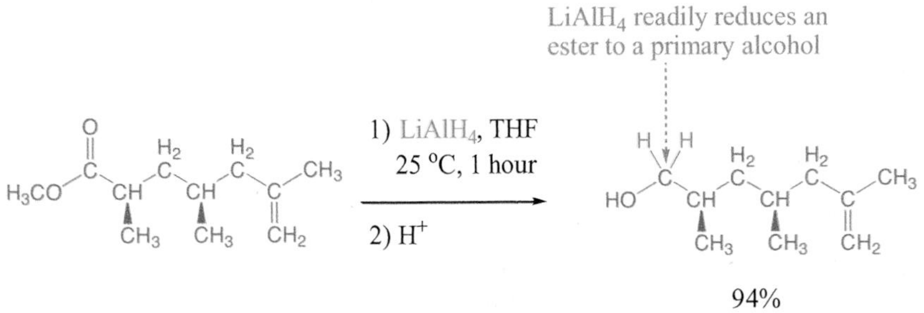

$LiAlH_4$ readily reduces an ester to a primary alcohol

1) $LiAlH_4$, THF, 25 °C, 1 hour
2) H^+

94%

(18-36)

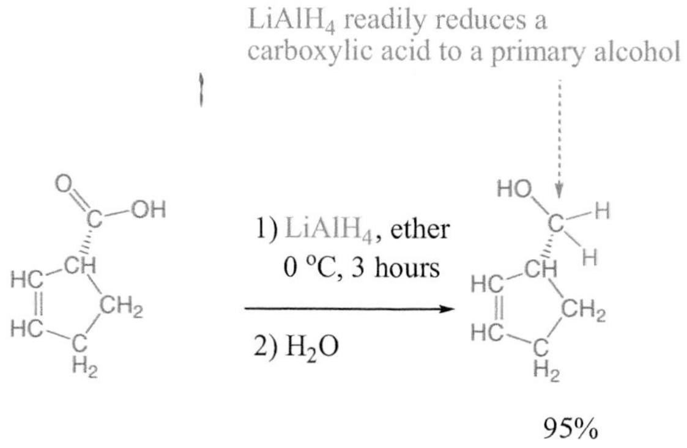

LiAlH$_4$ readily reduces a carboxylic acid to a primary alcohol

1) LiAlH$_4$, ether 0 °C, 3 hours
2) H_2O

95%

(18-37)

The mechanisms of the LiAlH$_4$ reductions of acid chlorides, acid anhydrides, and esters are essentially the same as those involving NaBH$_4$, shown previously in Equation 18-29. First nucleophilic addition-elimination takes place, with H$^-$ as the nucleophile. The aldehyde product is then attacked by a second equivalent of H$^-$ to produce an alkoxide anion (RO$^-$), which is subsequently protonated in an acid workup.

Your Turn 18.13. In the space provided here, draw the mechanism for the reaction in Equation 18-36. (You may use H$^-$ to represent LiAlH$_4$.)

The mechanism for the reduction of a carboxylic acid (Equation 18-38), however, is slightly different. Step 1 is a rapid proton transfer that produces a carboxylate anion, just as we saw previously when a carboxylic acid is treated with NaBH$_4$ (Equation 18-33). At the same time, the negatively-charged oxygen atom of the carboxylate anion forms a relatively strong bond to the aluminum atom. (This is analogous to the hydride transfer step we saw previously in Section 15.5.) Subsequently, steps 2 – 5 comprise the same mechanism that describes the reduction of an acid derivative with NaBH$_4$ (Equation 18-29).

Mechanism for the Reaction in Equation 18-37

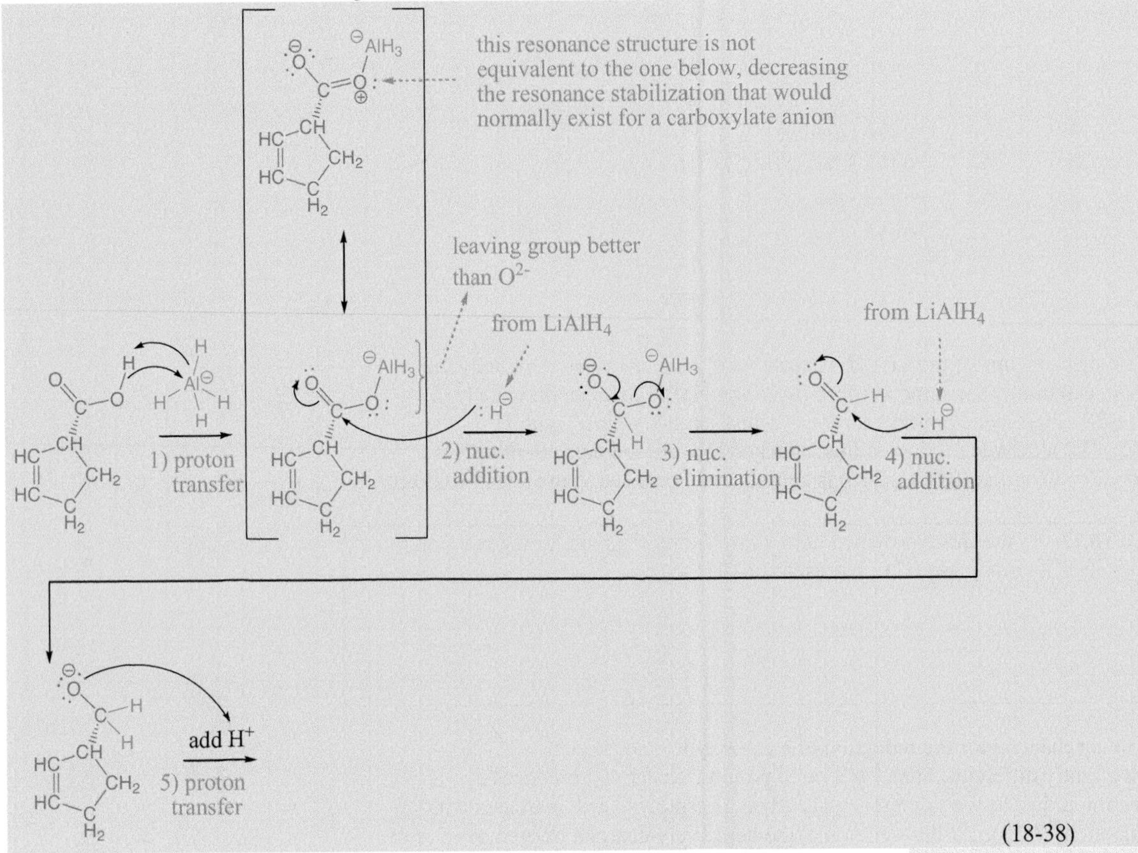

(18-38)

The formation of the O–Al bond in step 1 of Equation 18-38 facilitates the $LiAlH_4$ reduction of a carboxylic acid in two ways. First, as indicated in Equation 18-38, this bond removes the equivalence in the resonance structures normally observed for a carboxylate anion (RCO_2^-). Thus, the carbonyl group is not as highly resonance-stabilized as in a regular carboxylate anion and is therefore more susceptible to nucleophilic attack by H^-. Second, a better leaving group is generated; without the formation of the O–Al bond, the leaving group in a regular carboxylate anion would be an isolated oxygen atom bearing a -2 charge—a species that is much too unstable to depart on its own.

Comment [JMK33]: Margin note.
The formation of the relatively strong O-Al bond in step 1 of Equation 18-38 makes feasible the $LiAlH_4$ reduction of a carboxylic acid.

Another difference between $LiAlH_4$ and $NaBH_4$ is in the reaction with an amide. Whereas $NaBH_4$ cannot reduce an amide, $LiAlH_4$ can, as shown in Equation 18-39.

$LiAlH_4$ reduces an amide to an amine

$LiAlH_4$ / ether

98%

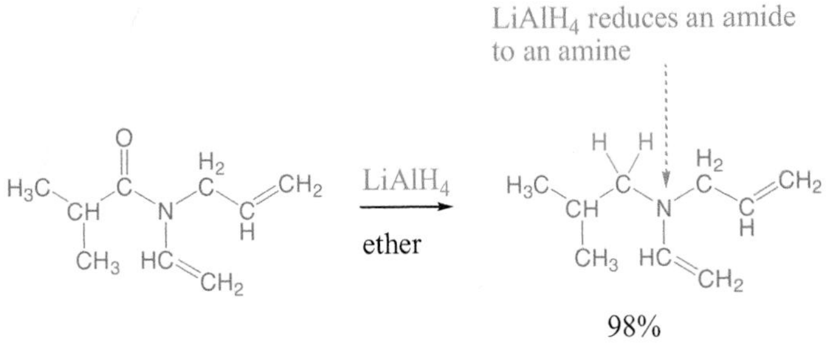

(18-39)

More specifically,

> $LiAlH_4$ reduces an amide ($RCONR_2$) to an amine ($RCNR_2$), preserving the overall backbone.

It should be particularly striking that the product is an amine, because $LiAlH_4$ reduces all of the other acid derivatives to primary alcohols. The reason for this difference stems, once again, from the relatively strong O–Al bond that forms, as we can see in the mechanism in Equation 18-40.

Mechanism for the Reaction in Equation 18-39

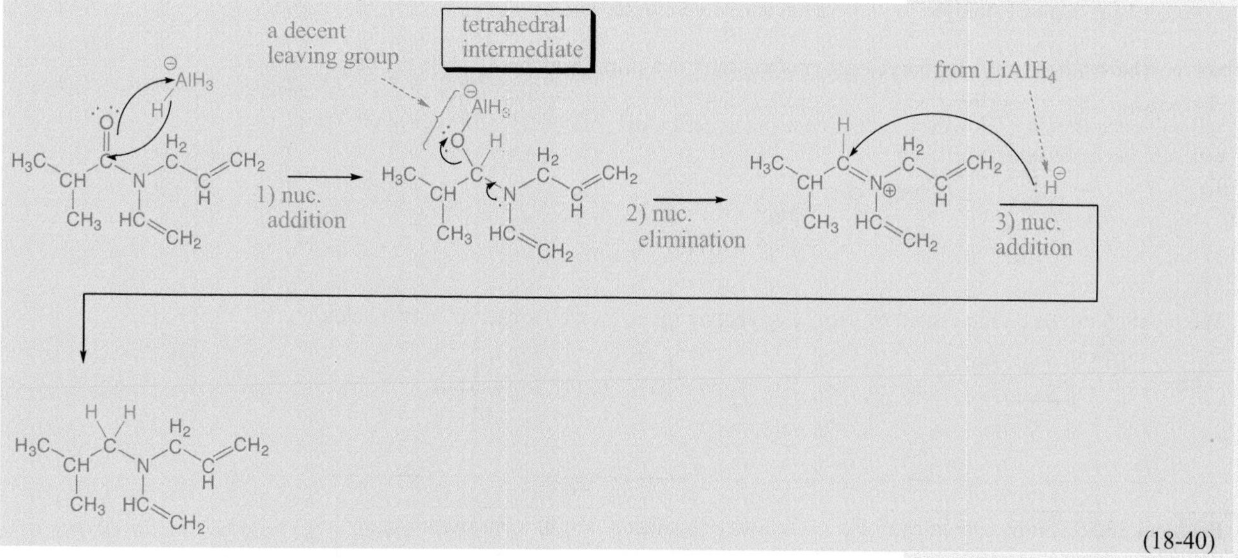

(18-40)

In step 1, H^- adds to the carbonyl group of the amide, and at the same time the O–Al bond forms. The tetrahedral intermediate that is produced contains the same $O{-}^{-}AlH_3$ leaving group we saw in the mechanism describing the reduction of carboxylic acids (Equation 18-38). In step 2, that leaving group departs, yielding an iminium ion, which is subsequently attacked by H^- in step 3 to yield the final product.

Your Turn 18.14. Below is the mechanism for the $LiAlH_4$ reduction of another amide, but the curved arrows have been omitted. (a) Supply the missing curved arrows. (b) Below each reaction arrow, write the name of the elementary step that is taking place. (c) Circle and label the tetrahedral intermediate.

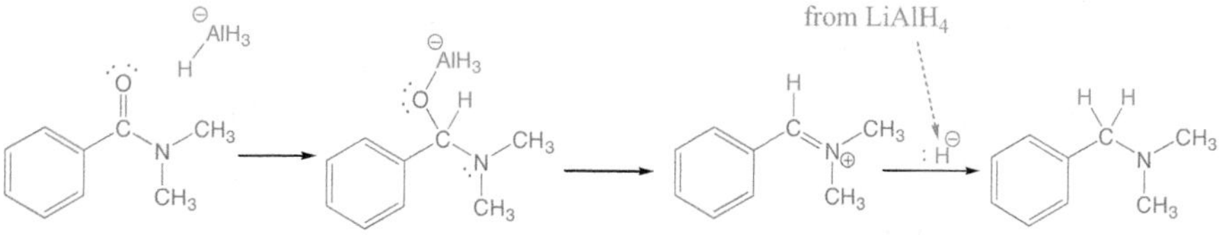

Problem 18.14. For each of the following reactions, draw the complete, detailed mechanism and predict the major product.

(a)

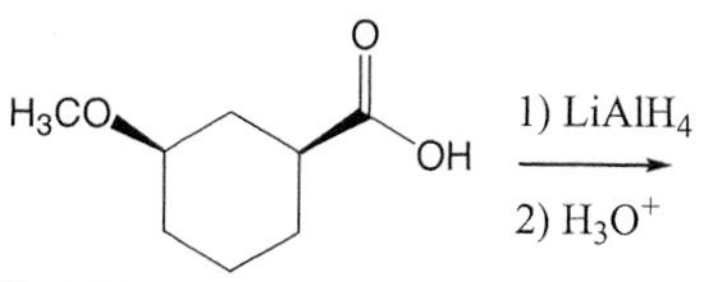

(b)

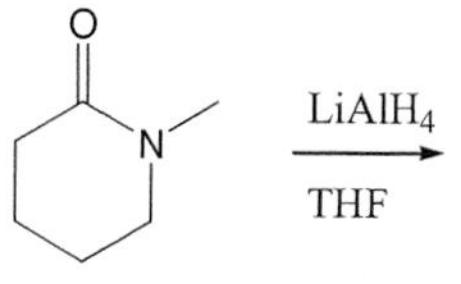

Solved Problem 18.5. Suggest how you would carry out the following transformation. (Hint: consider using a protecting group.)

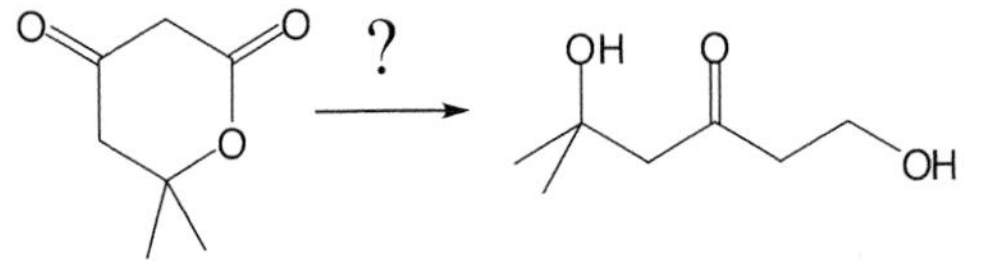

Think. Which of the groups in the starting compound must be reduced? Which should remain unchanged? Will the desired reduction also cause the reduction of the latter functional group? How can a protecting group be employed to prevent the undesired reductions?

Solve. The synthesis calls for the reduction of the ester to a primary alcohol, while the ketone remains unchanged. Such a reaction would proceed via nucleophilic addition-elimination at the ester carbon, and will open the ring. However, reduction using either $LiAlH_4$ or $NaBH_4$ will reduce the ketone as well, as shown below.

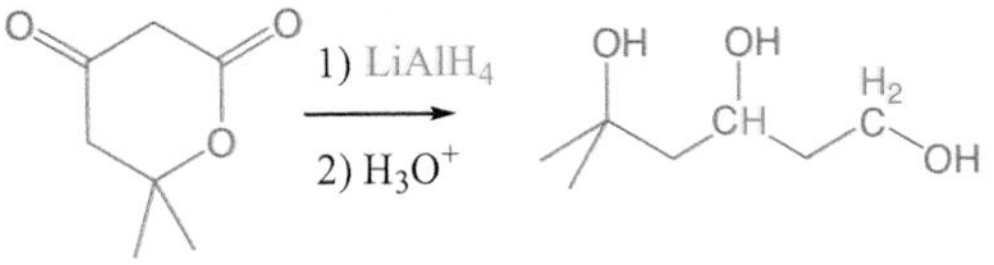

1) $LiAlH_4$ 2) H_3O^+

The problem can be circumvented by using a protecting group on the ketone, as shown below.

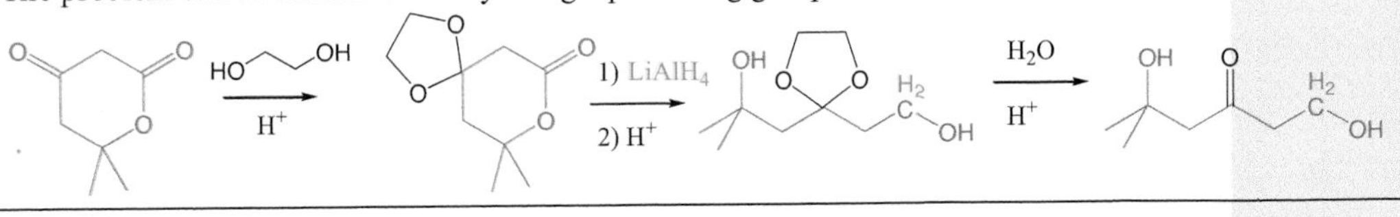

HO–CH₂CH₂–OH, H^+; 1) $LiAlH_4$ 2) H^+; H_2O, H^+

Problem 18.15. Show how to carry out the following synthesis. (Hint: consider using a protecting group.)

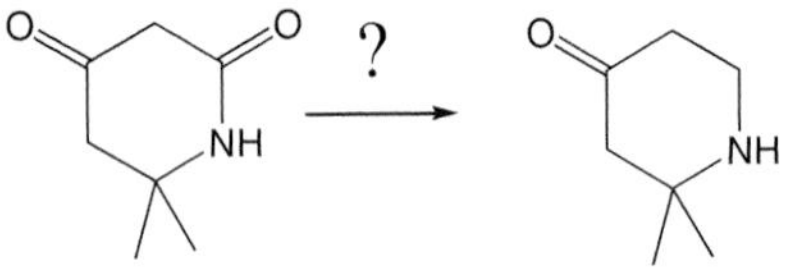

18.6c. Specialized Reducing Agents: Diisobutylaluminum Hydride (DIBAH) and Lithium Tri-*tert*-butoxyaluminum Hydride

Notice that the mechanism in Equations 18-29, which describes the hydride reduction of an acid derivative to a primary alcohol, proceeds through an aldehyde intermediate. That is, the aldehyde, once it is formed, quickly reacts with H^- in a second reduction. Some situations, however, might call for the reduction of an acid derivative to an aldehyde rather than to a primary alcohol. Two specialized reducing agents are commonly employed for such cases—**lithium tri-*tert*-butoxyaluminum hydride** and **diisobutylaluminum hydride (DIBAH)**. As we can see below, both of these compounds possess an Al–H bond and thus are hydride anion (H^-) sources, much the same as $LiAlH_4$ is.

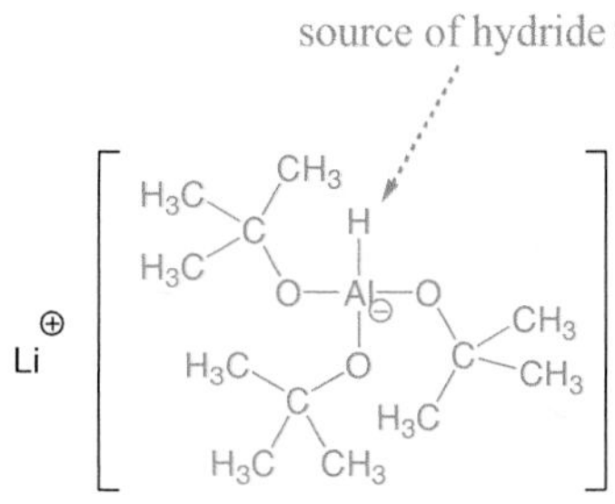

source of hydride ($H^{\ominus}$)

Lithium tri-*tert*-butoxyaluminum hydride
($LiAlH(Ot\text{-}Bu)_3$)

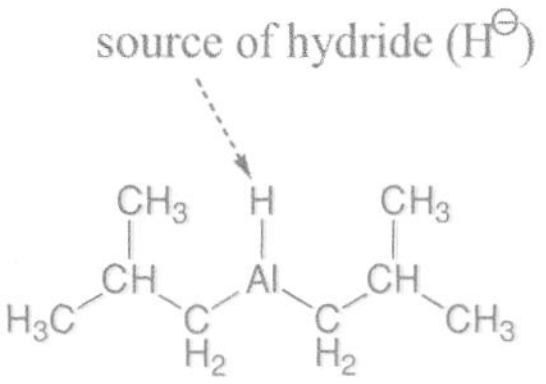

source of hydride ($H^{\ominus}$)

Diisobutylaluminum hydride
(DIBAH)

Examples of how these specialized reducing agents are employed are shown in Equations 18-41 and 18-42.

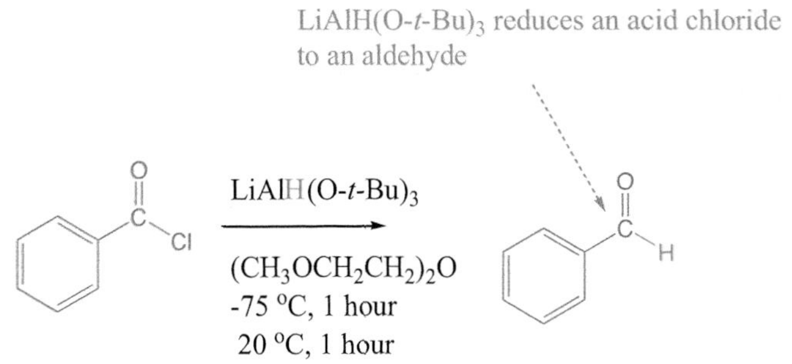

$LiAlH(O\text{-}t\text{-}Bu)_3$ reduces an acid chloride to an aldehyde

$LiAlH(O\text{-}t\text{-}Bu)_3$; $(CH_3OCH_2CH_2)_2O$; -75 °C, 1 hour; 20 °C, 1 hour

benzoyl chloride → benzaldehyde 73%

(18-41)

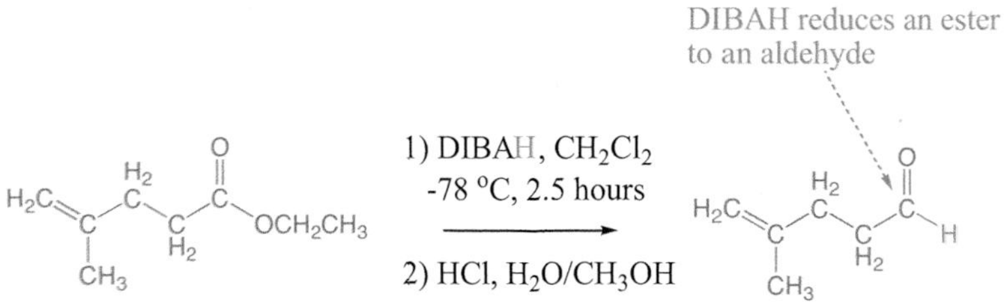

DIBAH reduces an ester to an aldehyde

1) DIBAH, CH_2Cl_2, -78 °C, 2.5 hours
2) HCl, H_2O/CH_3OH

ethyl 4-methylpent-4-enoate → 4-methylpent-3-enal 95%

(18-42)

Specifically,

- Lithium tri-*tert*-butoxyaluminum hydride is commonly used to reduce an acid chloride (RCOCl) to an aldehyde (RCH=O).
- Diisobutylaluminum hydride (DIBAH) is commonly used to reduce an ester (RCO_2R) to an aldehyde (RCH=O).

The mechanism by which lithium tri-*tert*-butoxyaluminum hydride reduces an acid chloride is shown in Equation 18-43.

Mechanism for the Reaction in Equation 18-41

stops at the aldehyde because a second addition of $H^{\ominus}$ from $LiAlH(Ot\text{-}Bu)_3$ is much slower than the first

from $LiAlH(Ot\text{-}Bu)_3$

1) nuc. addition

2) nuc. elimination

SLOW

(18-43)

This mechanism is essentially the same nucleophilic addition-elimination mechanism as the one by which $LiAlH_4$ operates, the only difference being the rate.

Reduction by lithium tri-*tert*-butoxyaluminum hydride occurs much more slowly than by $LiAlH_4$, allowing the reaction to take place in a controlled fashion.

Thus, we can take advantage of the fact that an aldehyde is less reactive than an acid chloride, making the second reduction slower than the first. Once the first reduction has come to completion, the reaction is simply stopped before the second reduction can proceed.

There are two reasons why the lithium tri-*tert*-butoxyaluminum hydride reduction is significantly slower than that involving $LiAlH_4$. One is the bulkiness of the *t*-butoxy groups, which introduces significant steric hindrance in the nucleophilic addition step. The second reason is that the reaction is carried out at very cold temperatures, around -75 °C. In fact, at room temperature, lithium tri-*tert*-butoxyaluminum hydride can rapidly reduce an acid chloride twice, all the way down to the alcohol (Equation 18-44).

at room temperature, $LiAlH(O\text{-}t\text{-}Bu)_3$ reduces an acid chloride twice, producing a primary alcohol

1) $LiAlH(O\text{-}t\text{-}Bu)_3$
25 °C
2) HCl

(18-44)

The reason that the reduction of an ester by DIBAH stops at the aldehyde is somewhat different from the reason that the reduction of an acid chloride by lithium tri-*tert*-butoxyaluminum hydride stops at the aldehyde. Specifically, it is *not* because the second reduction is slower than the first.

Instead, the reason that DIBAH reduction of an ester stops at the aldehyde stems from the fact that the tetrahedral intermediate that is formed (Equation 18-45) is relatively stable at -78 °C. In that tetrahedral intermediate, the oxygen atom from the initial carbonyl group has formed a bond to aluminum, much as we have seen previously in other mechanisms. This species persists until H_3O^+ is added. Effectively, the H_3O^+ "washes away" the Al-containing species, generating a hemiacetal that equilibrates with the aldehyde. Consequently,

In the DIBAH reduction of an ester, the aldehyde product and the reducing agent are not present in the reaction mixture at the same time, so the aldehyde cannot be further reduced to the alcohol.

Mechanism for the Reaction in Equation 18-39

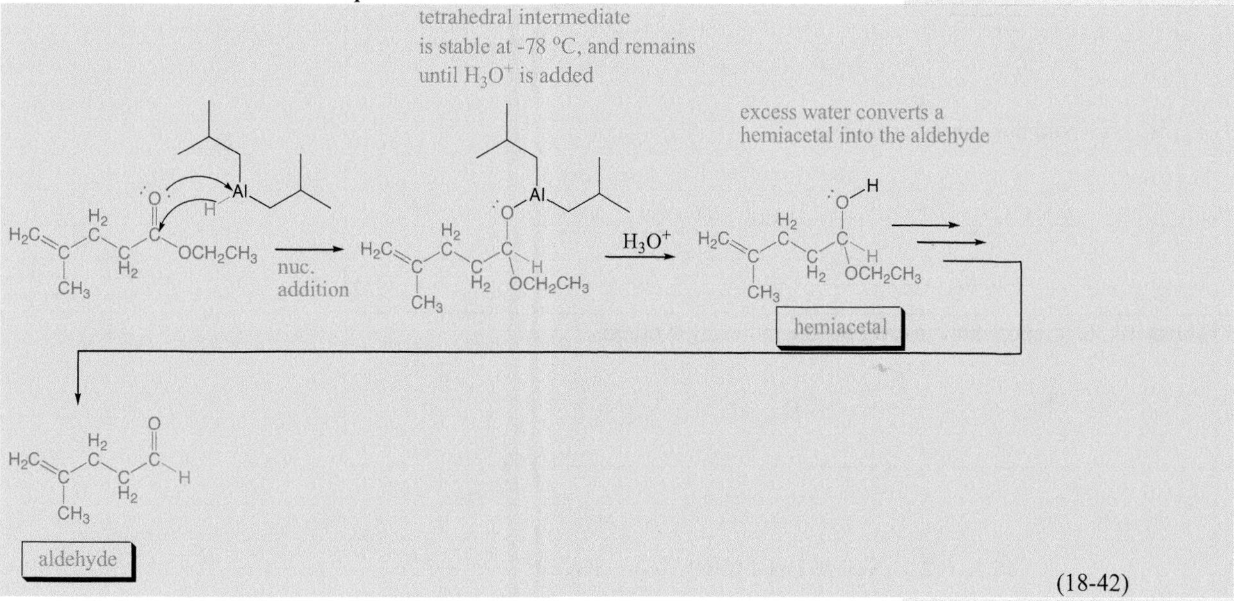

tetrahedral intermediate is stable at -78 °C, and remains until H_3O^+ is added

excess water converts a hemiacetal into the aldehyde

nuc. addition

H_3O^+

hemiacetal

aldehyde

(18-42)

The relative stability of the tetrahedral intermediate in the DIBAH reduction of an ester can be rationalized in part by charge stability. As shown below, elimination of the alkoxy leaving group from the tetrahedral intermediate would result in the generation of two additional charges—a negative charge on the oxygen atom of the leaving group (RO^-) and a positive charge on the oxygen atom bonded to Al.

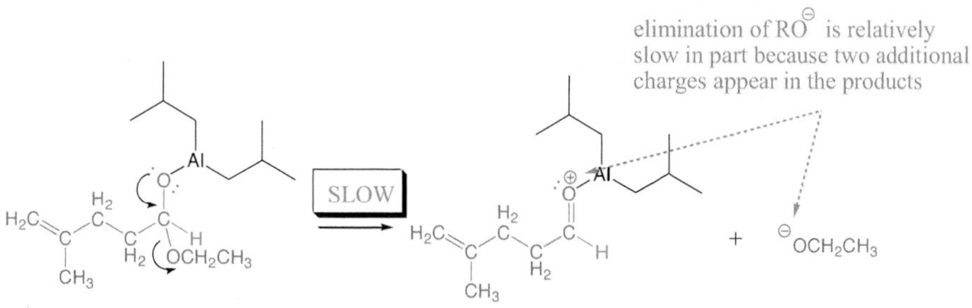

elimination of $RO^{\ominus}$ is relatively slow in part because two additional charges appear in the products

SLOW

+ $^{\ominus}OCH_2CH_3$

Solved Problem 18.6. Show how you would convert the following carboxylic acid into the aldehyde.

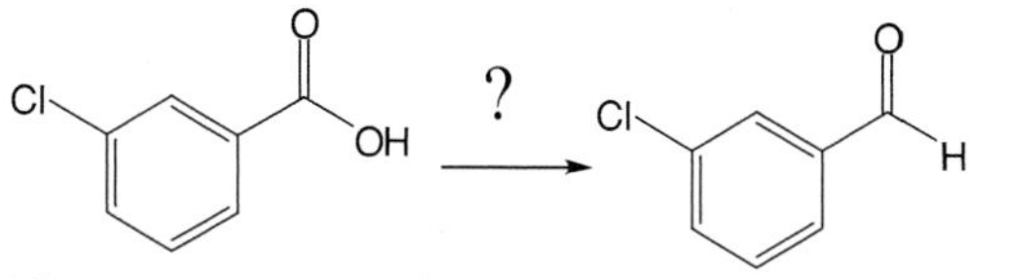

?

Think. What reactions do we know that can convert an acid derivative into an aldehyde? Can this be accomplished directly from a carboxylic acid?

Solve. We just learned that an aldehyde can be produced from an acid chloride using lithium tri-*tert*-butoxyaluminum hydride, or from an ester using DIBAH. Thus, we must convert the initial carboxylic acid into an acid chloride or an ester. We have not yet seen a way to convert a carboxylic acid into an acid chloride, but we have seen that diazomethane can convert the carboxylic acid into a methyl ester.

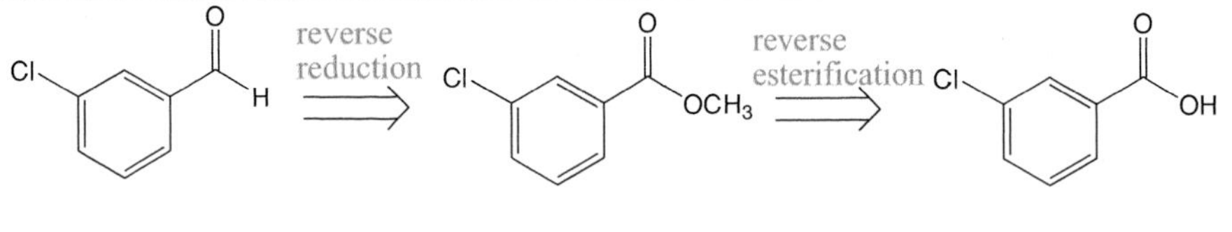

Cl, O, H ⟹ (reverse reduction) Cl, O, OCH_3 ⟹ (reverse esterification) Cl, O, OH

The synthesis would then appear as follows.

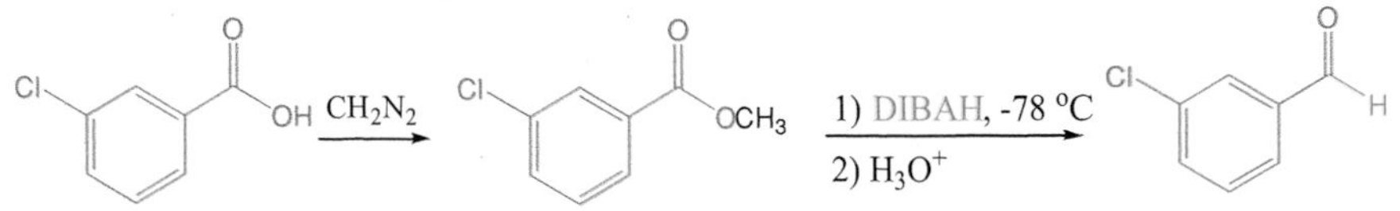

Cl, O, OH → (CH_2N_2) Cl, O, OCH_3 → (1) DIBAH, -78 °C 2) H_3O^+) Cl, O, H

Problem 18.16. Propose how to carry out the following synthesis.

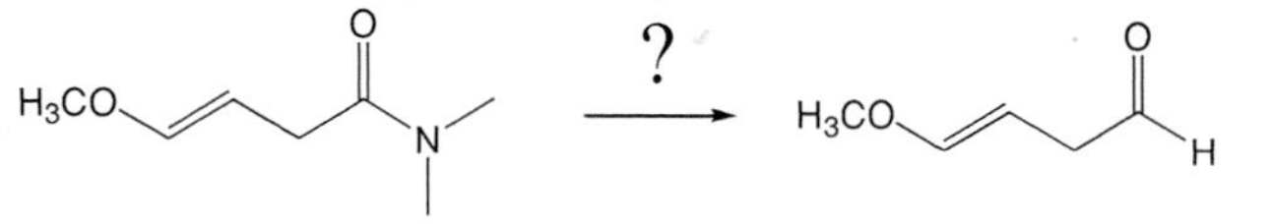

H_3CO, O, N → ? → H_3CO, O, H

18.7. ORGANOMETALLIC REAGENTS

In the previous section, we saw that hydride reagents can react with a carboxylic acid or acid derivative to produce an aldehyde, which can undergo further reduction to produce an alcohol. Although the mechanism for the formation of the aldehyde is essentially the same as other nucleophilic addition-elimination mechanisms we encountered earlier in this chapter, the product is *not* an acid or acid derivative because the nucleophile, H^-, is not a viable leaving group.

Alkyl anions (R^-) are other species that can act as nucleophiles but not as leaving groups. As we have seen in previous chapters, sources of R^- are organometallic compounds such as alkyllithium reagents (R-Li), Grignard reagents (R-MgBr), and lithium dialkyl cuprates (R_2CuLi). Thus, as with hydride reagents, the product of nucleophilic addition-elimination involving one of these organometallic reagents is *not* an acid derivative. We can see this explicitly in Equations 18-46 and 18-47, in which an acid derivative is treated with an alkyllithium or Grignard reagent, respectively.

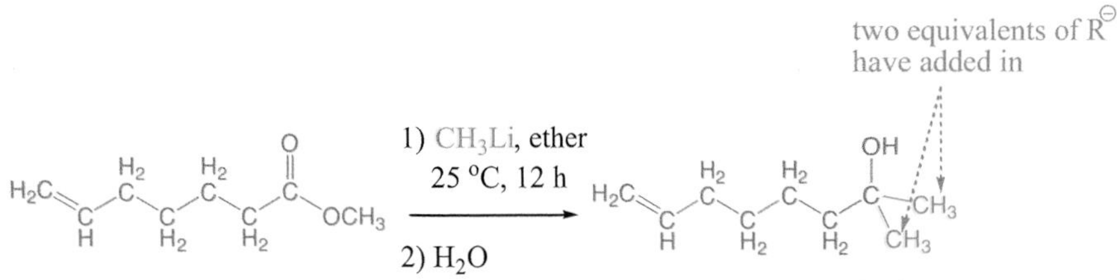

two equivalents of $R^{\ominus}$ have added in

$H_2C{=}CH{-}CH_2{-}CH_2{-}CH_2{-}CH_2{-}C(=O){-}OCH_3$ → 1) CH_3Li, ether 25 °C, 12 h 2) H_2O → $H_2C{=}CH{-}CH_2{-}CH_2{-}CH_2{-}CH_2{-}C(OH)(CH_3){-}CH_3$

methyl hept-6-enoate | 2-methyloct-7-en-2-ol 99% (18-46)

two equivalents of $R^{\ominus}$ have added in

1) CH_3CH_2MgBr, $N[(CH_2)_2O(CH_2)_2OCH_3)]_3$, ether/cyclohexane
2) H^+

benzoyl chloride → 3-phenylpentan-3-ol (18-47)

In general,

Acid chlorides (RCOCl), acid anhydrides (RCO_2COR), and esters (RCO_2R) can be treated with an alkyllithium (R-Li) or Grignard (R-MgBr) reagent to produce a tertiary alcohol (R_3COH).

Notice that in each case, in order to produce a tertiary alcohol, two equivalents of the R^- nucleophile must add to the acid derivative. This is explained by Equation 18-48, the mechanism of the reaction in Equation 18-47.

Mechanism of the Reaction in Equation 18-47

from CH_3CH_2MgBr — 1) nuc. addition — 2) nuc. elimination — ketone is not isolated — from CH_3CH_2MgBr — 3) nuc. addition — acid workup, add H^+ — 4) proton transfer (18-48)

This mechanism is essentially the same as the one in Equation 18-29, which describes the hydride reduction of an acid chloride to a primary alcohol. The first two steps comprise the usual nucleophilic addition-elimination mechanism, which produces a ketone in this case. That ketone, once it is produced, reacts with a second equivalent of R^- in step 3 to produce a tertiary alkoxide anion, RO^-. Acid workup in step 4 yields the tertiary alcohol as the final product. Notice that steps 3 and 4 comprise the mechanism for a typical alkyllithium or Grignard reaction involving a ketone, which we previously discussed in Section 15.6.

Your Turn 18.15. In the space provided here, draw the mechanism for the reaction in Equation 18-46.

Although similar mechanisms can be drawn involving carboxylic acids or amides, such reactions are generally avoided due to complications that arise. As we have seen, amides are significantly less reactive than esters, and carboxylic acids are acidic and can thus protonate the R^- nucleophile.

Comment [JMK34]: Margin note. Avoid alkyllithium and Grignard reactions involving carboxylic acids or amides.

Problem 18.17. For each of the following reactions, draw the complete, detailed mechanism and predict the major products.

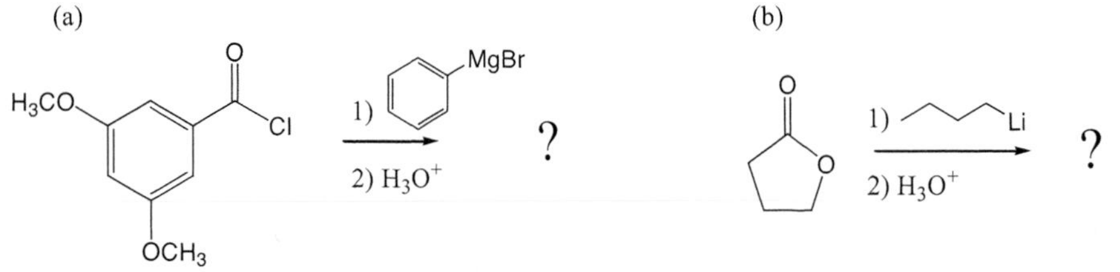

(a) (b)

H₃CO, OCH₃, Cl, O; 1) MgBr; 2) H_3O^+ ?

O, O; 1) Li; 2) H_3O^+ ?

Problem 18.18. Propose a synthesis for the following transformation.

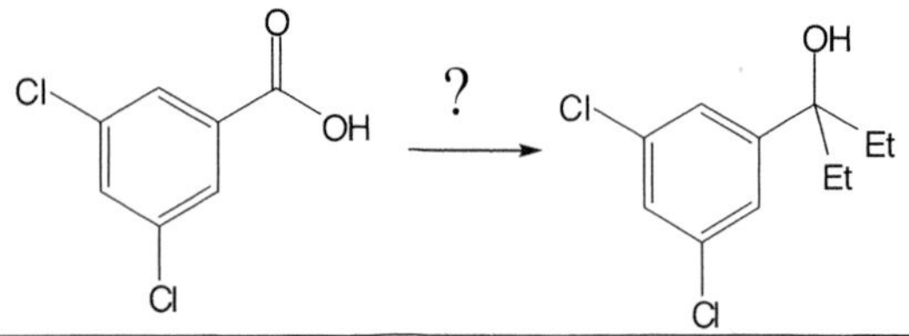

Cl, Cl, O, OH → ? → Cl, Cl, OH, Et, Et

Similar to what we saw with hydride reductions in the previous section, it can be advantageous to carry out reactions in which only one equivalent of R^- adds to an acid derivative, thus producing a ketone that can be isolated. One way to carry out such a reaction involves lithium dialkylcuprates, an example of which is shown in Equation 18-49.

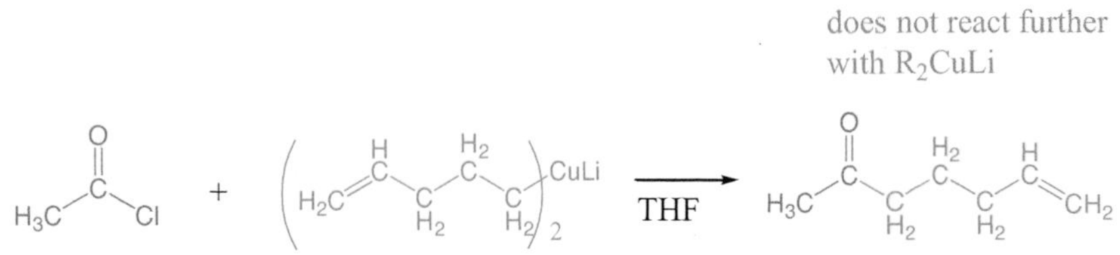

does not react further with R_2CuLi

ethanoyl chloride (acetyl chloride) + $(H_2C{=}CH{-}CH_2{-}CH_2)_2CuLi$ —THF→ hept-6-en-2-one 74%

(18-49)

Thus, in general,

An acid chloride (RCOCl) can be treated with a lithium dialkylcuprate (R_2CuLi) to produce a ketone ($R_2C{=}O$).

As we saw in Chapter 15, lithium dialkylcuprates are relatively weak R^- nucleophiles and therefore do not undergo direct addition to the carbonyl group of a ketone or aldehyde. They will, however, attack the carbonyl group of an acid chloride, because it is much more reactive than a ketone or aldehyde. As we can see, the nucleophilic addition-elimination product is a ketone, which does not react further with the lithium dialkylcuprate.

Not surprisingly, lithium dialkyl cuprates do not react with esters or amides, which are significantly more stable than acid chlorides. Thus, in order to convert an ester or amide into a ketone, we must first convert it into an acid chloride. We will learn how to do so in Chapter 19.

Problem 18.19. For each of the following reactions, draw the complete, detailed mechanism and the product. If no reaction takes place, write "no reaction."

(a) 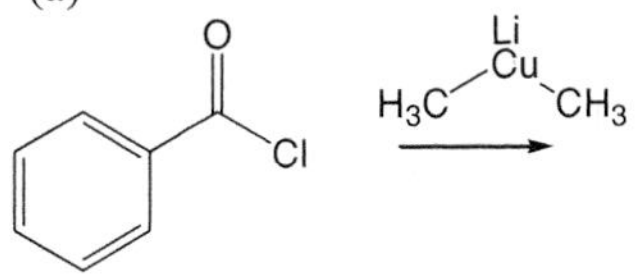 (b)

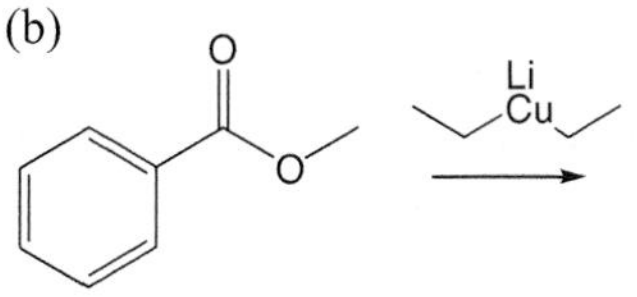

Li Cu H_3C CH_3 Cl O

O Li Cu O

(c)

O $(C_6H_5)_2CuLi$ N H

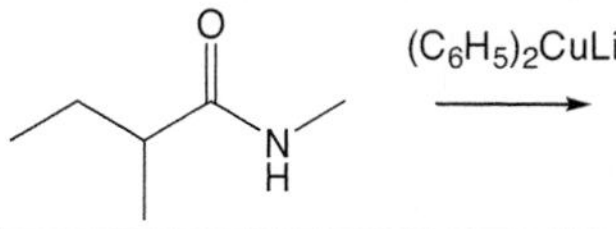

Solved Problem 18.7. Show how to carry out the following synthesis.

O O ? O H Cl

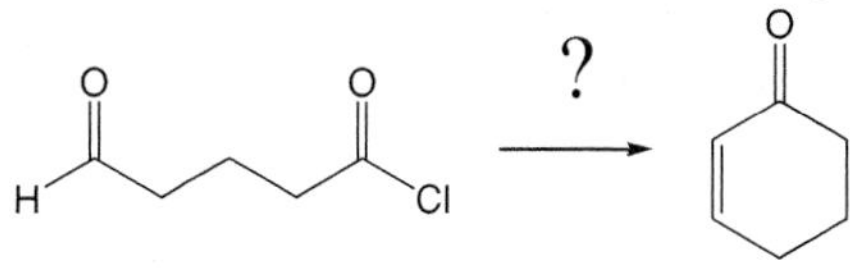

Think. What precursor can be used to produce the α,β-unsaturated ketone? To make that precursor from the starting compound, which carbonyl-containing functional group must gain an additional carbon-carbon bond? What reagent can be used to selectively react with that functional group?

Solve. The α,β-unsaturated ketone can be produced from an aldol condensation, as shown in the retrosynthetic analysis below. To make the precursor from the starting material, the Cl of the acid chloride must be replaced by a CH_3 group, which can be accomplished using $(CH_3)_2CuLi$.

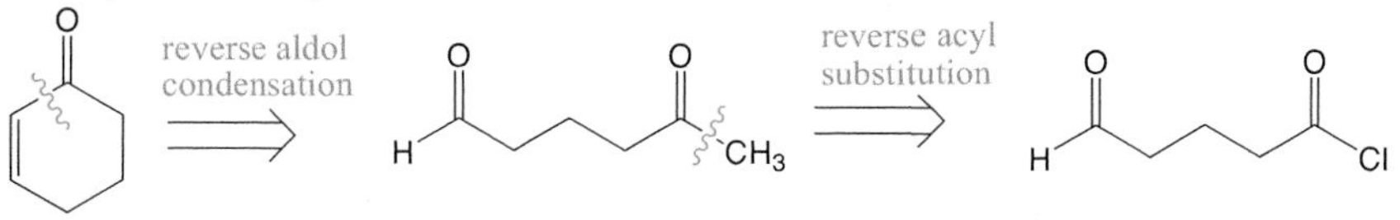

O reverse aldol condensation O O H CH_3 reverse acyl substitution O O H Cl

In the forward direction, the synthesis might appear as follows.

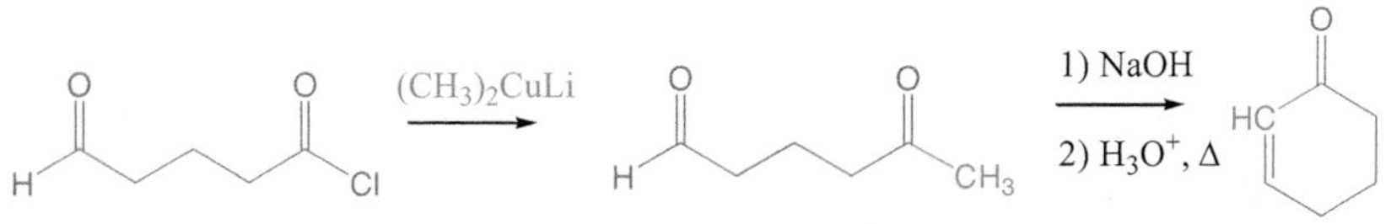

O O H Cl $(CH_3)_2CuLi$ O O H CH_3 1) NaOH 2) H_3O^+, Δ O HC

Problem 18.20. Show how to carry out the following synthesis.

O O Cl ? OH OH

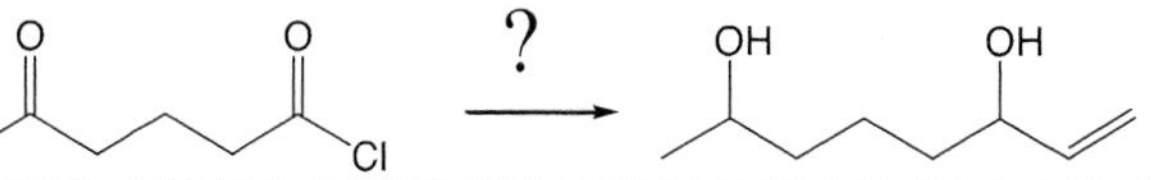

18.8. WRAPPING UP AND LOOKING AHEAD

The main thrust of this chapter is the general nucleophilic addition-elimination mechanism involving a carbonyl (C=O) group, shown previously in Equation 18-2. In short, with a sufficient leaving group bonded to the carbonyl carbon, a strong nucleophile can add to the carbonyl carbon in a first step, temporarily producing a tetrahedral intermediate. In a second step, the tetrahedral intermediate collapses to regenerate the carbonyl group and eliminate the leaving group. The net result is a nucleophilic acyl substitution.

Much of this chapter focused on the conversion of one acid derivative to another, which is observed if the reactant nucleophile can also act as a leaving group on a carbonyl carbon. For such conversions, the "stability ladder" in Figure 18-3 provides insight as to whether or not the reaction is energetically favorable. An interconversion is energetically favorable, and thus relatively easy to carry out, if the acid derivative that is produced is on a lower rung of the ladder than the starting acid derivative. Conversely, an interconversion is unfavorable, and thus more difficult to carry out, if the product derivative is on a higher rung of the ladder. And reactions in which the initial and final derivatives are on the same rung of the ladder, such as transesterification, tend to take place under equilibrium and are reversible.

We also saw acyl substitutions in which either the carbonyl-containing reactant or the carbonyl-containing product is *not* an acid derivative. For example, the haloform reaction converts a methyl ketone into a carboxylic acid, and is facilitated by alpha-halogenation, which first transforms the very poor CH_3 leaving group into a decent CX_3 leaving group. Other examples involve H^- and R^- nucleophiles, which cannot act as leaving groups in the product. Acyl substitution involving one of these nucleophiles produces either an aldehyde or ketone, respectively, and under normal conditions, the initial aldehyde or ketone is attacked a second time to produce a primary alcohol or tertiary alcohol.

This is the first of two chapters that discuss the nucleophilic addition-elimination mechanism. In Chapter 19, we will extend our discussion to include reactions involving weak nucleophiles. Many of the principles we learned in this chapter will be applied to those reactions as well. As we will see, however, the mechanisms involving weak nucleophiles are somewhat different. Moreover, the lower reactivity of a weak nucleophile has a significant impact on the feasibility of acyl substitution reactions, as well as on the conditions necessary to carry out some of those reactions.

CHAPTER SUMMARY AND KEY TERMS

- The general **nucleophilic addition-elimination mechanism** is shown below, and consists of two steps. First a nucleophile attacks the electron-poor atom of a polar π bond in a nucleophilic addition step, producing a high-energy **tetrahedral intermediate**. Second, the tetrahedral intermediate eliminates a leaving group initially bonded to the electron-poor atom of the polar π bond. (Section 18.1)

tetrahedral intermediate

H3C–C(=O)–L + :Nu⊖ → 1) nucleophilic addition → H3C–C(O⊖)(L)–Nu → 2) nucleophilic elimination → H3C–C(=O)–Nu + :L⊖

- When the leaving group is bonded to a carbonyl group, nucleophilic addition-elimination is called an **acyl substitution**. (Section 18.1a)

- In a **base-promoted transesterification reaction**, an ester reacts with an alkoxide anion (RO^-) to produce a new ester. (Section 18.1a)
- The first step of a nucleophilic addition-elimination reaction is the rate-determining step. (Section 18.1b)
- A transesterification reaction is reversible because the reactants and products are of roughly the same stability. (Section 18.1c)
- In a **saponification reaction**, an ester reacts with HO^- to produce an initial carboxylic acid that is rapidly and irreversibly deprotonated under the basic conditions of the reaction. (Section 18.2)
- The stability of a carboxylic acid derivative decreases in the order: amide < ester ≈ carboxylic acid < acid anhydride < acid chloride. (Section 18.3)
- The conversion of one carboxylic acid derivative into another can be carried out with relative ease if the acid derivative on the product side is more stable than that on the reactant side. By contrast, such a conversion is difficult if the acid derivative on the product side is higher in energy than that on the reactant side. (Section 18.3)
- The conversion of an amide ($RCONR_2$) to a carboxylic acid (RCO_2H) via nucleophilic addition-elimination is energetically unfavorable, but can be carried out with relative ease by treating an amide with HO^-. This is because the initial carboxylic acid that is formed is rapidly and irreversibly deprotonated under the basic conditions of the reaction. (Section 18.4)
- The **Gabriel synthesis** produces a primary amine from a corresponding alkyl halide. (Section 18.4)
- A **haloform reaction** converts a methyl ketone ($RCOCH_3$) into a carboxylic acid (RCO_2H). The CH_3 group is not a suitable leaving group, but under the conditions of the reaction, it is first converted into CX_3 (X = Cl, Br, I), which is a suitable leaving group. Subsequent acyl substitution involving HO^- as the nucleophile produces an initial carboxylic acid that is rapidly and irreversibly deprotonated under the basic conditions of the reaction. (Section 18.5)
- $NaBH_4$ readily reduces high-energy acid derivatives, such as acid chlorides ($RCOCl$) and acid anhydrides (RCO_2COR), to primary alcohols. Esters, which are significantly more stable, are reduced to primary alcohols more slowly. All of these reactions proceed through an aldehyde intermediate, which is reduced a second time to the alcohol. (Sections 18.6a)
- $LiAlH_4$ is a more powerful reducing agent than $NaBH_4$, and thus can also reduce acid chlorides, acid anhydrides, and esters to primary alcohols. (Section 18.6b)
- $LiAlH_4$ reduces carboxylic acids (RCO_2H) to primary alcohols, and reduces amides ($RCONR_2$) to amines (RCH_2NH_2). Such reactions are facilitated by the strong O-Al bond that forms in the mechanism. (Section 18.6b)
- **Diisobutylaluminum hydride (DIBAH)** and **lithium tri-*tert*-butoxyaluminum hydride** are two specialized reducing agents that can be used to reduce an acid derivative to an aldehyde. DIBAH reduces an ester to an aldehyde, and lithium tri-*tert*-butoxyaluminum hydride reduces an acid chloride to an aldehyde. (Section 18.6c)
- When an acid derivative such as an acid chloride, acid anhydride, or ester is treated with an alkyllithium reagent (R-Li) or Grignard reagent (R-MgBr), R^- adds twice to produce a tertiary alcohol. (Section 18.7)
- When an acid chloride ($RCOCl$) is treated with a lithium dialkyl cuprate, R^- adds once to produce a ketone. (Section 18.7)

REACTION TABLES

Table 18-1. Functional Group Transformations

	Starting Functional Group	Typical Reagents and Reaction Conditions	Functional Group Formed	Key Electron-Rich Species	Key Electron-Poor Species	Type of Mechanism	Discussed in Section(s)
(1)	RC(=O)OR' Ester	NaOR'' / ether	RC(=O)OR'' Ester	$^{\ominus}$OR''	RC(=O)OR' (δ^+ C)	Nucleophilic addition-elimination (transesterification)	18.1a
(2)	RC(=O)OR' Ester	1) NaOH 2) H^+	RC(=O)OH Carboxylic acid	$^{\ominus}$OH	RC(=O)OR' (δ^+ C)	Nucleophilic addition-elimination (saponification)	18.2
(3)	RC(=O)Cl Acid chloride	LiOR'	RC(=O)OR' Ester	$^{\ominus}$OR'	RC(=O)Cl (δ^+ C)	Nucleophilic addition-elimination	18.3
(4)	RC(=O)OC(=O)R Acid anhydride	NaOR'	RC(=O)OR' Ester	$^{\ominus}$OR'	RC(=O)OC(=O)R (δ^+ C)	Nucleophilic addition-elimination	18.3
(5)	RC(=O)OR' Ester	$LiNR''_2$	$RC(=O)NR''_2$ Amide	$^{\ominus}NR''_2$	RC(=O)OR' (δ^+ C)	Nucleophilic addition-elimination	18.3
(6)	$RC(=O)NR'_2$ Amide	1) NaOH 2) H^+	RC(=O)OH Carboxylic acid	$^{\ominus}$OH	$RC(=O)NR'_2$ (δ^+ C)	Nucleophilic addition-elimination	18.4
(7)	Phthalimide (NH)	1) KOH / EtOH 2) RBr 3) KOH / H_2O	H_2N—R Primary amine	$^{\ominus}$OH	N-R phthalimide (δ^+ C)	Nucleophilic addition-elimination (Gabriel synthesis)	18.4
(8)	RC(=O)Cl Acid chloride	1) $NaBH_4$ or $LiAlH_4$ 2) H^+	RCH_2OH Primary alcohol	$^{\ominus}$H	RC(=O)Cl (δ^+ C)	Nucleophilic addition-elimination (reduction)	18.6a and 18.6b
(9)	RC(=O)OC(=O)R Acid anhydride	1) $NaBH_4$ or $LiAlH_4$ 2) H^+	RCH_2OH Primary alcohol	$^{\ominus}$H	RC(=O)OC(=O)R (δ^+ C)	Nucleophilic addition-elimination (reduction)	18.6a and 18.6b

(10)	R–C(=O)–OR' Ester	1) $NaBH_4$ or $LiAlH_4$ 2) H^+	$R–CH_2–OH$ Primary alcohol	H^-	R–C(=O)–OR' (δ+ on C)	Nucleophilic addition-elimination (reduction)	18.6a and 18.6b
(11)	R–C(=O)–OH Carboxylic acid	1) $LiAlH_4$ 2) H^+	$R–CH_2–OH$ Primary alcohol	H^-	R–C(=O)–O–AlH_3^- (δ+ on C)	Nucleophilic addition-elimination (reduction)	18.6b
(12)	R–C(=O)–NR'_2 Amide	$LiAlH_4$ ether	R–CH_2–NR'_2 Amine	H^-	R–CH=$N^+R'_2$	Nucleophilic addition-elimination (reduction)	18.6b
(13)	R–C(=O)–Cl Acid chloride	LiAlH(O-*t*-Bu)$_3$ -78 °C	R–C(=O)–H Aldehyde	H^-	R–C(=O)–Cl (δ+ on C)	Nucleophilic addition-elimination (reduction)	18.6c
(14)	R–C(=O)–OR' Ester	1) DIBAH -78 °C 2) H_3O^+	R–C(=O)–H Aldehyde	H^-	R–C(=O)–OR' (δ+ on C)	Nucleophilic addition-elimination (reduction)	18.6c

Table 18-2. Reactions that Alter the Carbon Skeleton

	Reactant	Typical Reagent and Reaction Conditions	Product Formed	Key Electron-Rich Species	Key Electron-Poor Species	Type of Reaction	Discussed in Section(s)
(1)	R–C(=O)–CH_3 Methyl ketone	(X=Cl, Br, I) 1) X_2, NaOH 2) H^+	R–C(=O)–OH Carboxylic acid	OH^-	R–C(=O)–CX_3 (δ+ on C) (X=Cl, Br, I)	Nucleophilic addition-elimination (haloform reaction)	18.5
(2)	R–C(=O)–Cl Acid chloride	1) R'-Li or R'-MgBr 2) H^+	R–C(OH)(R')–R' Tertiary alcohol	R'^-	R–C(=O)–Cl (δ+ on C)	Nucleophilic addition-elimination (Grignard reaction)	18.7
(3)	R–C(=O)–O–C(=O)–R Acid anhydride	1) R'-Li or R'-MgBr 2) H^+	R–C(OH)(R')–R' Tertiary alcohol	R'^-	R–C(=O)–O–C(=O)–R (δ+ on C)	Nucleophilic addition-elimination (Grignard reaction)	18.7
(4)	R–C(=O)–OR' Ester	1) R'-Li or R'-MgBr 2) H^+	R–C(OH)(R')–R' Tertiary alcohol	R'^-	R–C(=O)–OR' (δ+ on C)	Nucleophilic addition-elimination (Grignard reaction)	18.7
(5)	R–C(=O)–Cl Acid chloride	R'_2CuLi	R–C(=O)–R'	R'^-	R–C(=O)–Cl (δ+ on C)	Nucleophilic addition-elimination (Grignard reaction)	18.7

PROBLEMS

21. Predict the product of the following sequence of reactions.

1) $NaBH_4$, EtOH
2) [acid chloride structure]

22. Predict the product for the reaction between *m*-ethylbenzoyl chloride and each of the following compounds. Draw the complete, detailed mechanism for each reaction. If no reaction is expected to occur, write "no reaction."

→ ?

m-ethylbenzoyl chloride

(a) NaOH, then H_3O^+ (b) CH_3NHLi (c) CH_3CH_2OK (d) $C_6H_5CO_2K$
(e) $(CH_3CH_2)_2CuLi$ (f) $LiAlH(O\text{-}t\text{-}Bu)_3$, -78 °C (g) CH_3Cl
(h) $NaBH_4$, EtOH (i) C_6H_5MgBr (excess), then H^+ (j) CH_3OCH_3

23. Predict the product for the reaction between acetic anhydride and each of the following compounds. If no reaction is expected to occur, write "no reaction." Draw the complete, detailed mechanism for each reaction.

(a) NaOH, then H_3O^+ (b) CH_3NHLi (c) CH_3CH_2OK (d) $C_6H_5CO_2K$
(e) NaBr (f) $CH_3CH_2OCH_2CH_3$ (g) 3-chloropentane
(h) hexanal

24. Predict the product for the reaction between methyl cyclohexanoate and each of the following. If no reaction is expected to occur, write "no reaction." For those reactions that do occur, draw the complete, detailed mechanism for each reaction.

(a) NaOH, then H_3O^+ (b) $CH_3CH_2CH_2ONa$, $CH_3CH_2CH_2OH$
(c) $LiAlH_4$, then H_3O^+
(d) $CH_3CH_2CH_2Li$ (excess), then H_3O^+ (e) $(CH_3CH_2)_2CuLi$
(f) NaBr (g) 3-chloropentane
(h) hexanal (i) CH_3Cl

25. Starting with acetyl chloride and using any other reagents necessary, propose how you would synthesize each of the following compounds.

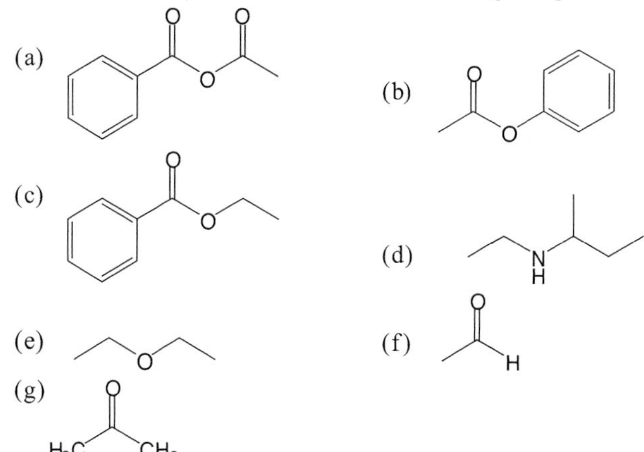

26. Using acetyl chloride as your only source of carbon, propose a synthesis of each of the following compounds. You may use any inorganic reagent necessary.

(a) ethyl acetate (b) 2-butanol (c) 3-methyl-3-pentanol
(d) 2-butanone (e) ethanamine (f) *N*-ethylacetamide
(g) *N,N*-diethylacetamide

27. Which of the following esters do you think will undergo saponification faster? Why?

$H_3C-C(=O)-O-CH_3$ OR $F_3C-C(=O)-O-CH_3$

28. Show how to synthesize the following molecule from any compounds containing 2 carbons. Draw the complete, detailed mechanism for that reaction.

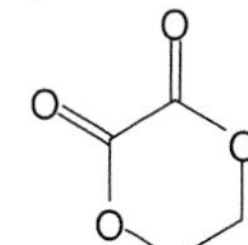

29. N,N-diacylamides can be prepared by treating an acyl chloride with lithium nitride in a 3-to-1 ratio, as shown below. Draw a complete, detailed mechanism for this reaction.

$RC(=O)Cl + Li_3N \longrightarrow N(C(=O)R)_3$

30. Barbituric acid can be prepared from malonic ester and urea, as shown below. Provide a complete, detailed mechanism for this reaction.

Et–O–C(=O)–CH₂–C(=O)–O–Et + H₂N–C(=O)–NH₂ —($EtO^{\ominus}$)→ barbituric acid

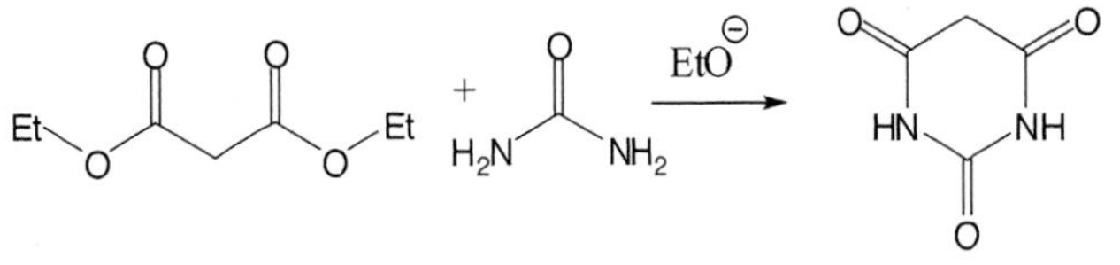

barbituric acid

31. Enamines can react with acyl chlorides via nucleophilic addition-elimination such as in the synthesis of a 1,3-diketone shown below. Provide a complete, detailed mechanism for this transformation.

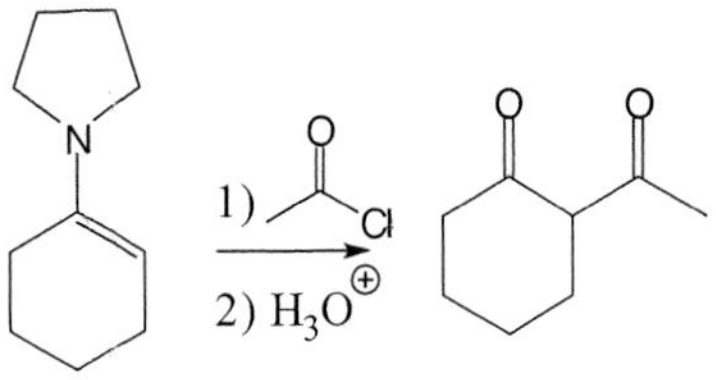

1) acetyl chloride (Cl)
2) $H_3O^{\oplus}$

32. An amidine has the general form R–C(=NH)–NH₂. Amidines are nitrogen analogs of carboxylic acids. As shown below, they can be hydrolyzed under basic conditions to form amides. (a) Propose a mechanism illustrating the conversion of an amidine into an amide. (b) Which do you think would be *more* susceptible to nucleophilic attack—an amidine or an amide? Explain.

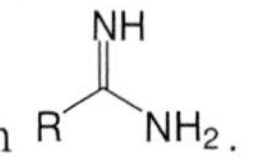

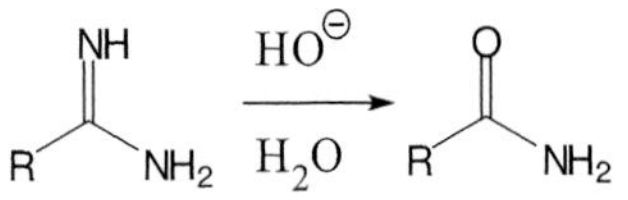

R–C(=NH)–NH₂ —($HO^{\ominus}$, H_2O)→ R–C(=O)–NH₂

33. (a) Propose a mechanism for the following substitution reaction.

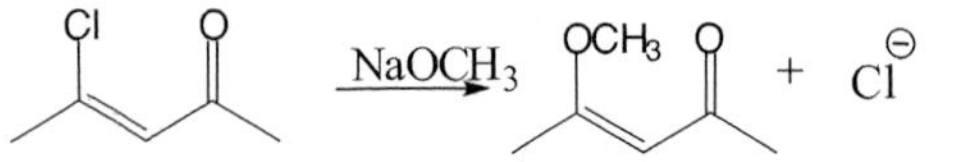

—($NaOCH_3$)→ product with OCH_3 + $Cl^{\ominus}$

(b) Explain why the following reaction does not lead to a similar substitution.

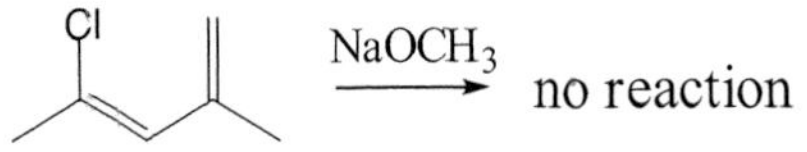

—($NaOCH_3$)→ no reaction

34. Propose a mechanism for the following reaction.

epoxide + C_2H_5O–C(=O)–CH₂–C(=O)–OC_2H_5 —($NaOC_2H_5$)→ lactone–C(=O)–OC_2H_5 + $C_2H_5O^{\ominus}$

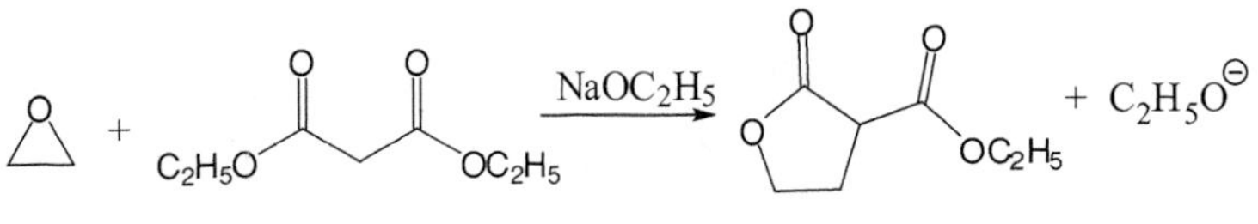

35. If a lactam (cyclic amide) contains an alkyl group with an amine functional group, treatment with lithium diisopropyl amide results in a ring-expanded lactam, as shown below. Prove a detailed mechanism for this reaction.

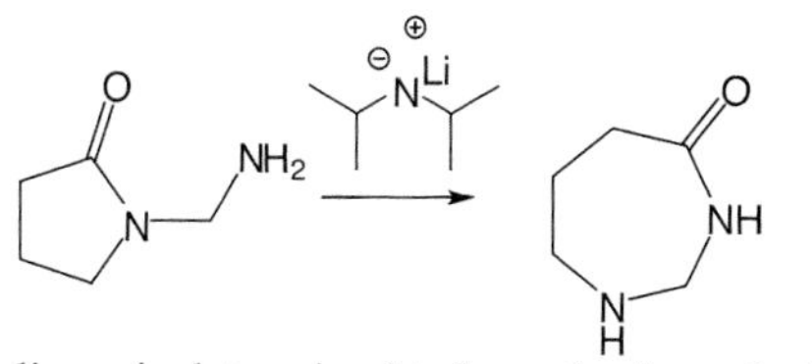

36. A pain reliever is determined to have the formula $C_8H_9NO_2$. Its IR spectrum is as follows

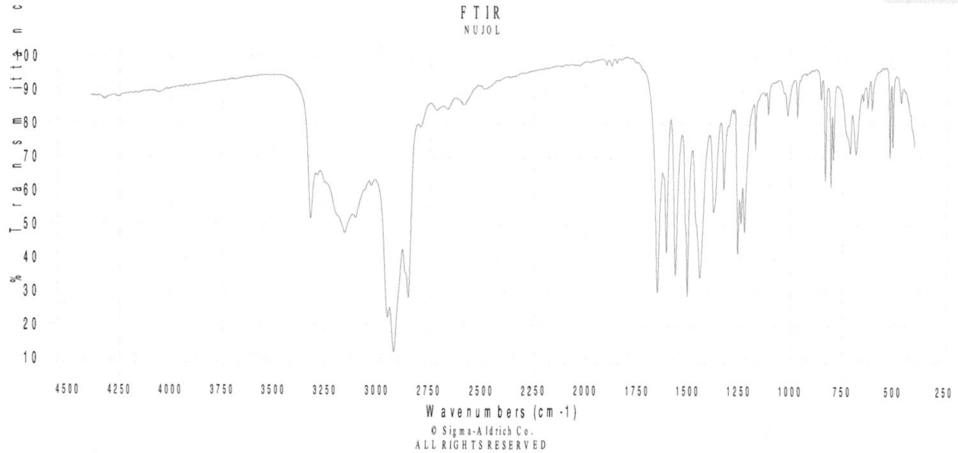

When it is heated in water under basic conditions, followed by an acid workup, two compounds are formed—acetic acid and a compound whose formula is C_6H_7NO and whose ^{1}H-NMR spectrum is shown below. Draw a structure for this compound and for the pain reliever.

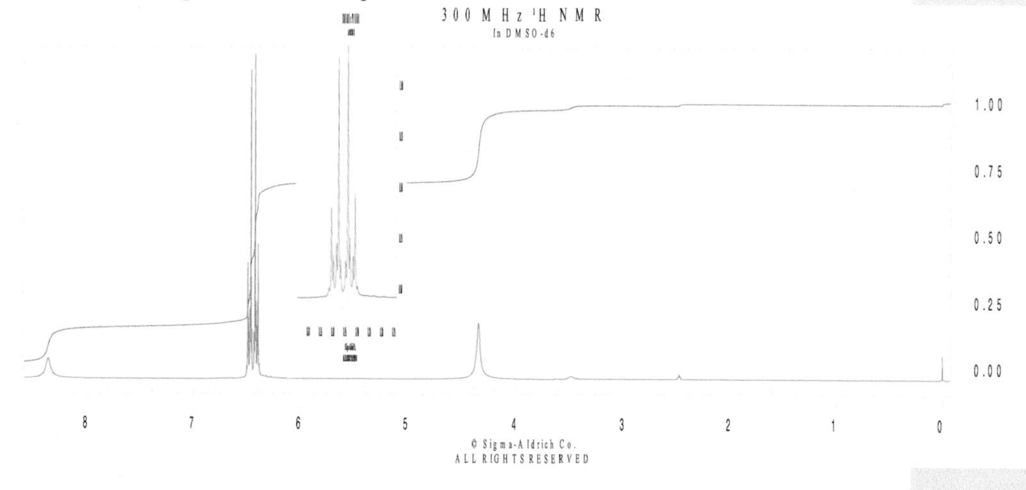

37. Draw the complete, detailed mechanism for the following reaction.

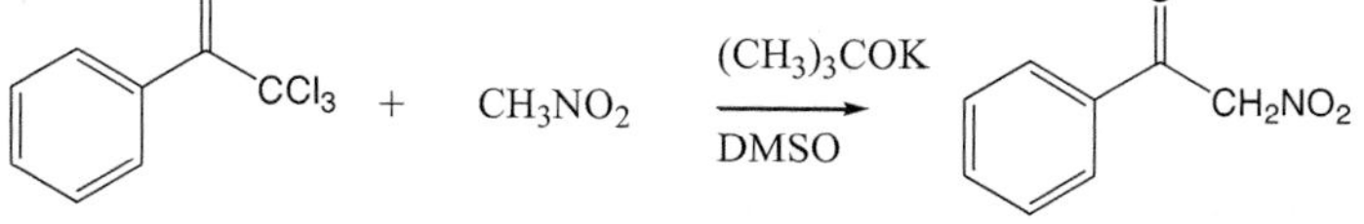

$$C_6H_5COCCl_3 + CH_3NO_2 \xrightarrow[\text{DMSO}]{(CH_3)_3COK} C_6H_5COCH_2NO_2$$

38. Draw a complete, detailed mechanism to account for the incorporation of ^{18}O twice into the acetate anion.

RCO_2^- $\underset{H_2{}^{18}O}{\overset{^{18}NaOH}{\rightleftharpoons}}$ $RC(^{18}O)^{18}O^-$

39. Which of the following compounds do you think will form a yellow solid when dissolved in a basic, aqueous solution of I_2?
(a) butanoic acid (b) 2-pentanone (c) 3-pentanone (d) cyclohexanone
(e) pentanal

40. When methyl 5-oxopentanoate is treated with vinyl Grignard, a compound is produced whose formula is $C_7H_{10}O_2$. In the IR spectrum of that product, an intense absorption appears at 1,740 cm^{-1}, and a weaker absorption appears at 1,650 cm^{-1}. In the ^{13}C-NMR spectrum of that product, six signals appear. The DEPT spectrum shows that there is one carbon that is bonded to no hydrogens, there are two CH carbons, and there are four CH_2 carbons.

methyl 5-oxopentanoate $\xrightarrow[\text{THF}]{CH_2{=}CHMgBr}$

41. When dimethyl phthalate is treated with lithium aluminum hydride, a compound is produced whose proton NMR spectrum is shown below.

dimethyl phthalate $\xrightarrow[\text{Et}_2\text{O, THF, -30 °C}]{LiAlH_4}$?

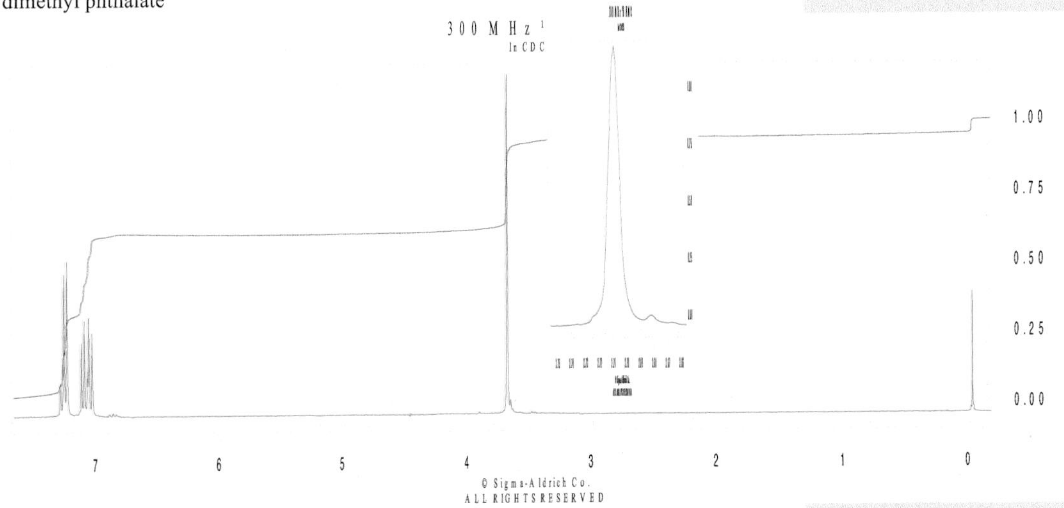

42. Show how to synthesize each of the following amines from an alkyl halide via a Gabriel synthesis.

(a) NH_2

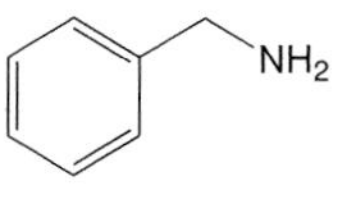

(b) NH_2

(c) NH_2 OCH_3

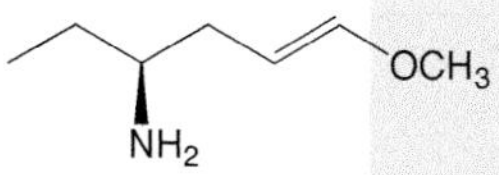

43. Supply the missing compounds A through D.

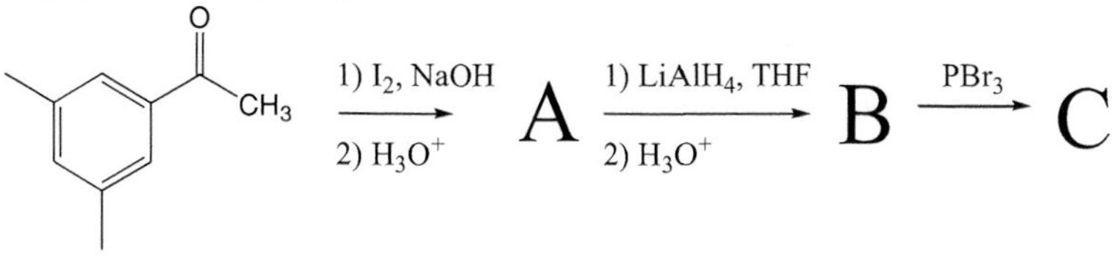

O, CH_3 — 1) I_2, NaOH; 2) H_3O^+ → A — 1) $LiAlH_4$, THF; 2) H_3O^+ → B — PBr_3 → C

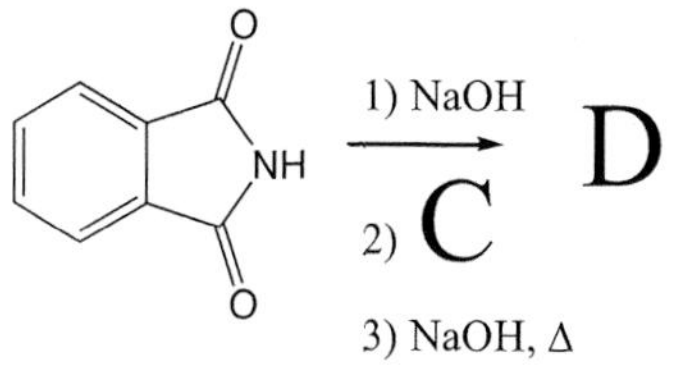

O, NH, O — 1) NaOH; 2) C; 3) NaOH, Δ → D

44. Supply the missing compounds A through G.

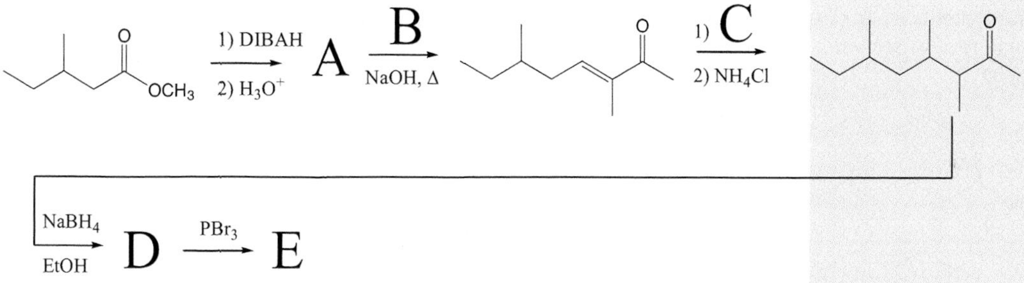

O, OCH_3 — 1) DIBAH; 2) H_3O^+ → A — B; NaOH, Δ → O — 1) C; 2) NH_4Cl → O

$NaBH_4$; EtOH → D — PBr_3 → E

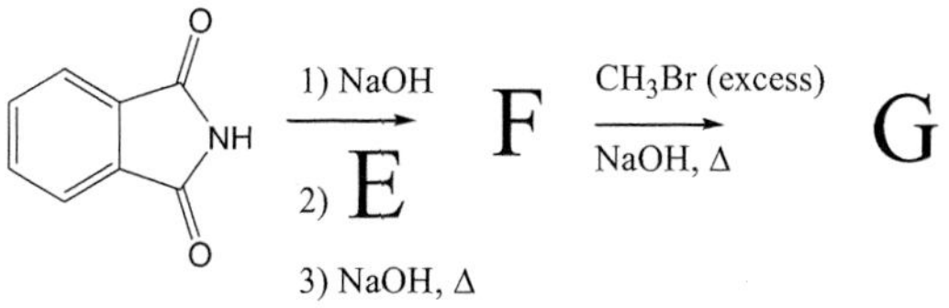

O, NH, O — 1) NaOH; 2) E; 3) NaOH, Δ → F — CH_3Br (excess); NaOH, Δ → G

45. Supply the missing reagents A through D.

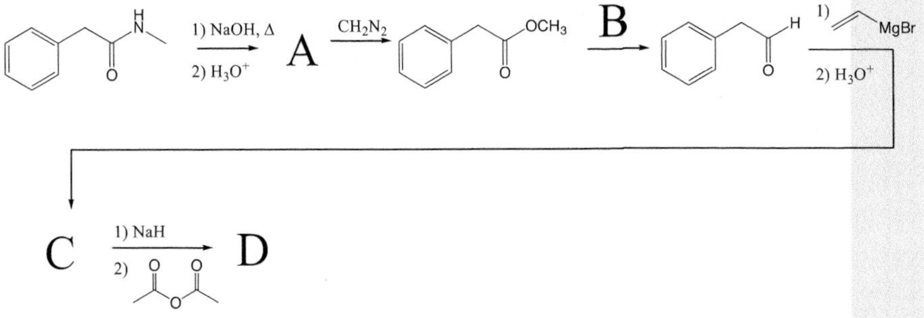

1) NaOH, Δ; 2) H_3O^+ → A; CH_2N_2 → OCH_3 B → H; 1) MgBr; 2) H_3O^+

C 1) NaH; 2) → D

46. Below is a proposed synthesis of a thioster from an ester. (a) Draw the mechanism by which this reaction would take place. (b) Argue whether or not this reaction would be energetically favorable.

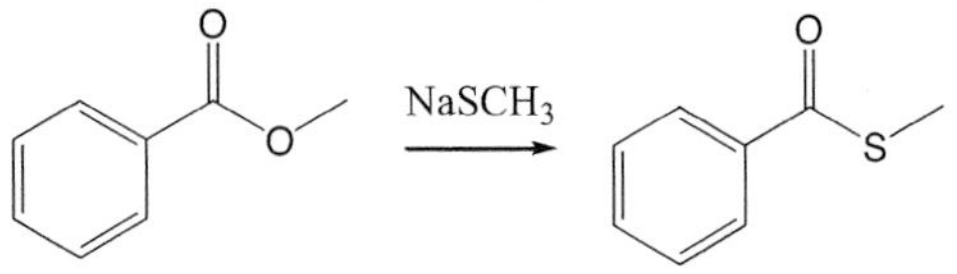

$NaSCH_3$ →

47. In the chapter, we mentioned that ancient civilizations synthesized soap by heating animal fat with wood ash, a source of HO^-. Animal fat consists of triesters, known as triglycerides, an example of which is shown below at left. (a) Assuming that the triglyceride reacts completely with HO^-, what are the products of this reaction? (b) Draw the complete, detailed mechanism that leads to those products. (c) Explain how those products can serve soap. (You may wish to review Section 2.9.)

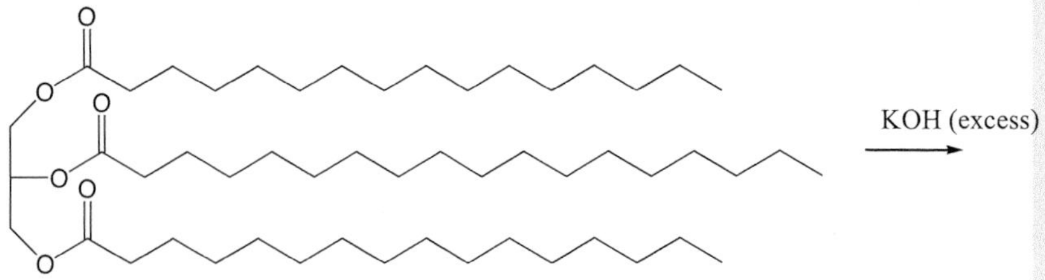

KOH (excess) →

Chapter 19. Nucleophilic Addition-Elimination Reactions. 2: Weak Nucleophiles

Introduction

Chapter 18 discussed reactions that proceed by the nucleophilic addition-elimination mechanism, which, as shown below, consists of two steps. In step 1, a nucleophile attacks the electron-poor carbon of a polar multiple bond to generate an unstable tetrahedral intermediate. In step 2, a leaving group is expelled from the tetrahedral intermediate, thus regenerating the multiple bond.

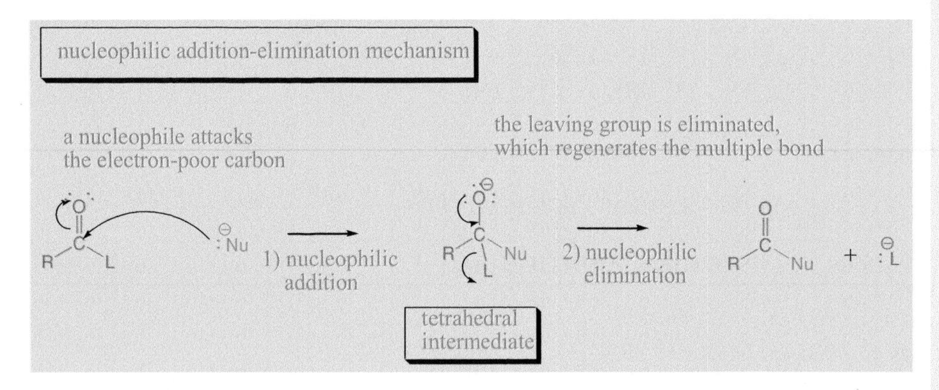

The specific reactions we examined in Chapter 18 were limited to ones involving *strong nucleophiles* in the addition step. For example, in a transesterification reaction, an alkoxide anion (RO^-) serves as the nucleophile, and in a Grignard reaction involving an ester, an alkanide anion (R^-) serves as the nucleophile.

In this chapter we will expand our discussion of nucleophilic addition-elimination reactions to include ones that involve *weak nucleophiles*. Fundamentally, nucleophilic addition-elimination reactions involving weak nucleophiles are quite similar to ones involving strong nucleophiles, but there are some key differences. We will see, for example, that nucleophilic addition-elimination reactions involving weak nucleophiles tend to proceed much slower than ones involving strong nucleophiles. Many such reactions therefore require acid- or base-catalysis. We will also see that mechanisms that describe reactions involving weak nucleophiles tend to consists of more steps than those in which strong nucleophiles are involved.

We will examine a wide variety of nucleophilic addition-elimination reactions involving weak nucleophiles. Most of our discussion will be on reactions in which a nucleophile attacks the carbonyl carbon of an acid derivative or a carboxylic acid, leading to acyl substitution. However, we will also examine reactions that involve nucleophilic attack at other polar π bonds, such as S=O and Cr=O bonds. Some reactions we will examine are oxidation reactions, and some alter a molecule's carbon skeleton. Given this variety of reactions, it will be particularly important for you to maintain focus on the mechanism, so that you can see clearly how all the reactions in this chapter are interrelated.

19.1. THE GENERAL NUCLEOPHILIC ADDITION-ELIMINATION MECHANISM INVOLVING WEAK NUCLEOPHILES: ALCOHOLYSIS AND HYDROLYSIS OF ACID CHLORIDES

In Section 18.3, we learned that an ester such as methyl benzoate can be produced from benzoyl chloride using methoxide anion (CH_3O^-), a relatively *strong* nucleophile (Equation 19-1). As we saw, the mechanism for this reaction is simply the two-step nucleophilic addition-elimination mechanism described in the introduction to this chapter.

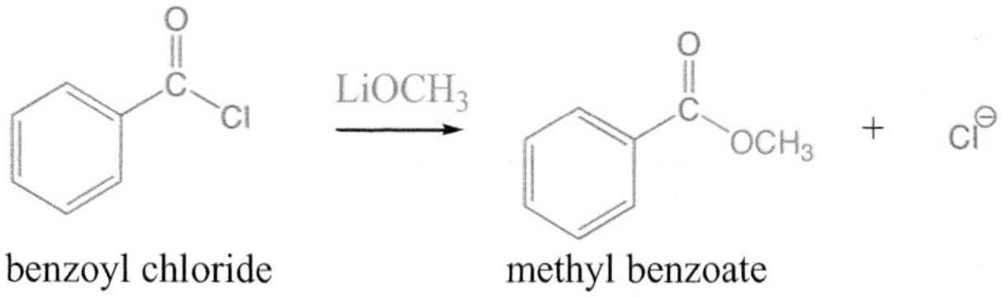

benzoyl chloride $\xrightarrow{LiOCH_3}$ methyl benzoate (84%) + $Cl^{\ominus}$

(19-1)

Another way to produce an ester from an acid chloride is simply to treat the acid chloride with an alcohol, a relatively *weak* nucleophile. An example is shown in Equation 19-2. Similarly, an acid chloride can be treated with water (another relatively weak nucleophile) to produce a carboxylic acid, as shown in Equation 19-3.

Comment [JMK35]: Margin note
An acid chloride will react with an alcohol or water to produce an ester or carboxylic acid, respectively.

an alcoholysis reaction

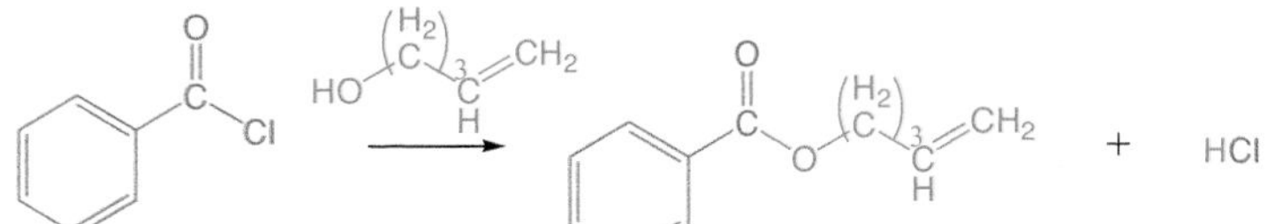

benzoyl chloride $\xrightarrow{HO(CH_2)_2CH{=}CH_2}$ 3-butenyl benzoate (71%) + HCl

(19-2)

a hydrolysis reaction

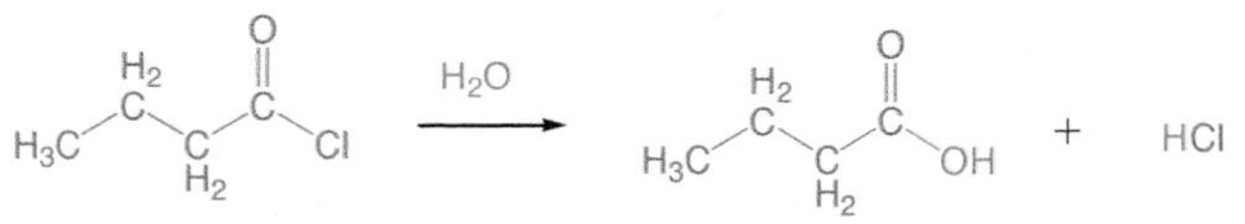

butanoyl chloride $\xrightarrow{H_2O}$ butanoic acid (77%) + HCl

(19-3)

The first of these reactions is called **alcoholysis** because the addition of the alcohol results in the breaking of a bond (*lysis* in Greek means "breaking"), in this case the C–Cl bond of the acid chloride. The second is called **hydrolysis**, given that the breaking of the bond in the acid chloride results from the addition of water.

The mechanism for the hydrolysis of an acid chloride is shown in Equation 19-4. The mechanism for alcoholysis is essentially the same, and is presented in Your Turn 19-1.

Mechanism for the Reaction in Equation 19-3

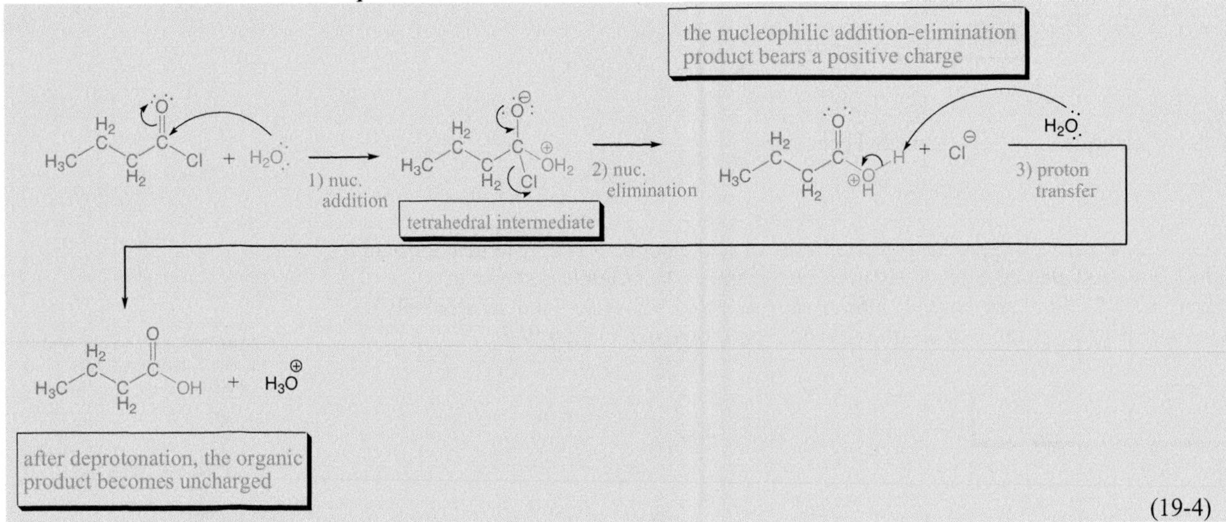

(19-4)

Notice that the first two steps of the mechanism consist of the usual nucleophilic addition and elimination steps. Water attacks the carbonyl carbon in the first step to produce the tetrahedral intermediate, which subsequently expels the Cl^- leaving group in the second step to reform the carbonyl bond. However, in a third step, a proton transfer takes place. As we can see, that proton transfer step is necessary in order to produce an uncharged product; without it, the OH group in the product would remain an OH_2^+ group.

Interestingly, HCl appears as a product in the overall reaction in Equation 19-3, but it does not appear in the mechanism in Equation 19-4. The reason is that the reaction involves water, in which HCl, because it is a strong acid, exists almost entirely as hydronium ion (H_3O^+) and chloride ion (Cl^-). This is consistent with the production of Cl^- in the second step of the mechanism, and H_3O^+ in the third step.

Your Turn 19.1. The mechanism for the alcoholysis reaction in Equation 19-2 is shown below, but the curved arrows have been omitted. (a) Draw in the appropriate curved arrows. (b) Write the name of the elementary step below each reaction arrow. (c) Circle and label the tetrahedral intermediate.

Problem 19.1. For each reaction, draw the complete, detailed mechanism and predict the major organic products.

(a) (b) H_2O

The free-energy diagram for an acid chloride hydrolysis is shown in Figure 19-1. As we can see, this free-energy diagram resembles the one that describes nucleophilic addition-elimination involving a strong nucleophile, shown previously in Figure 18-1. Namely, the first step produces a relatively high-energy tetrahedral intermediate, and involves a relatively large free energy of activation, $\Delta G^{\ddagger 0}$. Moreover, the second step is very favorable energetically, and involves only a small free energy activation. However, unlike the free-energy diagram involving a strong nucleophile, Figure 19-1 exhibits a third energy maximum. This accounts for the proton transfer that comprises the third step of the mechanism.

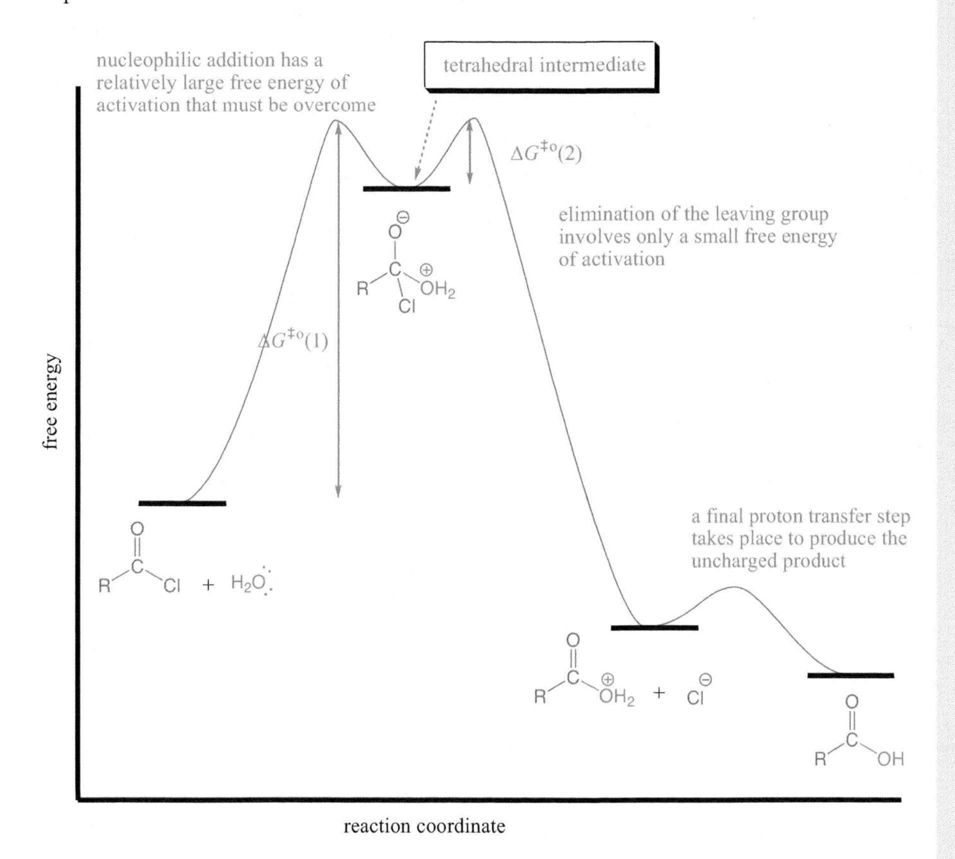

Figure 19-1. Free-energy diagram for the hydrolysis reaction of an acid chloride.
Step 1, nucleophilic addition, produces a high-energy tetrahedral intermediate, and involves a relatively large energy barrier, $\Delta G^{\ddagger 0}(1)$. Step 2, elimination of Cl^-, is very favorable energetically, and involves a small energy barrier, $\Delta G^{\ddagger 0}(2)$. Step 3 is a fast proton transfer step that produces an uncharged carboxylic acid.

Your Turn 19.2. The free-energy diagram for the alcoholysis reaction in Equation 19-2 is shown below. Draw the species involved in the reaction in the appropriate boxes provided, and label the tetrahedral intermediate.

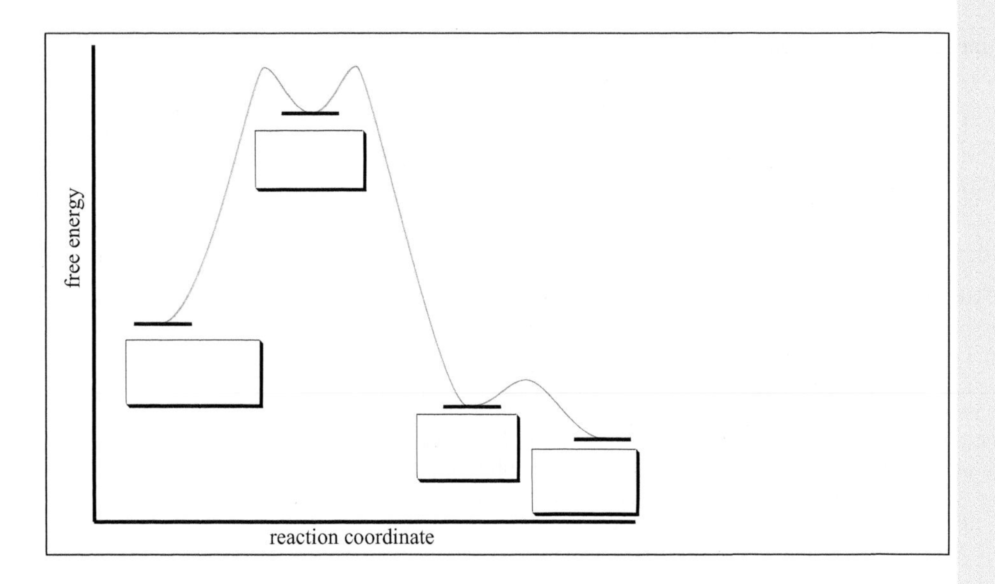

19.2. RELATIVE REACTIVITIES OF ACID DERIVATIVES: RATES OF HYDROLYSIS

Section 19.1 highlighted alcoholysis and hydrolysis reactions involving acid chlorides only, but such reactions are not limited only to acid chlorides. As shown in Equations 19-5 and 19-6, acid anhydrides can readily undergo alcoholysis and hydrolysis, producing esters and carboxylic acids, respectively. The mechanisms for these reactions are essentially the same as the one that describes the hydrolysis of an acid chloride, shown previously in Equation 19-4.

Comment [JMK36]: Margin note. Acid anhydrides react with alcohols and water to produce esters and carboxylic acids, respectively.

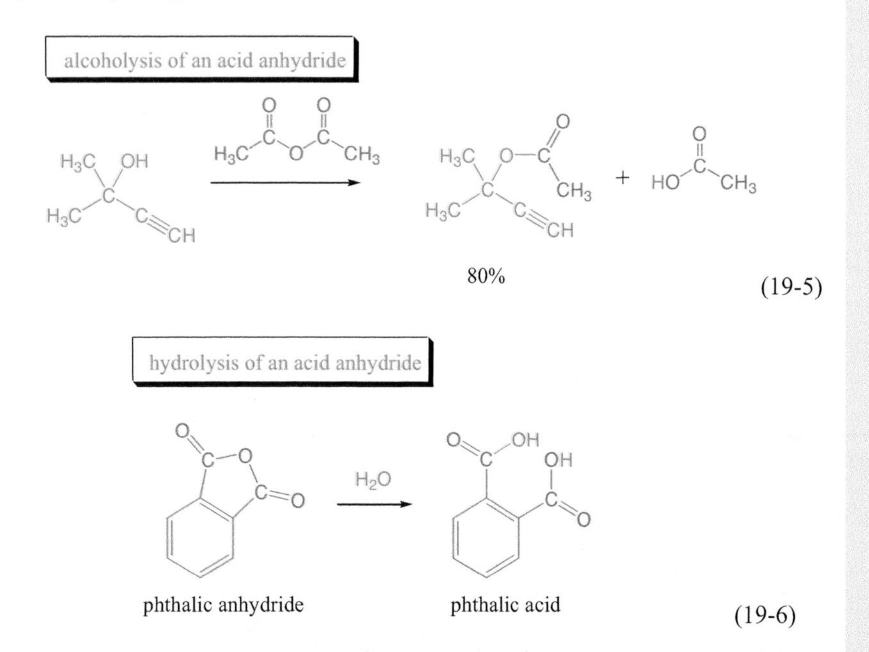

Problem 19.2. Draw the complete, detailed mechanisms for the reactions in Equations 19-5 and 19-6.

We can also envision similar reactions taking place when other acid derivates, such as esters or amides, are treated with water. However, as indicated in Table 19-1, such reactions are much too slow under normal conditions to be useful for synthesis.

Comment [JMK37]: Margin note. Esters and amides do not *readily* undergo hydrolysis.

Table 19-1. Relative reactivities of various carbonyl-containing species.

Carbonyl-containing species (leaving group in red)	Relative rate of hydrolysis	
$RC(O)Cl$	10^{11}	hydrolysis takes place readily
$RC(O)OC(O)R$	10^{7}	
$RC(O)H$, $RC(O)R$	-	
$RC(O)OH$, $RC(O)OR$	1	too slow to be useful for synthesis
$RC(O)NH_2$, $RC(O)NHR$, $RC(O)NR_2$	10^{-2}	
$RC(O)O^{\ominus}$	-	

Susceptibility to nucleophilic attack (increasing toward top)

To understand the relative hydrolysis rates of the species in Table 19-1, we must consider the *rate-determining-step* for the reaction. Just as we saw in the free-energy diagram for nucleophilic addition-elimination reactions involving strong nucleophiles (Figure 18-1), the step with the largest energy barrier in Figure 19-1 is nucleophilic addition. Thus,

> The rate-determining step in the hydrolysis of an acid derivative is the first step, nucleophilic addition.

With this in mind, let's examine Figure 19-2, which illustrates the free-energy diagrams for just the nucleophilic addition steps in the hydrolysis of various acid derivatives.

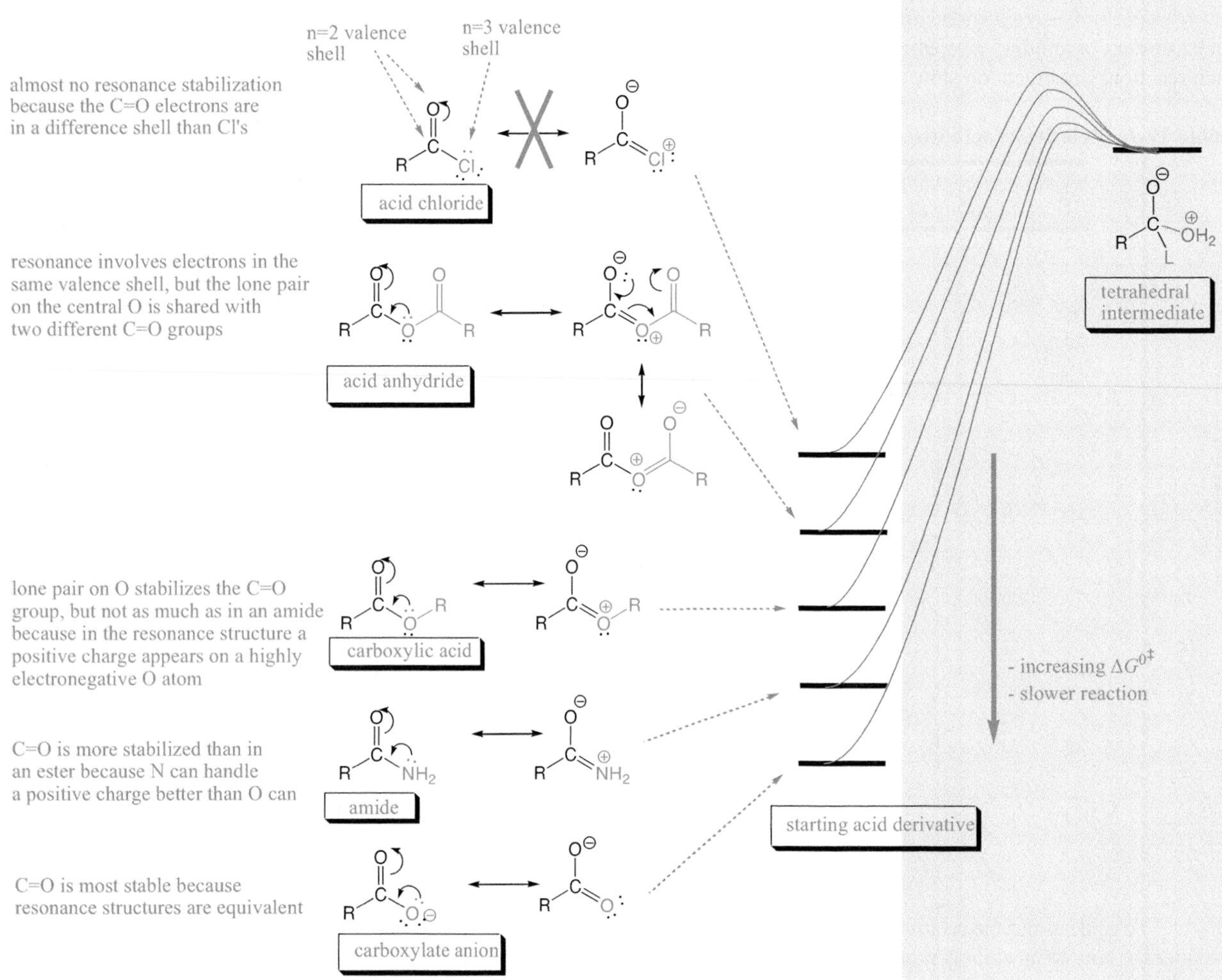

Figure 19-2. Relative reactivities of the acid derivatives.
Free-energy diagrams for just the nucleophilic addition steps in the hydrolysis of various acid derivatives. The different extents of resonance stabilization involving a lone pair on the leaving group lead to different free energies of activation. Carboxylate anions are the most stable due to the equivalence of the resonance structures. Amides are more stable than esters because the positive charge in the resonance structure is better accommodated by N than O. Acid anhydrides are less stable than esters because the lone pair is involved in resonance with two different carbonyl groups. Acid chlorides are the least stable because the valence electrons involved in resonance are from two different shells—the $n = 2$ shell for the C=O atoms, and the $n = 3$ shell for Cl.

The various acid derivatives differ in energy largely because they differ in the extent of *resonance stabilization* involving the carbonyl group and the leaving group. A carboxylate anion (RCO_2^-) is the most stable because it is the only one that has equivalent resonance structures. An amide is more resonance-stabilized than an ester because a positive charge is better accommodated by N than O. Thus, the contribution by an amide's resonance structure to the resonance hybrid is greater than that of an ester. The carbonyl group of an acid anhydride is less resonance-stabilized than that of an ester because the central oxygen's lone pair is involved in resonance with *two* carbonyl groups. Thus, the stabilization of each carbonyl group is diminished. Finally, an acid chloride is the highest in energy because the lone pair on Cl belongs to a different shell (n =3) than the valence electrons of the carbon and oxygen atoms belonging to the C=O group (n = 2). As we learned in Chapter 3, this leads to a relatively poor interaction among the valence orbitals, and thus diminishes any resulting stabilization.

According to the Hammond postulate (Section 9.3), these relative stabilities of the acid derivatives govern the sizes of the energy barriers for nucleophilic addition. The carboxylate anion, being the most stable, must traverse the largest energy barrier and thus takes place most slowly. On the other hand, the acid chloride, being the least stable, has the smallest energy barrier to overcome and thus takes place most quickly.

We can gain a better sense of the relative reactivities of the various acid derivatives by considering also the reactivities of aldehydes and ketones. Notice from Table 19-1 that acid chlorides and acid anhydrides are in fact more reactive than aldehydes and ketones, despite the fact that the carbonyl group of an aldehyde or ketone cannot be stabilized at all by resonance; the hydrogen and alkyl groups bonded to the carbonyl carbon do not possess a lone pair to participate in resonance. Primarily, this is due to *inductive effects*, as illustrated in Figure 19-3. With the resonance stabilization being relatively weak in acid chlorides and acid anhydrides, the electron-withdrawing effects by the electronegative atoms in the leaving group become very important. These *inductive effects increase the concentration of positive charge on the carbonyl carbon, making it more susceptible to nucleophilic attack.* By the same token, recall from Chapter 15 that inductive effects are also partly responsible for ketones being *less* reactive than aldehydes—the additional alkyl group in a ketone is electron-donating and therefore serves to decrease the concentration of positive charge on the carbonyl carbon.

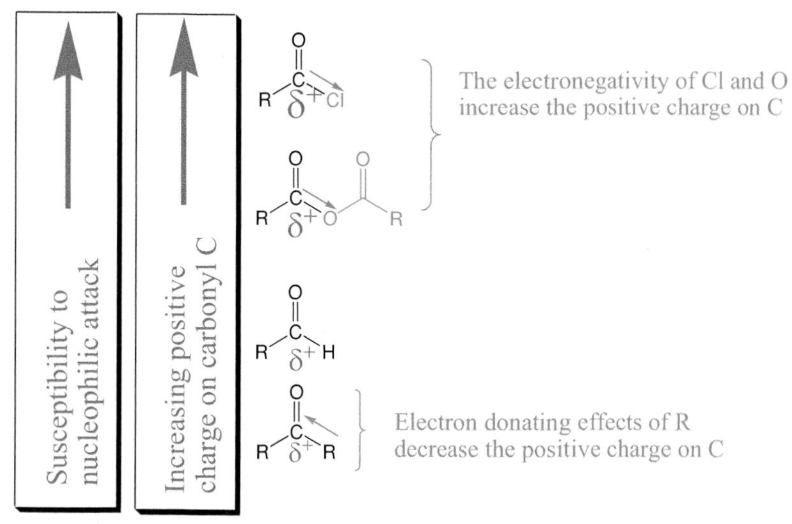

Figure 19-3. Inductive effects in various carbonyl-containing groups.
The carbonyl groups of acid chlorides and acid anhydrides are not stabilized very heavily by resonance, making inductive effects an important factor governing their relative reactivities. Because their leaving groups are electron-withdrawing, the concentration of positive charge on the carbonyl C is higher than it is in aldehydes. Thus, the C attracts nucleophiles more strongly, enhancing the rate of nucleophilic addition. By contrast, the electron-donating effect by an alkyl group decreases the concentration of positive charge on the carbonyl C, thus slowing down the rate of nucleophilic addition.

Solved Problem 19.1. Is the hydrolysis of phenyl acetate faster or slower than that of ethyl acetate? Explain.

phenyl acetate ethyl acetate

Think. How do resonance and inductive effects play a role in the reactivity of carboxylic acid derivatives? Are the carbonyl groups stabilized differently by resonance? By inductive effects? How so?

Solve. Phenyl acetate reacts faster because its carbonyl group is less stabilized by resonance than ethyl acetate's carbonyl group. In phenyl acetate, the lone pair of electrons on the oxygen of the leaving group is partly tied up in resonance with the benzene ring, making those electrons less available for resonance with the carbonyl group.

etc.

resonance with the benzene ring
makes these electrons less available
for resonance with the carbonyl group

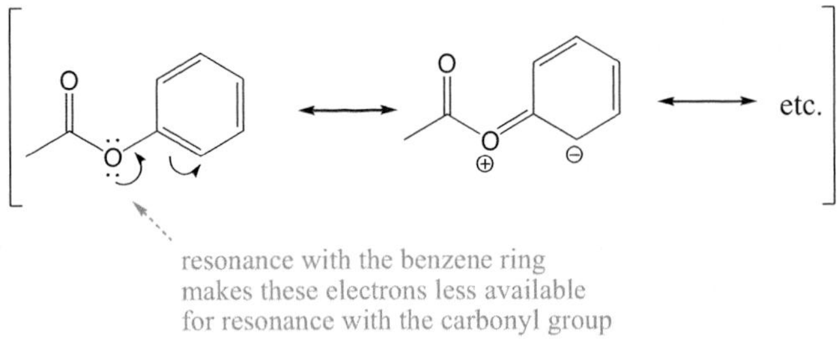

The inductive effects, on the other hand, are not expected to be much different in the two compounds, as both carbonyl groups are bonded to an alkyl group and an oxygen atom.

Problem 19.3. Which of the following do you think undergoes hydrolysis more quickly? Explain.

(a) 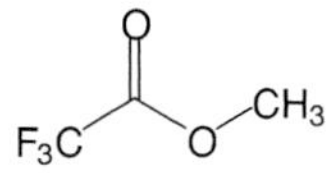 F_3C–CO–O–CH_3 OR H_3C–CO–O–CH_3

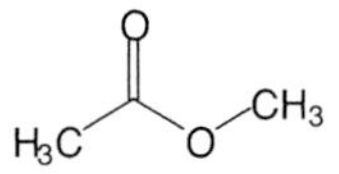

(b) 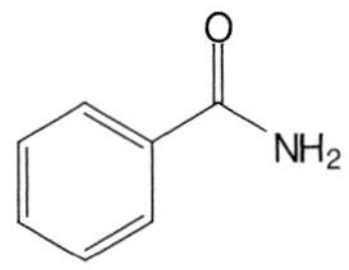 (benzene)–CO–NH_2 OR (cyclohexane)–CO–NH_2

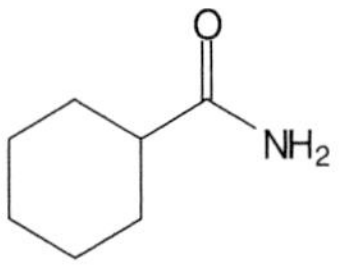

(c) 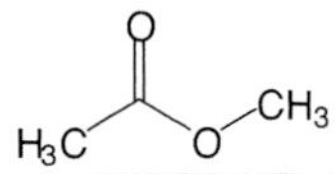 H_3C–CO–O–CH_3 OR H_3C–O–CO–O–CH_3

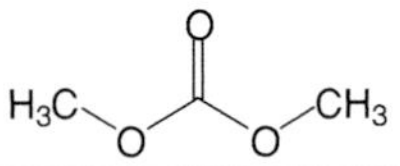

19.3. AMINOLYSIS OF ACID DERIVATIVES

In the previous two sections, we have seen that acid chlorides and acid anhydrides are reactive enough to undergo nucleophilic addition-elimination quite readily, even with weak nucleophiles such as water and alcohols. It should therefore be of no surprise that these acid derivatives can also undergo reaction with amines, which are even more nucleophilic than water or alcohols. Specifically, as shown in Equations 19-7 and 19-8, when an acid chloride or an acid anhydride is treated with an amine, an amide is produced via **aminolysis**.

aminolysis reactions

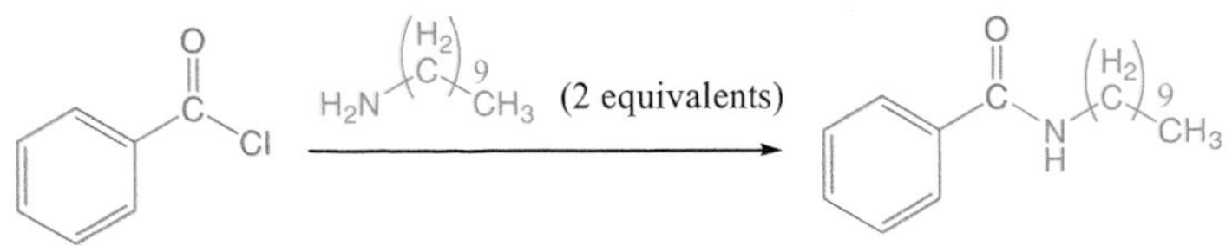

$H_2N(CH_2)_9CH_3$ (2 equivalents)

benzoyl chloride → *N*-decylbenzamide (19-7)

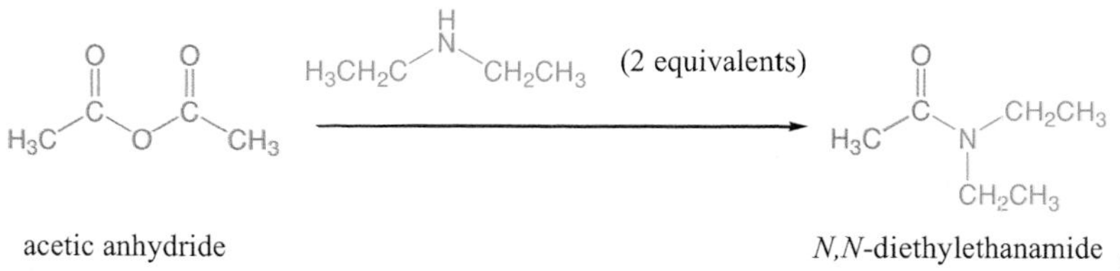

acetic anhydride $\xrightarrow{\text{H}_3\text{CH}_2\text{C-NH-CH}_2\text{CH}_3 \text{ (2 equivalents)}}$ *N,N*-diethylethanamide (19-8)

As we should expect, the mechanisms for these reactions are similar to the one for the hydrolysis of an acid chloride, shown previously in Equation 19-4. Indeed, as Equation 19-9 explicitly shows, this is the case for the aminolysis of an acid chloride. Step 1 of the mechanism is nucleophilic addition of the amine to produce the tetrahedral intermediate, followed by elimination of Cl^- in step 2. Finally, in step 3, a proton transfer produces the uncharged product.

Mechanism for the Reaction in Equation 19-7

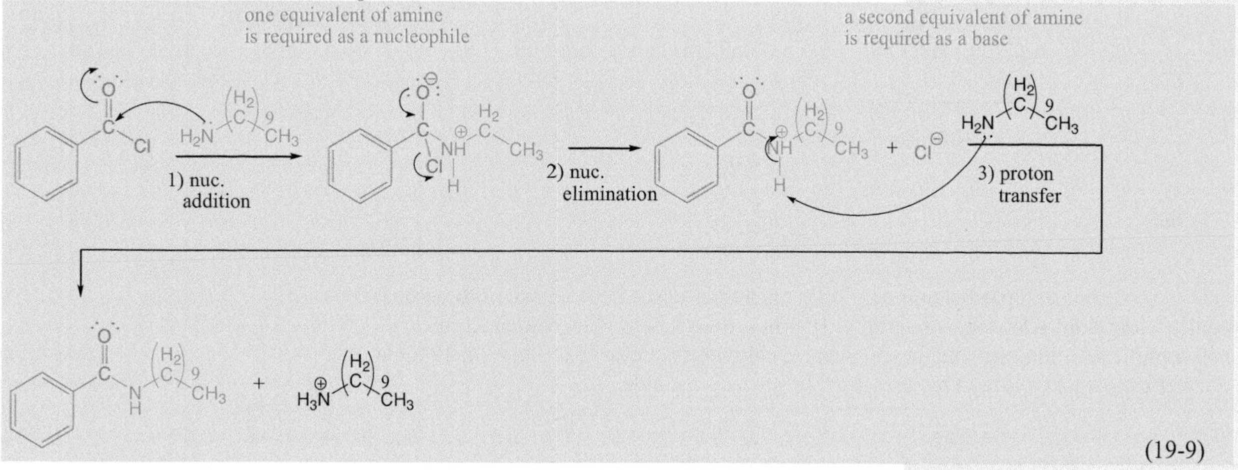

one equivalent of amine is required as a nucleophile

a second equivalent of amine is required as a base

1) nuc. addition

2) nuc. elimination

3) proton transfer

(19-9)

Problem 19.4. Draw the complete, detailed mechanism for the reaction in Equation 19-8.

An important aspect of the aminolysis reactions above is the need for two equivalents of the amine. The reason for such a requirement is evident from the mechanism. The first equivalent of the amine is used in step 1, in which the amine, acting as a nucleophile, attacks the carbonyl carbon of the acid chloride. The second equivalent of the amine is used in step 3, where it is irreversibly protonated by the elimination product from step 2.

If the amine is readily available and inexpensive, it may be acceptable to carry out an aminolysis reaction that extinguishes two equivalents of the amine. If, however, the amine is not easy to obtain or is simply expensive, then it is advantageous to use only one equivalent. In such cases, another amine such as pyridine or triethylamine can be added to the reaction mixture to act as a base, freeing up the desired amine to act as the nucleophile. For example, the aminolysis reaction in Equation 19-10 requires only one equivalent of the amine when one equivalent of pyridine is also present. Similarly, the aminolysis reaction in Equation 19-12 requires only one equivalent of the desired amine in the presence of one equivalent of triethylamine.

Comment [JMK38]: Margin note. Aminolysis of an acid chloride or acid anhydride requires two equivalents of amine.

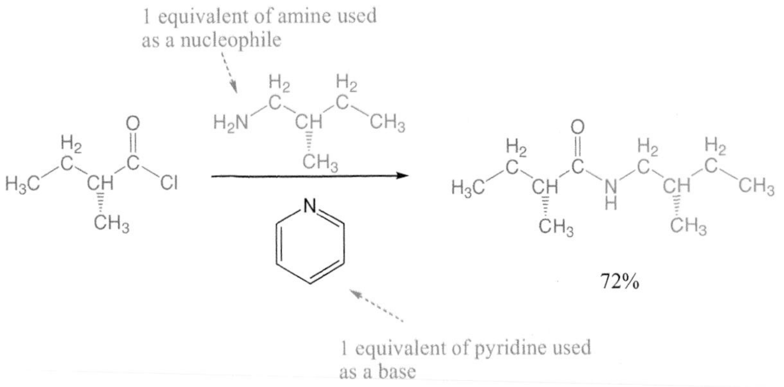

1 equivalent of amine used as a nucleophile

1 equivalent of pyridine used as a base

72%

(19-10)

1 equivalent of amine

$N(C_2H_5)_3$

70%

1 equivalent of triethylamine

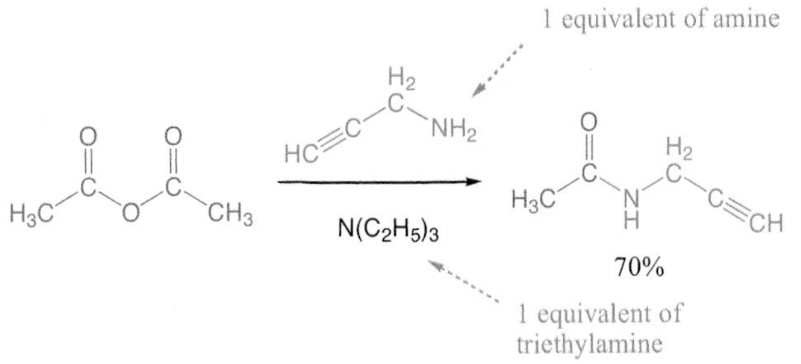

(19-11)

Pyridine and triethylamine are good choices as bases in these reactions because neither compound's N atom is bonded to H. Thus, even though they can undergo nucleophilic addition-elimination with an acid chloride or acid anhydride, a final proton transfer cannot take place to produce a stable uncharged amide.

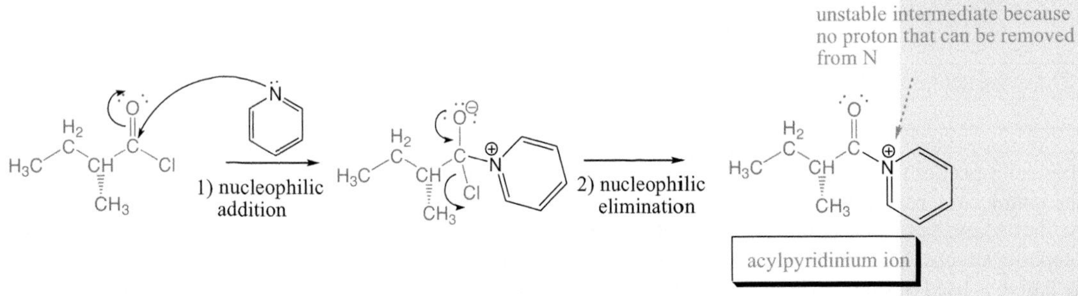

unstable intermediate because no proton that can be removed from N

1) nucleophilic addition

2) nucleophilic elimination

acylpyridinium ion

Instead, pyridine and triethylamine can remain free to act as bases in the final step, as shown for pyridine in Equation 19-12.

Mechanism of the Reaction in Equation 19-10

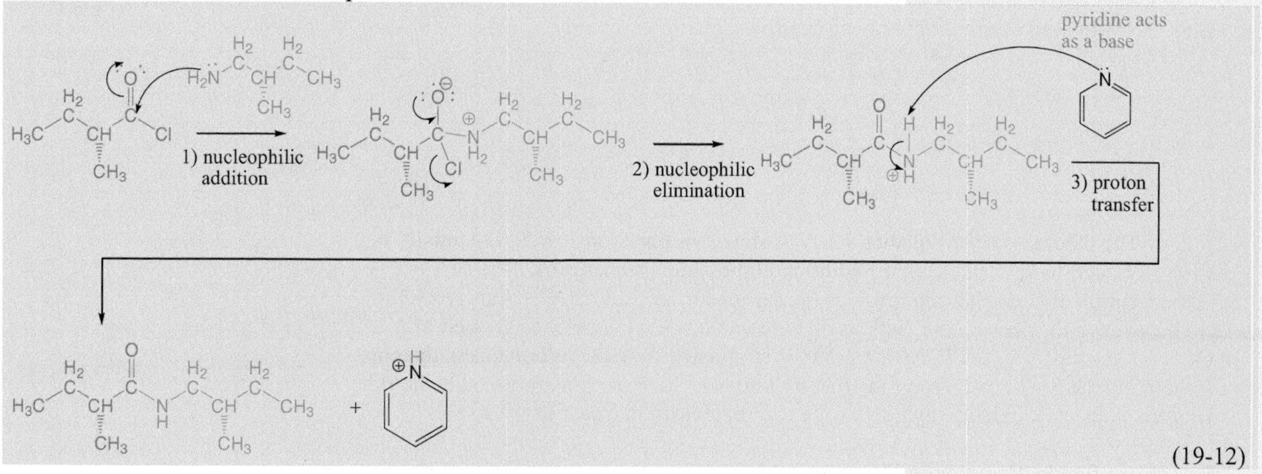

pyridine acts as a base

1) nucleophilic addition

2) nucleophilic elimination

3) proton transfer

(19-12)

Problem 19.5. Draw the complete, detailed mechanism for the reaction in Equation 19-11, in which triethylamine participates in a nucleophilic addition-elimination reaction with the anhydride.

19.4. SYNTHESIS OF ACID HALIDES: GETTING TO THE TOP OF THE STABILITY LADDER

In Section 18.3, we saw that an acid chloride appears at the top of the stability ladder and can thus be converted into any of the other acid derivatives with relative ease. This is true not only for reactions involving strong nucleophiles, but, as we have seen in this chapter, for weak nucleophiles like water, alcohols, and amines as well. In light of this, it can be extremely useful to produce acid chlorides from compounds that are more readily available.

Unfortunately, as we also learned in Section 18.3, it is not feasible to produce an acid chloride from a more stable acid derivative simply by treatment with Cl^-—although we can envision a mechanism for such a nucleophilic addition-elimination reaction, it would be unfavorable energetically. Consequently, in order to produce an acid chloride from a more stable acid derivative, other reagents must be used.

As shown in Equations 19-13 and 19-14, two such reagents are thionyl chloride ($SOCl_2$) and phosphorus trichloride (PCl_3). Of these, thionyl chloride is the more widely used reagent for chlorinating a carboxylic acid, due largely to the fact that the two byproducts, SO_2 and HCl, are gases that irreversibly bubble out of solution as they are produced.

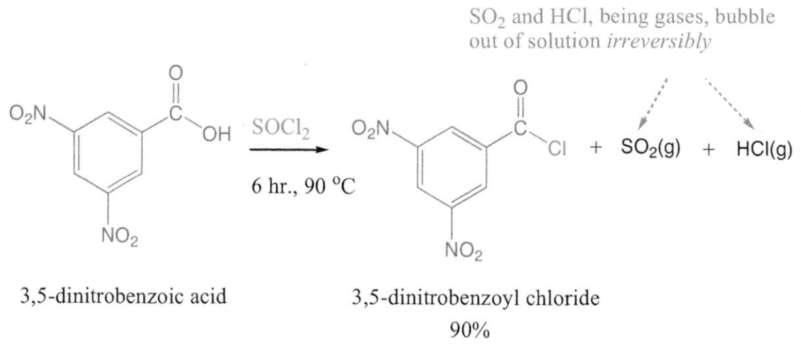

SO_2 and HCl, being gases, bubble out of solution *irreversibly*

$SOCl_2$, 6 hr., 90 °C

3,5-dinitrobenzoic acid → 3,5-dinitrobenzoyl chloride 90% + SO_2(g) + HCl(g)

(19-13)

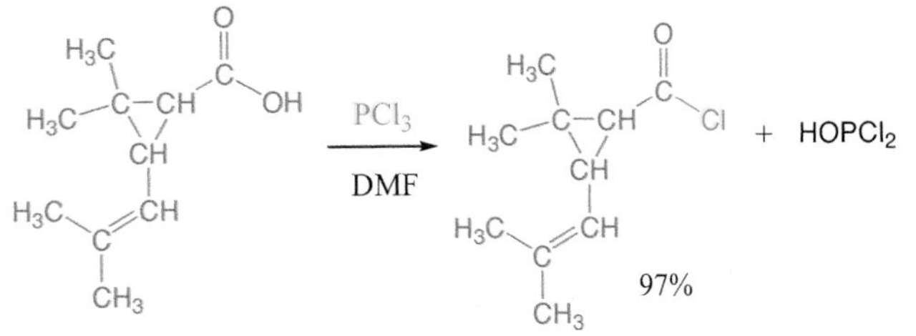

PCl3
DMF
+ HOPCl2
97%

(19-14)

The mechanism for Equation 19-13 is shown in Equation 19-15. Essentially it consists of back-to-back nucleophilic addition-elimination mechanisms. The first addition-elimination mechanism involves the carboxylic acid and $SOCl_2$; the carboxylic acid behaves as the nucleophile, with its OH group attacking the polar S=O bond of $SOCl_2$. In the next step, a Cl^- leaving group is eliminated from the intermediate, thereby regenerating the S=O bond. Thus, the first two steps in this mechanism resemble the first two steps in the acid chloride hydrolysis we saw previously in Equation 19-4.

Mechanism for the Reaction in Equation 9-13

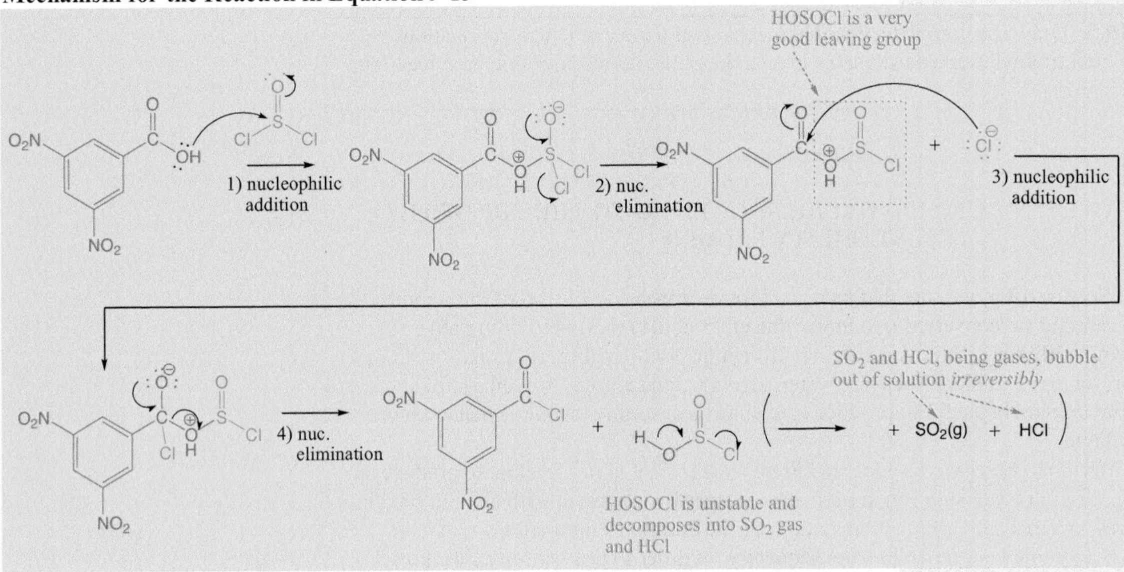

HOSOCl is a very good leaving group

1) nucleophilic addition

2) nuc. elimination

3) nucleophilic addition

4) nuc. elimination

SO2 and HCl, being gases, bubble out of solution *irreversibly*

+ SO2(g) + HCl

HOSOCl is unstable and decomposes into SO2 gas and HCl

(19-15)

As indicated, in the product of step 2, a very good leaving group, HOSOCl, is bonded to the carbonyl carbon. This sets the stage for a second nucleophilic addition-elimination reaction (steps 3 and 4), in which the chloride anion generated in step 2 replaces HOSOCl. Finally, in step 5, HOSOCl decomposes into SO_2 and HCl.

The mechanism for the reaction involving phosphorus trichloride (Equation 19-14) is shown in Your Turn 19.3, and is quite similar to the one involving thionyl chloride. The difference is that PCl_3 does not possess a polar π bond, so Cl^- is generated from an S_N2 step instead of an addition-elimination mechanism. This is essentially identical to the way in which Cl^- is produced from PCl_3 in the chlorination of an alcohol, which we examined previously in Section 10.1. Once the Cl^- nucleophile is generated, however, it enters into a nucleophilic addition-elimination mechanism with the carbonyl group to produce the carboxylic acid chloride.

Your Turn 19.3. The mechanism for the reaction in Equation 19-14 is shown below, but the curved arrows have been omitted. (a) Supply the missing curved arrows, and label each elementary step below its respective reaction arrow. (b) Circle and label the leaving group in the product of the first step.

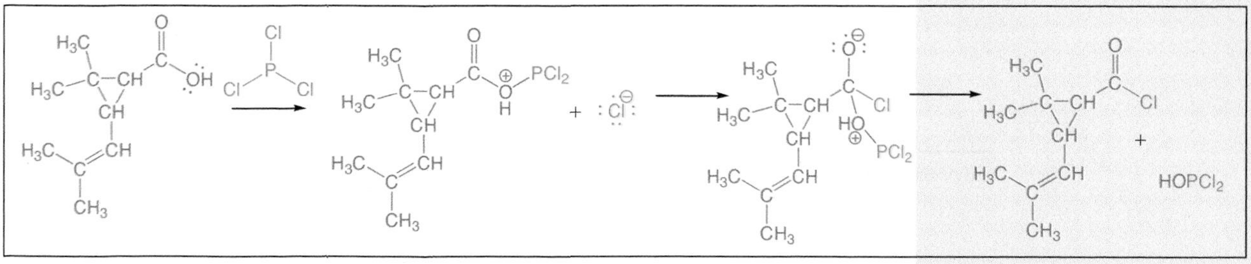

Solved Problem 19.2. Propose how you would carry out the following synthesis, in which an amide is converted into an acid anhydride.

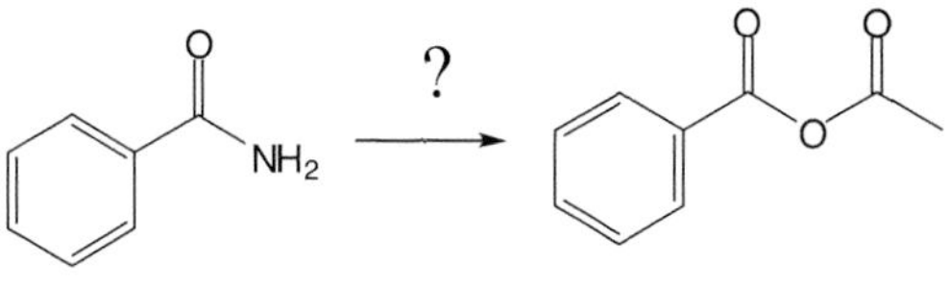

Think. What reactions do we know that transform an acid derivative lower on the stability ladder to one higher on the ladder? Can this transformation be done in a single step?

Solve. We know that $SOCl_2$ will transform a carboxylic acid into an acid chloride, from which any other acid derivative can be formed. In this case, we could treat benzoyl chloride with sodium acetate to arrive at the final anhydride, via an acyl substitution. Benzoyl chloride could be formed from benzoic acid using $SOCl_2$. Benzoic acid, in turn, could be formed from benzamide via hydrolysis.

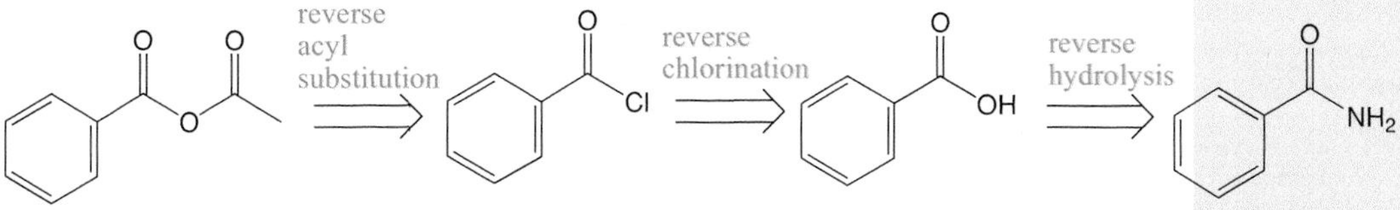

reverse acyl substitution; reverse chlorination; reverse hydrolysis

The overall synthesis would then appear as follows.

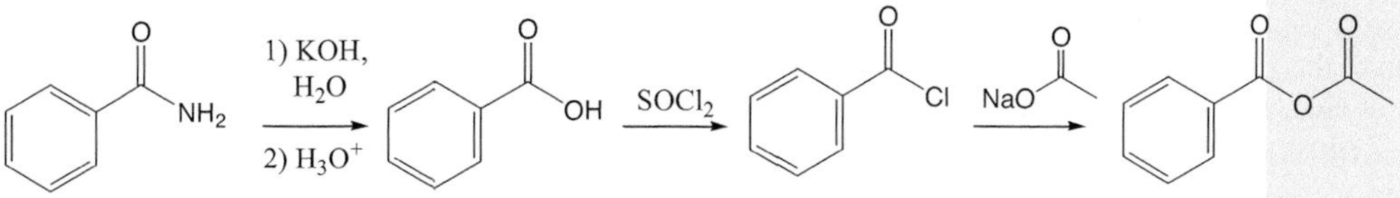

1) KOH, H_2O; 2) H_3O^+; $SOCl_2$; NaO

Problem 19.6. Propose a synthesis that would carry out the same transformation in Solved Problem 19.2, but does not involve benzoyl chloride as a synthetic intermediate.

19.4a. The Hell-Volhard-Zelinsky Reaction: Synthesizing Alpha-Bromo Carboxylic Acids

In Section 10.4, we learned that ketones and aldehydes undergo bromination at the alpha carbon by treating the ketone or aldehyde with molecular bromine (Br_2) in the presence of acid or base. In light of this, it might seem that, under similar conditions, carboxylic acids could undergo bromination at the alpha carbon to produce an α-bromo carboxylic acid. However, as indicated in Equation 19-16, this does not occur.

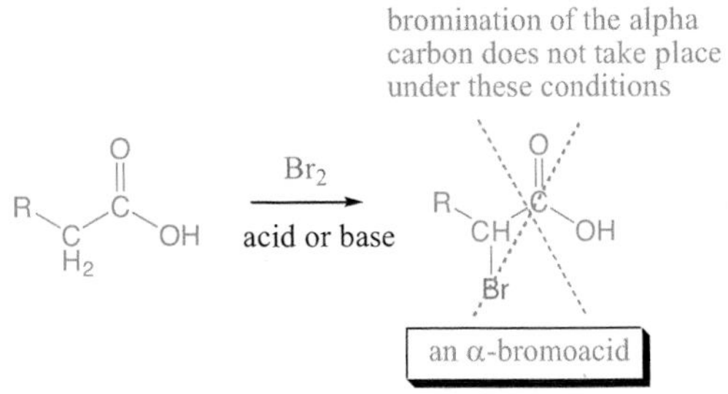

bromination of the alpha carbon does not take place under these conditions

$\mathrm{RCH_2COOH} \xrightarrow[\text{acid or base}]{Br_2} \mathrm{RCH(Br)COOH}$ (crossed out)

an α-bromoacid

(19-16)

We can understand why if we recall from Section 10.4 that α-bromination requires a key intermediate in which the α carbon is nucleophilic. Under basic conditions, that intermediate is an enolate anion, whereas under acidic conditions, it is an uncharged enol. With carboxylic acids, however, neither of these intermediates is feasible. As shown below, under basic conditions the carboxyl hydrogen is the one that is deprotonated instead of the alpha hydrogen. And under acidic conditions, the enol is unfavorable due to the resonance stabilization of the carbonyl group involving the hydroxyl group.

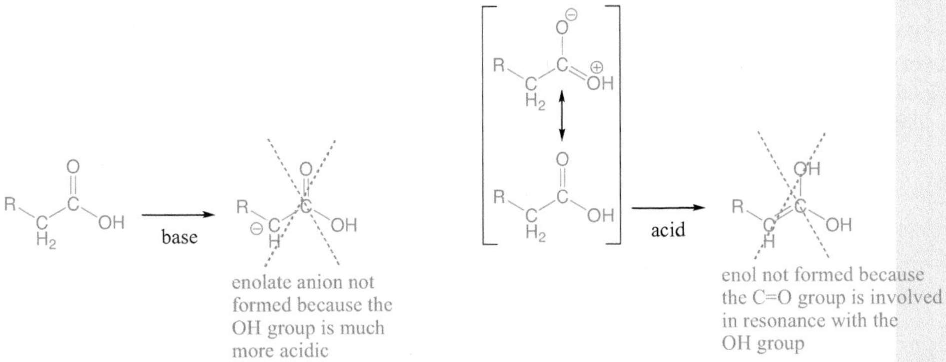

enolate anion not formed because the OH group is much more acidic

enol not formed because the C=O group is involved in resonance with the OH group

A clever solution to this problem is to carry out the bromination in the presence of a phosphorus trihalide or elemental phosphorus, as shown below. Such a bromination is called a **Hell-Volhard-Zelinsky reaction**.

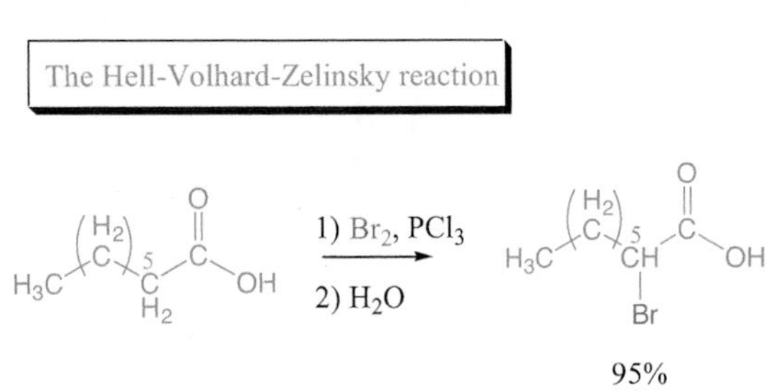

The Hell-Volhard-Zelinsky reaction

$\mathrm{H_3C(CH_2)_5CH_2COOH} \xrightarrow[\text{2) } H_2O]{\text{1) } Br_2,\ PCl_3} \mathrm{H_3C(CH_2)_5CH(Br)COOH}$ 95%

(19-17)

$\mathrm{C_6H_{11}CH_2COOH} \xrightarrow[\text{2) } H_2O]{\text{1) } Br_2,\ P,\ CCl_4,\ \text{reflux 3 hr.}} \mathrm{C_6H_{11}CH(Br)COOH}$ 21%

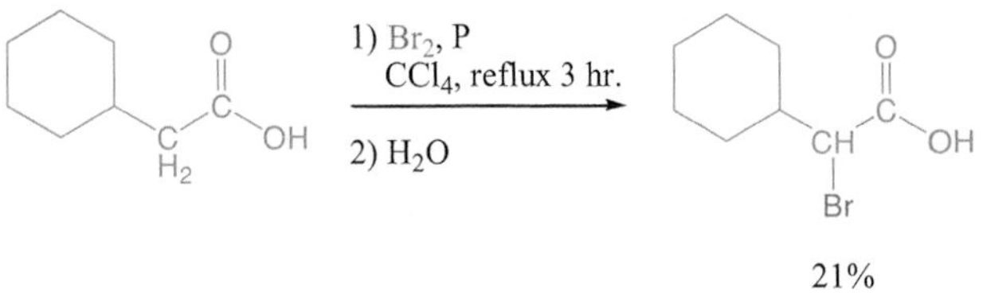

(19-18)

The role of phosphorus trichloride in the reaction in Equation 19-17 is shown in its partial mechanism in Equation 19-19. As we saw in the previous section, PCl_3 converts the carboxylic acid into an acid chloride, in which the carbonyl group is not stabilized significantly via resonance. Thus, the enol becomes more favorable, which facilitates the substitution reaction in the following steps to produce the α-bromo acid chloride. Subsequent treatment with water hydrolyzes the acid chloride to reform the carboxylic acid.

Partial mechanism of the Reaction in Equation 19-17

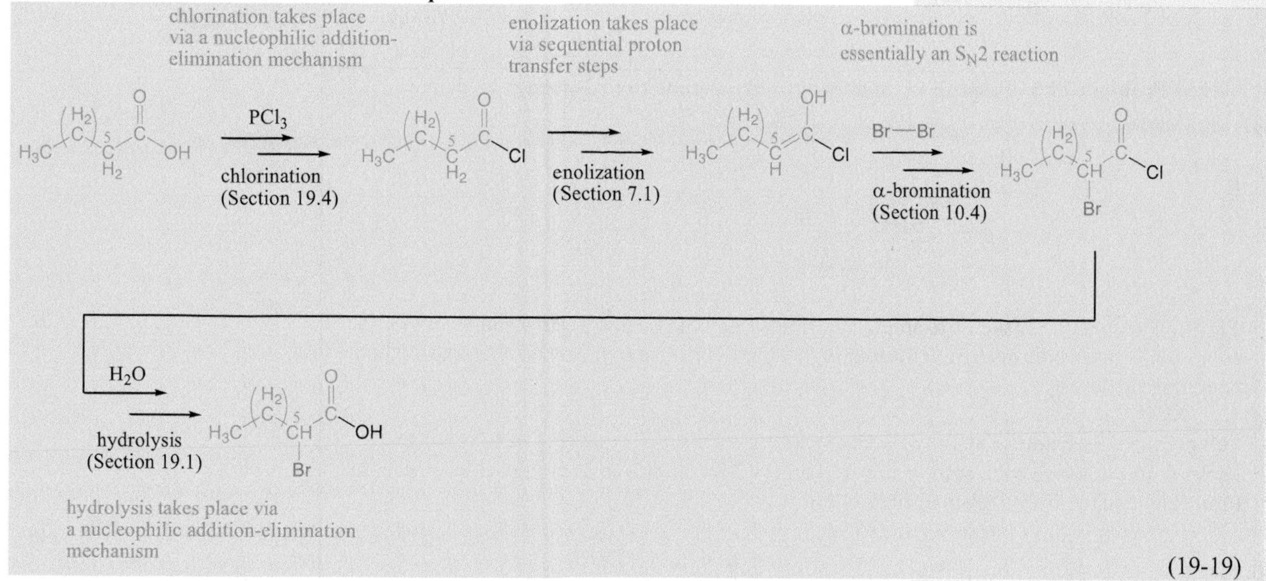

(19-19)

This mechanism is very similar to the one that describes the reaction in Equation 19-18 as well, because molecular bromine (Br_2) and elemental phosphorus react to form PBr_3. Thus, as shown in Your Turn 19.4, an α-bromo acid bromide is produced as an intermediate instead of an α-bromo acid chloride.

Your Turn 19.4. The partial mechanism for the HVZ reaction in Equation 19-18 is shown below, but the key intermediates have been omitted. Draw each intermediate.

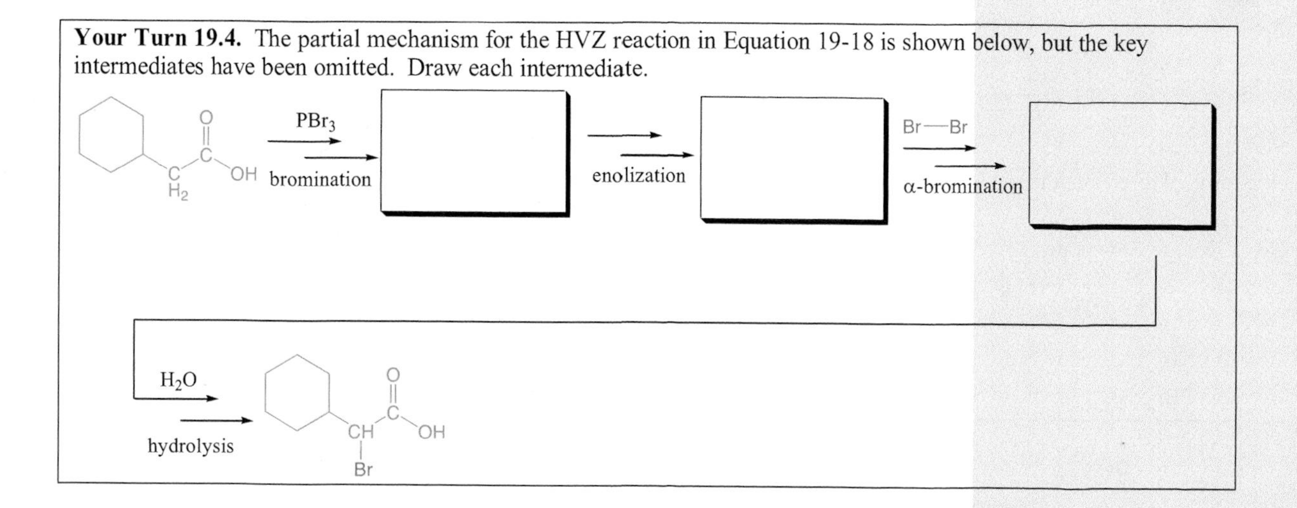

Not surprisingly, the excellent leaving group ability of the bromine atom makes α-bromoacids useful synthetic intermediates. For example, as shown below, they can be used to synthesize α-amino acids, the building blocks of proteins, via a nucleophilic substitution reaction with aqueous ammonia.

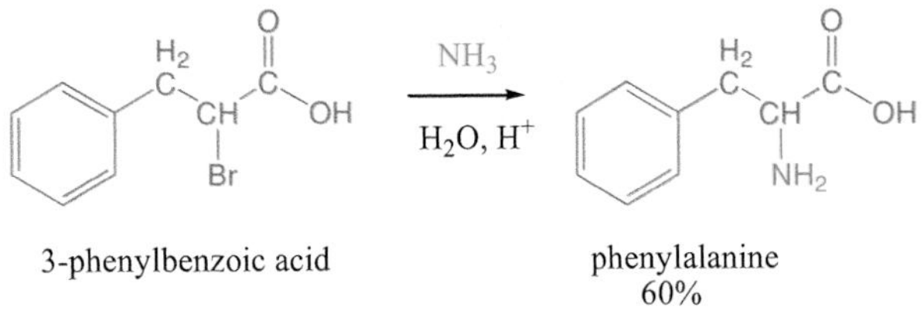

NH_3; H_2O, H^+

3-phenylbenzoic acid → phenylalanine 60%

(19-20)

Solved Problem 19.3. Propose a synthesis of phenylalanine from 2-phenyl-1-ethanol.

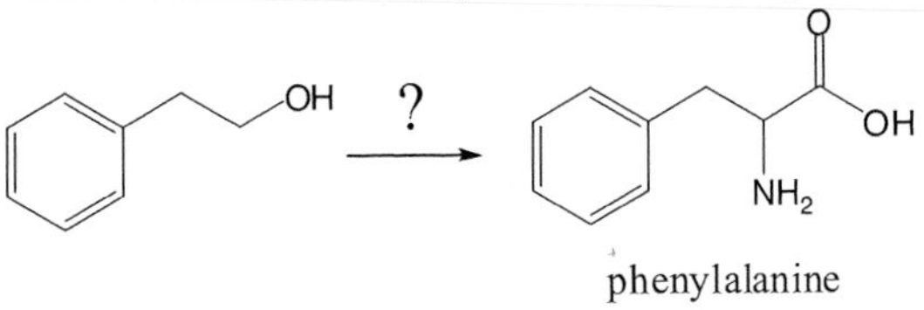

?

phenylalanine

Think. How can we make an α-amino acid from a carboxylic acid? How can we make the appropriate carboxylic acid from the starting material? Do we need to add a carbon-carbon bond? If so, how?

Solve. In a retrosynthetic analysis, we can apply a reverse S_N2 (thinking of NH_3 as the nucleophile) to arrive back at the product of an HVZ reaction—an α-bromoacid—which, in turn, can be made from 3-phenylbenzoic acid.

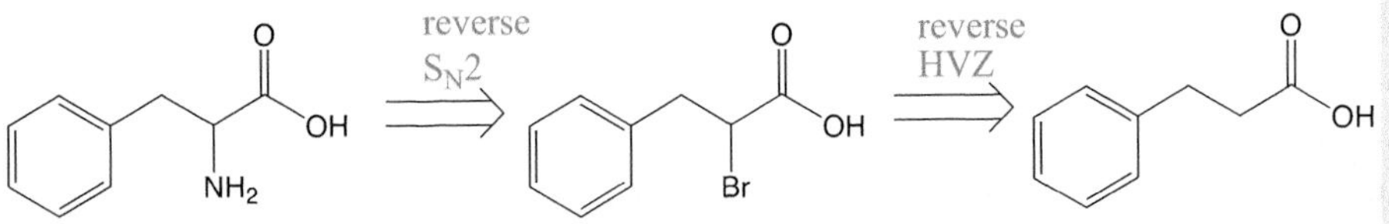

reverse S_N2 ⟹ reverse HVZ ⟹

This has one more carbon than the starting material. By reacting the CO_2 with the appropriate Grignard reagent, we can add a carbon and produce a carboxylic acid at the same time. That Grignard reagent can be made from the starting alcohol.

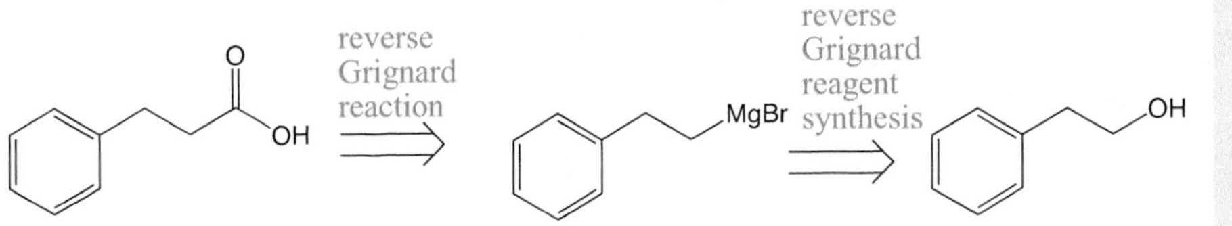

reverse Grignard reaction ⟹ reverse Grignard reagent synthesis ⟹

In the forward direction, the synthesis would appear as follows.

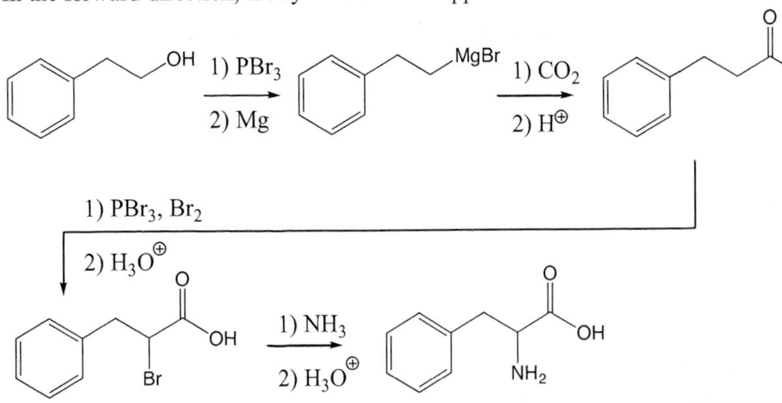

1) PBr_3 2) Mg → 1) CO_2 2) $H^{\oplus}$ →

1) PBr_3, Br_2 2) $H_3O^{\oplus}$ →

1) NH_3 2) $H_3O^{\oplus}$ →

Problem 19.7. Propose how to synthesize each of the following compounds from butanoic acid.

(a) (b) 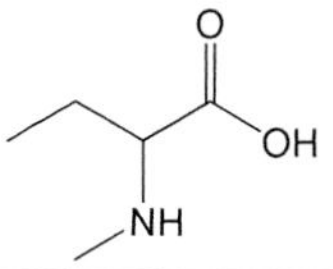 (c)

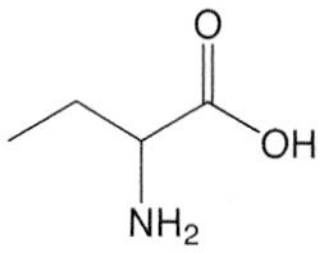

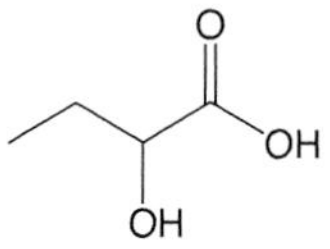

O OH NH_2 O OH NH O OH OH

19.5. SULFONYL CHLORIDES: SYNTHESIS OF MESYLATES, TOSYLATES, AND TRIFLATES

A sulfonyl chloride has the general form R–SO_2–Cl. With the Cl atom attached to a S=O bond, this structurally resembles $SOCl_2$, which we discussed in Section 19.4. Thus, it should be no surprise that sulfonyl chlorides undergo nucleophilic addition-elimination reactions readily, even with weak nucleophiles such as alcohols and amines.

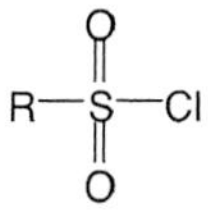

One of the most common uses of sulfonyl chlorides is to convert an alcohol into a **sulfonate ester**, $ROSO_2R'$, via a **sulfonation reaction**. Equations 19-21 through 19-23 show examples using methanesulfonyl chloride (abbreviated **mesyl chloride**, MsCl, or CH_3SO_2Cl), trifluoromethanesulfonyl chloride (abbreviated **trifyl chloride**, TfCl, or CF_3SO_2Cl) and *p*-toluenesulfonyl chloride (abbreviated **tosyl chloride**, TsCl, or CH_3-C_6H_4-SO_2Cl). As we first saw in Chapter 9, these sulfonate esters have excellent leaving groups that stabilize a negative charge via abundant resonance and inductive effects.

SULFONATION REACTIONS

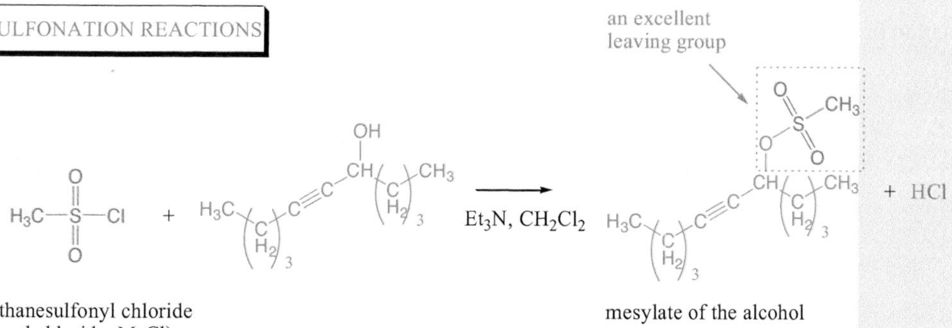

H_3C–SO_2–Cl + $H_3C(CH_2)_3C{\equiv}C$–CH(OH)–$(CH_2)_3CH_3$ $\xrightarrow{Et_3N,\ CH_2Cl_2}$ $H_3C(CH_2)_3C{\equiv}C$–CH(OSO_2CH_3)–$(CH_2)_3CH_3$ + HCl

methanesulfonyl chloride (mesyl chloride, MsCl)

an excellent leaving group

mesylate of the alcohol 78%

(19-21)

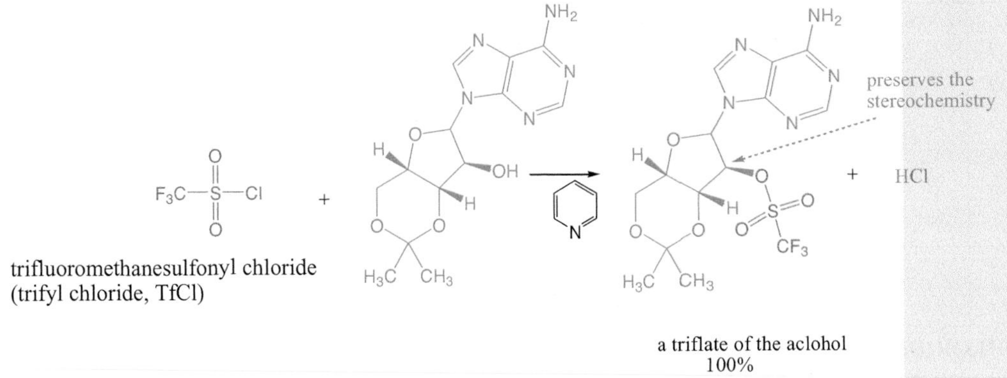

trifluoromethanesulfonyl chloride (trifyl chloride, TfCl)

preserves the stereochemistry

a triflate of the aclohol 100%

(19-22)

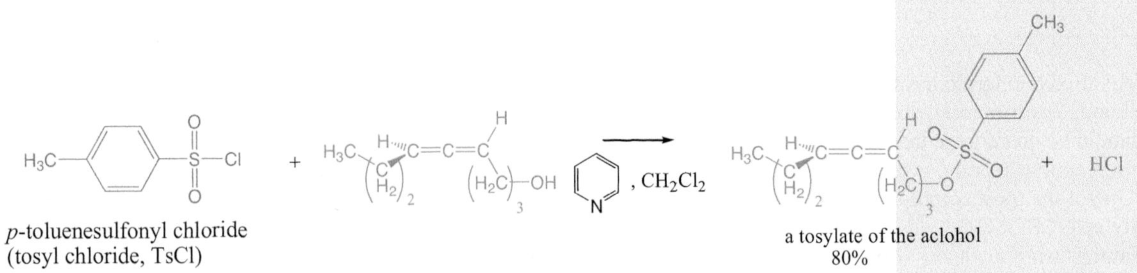

p-toluenesulfonyl chloride (tosyl chloride, TsCl)

, CH_2Cl_2

a tosylate of the aclohol 80%

(19-23)

Your Turn 19.5. Circle and label the leaving group in the product of Equation 19-22 as well as of Equation 19-23.

The mechanism for sulfonation is shown in Equation 19-24.

Mechanism for the Reaction in Equation 19-21

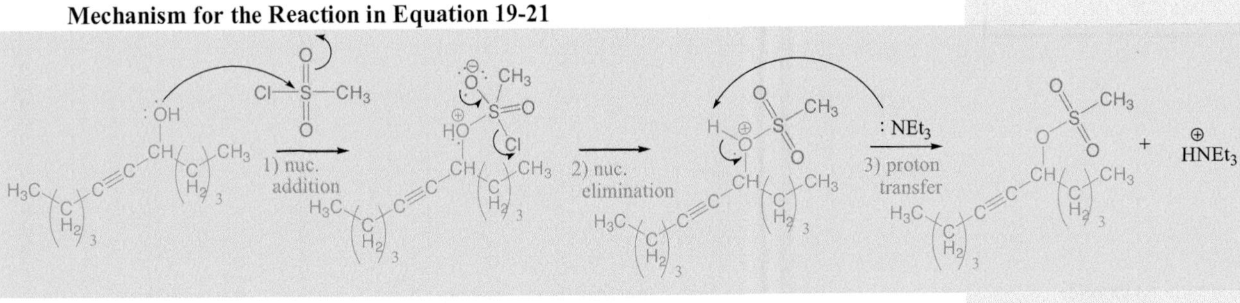

1) nuc. addition

2) nuc. elimination

: NEt_3

3) proton transfer

$\oplus$ $HNEt_3$

(19-24)

As we can see, it is essentially identical to the mechanism by which a carboxylic acid is produced via hydrolysis of an acid chloride, previously shown in Equation 19-4. In step 1, the nucleophilic oxygen atom of the OH group attacks the polar S=O bond of the sulfonyl chloride, temporarily placing a negative charge on the O. In step 2, the S=O bond is regenerated as the Cl^- leaving group is eliminated. Finally, in step 3, deprotonation occurs at the alcohol's oxygen atom to yield the uncharged overall product.

Notice the role that triethylamine and pyridine play in sulfonation reactions. As we can see from Equations 19-21 through 19-23, HCl appears as an overall product. Triethylamine and pyridine are weak bases that effectively absorb the HCl byproduct to prevent the solution from becoming too acidic. This is illustrated in the final step of the mechanism in Equation 19-24, in which triethylamine receives a proton.

Your Turn 19.6. The mechanism for the reaction in Equation 19-23 is shown below, but the curved arrows have been omitted. Supply the missing curved arrows, and write the name of each elementary step under the appropriate reaction arrow.

Problem 19.8. Draw the complete, detailed mechanism for the reaction in Equation 19-22.

Notice also from Equation 19-22 that sulfonation is stereospecific.

Sulfonation of an alcohol occurs with retention of configuration at the alcohol carbon.

The reason, as can be seen from the sulfonation mechanism in Equation 19-24, is simply that no bonds to the alcohol carbon are ever formed or broken in the process. As shown in Solved Problem 19.4, we can take advantage of this stereospecificity in synthesis, especially in a synthesis that calls for an S_N2 or E2 reaction.

Solved Problem 19.4. What is the major product of the following sequence of reactions?

1) TsCl

2) $(CH_3)_3CONa$

Think. What is the product of sulfonation of an alcohol, and what is the stereoselectivity that is associated with that reaction? What type of reaction is promoted by a strong, bulky base in the second step of this synthesis? What is the stereoselectivity associated with that reaction?

Solve. The first reaction is a sulfonation in which tosyl chloride (TsCl) converts the alcohol to a tosylate. Because the tosylate is an excellent leaving group, the presence of the strong, bulky base, $(CH_3)_3CONa$, promotes an E2 reaction. Recall that in an E2 reaction, the alkene that is favored is produced from the substrate conformation in which the H and the leaving group on adjacent carbons are *anti* to each other. That conformation is the one shown below, so the major product is the (E) alkene.

configuration is preserved in a sulfonation reaction

leaving group is *anti* to the adjacent H

only the (E) isomer is produced

Problem 19.9. Show how to carry out the following synthesis.

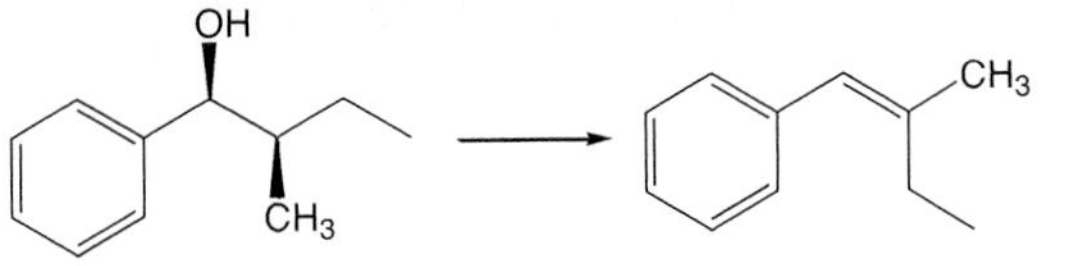

19.6. BASE- AND ACID-CATALYSIS IN NUCLEOPHILIC ADDITION-ELIMINATION REACTIONS

Thus far in this chapter, we have seen that weak nucleophiles, such as water, alcohols, and amines, react readily with acid halides, acid anhydrides, thionyl chloride, and sulfonyl chlorides. Even though the nucleophiles are weak, the polar π bonds (C=O and S=O) in such compounds are reactive enough to compensate. By contrast, we saw in Section 19.1 that esters are significantly less reactive at the carbonyl carbon due to resonance involving the leaving group. Thus, as shown below in Equation 19-25, under normal conditions esters do not undergo nucleophilic addition-elimination with weak nucleophiles like alcohols.

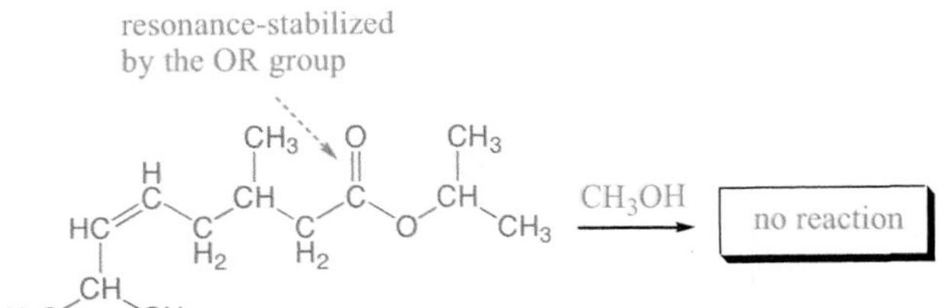

resonance-stabilized by the OR group

CH_3OH → no reaction

(19-25)

However, Equation 19-26 shows that with the addition of a small amount (i.e., a catalytic amount) of a base (sodium methoxide, CH_3ONa, in this case), transesterification takes place readily. Moreover, as indicated, the base is not consumed overall in the reaction, so the reaction is *base-catalyzed.*

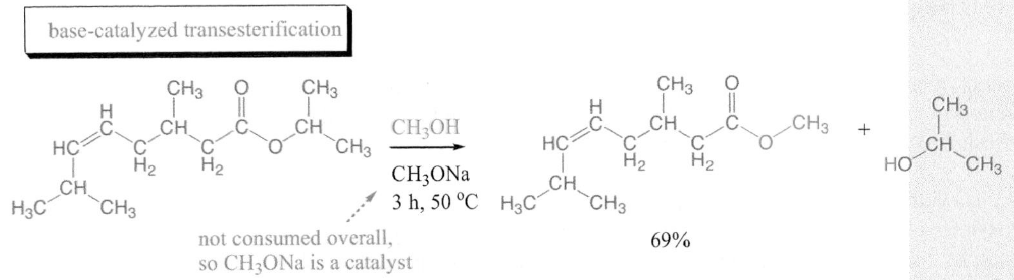

base-catalyzed transesterification

CH_3OH, CH_3ONa, 3 h, 50 °C → 69% +

not consumed overall, so CH_3ONa is a catalyst

(19-26)

The mechanism for this reaction, shown in Equation 19-27, explains why the reaction is catalyzed by the methoxide anion base. The rate is increased because in the nucleophilic addition in step 1 (the rate-determining step) the nucleophile that attacks the carbonyl carbon is methoxide anion, a strong nucleophile. By contrast, in the absence of methoxide anion (as in Equation 19-25), the nucleophile would have to be methanol, a weak nucleophile. The reason there is no net consumption of methoxide anion can be seen in step 3, a proton transfer step in which methoxide anion is regenerated.

Mechanism for the Reaction in Equation 19-26

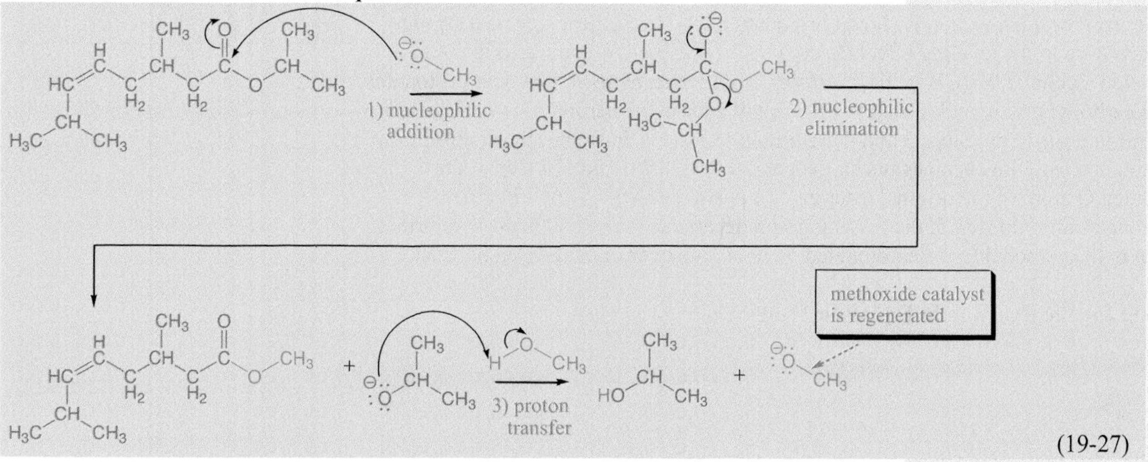

1) nucleophilic addition

2) nucleophilic elimination

methoxide catalyst is regenerated

3) proton transfer

(19-27)

Because water and alcohols have similar behaviors, it might also seem that a base can be used to catalyze the interconversion between esters and carboxylic acids. However, it cannot. Although the presence of hydroxide indeed facilitates the nucleophilic addition-elimination reaction, as shown in Equation 19-28, the carboxylic acid that is initially produced is acidic and thus reacts further with hydroxide. Consequently, the base is consumed in the overall reaction, making it a *base-promoted* reaction instead of a base-catalyzed reaction. In fact, this is an example of a *saponification reaction*, discussed previously in Section 18.2. As shown in Equation 19-29, a similar proton transfer takes place when a carboxylic is treated with an alkoxide anion, making it unfeasible to convert a carboxylic acid into an ester under basic conditions.

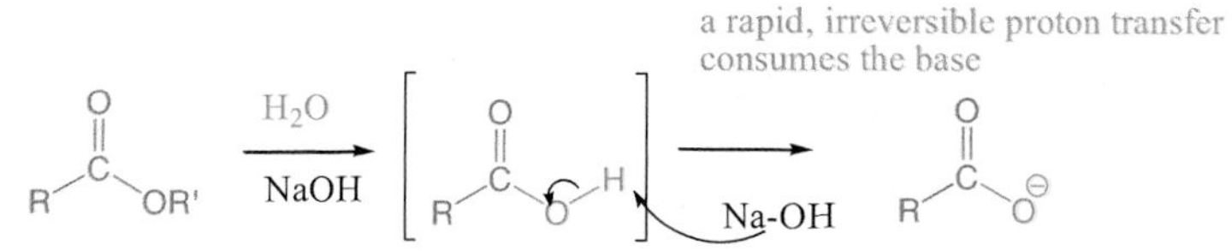

a rapid, irreversible proton transfer consumes the base

H_2O, NaOH; Na-OH

(19-28)

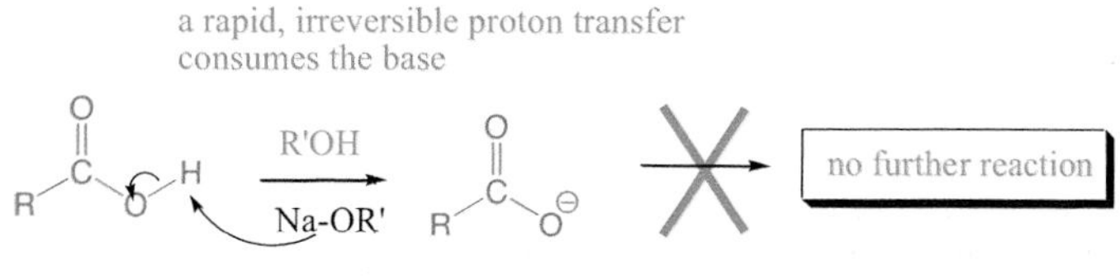

a rapid, irreversible proton transfer consumes the base

R'OH; Na-OR'

no further reaction

(19-29)

Transesterification can also be *acid*-catalyzed. For example, as shown in Equation 19-30, a catalytic amount of a strong acid, such as sulfuric acid, facilitates the production of hexyl acetate from methyl acetate and 1-hexanol.

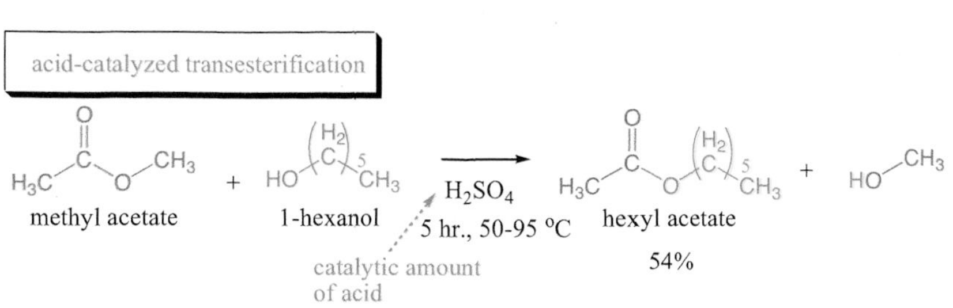

acid-catalyzed transesterification

methyl acetate + 1-hexanol → (H_2SO_4, 5 hr., 50-95 °C) hexyl acetate (54%) + $HO-CH_3$

catalytic amount of acid

(19-30)

The mechanism for this reaction is shown in Equation 19-31. Sulfuric acid is a strong acid, so according to the leveling effect (Section 6.2c), the predominant acid in solution is the protonated alcohol, $CH_3(CH_2)_5OH_2^+$. In step 1 of the mechanism, that acid protonates the ester's carbonyl group, and in step 2, the alcohol attacks the carbonyl carbon, yielding a tetrahedral intermediate. Steps 3 and 4 are proton transfers. In step 3, the O atom from the incoming nucleophile becomes uncharged, and thus is stabilized. In step 4, the singly-bonded O atom of the original ester gains a positive charge, which increases the leaving group ability. In step 5, the leaving group departs and the C=O bond is reformed, and in step 6, the carbonyl O is deprotonated, yielding the overall uncharged product.

Mechanism for the Reaction in Equation 19-30

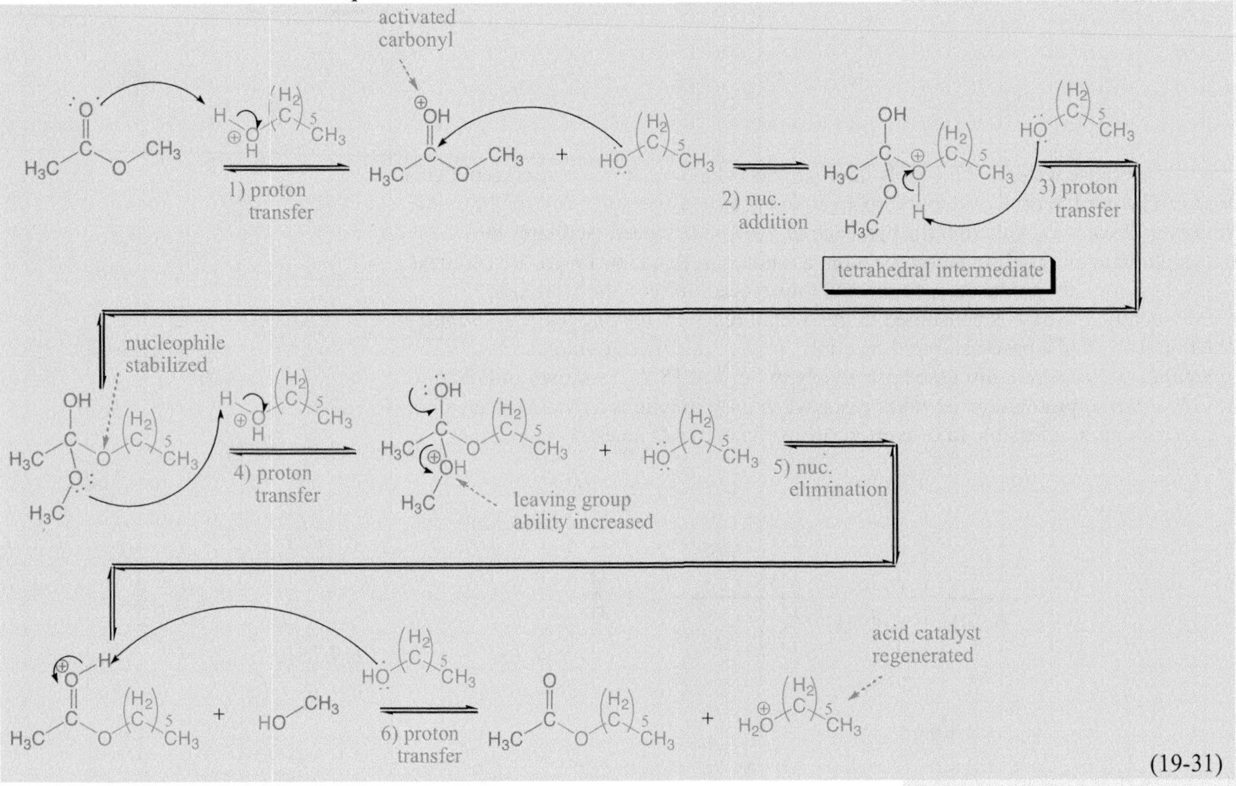

(19-31)

Looking at the mechanism, we can see why the presence of a strong acid catalyzes this reaction. Notice in step 2 that although the nucleophile is a relatively weak alcohol, the rate of nucleophilic addition (i.e., the rate-determining step) is enhanced due to the fact that the carbonyl group has become *activated* (Section 16.1) by the proton transfer from step 1. Moreover, notice that the strong acid used in step 1 is regenerated in step 6, so it is not consumed in the overall reaction.

Unlike what we saw previously under basic conditions, the conversion of an ester to a carboxylic acid can also be acid-catalyzed. Equation 19-32 shows an example of such an *ester-hydrolysis*.

acid-catalyzed ester hydrolysis

ester is hydrolyzed to a carboxylic acid

H_2O

H_2SO_4, acetic acid
reflux

94%

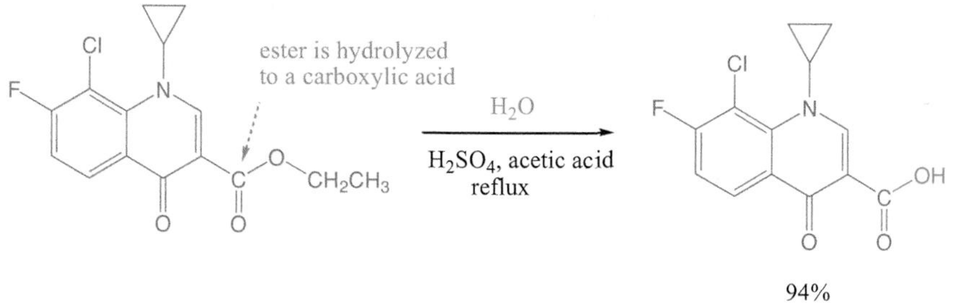

(19-32)

Likewise, as shown in Equation 19-33, the *esterification* of a carboxylic acid can be acid-catalyzed. This is an example of a **Fischer esterification reaction**, named after Emil Fischer, the German chemist and Nobel laureate who first reported such reactions.

Fischer esterification

CH_3CH_2OH

H_2SO_4, H_2O
2 hr., reflux

86%

carboxylic acid converted to an ester

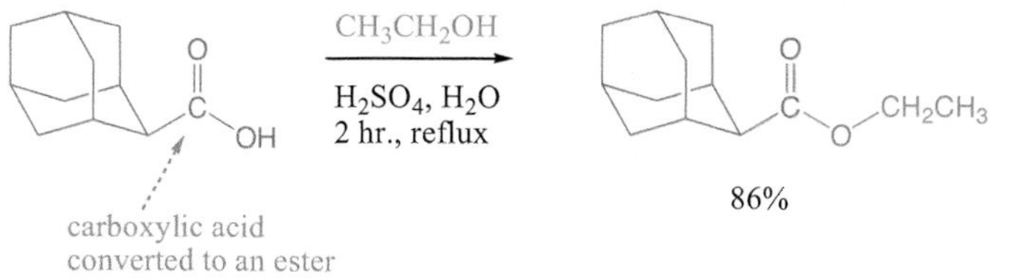

(19-33)

Your Turn 19.7. The mechanism for the Fischer esterification reaction in Equation 19-33 is shown below, but the curved arrows have been omitted. Supply the curved arrows for each step, and write the name of each elementary step below its reaction arrow.

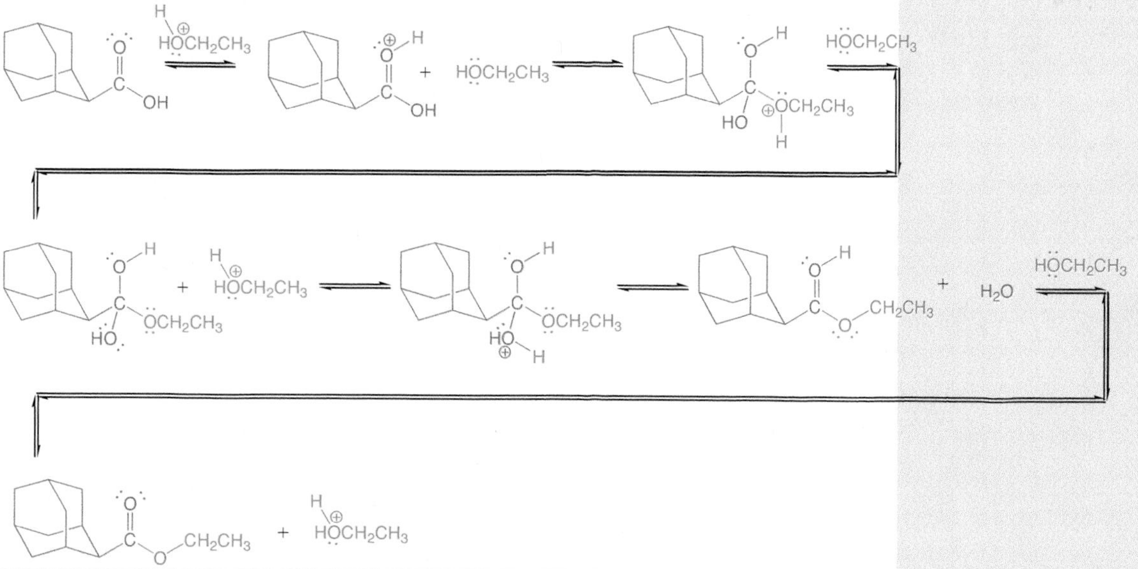

Problem 19.10. Draw the complete, detailed mechanism for the acid-catalyzed ester hydrolysis in Equation 19-32.

Acid-catalyzed acyl substitutions are not limited only to esters and carboxylic acids. Amides, which are even less reactive than esters or carboxylic acids, also do not react with weak nucleophiles under normal conditions. Under acidic conditions, however, amides can undergo acyl substitution via an addition-elimination mechanism. This is exemplified by the amide hydrolysis in Equation 19-34.

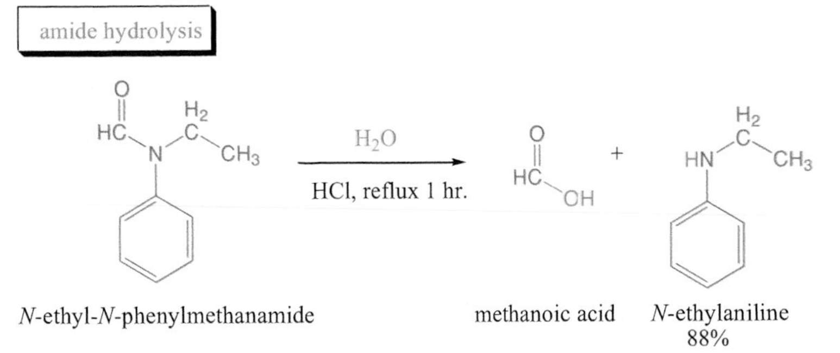

amide hydrolysis

H_2O

HCl, reflux 1 hr.

N-ethyl-*N*-phenylmethanamide

methanoic acid

N-ethylaniline
88%

(19-34)

The mechanism for this reaction, illustrated in Equation 19-35, is essentially the same as the one that describes acid-catalyzed esterification, shown previously in Equation 19-31. The carbonyl group is activated in step 1, which better facilitates nucleophilic addition of the weak nucleophile in step 2. In step 3, the charge on the oxygen atom from the nucleophile goes from +1 to 0, and is thus stabilized. The reverse is true for the nitrogen atom of the leaving group in step 4. In step 5, the amine leaving group departs and the C=O bond is simultaneously regenerated. Finally, in step 6, the newly-formed amine, which is weakly-basic, deprotonates the carbonyl oxygen.

Mechanism for the Reaction in Equation 19-34

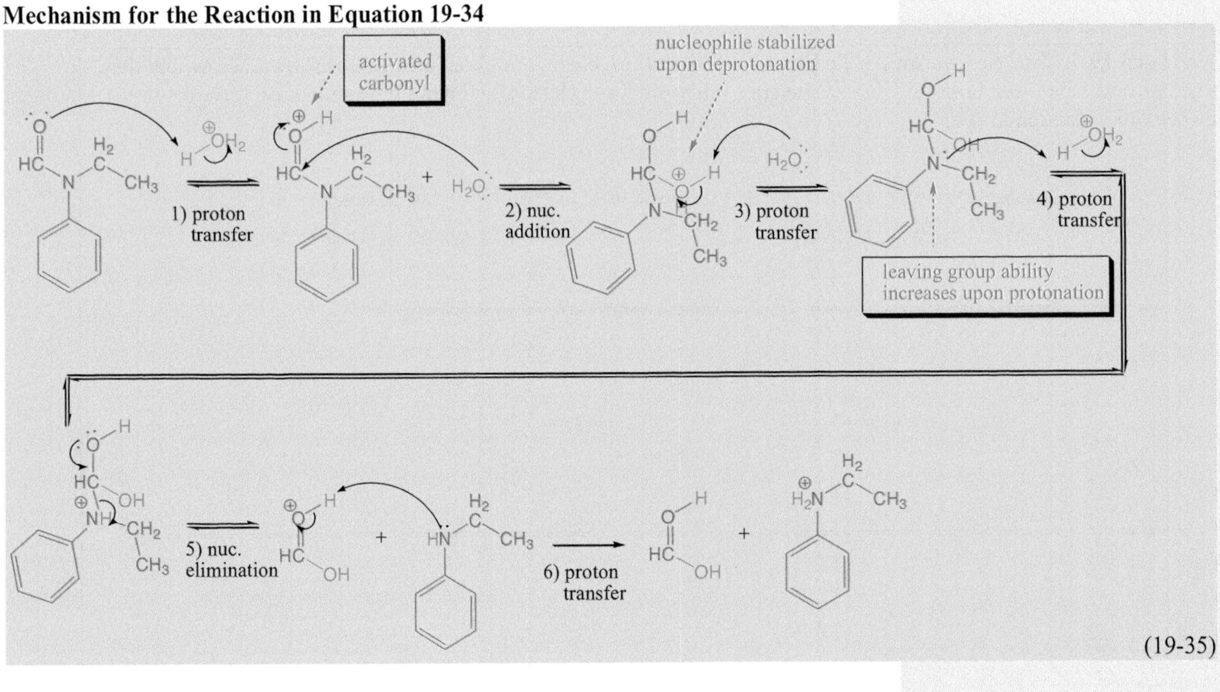

activated carbonyl

nucleophile stabilized upon deprotonation

1) proton transfer

2) nuc. addition

3) proton transfer

4) proton transfer

leaving group ability increases upon protonation

5) nuc. elimination

6) proton transfer

(19-35)

Problem 19.11. For each of the following reactions, draw the complete detailed mechanism and the overall products.

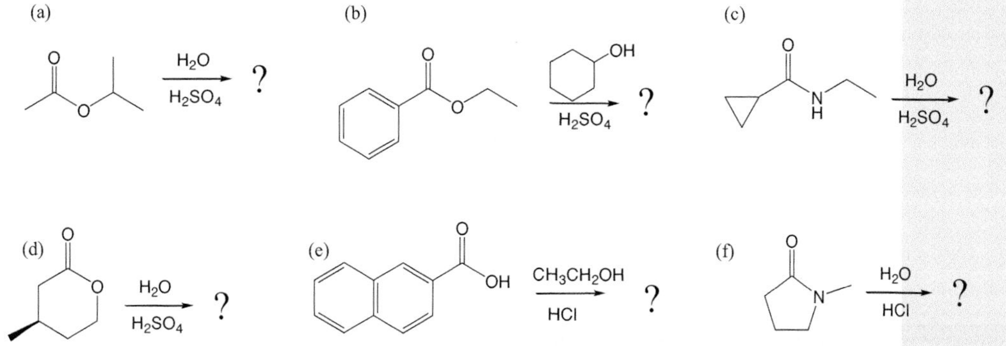

(a) $\xrightarrow[H_2SO_4]{H_2O}$?

(b) $\xrightarrow{H_2SO_4}$?

(c) $\xrightarrow[H_2SO_4]{H_2O}$?

(d) $\xrightarrow[H_2SO_4]{H_2O}$?

(e) $\xrightarrow[HCl]{CH_3CH_2OH}$?

(f) $\xrightarrow[HCl]{H_2O}$?

19.7. OXIDATIONS OF ALCOHOLS AND ALDEHYDES

In Chapters 15 and 18, we discussed a variety of important reduction reactions involving reducing agents such as $LiAlH_4$ and $NaBH_4$. As indicated below, such reactions frequently result in an increase in the number of C-H bonds or a decrease in the number of C-O bonds, which leads to a decrease in the oxidation state of carbon.

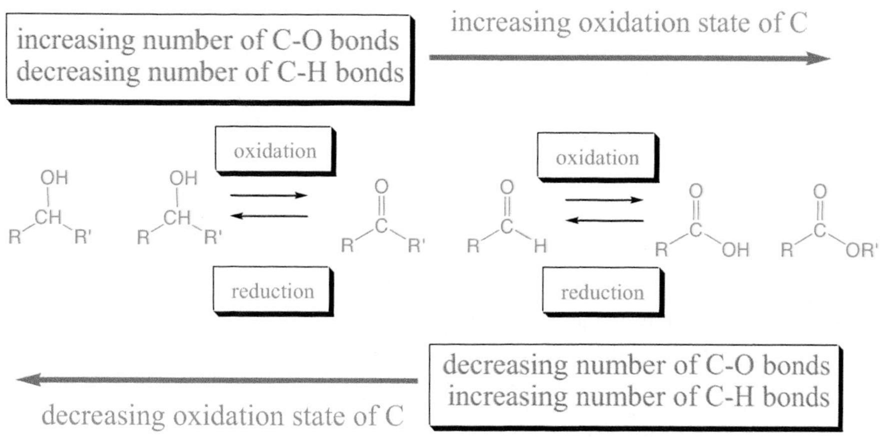

increasing number of C-O bonds
decreasing number of C-H bonds

increasing oxidation state of C

oxidation

reduction

oxidation

reduction

decreasing number of C-O bonds
increasing number of C-H bonds

decreasing oxidation state of C

To complement these reduction reactions, it is also important to be able to carry out oxidation reactions, which increase the oxidation state on carbon. As indicated above, this can be done by carrying out reactions that increase the number of C-O bonds or decrease the number of C-H bonds. In this section, we will examine two types of oxidizing agents that can be used for such reactions. Section 19.7a will discuss *chromic acid* as an oxidizing agent, and Section 19.7b will discuss *potassium permanganate*.

19.7a. Chromic acid oxidations of alcohols and aldehydes

Chromic acid, H_2CrO_4, is an important oxidizing agent in synthesis. As shown below, it is prepared by dissolving either chromium trioxide (CrO_3) or sodium dichromate ($Na_2Cr_2O_7$) in an acidic aqueous solution. Notice that in both reactions, a molecule of water is added to the starting material. Furthermore, notice that in all three forms—CrO_3, $Na_2Cr_2O_7$, and H_2CrO_4—the oxidation state of the chromium atom is +6.

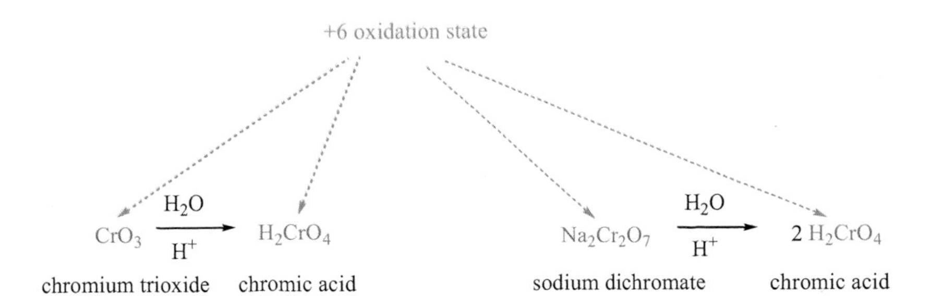

An example of a chromic acid oxidation is shown in Equation 19-36. As we can see,

Chromic acid oxidizes a secondary alcohol to a ketone.

a 2° alcohol

chromic acid

a ketone

$$\text{cyclooctanol} \xrightarrow[\text{water, acetone}]{H_2CrO_4 \;/\; H_2SO_4} \text{cyclooctanone (96\%)} \qquad (19\text{-}36)$$

cyclooctanol

cyclooctanone
96%

(19-36)

Your Turn 19.8. Verify that the reaction in Equation 19-36 is an oxidation by calculating the oxidation state of the carbon atom in red in the reactant ________ and in the product ____________.

The mechanism for this reaction is shown in Equation 19-37, and consists of seven steps. In step 1, the Cr=O is protonated and thus activated toward nucleophilic attack by the alcohol, a weak nucleophile. Step 2 is nucleophilic addition of the alcohol to the Cr=O bond. Proton transfers comprise steps 3 and 4, which serve to stabilize the newly-added nucleophile and to generate a very good water leaving group. In step 5, water departs and the Cr=O bond is regenerated. Deprotonation in step 6 produces a neutral **chromate ester**, and a final E2 step yields the overall ketone product.

Mechanism for the Reaction in Equation 19-36

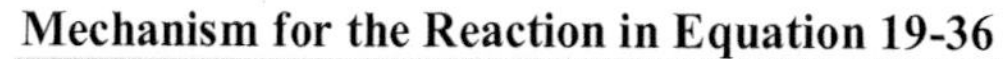

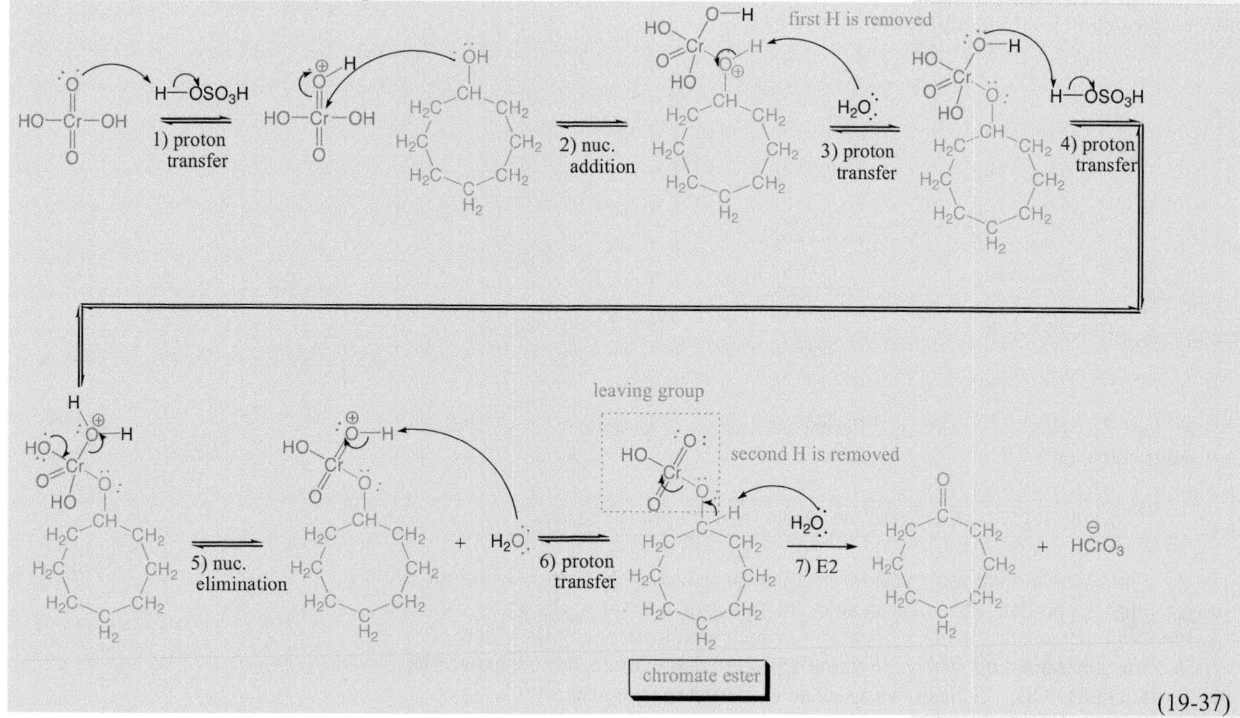

(19-37)

Although his mechanism might appear to be somewhat complex, notice that the first six steps are in fact identical to the six steps that comprise the *Fischer esterification* mechanism, discussed in Section 19.6. Instead of a normal ester, however, the product of step 6 is a *chromate ester*.

The final E2 step might also appear to be peculiar. Normally in an E2 step the leaving group is attached to a carbon atom, but in this case it is attached to oxygen. Nevertheless, realize that, as with any E2 step, the leaving group and a proton on adjacent atoms are eliminated, leaving behind an additional double bond. Here, the new double bond is C=O instead of C=C.

As you examine the mechanism in Equation 19-37, notice that there are two key steps in which hydrogen is removed from the starting alcohol. The first H is removed from the alcohol oxygen in the proton transfer in step 3, and the second H is removed from the adjacent carbon in the E2 step in step 7. In other words,

> Oxidation by chromic acid requires an OH group to be attached to a carbon atom that is bonded to at least one H.
>
> H or R–CH(OH)–R or H $\xrightarrow{H_2CrO_4}$ H or R–C(=O)–R or H

This is why, for example, the tertiary alcohol in Equation 19-38 is not oxidized when treated with chromic acid.

no hydrogen attached to the alcohol C

$\xrightarrow{H_2CrO_4}$ no reaction

(19-38)

On the other hand, a primary alcohol *is* oxidizable because the alcohol carbon is indeed bonded to H. An example is shown in Equation 19-39.

a primary alcohol is oxidizable because an H is bonded to the alcohol C

a carboxylic acid is produced from oxidation of a primary alcohol

H_2CrO_4 / H_2SO_4, water, acetone

pent-3-yn-1-ol → pent-3-ynoic acid 36%

(19-39)

Notice that the oxidation product is different from what we observe in the oxidation of a secondary alcohol.

Chromic acid oxidizes a primary alcohol to a carboxylic acid.

This should seem somewhat peculiar, because the mechanism in Equation 19-37 suggests that the product should be an aldehyde rather than a carboxylic acid. However, keep in mind that water is present in solution, which equilibrates with the aldehyde to produce the corresponding *hydrate* (Section 15.3). In that hydrate, notice that an OH is indeed attached to CH, which allows a second oxidation to take place.

H atoms removed from adjacent OH and CH groups in a chromic acid oxidation

no OH present

H atoms removed from adjacent OH and CH groups in a chromic acid oxidation

H_2CrO_4 → [aldehyde] ⇌ H_2O → an aldehyde hydrate → H_2CrO_4 →

(19-40)

Given the role that water plays in the oxidation of a primary alcohol to a carboxylic acid, we can see that in the absence of water, the oxidation would have to stop at the aldehyde. However, chromic acid itself cannot be used in such an oxidation, because, as we saw previously, water is required to produce chromic acid. Instead, as indicated in Equation 19-41, **pyridinium chlorochromate (PCC)** can be used as the oxidizing agent.

pyridinium chlorochromate (PCC)

oxidation stops at the aldehyde because no water is present

• CrO_3 • $Cl^\ominus$

CH_2Cl_2

91%

(19-41)

In other words,

> Pyridinium chlorochromate (PCC) oxidizes a primary alcohol to an aldehyde.

Pyridinium chlorochromate contains the same Cr^{+6} species as in chromic acid. Unlike chromic acid, however, pyridinium chlorochromate is soluble in non-aqueous solvents like dichloromethane, CH_2Cl_2, which allows oxidation to take place in the absence of water.

Solved Problem 19.5. Show how to synthesize the following compound using alcohols of 7 or fewer carbons as your only carbon source.

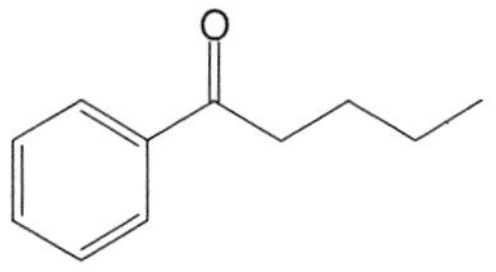

O

Think. Which carbon-carbon bond can we "disconnect" in a retrosynthetic analysis? By reversing what reaction? Are there any oxidations of alcohols that require stopping at the aldehyde?

Solve. A Grignard reaction forms a carbon-carbon bond, yielding an alcohol. Our target is a ketone that could be the result of oxidizing a Grignard product. Our retrosynthetic analysis may therefore begin with the following transforms.

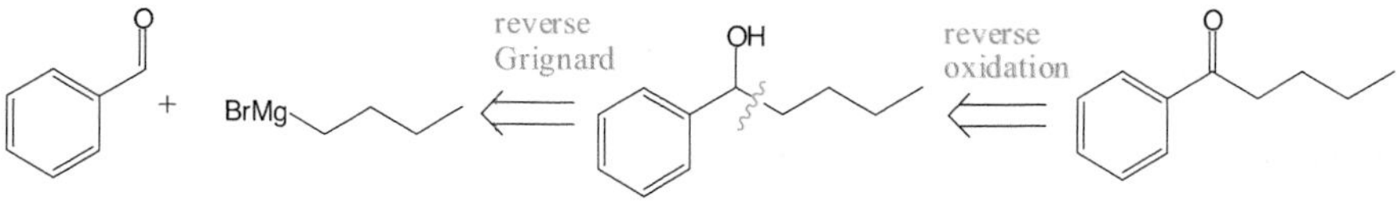

O + BrMg ⟸ reverse Grignard OH ⟸ reverse oxidation O

The Grignard reagent can be prepared from an alkyl bromide, which in turn can be produced from an alcohol using PBr_3.

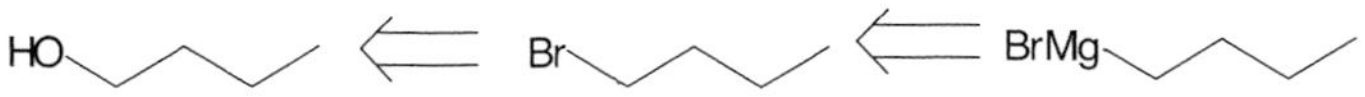

HO ⟸ Br ⟸ BrMg

Benzaldehyde, on the other hand, can be made simply from benzyl alcohol via an oxidation.

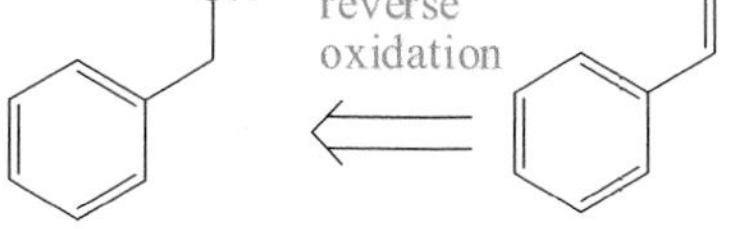

OH ⟸ reverse oxidation O

There are two oxidations of alcohols required in this synthesis. One is an oxidation to an aldehyde that requires an aqueous-free solvent and thus PCC as the oxidizing agent. The other is an oxidation to a ketone, which can take place in water, thus allowing us to use H_2CrO_4 as the oxidizing agent. The overall synthesis appears as follows.

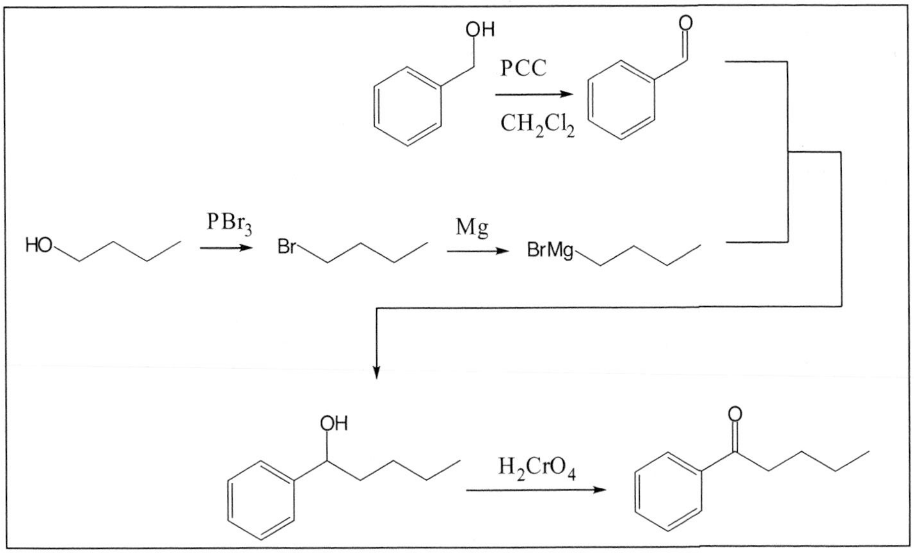

PCC
CH_2Cl_2
HO
PBr_3
Br
Mg
BrMg
OH
H_2CrO_4

Problem 19.9. Show how to synthesize the compound in Solved Problem 19.5 beginning with bromobenzene and any alcohol.

19.7b. Permanganate oxidations of alcohols and aldehydes

Potassium permanganate, $KMnO_4$, is another common oxidizing agent; it is an ionic compound consisting of the potassium cation, K^+, and the permanganate anion, MnO_4^-. Structurally, MnO_4^- resembles H_2CrO_4, as shown below. In both compounds, a central metal atom is bonded to 4 oxygen atoms, thus giving the metal atom a high positive oxidation state; that oxidation state is +6 for H_2CrO_4 and +7 for MnO_4^-.

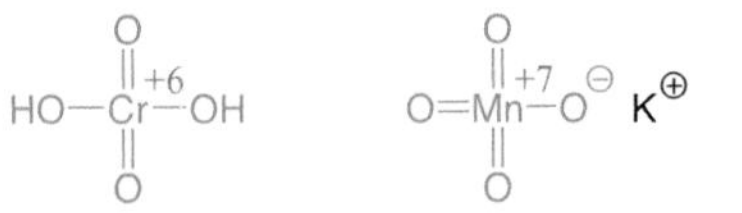

chromic acid

potassium permanganate

Given its structural similarity to chromic acid, it should be no surprise that potassium permanganate can be used to oxidize alcohols, as shown in Equation 19-42 and 19-43.

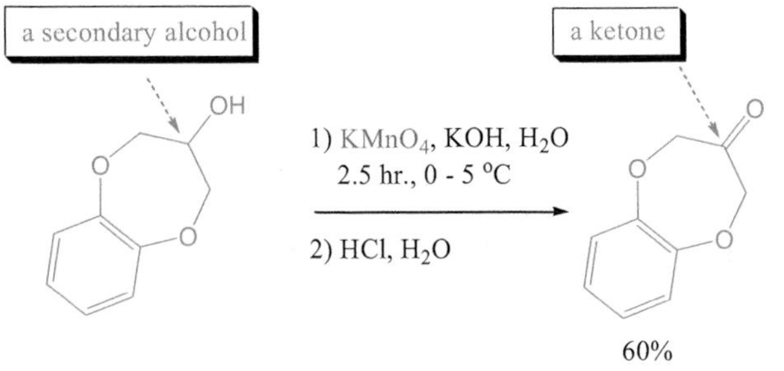

a secondary alcohol

a ketone

1) $KMnO_4$, KOH, H_2O
2.5 hr., 0 - 5 °C

2) HCl, H_2O

60%

(19-42)

a primary alcohol — a carboxylic acid

$KMnO_4$, H_2O

phenylmethanol (benzyl alcohol) → benzoic acid 75%

(19-43)

As we can see,

Potassium permanganate ($KMnO_4$) oxidizes primary alcohols to carboxylic acids, and secondary alcohols to ketones.

Given the similar reactions that can be carried out by chromic acid and potassium permanganate, it might seem that the choice is arbitrary. However, it is not. All else being equal, *potassium permanganate should be used instead of chromic acid in the oxidation of alcohols*. There are two main reasons why.

- Potassium permanganate is less expensive than chromic acid.
- Chromic acid and its byproducts are highly toxic and pose serious environmental hazards.

On the other hand, chromic acid has one major advantage.

Chromic acid is more selective than potassium permanganate.

As we will see in Chapters 21 and 23, $KMnO_4$ can oxidize a variety of groups in addition to alcohols and aldehydes, including alkenes, alkynes, and alkylbenzenes. Therefore, chromic acid's greater selectivity makes it the oxidizing agent of choice when these other groups are present.

Problem 19.10. Determine the structures of A and B in the following sequence of reactions.

OH

1) $KMnO_4$, $HO^{\ominus}$, heat; 2) $H_3O^{\oplus}$ → A; 1) MgBr; 2) $H_3O^{\oplus}$ → B

19.8. BAEYER-VILLIGER OXIDATIONS

In the previous section, we saw that chromic acid oxidations proceed via an acid-catalyzed nucleophilic addition-elimination mechanism. Another oxidation reaction that proceeds via a nucleophilic addition-elimination mechanism under acidic conditions is the **Baeyer-Villiger oxidation**, named after the German chemist Adolf Baeyer and the Swiss chemist Victor Villiger. An example of such an oxidation is shown in Equation 19-44, in which a ketone is oxidized to an ester by a **peroxyacid**, (RCO_3H).

Baeyer-Villiger oxidation

meta-chloroperbenzoic acid, MCPBA (a peroxyacid)

CF_3SO_3H, CH_2Cl_2

diphenylmethanone

phenyl benzoate 100%

(19-44)

The mechanism for this reaction is shown in Equation 19-45. As we can see, after the ketone's carbonyl group has been activated by protonation in step 1, the relatively weak peroxyacid nucleophile attacks the carbonyl carbon in step 2. After a proton is removed from the peroxyacid's oxygen atom in step 3, an alkyl group departs from the carbonyl carbon in step 4. Simultaneously, the alkyl group forms a bond to an oxygen atom from the peroxyacid, breaking the peroxyacid's O-O bond in the process. Finally, in step 5, the ester's carbonyl group is deprotonated, yielding the overall uncharged ester product.

Mechanism for the Reaction in Equation 19-44

1) proton transfer

2) nucleophilic addition

3) proton transfer

weak O-O bond is broken

4) nuc. elimination

negative charge is resonance-stabilized over two O atoms

5) proton transfer

$C_6H_5^{\ominus}$ leaves at the same time it forms a bond to O from the peroxyacid

(19-45)

It may seem peculiar that C_6H_5 acts as the leaving group in this mechanism, because the leaving group ability of $C_6H_5^-$ is extremely poor. Here, however, there are two factors that facilitate the breaking of the $C-C_6H_5$ bond. First, in the products of that step, a negative charge never appears on C_6H_5, but rather appears on a carboxylate anion (RCO_2^-), and is thus resonance-stabilized over two oxygen atoms. Second, there is a significant driving force provided by the fact that the O-O bond of the peroxyacid is rather weak. In the step where the C_6H_5 group leaves, the weak O-O bond is replaced by a much stronger C-O bond.

Notice that the ketone in Equation 19-44 is *symmetric*—i.e., the carbonyl group is bonded to identical alkyl groups. But, as we can see from Equations 19-46 and 19-47, Baeyer-Villiger oxidations can be carried out on *unsymmetric* ketones and aldehydes as well.

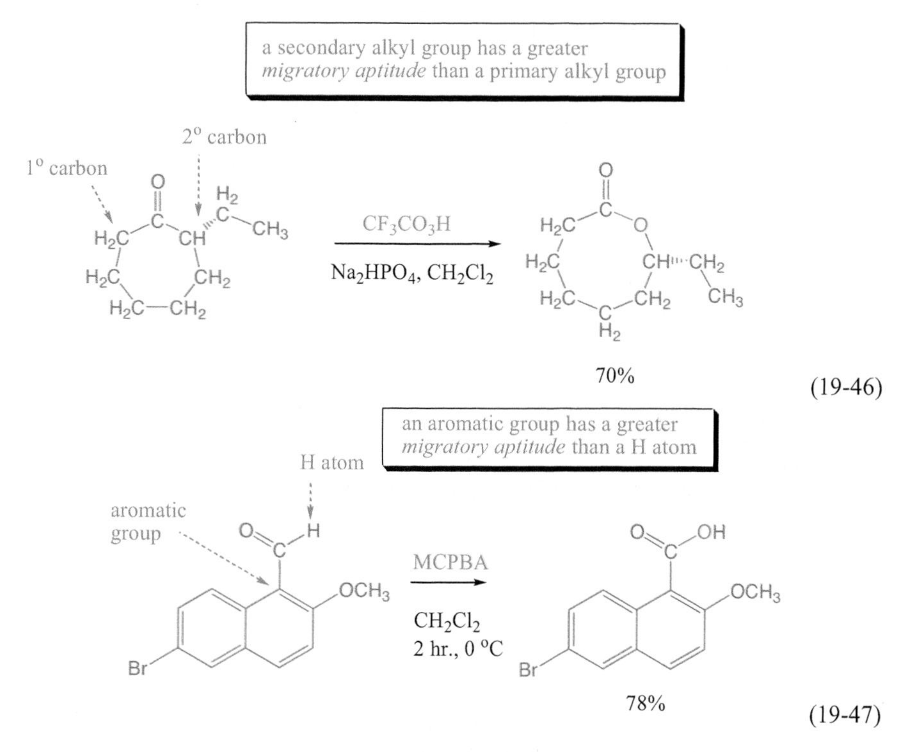

When a ketone is symmetric, the same ester product would be produced regardless of which alkyl group departs from the carbonyl carbon. By contrast, in Equations 19-46 and 19-47, there are two possible oxidation products, depending upon which group departs from the carbonyl carbon. Frequently, however, one group has a greater tendency to depart than the other. This tendency is called the group's **migratory aptitude**. From Equation 19-46, for example, we can see that a secondary alkyl group has a greater migratory aptitude than a primary alkyl group does. And Equation 19-47 indicates that a hydrogen atom has a greater migratory aptitude than does an aromatic group.

Migratory aptitudes have been determined empirically as follows:

migratory aptitude in a Baeyer-Villiger oxidation

methyl < 1° alkyl < 2° alkyl < 3° alkyl < aryl < H

It should be noted that the reason for these relative migratory aptitudes is not fully known. However, it is useful to see that the relative order is similar to the one for cation stability.

Problem 19.11. Predict the major product of each of the following reactions.

(a) $C_6H_5C(=O)CH_2CH_3$ $\xrightarrow[CH_2Cl_2]{CF_3CO_3H}$?

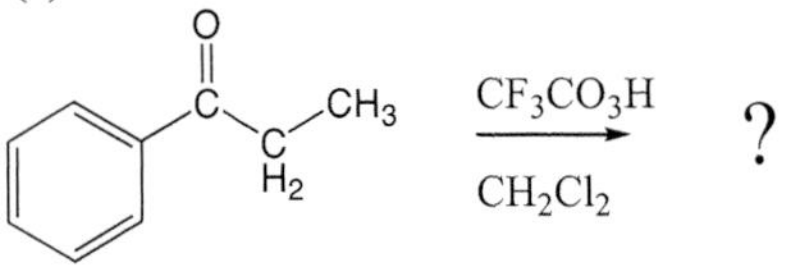

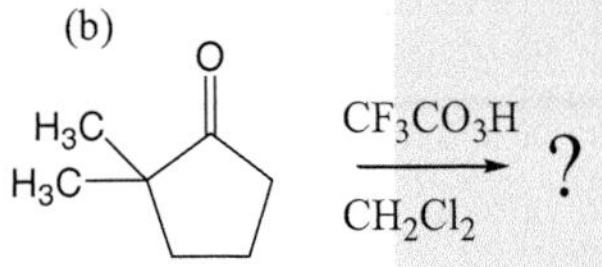

(b) 2,2-dimethylcyclopentanone $\xrightarrow[CH_2Cl_2]{CF_3CO_3H}$?

(c) $C_6H_5C(=O)CH_2C_6H_5$ $\xrightarrow[CH_2Cl_2]{MCPBA}$?

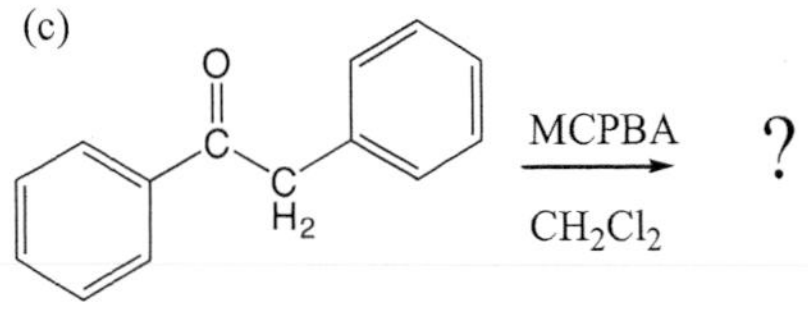

Problem 19.12. In the mechanism in Equation 19-45, the hydroxyl (OH) oxygen of the peroxyacid is shown as the nucleophile. Why is that oxygen more nucleophilic than the adjacent oxygen?

19.9 CLAISEN CONDENSATIONS

In Section 19.6, we saw that under normal conditions, weak nucleophiles such as water and alcohols do not react readily with esters. Under basic conditions, however, these weak nucleophiles can be converted into strong ones through a simple deprotonation, thus catalyzing an acyl substitution reaction.

By the same token, carbonyl compounds with alpha hydrogens can be converted into enolate anions ($^{\ominus}$:CH–C(=O)–), relatively strong carbon-nucleophiles, by treatment with a sufficiently strong base. As we saw in previous chapters, for example, this was the basis for generating the enolate nucleophile in α-alkylation reactions (Section 10.3) and α-halogenation reactions (Section 10.4). It was also the basis for generating the enolate nucleophile in aldol reactions (Section 16.4).

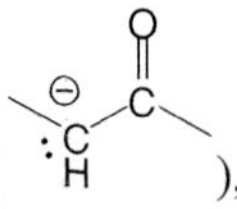

Not surprisingly, then, enolate anions can also act as carbon-nucleophiles in nucleophilic addition-elimination reactions. In this context, our focus throughout this section will be on the *Claisen condensation reaction*, in which an ester is the acid derivative that undergoes nucleophilic attack.

19.9a. The general Claisen condensation mechanism

The Claisen condensation reaction is exemplified by the reaction in Equation 19-48. As we can see, when ethyl ethanoate (ethyl acetate) is treated with sodium ethoxide, followed by acid work-up, ethyl 3-oxobutanoate, a **β-ketoester**, is produced. This is a *condensation* reaction because overall two ester molecules are fused together at the expense of the elimination of a smaller molecule, a molecule of ethanol. Moreover, it is named after Rainer Ludwig Claisen, who developed the reaction.

Claisen condensation

1) $NaOCH_2CH_3$, CH_3CH_2OH reflux 4 hr.
2) $H_3O^{\oplus}$

a β-ketoester

ethyl ethanoate (ethyl acetate) → ethyl 3-oxobutanoate (ethyl acetoacetate) + $HOCH_2CH_3$

68%

(19-48)

As shown in the mechanism (Equation 19-49), an enolate anion is generated in step 1 when the ethoxide anion deprotonates the ester at the alpha carbon. In step 2, that enolate anion attacks the carbonyl carbon of a second molecule of the ester, forming a new carbon-carbon bond. An ethoxide anion is then eliminated in step 3, producing an initial β-ketoester, which is quickly deprotonated in step 4. Acid workup in step 5 replenishes the β-ketoester.

Mechanism for the Reaction in Equation 19-48

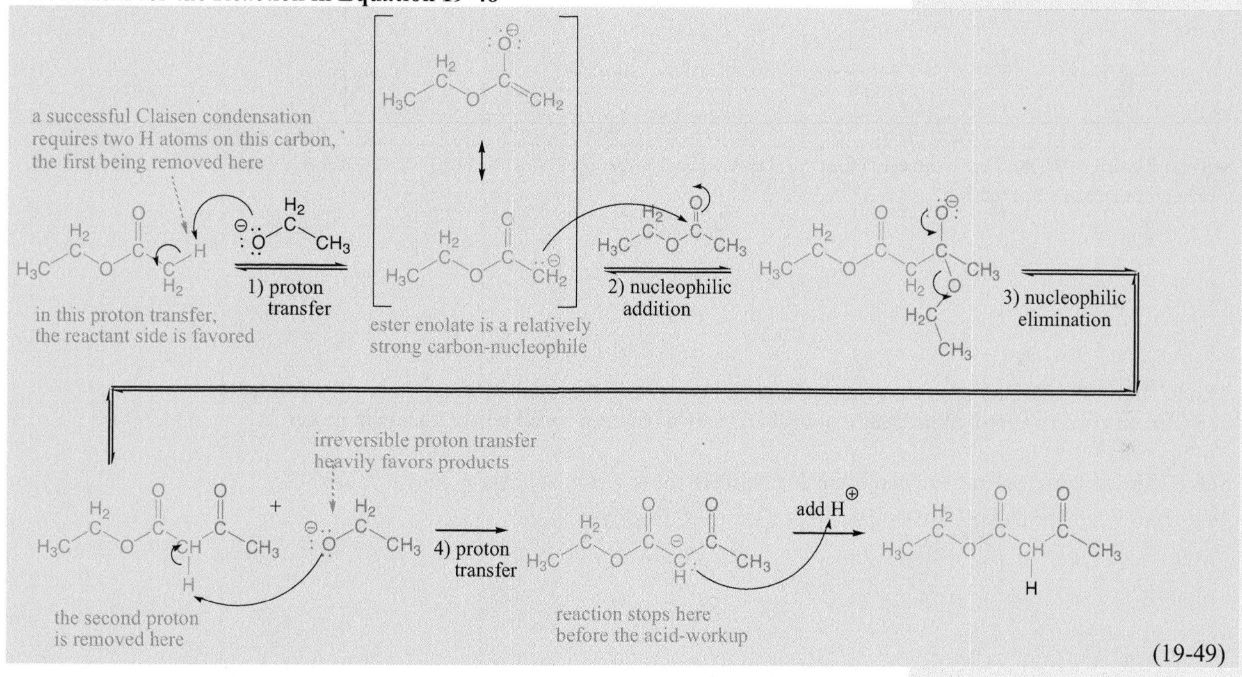

(19-49)

The reversibilities of the two proton transfer steps in this mechanism play important roles. Notice that the first proton transfer, in step 1, is reversible and somewhat favors the reactant side. Thus, only a small fraction of the initial ester exists in the form of the enolate anion at any given time, which allows the enolate anion and the uncharged ester to coexist for the subsequent nucleophilic addition step. By contrast, the second proton transfer is irreversible, heavily favoring the product side. This is important because the first three steps are reversible, slightly favoring the overall reactants. The deprotonation in step 4 effectively removes the β-ketoester product of the equilibrium as it is formed and, according to Le Châtelier's principle, the equilibrium shifts continuously toward products.

The necessity for these proton transfer steps places a significant restriction on an ester that can participate in a Claisen condensation.

A successful Claisen condensation generally requires two alpha protons on the initial ester.

The first proton is removed to produce the enolate nucleophile, and the second is removed to shift the addition-elimination equilibrium toward products. Thus, as shown below, an ester that possesses only one alpha hydrogen does not produce a β-ketoester that can be isolated.

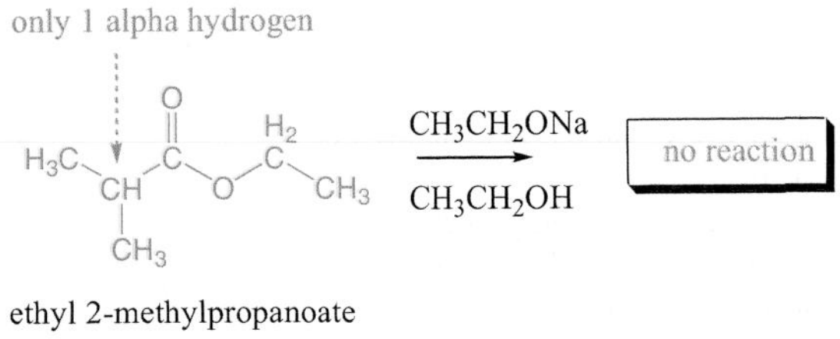

only 1 alpha hydrogen

CH_3CH_2ONa / CH_3CH_2OH → no reaction

ethyl 2-methylpropanoate

Problem 19.13. Draw the complete, detailed mechanism for the following reaction and predict the major product.

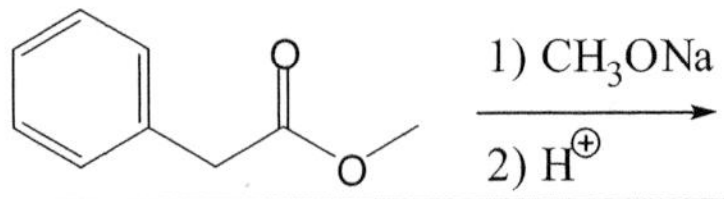

1) CH_3ONa
2) $H^{\oplus}$

Solved Problem 19.6. Draw the ester that can be used to synthesize the following compound using a Claisen condensation reaction.

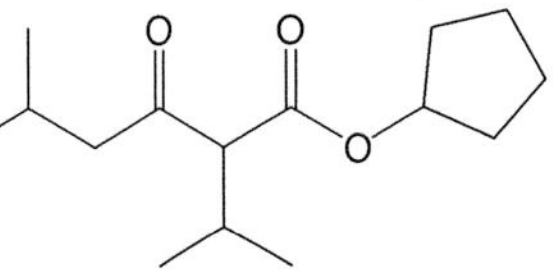

Think. In the β-ketoester product, which carbon-carbon bond is the one that would have been formed in a Claisen condensation? Which carbon would have been bonded to the alkyoxy leaving group?

Solve. The new carbon-carbon bond is the one between the α and β carbons, as shown below. Moreover, the leaving group would have been attached to the β carbon.

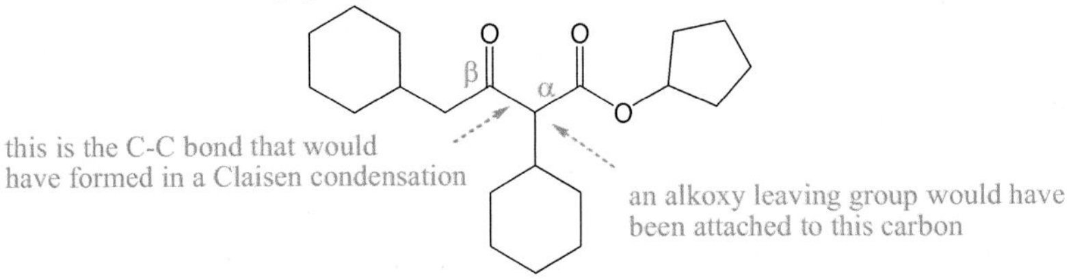

this is the C-C bond that would have formed in a Claisen condensation

an alkoxy leaving group would have been attached to this carbon

Therefore, we can apply a transform that reverses a Claisen condensation by disconnecting that carbon-carbon bond and reattaching the leaving group, as shown below. As we can see, this yields two esters that are identical.

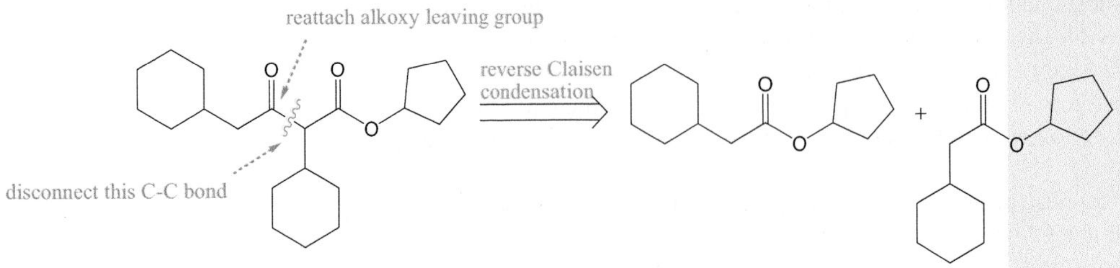

reattach alkoxy leaving group

reverse Claisen condensation

disconnect this C-C bond

Problem 19.14. Show how to synthesize the compound below using a Claisen condensation reaction.

19.9b. Importance of solvent and base in Claisen condensations

In the mechanism in Equation 19-49, the ethoxide anion ($CH_3CH_2O^-$) is shown to behave as a base to generate the ester enolate nucleophile. Realize, however, that the ethoxide anion is a strong nucleophile itself, so it can also participate in a nucleophilic addition-elimination reaction with the ester. In fact, these are the conditions for a base-catalyzed transesterification reaction, which we discussed in Section 19.6.

For the specific Claisen condensation reaction in Equation 19-48, however, transesterification does not pose a problem, because both the nucleophile and the leaving group are $CH_3CH_2O^-$. Thus, the transesterification product is identical to the reactant, as shown in Equation 19-50.

transesterification that would take place in the reaction in Equation 19-48

no different from starting ester

(19-50)

On the other hand, other choices of base could lead to undesired products. For example, if the base is an alkoxide other than ethoxide, as in Equation 19-51, transesterification would produce an ester that is different from the starting material. Alternatively, if hydroxide is used as the base, as in Equation 19-52, then *saponification* (Section 18.2) would irreversibly convert the ester into a carboxylate anion.

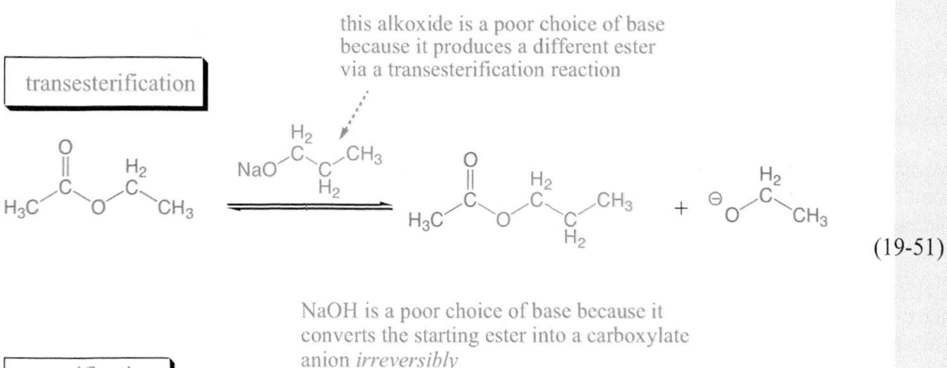
this alkoxide is a poor choice of base because it produces a different ester via a transesterification reaction
transesterification
NaO

(19-51)

saponification

NaOH is a poor choice of base because it converts the starting ester into a carboxylate anion *irreversibly*

NaOH

(19-52)

These complications can be avoided by adhering to the following guideline.

For a Claisen condensation reaction, an alkoxide anion (RO^-) can be used as the base if it is identical to the alkoxy group (–OR) bonded to the ester's carbonyl carbon. In other words, the alkyl groups indicated below should be identical.

same R groups

R'C(=O)OR —NaOR→

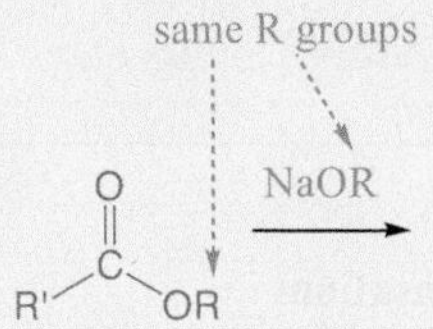

Your Turn 19.9. In the space provided here, draw the complete, detailed mechanisms for the reactions in Equations 19-51 and 19-52.

19-51)

19-52)

The wrong choice of solvent can also lead to an unwanted transesterification or saponification reaction. If, for example, the solvent for the reaction in Equation 19-48 were another alcohol such as 1-propanol, $CH_3CH_2CH_2OH$, the added ethoxide anion would deprotonate 1-propanol to generate the 1-propoxide anion, $CH_3CH_2CH_2O^-$, thereby causing the transesterification reaction in Equation 19-51 to ensue. Alternatively, if water were used as the solvent, then HO^- would be produced, and the saponification reaction in Equation 19-52 would take place.

In light of these proton transfer reactions that can occur, we arrive at the following guideline for the proper choice of solvent in a Claisen condensation reaction.

When using an alcohol as a solvent for a Claisen condensation reaction, choose the alcohol to be the conjugate acid of the alkoxide leaving group attached to the carbonyl carbon. In other words, the alkyl groups indicated below should be identical.

R'C(=O)OR —ROH→

same R groups

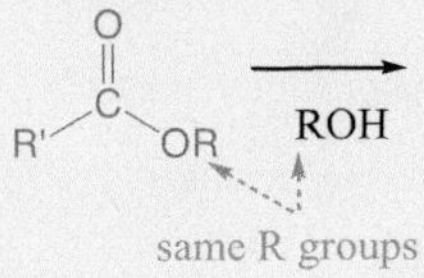

This choice of solvent ensures that deprotonation of the solvent by the added base does not produce a different base. In the case of the reaction in Equation 19-48, deprotonation of ethanol would produce ethoxide anion, the same as the base that is added.

Your Turn 19.10. In the space provided here, write the proton transfer equilibrium that would take place if 1-propanol is used as the solvent for the reaction in Equation 19-48. Do the same if water were used as the solvent and if ethanol were used as the solvent.

1-propanol:

water:

ethanol:

Solved Problem 19.7. Identify the appropriate base-solvent pair to accomplish a Claisen condensation with the ester below.

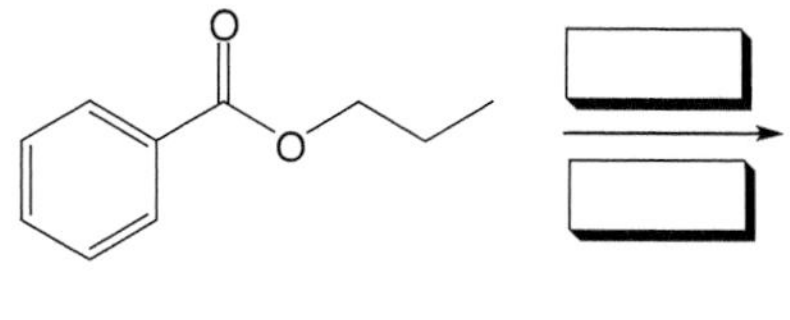

Think. What is the leaving group on the ester? What choice of base would ensure that a nucleophilic addition-elimination would leave us with the same ester? What solvent could be used so that, if it were to be deprotonated, the base that would be produced would be the same as the base that is added?

Solve. The leaving group is $CH_3CH_2CH_2O^-$. Therefore, if we were to add $NaOCH_2CH_2CH_3$ as the base, nucleophilic addition-elimination would leave us with the same ester. $CH_3CH_2CH_2OH$ should therefore be the solvent, because if it were to be deprotonated, it would yield $CH_3CH_2CH_2O^-$, the same as the added base. Overall, the reaction would appear as:

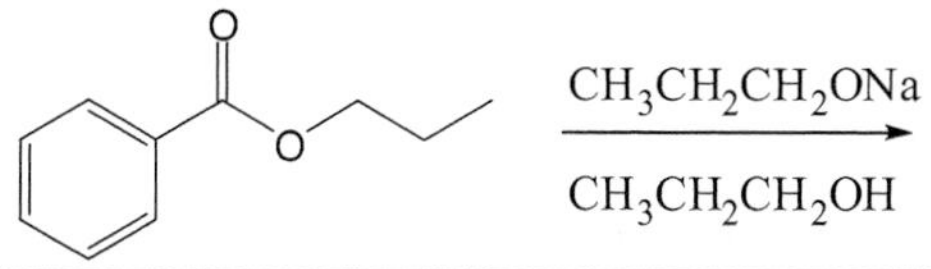

$CH_3CH_2CH_2ONa$ / $CH_3CH_2CH_2OH$

Problem 19.15. Identify the appropriate base-solvent pair to accomplish a Claisen condensation with each ester below.

(a)

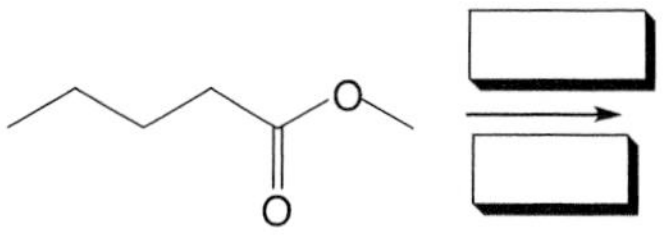

(b)

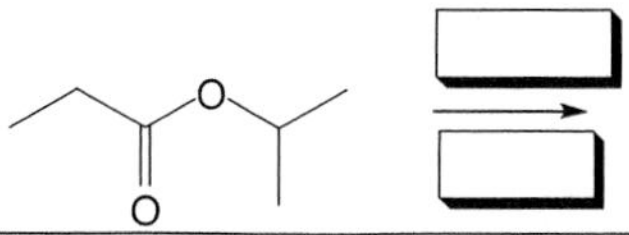

Problem 19.16. The Claisen condensation below proceeds without an unwanted transesterification, even though the choice of base is not the same as the leaving group. Explain why.

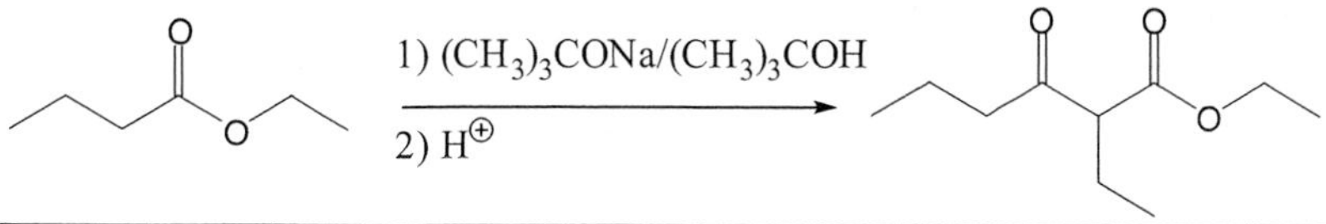

1) $(CH_3)_3CONa/(CH_3)_3COH$
2) $H^{\oplus}$

19.9c. Crossed Claisen condensation reactions

The Claisen condensation reactions we examined in the previous section involve two molecules of the same ester. Claisen condensations can also involve two *different* esters—so-called **crossed Claisen condensation reactions**. However, such reactions require special considerations because, just as we saw with crossed *aldol* reactions (Section 16.7), crossed Claisen reactions can potentially lead to a mixture of condensation products.

For example, the reaction in Equation 19-53 would produce a mixture of four β-ketoesters. This is because two different ester enolates can be generated as nucleophiles and two different uncharged esters can be attacked by those nucleophiles.

four different β-ketoesters can be produced from this crossed Claisen condensation reaction

1) CH_3ONa, CH_3OH

2) $H^{\oplus}$

(a) (b) (c) (d)

(19-53)

Problem 19.17. Draw a complete, detailed mechanism for the formation of *each* product in Equation 19-53.

One way to circumvent this problem is to ensure that one of the esters has no alpha hydrogens. (We previously saw that this strategy employed with crossed aldol reactions.) Some common examples of such esters are shown below.

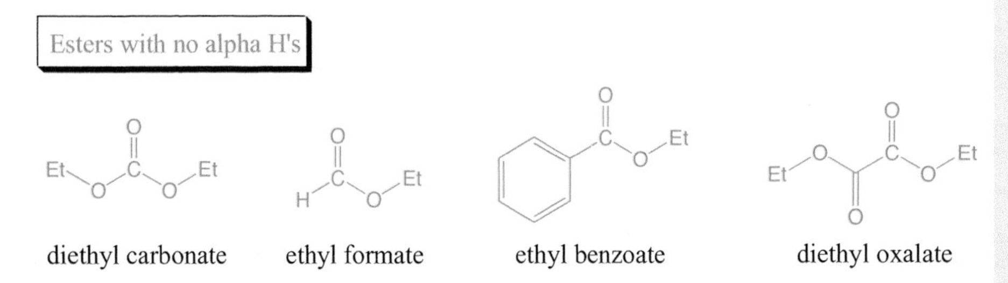

Because these esters have no alpha hydrogens, they can be dissolved in solution with an alkoxide base and no Claisen condensation takes place. A second ester that has alpha hydrogens can then be added slowly to this solution. As the ester with alpha hydrogens comes in contact with the base, its enolate anion is produced and the crossed Claisen condensation is initiated. An example is shown in Equation 19-54 using ethyl formate as the ester with no alpha hydrogens.

this ester has no alpha hydrogens

this ester has two alpha hydrogens

+ NaOEt / EtOH

1)

2) $H^{\oplus}$

45%

(19-54)

If both esters possess alpha hydrogens, it is still possible to carry out an effective crossed Claisen condensation reaction that produces exclusively one β-ketoester. The key is to use a base like lithium diisopropylamide, which *irreversibly and quantitatively* converts one of the esters into its enolate anion prior to introducing the second ester. (This is another strategy that was discussed in the context of crossed aldol reactions, Section 16.7.) With only the ester enolate present, no Claisen condensation can take place until the second (uncharged) ester is added. For example, as shown in Equation 19-55, methyl butanoate can be treated with LDA prior to the addition of methyl acetate.

LDA irreversibly deprotonates the ester to produce the ester enolate quantitatively, so the enolate is never in the presence of its own ester

+ LDA/ether

1)

2) $H^{\oplus}$

methyl butanoate

(19-55)

Not surprisingly, aldehyde and ketone enolate anions can also undergo nucleophilic addition-elimination with an ester. Equation 19-56 shows how this can occur with an ester that has no alpha hydrogens, and Equation 19-57 shows how this can occur with an ester that does have alpha hydrogens.

+ *t*-BuOK / DMF

1)

50 °C, 0.45 hr

2) H_2SO_4, H_2O

80%

(19-56)

+ $NaNH_2$ / ether

1)

reflux, 2 hr

2) H^+

57%

(19-57)

Solved Problem 19.8. Show how you would synthesize the following β-ketoester via a Claisen condensation reaction.

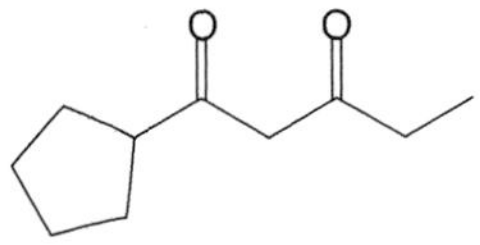

Think. Which carbon-carbon bond(s) can be "disconnected" in a reverse Claisen condensation? Does this transform suggest a self-Claisen condensation reaction or a crossed Claisen? Can we use a base that reversibly deprotonates an alpha hydrogen or should we use one that brings about an irreversible deprotonation?

Solve. A transform that reverses Claisen condensation disconnects a carbonyl's alpha carbon from the carbonyl group at the beta position, as shown below; the carbonyl at the beta position is part of an ester in the reactants. Given that the two carbonyl-containing precursors are not identical esters, a crossed Claisen condensation reaction is in order.

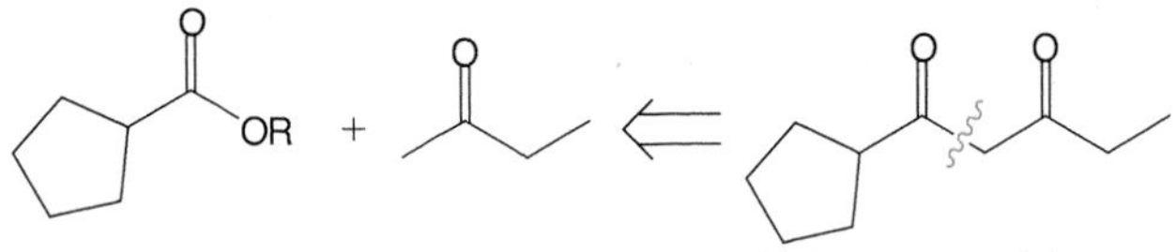

OR +

In the forward direction, 2-butanone would be converted into an enolate nucleophile via deprotonation at the alpha carbon. Because the ester contains an alpha proton of its own, generating the enolate nucleophile should be done irreversibly prior to the addition of the ester. Overall, the synthesis would appear as follows.

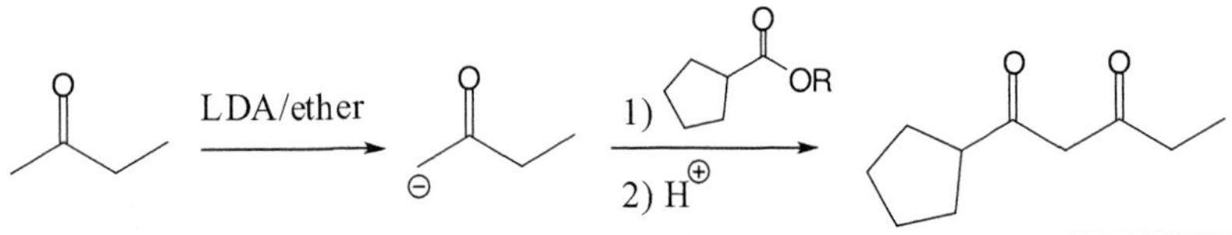

LDA/ether

1) OR

2) $H^{\oplus}$

Problem 19.18. Devise another synthesis of the β-ketoester in Solved Problem 19.8 without using OR .

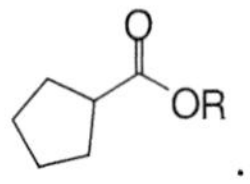

19.9d. Intramolecular Claisen condensation reactions: The Dieckmann consdensation

Yet another similarity between the Claisen condensation and the aldol reaction is the potential for an *intramolecular* reaction, ultimately producing a ring. An example of such a **Dieckmann condensation** is shown in Equation 19-58, and, as we can see, can be considered whenever two ester functional groups appear on the same molecule. As with most cyclization reactions, Dieckmann condensations occur most readily when the reaction leads to the formation of a 5- or 6-membered ring.

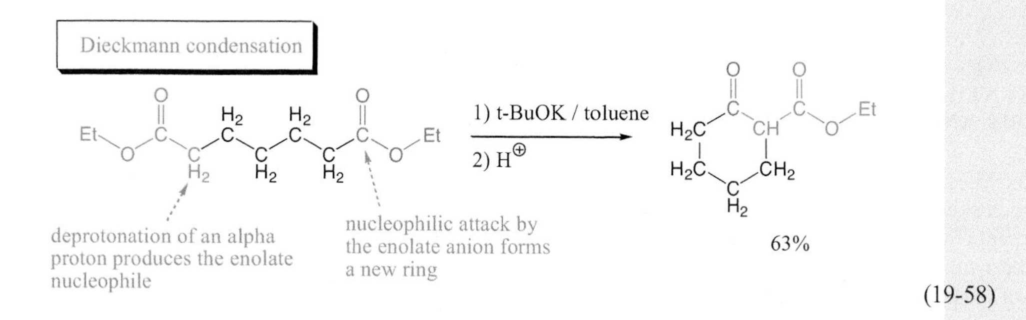
Dieckmann condensation
1) t-BuOK / toluene
2) H⊕
deprotonation of an alpha proton produces the enolate nucleophile
nucleophilic attack by the enolate anion forms a new ring
63%

(19-58)

Problem 19.19. Draw the complete, detailed mechanism for the reaction in Equation 19-58.

An intramolecular nucleophilic addition-elimination reaction on an ester can also occur if the enolate anion is that of a ketone or aldehyde. For example, methyl 6-oxo-6-phenylhexanoate cyclizes when treated with sodium amide to yield the 5-membered ring product shown in Equation 19-59.

ketones are more acidic than esters

$NaNH_2$

benzene

methyl 6-oxo-6-phenylhexanoate

90%

(19-59)

Notice in the reactant in Equation 19-59 that there are H atoms on the alpha carbons of both the ketone and the ester functional groups. However, deprotonation takes place almost exclusively at the ketone's alpha carbon, generating the ketone enolate anion instead of the ester enolate anion. This is because *ketones (and aldehydes) are substantially more acidic than esters*.

Your Turn 19.11. Verify the above statement about the relative acidities of ketones and esters by looking up or estimating the pK_a values of each functional group.

Ketone: _______________ Ester: _______________

Problem 19.20. Draw the complete, detailed mechanism for the following reaction and predict the major product.

1) NaOEt, EtOH

2) H⊕

Problem 19.21. Draw the acyclic di-carbonyl compound that can be used to synthesize the following cyclic β-ketoaldehyde.

19.10. ORGANIC SYNTHESIS: DECARBOXYLATION, THE MALONIC ESTER SYNTHESIS, AND THE ACETOACETIC ESTER SYNTHESIS

Organic synthesis relies substantially on visual cues in the target molecule, such as the structure of the carbon skeleton, as well as the identity and relative positioning of each functional group present within the molecule. Therefore, the level of challenge of a synthesis is increased if the synthesis employs a reaction that removes a functional group entirely, given that some of those visual cues disappear with it. This was the case, for example, with reactions that convert the carbonyl group (C=O) of a ketone or aldehyde into a methylene (CH_2) group (Section 17.3). It was also the case with the catalytic hydrogenation of an alkene or alkyne, producing an alkane (Section 17.5).

Decarboxylation is another synthetically useful reaction in which a functional group is removed entirely from a molecule. As its name suggests, the specific functional group that is removed is a carboxylic acid. As indicated in Equation 19-60, decarboxylation takes place readily when a **β-keto acid** is heated, via the loss of a molecule of carbon dioxide.

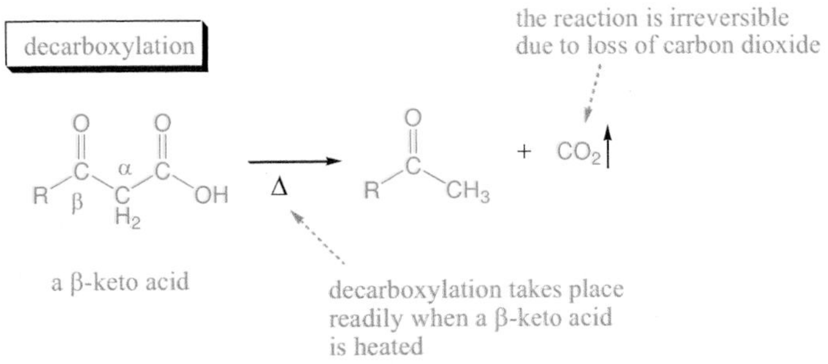

decarboxylation

the reaction is irreversible due to loss of carbon dioxide

+ CO_2↑

Δ

a β-keto acid

decarboxylation takes place readily when a β-keto acid is heated

(19-60)

The mechanism for the decarboxylation is shown in Equation 19-61. Loss of CO_2 takes place in a single step through the cyclic movement of six electrons—this is an example of a **pericyclic reaction**, a class of reactions that will be discussed in greater detail in Chapter 24. Notice that the immediate product of decarboxylation is an *enol*, which tautomerizes to the more stable *keto* form in two proton transfer steps (Section 7.1).

Mechanism of the Reaction in Equation 19-60

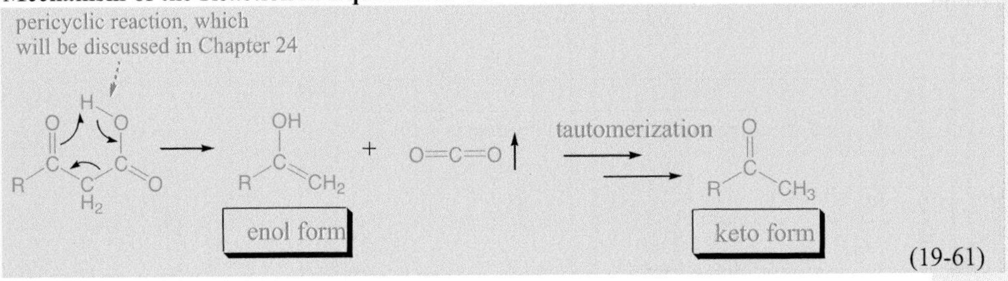

pericyclic reaction, which will be discussed in Chapter 24

+ O=C=O↑

tautomerization

enol form

keto form

(19-61)

As we will see, decarboxylation is a key step in both the **malonic ester synthesis** and the **acetoacetic ester synthesis**. These syntheses begin with malonic ester or acetoacetic ester (shown below) and, as we will see shortly, lead to the formation of carboxylic acids and ketones, respectively.

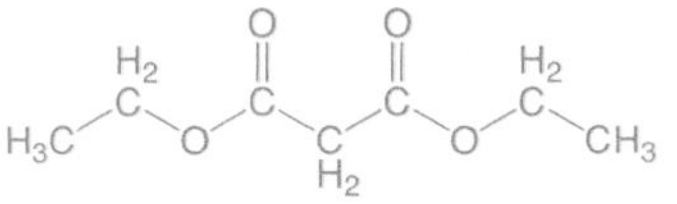

(malonic ester)
diethyl malonate

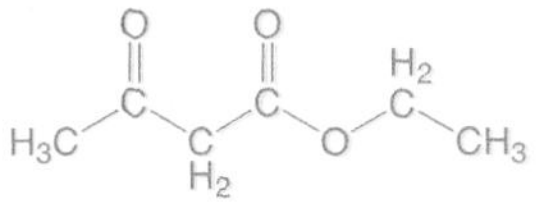

(acetoacetic ester)
ethyl 2-oxobutanoate

Neither of these compounds is a β-keto acid, so neither can undergo decarboxylation directly. However, as shown in Equations 19-62 and 19-63, both can undergo hydrolysis to become a β-keto acid, after which decarboxylation can occur—overall, acetoacetic ester is converted into acetone, whereas malonic ester is converted into acetic acid. Notice that in the hydrolysis step, *both* ester functional groups of malonic ester are converted into carboxylic acids, prior to decarboxylation.

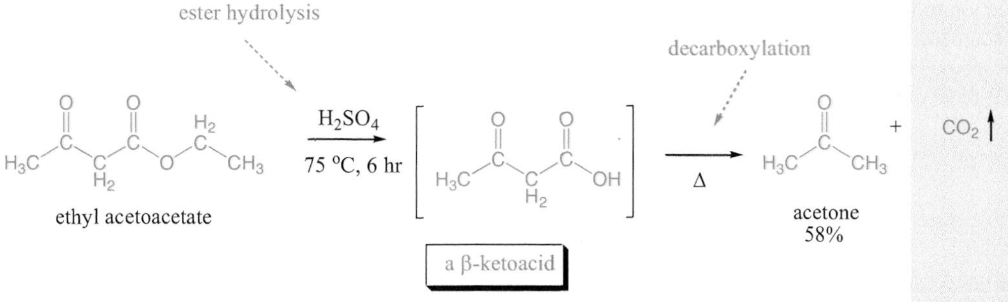

ester hydrolysis

decarboxylation

H_2SO_4, 75 °C, 6 hr

Δ

ethyl acetoacetate

a β-ketoacid

acetone
58%

$+ \; CO_2 \uparrow$

(19-62)

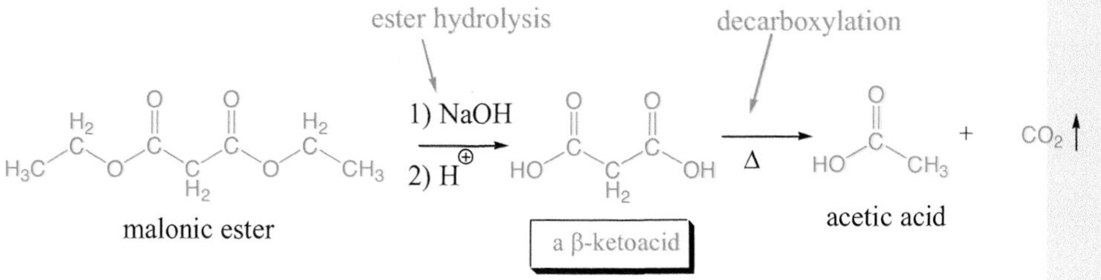

ester hydrolysis

decarboxylation

1) NaOH
2) $H^{\oplus}$

Δ

malonic ester

a β-ketoacid

acetic acid

$+ \; CO_2 \uparrow$

(19-63)

19.10a. Synthesis of monoalkylated acetone and acetic acid

The goal of an acetoacetic ester or malonic ester synthesis is not merely to produce acetone or acetic acid; there are less expensive ways to synthesize those compounds. Rather, prior to the hydrolysis-decarboxylation sequence of reactions, we can take advantage of the special reactivity of the CH_2 group between the two carbonyl functional groups. Malonic ester and acetoacetic ester are examples of **active methylene compounds**. In each of these compounds, the methylene (i.e., CH_2) group flanked by the two carbonyl groups is unusually acidic; thus, one of the methylene hydrogens can be removed *irreversibly* by a moderately strong base such as $CH_3CH_2O^-$.

Your Turn 19.12. Verify the above statement that an *active methylene compound* can be irreversibly deprotonated by using the appropriate pK_a values to estimate the equilibrium constant, K_{eq}, for the following reaction.

EtOC(=O)CH$_2$C(=O)OEt + $CH_3CH_2O^{\ominus}$ ⇌ EtOC(=O)CH$^{\ominus}$C(=O)OEt + CH_3CH_2OH K_{eq} = [ ]

pK_a = [ ] pK_a = [ ]

The resulting enolate anion is highly nucleophilic, and can react with a suitable alkyl halide in an S_N2 reaction to form a new carbon-carbon bond (Equations 19-64 and 19-65). These alkylated acetoacetic and malonic esters can then be hydrolyzed and subsequently undergo decarboxylation, just as we saw with the unsubstituted compounds in Equations 19-62 and 19-63 above.

ethyl acetoacetate —NaOEt, EtOH→ enolate (nucleophilic carbon) —$H_2C{=}C(CH_3)CH_2Br$ (S_N2 reaction)→ alkylated ester —1) NaOH, H_2O; 2) H_2SO_4, H_2O, Δ→ an α-alkylated acetone, 55% (19-64)

malonic ester —NaOEt, EtOH→ enolate (nucleophilic carbon) —bromocyclohexane (S_N2 reaction)→ alkylated ester —1) KOH, H_2O; 2) H_2SO_4, H_2O, Δ→ an α-alkylated acetic acid, 38% (19-65)

Notice that the products of these reactions are α-alkylated acetone (Equation 19-64) and α-alkylated acetic acid (Equation 19-65). Therefore, when synthesizing one of these derivatives, acetoacetic ester or malonic ester may be viable options.

Solved Problem 19.9. Show how you would synthesize 2-hexanone beginning with acetoacetic ester.

acetoacetic ester —?→ 2-hexanone

Think. What would the precursor look like before decarboxylation? How could that precursor be produced from acetoacetic ester?

Solve. Recognizing that 2-hexanone is an α-alkylated acetone, we can first perform a reverse-decarboxylation, given that decarboxylation is the last step in an acetoacetic ester synthesis.

reverse decarboxylation

OH

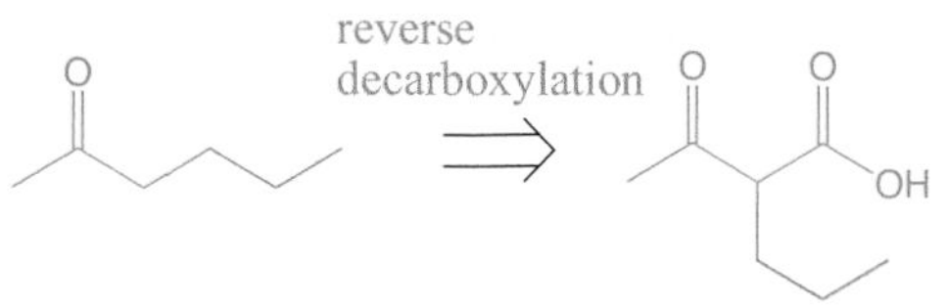

Continuing the retrosynthesis, we then perform a reverse hydrolysis and a reverse alkylation to bring us back to the starting acetoacetic ester.

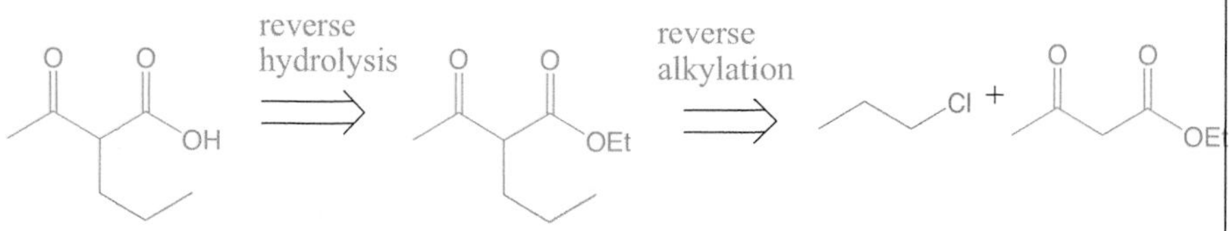

reverse hydrolysis

reverse alkylation

OH OEt Cl + OEt

In the forward direction, the synthesis would appear as follows.

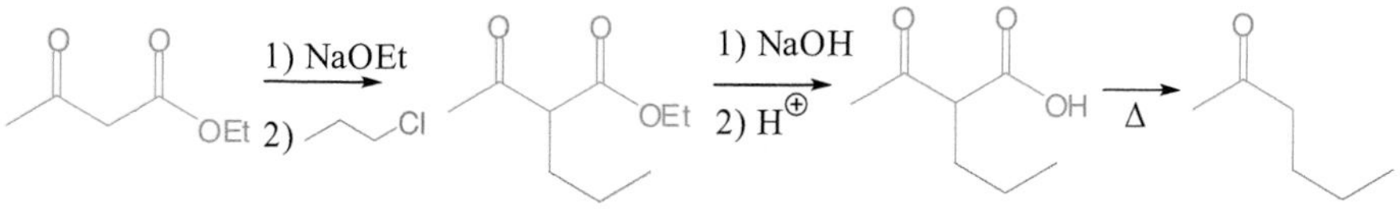

1) NaOEt 2) Cl

1) NaOH 2) $H^{\oplus}$

Δ

Problem 19.22. Outline a synthesis of 3-methylbutanoic acid from either acetoacetic ester or malonic ester.

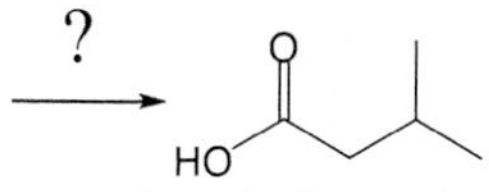

?

HO

3-methylbutanoic acid

19.10b. Synthesis of dialkylated acetone and acetic acid

Both the acetoacetic ester synthesis and the malonic ester synthesis also lend themselves to *dialkylation* at the active methylene group, given that there are two acidic hydrogens. Examples are shown in Equations 19-66 and 19-67. Notice that the two alkyl groups can either be the same or they can be different.

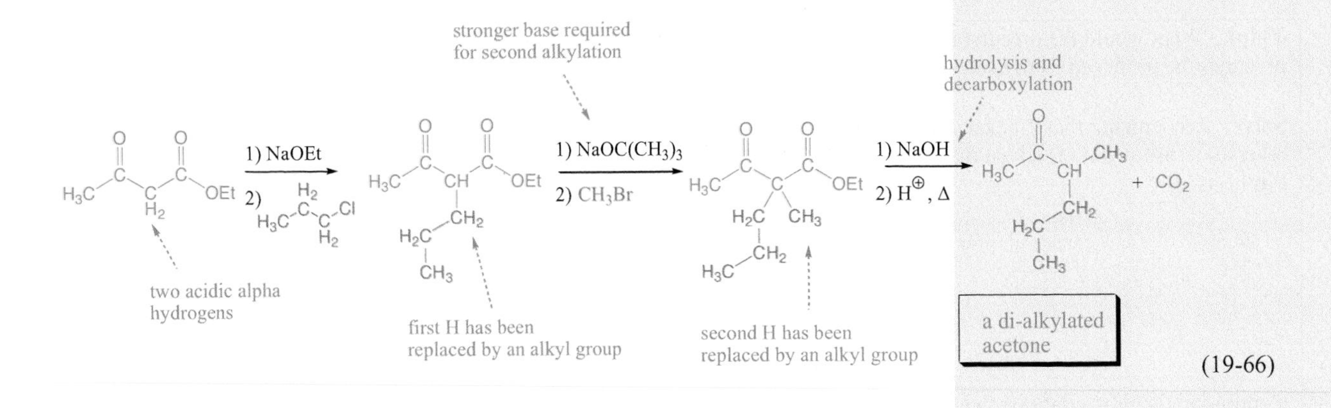

(19-66)

stronger base required for second alkylation

hydrolysis and decarboxylation

1) NaOEt
2) H_3C-CH_2-Cl

1) $NaOC(CH_3)_3$
2) H_3C-CH_2-Cl

1) NaOH
2) $H^{\oplus}$, Δ

+ CO_2

two acidic alpha hydrogens

first H has been replaced by an alkyl group

second H has been replaced by an alkyl group

a di-alkylated acetic acid

(19-67)

In both cases, alkylation of the methylene carbon is carried out twice prior to hydrolysis and decarboxylation. Notice, however, the base in the second alkylation is the *t*-butoxide anion, $(CH_3)_3CO^-$. This is because the second deprotonation is more difficult than the first, so it requires a stronger base. The reason that the second deprotonation is more difficult is that the alkyl group added in the first alkylation is electron-donating, and thus destabilizes the resulting enolate anion.

Your Turn 19.13. In the figure provided here, draw an arrow representing the inductive electron donation by the alkyl group. Do the alkyl group's effects increase or decrease the concentration of negative charge? ____________

R

Problem 19.23. Show how you would synthesize 2-ethylhexanoic acid from malonic ester.

19.11. ORGANIC SYNTHESIS: PROTECTING CARBOXYLIC ACIDS AND AMINES

Chapter 17 introduced the concept of the *protecting group.* The general approach is quite straightforward: In the anticipation of an undesired reaction involving a particular functional group, (1) protect that functional group by temporarily converting it into another one that is unreactive under the conditions for the desired reaction, (2) perform the desired reaction, and (3) deprotect the functional group by converting it back to its original form. In Chapter 17, we specifically examined how to protect ketones, aldehydes, and alcohols. Here, we will examine how to protect carboxylic acids and amines, which employ nucleophilic addition-elimination reactions, the topic of this chapter and Chapter 18.

19.11a. Protection of carboxylic acids

The acidity of a carboxyl group (RCO_2H) can easily interfere with a synthesis, so it might be desirable to suppress that acidity. Commonly this is done by converting the carboxylic acid to an ester, which effectively replaces the acidic hydrogen by an alkyl group. Methyl esters are popular choices, and can be made by reacting the carboxylic acid with methanol (Fischer esterification, Section 19.6) or with diazomethane (Section 10.5), as shown in Equation 19-68. Benzyl esters (Equation 19-69) are also popular choices.

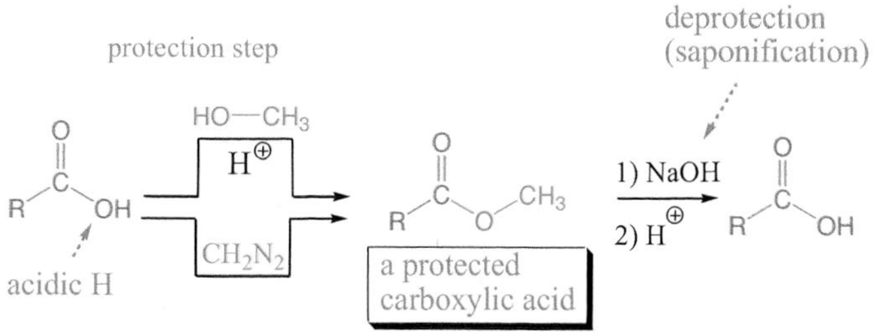

protection step: $HO{-}CH_3$, $H^{\oplus}$ or CH_2N_2 (acidic H) → a protected carboxylic acid; deprotection (saponification): 1) NaOH, 2) $H^{\oplus}$

(19-68)

protection (Fischer esterification): $HOCH_2C_6H_5$, $H^{\oplus}$ (acidic H) → protected carboxylic acid (a benzyl ester); deprotection: H_2, Pd → RCO_2H + $H_3C{-}C_6H_5$

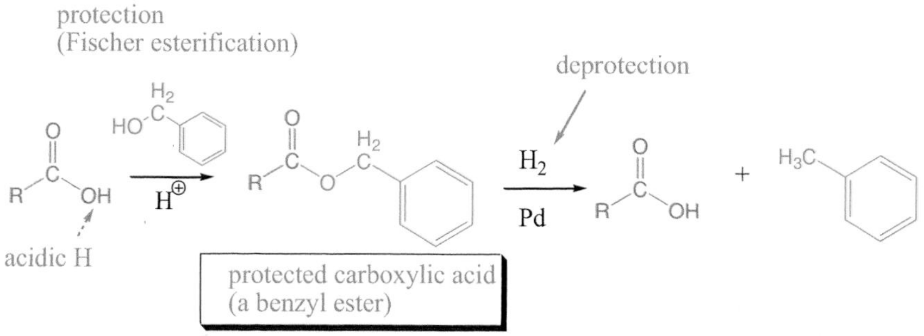

(19-69)

Removal of the ester protecting group can be accomplished by a saponification reaction in aqueous base (Equation 19-68). Benzyl esters have the special capability of being removed by reaction with hydrogen gas and a catalyst at room temperature (Equation 19-69). As we can see, toluene is formed as a by-product.

With these protection and deprotection steps in mind, suppose that we wish to carry out the following synthesis.

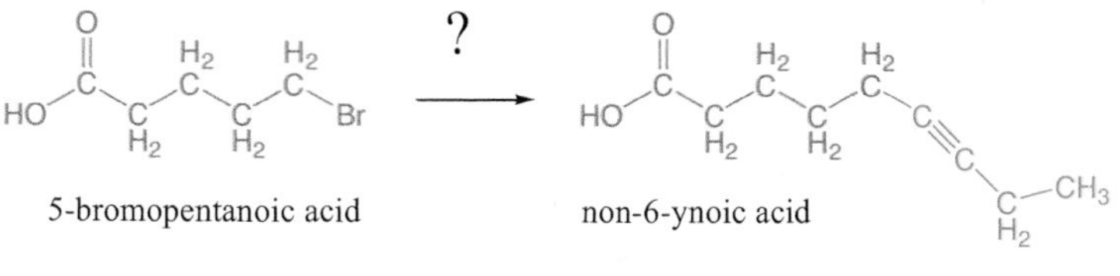

5-bromopentanoic acid —?→ non-6-ynoic acid

(19-70)

It might at first appear that the synthesis could be carried out simply by using $NaC{\equiv}CCH_2CH_3$ in an S_N2 reaction. However, as shown in Equation 19-71, this alkynide anion is a relatively strong base and will rapidly deprotonate the carboxylic acid. The resulting carboxylate anion is nucleophilic, and could then attack the alkyl halide in an intramolecular S_N2 reaction, yielding an undesired cyclic product.

NaC≡CCH2CH3 proton transfer SN2 + Br⊖

(19-71)

To circumvent this problem, we can first convert the carboxylic acid into an ester, as shown in Equation 19-72. Therefore, no acidic protons remain when the alkynide anion is introduced, leaving the alkynide anion free to displace bromide in an S_N2 reaction. Once the substitution reaction has come to completion, the ester can be hydrolyzed back into a carboxylic acid.

no acidic proton; remains free to act as a nucleophile; ester hydrolysis regenerates the carboxylic acid

CH_3OH / H_2SO_4; NaC≡CCH2CH3; 1) NaOH 2) H_3O^+

(19-72)

19.11b. Protection of amines

Amino groups are susceptible to oxidation and are also susceptible to deprotonation by very strong bases, such as Grignard and alkyllithium reagents. They are also moderately strong nucleophiles. Therefore, if we want to suppress these reactivities, we must use a protecting group.

One way to protect an amine is to convert it to an amide by reacting it with an acid chloride, as we have seen previously in Equation 19-3. Amides are less susceptible to oxidation and are less nucleophilic because of the resonance stabilization involving the carbonyl group and the lone pair on N (Figure 19-2). Furthermore, secondary amines result in tertiary amides, which have no N-H bonds and are therefore not susceptible at all to deprotonation of the nitrogen atom.

We must be careful about using amides as protecting groups for amines, because freeing the amine (i.e., deprotecting) requires relatively harsh acidic conditions (Equation 19-73). If there are other functional groups that are sensitive to acid, such as alcohols and ethers, then protecting an amine in the form of an amide may not be wise.

a protected amine; de-protection (hydrolysis)

$H_3O^{\oplus}$, Δ

(19-73)

To illustrate how an amide protecting group might be used in synthesis, suppose that we wish to carry out the following transformation in which a primary alcohol is oxidized to a carboxylic acid.

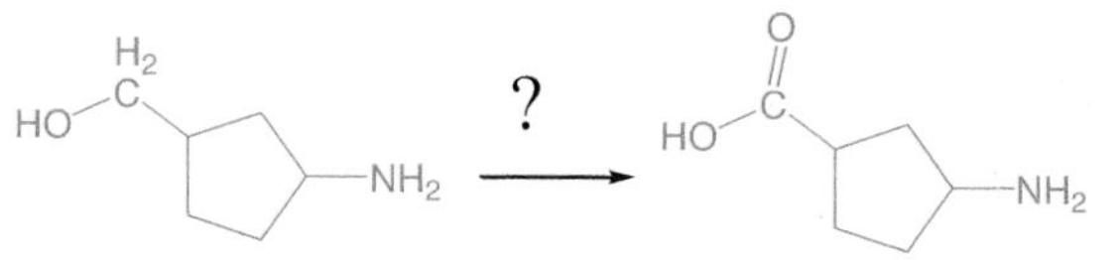

?

It may at first appear that we can accomplish this using a simple oxidation using chromic acid, H_2CrO_4 (Equation 19-74). However, H_2CrO_4 will also oxidize the primary amine to a nitro group, as shown.

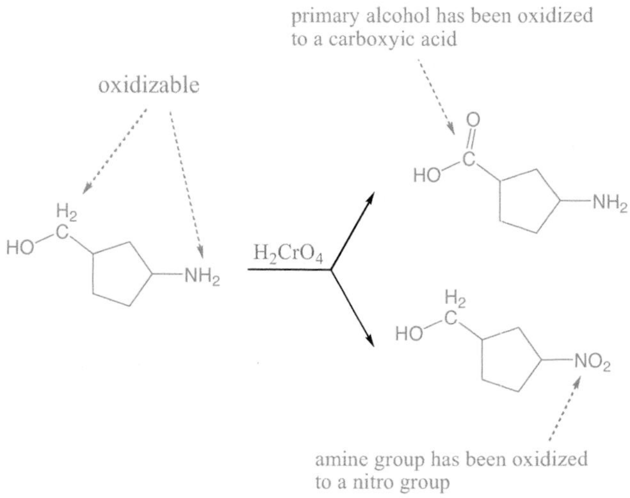

primary alcohol has been oxidized to a carboxyic acid

oxidizable

H_2CrO_4

amine group has been oxidized to a nitro group

(19-74)

Instead, converting the amine to an amide will suppress the reactivity of the NH_2 group, allowing the oxidation to take place only at the alcohol (Equation 19-75).

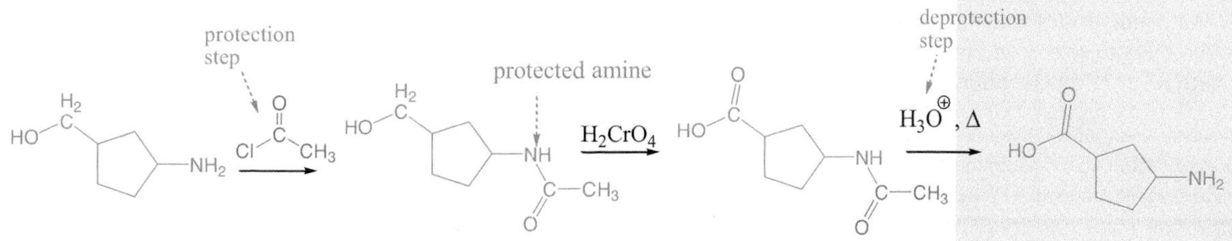

protection step

protected amine

H_2CrO_4

deprotection step

$H_3O^{\oplus}$, Δ

(19-75)

19.12 FUNCTIONAL GROUP CHEMISTRY

As we have seen throughout Chapters 18 and 19, there are a variety of functional groups that can participate in nucleophilic addition-elimination reactions. These functional groups include acid chlorides, acid anhydrides, esters, carboxylic acids, and amides, each of which possesses a polar C=O bond to which a leaving group is attached. Ketones and aldehydes can also participate in nucleophilic addition-elimination reactions, even though, under normal conditions, very poor leaving groups are attached to the carbonyl carbon. Moreover, functional groups containing polar π bonds other than the C=O bond, such as the S=O and Cr=O bonds, can also participate in nucleophilic addition-elimination reactions.

As usual, aspects that have been discussed in previous *Functional Group Chemistry* sections appear gray. New aspects that have been discussed in Chapters 18 and 19 appear green.

19.12a. Acid halides

Acid halides are highly reactive compounds, susceptible, in particular, to nucleophilic attack at the carbonyl carbon by a variety of nucleophiles, both strong and weak. For example, an acid chloride undergoes acyl substitution with water, alcohols, and amines to produce carboxylic acids, esters, and amides, respectively. Substitution with a carboxylate anion (RCO_2^-) will produce an acid anhydride.

Acid chlorides can also be reduced by R^- and H^- nucleophiles. Alkyllithium or Grignard reagents will lead to two additions of R^- to produce tertiary alcohols, whereas the weaker lithium dialkylcuprate will lead to a single addition to produce ketones. Treatment with $NaBH_4$ or $LiAlH_4$ will lead to two additions of H^- to produce primary alcohols, whereas lithium tri-*tert*-butoxyaluminum hydride will lead to a single addition to produce aldehydes.

Additionally, acid halides, in the enol form, are nucleophilic at the alpha carbon. This allows alpha halogenation to take place, as in the Hell-Volhard-Zelinsky reaction (Section 19.4a).

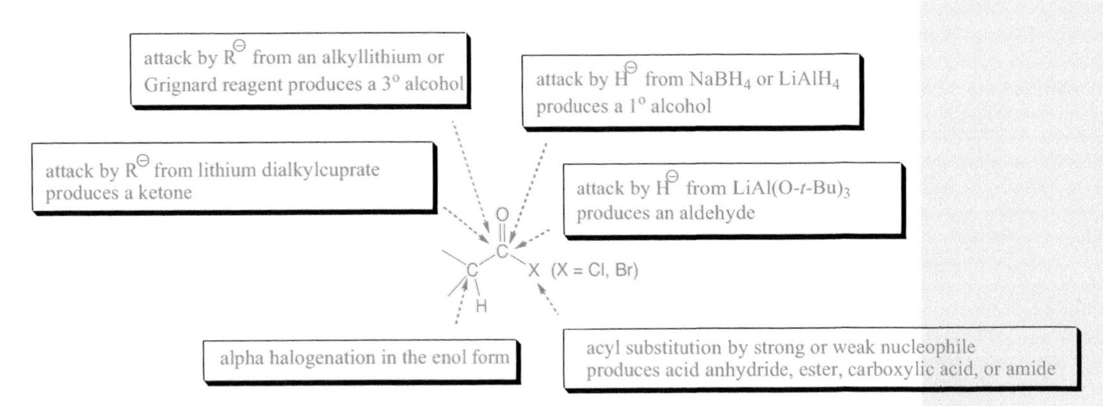

19.12b. Acid anhydrides

Acid anhydrides are similar in reactivity to acid halides, susceptible to acyl substitution by both strong and weak nucleophiles. Reduction also takes place when treated with R^- or H^- nucleophiles.

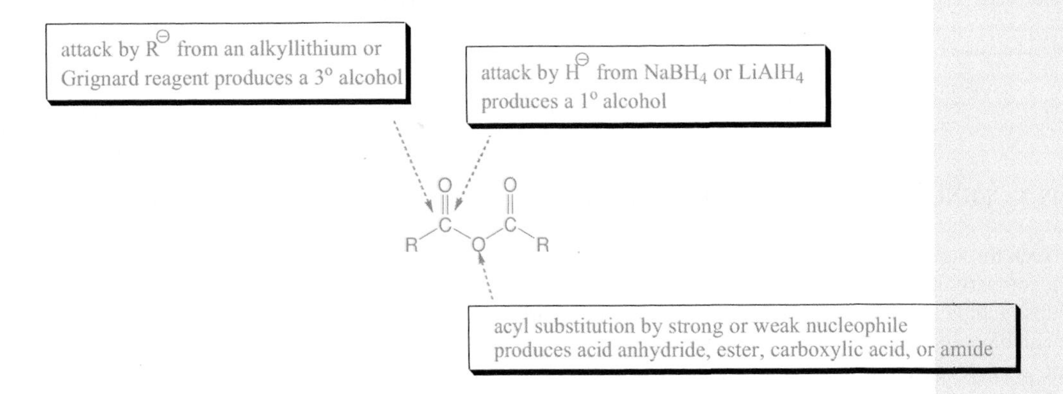

19.12c. Esters

Esters, like acid halides and acid anhydrides, undergo nucleophilic acyl substitution with strong nucleophiles like hydroxide and alkoxide anions. However, esters, owing to their greater stability, do not react readily with weak nucleophiles like water or alcohols under normal conditions. By contrast, many such reactions do take place readily under basic or acidic conditions. Under basic conditions, the reaction can be catalyzed if the weak nucleophile can be converted into a strong nucleophile by deprotonation. Under acidic conditions, catalysis can take place by protonating the carbonyl oxygen, and thus activating it.

Strong R^- nucleophiles, such as alkyllithium and Grignard reagents, add twice to the ester's carbonyl carbon to produce a tertiary alcohol. Strong H^- nucleophiles, such as $NaBH_4$ and $LiAlH_4$, also add twice, reducing an ester to a primary alcohol. Diisobutylaluminum hydride (DIBAH), a specialized reducing agent, adds a single H^- to the carbonyl carbon to produce an aldehyde.

The alpha carbon of an ester is weakly acidic, so it can be deprotonated under strongly basic conditions. The resulting ester enolate anion is highly nucleophilic, and can thus attack the carbonyl carbon of another ester in a Claisen condensation, or an alkyl halide in an alpha alkylation.

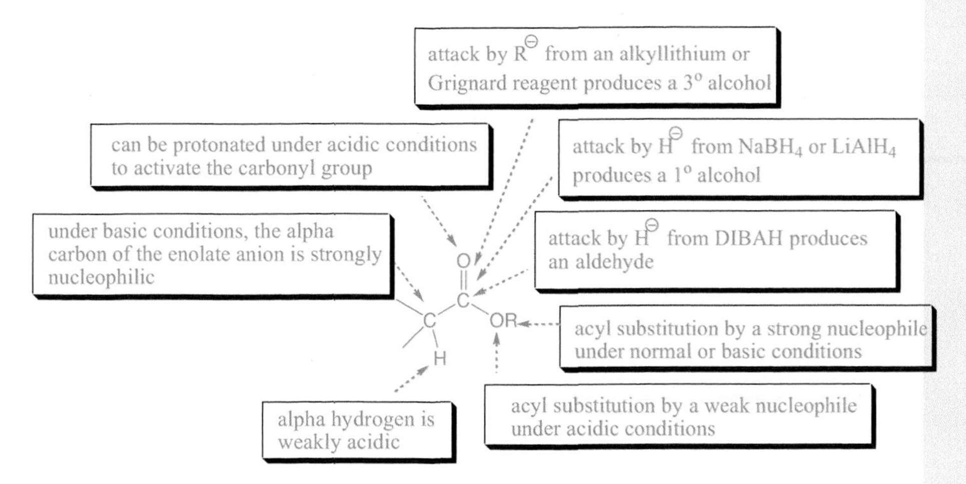

19.12d. Carboxylic acids

The reactivity at the carbonyl group of a carboxylic acid is very similar to that of an ester's carbonyl group. Thus, acyl substitution can take place with weak nucleophiles under acidic conditions via acid catalysis. Unlike esters, however, carboxylic acids tend *not* to react with strong nucleophiles, owing to the acidity of the carboxyl proton. One exception is $LiAlH_4$, which reduces a carboxylic acid to a primary alcohol.

Additionally, thionyl chloride ($SOCl_2$) can be used to convert the OH group to Cl, yielding an acid chloride.

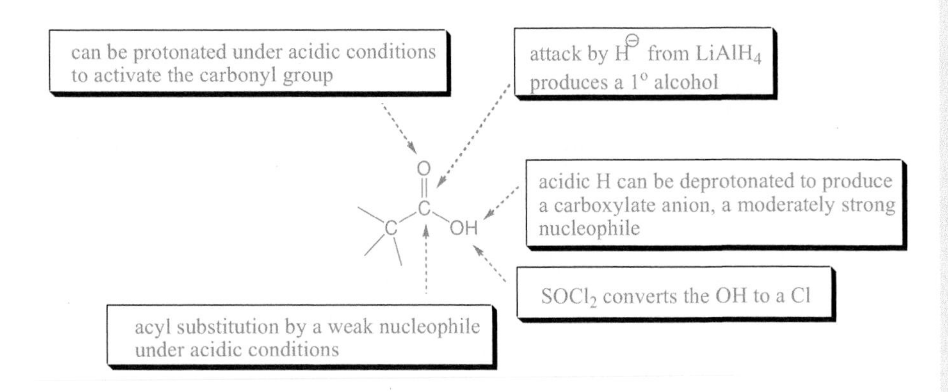

19.12e. Amides

The carbonyl group of an amide is even more stable than that of a carboxylic acid. Therefore, under normal conditions, amides tend not to undergo nucleophilic acyl substitution, even with relatively strong nucleophiles. Under strongly acidic or basic conditions, however, an amine can be hydrolyzed to a carboxylic acid. Additionally, $LiAlH_4$, a strong reducing agent, will reduce an amide to an amine.

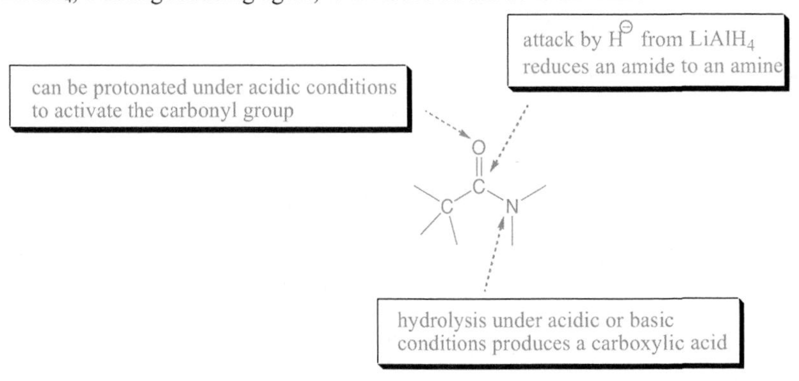

19.12f. Ketones

Normally, ketones are not susceptible to acyl substitution because the alkyl groups that are attached to the carbonyl carbon are very poor leaving groups. However, methyl ketones can undergo acyl substitution with hydroxide, producing carboxylic acids, after conversion to a trihalomethyl ketone. These are haloform reactions. Additionally, an alkyl group can behave as a leaving group after nucleophilic addition by a peroxyacid in a Baeyer-Villiger oxidation, in large part due to the breaking of the peroxyacid's weak O-O bond.

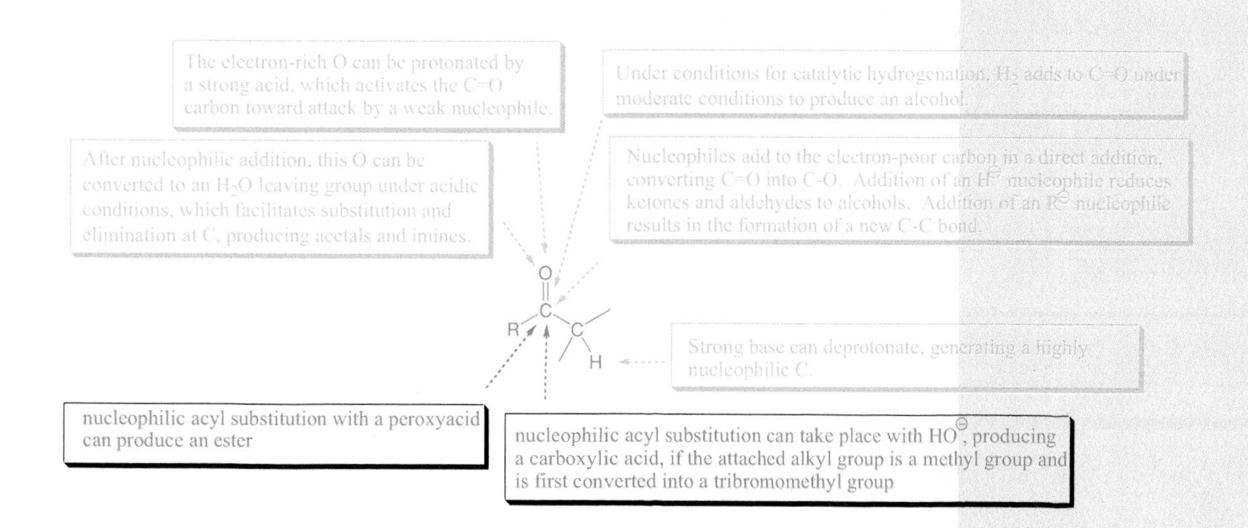

19.12g. Aldehydes

Like ketones, aldehydes, under normal conditions, do not possess suitable leaving groups for nucleophilic acyl substitution. However, treatment with a peroxyacid facilitates the departure of H from the carbonyl group, producing a carboxylic acid. Additionally, in aqueous solution, the hydrate can be oxidized to a carboxylic acid by chromic acid.

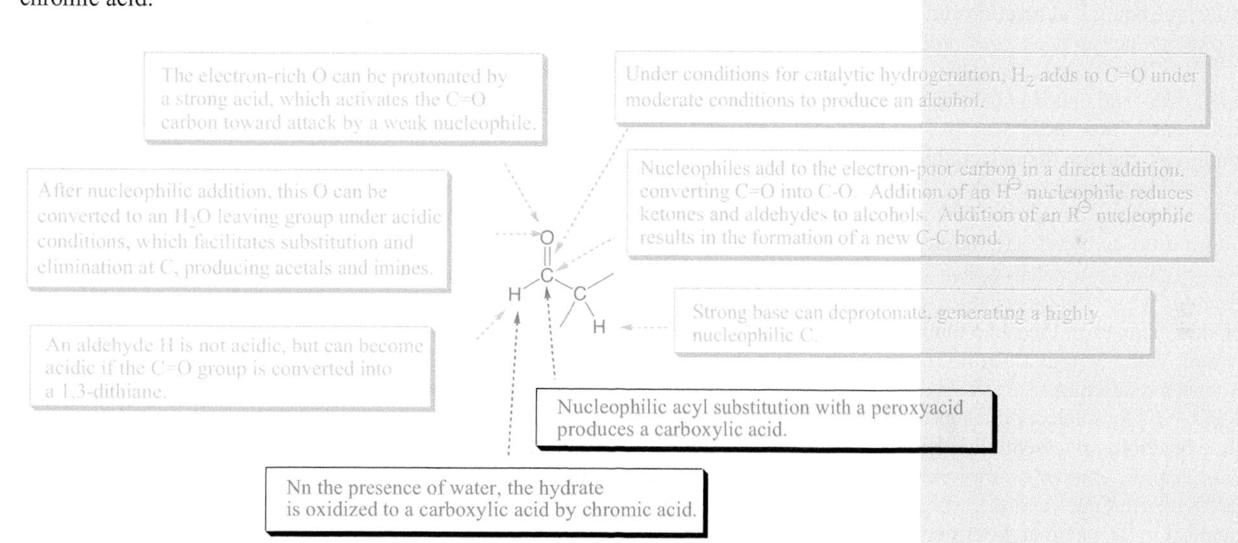

19.12h. Alcohols

Under normal conditions, alcohols do not readily undergo nucleophilic substitution or elimination because of the poor HO^- leaving group. Sulfonyl chlorides, however, can convert alcohols into sulfonate esters, which possess excellent leaving groups for nucleophilic substitution and elimination.

Additionally, alcohols are oxidizable. Chromic acid or potassium permanganate will oxidize a primary alcohol to a carboxylic acid, and a secondary alcohol to a ketone. Pyridinium chlorochromate, PCC, will oxidize a primary alcohol to an aldehyde.

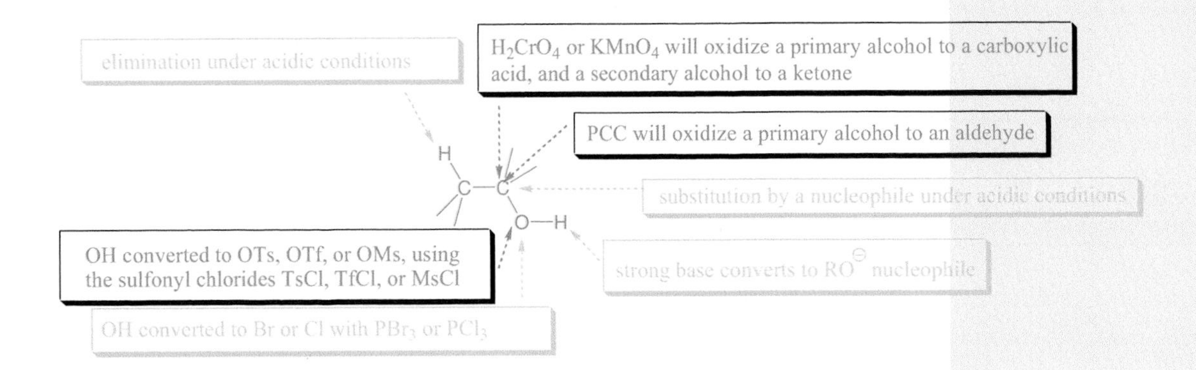

19.13. WRAPPING UP AND LOOKING AHEAD

Chapter 19 was the second of two chapters discussing nucleophilic addition-elimination reactions. Whereas Chapter 18 focused on such reactions involving strong nucleophiles, this chapter's focus was on reactions involving weak nucleophiles. Highly reactive acid derivatives such as acid chlorides and acid anhydrides react readily with weak nucleophiles, including water, alcohols, and amines, to produce carboxylic acids, esters, and amides, respectively. The mechanism that describes these reactions is nearly identical to the one that describes reactions involving strong nucleophiles, the only difference being that reactions involving weak nucleophiles require a final proton transfer step to produce an uncharged product.

Carboxylic acids, esters, and amides are less reactive than acid chlorides or acid anhydrides, and thus do not react as readily with weak nucleophiles under normal conditions. Thus, these reactions are frequently base- or acid-catalyzed. Under basic conditions, the rate of nucleophilic addition-elimination is enhanced by deprotonating the nucleophile, thereby converting it into a strong nucleophile. Under acidic conditions, the reaction rate is enhanced by protonating the oxygen atom of a carbonyl group, which *activates* the carbonyl carbon toward nucleophilic attack.

Similar to what we saw in Chapter 18, many nucleophilic addition-elimination reactions we saw in this chapter serve to convert one carboxylic acid derivative into another. However, the same fundamental mechanism describes other important reactions as well. For example, treatment of an alcohol with a sulfonyl chloride (RSO_2–Cl) produces a sulfonate ester (RSO_2–OR'), which possesses an excellent leaving group (RSO_2–O^-) for nucleophilic substitution and elimination reactions. The mechanisms for these reactions are essentially identical to the ones that describe the alcoholysis of acid chlorides. As another example, chromic acid (H_2CrO_4) oxidizes an alcohol via a chromate ester intermediate, which is itself produced by a mechanism that is essentially identical to the one that describes Fischer esterification.

With the completion of this chapter, we have essentially completed our set of chapters on "nucleophilic" reactions. Chapters 9 through 11 discussed nucleophilic substitution and elimination reactions; Chapters 15 and 16 discussed nucleophilic addition reactions; and Chapters 18 and 19 discussed nucleophilic addition-elimination reactions. For each of these types of reactions, a key step in the mechanism shows the formation of a bond involving a lone pair of electrons from a nucleophile.

Beginning in Chapter 20, our focus will shift to "electrophilic" reactions. As we will see, these reactions differ from the ones we have discussed so far primarily in the source of the electrons used to form a bond between key electron-rich and electron-poor species. Namely, in electrophilic reactions, that source of electrons is typically from a nonpolar π bond instead of a lone pair.

APPLICATIONS TO BIOLOGY AND BIOCHEMISTRY

19.14 DETERMINING THE PRIMARY STRUCTURE VIA AMINO ACID SEQUENCING: EDMAN DEGRADATION

Recall from Section 1.12a that proteins are large molecules constructed from α-amino acids, and each of the 20 possible amino acids is distinguished by the identity of its side group, R. As shown below, each pair of amino acids in a protein is joined via an amide functional group, also called a **peptide linkage** or **peptide bond**.

amino acids in a protein are connected by an amide functional group, also called a peptide linkage or peptide bond

N-terminus

C-terminus

complete hydrolysis of the amides liberates the individual amino acids

6 N HCl, 110 °C, 24 h

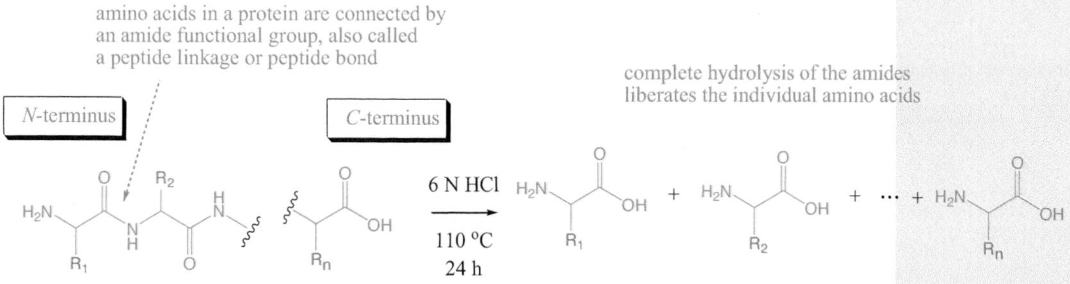

(19-76)

The fact that amino acids are joined by amide groups is critical to the stability of proteins. As we saw in Section 18.3, amides are among the most stable acid derivatives, and therefore require relatively extreme conditions to react. For example, as shown in Equation 19-76 above, the complete hydrolysis of a protein can take place under strongly acidic conditions and elevated temperatures.

Such a complete hydrolysis can be useful in determining the relative amounts of each type of amino acid in a protein. To do so, the product mixture is injected into an *amino acid analyzer*, which is a type of chromatograph (see Interchapter 1). Each amino acid, having a characteristic retention time on the column, is separated and quantified.

However, complete hydrolysis cannot tell us the **primary structure** of the protein—i.e., the specific sequence of amino acids from the ***N*-terminus** (the end with the free amino group) to the ***C*-terminus** (the end with the carboxyl group). This sequence is important, because it is what gives a protein its specific function—frequently, proteins that differ by the identity of just one amino acid at a specific site, or **residue**, have very different biological properties.

One way to determine a protein's sequence is **Edman degradation**. The basis of Edman degradation is to remove and detect one amino acid at a time, from the *N*-terminus. As shown below, the removal of each *N*-terminal amino acid consists of three steps.

In the first step, the protein is treated with phenyl isothiocyanate. The free amine of the *N*-terminal amino acid adds to the polar C=N bond in a nucleophilic addition reaction, producing a phenylthiocarbamoyl (PTC) derivative that contains the side group (in this case, R_1). In the second step, under mildly acidic conditions, the *N*-terminal amino acid cleaves in the form of a thiazolone, via a nucleophilic addition-elimination mechanism. The thiazolone is then extracted into an organic solvent, and when treated with HCl, it undergoes another nucleophilic addition-elimination mechanism, rearranging to a more stable phenylthiohydantoin (PTH) derivative. The PTH derivative is then identified using either chromatographic or mass spectrometric techniques. The entire process is repeated with the remainder of the protein.

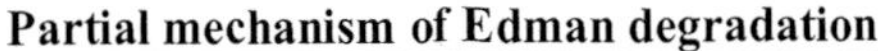

Partial mechanism of Edman degradation

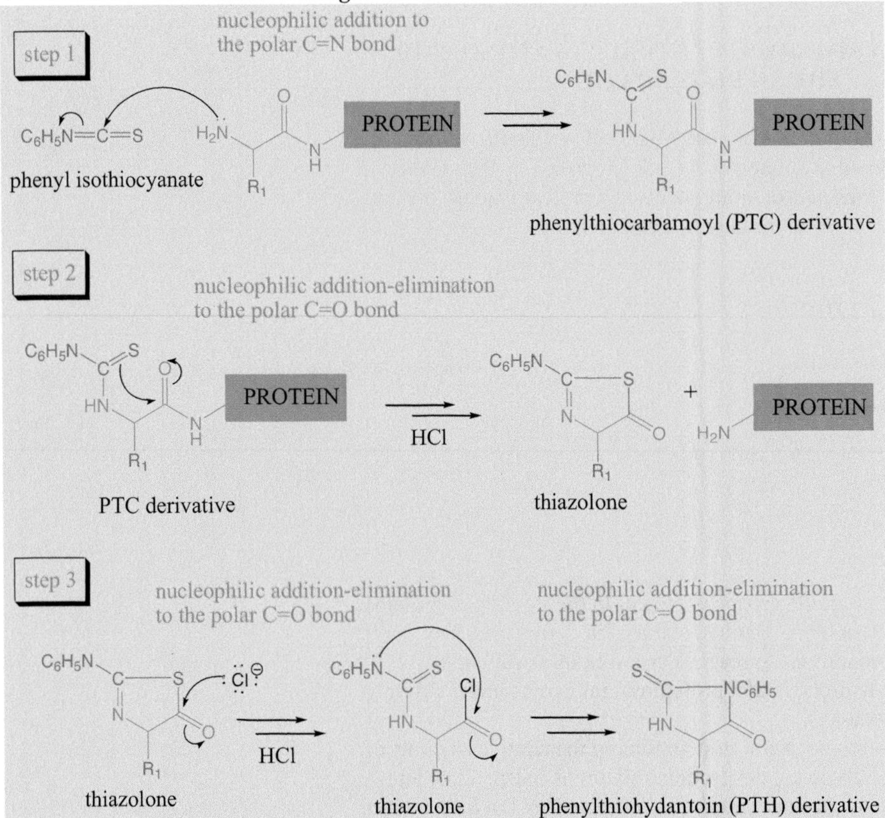

Theoretically, the entire sequence of a protein can be determined in this manner. However, sequencing proteins via Edman degradation becomes impractical when the protein exceeds roughly 30 amino acids, because side products accumulate and interfere with the results. In such cases, the protein can be *partially* hydrolyzed using dilute acid—hydrolysis takes place at essentially random locations in the protein to produce smaller polypeptides. Those smaller polypeptides can be sequenced using Edman degradation, and the sequence of the original protein can then be pieced together from the results.

Suppose, for example, the partial hydrolysis of a protein yielded three smaller polypeptides, whose sequences were determined to be the ones shown below at left. As shown at right, certain portions of the peptides have the same sequence—specifically, the Ser-His sequence in peptides 1 and 3 (red), and the Gln-His-Leu sequence in peptides 2 and 3 (blue). Assuming those sequences come from the same portions of the original protein, we can piece together the overall sequence, as shown.

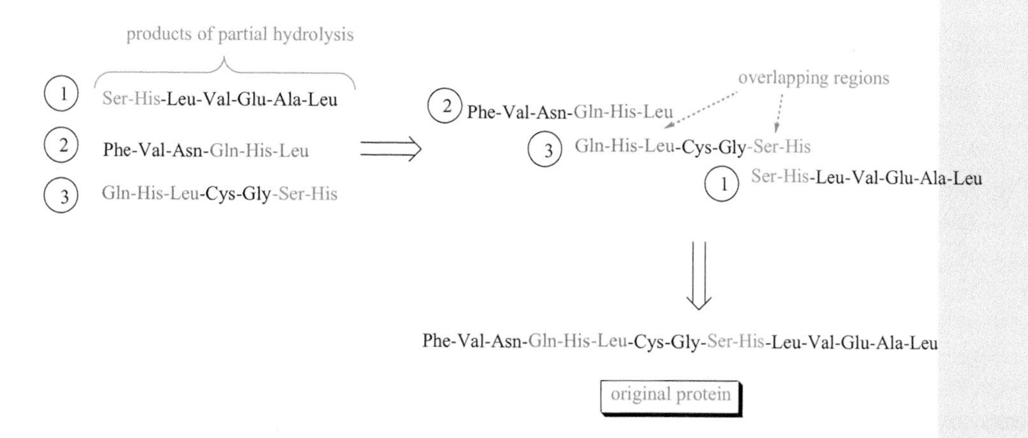

19.15. SYNTHESIS OF PEPTIDES

Once a protein is sequenced, it is often desirable to be able to produce it synthetically. Consider, for example, the story of type 1 diabetes. Historically, people with this condition required routine injections of pig insulin. In 1978, however, human insulin was synthesized, and soon after became less expensive and more readily available than pig insulin.

To synthesize a protein, amino acids must be joined together by amide bonds, produced from the amine group of one amino acid and the carboxylic acid group of another. Under normal conditions, such reactions are slow (see Section 19.2), so to facilitate them, **dicyclohexylcarbodiimide (DCC)** is typically used, as shown in Equation 19-77.

amide is produced

$$RC(=O)OH + H_2N{-}R' \xrightarrow{\text{DCC}} RC(=O){-}NH{-}R' \qquad (19\text{-}77)$$

Comment [JMK39]: Margin note

N=C=N

DCC

The mechanism for this reaction is shown in Equation 19-78. In the first two steps, DCC undergoes a nucleophilic addition reaction with the carboxylic acid group to produce an *O*-acyl isourea derivative, which contains a good leaving group on the carbonyl carbon. Subsequently, the *O*-acyl isourea undergoes a nucleophilic addition-elimination reaction with the amine group, producing the amide and *N,N'*-dicyclohexyl urea.

Mechanism for the reaction in Equation 19-77

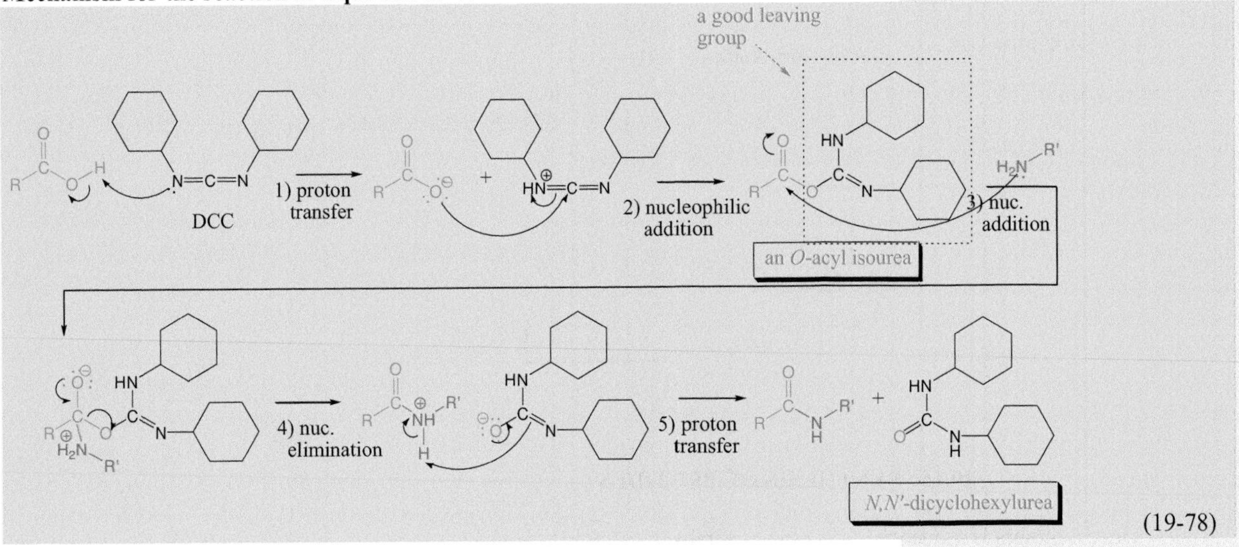

a good leaving group

DCC

1) proton transfer

2) nucleophilic addition

an *O*-acyl isourea

3) nuc. addition

4) nuc. elimination

5) proton transfer

N,N'-dicyclohexylurea

(19-78)

With this understanding, DCC can be used to couple together amino acids. However, because each amino acid has both an amine and a carboxylic acid group, multiple different couplings can take place. For example, if a mixture of glycine and alanine is treated with DCC, four different couplings will take place to produce a mixture of four dipeptides, as shown in Equation 19-79.

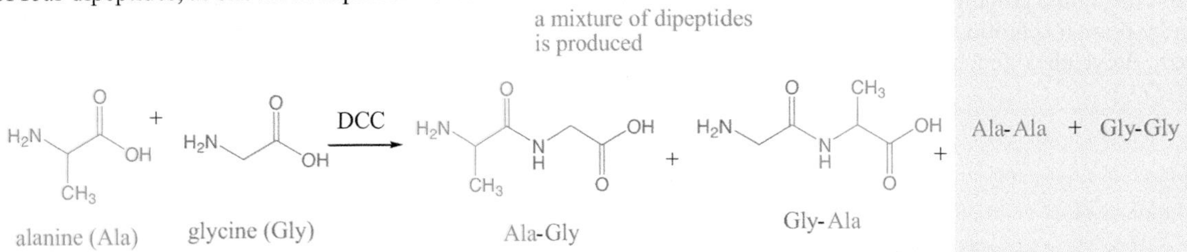

a mixture of dipeptides is produced

alanine (Ala) + glycine (Gly) —DCC→ Ala-Gly + Gly-Ala + Ala-Ala + Gly-Gly

(19-79)

To carry out one of these couplings selectively, the groups that we wish *not* to react must be *protected*. For example, suppose we wish to couple together alanine (Ala) and Glycine (Gly) to produce Ala-Gly (Equation 19-80).

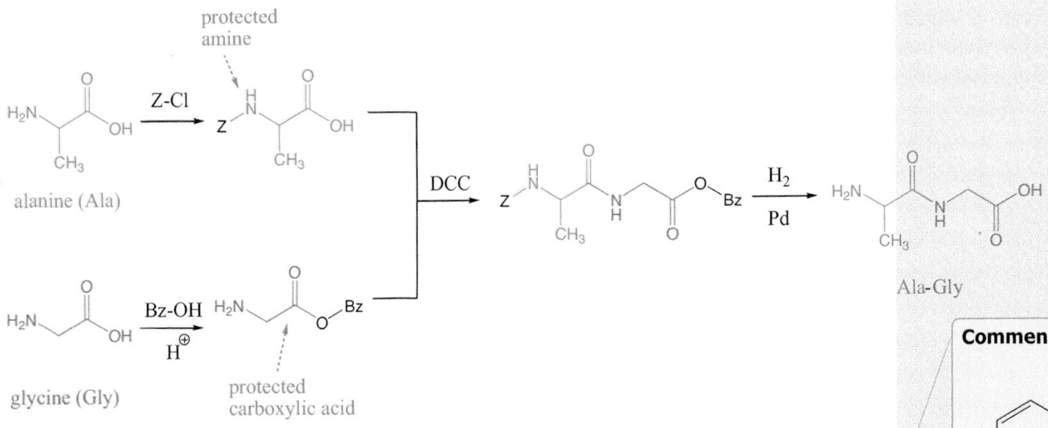

protected amine

alanine (Ala) —Z-Cl→

glycine (Gly) —Bz-OH, $H^{\oplus}$→

protected carboxylic acid

—DCC→ —H_2, Pd→ Ala-Gly

The amine group of Ala and the carboxylic acid group of Gly must be protected. The amine is commonly protected with benzyl chloroformate (Z-Cl)—the reaction is

Comment [JMK40]: Margin note

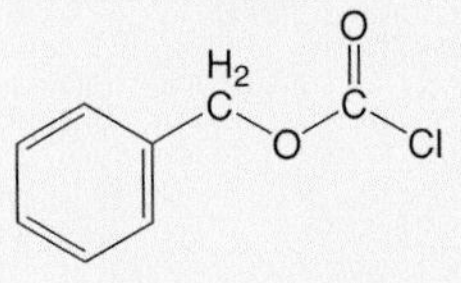

benzyl chloroformate = Z-Cl

essentially an aminolysis (Section 19.3) to produce a carbamate, which has reactivity similar to an amide. The carboxylic acid group is protected as an ester, by treatment with benzyl alcohol under acidic conditions—this is a Fischer esterification (Section 19.6). Once the necessary groups are protected, DCC is used to couple the amino acids together. Conveniently, both protecting groups can be removed in a single step, using catalytic hydrogenation.

These steps can be repeated to attach additional amino acids. However, because the process takes place entirely in solution, the products must be purified after each step. Not only is this tedious, but it also leads to significant loss of product. R. B. Merrifield solved these problems by designing a *solid phase* synthesis, for which he was awarded the 1984 Nobel Prize in chemistry.

The basis of this **Merrifield synthesis**, outlined in Figure 19-4, begins with polymer beads that terminate with benzyl chloride groups. The *C*-terminal amino acid, whose amine is protected with a *t*-butoxycaronyl (BOC) group, is then added to the polymer beads (step 1). An S_N2 reaction ensues, joining the amino acid to the polymer bead via an ester linkage. In step 2, the amine group of the newly joined amino acid is deprotected under acidic conditions, and in step 3, a second BOC-protected amino acid is added in the presence of DCC. A new peptide bond is produced, according to the mechanism in Equation 19-78, resulting in a BOC-protected dipeptide attached to the polymer bead. Steps 2 and 3 are then repeated for each amino acid that is to be added to the protein, working from the *C*-terminus to the *N*-terminus. Once the protected *N*-terminal amino acid has joined, hydrogen bromide is added, which simultaneously releases the protein from the bead and deprotects the *N*-terminal amino acid.

Solid phase synthesis is so simple in its execution that the process has been automated. It is now possible to use a "peptide synthesizer" to make peptides of over 100 amino acid residues. The addition of each residue takes about four hours, which is about 250 times slower than the natural process that makes a protein in a cell. However, the Merrifield synthesis is quite effective at making peptides when it is not possible to do so other ways, such as cloning the protein using recombinant DNA techniques.

Comment [JMK41]: Margin note

$HO-CH_2-C_6H_5$

benzyl alcohol = Bz-OH

Comment [JMK42]: Margin note

$(H_3C)_3C-O-C(=O)-$ = Boc

The Merrifield Synthesis of a Protein

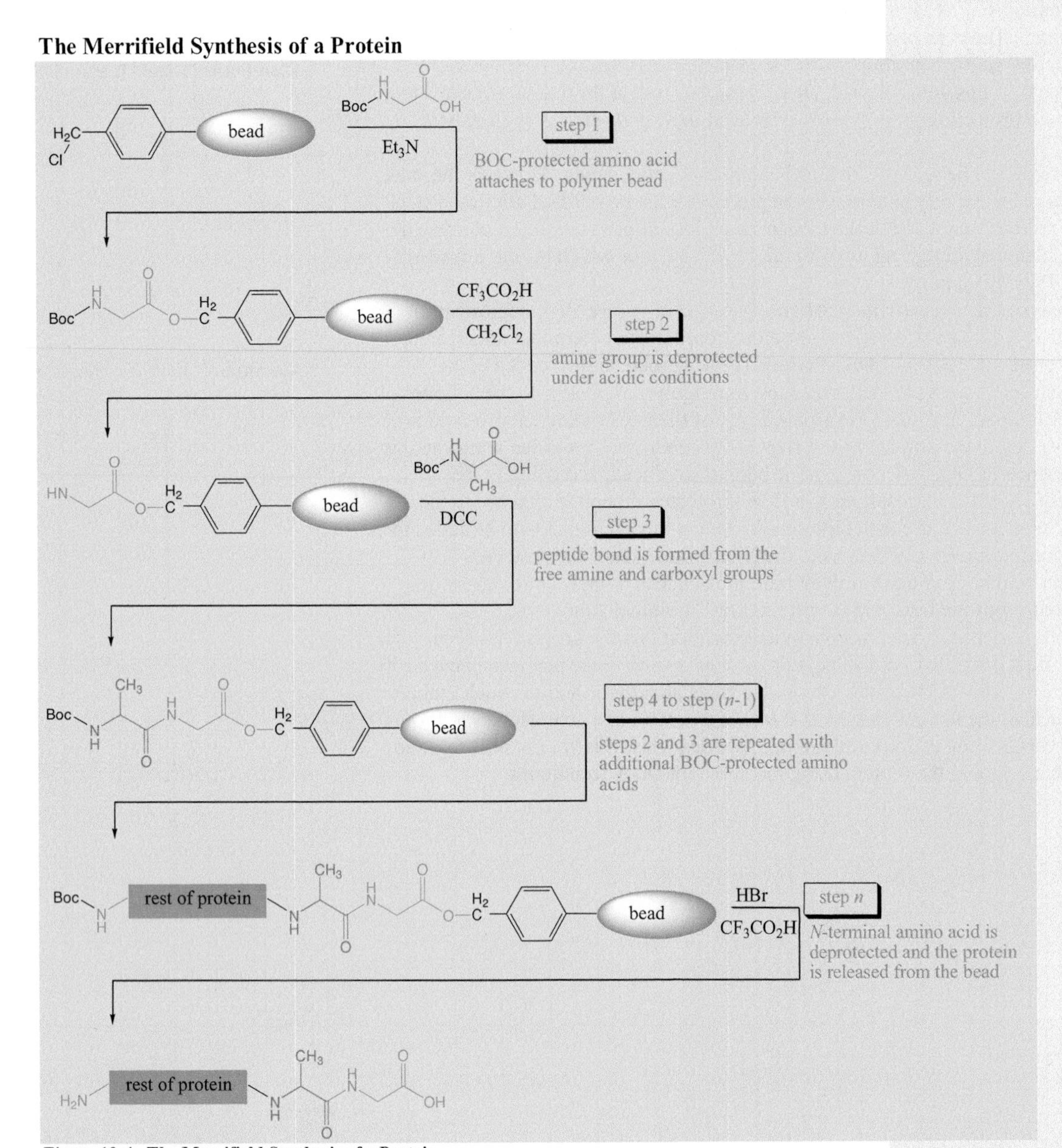

Figure 19-4. The Merrifield Synthesis of a Protein
The solid phase synthesis protocol developed by R. B. Merrifield. Ar represents an aromatic ring which is part of the structure of an insoluble polystyrene bead.

Solid phase synthesis is so simple in its execution that the process has been automated. It is now possible to use a "peptide synthesizer" to make peptides of over 100 amino acid residues. The addition of each residue takes about four hours, which is about 250 times slower than the natural process that makes a protein in a cell. However, the Merrifield synthesis is quite effective at making peptides when it is not possible to clone the protein using recombinant DNA techniques.

REACTION TABLES

Table 19-2. Functional Group Transformations

	Starting Functional Group	Typical Reagents and Reaction Conditions	Functional Group Formed	Key Electron-Rich Species	Key Electron-Poor Species	Type of Mechanism	Discussed in Section(s)
(1)	RC(=O)Cl Acid chloride	H_2O →	RC(=O)OH Carboxylic acid	$H_2\ddot{O}$: δ^-	RC(δ^+)(=O)Cl	Nucleophilic addition-elimination (hydrolysis)	19.1
(2)	RC(=O)Cl Acid chloride	R"OH →	RC(=O)OR" Ester	R"ÖH δ^-	RC(δ^+)(=O)Cl	Nucleophilic addition-elimination (alcoholysis)	19.1
(3)	RC(=O)OC(=O)R Acid anhydride	H_2O →	RC(=O)OH Carboxylic acid	$H_2\ddot{O}$: δ^-	RC(δ^+)(=O)OC(=O)R	Nucleophilic addition-elimination (hydrolysis)	19.2
(4)	RC(=O)OC(=O)R Acid anhydride	R"OH →	RC(=O)OR" Ester	R"ÖH δ^-	RC(δ^+)(=O)OC(=O)R	Nucleophilic addition-elimination (alcoholysis)	19.2
(5)	RC(=O)Cl Acid chloride	R''_2NH → Et_3N or pyridine	RC(=O)NR''_2 Amide	$R''_2\ddot{N}H$ δ^-	RC(δ^+)(=O)Cl	Nucleophilic addition-elimination (aminolysis)	19.3
(6)	RC(=O)OC(=O)R Acid anhydride	R''_2NH → Et_3N or pyridine	RC(=O)NR''_2 Amide	$R''_2\ddot{N}H$ δ^-	RC(δ^+)(=O)OC(=O)R	Nucleophilic addition-elimination (aminolysis)	19.3
(7)	RC(=O)OH Carboxylic acid	$SOCl_2$ →	RC(=O)Cl Acid chloride	$Cl^⊖$	RC(δ^+)(=O)–O⊕(H)–S(=O)Cl	Back-to-back nucleophilic addition-elimimination	19.4
(8)	R–CH_2–C(=O)OH Carboxylic acid	Br_2, P →	R–CH(Br)–C(=O)OH	R–C(H)(δ^-)=C(OH)Br	Br—Br	Hell-Volhard-Zelinsky reaction	19.4a
(9)	R—OH Alcohol	Cl–S(=O)(=O)–R' →	RO–S(=O)(=O)–R' Sulfonate ester	RÖH δ^-	Cl–S(δ^+)(=O)(=O)–R'	Nucleophilic addition-elimination	19.5
(10)	RC(=O)OR' Ester	R"OH → $R''O^⊖$	RC(=O)OR" Ester	$^⊖OR''$	RC(δ^+)(=O)OR'	Base-catalyzed nucleophilic addition-elimination (transesterification)	19.6

(11)	RC(=O)OR′ Ester	R″OH, $H^{\oplus}$ →	RC(=O)OR″ Ester	$R\ddot{O}H$ (δ−)	RC(=$\overset{\oplus}{O}$H)OR′	Acid-catalyzed nucleophilic addition-elimination (transesterification)	19.6
(12)	RC(=O)OR′ Ester	H_2O, $H^{\oplus}$ →	RC(=O)OH Carboxylic acid	$H_2\ddot{O}$ (δ−)	RC(=$\overset{\oplus}{O}$H)OR′	Acid-catalyzed nucleophilic addition-elimination (hydrolysis)	19.6
(13)	RC(=O)OH Carboxylic acid	R″OH, $H^{\oplus}$ →	RC(=O)OR″ Ester	$R\ddot{O}H$ (δ−)	RC(=$\overset{\oplus}{O}$H)OH	Acid-catalyzed nucleophilic addition-elimination (Fischer esterification)	19.6
(14)	RCH_2OH Primary alcohol	H_2CrO_4 (or $KMnO_4$) →	RC(=O)OH Carboxylic acid	$R\ddot{O}H$ (δ−)	HO–C(=$\overset{\oplus}{O}$H)(=O)–OH	Acid-catalyzed nucleophilic addition-elimination (oxidation)	19.7
(15)	RCH_2OH Primary alcohol	PCC →	RC(=O)H Aldehyde	$R\ddot{O}H$ (δ−)	HO–C(=$\overset{\oplus}{O}$H)(=O)–OH	Acid-catalyzed nucleophilic addition-elimination (oxidation)	19.7
(16)	RCH(OH)R′ Secondary alcohol	H_2CrO_4 (or $KMnO_4$) →	RC(=O)R′ Ketone	$R\ddot{O}H$ (δ−)	HO–C(=$\overset{\oplus}{O}$H)(=O)–OH	Acid-catalyzed nucleophilic addition-elimination (oxidation)	19.7
(17)	RC(=O)H Aldehyde	R″C(=O)OOH →	RC(=O)OH Carboxylic acid	R″C(=O)O$\ddot{O}$H (δ−)	RC(=$\overset{\oplus}{O}$H)H	Acid-catalyzed nucleophilic addition-elimination (Baeyer-Villiger oxidation)	19.8

Table 19-3. Reactions that alter the carbon skeleton

	Reactant	Typical Reagent and Reaction Conditions	Product Formed	Key Electron-Rich Species	Key Electron-Poor Species	Type of Reaction	Discussed in Section(s)
(1)	RC(=O)R′ Ketone	R″C(=O)OOH →	RC(=O)OR′ Ester	R″C(=O)O$\ddot{O}$H (δ−)	RC(=$\overset{\oplus}{O}$H)R′	Acid-catalyzed nucleophilic addition-elimination (Baeyer-Villiger oxidation)	19.8

(2)	Ester	1) NaOR" 2) H^+	β-ketoester		δ^+	Base-promoted nucleophilic addition-elimination (Claisen condensation)	19.9
(3)	Acetoacetic ester	1) NaOEt 2) R-Br 3) H_3O^+, heat	Alkyl-substituted acetone		δ^+ R—Br	Acetoacetic ester synthesis	19.10
(4)	Malonic ester	1) NaOEt 2) R-Br 3) H_3O^+, heat	Alkyl-substituted acetic acid		δ^+ R—Br	Malonic ester synthesis	19.10

CHAPTER SUMMARY AND KEY TERMS

- The general mechanism for nucleophilic addition-elimination involving a weak nucleophile (H-Nu) is similar to the one involving a strong nucleophile, but includes a proton transfer step in order to produce an uncharged product. This mechanism describes the **hydrolysis**, **alcoholysis**, and **aminolysis** of both an acid chloride and an acid anhydride. (Sections 19.1 and 19.3)

tetrahedral intermediate

1) nuc. addition → 2) nuc. elimination → 3) proton transfer (base)

- The reactivity of an acid derivative decreases with increasing resonance stabilization of the carbonyl group, and also decreases with decreasing electron-withdrawing effects by the leaving group. Overall, the relative reactivities of acid derivatives decrease in the order:

acid chloride > acid anhydride > ester ≈ carboxylic acid > amide

- **Thionyl chloride** ($SOCl_2$) converts a carboxylic acid to an acid chloride (the acid derivative at the top of the reactivity hill), from which any other acid derivative can be produced. (Section 19.4)
- The **Hell-Volhard-Zelinsky reaction** produces an alpha-bromo carboxylic acid from a carboxylic acid. The key is to convert the carboxylic acid into an acid bromide, which is enolizable, and is thus nucleophilic at the alpha carbon. (Section 19.4a)
- Treatment of an alcohol with a **sulfonyl chloride** produces a **sulfonate ester**. Thus, a poor HO^- leaving group is converted into an excellent **alkylsulfonate** leaving group for nucleophilic substitution and elimination reactions. Examples

include **mesylate** (OMs), **tosylate** (OTs), and **triflate** (OTf) leaving groups. (Section 19.5)

- Carboxylic acids, esters, and amides are relatively stable and thus do not react readily with weak nucleophiles under normal conditions. However, nucleophilic acyl substitution can be base-catalyzed or acid-catalyzed. Base-catalysis involves deprotonating the nucleophile to convert it into a strong nucleophile. Acid-catalysis involves protonating the carbonyl oxygen to activate the carbonyl carbon. (Section 19.6)
- The **Fischer esterification reaction** produces an ester from a carboxylic acid under highly acidic conditions, and is described by the acid-catalyzed acyl substitution mechanism. (Section 19.6)
- Oxidation of a primary alcohol to a carboxylic acid or a secondary alcohol to a ketone proceeds through a **chromate ester** intermediate, which undergoes an elimination reaction to produce a C=O bond. The chromate ester is produced via a mechanism that is essentially identical to the one that describes Fischer esterification. (Section 19.7a)
- Oxidation of a primary alcohol by **pyridinium chlorochromate** (PCC) stops at the aldehyde because the reaction takes place in a nonaqueous medium. (Section 19.7a)
- Oxidation of an alcohol by **potassium permanganate** ($KMnO_4$) produces the same ketone and carboxylic acid products that would be produced by chromic acid. (Section 19.7b)
- The **Baeyer-Villiger oxidation** produces carboxylic acids from aldehydes, and produces esters from ketones. In such reactions, a hydrogen or alkyl group departs from the carbonyl carbon, facilitated by the breaking of the weak O-O bond from a **peroxyacid** (RCO_3H). (Section 19.8)
- In a **Claisen condensation reaction**, an ester with at least two alpha protons is treated with a strong base to produce a **β-ketoester**. In such reactions, the base deprotonates the alpha carbon of one ester to produce an ester enolate anion, which acts as a nucleophile and attacks the carbonyl carbon of a second ester. (Section 19.9a)
- If the base in a Claisen condensation is nucleophilic, it must be identical to the alkoxide leaving group on the ester. If the solvent can be deprotonated to become strongly nucleophilic, it must be the conjugate acid of the base that is used. (Section 19.9b)
- In a **crossed Claisen condensation reaction**, the enolate anion that acts as the nucleophile derives from an ester that is different from the ester it attacks. Synthetically useful crossed Claisen condensations take specific measures to ensure that only one ester enolate anion is present, and only one uncharged ester can be attacked. (Section 19.9c)
- A **Dieckmann condensation** is an intramolecular Claisen condensation, and is favored when a 5- or 6-membered ring can be formed. (Section 19.9d)
- A **β-ketoacid** can undergo **decarboxylation** upon heating under acidic conditions. The result is loss of CO_2, leaving behind a ketone or carboxylic acid. Decarboxylation is employed in the **acetoacetic ester synthesis** to produce an alkyl-substituted ketone, as well as the **malonic ester synthesis** to produce an alkyl-substituted carboxylic acid. (Section 19.10)
- Carboxylic acids are frequently protected as a methyl or benzyl ester. Deprotection takes place upon treatment of either of these esters with hydroxide, in a saponification reaction. Alternatively, deprotection of a benzyl ester can take place by catalytic hydrogenation. (Section 19.11a)
- Amines are frequently protected as amides. Deprotection typically requires acid-catalyzed hydrolysis. (Section 19.11b)

PROBLEMS

24. Show how each of the following compounds can be synthesized from an acid chloride and either water, an alcohol, or an amine. For each reaction, provide the complete, detailed mechanism.

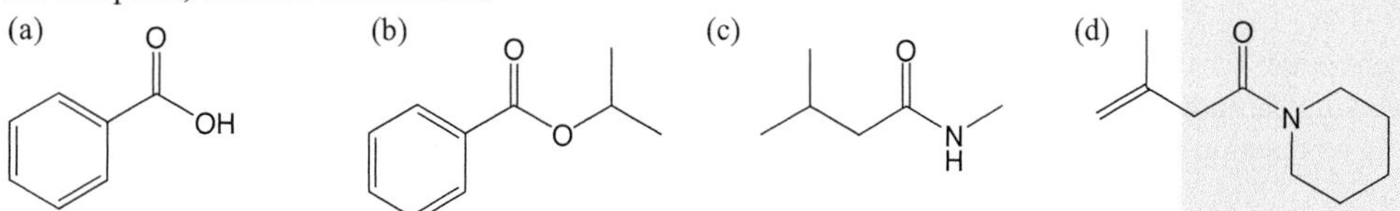

25. For each of the following reactions, draw the complete, detailed mechanism as well as the products.

(a)

(b)

(2 equiv.)

(c)

(d)

26. A *thioester* is the sulfur analog of an ester, as shown below. Do you think a thioester would undergo hydrolysis faster or slower than an ester under normal conditions? Explain your reasoning.

a thioester

27. Predict the product of the following sequence of reactions.

H

1) $NaBH_4$, EtOH

2)

Cl

28. Predict the product for the reaction between *m*-ethylbenzoyl chloride and each of the following compounds. Draw the complete, detailed mechanism for each reaction. If no reaction is expected to occur, write "no reaction."

O

Cl → ?

m-ethylbenzoyl chloride

(a) H_2O (b) CH_3NH_2 (c) (S)-2-butanol (d) diethyl ether

29. Predict the product for the reaction between acetic anhydride and each of the following compounds. If no reaction is expected to occur, write "no reaction." Draw the complete, detailed mechanism for each reaction.
(a) H_2O (b) CH_3NH_2, pyridine (c) (S)-2-butanol
(d) diethyl ether

30. Predict the product for the reaction between methyl cyclohexanoate and each of the following. If no reaction is expected to occur, write "no reaction." For those reactions that do occur, draw the complete, detailed mechanism for each reaction. (Hint: pay attention to the reaction conditions.)
(a) H_2O, $H^{\oplus}$ (b) H_2O, $OH^{\ominus}$ (c) $CH_3CH_2CH_2OH$, $CH_3CH_2CH_2ONa$
(d) 2-propanol, $H^{\oplus}$ (e) 2-propanamine (excess), $H^{\oplus}$ (f) 1-propanol

31. Starting with acetic acid and using any other reagents necessary, propose how you would synthesize each of the following compounds.

(a)
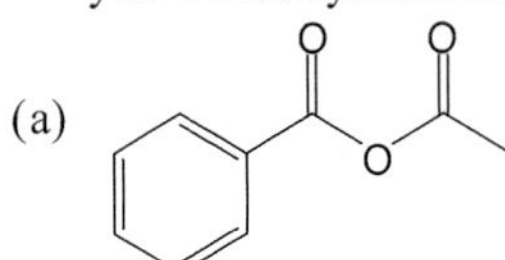

(b)
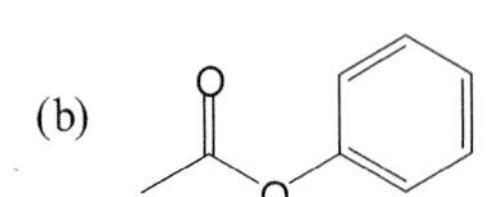

(c)
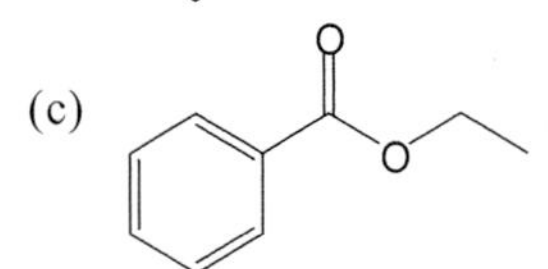

(d)
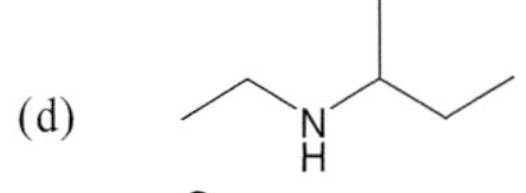

(e)
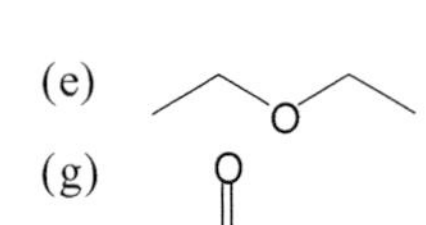

(f)

H

(g)

H_3C CH_3

32. Using acetic acid as your only source of carbon, propose a synthesis of each of the following compounds. You may use any inorganic reagent necessary.

(a) ethyl acetate (b) 2-butanol (c) 3-methyl-3-pentanol
(d) 2-butanone (e) ethanamine (f) *N*-ethylacetamide
(g) *N,N*-diethylacetamide

33. Aspirin (acetylsalicylic acid) is made by treating salicylic acid with acetic anhydride, as shown below. Draw the complete, detailed mechanism for this reaction and draw the product.

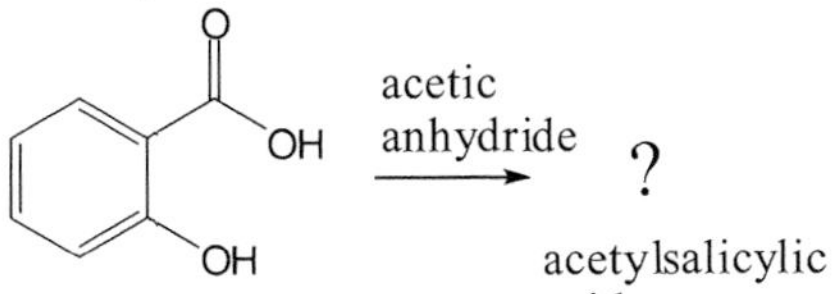

salicylic acid —acetic anhydride→ ? acetylsalicylic acid

34. In each of the following reactants, a carboxylic acid is separated from an alcohol group by 4 carbons. When heated in the presence of acid, only the first compound forms a lactone. Explain why.

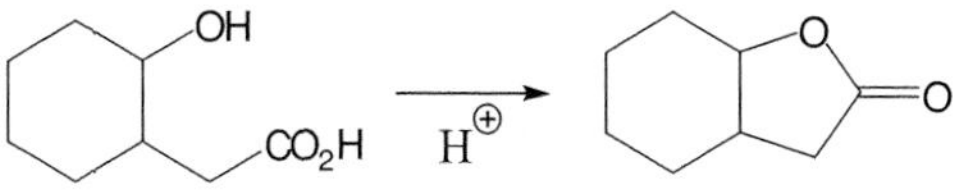

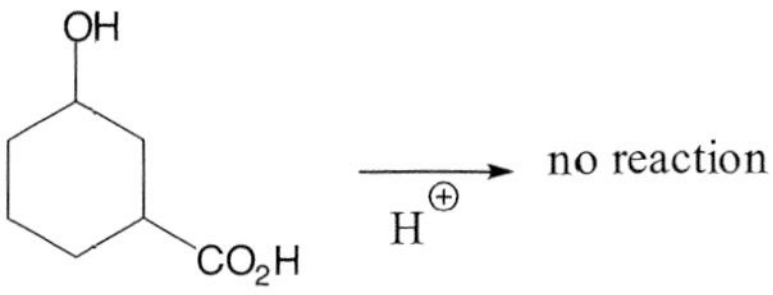

OH, CO_2H —$H^{\oplus}$→ lactone

OH, CO_2H —$H^{\oplus}$→ no reaction

35. In the chapter, we saw that the hydrolysis of an ester can be sped up by both acidic and basic conditions. Aminolysis of an ester can be sped up by acidic conditions, but cannot by basic conditions. Explain why.

36. When phosgene is treated with excess methanol, a product is formed whose proton NMR spectrum shows one peak—a singlet at 3.8 ppm. Provide a complete, detailed mechanism for this reaction.

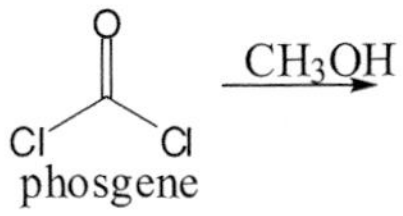

phosgene —CH_3OH→

37. One method for synthesizing lactones (cyclic esters) involves treating a hydroxyacid with 2-pyridinethiol, followed by heating under reflux. The mechanism proceeds through a 2-pyridinethiol ester, as indicated.

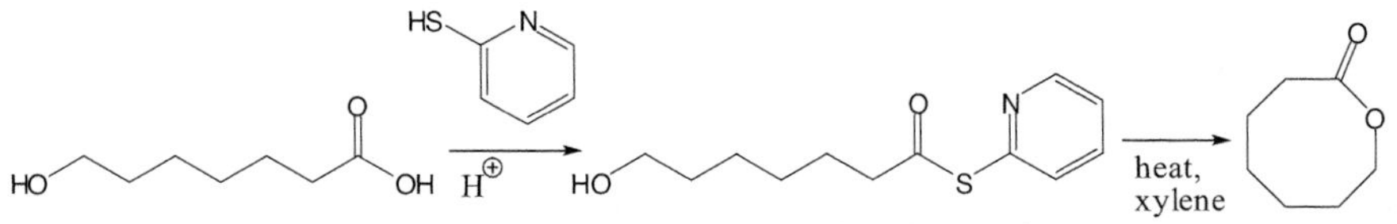

HS N HO OH $H^{\oplus}$ HO S N heat, xylene O O

(a) Provide a complete, detailed mechanism for this reaction.
(b) If benzenethiol (C_6H_5SH) is used instead of 2-pyridinethiol, the conversion is much less effective. This suggests that the nitrogen atom is instrumental in the above mechanism. Explain the nitrogen atom's role.

38. An acid anhydride can be formed under equilibrium conditions by reacting an ester with a carboxylic acid, as shown below. Reasonable yield is achieved if the equilibrium can be shifted using Le Châtelier's principle.

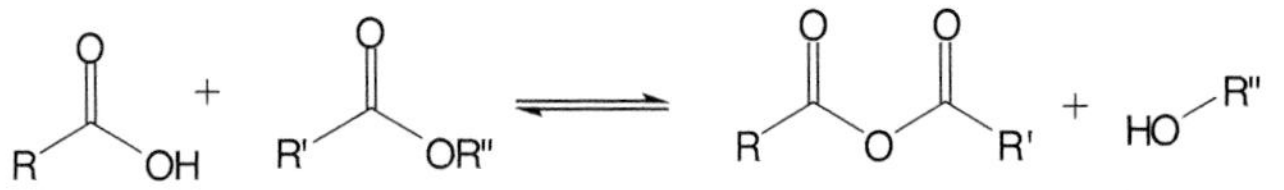

R OH + R' OR" ⇌ R O R' + HO R"

(a) Provide a complete, detailed mechanism for this reaction.
(b) In general, the above equilibrium favors the reactants. However, if the ester that is used is the following, the equilibrium favors the products. Explain why.

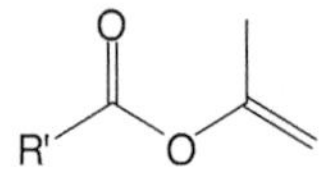

R' O

39. When a methyl ester is hydrolyzed under acidic conditions in oxygen-18 labeled water, the ^{18}O isotope ends up in the alcohol product. When a t-butyl ester is hydrolyzed under the same conditions, the labeled oxygen ends up in the carboxylic acid.

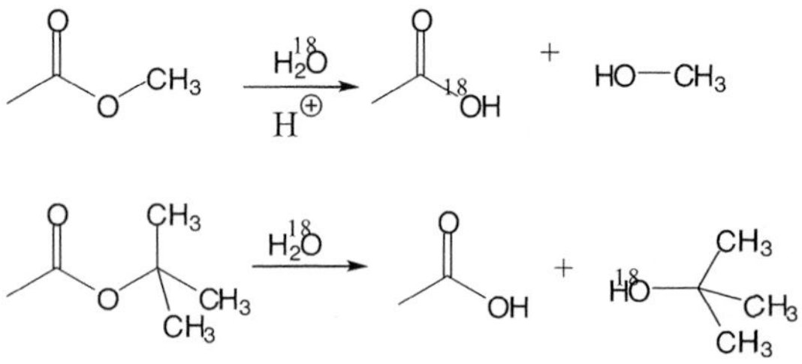

O CH3 $\xrightarrow[H^{\oplus}]{H_2^{18}O}$ ^{18}OH + HO—CH3

O CH3 CH3 CH3 $\xrightarrow{H_2^{18}O}$ OH + $H^{18}O$ CH3 CH3 CH3

(a) Propose mechanisms to account for each of these observations.
(b) Explain why each ester undergoes the respective mechanism.

40. Treatment of a δ-lactone with ammonia yields a hydroxyamide. On the other hand, if a β-lactone is treated with ammonia, a β-amino acid is formed. Provide the detailed mechanism for each of these reactions and explain these observations.

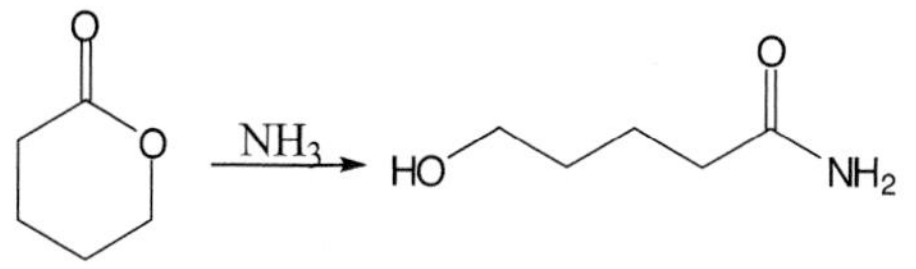

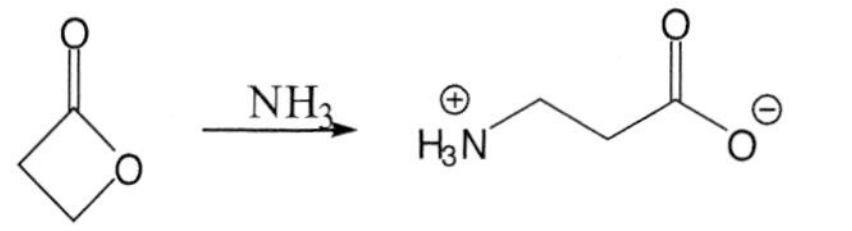

O, O, NH_3, HO, O, NH_2

O, O, NH_3, ⊕, H_3N, O, O, ⊖

41. Propose a mechanism for the following reaction.

O, O, OEt, NH_2OH, $H^{\oplus}$, O, N, O

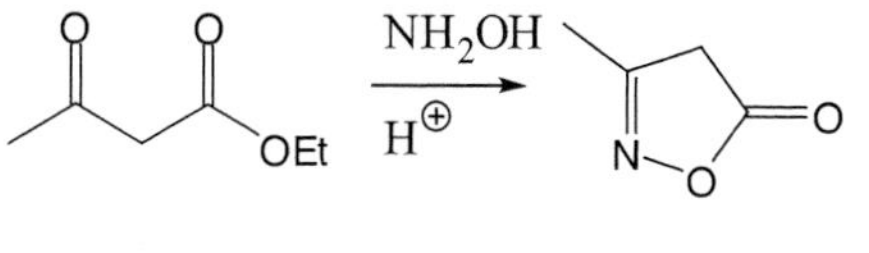

42. Draw the complete, detailed mechanism for each of the following reactions and predict the major product.

(a) O, OMe, O, OMe; $NaOCH_3$ / CH_3OH

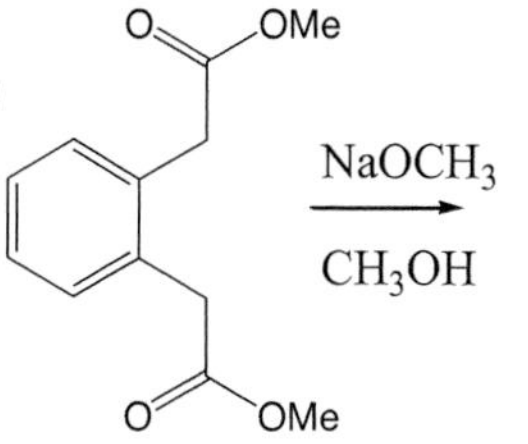

(b) O, O; 1) LDA, 2) ethyl acetate, 3) $H_3O^{\oplus}$

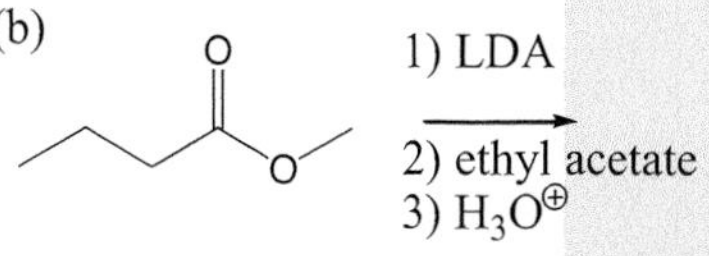

43. Draw the complete, detailed mechanism for each of the following reactions and predict the major product.

(a) ethyl 3-methylbutanoate $\xrightarrow[\text{EtOH}]{\text{NaOEt}}$

(b) ethyl propanoate + ethyl benzoate $\xrightarrow[\text{EtOH}]{\text{NaOEt}}$

(c) ethyl butanoate + diethyl carbonate $\xrightarrow[\text{EtOH}]{\text{NaOEt}}$

44. Draw structures for compounds A through H.

(a) ethyl acetoacetate $\xrightarrow[\text{2) chlorocyclohexane}]{\text{1) NaOEt, EtOH}}$ A $\xrightarrow[\text{2) } H_3O^{\oplus}\text{, heat}]{\text{1) NaOH, } H_2O}$ B

(b) A $\xrightarrow[\text{2) 1-chloropropane}]{\text{1) NaOC(CH}_3)_3,\ (\text{CH}_3)_3\text{COH}}$ C $\xrightarrow[\text{2) H}_3\text{O}^{\oplus}\text{, heat}]{\text{1) NaOH, H}_2\text{O}}$ D

(c) diethyl malonate $\xrightarrow[\text{2) bromophenylmethane}]{\text{1) NaOEt, EtOH}}$ E $\xrightarrow[\text{2) H}_3\text{O}^{\oplus}\text{, heat}]{\text{1) NaOH, H}_2\text{O}}$ F

(d) E $\xrightarrow[\text{2) 1-iodopentane}]{\text{1) NaOC(CH}_3)_3,\ (\text{CH}_3)_3\text{COH}}$ G $\xrightarrow[\text{2) H}_3\text{O}^{\oplus}\text{, heat}]{\text{1) NaOH, H}_2\text{O}}$ H

45. Draw the complete, detailed mechanism for the following reaction.

EtO(C=O)CH$_2$(C=O)OEt + $CH_3C(=O)CH=CH_2$ $\xrightarrow[\text{EtOH}]{\text{NaOEt}}$ (cyclohexane-1,3-dione bearing CO_2Et)

46. A student carries out the following sequence of reactions. The IR and ^{13}C-NMR spectra are shown. Draw structures for A through C.

EtO(C=O)CH$_2$(C=O)OEt $\xrightarrow[\text{2) Br(CH}_2)_6\text{Br}]{\text{1) NaOEt, EtOH}}$ A $\xrightarrow[(\text{CH}_3)_3\text{COH}]{\text{NaOC(CH}_3)_3}$ B $\xrightarrow[\text{2) H}_3\text{O}^{\oplus}\text{, heat}]{\text{1) NaOH, H}_2\text{O}}$ C

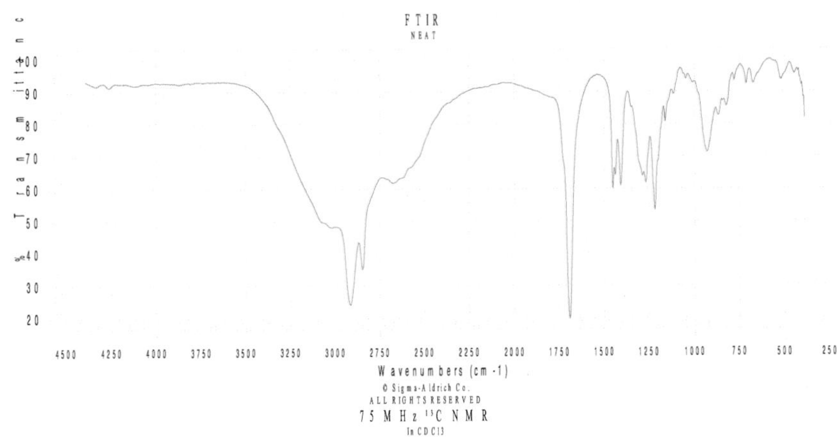

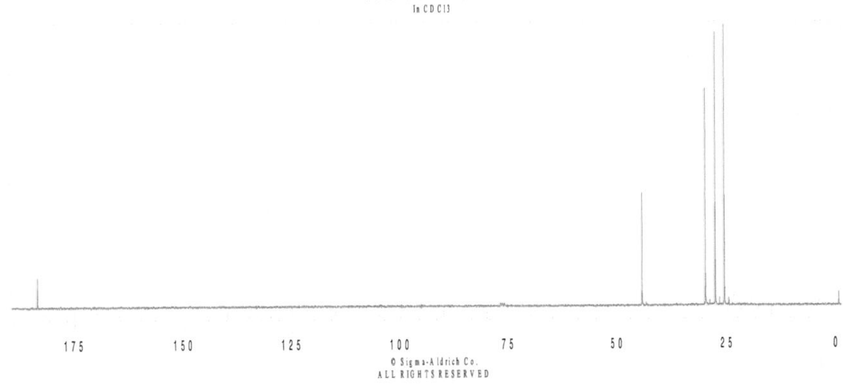

47. A student treated methyl 2-methylpropanoate with sodium methoxide dissolved in methanol. After refluxing the solution for 2 hours, she analyzed the mixture by NMR, IR, and mass spectrometry. Those spectra are shown below. The student was disappointed to find that she did not synthesize any of her intended product. (a) Draw the mechanism of the reaction the student was expecting, and draw the expected product. (b) Explain why the student did not observe any of that product formed.

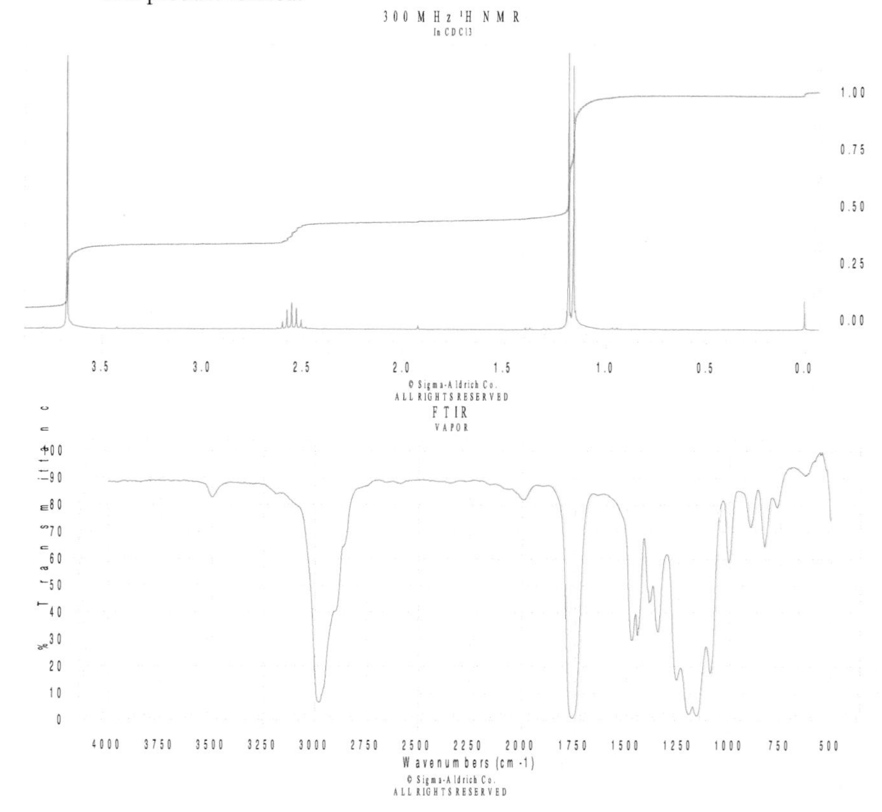

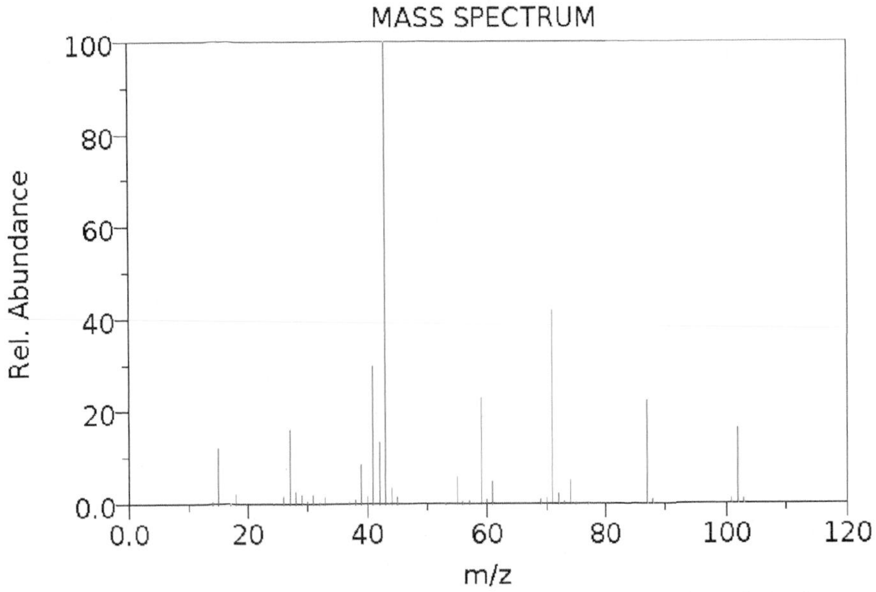

NIST Chemistry WebBook (http://webbook.nist.gov/chemistry)

48. Predict the major product of each of the following reactions. If no reaction is expected, write "no reaction."

(a) 2-methylcyclobutanone $\xrightarrow[H_2SO_4]{CrO_3}$

(b) 3-methylbutanal $\xrightarrow[H_2SO_4]{Na_2Cr_2O_7}$

(c) 5-chloro-1-pentanol $\xrightarrow{\text{pyridinium } NH \bullet CrO_3 \bullet Cl^{\ominus}}$

(d) 5-chloro-1-pentanol $\xrightarrow{H_2CrO_4}$

(e) 1-methylcyclohexanol $\xrightarrow{KMnO_4}$

(f) 2-methylcyclohexanol $\xrightarrow{KMnO_4}$

(g) phenol $\xrightarrow{\text{pyridinium } NH \bullet CrO_3 \bullet Cl^{\ominus}}$

49. Draw the structures of A, B, and C in the following sequence of reactions.

benzophenone $\xrightarrow[2)\ H^{\oplus}]{1)\ LiAlH_4}$ A $\xrightarrow[\text{pyridine}]{TsCl}$ B $\xrightarrow[DMSO]{NaCN}$ C

50. Draw the major product of each of the following sequences of reactions performed on methyl 3-cyclohexylpropanoate.

(a) [methyl 3-cyclohexylpropanoate] $\xrightarrow[\text{heat}]{H_3O^{\oplus}}$ A $\xrightarrow{SOCl_2}$ B $\xrightarrow{NH_3}$ C $\xrightarrow{LiAlH_4}$ D

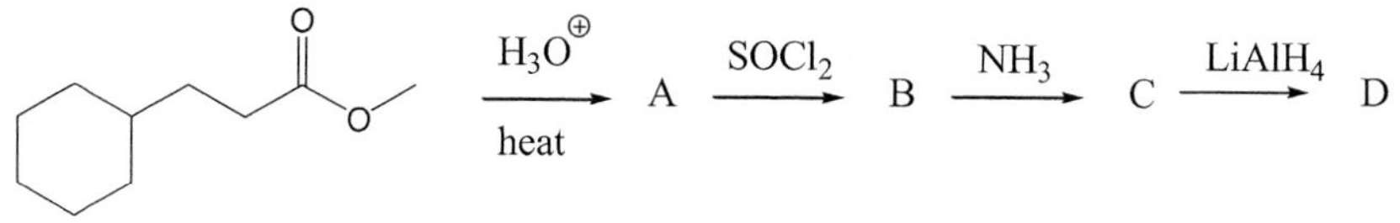

(b) A $\xrightarrow[\text{2) } H_3O^{\oplus}]{\text{1) } PBr_3,\ Br_2}$ G $\xrightarrow{NaCN}$ H $\xrightarrow[\text{heat}]{H_3O^{\oplus}}$ I

(c) [methyl 3-cyclohexylpropanoate] $\xrightarrow[\text{2) } H_3O^{\oplus}]{\text{1) DIBAH, -78 °C}}$ J $\xrightarrow[\text{2) } H^{\oplus}]{\text{1) PhMgBr}}$ K $\xrightarrow{H_2CrO_4}$ L

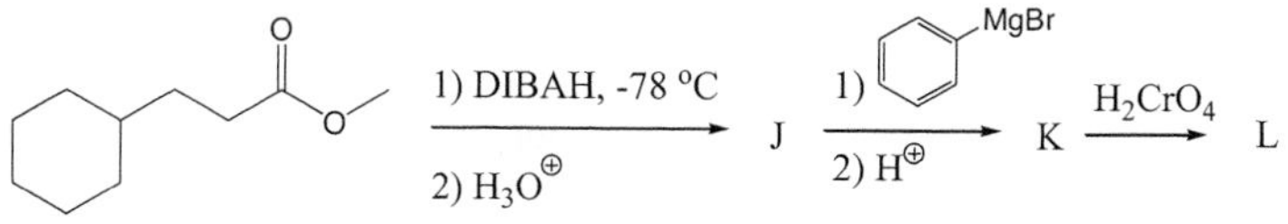

(d) [methyl 3-cyclohexylpropanoate] $\xrightarrow[\text{2) } H^{\oplus}]{\text{1) } LiAlH_4}$ M $\xrightarrow[\text{pyridine}]{TsCl}$ N $\xrightarrow[\text{DMSO}]{CH_3CH_2SH}$ O

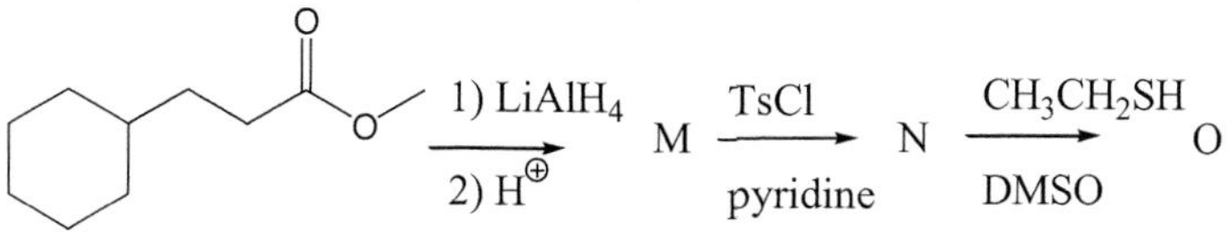

51. Suggest how you carry out each of the following syntheses.

(a) [4-methyl-2-pentanone] ⟶ [5-methyl-3-oxohexanal]

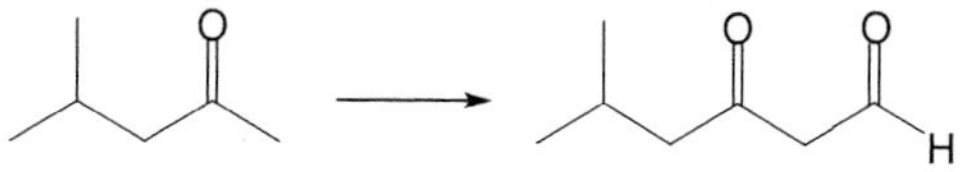

(b) [4-methyl-2-pentanone] ⟶ [product bearing a –CH₂CHO group]

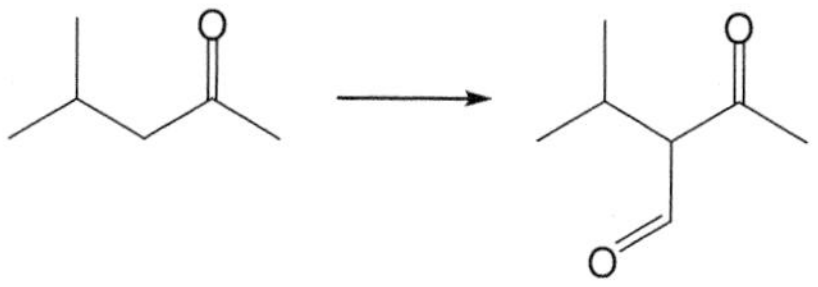

52. Draw the complete, detailed mechanism for the following reaction.

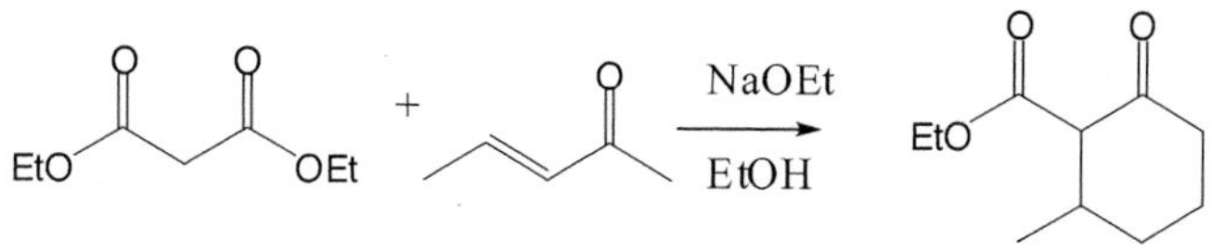

[diethyl malonate] + [3-penten-2-one] $\xrightarrow[\text{EtOH}]{\text{NaOEt}}$ [ethyl 2-methyl-6-oxocyclohexane carboxylate product]

53. Devise a synthesis of methyl-1,3-pentanediol. Your carbon source must only be alcohols containing 3 or fewer carbons, and you may use any inorganic reagents.

54. Show how you would synthesize 3-oxo-2-methylpentanal. Your carbon source must only be alcohols containing 3 or fewer carbons, and you may use any inorganic reagents. (Hint: consider using a protecting group.)

55. Show how you would synthesize 1-pentanoic acid from 1,3-propanedioic acid, using any reagents necessary.

56. Show how you would carry out the following synthesis, using any reagents necessary.

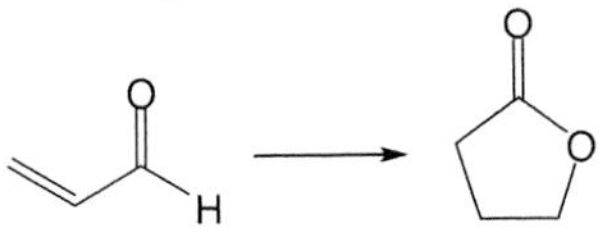

57. Why do you suppose that the following Claisen condensation does not work?

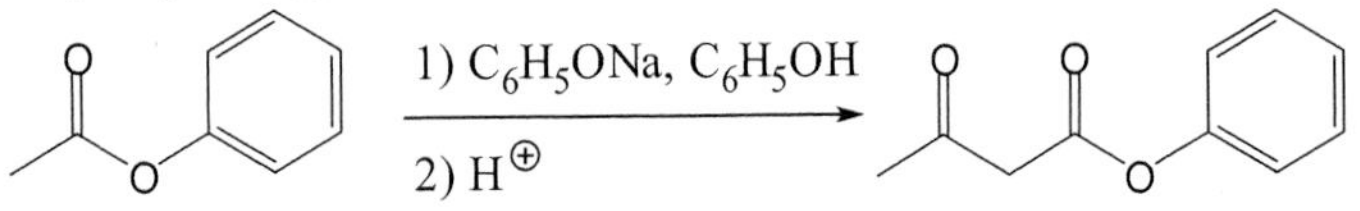

1) C_6H_5ONa, C_6H_5OH

2) $H^{\oplus}$

58. A 1,2-dicarbonyl compound can be synthesized from an aldehyde and an ester, according to the scheme below. Provide the structure for each of the missing intermediates, and draw a complete, detailed mechanism for the conversion of one into the other.

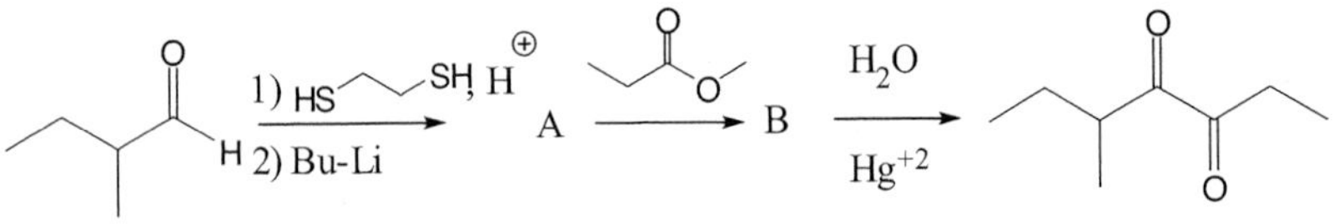

1) HS⁀SH, $H^{\oplus}$ 2) Bu-Li → A → B; H_2O, Hg^{+2}

59. In the McFayden-Stevens reaction, an acyl chloride is converted to an aldehyde. First the acid chloride is reacted with hydrazine, H_2NNH_2, the product of which is reacted with benzenesulfonyl chloride. The result is a 1-acyl-2-benzenesulfonylhydrazide, which, when heated under basic conditions, decomposes into the aldehyde. Provide the detailed mechanism showing the conversion of the acyl chloride into the 1-acyl-2-benzenesulfonylhydrazide.

1) H_2NNH_2 2) $C_6H_5SO_2Cl$; Na_2CO_3, heat

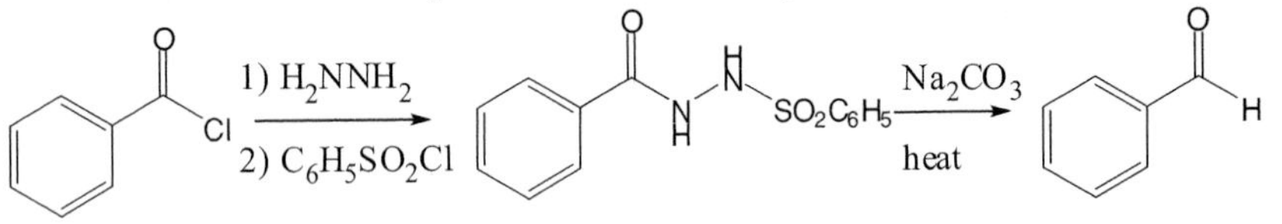

benzoyl chloride   1-benzoyl-2-benzenesulfonylhydrazide

60. An imino chloride can be prepared from an amide according to the reaction below. Propose a mechanism for this reaction.

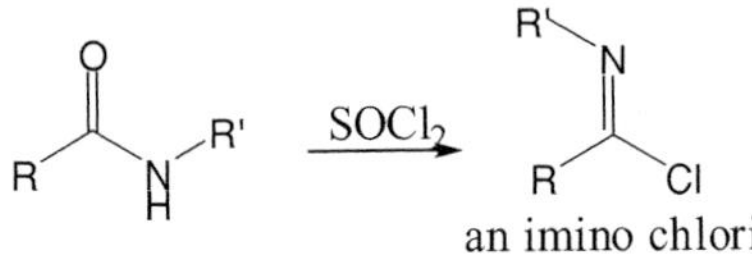

$SOCl_2$

an imino chloride

61. Draw a complete, detailed mechanism for the following reaction.

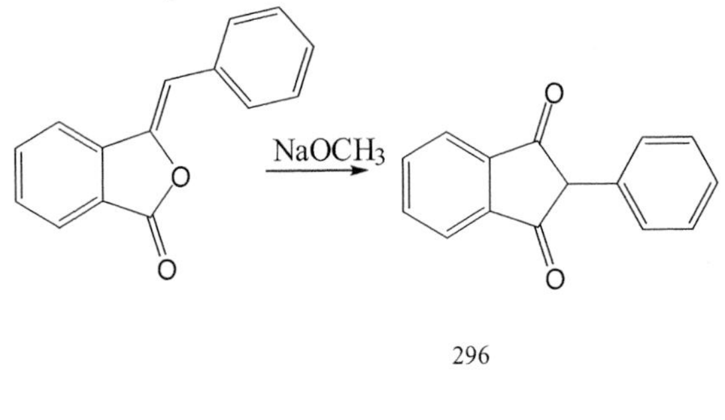

$NaOCH_3$

62. The Gabriel-malonic ester synthesis is used to make α-amino acids, as shown below.

CO_2Et / N—CH / CO_2Et —— 1) NaOEt, EtOH; 2) R-Br ——→ A —— $H_3O^{\oplus}$, heat ——→ H_2N—CH(R)—CO_2H

an α-aminoacid

Draw the complete, detailed mechanism for this reaction and draw the structure of the intermediate A.

63. Diazomethane can be used to bring about a *ring expansion* of a cyclic ketone, as shown below. (a) Propose a mechanism for this reaction. (b) Suggest why this reaction is capable of converting a less stable 6-membered ring to a more stable 7-membered ring.

CH_2N_2, ether ——→ + N_2

64. If a sulfonyl chloride is treated with an amine, a **sulfonamide** is produced, as shown below. This reaction is a key step in the synthesis of **sulfa drugs**, which constitute an important class of antibiotics. Draw a complete, detailed mechanism for this reaction.

R—SO_2—Cl —— H_2N—R' ——→ R—SO_2—NH—R'

a sulfonamide

65. A liquid, which is insoluble in water, reacts in acidic water to form an insoluble solid product. That product is soluble in water under basic conditions. The ^1H-NMR and ^{13}C-NMR spectra of the reactant are shown below. Provide a structure for both the reactant and the product.

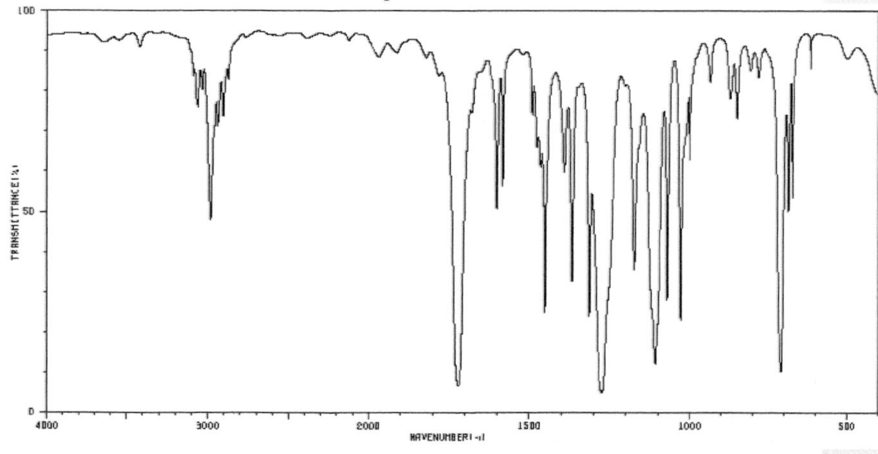

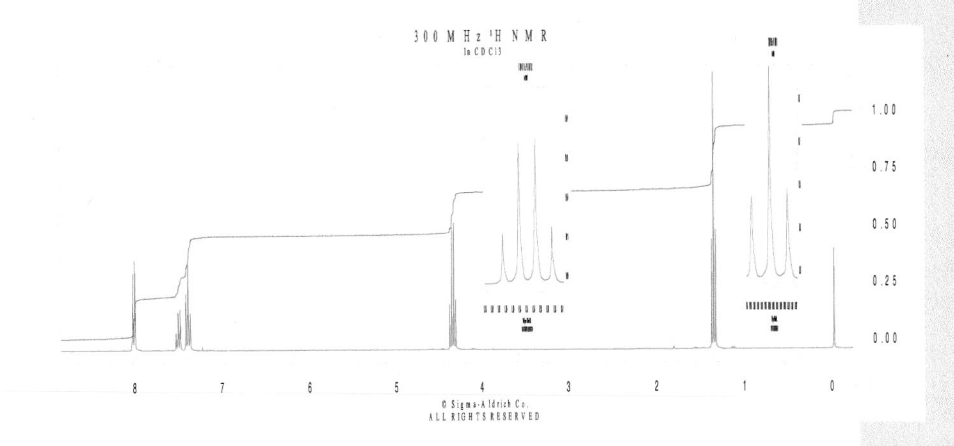

66. A compound is treated with excess acetyl chloride. The product is a compound whose formula is $C_6H_{10}O_4$. The IR and ^{1}H-NMR spectra of the product are shown below. Draw structures for both the product and the reactant.

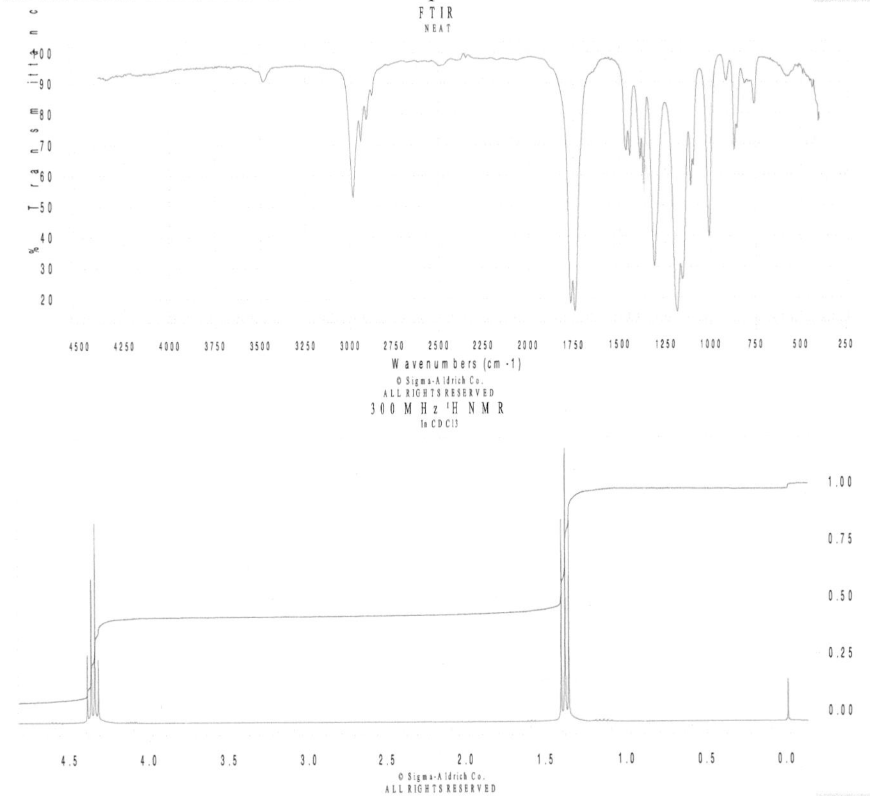

67. The following is an example of the *Favorskii reaction*, which involves an R^- leaving group in a nucleophilic addition-elimination reaction. (a) Draw the complete, detailed mechanism for this reaction and explain why R^- can act as a leaving group. (b) Suggest how you can synthesize an ester from cyclopropanone using this reaction.

$$\text{cyclopropanone} \xrightarrow[H_2O]{NaOH} \text{CH}_3\text{CH}_2\text{COOH}$$

68. During the hydrolysis of proteins, some amino acids like tryptophan do not survive the reaction conditions. Other amino acids like asparagine and glutamine are modified. Referring to the interchapters that show the structures of the twenty common amino acids, write the structures of the two amino acids that are formed when asparagine and glutamine decompose in hot, concentrated HCl.

Chapter 20. Electrophilic Addition to Nonpolar π Bonds. 1: Addition of a Brønsted Acid

Introduction

As we have seen throughout this book, bond formation is frequently driven by the flow of electrons from an electron-rich species to an electron-poor species. In the reactions we have discussed so far, the electron-rich species, acting as a nucleophile or base, typically possesses an atom that not only has a partial or full negative charge, but also has a lone pair of electrons. In such cases, those electrons are the ones used to form the new bond.

This chapter and Chapter 21 will discuss **electrophilic addition reactions**, whose mechanisms contain an *electrophilic addition step* (or a variation of it). Recall from Section 7.6 that in an electrophilic addition step, the electrons used to form a new bond originate from a nonpolar π bond, such as the C=C double bond of an alkene or a C≡C triple bond of an alkyne. These bonds are relatively electron-rich because there are multiple electrons confined to the region between two atoms (Figure 20-1a). Thus, alkenes and alkynes tend to react with **electrophiles**, electron-poor species.

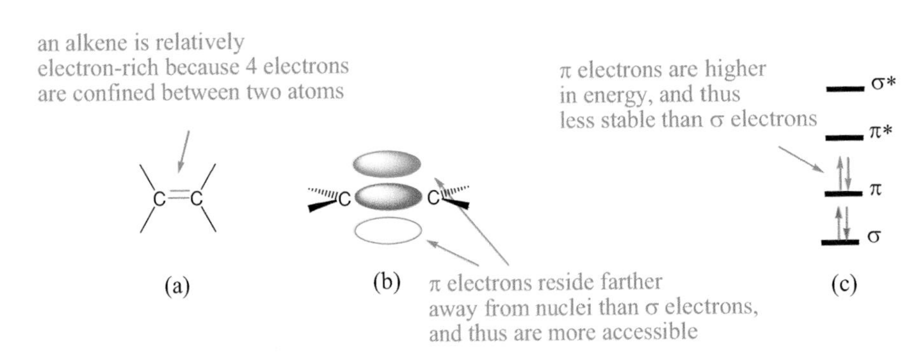
an alkene is relatively electron-rich because 4 electrons are confined between two atoms
C=C
(a)
C
C
(b)
π electrons reside farther away from nuclei than σ electrons, and thus are more accessible
π electrons are higher in energy, and thus less stable than σ electrons
σ*
π*
π
σ
(c)

Figure 20-1. Relative Reactivity of π Electrons
(a) The electrons comprising a nonpolar π bond are relatively electron-rich because there are multiple electrons confined to the region between two atoms. In general, π electrons are more reactive than σ electrons because π electrons are (b) more easily accessible spatially, and (c) higher in energy.

Two other factors contribute to the reactivity of the π electrons of a nonpolar double or triple bond. One is the fact that π electrons are, on average, located farther away from a molecule's nuclei than σ electrons are, as shown in Figure 20-1b. Thus, π electrons are more accessible spatially. The second factor is the relative energy of the π electrons. As indicated by Figure 20-1c, π electrons are higher in energy, and thus less stable than σ electrons.

There are a variety of electrophilic addition reactions we will examine in this chapter and the next. As we will see, the complexity of such reactions can vary greatly. Some are stepwise additions, whose mechanisms consist of two or more steps, while others are concerted, taking place in a single step. Some even result in the formation of rings. Realizing the complexity that electrophilic addition reactions can have, we will begin with the addition of a Brønsted acid (HA) to an alkene, a prototype of electrophilic addition reactions. We will then explore the intricacies of the other electrophilic addition mechanisms.

CHAPTER OBJECTIVES
Upon completion of this chapter you should be able to:

- Draw the general mechanism of the addition of a strong Brønsted to an alkene or alkyne.
- Predict the major products of the addition of a strong Brønsted acid to an alkene or alkyne, including both regiochemistry and stereochemistry.
- Explain the role of an acid catalyst in the addition of a weak Brønsted acid to an alkene or alkyne.
- Predict the major product of hydration of an alkyne, and draw the mechanism for its formation.
- Identify the products of 1,2- and 1,4-addition to a conjugated diene, and draw the mechanisms for their formation.
- Predict the major product of electrophilic addition to a conjugated diene under kinetic control and under thermodynamic control, and explain why they can differ.
- Specify the reason that benzene rings tend not to participate in electrophilic addition reactions.
- Utilize electrophilic addition reactions to protect alcohol groups in synthesis.

20.1. THE GENERAL ELECTROPHILIC ADDITION MECHANISM: ADDITION OF A STRONG BRØNSTED ACID TO AN ALKENE

Equation 20-1 shows a prototypical electrophilic addition reaction, in which cyclohexene reacts with HCl, a strong Brønsted acid, to produce chlorocyclohexane, the **adduct** (i.e., addition product). As we can see, one alkene carbon forms a new bond to H, and the other one forms a new bond to Cl. The HCl molecule is said to add across the C=C double bond. Similarly, in the reaction in Equation 20-2, H_2SO_4 adds across the C=C double bond in 1,2-diphenylethene.

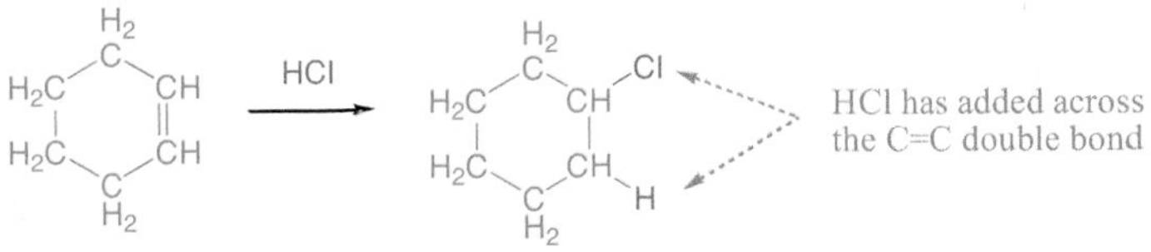

HCl

HCl has added across the C=C double bond

cyclohexene → chlorocyclohexane 95%

(20-1)

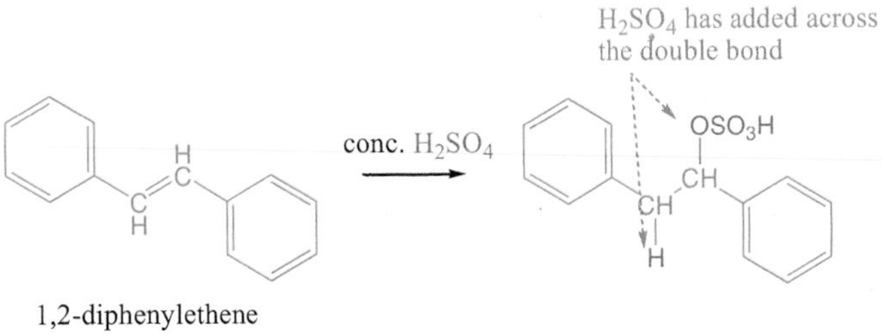

H_2SO_4 has added across the double bond

conc. H_2SO_4

1,2-diphenylethene

(20-2)

Your Turn 20.1. In the space provided, describe what takes place in the reaction below.

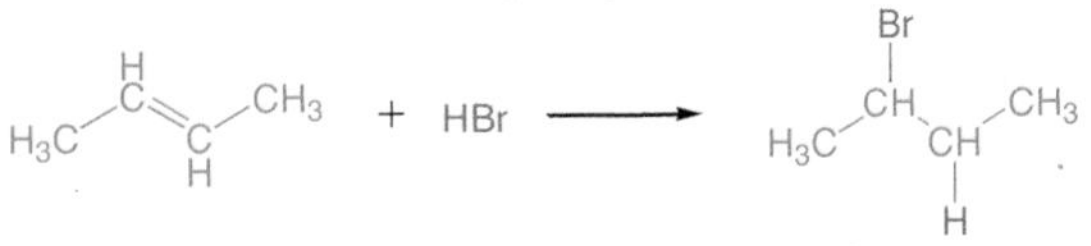

+ HBr →

2-butene → 2-bromobutane

These reactions take place via a two-step mechanism, as illustrated in Equation 20-3 for the addition of HCl.

Mechanism for the Reaction in Equation 20-1

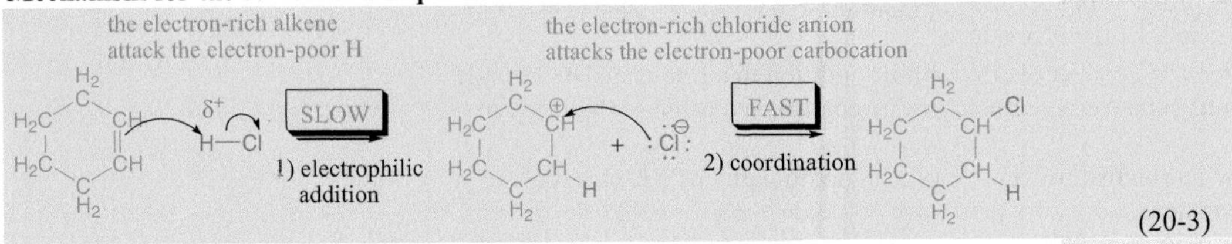
the electron-rich alkene attack the electron-poor H
SLOW
1) electrophilic addition
the electron-rich chloride anion attacks the electron-poor carbocation
FAST
2) coordination

(20-3)

As we can see, step 1 is an electrophilic addition step, in which a pair of electrons from the electron-rich π bond forms a bond to the acid's electron-poor hydrogen atom. This leaves one of the initial alkene carbons with only three bonds, giving it a +1 formal charge. Furthermore, Cl^- is produced as a result of the concurrent breaking of the H–Cl bond. Step 2 is a coordination step, whereby Cl^- forms a bond to the carbocation. This step is identical to the second step of the S_N1 mechanism we saw in Chapter 8.

Your Turn 20.2. The mechanism for the addition of HBr across the double bond in cyclohexene is shown below, but the curved arrows have been omitted. The mechanism is essentially identical to the one in Equation 20-3. Supply the missing curved arrows, and write the name of each elementary step below the appropriate reaction arrow. Also, in each step, label the appropriate electron-rich and electron-poor sites.

H_2C–CH=CH (cyclohexene) + H—Br ⟶ (cyclohexyl cation, $\overset{\oplus}{C}H$) + $:\ddot{Br}:^{\ominus}$ ⟶ (bromocyclohexane, CH–Br)

Problem 20.1. For each of the following reactions, draw the complete, detailed mechanism and predict the major product.

(a) H_3C–CH_2–CH=CH–CH_2–CH_3 $\xrightarrow{HCl}$?

(b) 1,2-dimethylcyclopentene (CH_3, H_2C, C–CH_3, H_2) $\xrightarrow{HI}$?

(c) cyclohexene $\xrightarrow{H_2SO_4}$?

(d) $\xrightarrow{HBr}$?

Problem 20.2. Show how each of the following compounds can be produced from an alkene.

(a)

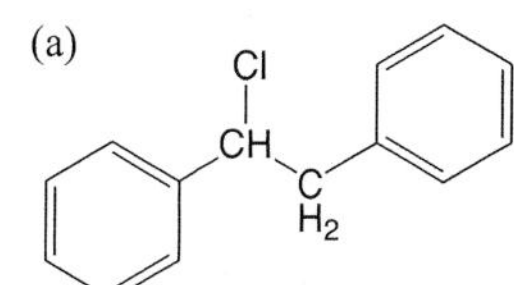

(b)

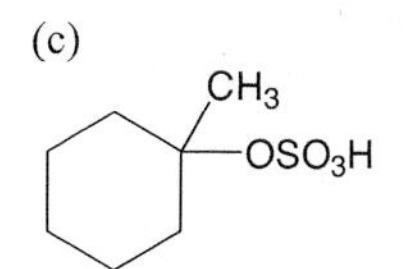

(c) C_6H_{10}(CH_3)–OSO_3H

Notice in Equation 20-3 that step 1 is much slower than step 2. Thus,

> In an electrophilic addition of a Brønsted acid to an alkene, the rate-determining step is step 1, addition of the H^+ electrophile.

The reason stems from the fact that the intermediates are substantially higher in energy than either the reactants or products, as can be seen from the reaction free-energy diagram shown in Figure 20-2. Thus, the first step has a much larger energy barrier than does the second step. The high energy of the intermediates, in turn, is due both to the lack of an octet on carbon, as well as the presence of two charges.

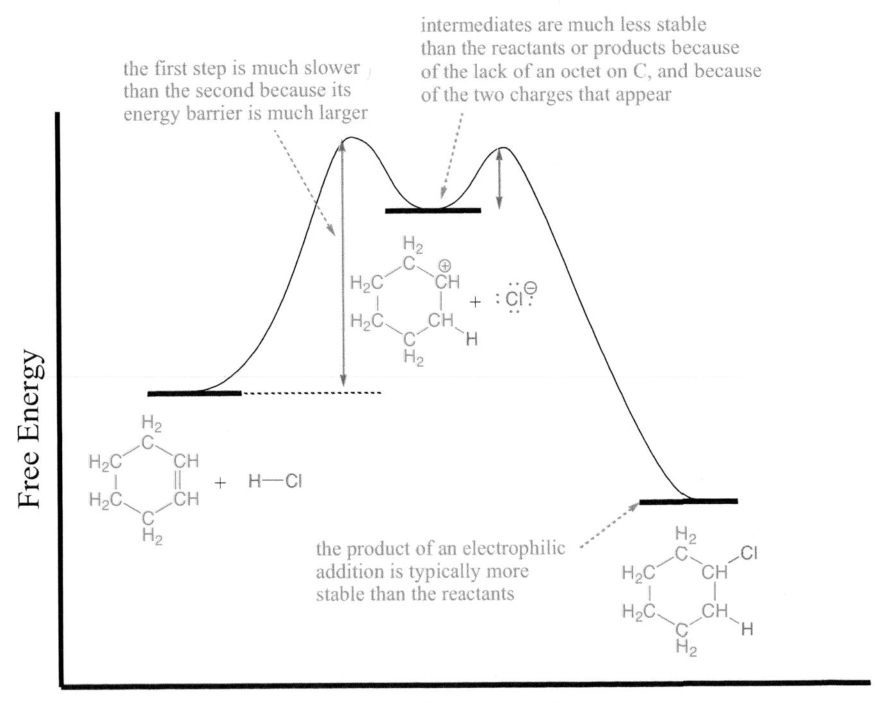

Figure 20-2. Reaction Energy Diagram for the Electrophilic Addition of a Strong Acid to an Alkene
The intermediates are much higher in energy than the reactants or products, due to the lack of an octet on carbon, as well as the presence of two charges. Thus, the first step has a much larger energy barrier, and is thus much slower than the second step. Consequently, the first step is rate-determining.

As indicated in the figure, the product of an electrophilic addition reaction is typically more stable than the reactants. Thus,

> In general, electrophilic addition reactions are energetically quite favorable.

This is explained by the fact that the sum of the bond energies in the product is greater than that in the reactants. As indicated below, a C=C double bond and a single bond to H are replaced by three single bonds. The double bond consists of a σ bond and a π bond, whereas each single bond consists of a σ bond only. Thus, the overall change in bond energy is largely accounted for by the gain of a σ bond at the expense of the loss of a π bond. Because a σ bond is stronger than a π bond (Section 3.6), the total bond energy increases during the course of the reaction.

σ bond + π bond   σ bond   σ bond   σ bond   σ bond

C=C + H—A ⟶ H—C—C—A

because a π bond is weaker than
a σ bond, the total bond energy is greater
in the product than in the reactants

> **Your Turn 20.3.** Verify that the addition of HCl across a C=C double bond is energetically favorable by using the table of bond energies from Chapter 1 to estimate ΔH^0_{rxn}.

$\Delta H^0{}_{rxn} = \left(\underset{C{=}C}{\_\_\_\_\_\_} \text{ kJ/mol} + \underset{H{-}Cl}{\_\_\_\_\_\_} \text{ kJ/mol}\right) - \left(\underset{C{-}C}{\_\_\_\_\_\_} \text{ kJ/mol} + \underset{H{-}C}{\_\_\_\_\_\_} \text{ kJ/mol} + \underset{C{-}Cl}{\_\_\_\_\_\_} \text{ kJ/mol}\right) = \_\_\_\_\_\_ \text{ kJ/mol}$

sum of energies of bonds lost

sum of energies of bonds gained

20.2. REGIOCHEMISTRY: MARKOVNIKOV'S RULE

Notice that in the addition of a Brønsted acid across a double bond, the hydrogen atom can bond to either of two possible carbon atoms. In each of the reactions we have examined thus far, the alkene is *symmetric* (i.e., the groups attached to one of the alkene carbons are identical to the groups attached to the other), so the same adduct is produced regardless of which alkene carbon gains the bond to hydrogen. By contrast, with an *asymmetric* alkene, two constitutional isomers can be produced. For example, as shown in Equation 20-4, propene can react with hydrochloric acid to produce 1-chloropropane and 2-chloropropane.

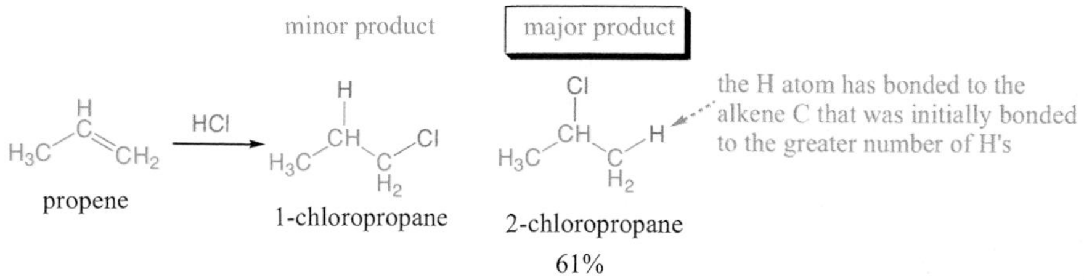

minor product

major product

$H_3C{-}CH{=}CH_2$ → (HCl) $H_3C{-}CH_2{-}CH_2{-}Cl$ + $H_3C{-}CHCl{-}CH_3$

propene

1-chloropropane

2-chloropropane 61%

the H atom has bonded to the alkene C that was initially bonded to the greater number of H's

(20-4)

Notice, however, that 2-chloropropane is the major product. This is consistent with the generalization put forth in 1865 by the Russian chemist Vladimir Markovnikov, which is now known as **Markovnikov's rule**.

Markovnikov's Rule

The addition of a hydrogen halide to an alkene favors the product in which the hydrogen atom adds to the alkene carbon that is initially bonded to the greater number of hydrogen atoms.

Thus, in the addition of HCl to propene shown above, the hydrogen atom forms a bond to the terminal alkene carbon—the terminal alkene carbon is initially bonded to two hydrogen atoms, whereas the central carbon is initially bonded to only one. This type of regioselectivity is called **Markovnikov addition**. In Chapter 21, we will see examples of electrophilic addition with the opposite regioselectivity—so-called **non-Markovnikov addition**.

Although Markovnikov's rule resulted from observations made solely on hydrogen halides, it holds for Brønsted acids in general. For example, as shown in the addition of sulfuric acid across the C=C double bond in dodec-1-ene, H adds primarily to C1 instead of C2. The former is initially bonded to two hydrogens, whereas the latter is initially bonded to just one.

H atom adds to the alkene carbon initially bonded to the greater number of H atoms

minor product

major product

$$H_3C(CH_2)_9CH{=}CH_2 \xrightarrow{H_2SO_4} H_3C(CH_2)_9CH(H)CH_2OSO_3H + H_3C(CH_2)_9CH(OSO_3H)CH_2H \quad (78\%) \qquad (20\text{-}5)$$

Markovnikov's work was carried out without knowing the mechanism. He therefore did not know the reason for the regioselectivity he observed. Understanding the mechanisms for these reactions (Equation 20-3), however, we can now rationalize his observations.

To begin, recall from Section 20.1 that the overall product of an electrophilic addition reaction is significantly more stable than the overall reactants. Thus,

> Electrophilic addition reactions tend to be irreversible and generally take place under *kinetic control.*

Therefore, the major product is the one that is produced the fastest.

Also recall from Section 20.1 that the first step of the mechanism—formation of the carbocation intermediate—is the rate-determining step of the overall reaction. Thus, the adduct that is produced most rapidly derives from the carbocation intermediate that is produced most rapidly.

With this in mind, let's examine Figure 20.3, the free energy diagrams for the formation of 1-chloropropane (red curve) and 2-chloropropane (blue curve) from propene. Notice that the carbocation that is produced by the addition of a proton to the terminal carbon (blue curve) is lower in energy than the one that is produced by the addition of a proton to the central carbon (red curve). This is because the former is a secondary carbocation, whereas the latter is a primary one.

Consequently, according to the Hammond postulate (Section 9.3), production of the secondary carbocation involves a smaller energy barrier than does production of the primary carbocation, so the secondary carbocation is produced faster than the primary one. In other words, the adduct that derives from the secondary carbocation, 2-chloropropane, is produced faster than the one that derives from the primary carbocation, 1-chloropropane, making 2-chloropropane the major product in these kinetically controlled reactions.

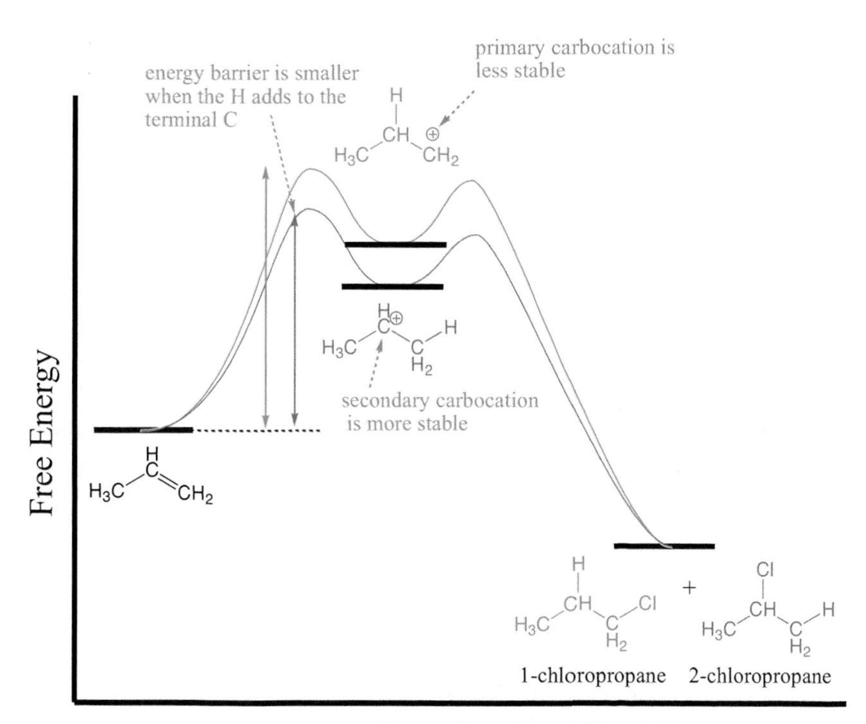

Figure 20-3. Markovnikov's Rule and Relative Energy Barriers in Electrophilic Addition
Electrophilic addition of H-Cl to propene to form 2-bromopropane is represented by the blue curve. Formation of 1-chloropropane via the same reaction is represented by the red curve. The faster rate of the former reaction is consistent with a smaller energy barrier, which, in turn, is consistent with a more stable carbocation intermediate.

Your Turn 20.4. The free-energy diagrams for the reactions that produce the isomeric adducts in Equation 20-5 are shown in the figure below. Complete the diagram by drawing the carbocation intermediates in the appropriate boxes provided.

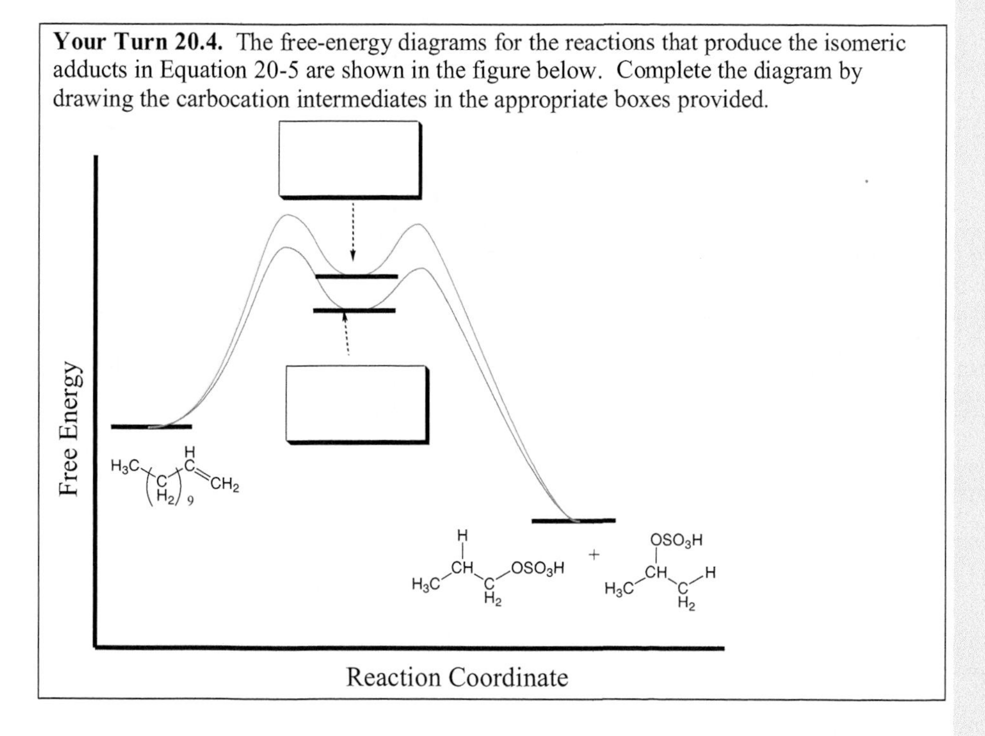

In light of the above analysis, we can rewrite Markovnikov's rule from the perspective of the mechanism:

Mechanistic version of Markovnikov's rule

The major product of an electrophilic addition of a Brønsted acid to an alkene is the one that proceeds through the more stable carbocation intermediate.

Although this form of Markovnikov's rule may at first seem to be redundant to the one presented earlier, it is in fact much more powerful as a predictive tool. This is because the degree of alkyl substitution is not the only factor that affects carbocation stability, and is frequently not the most important factor. This is illustrated in Solved Problem 20.1.

Solved Problem 20.1. Predict the major product of the following reaction.

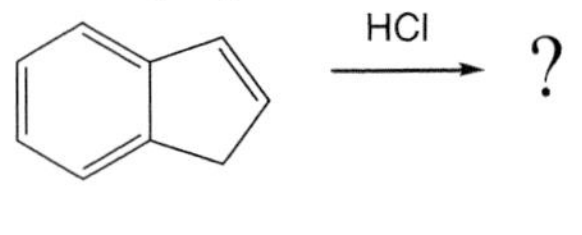

HCl
?

Think. Which C=C double bond will undergo electrophilic addition? What are the *possible* products, and the corresponding carbocation intermediates from which they derive? Which carbocation intermediate is more stable?

Solve. The right-most C=C double bond is the one that will undergo electrophilic addition. The others comprise the benzene ring, and are thus much less reactive. The two possible products of HCl addition differ by which carbon atom gains the H atom and which gains the Cl atom, as shown below.

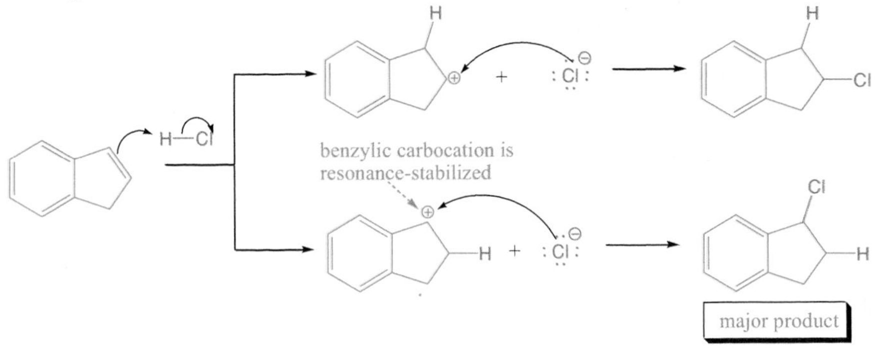

H—Cl
H + :Cl: → Cl
benzylic carbocation is resonance-stabilized
H + :Cl: → Cl H

major product

In this case, both alkene carbons are initially bonded to one hydrogen atom, so the original form of Markovnikov's rule is not applicable. However, we can predict the major product by identifying the more stable carbocation intermediate. As indicated above, the bottom carbocation is benzylic and therefore is resonance-stabilized, giving it significantly greater stability than the one at the top. Thus, the product that derives from it is the major product.

Problem 20.3. Draw the detailed mechanism for the reaction of each of the following with HCl and predict the major product.

(a) (b) (c) O (d) NO_2

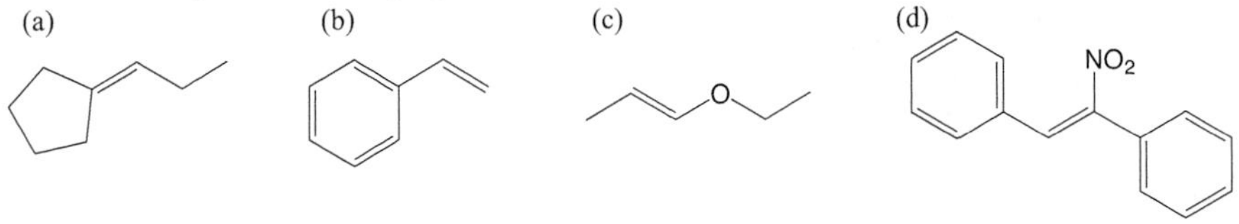

Problem 20.4. Show how each of the following compounds can be synthesized from two different alkenes.

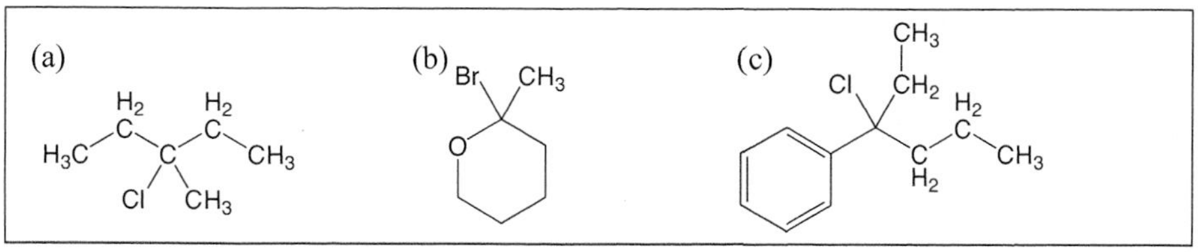

(a) (b) (c)

20.3. CARBOCATION REARRANGEMENTS

When 3-methylbut-2-ene is treated with hydrochloric acid (Equation 20-6), significant amounts of both 2-chloro-3-methylbutane and 2-chloro-2-methylbutane are produced.

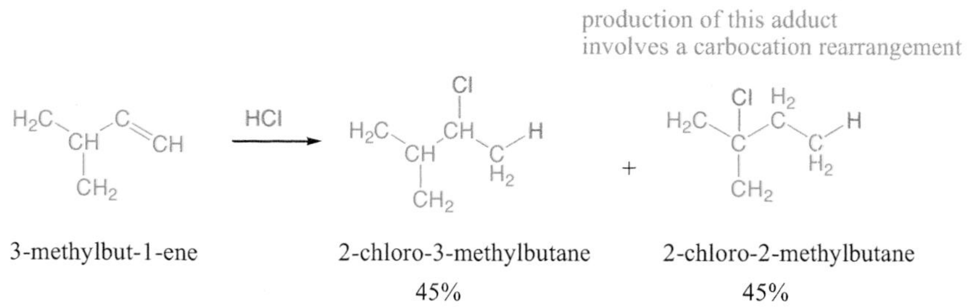

production of this adduct involves a carbocation rearrangement

HCl

3-methylbut-1-ene → 2-chloro-3-methylbutane 45% + 2-chloro-2-methylbutane 45% (20-6)

It should not be surprising that 2-chloro-3-methylbutane is produced, because it is the product of a normal Markovnikov addition of HCl across the C=C double bond. Specifically, H adds to the terminal alkene carbon and Cl adds to the adjacent secondary alkene carbon. By contrast, 2-chloro-2-methylbutane does not appear to be the product of addition of HCl across the double bond, because the carbon atom to which the chlorine atom attaches is not initially part of the double bond.

As with any mechanism that proceeds through a carbocation intermediate,

> Electrophilic addition of a Brønsted acid across a C=C double bond is susceptible to carbocation rearrangements.

Recall from Chapter 8 that carbocation rearrangements are fast! In this case, a 1,2-hydride shift can account for the formation of the 2-chloro-2-methylbutane, as shown in the mechanism in Equation 20-7. Notice that this 1,2-hydride shift transforms a less stable secondary carbocation to a more stable tertiary carbocation prior to the attack of the Cl^- nucleophile.

Mechanism for the Reaction in Equation 20-6

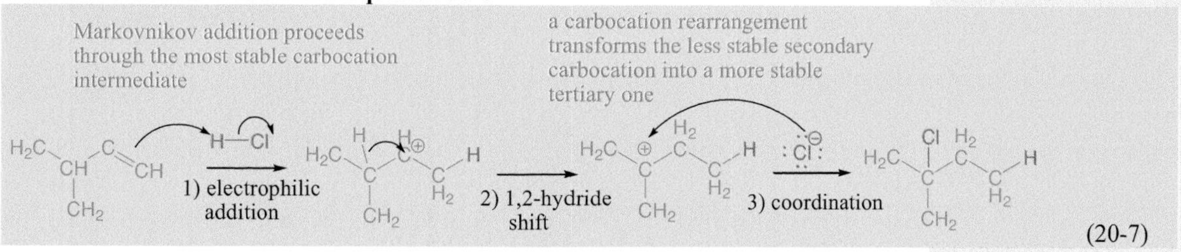

Markovnikov addition proceeds through the most stable carbocation intermediate

a carbocation rearrangement transforms the less stable secondary carbocation into a more stable tertiary one

1) electrophilic addition → 2) 1,2-hydride shift → 3) coordination (20-7)

Be aware that 1,2-methyl shifts also take place quickly, and can therefore appear in the mechanism of an electrophilic addition reaction. An example is illustrated in Solved Problem 20.2.

Solved Problem 20.2. For the reaction below, draw the complete, detailed mechanism and predict the major product.

HBr
?

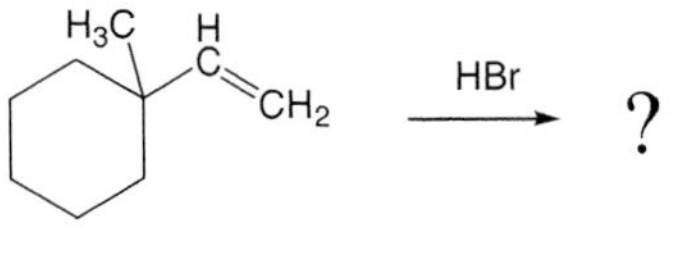

Think. What carbocation intermediate is produced upon addition of H^+? Can that carbocation intermediate undergo a 1,2-hydride shift or a 1,2-methyl shift to attain greater stability?

Solve. In step 1 of this electrophilic addition reaction, H^+ adds to the terminal alkene carbon to produce a secondary carbocation intermediate, as shown below. (Addition of H^+ to the internal alkene carbon would instead produce a less stable primary carbocation intermediate.)

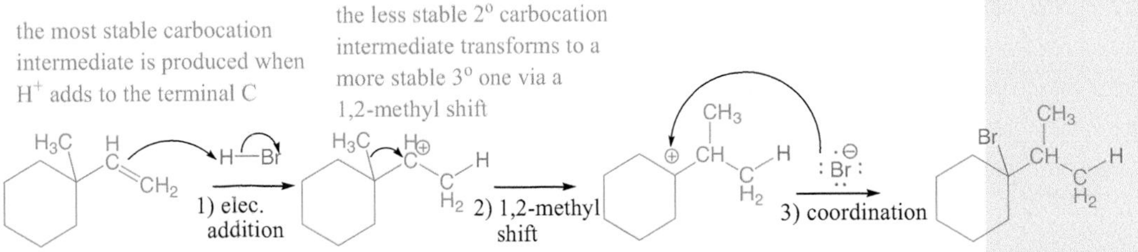

the most stable carbocation intermediate is produced when H^+ adds to the terminal C

the less stable 2° carbocation intermediate transforms to a more stable 3° one via a 1,2-methyl shift

1) elec. addition

2) 1,2-methyl shift

3) coordination

That carbocation intermediate rapidly converts to a more stable tertiary one via a 1,2-methyl shift. After coordination involving Br^- in the third step, the reaction is complete.

Problem 20.5. Draw the complete, detailed mechanism for each of the following reactions and predict the major product.

(a) HI → ?

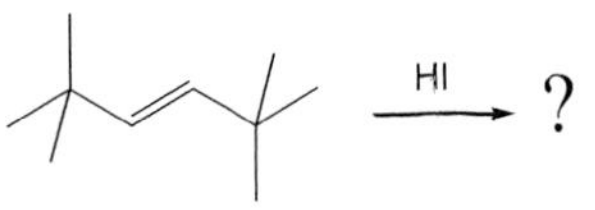

(b) HCl → ?

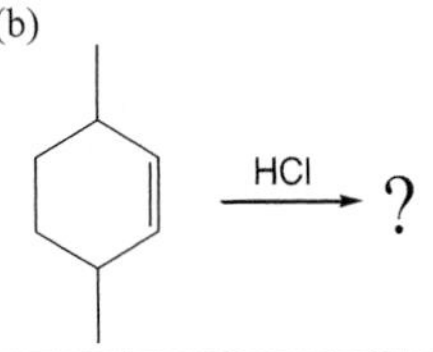

(c) H_2SO_4 → ?

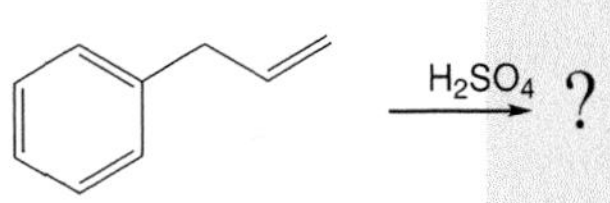

Problem 20.6. Each of the following deuterated bromoalkanes can be produced by treating an alkene with deuterium bromide (DBr). Draw the corresponding alkenes.

(a)

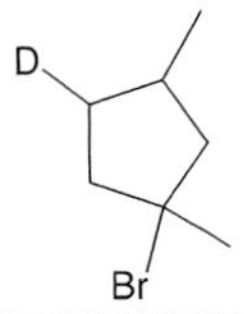

(b)

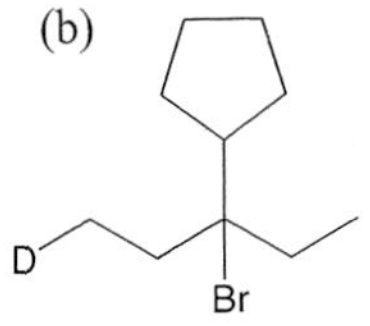

(c)

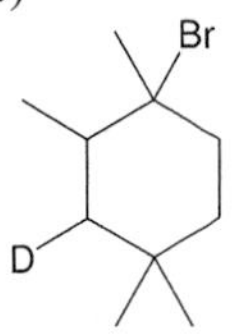

20.4. STEREOCHEMISTRY

In an electrophilic addition reaction involving an alkene, both alkene carbons, which are initially planar, become tetrahedral in the product. Thus, it is possible for new stereocenters to be produced during the course of the reaction. Depending upon the symmetry of the product, stereochemistry may or may not be of concern.

In the reaction we saw previously in Equation 20-1 (shown again in Equation 20-8), such stereochemistry is *not* a concern. As we can see, neither alkene carbon becomes a stereocenter, and the product is achiral; in the product, none of the carbon atoms is bonded to four *different* groups.

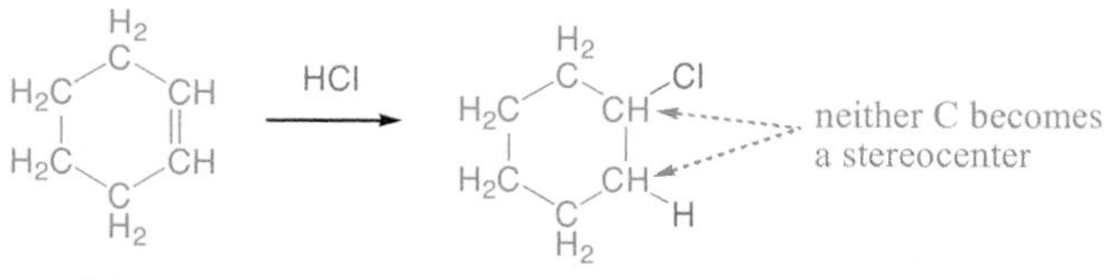

HCl

neither C becomes a stereocenter

cyclohexene chlorocyclohexane

(20-8)

By contrast, in the reaction we saw previously in Equation 20-2 (shown again in Equation 20-9), a single stereocenter is formed, and the product is indeed chiral. Because the starting material and the conditions under which the reaction takes place are achiral, a racemic mixture of enantiomers must be produced.

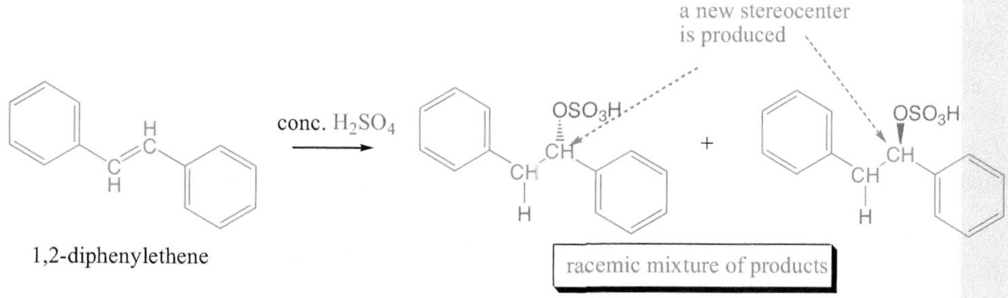

a new stereocenter is produced

conc. H_2SO_4

1,2-diphenylethene

racemic mixture of products

(20-9)

Your Turn 20.5. In the electrophilic addition reaction we saw previously in Equation 20-5, the major product has gained a stereocenter. Mark that stereocenter with an asterisk (*).

Similarly, when D-Br (whose reactivity is nearly identical to that of HBr) reacts with an achiral alkene such as cyclohexene (Equation 20-10), the product molecules are chiral. Unlike the ones in Equation 20-9, however, these product molecules contain two stereocenters, so there are $2^n = 2^2 = 4$ stereoisomers that exist. Which of these stereoisomers are produced, and what are their relative abundances?

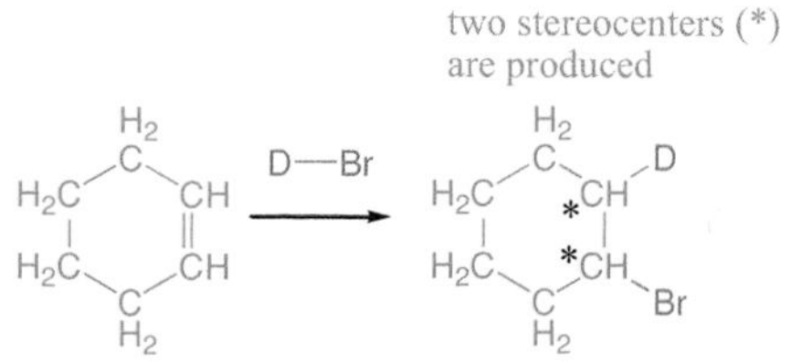

two stereocenters (*) are produced

D—Br

(20-10)

To answer these questions, we turn to the mechanism. The addition of DBr takes place in two steps, as shown in Equation 20-11, similar to the general mechanism in

Equation 20-3. In the first step, D^+ (just like H^+) forms a bond to an alkene carbon, producing a carbocation intermediate. In the second step, Br^- forms a bond to the positively charged carbon atom.

Mechanism for the Reaction in Equation 20-10

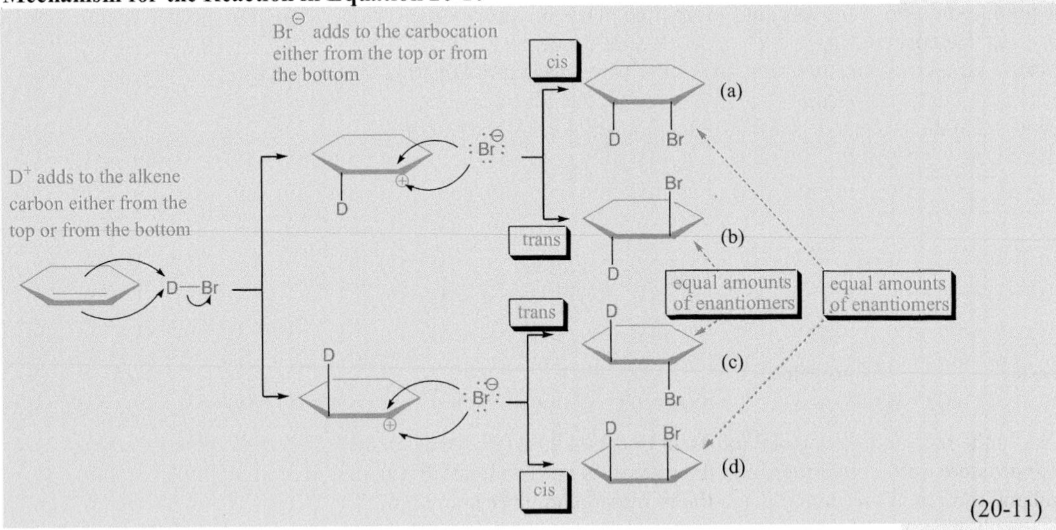

(20-11)

Notice that in the first step, D^+ can form a bond to the alkene carbon from either side of the carbon's plane, producing one of two enantiomeric carbocations. In the second step, Br^- can attack the positively charged carbon atom from either side of the plane—either *syn* to (i.e., on the same side as) or *anti* to (i.e., on the opposite side from) the D. This gives rise to two *cis* and two *trans* isomers. Therefore, the reaction produces a mixture of all four of the aforementioned stereoisomers.

To address the question of the relative abundance of these stereoisomers, realize that the two *cis* isomers are enantiomers, and, likewise, the two *trans* isomers are enantiomers. Because the starting material and the environment are achiral, each of these enantiomeric pairs is produced as a racemic mixture. By contrast, *cis* and *trans* isomers are diastereomers, so they must be produced in unequal amounts.

Problem 20.7. Draw the complete mechanism for the formation of all products formed in the following reaction. Which products, if any, will be formed in equal amounts?

$H_3C(D)C{=}C(D)CH_3 \xrightarrow{HCl} ?$

20.5. ADDITION OF A WEAK ACID: ACID CATALYSIS

Thus far we have examined the addition of only strong acids to alkenes. What about weak acids?

As indicated in Equation 20-12, if an alkene is treated with water—a weak acid—under neutral conditions, effectively no reaction occurs.

$H_3C-CH_2-CH=CH_2 \xrightarrow{H_2O}$ no reaction

(20-12)

This is because with water as the acid, the first step of the general electrophilic addition mechanism (Equation 20-3) is too unfavorable to take place at a reasonable rate. Not only does the first step produce a carbocation, but it also produces HO^-, a relatively unstable anion. (See Your Turn 20.6.)

Your Turn 20.6. In the space provided here, draw the hypothetical two-step mechanism mentioned above, in which water adds across the double bond in Equation 20-12 according to the mechanism in Equation 20-3. Circle and label the unstable HO^- intermediate.

By contrast, as Equation 20-13 shows,

The addition of water to an alkene takes place readily in the presence of a strong acid, such as sulfuric acid, producing an alcohol.

This is an example of an **acid-catalyzed hydration reaction**.

acid-catalyzed hydration

$H_3C-CH_2-CH=CH_2 \xrightarrow[H_2SO_4]{H_2O} H_3C-CH_2-CH(OH)-CH_2-H$

but-1-ene → butan-2-ol, 90%

water has added across the C=C double bond

(20-13)

The mechanism for the hydration reaction is shown in Equation 20-14. Due to the leveling effect, H_3O^+ is the strongest acid that can exist in significant amounts in water. Being a strong Brønsted acid, H_3O^+ can protonate the alkene to produce a carbocation intermediate, as illustrated in step 1. Notice that this step adheres to Markovnikov's rule—the proton adds to the terminal carbon so as to give the most stable carbocation intermediate. In step 2, that carbocation intermediate is attacked by a weak H_2O nucleophile. A final deprotonation in step 3 removes the positive charge from the adduct, yielding a stable, uncharged product.

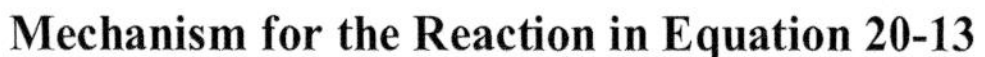

Mechanism for the Reaction in Equation 20-13

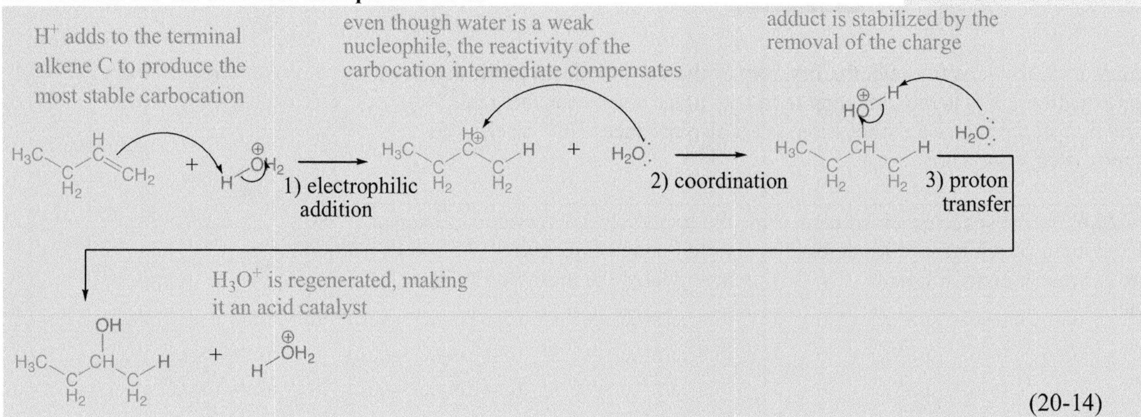

(20-14)

Water is not the only weak nucleophile that can add across a C=C double bond. As illustrated in Solved Problem 20.3, an alcohol can also undergo such a reaction in what is called an **acid-catalyzed alkoxylation reaction**.

Solved Problem 20.3. Draw the complete, detailed mechanism for the following reaction and predict the products.

$$\xrightarrow[H_2SO_4]{CH_3OH} \ ?$$

Think. What is the electrophile with which the alkene can react? To which alkene carbon does that electrophile add? What can behave as the nucleophile?

Solve. The strongest acid that can exist in methanol is $CH_3OH_2^+$, which can react with the alkene in an electrophilic addition step. Formally, H^+ from this acid adds to the terminal carbon, producing a secondary, resonance-stabilized carbocation intermediate. (This is consistent with Markovnikov's rule.) In a second step, CH_3OH can behave as a nucleophile, forming a bond to the positively charged carbon. In a third step, methanol acts as a base to remove a proton from the adduct, yielding an uncharged product. Overall, this is the same mechanism as in 20-14. Unlike Equation 20-14, the product here is an *ether*.

Problem 20.8. Draw the complete, detailed mechanism for each of the following reactions and predict the products.

(a) cyclohexene $\xrightarrow[\text{HCl}]{H_2O}$?

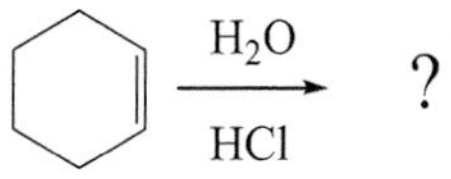

(b) stilbene $\xrightarrow[\text{HCl}]{H_2O}$?

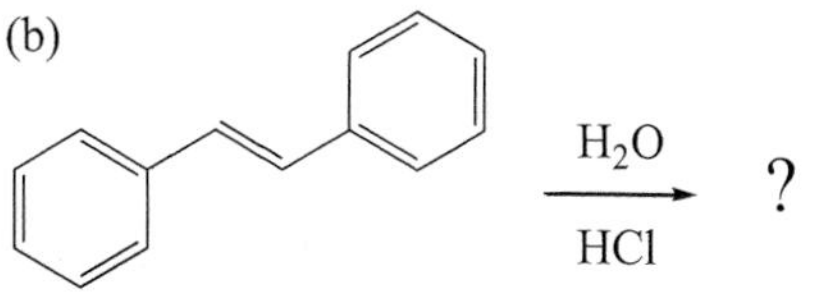

(c) $\xrightarrow[H_2SO_4]{CH_3CH_2OH}$?

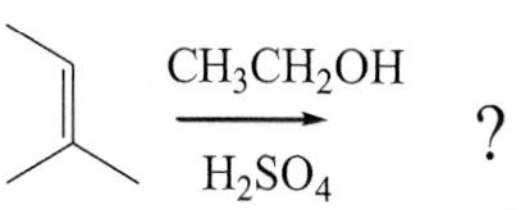

(d) $\xrightarrow[H_2SO_4]{\text{acetic acid (OH)}}$?

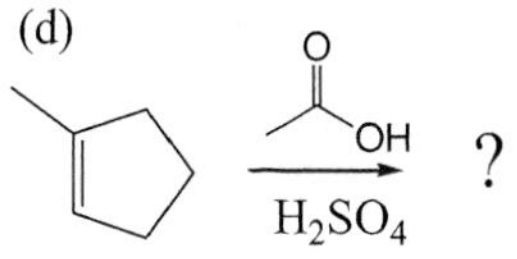

Problem 20.9. Show how to synthesize each of the following compounds from an alkene.

(a) OH

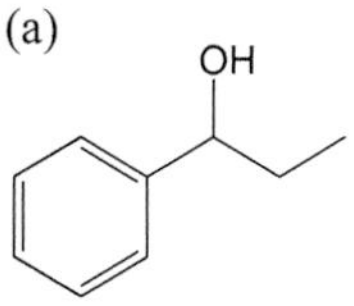

(b) OCH_3

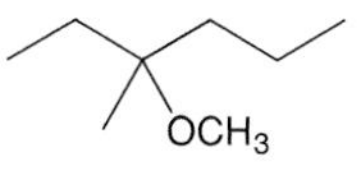

(c) OH

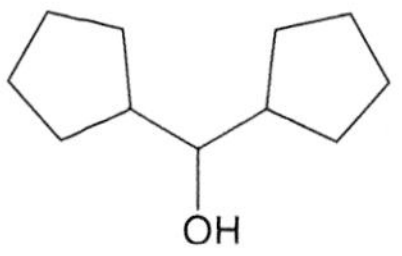

20.6. ELECTROPHILIC ADDITION OF A STRONG BRØNSTED ACID TO AN ALKYNE

Like the C=C double bond of an alkene, the C≡C triple bond of an alkyne is relatively electron-rich—the six electrons of the C≡C triple bond reside largely in the region between the two carbon atoms, and the π electrons are relatively easily accessible. Therefore, we should expect alkynes to undergo electrophilic addition with strong Brønsted acids in much the same way as alkenes do. Namely, we should expect a hydrogen halide to add across the triple bond, which would produce a vinylic halide.

Indeed, as shown in Equation 20-15, when an alkyne such as 1-hexyne is treated with HBr, some vinylic bromide is produced, resulting from a single addition of HBr across the triple bond.

a single addition of HBr across the triple bond produces a vinylic bromide

$H_3C-CH_2-CH_2-CH_2-C\equiv CH \xrightarrow[15\ ^\circ C,\ 6\ h]{HBr} H_3C-CH_2-CH_2-CH_2-C(Br)=CH_2$

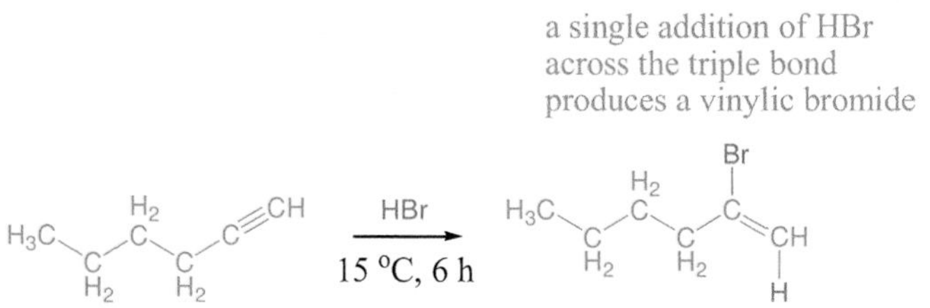

1-hyexyne — 2-bromo-1-hexene < 8% (20-15)

The mechanism for this reaction is shown in Equation 20-16.

Mechanism for the Reaction in Equation 20-15

Markovnikov addition proceeds through the more stable carbocation intermediate

1) electrophilic addition

2) coordination

(20-16)

As in electrophilic addition to an alkene, a hydrogen halide adds to an alkyne in a Markovnikov fashion, proceeding through the more stable of two possible carbocation intermediates. In this case, we can see that H^+ adds to the terminal carbon in step 1 to produce a secondary carbocation. In step 2, Br^- attacks the positively charged carbon in a coordination step.

Your Turn 20.7. The mechanism for the addition of HCl to 1-hexyne is shown below, but the curved arrows have been omitted. Supply the missing curved arrows, and under each reaction arrow write the appropriate name of the elementary step taking place.

As indicated in Equation 20-15,

Electrophilic addition of a single equivalent of a strong Brønsted acid to an alkyne generally gives poor yield, and thus is not very useful in synthesis.

This is in large part due to the fact that in the carbocation intermediate, the positive charge is on a vinylic carbon. That carbon is *sp*-hybridized (notice that only two electron groups are attached to it), and thus has a relatively high effective electronegativity (Section 3.11). Consequently, the positive charge is rather poorly stabilized, which makes the reaction proceed slowly.

Stereochemistry becomes a concern in these reactions when one equivalent of a hydrogen halide adds to an internal alkyne, as is the case in Equation 20-17. Because the product is an alkene, both *E* and *Z* configurations exist. Typically, however, the major product is produced from *anti* addition across the alkyne; in this case, it is the *Z* isomer. Why this is so is still not completely understood.

the major product is from *anti* addition

HBr

2-butyne

(Z)-2-bromo-2-butene

(20-17)

Notice that the product of a single addition of a hydrogen halide to an alkyne has a C=C double bond. Thus, with excess hydrogen halide, a second addition can take place to produce a dihaloalkane. An example is shown in Equation 20-18, in which propyne is treated with excess HBr, and is allowed to react for four days.

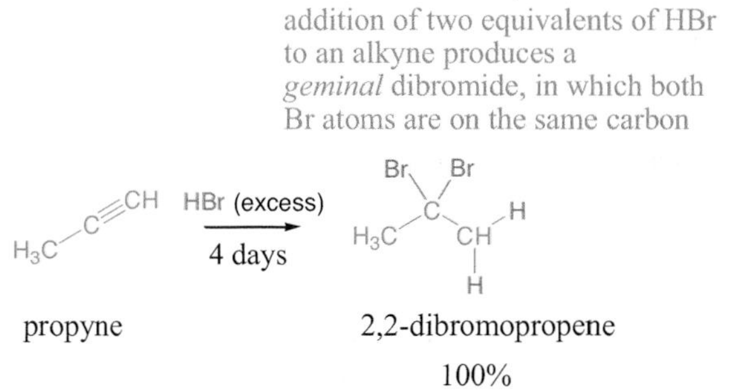

addition of two equivalents of HBr to an alkyne produces a *geminal* dibromide, in which both Br atoms are on the same carbon

$H_3C{-}C{\equiv}CH$ —HBr (excess), 4 days→ $H_3C{-}CBr_2{-}CH_3$

propyne 2,2-dibromopropene 100% (20-18)

Such reactions are highly regioselective, as can be seen from Equation 20-18. Specifically,

> When two equivalents of a hydrogen halide add to an alkyne, both halogen atoms end up on the same carbon atom in the product, producing what is called a **geminal dihalide**.

The reason for this regioselectivity is explained, once again, by the mechanism, shown in Equation 20-19.

Mechanism for the Reaction in Equation 20-18

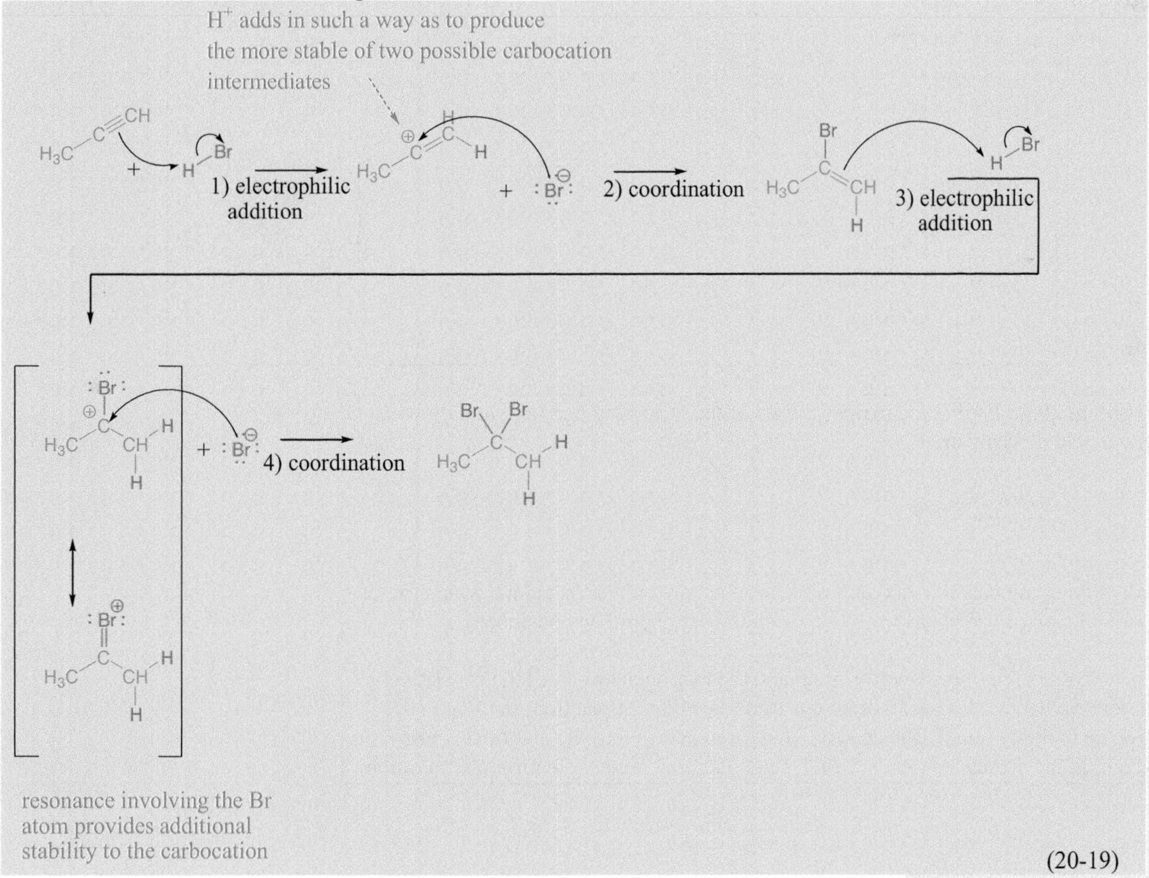

H^+ adds in such a way as to produce the more stable of two possible carbocation intermediates

1) electrophilic addition

2) coordination

3) electrophilic addition

4) coordination

resonance involving the Br atom provides additional stability to the carbocation

(20-19)

The first two steps of the mechanism are identical to those in Equation 20.16. In step 1, H^+ adds to the terminal carbon in order to produce the most stable carbocation intermediate (i.e., Markovnikov addition), and step 2 is coordination involving the newly formed carbocation and bromide ions. In step 3, H^+ adds to the terminal carbon of the alkene group. As indicated, this allows the carbocation that is produced to be stabilized by resonance involving a lone pair of electrons from bromine—no such resonance stabilization would be present if the H^+ were to add to the central carbon atom. Finally, in step 4, a second bromide anion attacks the positively charged carbon to produce the uncharged geminal dibromide.

Your Turn 20.8. The mechanism for the addition of HCl to 1-hexyne is shown below, but the curved arrows have been omitted. Supply the missing curved arrows, and under each reaction arrow write the appropriate name of the elementary step taking place. Also, draw the missing resonance structure in the box provided.

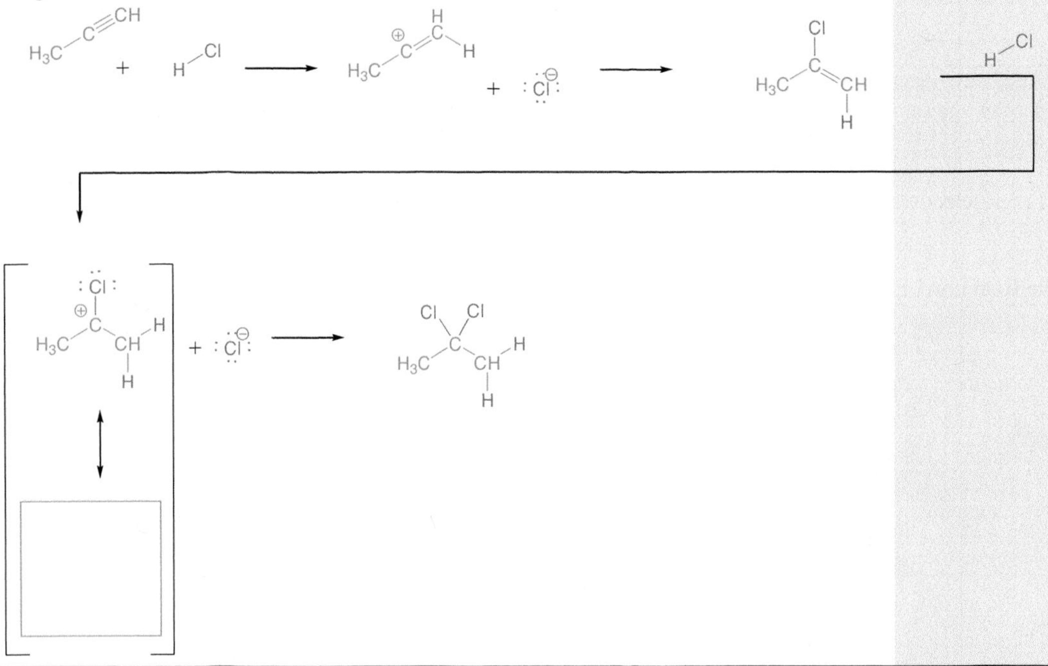

H3C–C≡CH + H–Cl ⟶ H3C–C⊕=CH2 + :Cl:⊖ ⟶ H3C–C(Cl)=CH2 + H–Cl ⟶ [H3C–C⊕(Cl:)–CH3 ↕ (box)] + :Cl:⊖ ⟶ H3C–C(Cl)(Cl)–CH3

Solved Problem 20.4. Predict the major product of the following reaction, and draw its complete, detailed mechanism.

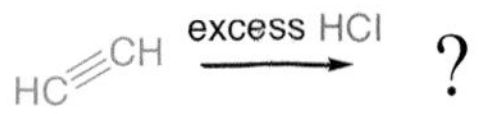

$$HC{\equiv}CH \xrightarrow{\text{excess HCl}} ?$$

Think. Identifying the electron-rich and electron-poor sites in the reactants, what type of reaction will take place? What aspects of regiochemistry should be considered?

Solve. The alkyne is relatively electron-rich, and the hydrogen atom of HCl is relatively electron-poor. So the conditions favor an electrophilic addition reaction, in which HCl adds across the multiple bond. The product of such an addition to the alkyne is a vinyl halide, which, in the presence of excess HCl, can undergo a second electrophilic addition.

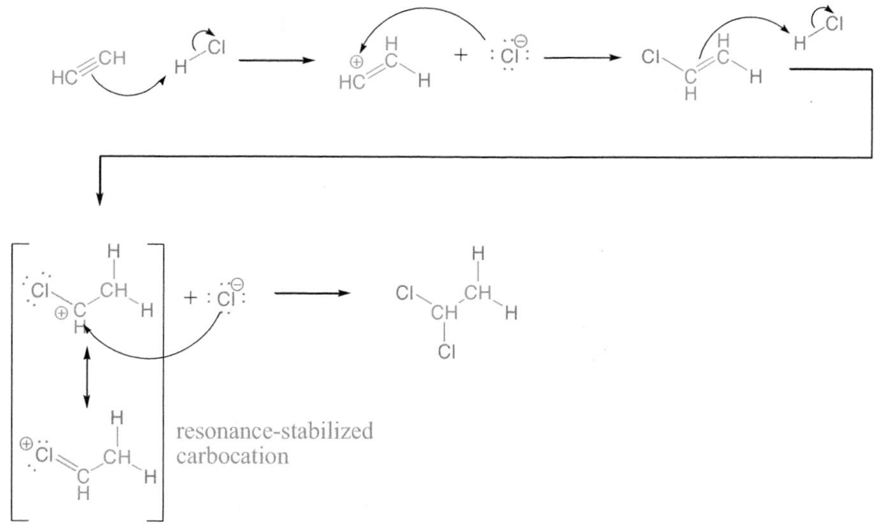

HC≡CH H–Cl → $\oplus$HC=CH–H + :Cl:$^{\ominus}$ → Cl–CH=CH–H → H–Cl

[:Cl–$\oplus$C(H)–CH(H)–H ↔ $\oplus$Cl=C(H)–CH(H)–H] + :Cl:$^{\ominus}$ → Cl–CH(Cl)–CH(H)–H

resonance-stabilized carbocation

In the first addition, regiochemistry is not a concern because the alkyne is symmetric—the same vinyl halide is produced regardless of which carbon forms the new bond to H^+. In the second addition, however, regiochemistry is a concern, because the vinyl halide is not symmetric. Addition of the H^+ is favored at the C atom that is *not* bonded to Cl, in order to produce a resonance-stabilized carbocation intermediate.

Problem 20.10. For each of the following reactions, draw the complete, detailed mechanism, and predict the major product.

(a) Ph–C≡C–Ph $\xrightarrow{\text{excess HCl}}$?

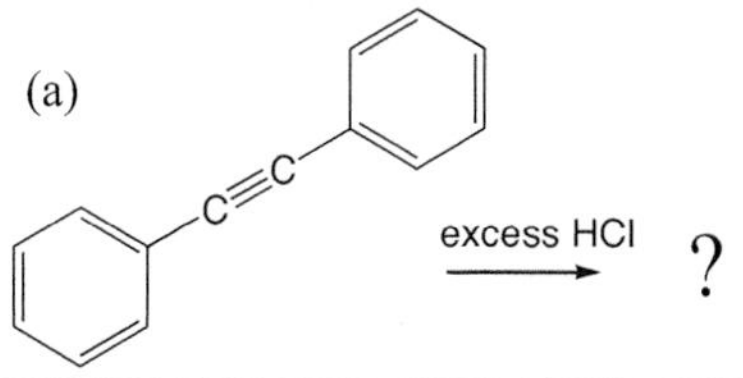

(b) H_3C–C(H)=C(Cl)–CH_3 $\xrightarrow{\text{HBr}}$?

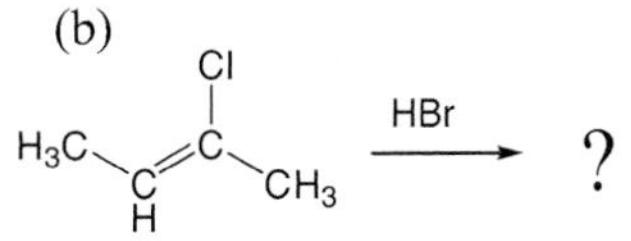

Problem 20.11. Show how to synthesize each of the following compounds from an alkyne.

(a) H_3C–$C(H_2)$–$C(H_2)$–C(Cl)(Cl)–CH_3

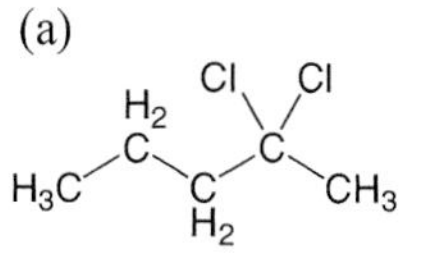

(b) H_3C–$C(H_2)$–C(D)=C(Br)–$C(H_2)$–CH_3

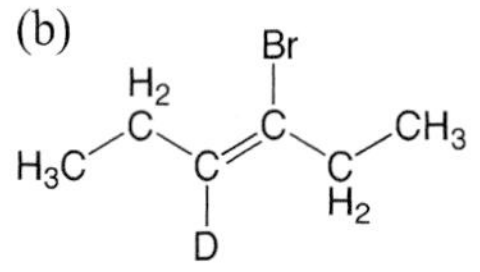

20.7. ACID-CATALYZED HYDRATION OF AN ALKYNE: SYNTHESIS OF A KETONE

In Section 20.5, we saw that when an alkene is treated with water under acidic conditions, water adds across the double bond to produce an alcohol. Therefore, it makes sense that a similar reaction should take place when an alkene is subjected to the same conditions. Indeed, Equation 20-20 shows that a reaction does take place, but the product does not possess an alcohol group. Instead,

Acid-catalyzed hydration of an alkyne produces a ketone.

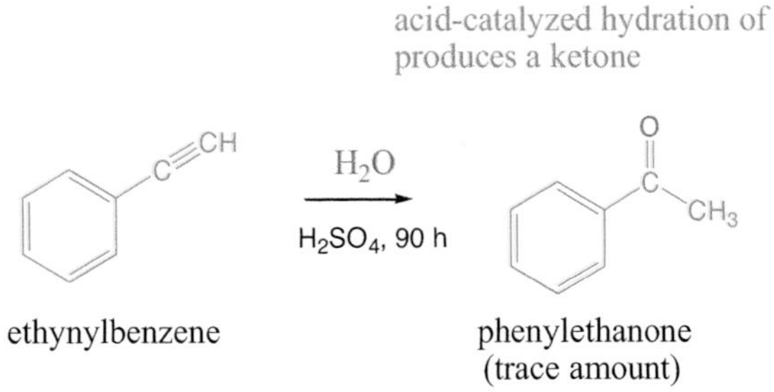

acid-catalyzed hydration of an alkyne produces a ketone

ethynylbenzene $\xrightarrow[H_2SO_4,\ 90\ h]{H_2O}$ phenylethanone (trace amount)

(20-20)

The production of a ketone is explained by the mechanism in Equation 20-21. As we can see, the first three steps are the same as the ones that comprise the mechanism of acid-catalyzed hydration of an alkene, shown previously in Equation 20-14. Step 1 is electrophilic addition of H^+, which obeys Markovnikov's rule, and produces a relatively unstable vinylic carbocation intermediate. In step 2, water behaves as a nucleophile, attacking the positively charged carbon of that intermediate. Deprotonation in step 3 produces the uncharged alcohol group, which is attached to an alkene carbon. Thus, it is an *enol*.

Under these acidic conditions, the enol rapidly tautomerizes to the more stable *keto* form in two steps. First, in step 4, a proton adds to the terminal carbon. Then, in step 5, the oxygen atom is deprotonated, yielding the final uncharged ketone.

Mechanism for the Reaction in Equation 20-20

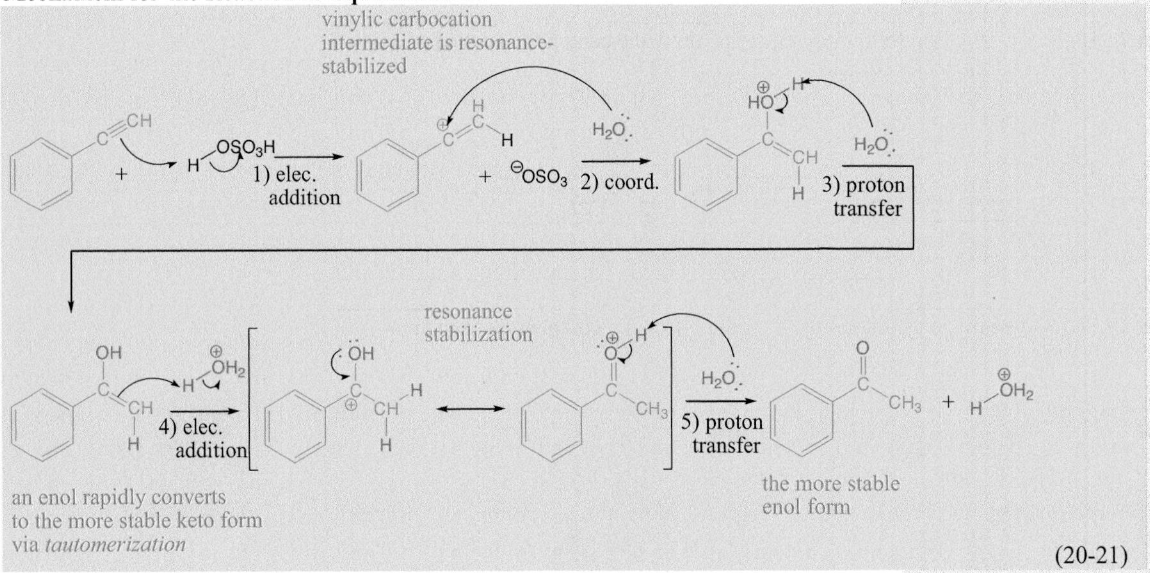

vinylic carbocation intermediate is resonance-stabilized

1) elec. addition

2) coord.

3) proton transfer

resonance stabilization

4) elec. addition

5) proton transfer

an enol rapidly converts to the more stable keto form via *tautomerization*

the more stable enol form

(20-21)

There are two important aspects of this reaction to take note of. First, the product is a ketone instead of an aldehyde. This is an outcome of Markovnikov's rule, which dictates that in the first step, H^+ should add preferentially to the terminal carbon to give the more stable carbocation intermediate. Thus, in the second step, water must add to the internal carbon atom. An aldehyde is not favored because its production would require the proton to add to the internal carbon atom in the first step, which would produce the less stable carbocation intermediate (see Your Turn 20.9).

Your Turn 20.9. In the space provided here, draw the carbocation intermediate that must be produced in order to produce an aldehyde from the acid-catalyzed hydration of ethynylbenzene. Explain why it is less stable than the carbocation intermediate shown in Equation 20-21.

The second aspect to take note of is that the product yield of the reaction in Equation 20-20 is very low; only a trace amount of ketone is produced. Thus, such a reaction is not very useful synthetically. The reason for such a low yield is that the addition of H^+ in the first step of the mechanism produces a vinylic carbocation intermediate, which, as was discussed in the previous section, is in general highly unstable. In other words, the first step of the mechanism is excessively unfavorable.

This problem can be circumvented by using a Brønsted acid that is significantly stronger than sulfuric acid, thus making the first step of the mechanism more favorable. Examples of such acids include trifluoromethanesulfonic acid, CF_3SO_3H (TfOH), and trifluoromethanesulfonamide, $(CF_3SO_2)_2NH$ (Tf_2NH). As we can see in Equations 20-22 and 20-23, a relatively high yield of the ketone product can be obtained from a catalytic amount of one of these acids.

acid-catalyzed hydration of an alkyne is facilitated by acids that are significantly stronger than H_2SO_4

ethynylbenzene $\xrightarrow[\text{cat. TfOH, 48 h}]{H_2O}$ phenylethanone 93% (20-22)

oct-4-yne $\xrightarrow[\text{cat. } Tf_2NH\text{, 48 h}]{H_2O}$ octan-4-one 64% (20-23)

Your Turn 20.10. Verify that trifluoromethanesulfonic acid is a significantly stronger acid than sulfuric acid by looking up their pK_a values and writing them in the spaces provided here.

H_2SO_4 ________ TfOH ________

Another way to circumvent the problem associated with the acid-catalyzed hydration of an alkyne is to incorporate a mercury (II) catalyst, Hg^{2+}. An example is shown in Equation 20-24. However, with the presence of a mercury (II) catalyst, the reaction proceeds through a mechanism that will be discussed in Chapter 21.

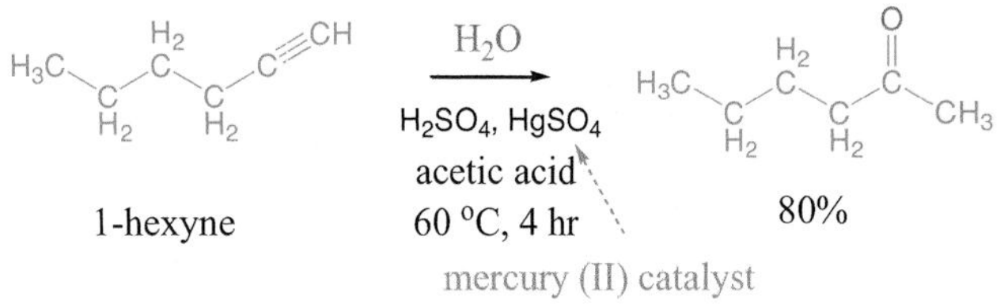

$H_3C-CH_2-CH_2-CH_2-C\equiv CH$ (1-hexyne) $\xrightarrow[\text{H}_2\text{SO}_4,\ \text{HgSO}_4,\ \text{acetic acid},\ 60\ ^\circ\text{C, 4 hr}]{\text{H}_2\text{O}}$ $H_3C-CH_2-CH_2-CH_2-C(=O)-CH_3$ 80%

mercury (II) catalyst

(20-24)

Problem 20.12. Draw the complete, detailed mechanism for the following reaction, and predict the major product.

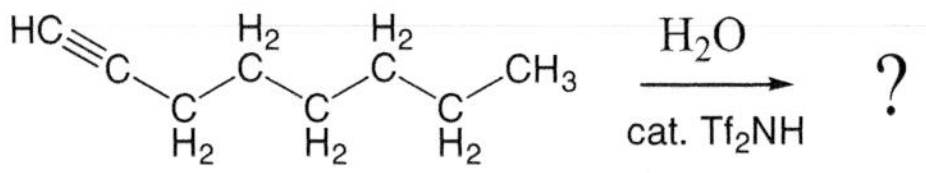

$HC\equiv C-CH_2-CH_2-CH_2-CH_2-CH_2-CH_3 \xrightarrow[\text{cat. Tf}_2\text{NH}]{\text{H}_2\text{O}}$?

20.8. ELECTROPHILIC ADDITION OF A BRØNSTED ACID TO A CONJUGATED DIENE: 1,2-ADDITION AND 1,4-ADDITION

A conjugated diene, such as 1,3-butadiene, is electron-rich and therefore undergoes electrophilic addition with Brønsted acids—an example is shown in Equation 20-25 with HCl as the acid. Interestingly, this reaction yields a mixture of isomeric products. One product, 3-chloro-1-butene, appears to be as expected—the H and Cl atoms have added across one of the double bonds with Markovnikov regiochemistry. The other product, 1-chloro-2-butene, cannot be produced simply by the addition of HCl across one of the double bonds, because the double bond in the product is in a different location than either of the double bonds in the reactant species.

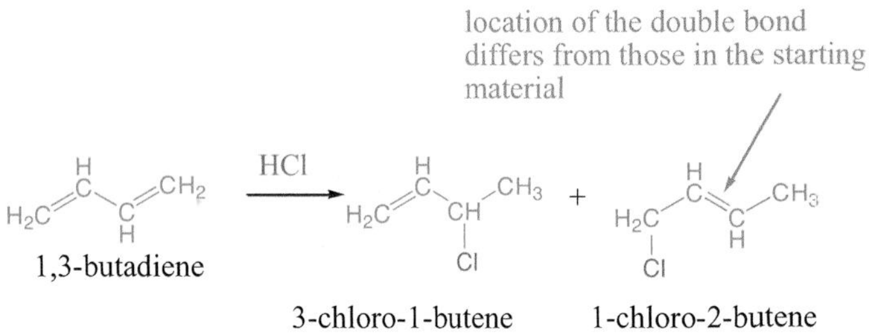

location of the double bond differs from those in the starting material

$H_2C=CH-CH=CH_2$ (1,3-butadiene) $\xrightarrow{\text{HCl}}$ $H_2C=CH-CH(Cl)-CH_3$ (3-chloro-1-butene) + $ClH_2C-CH=CH-CH_3$ (1-chloro-2-butene)

(20-25)

Both of these products are produced from the same general mechanism, as indicated in Equation 20-26. In step 1, a proton adds to a π bond, and in step 2, the chloride anion attacks the newly formed carbocation intermediate in a coordination step.

Mechanism for the Reaction in Equation 20-25

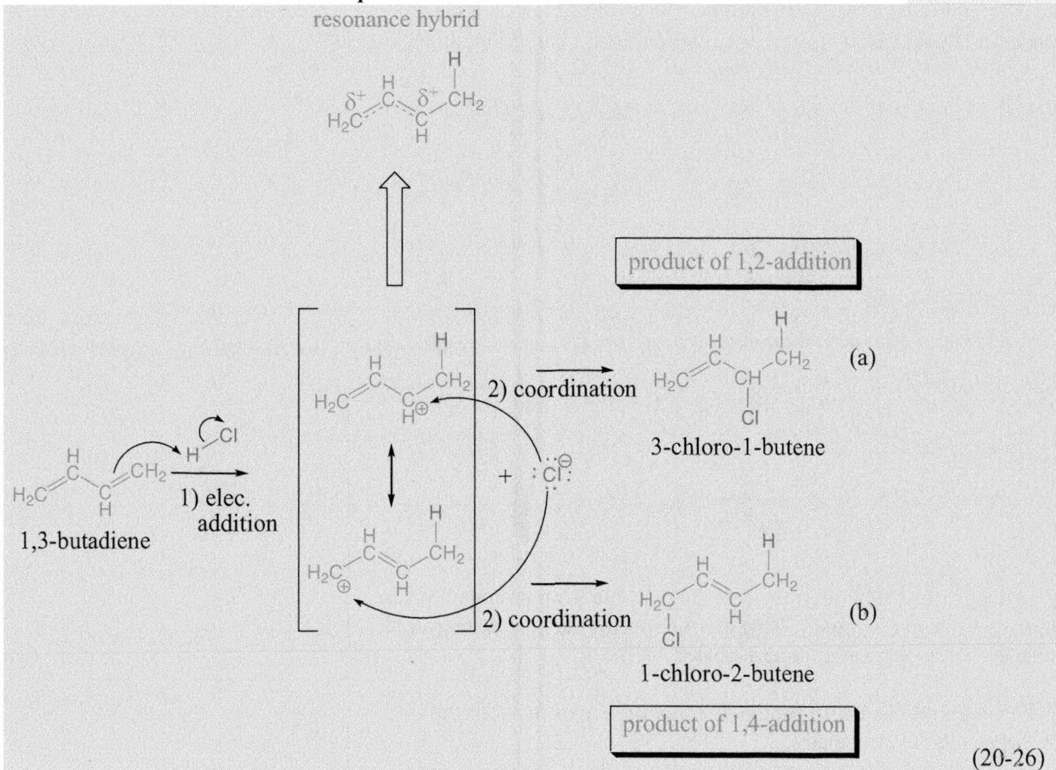

(20-26)

It is important to realize that both products are produced from the *same carbocation intermediate*. As indicated above, this intermediate has two resonance structures—one with the positive charge on carbon-1 and one with the positive charge on carbon-3. Therefore, in the resonance hybrid, each of those two carbon atoms bears a partial positive charge, and consequently can be attacked by chloride. Attack on one of those carbon atoms (Equation 20-26a) yields 3-chloro-1-butene, and attack on the other carbon atom yields 1-chloro-2-butene.

Notice that in the 3-chloro-1-butene product, the H and Cl atoms that had added to the diene are separated by two carbon atoms—therefore, this is the product of **1,2-addition**. On the other hand, 1-chloro-2-butene is the product of **1,4-addition** because the H and Cl atoms that had added to the diene are separated by four carbon atoms.

Your Turn 20.11. In the following reaction, determine which product is produced from 1,2-addition, and which is produced from 1,4-addition.

Notice also that in the first step of the mechanism, addition of the proton occurs so as to give *the most stable carbocation intermediate*, in accord with Markovnikov's rule, just as we saw previously in the electrophilic addition to propene (Equation 20-4).

The carbocation intermediate shown in Equation 20-26, which is produced by the addition of a proton to a terminal carbon, is *resonance stabilized.* If, on the other hand, one of the internal carbon atoms were to gain the proton, the positive charge in the resulting carbocation would be *localized* on a primary carbon, as shown in Equation 20-27.

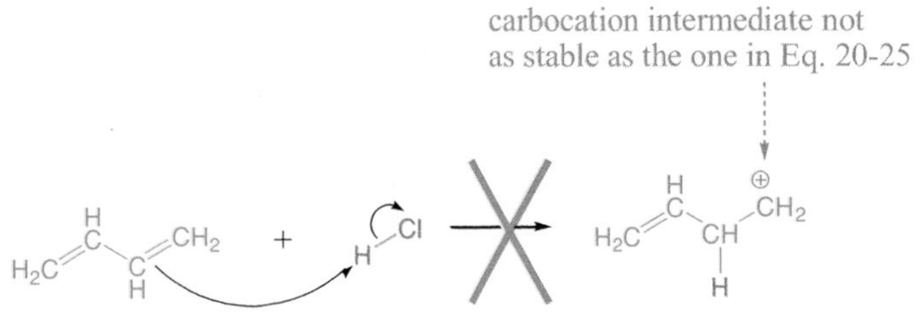

carbocation intermediate not as stable as the one in Eq. 20-25

(20-27)

Solved Problem 20.5. Draw the major 1,2-addition and 1,4-addition products of the following reaction.

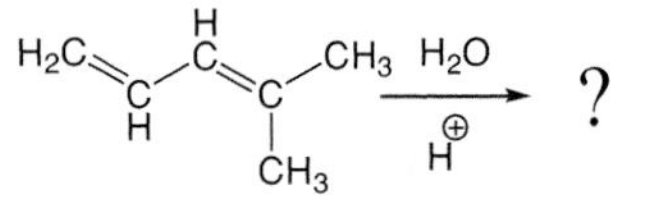

Think. How many distinct carbocation intermediates are possible from protonation of a double bond? Which one is the most stable? What are the species that can be produced upon nucleophilic attack of that carbocation intermediate?

Solve. Each of the alkene groups can gain a proton at either of its carbon atoms, giving rise to four possible carbocation intermediates.

(a) (b) (c) (d)

positive charge resonance delocalized over 2° and 3° carbons

positive charge resonance delocalized over 2° and 1° carbons

most stable carbocation intermediate

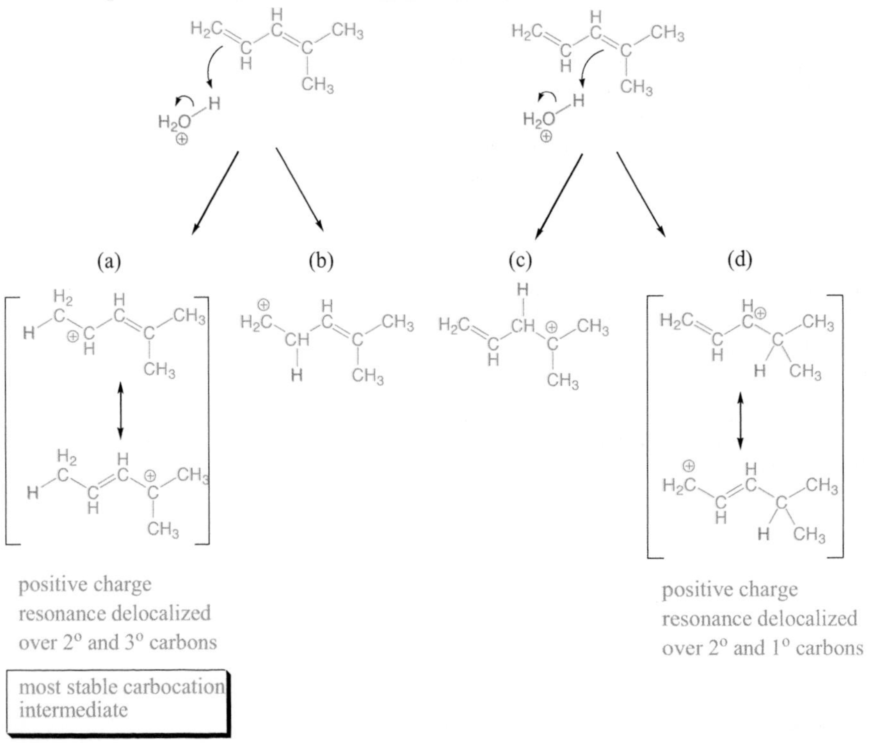

Intermediate (a) is the most stable. Intermediates (a) and (d) are more stable than (b) and (c) due to resonance delocalization of the positive charge. Intermediate (a) is more stable than (d) because the positive charge is shared on a 3° carbon.

With the most stable intermediate identified, the 1,2- and 1,4-addition products are obtained by attack of the nucleophile, H_2O, on the carbon atoms sharing the positive charge.

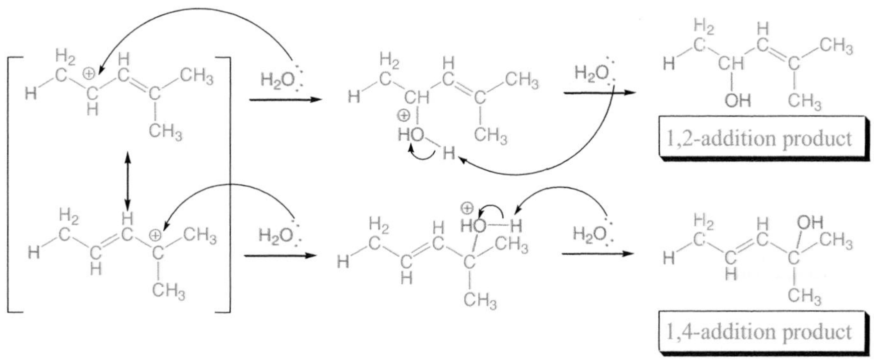

1,2-addition product

1,4-addition product

Problem 20.13. Draw the complete detailed mechanism for the formation of the major 1,2- and 1,4-addition products of the following reaction.

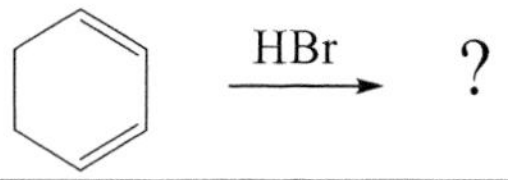

HBr → ?

Problem 20.14. When an unknown conjugated diene is treated with hydrogen chloride, a mixture of two chloralkenes is produced, as shown below. Draw the conjugated diene that was used as the reactant, and draw the complete, detailed mechanism that leads to the formation of each product.

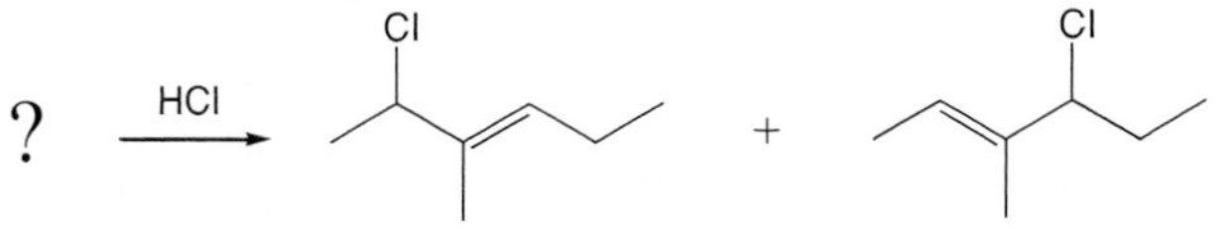

? —HCl→ +

20.9. KINETIC VS. THERMODYNAMIC CONTROL IN ELECTROPHILIC ADDITION TO A CONJUGATED DIENE

As we discussed in the previous section, electrophilic addition to 1,3-butadiene yields a mixture of addition products—a 1,2-adduct and a 1,4-adduct—from the same carbocation intermediate. Which adduct is the major product? Interestingly, the answer to that question can depend upon the *temperature* at which the reaction is carried out. If, for example, the electrophilic addition of HCl to 1,3-butadiene is carried out at room temperature, the 1,4-adduct is the major product (Equation 20-28). However, if the reaction is carried out at cold temperatures, the 1,2-adduct is the major product (Equation 20-29).

major product at warm temperatures

$H_2C{=}CH{-}CH{=}CH_2$ (1,3-butadiene) $\xrightarrow[20\ ^\circ C]{HCl}$ $H_2C{=}CH{-}CH(Cl){-}CH_3$ (3-chloro-1-butene; 25% of adduct mixture) + $ClH_2C{-}CH{=}CH{-}CH_3$ (1-chloro-2-butene; 75% of adduct mixture) (20-28)

major product at cold temperatures

$H_2C{=}CH{-}CH{=}CH_2$ (1,3-butadiene) $\xrightarrow[-80\ ^\circ C]{HCl}$ $H_2C{=}CH{-}CH(Cl){-}CH_3$ (3-chloro-1-butene; 80% of adduct mixture) + $ClH_2C{-}CH{=}CH{-}CH_3$ (1-chloro-2-butene; 20% of adduct mixture) (20-29)

The reason we observe these temperature effects is that the temperature at which the reaction is run governs whether the reaction is *reversible* or *irreversible*. At low temperatures, the product molecules do not possess enough energy to climb over the energy barrier in the reverse direction to reform reactants at a significant rate, effectively making electrophilic addition to the diene irreversible. By contrast, at high temperatures, the product molecules do possess enough energy to make the reaction reversible. Combining this information with what we learned in Section 9.12:

- At low temperatures, electrophilic addition to a conjugated diene takes place under *kinetic control*, so the major product is the one that is produced most rapidly.
- At high temperatures, electrophilic addition to a conjugated diene takes place under *thermodynamic control*, so the major product is the one that is most stable.

Therefore, based on the temperatures reported in Equations 20-28 and 20-29, the 1,4-adduct must be the thermodynamic product and the 1,2-adduct must the kinetic product.

Your Turn 20.12. In Equations 20-28 and 20-29, label each product as either the "kinetic product" or the "thermodynamic product."

We can rationalize the 1,4-adduct being the thermodynamic product by the stability of the alkene group. As shown below, the alkene group in the 1,4-adduct is *di-substituted* (i.e., bonded to two alkyl groups), whereas that in the 1,2-adduct is only *mono-substituted.* Recall from Section 5.9 that the more highly substituted an alkene is, the more stable it is.

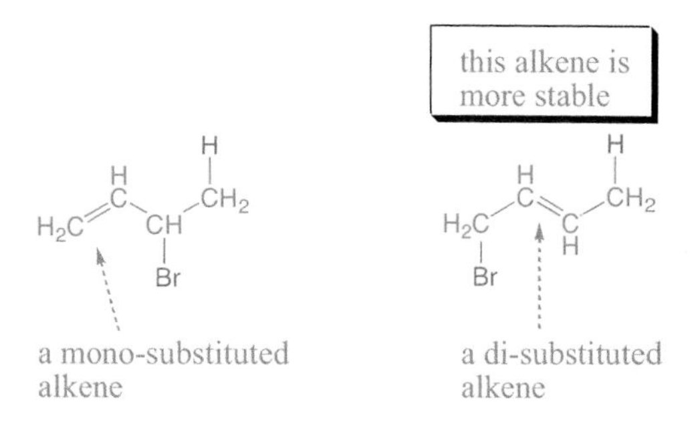

Your Turn 20.13. For each of the alkene products above, circle each alkyl group bonded to the alkene carbons, verifying that one is a monosubstituted alkene and the other is a disubstituted alkene.

The reason that the 1,2-adduct is the kinetic product is simply a result of the location of Br^- after completion of the first step of the mechanism. Upon addition of the proton to the diene, Br^- is closer to C-2 than it is to C-4 (Equation 20-30). Therefore, the resonance delocalized positive charge—which is shared over C-2 and C-4—is initially better stabilized on C-2 than it is on C-4, because it is closer to the negative charge on Br^-. With a greater concentration of positive charge on C-2, Br^- attacks C-2 more quickly than it attacks C-4.

$Br^{\ominus}$ stabilizes this positive charge better

1,2-adduct formed faster

(20-30)

In the case of electrophilic addition to 1,3-butadiene, the kinetic and thermodynamic products are different—the 1,2-adduct is the kinetic product and the 1,4-adduct is the thermodynamic product. However, this is not always the case, as illustrated in Solved Problem 20.6.

Solved Problem 20.6. Determine the major thermodynamic and kinetic products in the following reaction, and draw the complete, detailed mechanism for the formation of each.

HI

Think. What are the *possible* carbocation intermediates? What is the most stable carbocation intermediate? What are the adducts that can be produced upon nucleophilic attack of that carbocation intermediate? Which of those adducts is produced the fastest? Which is the more stable one?

Solve. The most stable carbocation intermediate (below) is produced by the addition of a proton to C-4, because the positive charge is resonance delocalized over two C atoms in the chain as well as the benzene ring. The 1,2- and 1,4-adducts are therefore as follows.

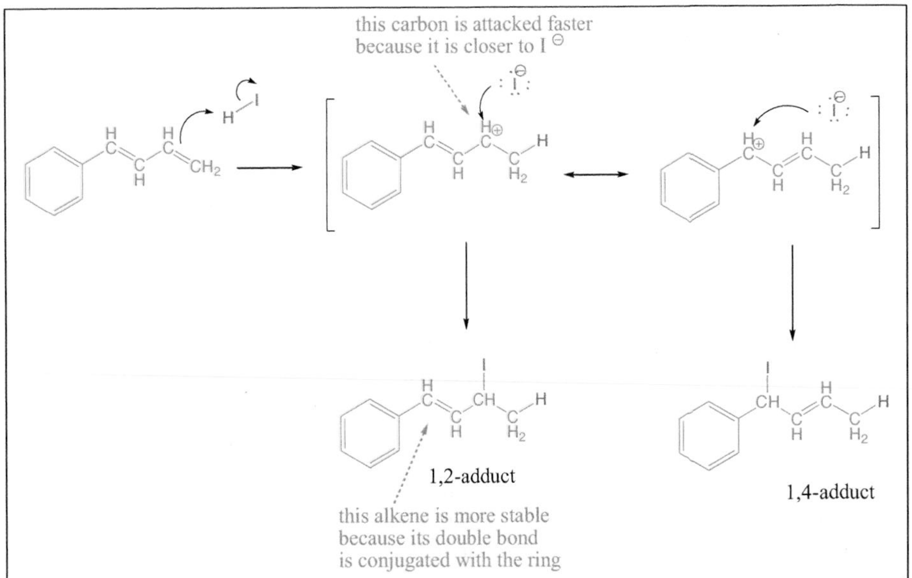

this carbon is attacked faster because it is closer to $I^{\ominus}$

1,2-adduct

1,4-adduct

this alkene is more stable because its double bond is conjugated with the ring

The kinetic product is the 1,2-adduct, for the same reasons as described previously—the I^- that is produced in the first step is closer to the 3-carbon than the 1-carbon, so it attacks the 3-carbon more rapidly. Furthermore, the 1,2-adduct is also the thermodynamic product because the double bond is *conjugated* with the benzene ring. By contrast, in the 1,4-adduct, the double bond is isolated.

Problem 20.15. Determine the major thermodynamic and kinetic products in the following reaction, and draw the complete, detailed mechanism for the formation of each.

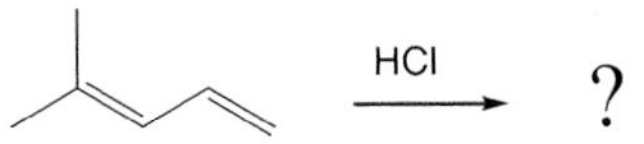

HCl ?

20.10. BENZENE AND ELECTROPHILIC ADDITION

Benzene has resonance structures that depict three conjugated carbon-carbon double bonds, indicating that it is an electron-rich species. Thus, we might expect benzene to undergo electrophilic addition reactions similar to ones that involve 1,3-butadiene. However,

> Benzene tends not to undergo addition reactions with electrophilic species like HCl, HBr, or H_3O^+.

We can see why this is so simply by examining Equation 20-31, which shows the generic addition of a Brønsted acid, HA, to benzene. In order for HA to add to benzene, one of the double bonds of the ring must be converted to a single bond. In so doing, *benzene must lose its aromaticity*! As we learned in Chapter 12, aromaticity is a very heavily stabilizing factor, making such reactions highly unfavorable energetically.

aromaticity destroyed!

A

H

HA

(20-31)

As we will see in Chapters 22 and 23, benzene and other aromatic species will react with electrophiles that are much stronger than the ones we have encountered in this chapter. However, the reaction is a *substitution* instead of an addition. A substitution ensures that the aromaticity is not lost in the formation of the products.

20.11. ORGANIC SYNTHESIS: PROTECTING ALCOHOL GROUPS

In Section 17.4b, we learned that ketones, aldehydes, and alcohols can be protected by temporarily converting them into ether groups. This is because the ether functional group is relatively unreactive in neutral and basic conditions.

Earlier in this chapter (Section 20.5), we saw that ethers can also be produced by the acid-catalyzed electrophilic addition of an alcohol across a C=C double bond, as shown in Equation 20-32. Therefore, we can use this reaction to protect alcohols.

an alcohol can be protected by temporarily converting it to an ether, which is unreactive under neutral and basic conditions

C=C + ROH ⇌ ($H^{\oplus}$) H—C—C—OR

an alkene an alcohol an ether

(20-32)

One of the most common alkenes used to protect alcohols is methylpropene, which leads to a *tert*-butyl ether. An example is shown in Equation 20-33.

methylpropene is used to protect the alcohol

in the form of an ether, the alcohol is protected from bases and nucleophiles

this alcohol is a byproduct that is discarded

the starting alcohol is recovered

R—OH → ($H_2C=C(CH_3)CH_3$, $H^{\oplus}$) RO—C(CH_3)(CH_3)—CH_2—H → R—OH + HO—C(CH_3)(H_3C)CH_3

an alcohol a *t*-butyl ether 2-methyl-2-propanol

(20-33)

The popularity of methylpropene as a protecting group derives from the fact that the intermediate carbocation that is produced in the acid-catalyzed addition reaction is tertiary, so it is stabilized by three attached alkyl groups. Thus, protection of the alcohol is quite facile.

Removal of the protecting group to regenerate the alcohol simply entails treating the *tert*-butyl ether with dilute aqueous acid. A relatively fast S_N1 reaction ensues, yielding 2-methyl-2-propanol as a byproduct. This deprotection step is aided in two ways: (1) The acidic conditions produce a protonated ether, which possesses a very good ROH leaving group, and (2) the carbocation generated upon the departure of the leaving group is, once again, a 3° carbocation.

Problem 20.16. Draw the complete, detailed mechanism for the protection and the deprotection step in Equation 20-33.

Another alkene that is commonly used to protect alcohols is **dihydropyran** (DHP), as shown in Equation 20-34. Protection and deprotection proceed by the same mechanisms by which the reactions in Equation 20-33 proceed; generation of the carbocation intermediate in both steps is facilitated by resonance stabilization involving a lone pair of electrons from oxygen.

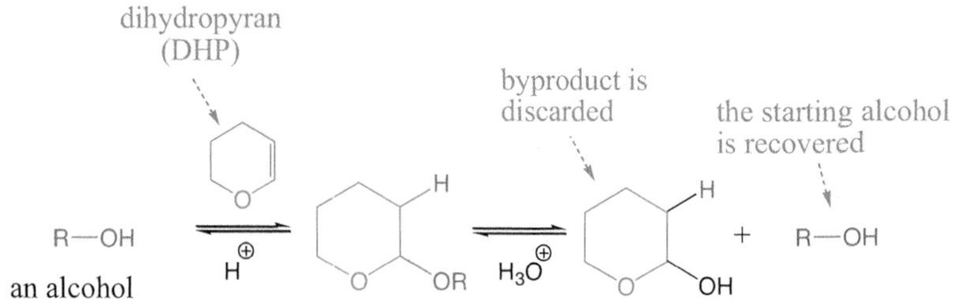

dihydropyran (DHP)

byproduct is discarded

the starting alcohol is recovered

R—OH

an alcohol

$H^{\oplus}$

$H_3O^{\oplus}$

+ R—OH

(20-34)

Problem 20.17. Draw the complete, detailed mechanisms for each step in Equation 20-34, and draw both resonance structures of the carbocation intermediate that is formed.

Solved Problem 20.7. A student attempted to carry out the following reaction, but it did not work. Suggest why, and propose a synthesis route that would circumvent this problem.

1) PhMgBr

2) $H_3O^{\oplus}$

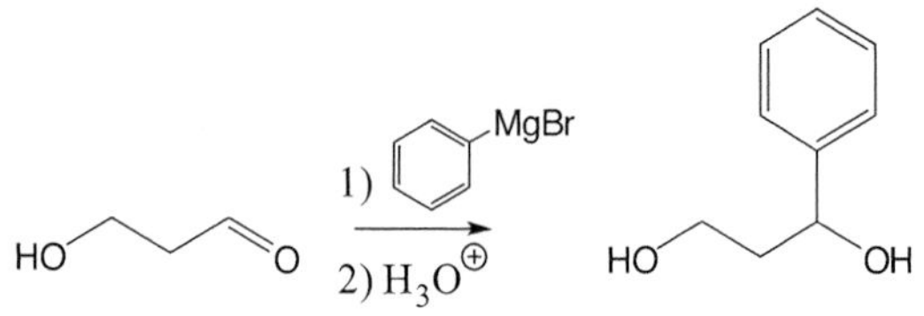

Think. What type of reaction does the student intend to carry out? What alternative reaction can take place, and what type of functional group does that reaction involve? Can that functional group be protected?

Solve. In order for the reaction to take place as planned, the Grignard reagent must act as a nucleophile, attacking the carbonyl group. However, a Grignard reagent is also a very strong base, and the alcohol group on the hydroxyaldehyde is mildly acidic. Instead of the intended nucleophilic addition, the following proton transfer reaction occurs, which destroys the Grignard reagent.

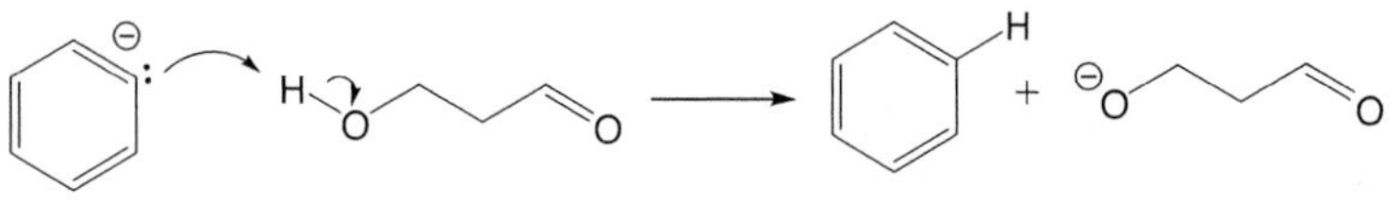

To circumvent this problem, we can protect the alcohol group before performing the Grignard reaction. Once the Grignard reaction is complete, the product is deprotected.

Notice that because the acid workup step of the Grignard reaction requires acidic aqueous conditions, the acid work-up and deprotection occur together.

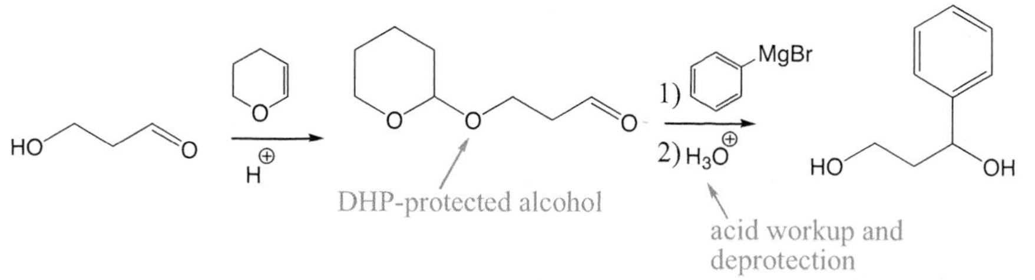

HO ... O, DHP, $H^{\oplus}$ → DHP-protected alcohol; 1) PhMgBr 2) $H_3O^{\oplus}$ → HO ... OH (acid workup and deprotection)

Problem 20.18. Show how to carry out the following synthesis.

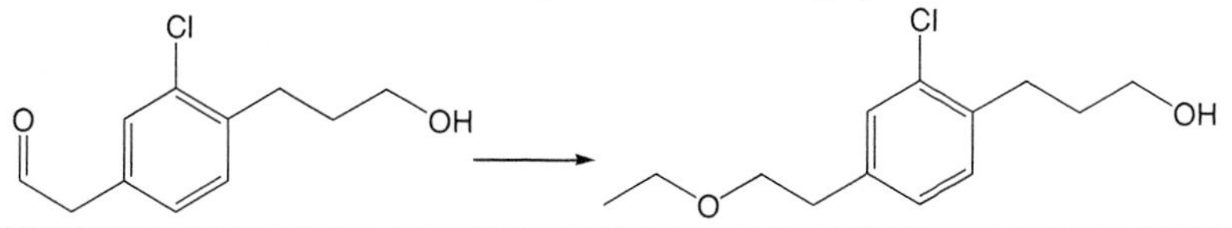

20.12. WRAPPING UP AND LOOKING AHEAD

This chapter introduced electrophilic addition reactions, using, as the prototype reaction, the addition of a hydrogen halide to an alkene. Such a reaction proceeds by a mechanism that consists of two steps—addition of a proton to the alkene, which produces a carbocation intermediate, followed by coordination of a nucleophile to the newly formed carbocation intermediate.

The appearance of a carbocation intermediate in the mechanism explains two important aspects of the reaction. One is the regioselectivity that is described by *Markovnikov's rule*—namely, the mechanism proceeds through the most stable carbocation intermediate. The second aspect of such reactions is the rearrangement of the carbon skeleton that is occasionally observed, expected of carbocations that can become more stable via a 1,2-hydride or 1,2-methyl shift.

With a solid foundation of the prototypical electrophilic addition reaction, we subsequently explored electrophilic addition reactions involving other Brønsted acids and other functional groups containing nonpolar π bonds. We saw, for example, that the addition of a weak acid, such as water or an alcohol, can take place via acid catalysis. And the π bond that undergoes electrophilic addition can be part of an alkyne or a diene.

Special attention must be paid when an alkyne or conjugated diene undergoes electrophilic addition. For example, when water adds to an alkyne, a ketone or aldehyde is produced via an unstable enol intermediate. And electrophilic addition to a conjugated diene can take place via 1,2- or 1,4-addition, with the major product frequently governed by the temperature at which the reaction is carried out.

This was the first of two chapters dealing with electrophilic addition reactions. In Chapter 21, our focus will turn toward electrophiles that are *not* Brønsted acids. Interestingly, as we will see, many of those reactions proceed through mechanisms that involve a cyclic transition state, and have regioselectivity or stereoselectivity that make them quite useful for synthesis.

APPLICATIONS TO BIOLOGY AND BIOCHEMISTRY

20.13. TERPENE BIOSYNTHESIS: CARBOCATION CHEMISTRY IN NATURE

In Section 2.10c, we saw that many natural products are *terpenes* or *terpenoids*, including essential oils from plants, as well as steroids. More importantly, we saw that terpenes and terpenoids are distinguished from other natural products by the structure of their carbon backbone. Namely, the carbon backbone of a terpene or terpenoid consists of multiple *isoprene* units linked together by their terminal carbons.

One of the keys to terpene synthesis in nature is isopentenyl pyrophosphate, which itself is produced in several steps from acetic acid (Equation 20-35). As you can see, isopentenyl pyrophosphate has the same carbon structure as the fundamental isoprene unit.

Comment [JMK43]: Margin note 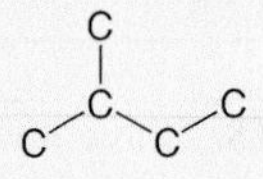
isoprene unit

Comment [JMK44]: Margin note 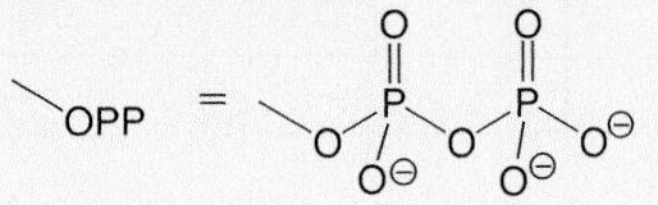
OPP =

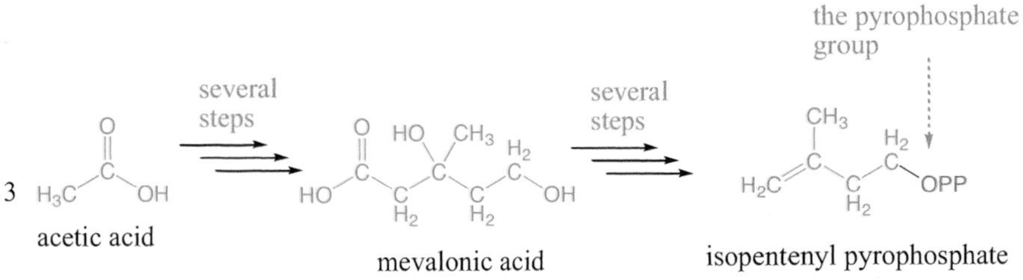

3 acetic acid → (several steps) → mevalonic acid → (several steps) → isopentenyl pyrophosphate (the pyrophosphate group) (20-35)

Some isopentenyl pyrophosphate reacts with an enzyme (a protein catalyst), isomerizing to dimethylallyl pyrophosphate. As shown in Equation 20-36, the first step is electrophilic addition of a proton, and the second step is the elimination of a different proton. Notice that the electrophilic addition step produces the most stable carbocation intermediate, thus adhering to Markovnikov's rule (Section 20.2). Also, notice that the elimination step produces the most highly substituted alkene product, adhering to Zaitsev's rule (Section 9.10).

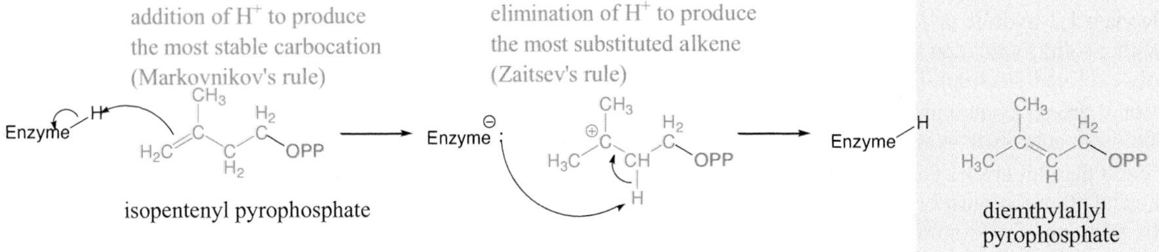

addition of H^+ to produce the most stable carbocation (Markovnikov's rule)

elimination of H^+ to produce the most substituted alkene (Zaitsev's rule)

isopentenyl pyrophosphate → diemthylallyl pyrophosphate (20-36)

Dimethylallyl pyrophosphate then reacts with isopentenyl pyrophosphate, according to Equation 20-37, to produce a carbocation intermediate that contains ten carbon atoms. This step is essentially an electrophilic addition reaction—the pyrophosphate group is a very good leaving group, making the carbon to which it is attached significantly electrophilic. Subsequently, the newly-formed carbocation intermediate can undergo elimination to produce geranyl pyrophosphate, both in its *E* and *Z* configurations.

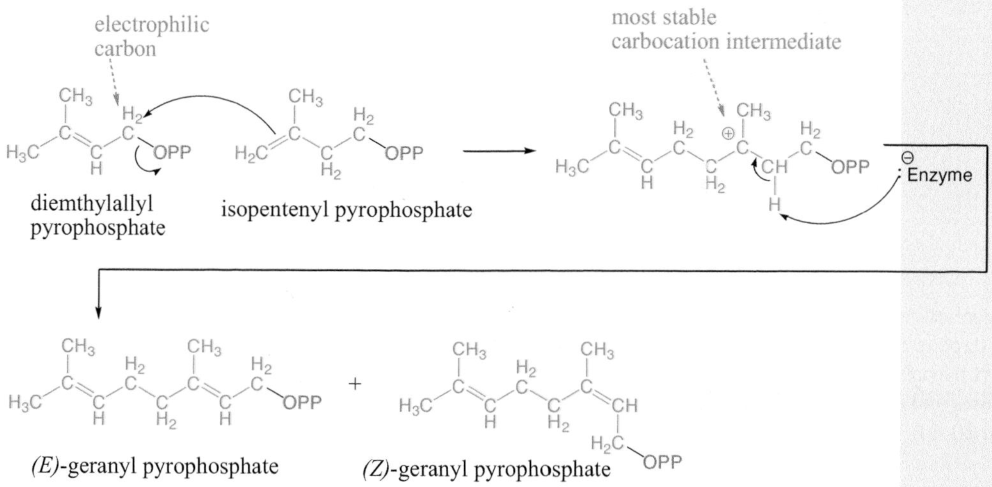

electrophilic carbon

most stable carbocation intermediate

diemthylallyl pyrophosphate

isopentenyl pyrophosphate

(*E*)-geranyl pyrophosphate

(*Z*)-geranyl pyrophosphate

(20-37)

The *Z* form of geranyl pyrophosphate can then react in a number of ways to produce various terpenes and terpenoids containing ten carbons. For example, as shown in Equation 20-38, it can undergo an intermolecular electrophilic addition reaction to produce a six-membered ring carbocation intermediate. Subsequent elimination of a proton yields limonene, a monoterpene that is a constituent of citrus oils.

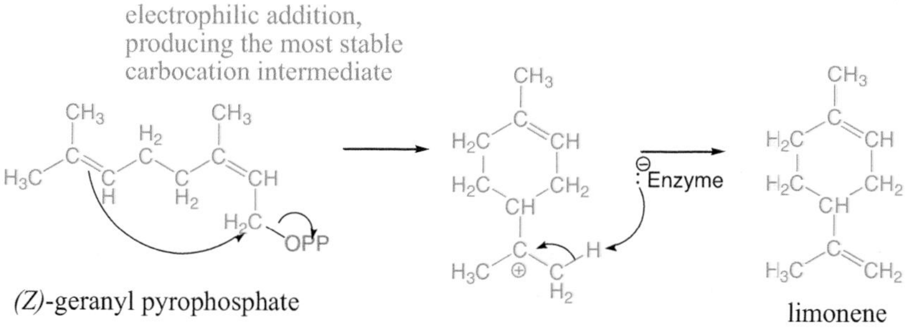

electrophilic addition, producing the most stable carbocation intermediate

(*Z*)-geranyl pyrophosphate

limonene

(20-38)

Alternatively, (*Z*)-geranyl pyrophosphate can undergo nucleophilic substitution with water to produce geraniol (Equation 20-39), found in oils of the rose and geranium plants.

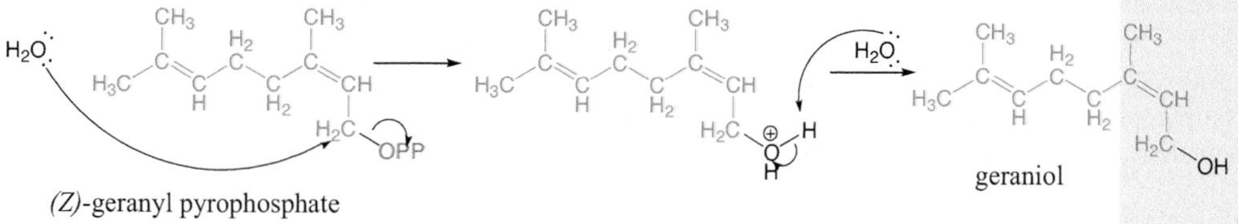

(*Z*)-geranyl pyrophosphate

geraniol

(20-39)

Problem 20.19. The *Z* form of geranyl pyrophosphate can react with water to produce α-terpineol and terpin hydrate, terpenoids found in natural oils. Draw the mechanism for each of these reactions.

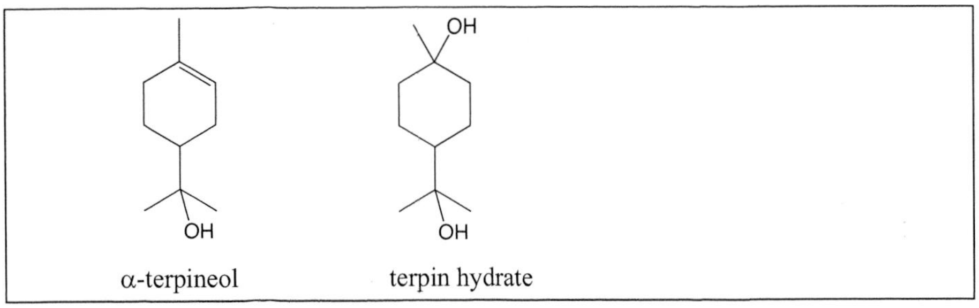

OH

OH OH

α-terpineol terpin hydrate

The *E* form of geranyl pyrophosphate can be used to further grow the carbon chain in the synthesis of terpenes and terpenoids. For example, geranyl pyrophosphate can react with isopentenyl pyrophosphate to produce a carbocation intermediate containing 15 carbon atoms, and subsequent elimination of a proton produces farnesyl pyrophosphate (Equation 20-40)

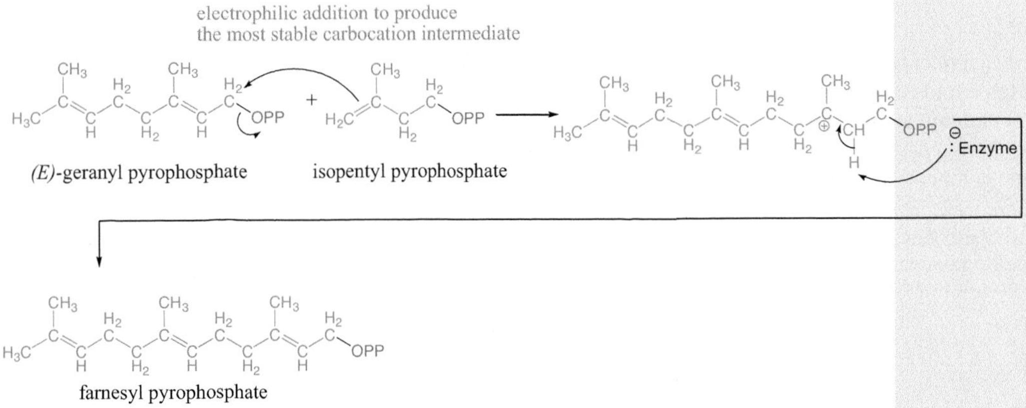

electrophilic addition to produce
the most stable carbocation intermediate

(*E*)-geranyl pyrophosphate + isopentyl pyrophosphate → [carbocation intermediate] : Enzyme

farnesyl pyrophosphate

(20-40)

Farnesyl pyrophosphate can undergo hydrolysis with water to produce farnesol (Equation 20-41)—a pheromone for some insects, and an oil used to enhance the aroma of perfumes.

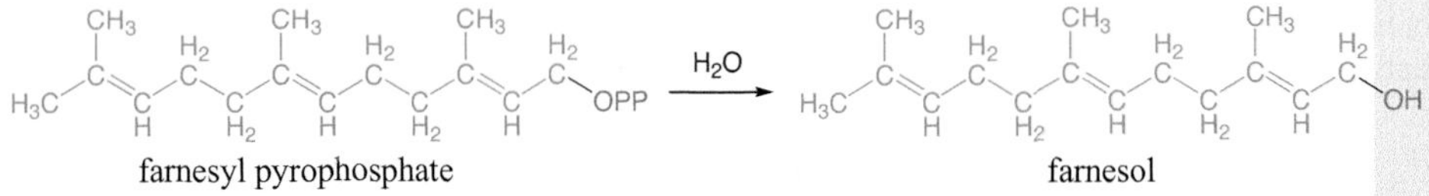

farnesyl pyrophosphate $\xrightarrow{H_2O}$ farnesol

(20-41)

Alternatively, two farnesyl pyrophosphate molecules can couple together in a "tail-to-tail" fashion to produce squalene, a triterpene (Equation 20-42).

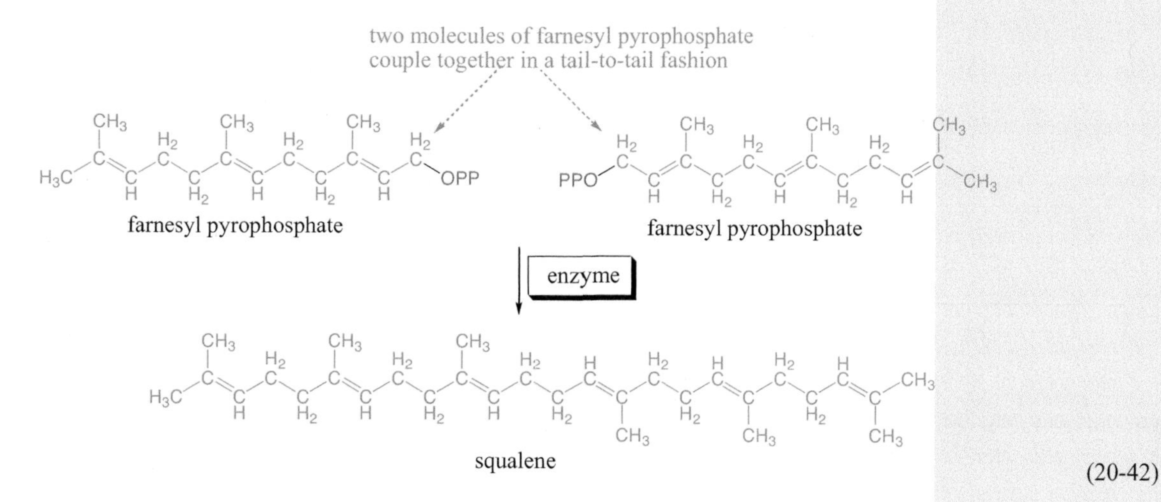

(20-42)

Squalene is an important terpene, because it is the precursor to cholesterol, from which all other steroid hormones are biosynthesized. As shown in Equation 20-41, squalene is oxidized by the enzyme squalene epoxidase in the presence of oxygen, producing squalene oxide. Under acid catalysis, the epoxide ring is electrophilic at the tertiary carbon that is indicated, which facilitates an electrophilic addition step that involves three alkene groups simultaneously. Three new carbon-carbon bonds are formed, resulting in three new rings—two that are six-membered, and one that is five-membered. Notice that when each p bond is broken, the pair of electrons remains associated with the *less* alkyl-substituted alkene carbon, which is what we would expect in a Markovnikov addition. Thus, in the carbocation that is produced, the positive charge is on a tertiary carbon.

In the next step, a 1,2-alkyl shift converts the five-membered ring into an additional six-membered ring, and the positive remains on a tertiary carbon. Subsequently, another electrophilic addition takes place, yielding the protosterol cation—in that step, the final ring is formed. Lanosterol is produced when a proton is eliminated, which also causes the shifting of two methyl groups and two other protons. From lanosterol, several additional steps are required to produce cholesterol.

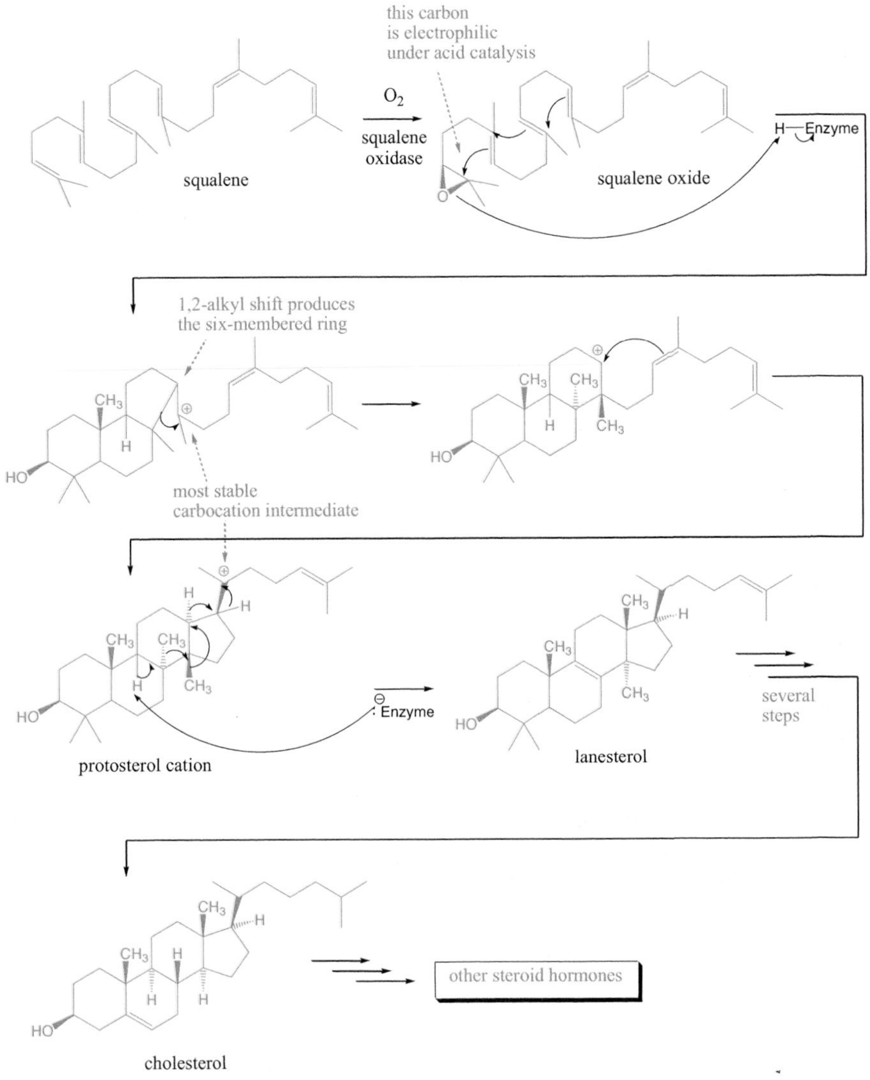
this carbon
is electrophilic
under acid catalysis
O2
squalene
oxidase
squalene
squalene oxide
H—Enzyme
1,2-alkyl shift produces
the six-membered ring
most stable
carbocation intermediate
protosterol cation
:Enzyme
lanesterol
several
steps
cholesterol
other steroid hormones

CHAPTER SUMMARY AND KEY TERMS

- A strong Brønsted acid, such as HCl or HBr, has an electron-poor proton, and thus is characterized as an **electrophile**. Such acids can therefore react with the nonpolar π bond of an alkene, which is relatively electron-rich. An **electrophilic addition reaction** ensues, in which the Brønsted acid adds across a C=C double bond—the proton to one carbon, and the conjugate base to the other. (Section 20.1)
- In the addition of a Brønsted acid to an alkene, the rate-determining step is the addition of the proton, which is step 1 of the general mechanism. (Section 20.1)
- The *regiochemistry* of the addition of a Brønsted acid across a C=C double bond is described by **Markovnikov's rule**. In turn, Markovnikov's rule derives from the fact that the addition of a proton to an alkene takes place so as to produce the most stable carbocation intermediate. (Section 20.2)
- Because the mechanism for the addition of a Brønsted acid to an alkene proceeds through a carbocation intermediate, such reactions are susceptible to carbocation rearrangements. (Section 20.3)

- Stereochemistry is a concern in electrophilic addition reactions involving alkenes if one of the alkene carbons becomes a stereocenter in the product. If the starting alkene is achiral, then any chiral products must be produced as a racemic mixture of enantiomers. (Section 20.4)
- Weak Brønsted acids, such as water and alcohols, can add across the double bond of an alkene under acid catalysis. When water adds, the reaction is an **acid-catalyzed hydration reaction**. (Section 20.5)
- An alkyne can undergo electrophilic addition of a Brønsted acid to produce a vinyl-substituted alkene. As with electrophilic addition to an alkene, the regiochemistry of the addition to an alkyne is described by Markovnikov's rule. (Section 20.6)
- When two equivalents of a hydrogen halide add to a C≡C triple bond, the major product is a **geminal dihalide**. This is an extension of Markovnikov's rule—during the addition of the second equivalent of the acid, the carbocation intermediate that is produced is resonance-stabilized if the positive charge appears on the carbon atom already attached to the halogen atom. (Section 20.6)
- The acid-catalyzed hydration of an alkyne produces an enol, which quickly undergoes tautomerization to produce a ketone. (Section 20.7)
- A conjugated diene undergoes electrophilic addition via **1,2-addition** and **1,4-addition**, producing a mixture of products. Both mechanisms involve precisely the same carbocation intermediate, in which the positive charge is resonance-delocalized over two carbon atoms. (Section 20.8)
- At cold temperatures, electrophilic addition to a conjugated diene takes place under kinetic control, and at warm temperatures, it takes place under thermodynamic control. The product of 1,2-addition is typically the kinetic product. The thermodynamic product is usually the one in which the alkene product is best stabilized, either by alkyl substitution or by conjugation. (Section 20.9)
- Benzene does not undergo electrophilic addition with Brønsted acids, because doing so would destroy the aromaticity of the ring. (Section 20.10)
- Alkenes such as 2-methylpropene and dihydropyran (DHP) can be used to protect alcohols. Under acidic conditions, an alcohol will add to one of these alkenes to produce a *tert*-butyl ether or acetal, respectively, both of which are unreactive under neutral and basic conditions. The original alcohol is recovered by treatment with aqueous acid. (Section 20.11)

REACTION TABLES

Starting Functional Group	Typical Reagent Required	Functional Group Formed	Comments	Discussed in Section(s)
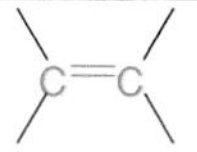 C=C Alkene	$\xrightarrow[X = Cl, Br, I]{HX, CCl_4}$	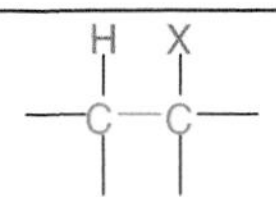 H–C–C–X Alkyl halide	Markovnikov addition	20.1
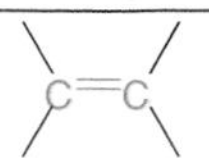 C=C Alkene	$\xrightarrow[H^{\oplus}]{H_2O}$	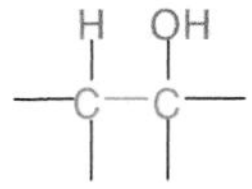 H–C–C–OH Alcohol	Markovnikov addition, acid catalysis	20.5
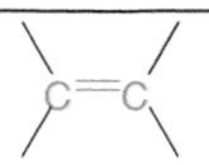 C=C Alkene	$\xrightarrow[H^{\oplus}]{ROH}$	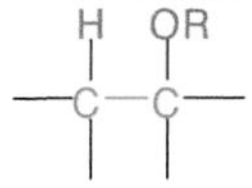 H–C–C–OR	Markovnikov addition, acid catalysis	20.5

		Ether		
—C≡C— Alkyne	HX (1 equiv) → X = Cl,Br,I	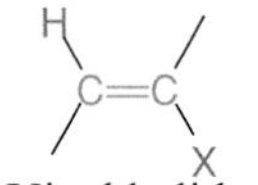 Vinyl halide	Markovnikov addition, predominantly *trans*	20.6
—C≡C— Alkyne	HX (2 equiv) → X = Cl,Br,I	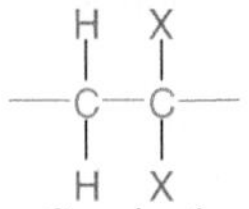 Geminal dihalide		20.6
—C≡C— Alkyne	H_2O → TfOH or Tf_2NH	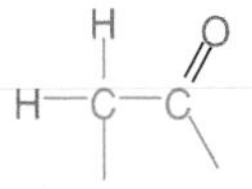 Ketone	Markovnikov addition of H_2O, keto-enol tautomerization	20.7
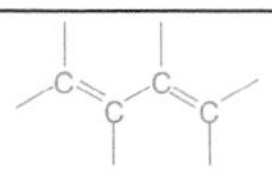 Conjugated diene	HX (1 equiv), cold → X = Cl,Br,I	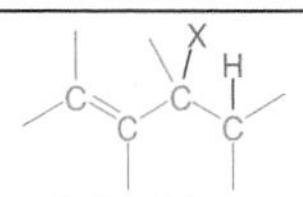 1,2-adduct	Kinetic control	20.8; 20.9
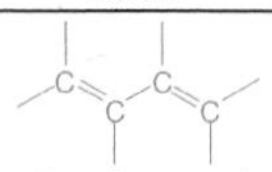 Conjugated diene	HX (1 equiv), warm → X = Cl,Br,I	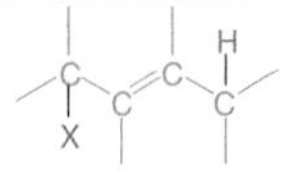 1,4-adduct	Thermodynamic control	20.8; 20.9

PROBLEMS

20. Cyclohexene can react with hydrogen halides, HX, to yield the various halocyclohexanes, $C_6H_{11}X$. Rank HF, HCl, HBr, and HI in order of *increasing* reaction rate. Explain. (Hint: What is the rate determining step?)

21. Rank the following alkenes in order of increasing rate of electrophilic addition of HCl. Explain. (Hint: What is the rate determining step?)

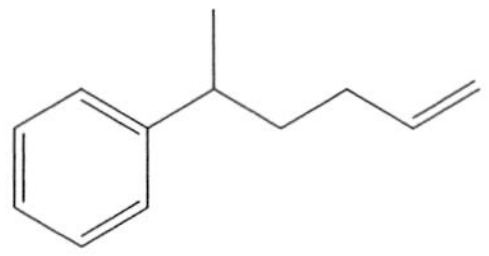

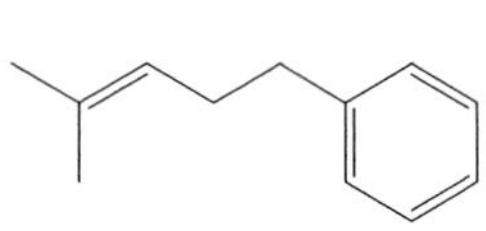

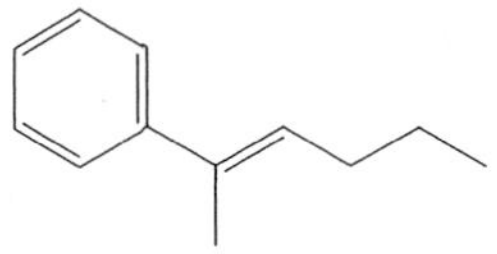

22. Which of the following alkenes will produce 1-chloro-1,2-dimethyl-1-phenylpropane as the major product when treated with HCl? Explain.

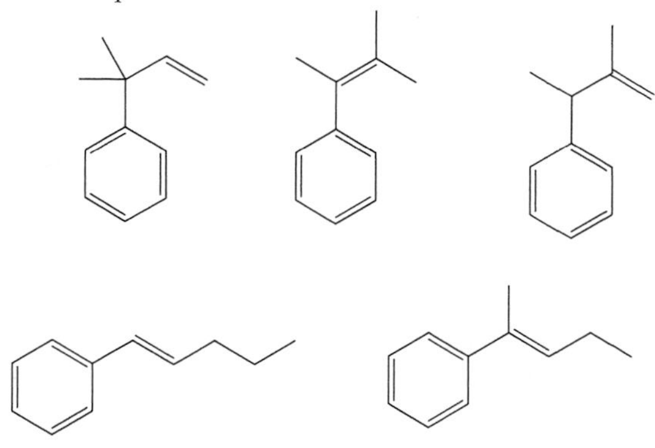

23. Predict the major product(s) for each of the following reactions
    a. 4-chloro-1-butene + HBr $\longrightarrow$
    b. 1-chloro-1-butene + HBr $\longrightarrow$
    c. 4,4-dimethylcyclopentene + H_2O, H^+ $\longrightarrow$
    d. propyne + 2 HCl $\longrightarrow$
    e. cyclopentylethene $\xrightarrow{H_3O^+}$

24. Each of the following compounds can be produced from an alkene, using a single electrophilic addition reaction. Write that reaction, and draw its complete, detailed mechanism.
    a. 4-chloro-1,2-dimethylcyclohexane
    b. 2-chloro-1,2-dimethylcyclohexane
    c. 1-bromo-1,1-diphenylbutane
    d. 1,1-dichloropentane

25. Each of the following compounds can be produced from an alkene, using a single electrophilic addition reaction. Write that reaction, and draw its complete, detailed mechanism.
    a. pentan-2-ol
    b. 3,5-dimethylpentan-3-ol
    c. 1-methoxy-1,4-dimethylcyclohexane
    d. cyclopentylmethoxyphenylmethanol

26. Each of the following compounds can be produced from an alkyne, using a single electrophilic addition reaction. Write that reaction, and draw its complete, detailed mechanism.
    a. 1,1-dichloro-2-cyclopentyl-1-phenylethane
    b. D H Br
    c. 3,3-dibromohex-3-ene
    d. Cl Cl

27. Each of the following compounds can be produced from an alkyne, using a single electrophilic addition reaction. Write that reaction, and draw its complete, detailed mechanism.

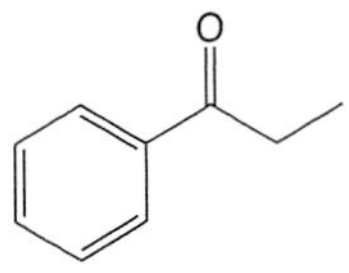

a. 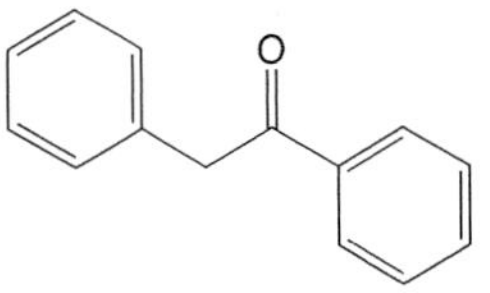 b.

28. In the chapter, we mentioned that electrophilic addition to an internal alkyne generally leads to a *mixture* of isomeric adducts. However, the acid catalyzed hydration of the following internal alkyne leads to only a single product. Draw the product and explain why a mixture of adducts is not produced.

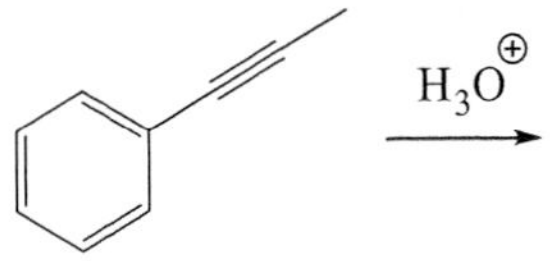

$H_3O^{\oplus}$

29. Outline how you would synthesize 1-methylcyclohexanol from two *different* alkenes.

30. Outline how you would carry out each of the following transformations. (Hint: Two or more separate reactions may be required.)

a. ?

b. ?

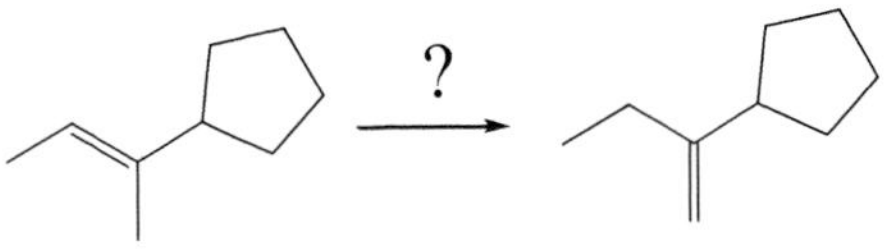

31. Consider the following addition of HBr.

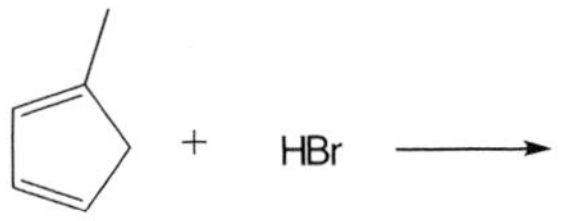

+ HBr

a. Draw all four carbocation intermediates possible upon protonation of the diene, and identify the most stable one.
b. Draw both halogenated products formed by attack of Br^- on that carbocation.
c. Which of those products would you expect to be formed in the greatest amount at low temperatures?
d. Which would you expect to be formed in the greatest amount at high temperatures?

32. Consider the following addition of HBr.

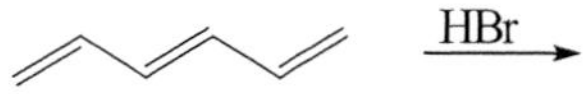

HBr

a. There are three carbocation intermediates possible from protonation of this triene. Draw all three of them and identify the most stable one.
b. Draw all halogenated products formed by attack of Br^- on that carbocation.
c. Which of those products would you expect to be formed in the greatest amount at low temperatures?
d. Which would you expect to be formed in the greatest amount at high temperatures?

33. In the chapter, we learned that the addition of HBr to 1,3-butadiene results in 1,2-addition at cold temperatures and 1,4-addition at warm temperatures.

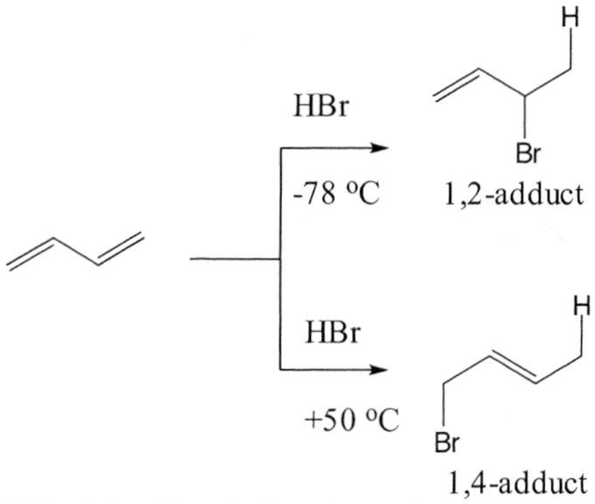

HBr, -78 °C → 1,2-adduct (H, Br)

HBr, +50 °C → 1,4-adduct (H, Br)

If the 1,2-adduct is first formed at cold temperatures and then warmed up, the 1,4 adduct is formed, as shown below. Draw a mechanism for this isomerization.

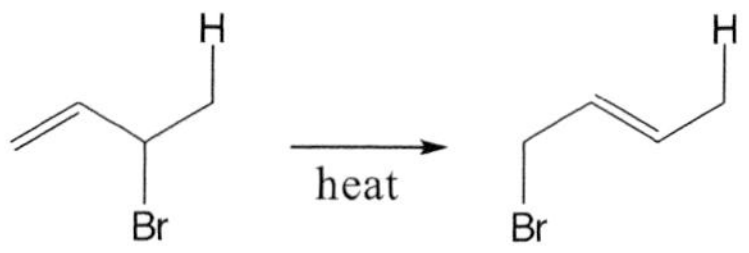

(H, Br) —heat→ (H, Br)

34. Draw the complete, detailed mechanism for the addition of HCl to dihydropyran and predict the major product.

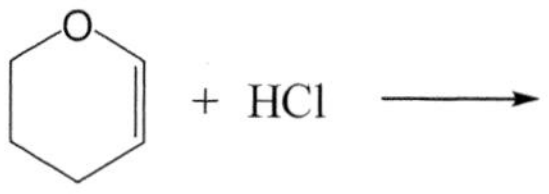

O + HCl →

35. Determine the structures of compounds A through L below.

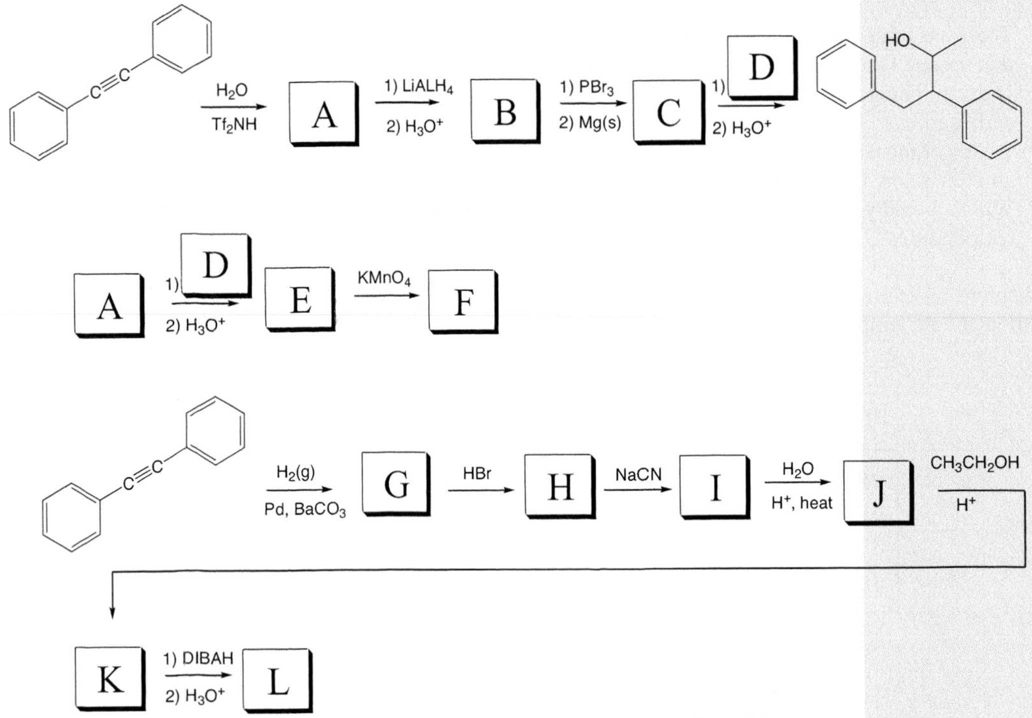

C≡C — H_2O / Tf_2NH → A — 1) $LiALH_4$ 2) H_3O^+ → B — 1) PBr_3 2) Mg(s) → C — 1) D 2) H_3O^+ → HO

A — 1) D 2) H_3O^+ → E — $KMnO_4$ → F

C≡C — $H_2(g)$ / Pd, $BaCO_3$ → G — HBr → H — NaCN → I — H_2O / H^+, heat → J — CH_3CH_2OH / H^+ → K — 1) DIBAH 2) H_3O^+ → L

36. Show how to synthesize each of the following compounds beginning with 1-phenylpropyne, using any other reagents necessary. (Hint: Two or more separate reactions may be required.)

a. 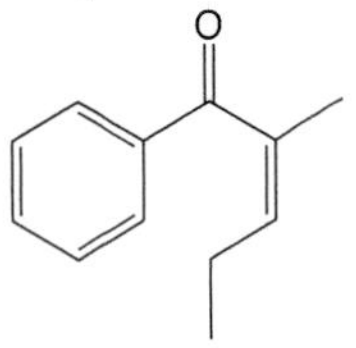 O

b. 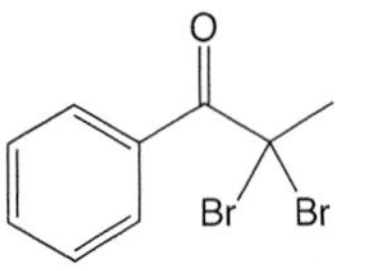 O Br Br

c. 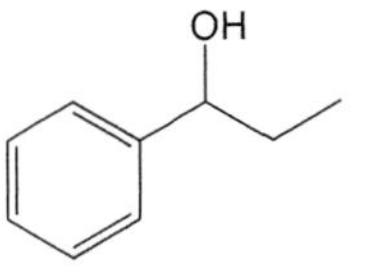 OH

d. 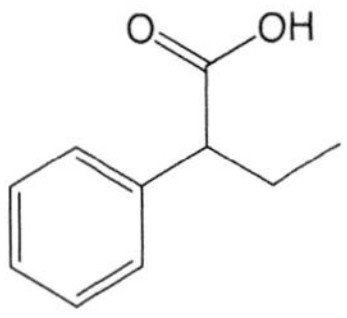 O OH

e. 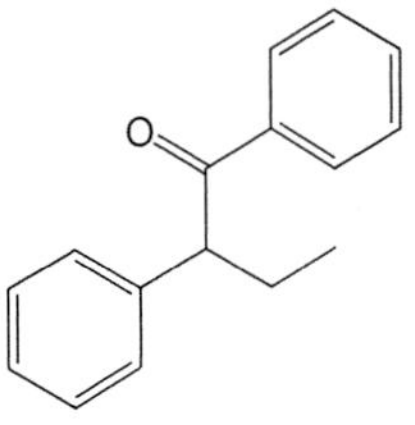 O

37. A compound, C_8H_6, is treated with H_2 over a Pd/$BaCO_3$ catalyst, followed by HBr, to yield a compound with the following IR and ^{1}H-NMR spectra. Draw the structure of the initial compound.

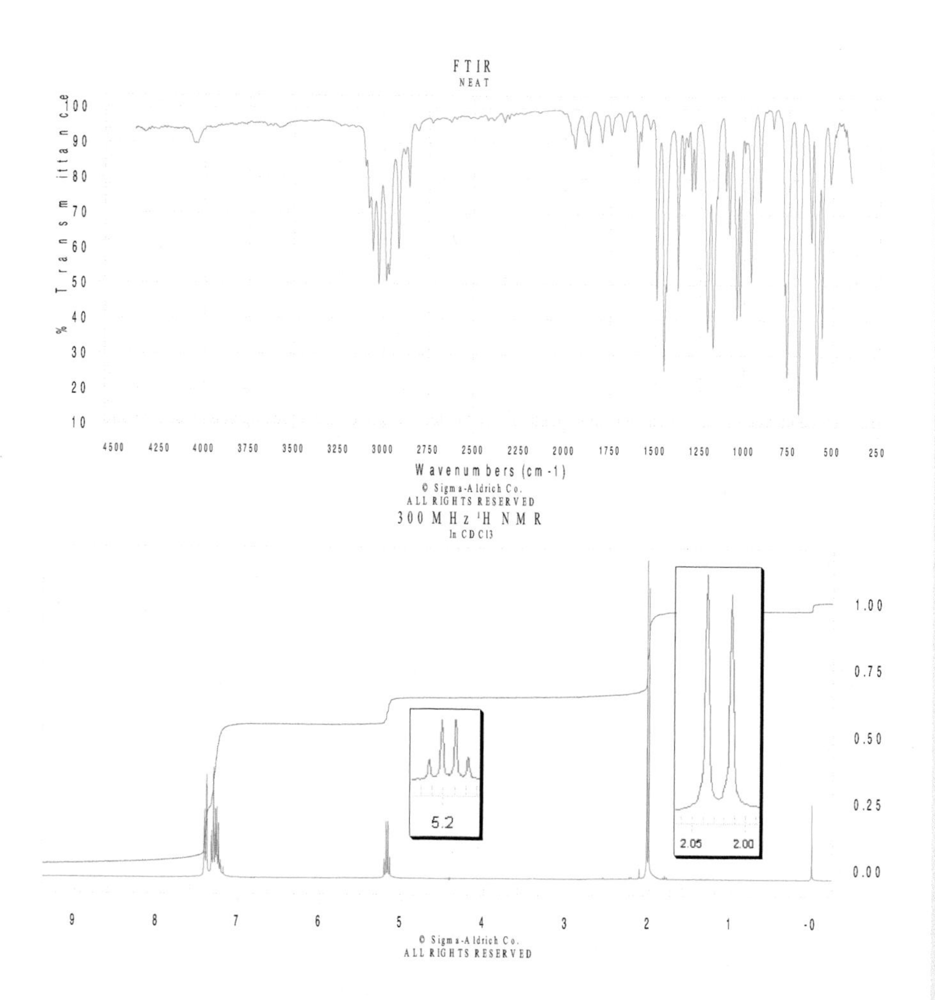

38. When phenylbut-2-yn-1-one is treated with water in the presence of a catalytic amount of trifluoromethanesulfonic acid, the compound that is produced has the formula $C_{10}H_{10}O_2$. The ^{1}H-NMR spectrum of that compound is shown below. (a) Draw the complete, detailed mechanism for this reaction, and draw the product. (b) Explain why the reaction exhibits this regioselectivity.

O

H_2O / TfOH → ?

phenylbut-2-yn-1-one

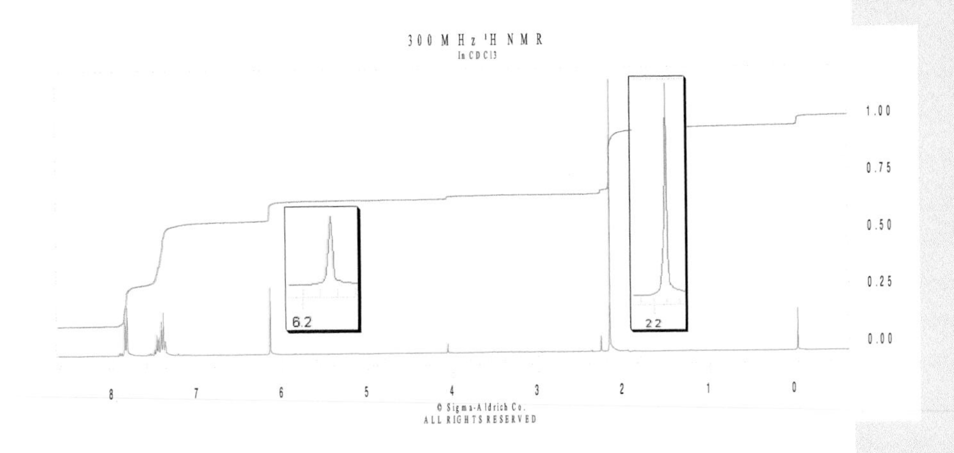

39. The major product of the reaction below has the formula C_4H_7ClO, and yields the IR and ¹H-NMR spectra shown below. (a) Draw the complete, detailed mechanism of this reaction and draw the major product. (b) Explain why the reaction exhibits this regioselectivity.

$$H_2C{=}CH{-}C({=}O){-}CH_3 \xrightarrow{HCl} C_4H_7ClO$$

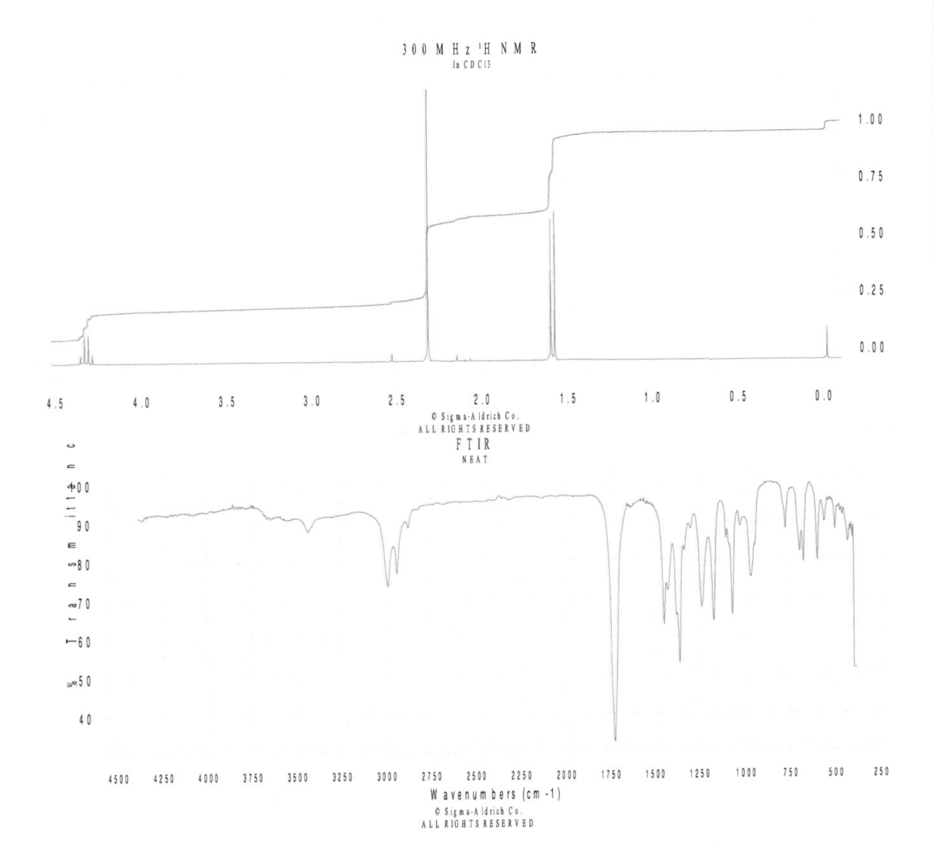

40. As we will see in greater detail in Chapter 22, $AlCl_3$ is a powerful Lewis acid that effectively catalyzes the dissociation of an alkyl chloride, R-Cl, into its respective ions, R^+ and Cl^-.

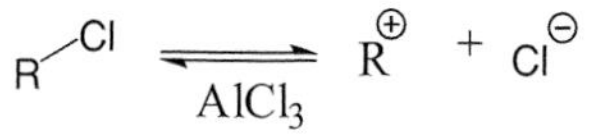

$$R\text{-}Cl \underset{AlCl_3}{\rightleftharpoons} R^{\oplus} + Cl^{\ominus}$$

(a) Propose a mechanism for the addition of RCl across a double bond, as shown in the reaction below.

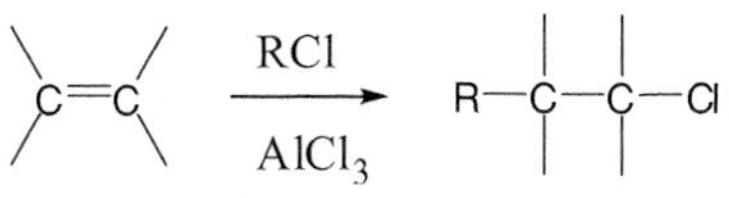

$$\text{C=C} \xrightarrow[AlCl_3]{RCl} \text{R—C—C—Cl}$$

(b) Using that mechanism, what are the two possible isomers that can be formed when 2-methylpropene is treated with 2-chloropropene in the presence of $AlCl_3$? Which one is the major product? Explain.

41. As we will learn in Chapters 25 and 26, a polymer is a very large molecule that contains many repeating units called monomers. The reaction below, for example, shows how styrene reacts to form polystyrene.

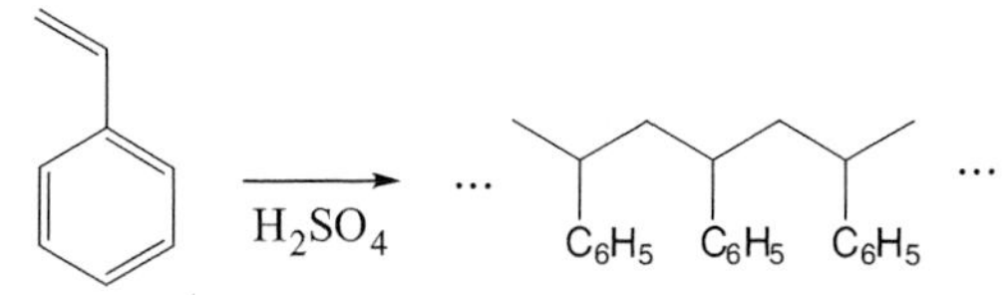

$$\xrightarrow{H_2SO_4}$$

... C_6H_5 C_6H_5 C_6H_5 ...

styrene polystyrene

The reaction is *initiated* by the electrophilic addition of H^+ from an acid like sulfuric acid, which generates an initial carbocation. Afterwards, that carbocation behaves as an electrophile in the presence of another molecule of styrene, resulting in yet another carbocation. This reaction can repeat many thousands of times to build up the polymer. With this in mind, draw the detailed mechanism that illustrates the initiation of the polymerization reaction and the addition of the first two monomers, as shown below.

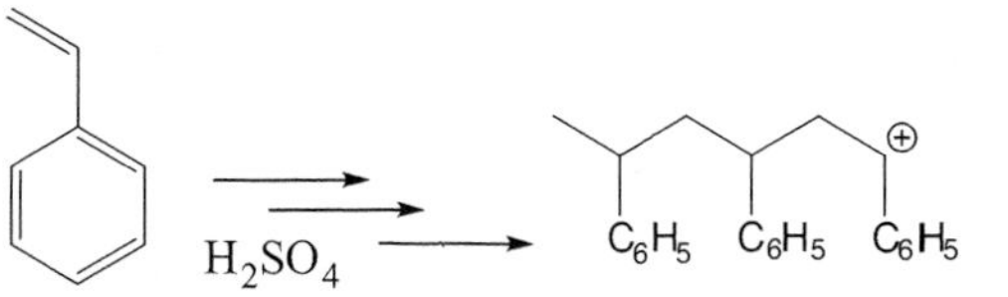

$$\xrightarrow{H_2SO_4} \rightarrow \rightarrow$$

C_6H_5 C_6H_5 C_6H_5 ⊕

42. Propose a synthesis for the following transformation. (Hint: You may need to incorporate two or more separate reactions.)

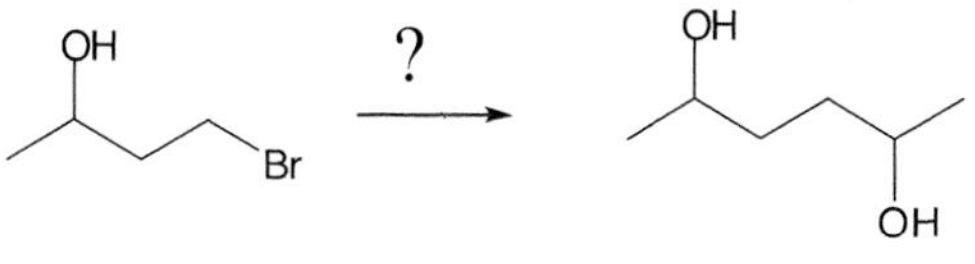

OH Br $\xrightarrow{?}$ OH OH

43. Treatment of but-1-en-3-yne with hydrogen bromide produces 4-bromobuta-1,2-diene, which is an allene. Draw the complete, detailed mechanism for this reaction.

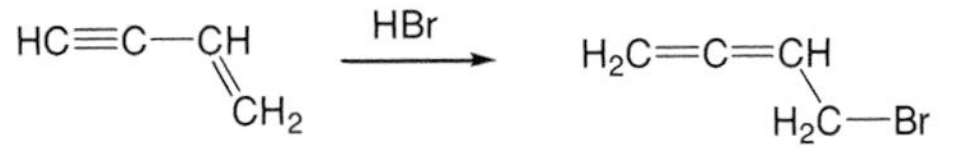

HC≡C—CH=CH₂ —HBr→ H₂C=C=CH—CH₂—Br

but-1-en-3-yne   4-bromobuta-1,2-diene

44. Propose a mechanism for the following reaction, in which HCl adds to 1,6-heptadiene.

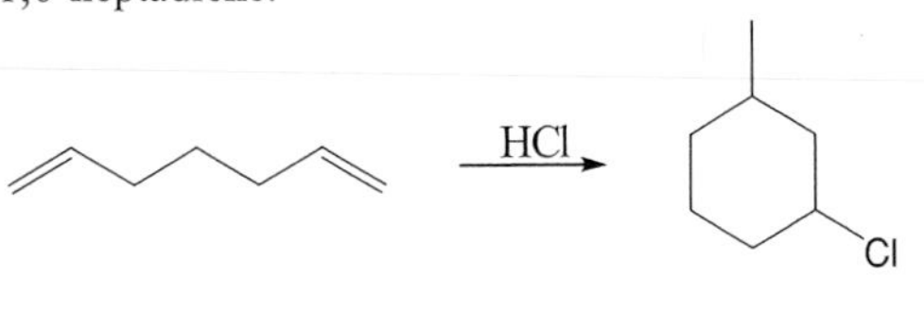

HCl

Cl

45. Cyclobutylidenecyclobutane reacts with aqueous acid to produce a compound whose formula is $C_8H_{14}O$. The IR spectrum of that product contains a broad, intense absorbance centered around 3,400 cm^{-1}. No IR absorbances appear between 1,600 cm^{-1} and 1,800 cm^{-1}. The ^{13}C-NMR spectrum contains five signals, and the DEPT spectrum indicated that three of them are CH_2 signals, one is a CH signal, and one is a C signal. (a) Draw the structure of the compound that is produced. (b) Draw the complete, detailed mechanism that leads to the formation of that compound. (c) What are the driving forces for this reaction?

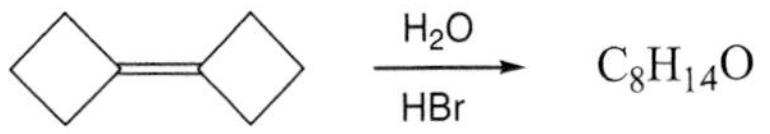

H_2O, HBr → $C_8H_{14}O$

cyclobutylidenecyclobutane

46. Treatment of 1,2-propadiene (an allene) with hydrogen bromide produces 2-bromopropene as the major product. This suggests that the more stable carbocation intermediate is produced by the addition of a proton to a terminal carbon rather than to the central carbon. (a) Draw both carbocation intermediates that can be produced by the addition of a proton to the allene. (b) Explain the relative stabilities of those intermediates. (Hint: It may help to draw the orbital picture of the intermediates.)

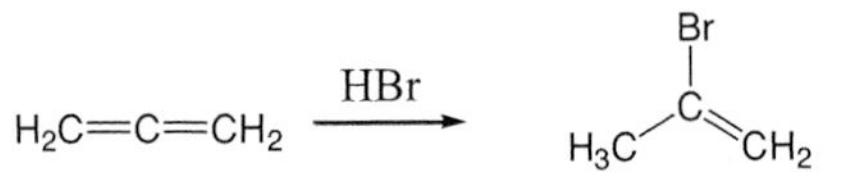

$H_2C{=}C{=}CH_2$ —HBr→ H_3C—C(Br)=CH_2

1,2-propadiene   2-bromopropene

Chapter 21. Electrophilic Addition to Nonpolar π Bonds 2: Reactions Involving Cyclic Transition States

Introduction

Chapter 20 discussed reactions in which a Brønsted acid adds to a C=C double bond of an alkene or a C≡C triple bond of an alkyne. In such reactions, the π bond of the alkene or alkyne is relatively electron-rich, whereas the proton (H^+) from the Brønsted acid is electron-poor. Thus, the proton acts as an *electrophile*, and as it adds to the alkene or alkyne, a carbocation intermediate is produced. Subsequently, that carbocation intermediate is attacked by a nucleophile.

Here we will see that species other than protons can act as electrophiles, and thus can also add to an alkene or alkyne. Examples include molecular halogens like Cl_2 and Br_2, peroxyacids (RCO_3H), carbenes (R_2C:), borane (BH_3), and oxidizing agents like OsO_4 and $KMnO_4$. Unlike the electrophilic addition of a Brønsted acid, all of these reaction mechanisms involve a step whose transition state is cyclic. As we will see, this prevents the formation of a carbocation intermediate, and therefore has significant consequences on the outcomes of the reactions.

We begin this chapter with a brief look at a key elementary step that comprises several of the above reactions—electrophilic addition to form a three-membered ring. We then examine the details of several reactions that proceed by such a step, including carbene addition, halogenation, oxymercuration, and epoxide formation. Next, we examine hydroboration, which proceeds through a 4-membered ring transition state. Finally, we discuss *syn*-hydroxylation and oxidative cleavage reactions, all of which proceed through 5-membered ring transition states.

CHAPTER OBJECTIVES
Upon completion of this chapter you should be able to:

- Recognize when electrophilic addition to an alkene or alkyne favors the formation of a three-membered ring instead of a carbocation intermediate, and draw the mechanism for such a step.
- Show how carbene and dichlorocarbene are produced from their respective precursors, and draw the mechanism of their reaction with an alkene or alkyne.
- Describe the role of the halonium ion intermediate in the addition of a molecular halogen to an alkene or alkyne, and predict the products of such reactions, including stereochemistry and regiochemistry.
- Explain the importance of the oxymercuration-reduction reaction, and draw its complete mechanism.
- Show how an epoxide is produced in the reaction of a peroxyacid with an alkene.
- Draw the detailed mechanism of hydroboration-oxidation of an alkene or alkyne, and predict the products of such a reaction, including stereochemistry and regiochemistry.
- Explain the role of disiamylborane in the hydroboration-oxidation of an alkyne.
- Specify the conditions for the *syn*-hydroxylation of an alkene or alkyne, and draw the mechanism.
- Identify the various oxidative cleavage reactions, and explain how and why the products of such reactions can differ.

21.1. ELECTROPHILIC ADDITION VIA A 3-MEMBERED RING: THE GENERAL MECHANISM

The mechanisms of all of the electrophilic addition reactions we saw in Chapter 20 include a step in which a carbocation is produced. Recall that such a step is in general highly unfavorable, due in large part to the loss of an octet on a carbon atom, as indicated in Equation 21-1.

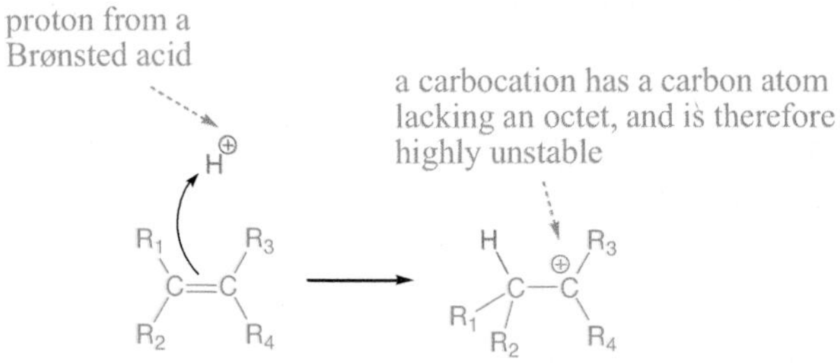

proton from a Brønsted acid

a carbocation has a carbon atom lacking an octet, and is therefore highly unstable

$$R_1R_2C{=}CR_3R_4 + H^{\oplus} \longrightarrow H(R_1)(R_2)C{-}C^{\oplus}R_3R_4 \quad (21\text{-}1)$$

However, if the electrophilic atom on the electrophile has a lone pair of electrons, then addition can take place in such a way as to avoid breaking an octet. This is illustrated in Equation 21-2, in which "E:" represents a generic electrophile that possesses a lone pair of electrons.

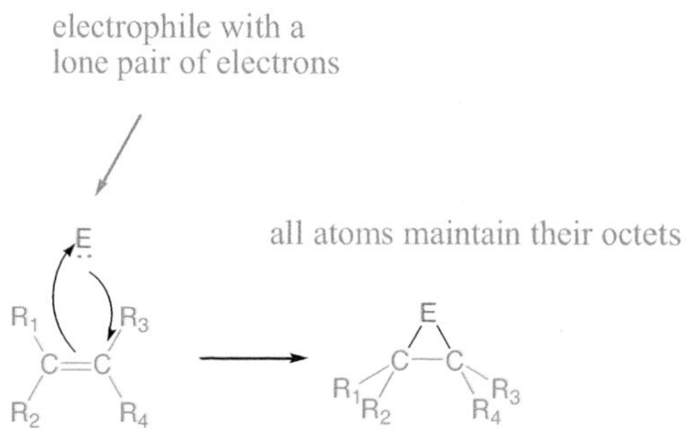

electrophile with a lone pair of electrons

all atoms maintain their octets

(21-2)

In this step, two new E–C bonds are formed simultaneously to produce a three-membered ring. One of those bonds is formed by the electrons from the initial carbon-carbon π bond, and the other is formed by the lone pair of electrons from the electrophile. As we can see, each of the carbon atoms that forms a new bond to the electrophile maintains its octet throughout the course of the reaction step. The reason is that as one of those carbon atoms loses its share of the two π electrons, it gains a share of two electrons in the new σ bond to the electrophile.

Notice in Equation 21-2 that in the reaction involving an alkene as the reactant, two carbon atoms re-hybridize from sp^2 to sp^3. Therefore, *stereochemistry* can be a concern. In such cases, stereochemistry is governed by the following rules.

- The *cis/trans* relationship is conserved for the groups attached to the alkene carbons in Equation 21-2. Groups that are on the same side of the double bond in the reactant must end up on the same side of the plane of the three-membered ring in the product (and vice versa).
- If the cyclic product in Equation 21-2 is chiral, then a mixture of stereoisomers is produced—a racemic mixture of enantiomers if the original alkene is achiral, or an unequal mixture of diastereomers if the original alkene is chiral.

The spirit of these rules is captured by Equation 21-3.

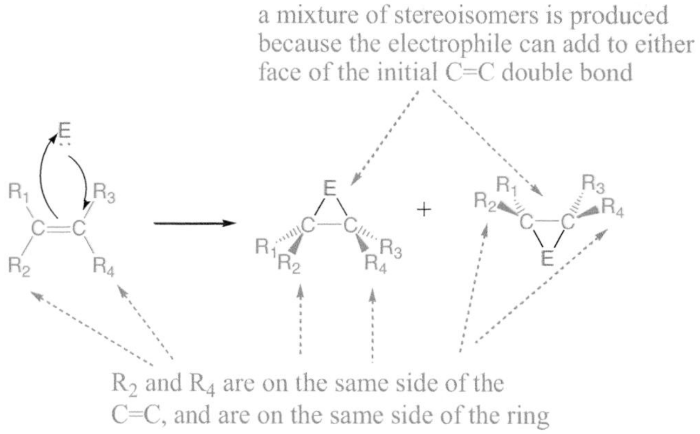

a mixture of stereoisomers is produced because the electrophile can add to either face of the initial C=C double bond

R_2 and R_4 are on the same side of the C=C, and are on the same side of the ring

(21-3)

The reason for the conservation of stereochemistry in such reactions is that both C–E bonds are formed simultaneously. Normally, if a C=C double bond is converted into a C–C single bond, rotation about that single bond can lead to scrambling of the *cis/trans* relationship among the groups attached to those carbon atoms. In this case, however, that single bond is formed as part of a ring, so free rotation cannot take place.

The reason the reaction produces a mixture of stereoisomers is that an alkene functional group is planar, and the electrophile can add to either face of the alkene. One stereoisomer is produced by the addition of the electrophile to one face, and the second is produced by addition to the other face. If the initial alkene is achiral, then it possesses a plane of symmetry, and addition to each face of the alkene is equally likely. By contrast, if the initial alkene is chiral, then it possesses no plane of symmetry, making electrophilic addition to one face more likely than addition to the other.

Your Turn 21.1. Match each curved arrow notation on the left with a product on the right. Write "racemic" next to each product that will be produced as a racemic mixture.

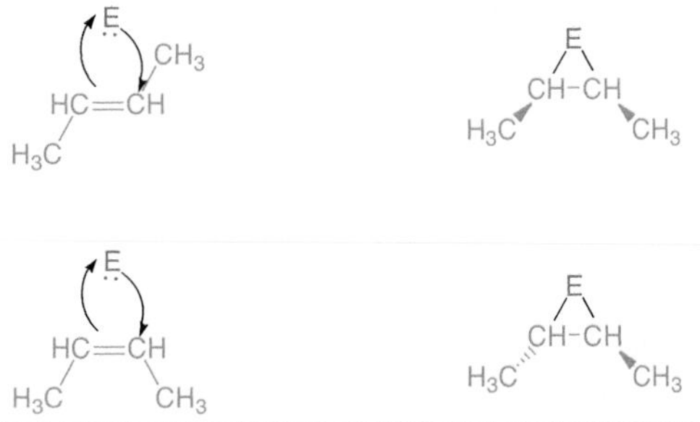

E
CH$_3$
HC=CH
H$_3$C

E
CH-CH
H$_3$C CH$_3$

E
HC=CH
H$_3$C CH$_3$

E
CH-CH
H$_3$C CH$_3$

Having examined this elementary step in a generic fashion, let's now turn our attention toward four specific reaction mechanisms in which it appears. Section 21.2 will discuss the electrophilic addition of a carbene to an alkene, in which the three-membered ring product is stable and can be isolated. In the other three reactions—electrophilic addition involving molecular halogens in Section 21.3, oxymercuration-reduction in Section 21.4, and epoxide formation in Section 21.5—the three-membered ring that is produced is a reactive intermediate.

21.2. ELECTROPHILIC ADDITION OF CARBENES: FORMATION OF CYCLOPROPANE RINGS

Mechanistically, the simplest of the reactions we will see in this section is that between an alkene and a **carbene**. A carbene is a species containing a carbon atom possessing two bonds and a lone pair of electrons, as shown below. Like a carbocation, a carbene possesses a carbon that lacks an octet (it is surrounded by only six electrons—two single bonds and one lone pair of electrons) and is therefore *highly* electron-poor. Unlike a carbocation, however, the electron-poor atom of a carbene has a formal charge of 0.

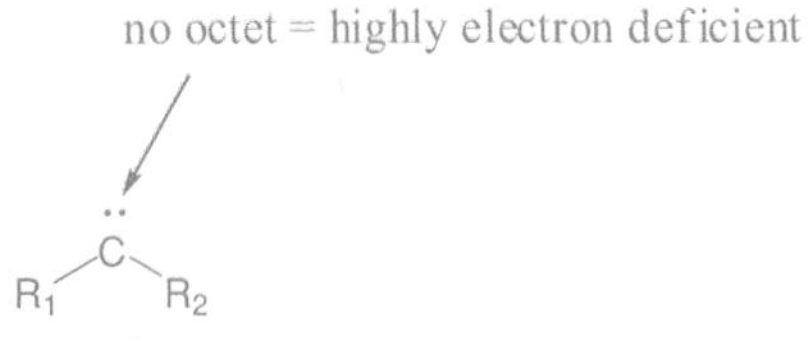

no octet = highly electron deficient

C
R$_1$ R$_2$

a carbene

Your Turn 21.2. Using the method we learned in Chapter 1, calculate the formal charge on the carbene carbon and show your work here.

Due to their high reactivity, carbenes have very short lifetimes and therefore cannot be isolated. Consequently, *we cannot simply add a carbene as a reagent.* Instead,

> Carbenes must be generated *in situ* (i.e., "on site") from precursors that can be added as reagents.

Diazomethane, CH_2N_2, is one precursor from which a carbene can be made. An example of how it is used is shown in Equation 21-4, illustrating that it leads to the production of a new cyclopropane ring.

new cyclopropane ring

$$+ \; CH_2N_2 \xrightarrow{h\nu} \; + \; N_2(g)$$

80%

(21-4)

The complete mechanism for this reaction is shown in Equation 21-5. In the first step, the C-N bond in diazomethane is broken, which produces carbene. Aiding this step is the fact that $N_2(g)$ is produced—not only is molecular nitrogen a very stable leaving group, but it is also a gas, so it escapes the reaction mixture *irreversibly*. In the second step, the carbene reacts with the alkene to generate the three-membered ring via the same mechanism as in Equation 21-2.

Mechanism for the Reaction in Equation 21-4

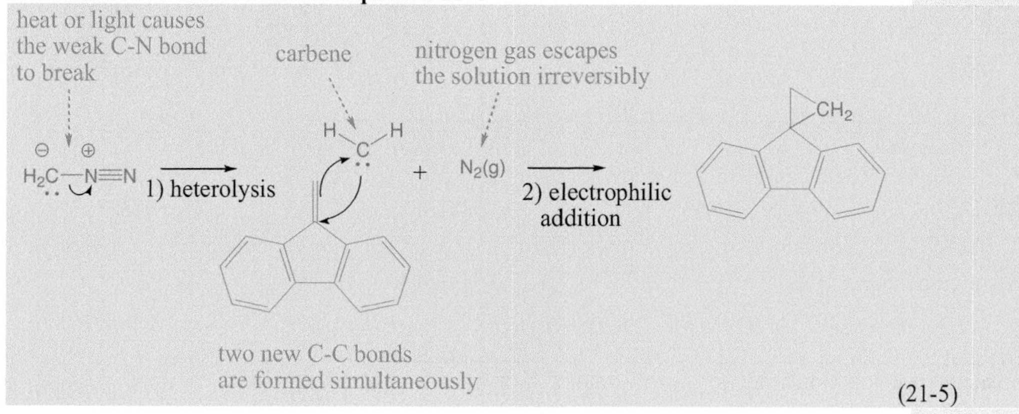

(21-5)

> **Problem 21.1.** Draw the complete, detailed mechanism for the following reaction and predict the major products.
>
> $$\xrightarrow[\text{heat}]{CH_2N_2}$$

> **Problem 21.2.** A compound with formula C_4H_6 is treated with CH_2N_2 in the presence of light. The ^{1}H-NMR spectrum of the product exhibits a singlet at 0.73 ppm. Draw the reactant and the product of this reaction.

Chloroform ($CHCl_3$) is another precursor that can be used to generate a carbene. Equation 21-6 provides an example, in which chloroform is treated with a strong base in the presence of *trans*-pent-2-ene, once again producing a cyclopropane ring. We can see from Equation 21-6 that the carbene that is generated from chloroform must be dichloromethylene (Cl_2C:), also called **dichlorocarbene**, which is different from the one generated from diazomethane.

cyclohexene + $CHCl_3$ $\xrightarrow[\text{45 h, 40 - 45 °C}]{\text{NaOH, } CH_2Cl_2}$ 7,7-dichlorobicyclo[4.1.0]heptane (52%)   (21-6)

As shown in the mechanism Equation 21-7, the base first deprotonates chloroform, which is mildly acidic (pK_a = 24). Next, Cl^- is eliminated in a heterolysis step to generate dichloromethylene. Although Cl^- is a good leaving group, this step occurs quite slowly because the carbene that is produced is very unstable. In the final step, the carbene adds to the alkene, producing the cyclopropane ring.

Mechanism for the Reaction in Equation 21-6

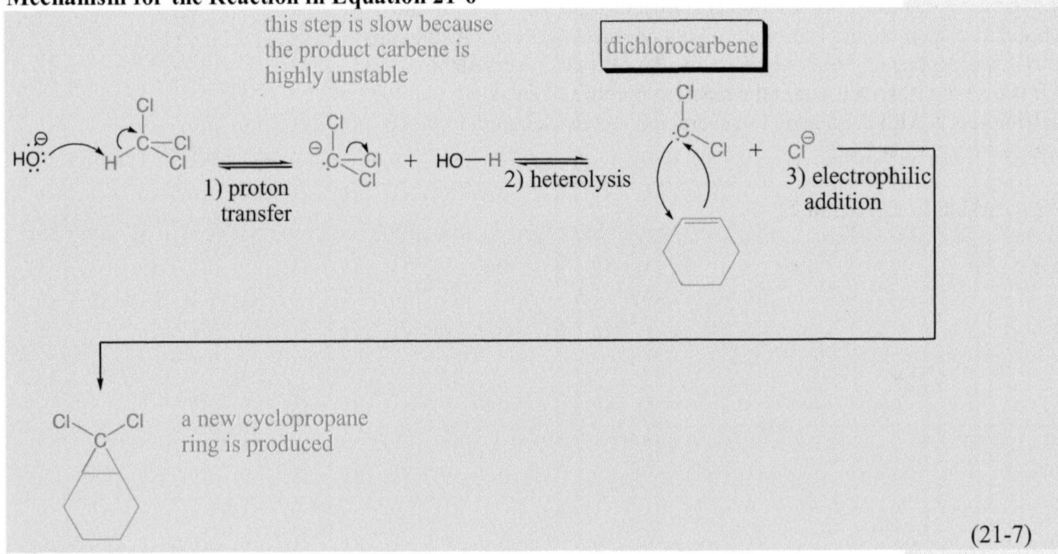

(21-7)

Your Turn 21.3. The reaction below is similar to the one in Equation 21-6.

cyclopentene + $CHBr_3$ $\xrightarrow{\text{NaOH}}$ 6,6-dibromobicyclo[3.1.0]hexane

The mechanism for this reaction is given below, but the curved arrow notation has been omitted. Complete the mechanism by adding the curved arrows, and write the name of each elementary step below the appropriate reaction arrow.

HO:⊖ H–CBr₃ ⇌ ⊖:CBr₃ + HO–H ⇌ :CBr₂ + Br⊖

Br Br C (dibromocyclopropane fused to cyclopentane)

Problem 21.3. Draw the complete, detailed mechanism for the following reaction. Using the mechanism, predict the products, paying attention to stereochemistry.

$$\xrightarrow[NaOC(CH_3)_3]{CHBr_3} ?$$

Problem 21.4. Suggest how the following compound can be formed from two different alkenes via carbene addition.

$$\xrightarrow{?}$$ Cl, Cl

21.3. ELECTROPHILIC ADDITION INVOLVING MOLECULAR HALOGENS: SYNTHESIS OF 1,2-DIHALIDES AND HALOHYDRINS

The previous section highlighted the reactions of carbenes with alkenes. The highly electrophilic carbon atom of the carbene possesses a lone pair of electrons, which is what facilitates the formation of a three-membered ring. Carbenes are not the only species in which an electrophilic atom possesses a lone pair of electrons. As we will see in this section, molecular halogens, such as Cl_2 and Br_2, share that feature with carbenes, and can therefore react with an alkene to produce a three-membered ring. Unlike what is observed with carbenes, however, the three-membered ring that is produced from a molecular halogen is an unstable intermediate, and reacts further to produce relatively stable products such as a *1,2-dihalide* or a *halohydrin*.

21.3a. Synthesis of 1,2-Dihalides

When cyclohexene is treated with molecular bromine (Br_2) in tetrachloromethane (CCl_4), also called carbon tetrachloride, a racemic mixture of *trans*-1,2-dibromocyclohexane (Equation 21-8) is produced.

products of *anti* addition only

cyclohexene $\xrightarrow[CCl_4]{Br_2}$ *trans*-1,2-dibromocyclohexane (59%) — two enantiomers shown: Br / Br + Br / Br

(21-8)

In other words,

Molecular bromine undergoes *anti* addition to a C=C double bond.

It might seem peculiar that such a reaction should take place at all, because Br_2 does not appear to possess an electron-poor atom. However, recall that we have seen Br_2 behave as an electrophile once before—in an S_N2 reaction in the bromination of enols and enolate anions (Section 10.4). As the electron-rich π bond approaches Br_2, Br_2 becomes *polarized*, temporarily making one of the Br atoms electron-poor (Figure 21-1).

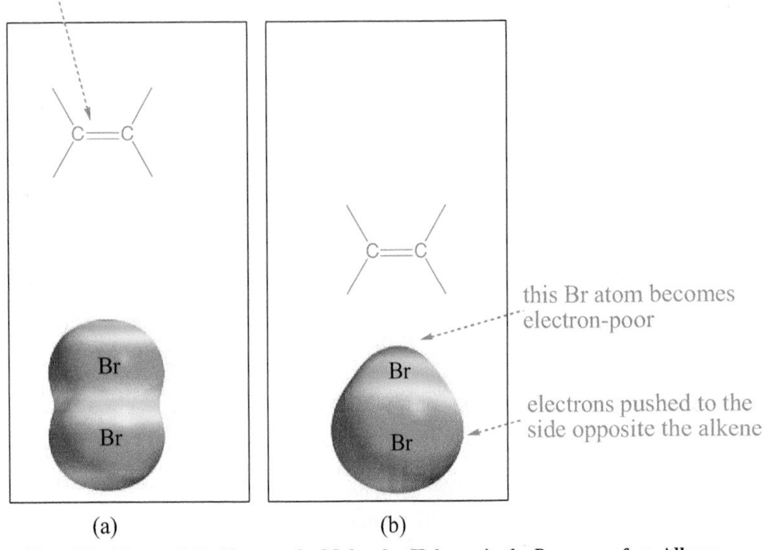

Figure 21-1. The Electrophilic Nature of a Molecular Halogen in the Presence of an Alkene
(a) When it is isolated from other species, Br_2 is not electron-poor. (b) As the electron-rich alkene approaches the Br_2 molecule, electrons of Br_2 are repelled to the side opposite the alkene, temporarily generating an electron-poor site on the Br atom closer to the alkene. Subsequent flow of electrons takes place between the electron-rich alkene and the electron-poor Br atom.

In order to account for the stereospecificity of the reaction in Equation 21-8, the mechanism must *not* proceed through a carbocation intermediate—otherwise, both *syn* and *anti* addition would take place (see again Section 20.4). Instead, as shown in Equation 21-9, the mechanism proceeds through a **bromonium ion intermediate** (possessing a positively charged bromine atom), which is produced in step 1. The formation of that bromonium ion is driven by the flow of electrons from the electron-rich π bond to the electron-poor Br atom. Similar to the reaction in Equation 21-2, a lone pair of electrons on Br forms a bond back to one of the alkene carbons in order to avoid breaking the carbon atom's octet, resulting in a three-membered ring. In this case, the ring consists of two carbon atoms and one bromine atom. Simultaneously, the weak Br-Br bond breaks, and one of the atoms leaves as bromide ion.

Mechanism for the Reaction in Equation 21-8

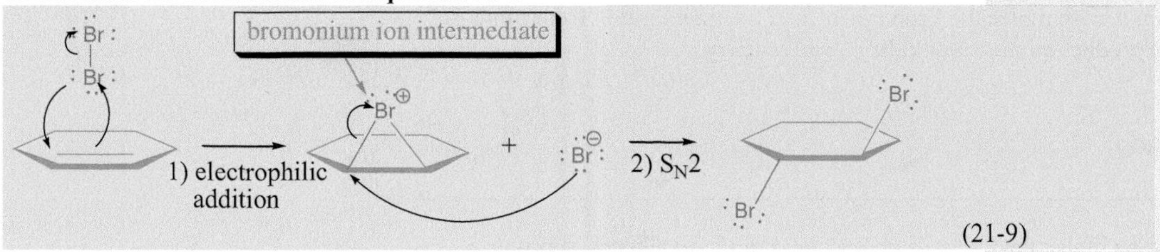

(21-9)

The second step of the mechanism is an S_N2 reaction—the bromide ion produced in step 1 acts as the nucleophile, and the positively charged Br atom in the ring acts as the leaving group. This is exactly the same step we saw in the opening of a protonated epoxide ring in Section 10.7, where a positively charged oxygen atom behaves as the leaving group.

Notice from Equation 21-9 that the S_N2 reaction in the second step is precisely what demands that the two Br atoms add to the alkene in an *anti* fashion. Recall from Section 8.5b that in an S_N2 reaction, the nucleophile must attack from the side *opposite the leaving group*. The only way to achieve *syn* addition would be for the Br^- nucleophile to attack from the same side on which the leaving group leaves—something that is forbidden in an S_N2 reaction.

Notice also that in the second step in Equation 21-9, nucleophilic attack can occur at either carbon atom of the three-membered ring, giving rise to a mixture of stereoisomers. This is illustrated in Equation 21-10. If the bromonium ion intermediate is achiral, as is the case in Equation 21-8, then a *racemic* mixture of enantiomers is produced.

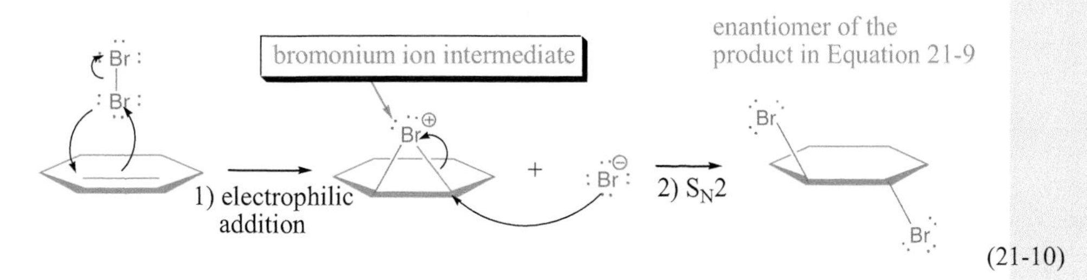

(21-10)

Solved Problem 21.1. Predict the products of the following reaction. Do you expect the product mixture to be optically active? Why or why not?

Br_2, CCl_4

Think. What reaction takes place between Br_2 and an alkene? Are the product molecules chiral? How does chirality relate to optical activity?

Solve. Br_2 undergoes *anti*-addition across the double bond, yielding the following mixture of products.

Br ... Br + Br ... Br

Each product molecule is chiral. Whereas the products in Equation 21-8 are enantiomers, here the two products are diastereomers. Therefore, they are formed in unequal amounts and, furthermore, do not have equal and opposite values of $[\alpha]_D^{20}$. Thus, the product solution will be optically active.

Problem 21.5. Draw the product(s) that would be produced from reacting each of the following compounds with molecular bromine in carbon tetrachloride. Determine whether or not the product mixture would be optically active.

(a) HO_2C–CH=CH–CO_2H (b) (c) (d) Br

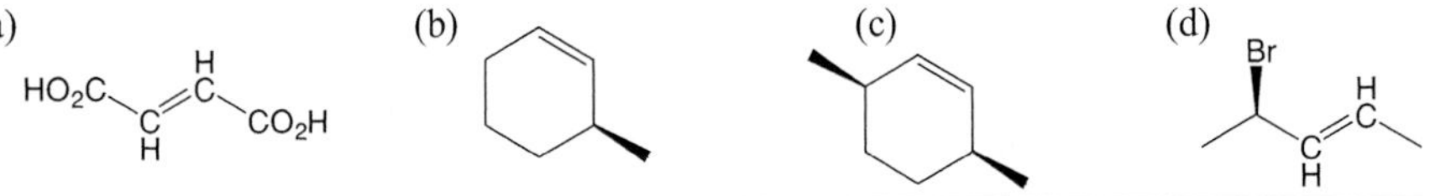

The chlorine molecule, Cl_2, also undergoes addition to alkenes to produce vicinal dichlorides (Equation 21-11). As in the addition of molecular bromine, molecular chlorine adds in an *anti* fashion to the double bond. The mechanism is similar, proceeding through a **chloronium ion intermediate** so as to avoid breaking carbon's octet (see Your Turn 21.4).

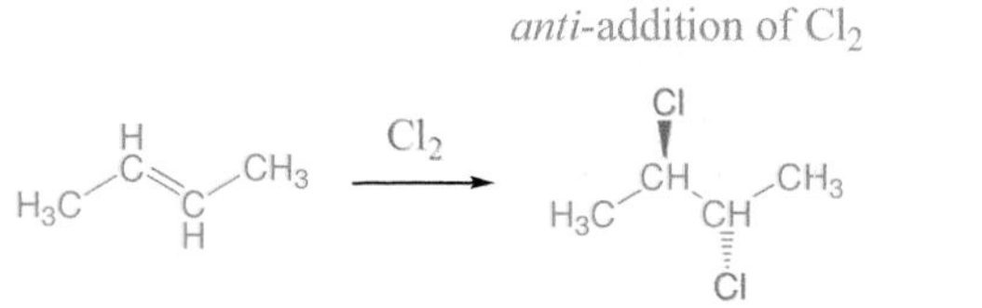

anti-addition of Cl_2

H_3C–CH=CH–CH_3 —Cl_2→ H_3C–CH(Cl)–CH(Cl)–CH_3

trans-but-2-ene (2*R*,3*S*)-2,3-dichlorobutane

73% (21-11)

Your Turn 21.4. The mechanism for the reaction in Equation 21-11 is shown below, but the curved arrow notation has been omitted. Complete the mechanism by adding the curved arrows, and write the name of each elementary step under the appropriate reaction arrow. Label the chloronium ion intermediate.

H_3C–CH=CH–CH_3 + :Cl–Cl: → H_3C–CH–CH–CH_3 (bridged $Cl^{\oplus}$) + $:Cl:^{\ominus}$ → H_3C–CH(Cl)–CH(Cl)–CH_3

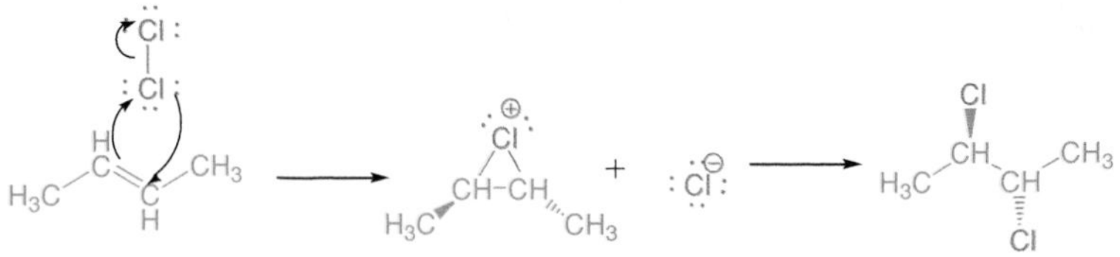

Not surprisingly, molecular fluorine (F_2) and molecular iodine (I_2) react with alkenes as well. However, these reactions are not very useful in organic synthesis. Molecular fluorine reacts explosively with alkenes, whereas iodine reacts too slowly. Therefore, we will not discuss these reactions any further.

Problem 21.6. Treatment of an alkene with molecular chlorine in carbon tetrachloride yields a racemic mixture of *(R,R)*-3,4-dichloro-2-methylhexane and its enantiomer. Draw the structure of the initial alkene.

Molecular bromine and molecular chlorine add to alkynes in much the same way they add to alkenes. For example, treatment of 2-hexyne with *one equivalent* of Br_2 yields 1,2-dibromooct-1-ene (Equation 21-12). With *excess* Br_2, on the other hand, the alkyne undergoes two additions to yield the tetrabromide (Equation 21-13).

oct-1-yne $\xrightarrow[\text{CH}_2\text{Cl}_2,\ 16\ \text{h},\ 25\ ^\circ\text{C}]{\text{Br}_2\ (1\ \text{eq.})}$ (*E*)-1,2-dibromooct-1-ene 65% + (*Z*)-1,2-dibromooct-1-ene 19% (21-12)

two equivalents of Br_2 add to an alkyne

oct-1-yne $\xrightarrow{\text{Br}_2\ (\text{excess})}$ 1,1,2,2-tetrabromooctane (21-13)

Notice in Equation 21-12 that a mixture of both *E* and *Z* isomers is formed. In other words,

> The addition of Br_2 to alkynes is not entirely stereospecific.

This means that the reaction must not proceed cleanly through a bromonium ion intermediate—otherwise, only *anti*-addition would take place, producing the *E* isomer exclusively. Why is this so?

Essentially, it is because of ring strain (Equation 21-14). When a bromonium ion intermediate is produced from an alkyne, the resulting three-membered ring consists of two sp^2-hybridized carbon atoms, whose ideal angles are 120°. By contrast, when a bromonium ion intermediate is produced from an alkene, those two carbon atoms are sp^3-hybridized, whose ideal angles are 109.5°. Therefore, the latter carbons can better handle the small angles required for the three-membered ring, which are near 60°.

alkynes do not react with molecular bromine to produce a bromonium ion intermediate, because the sp^2-hybridized carbon atoms would be too highly strained

(21-14)

21. 3b. Synthesis of Halohydrins

In the previous section (Equation 21-8), we saw that if an alkene reacts with molecular bromine in carbon tetrachloride, a vicinal dibromide is produced. If, however, the same reaction is carried out in water, as shown in Equation 21-15, a **bromohydrin** is produced instead. We can view the formation of a bromohydrin as the *net* addition of HO-Br across the double bond. Similarly, a **chlorohydrin** is produced when an alkene is treated with molecular chlorine in water (Equation 21-16).

water is the solvent

Br_2, H_2O

anti-addition of HO and Br

cyclohexene → *trans*-2-bromocyclohexanol

a bromohydrin

(21-15)

water is the solvent

Cl_2, H_2O

anti-addition of HO and Cl

(E)-but-2-ene → *(2S,3R)*- and *(2R,3S)*-3-chlorobutan-2-ol

a chlorohydrin

(21-16)

Notice that these reactions are *stereospecific*. Namely,

> In the formation of a **halohydrin** from an alkene, the OH group and the halogen atom add *anti* to each other.

This stereospecificity is the same as in the addition of Br_2 or Cl_2 across a double bond (recall Equations 21-8 and 21-11), strongly suggesting that halohydrin formation, too, proceeds through a *halonium ion intermediate*. This is illustrated in the mechanism in Equation 21-17.

Mechanism for the Reaction in Equation 21-15

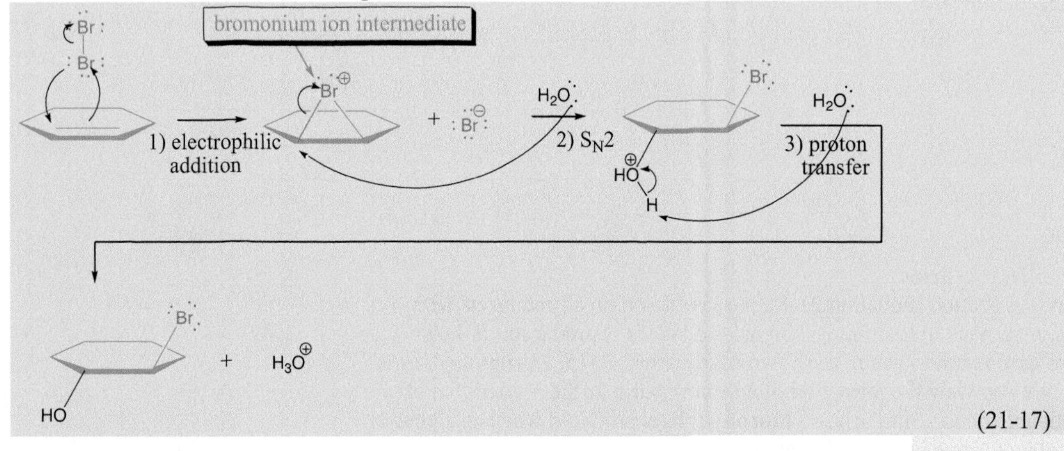

(21-17)

The first two steps are essentially the same as the ones in Equation 21-9, in which molecular bromine adds to an alkene. Step 1 is electrophilic addition that produces the bromonium ion intermediate, and step 2 is an S_N2 reaction. In contrast to the mechanism in Equation 21-9, however, the ring is opened in step 2 via nucleophilic attack by water instead of attack by Br^-. Finally, in step 3, a proton transfer produces the uncharged bromohydrin.

It might seem counterintuitive that water acts as the nucleophile in step 2, even though the much stronger Br^- nucleophile is present in solution. However, keep in mind the relative concentrations of the two nucleophiles. The Br^- ion is produced in step 1, which is a slow step because of the relatively unstable bromonium ion intermediate that is also produced. Thus, the concentration of Br^- is maintained at a very low concentration throughout the reaction. By contrast, water is the solvent, and is present in very high concentrations (the concentration of pure water is 55 mol/L). Therefore, the bromonium ion intermediate is much more likely to encounter a water molecule than a bromide ion.

Your Turn 21.5. The mechanism for the reaction in Equation 21-16 is shown below, but the curved arrow notation has been omitted. Complete the mechanism by drawing in the curved arrows. Also, write the name of each elementary step below the appropriate reaction arrow.

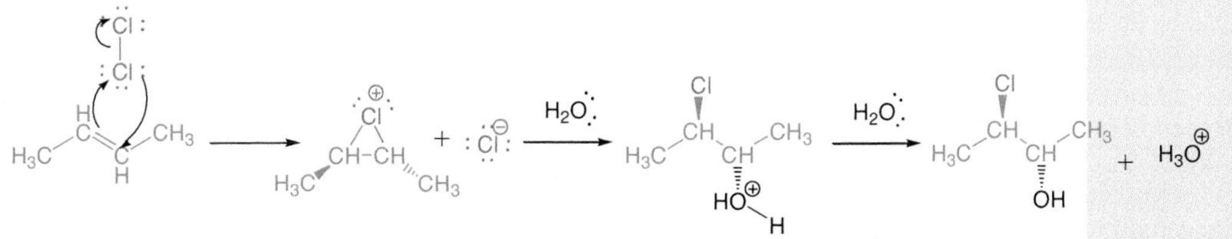

Problem 21.7. Draw the complete, detailed mechanism leading to the formation of the second enantiomer shown in Equation 21-15, which is not shown in Equation 21-17.

Solved Problem 21.2. When the reaction in Equation 21-15 is carried out in an aqueous NaCl solution instead of pure water, *trans*-1-bromo-2-chlorocyclohexane is produced along with the bromohydrin. Draw a complete mechanism that accounts for the formation of the dihalo compound.

Think. How can you account for the stereospecificity of the reaction—that is, the formation of only the *trans* isomer? What nucleophiles are present in solution?

Solve. To account for the *trans* stereospecificity, the reaction must proceed through a bromonium ion intermediate. To open the ring and form a C-Cl bond, Cl^- in solution must act as the nucleophile.

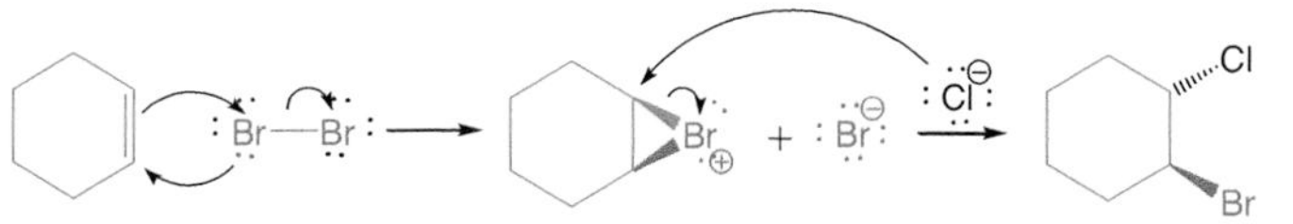

(plus enantiomer)

cyclohexene

trans-1-bromo-2-chlorocyclohexane

Problem 21.8. Draw the complete, detailed mechanism of the reaction in Equation 21-15 if it were to take place in ethanol instead of water.

Regiochemistry becomes a concern with halohydrin formation if the alkene reactant is *unsymmetrical.* With chemically distinct carbon atoms, two possible constitutional isomers can be produced, depending upon which carbon atom ends up bonded to the halogen atom, and which carbon atom ends up bonded to the alcohol group. This is the case, for example, with the reaction in Equation 21-18.

carbon atoms are distinct

major product

phenylethene $\xrightarrow[H_2O]{Br_2}$ 2-bromo-1-phenylethan-1-ol 78% + (2-bromo-2-phenylethan-1-ol)

(21-18)

Notice, however, that the first of these products is the major product. Why?

The answer can be understood from the mechanism, which is presented in Equation 21-19.

Mechanism for the Reaction in Equation 21-18

this C acquires more of bromine's positive charge than does the other C of the ring because this C is conjugated to the benzene ring and is also more highly substituted

water attacks the carbon atom that acquires the greater amount of positive charge

(21-19)

Notice that the specific isomer that is formed is dictated by the second step of the mechanism—nucleophilic attack by water. Although attack can occur at either carbon atom of the three-membered ring, attack is favored at carbon-1 instead of carbon-2. Recall that we saw a very similar mechanistic step in Equation 10-57 of Section 10.7b, in which a protonated epoxide acts as a substrate in an S_N2 reaction. Despite the fact that the positive charge is formally represented on the heteroatom—in this case Br—it is actually shared among the three atoms of the ring. Given that C-1 is conjugated to the benzene ring and is also a secondary carbon, it can better handle a positive charge than C-2, an isolated primary carbon. Therefore, C-1 bears more of a share of that positive charge than does C-2. As a result, when the water nucleophile approaches the two carbons, it is more attracted to C-1 than it is to C-2.

Problem 21.8. Draw a complete, detailed mechanism for the following reaction and predict the major product, paying attention to both regiochemistry and stereochemistry.

$\xrightarrow[H_2O]{Cl_2}$?

21.4. OXYMERCURATION-REDUCTION: ADDITION OF WATER

In Chapter 20, we saw that water can undergo an acid-catalyzed addition to an alkene or alkyne, producing an alcohol or ketone, respectively. Because the reaction proceeds through a carbocation intermediate, we observe *Markovnikov addition* of water. However, one drawback of such a reaction is that carbocation rearrangements are possible. An example is shown in Equation 21-20.

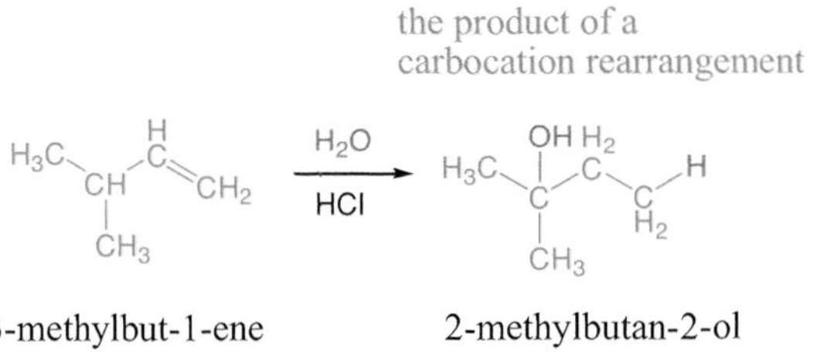

the product of a carbocation rearrangement

H_2O, HCl

3-methylbut-1-ene → 2-methylbutan-2-ol (21-20)

Your Turn 21.6. Review the mechanism that accounts for the formation of products in Equation 21-20 and draw it in the space provided here.

An alternate method to add water across a double bond is **oxymercuration-reduction** (also called **oxymercuration-demercuration**), an example of which is shown in Equation 21-21. The alkene is first treated with mercury(II) acetate, $Hg(OAc)_2$, in a water-THF solution, and is followed by reduction with sodium borohydride.

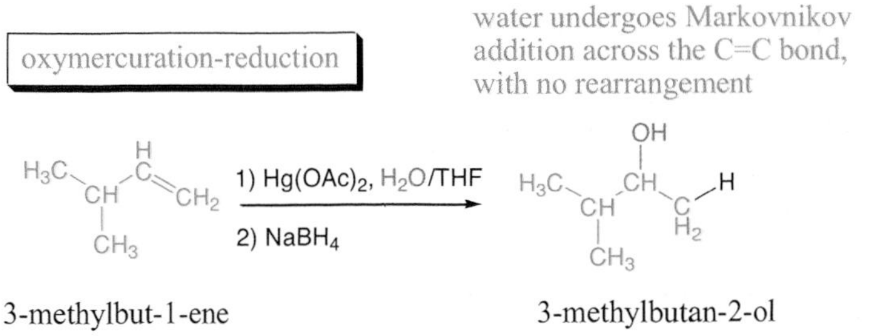

oxymercuration-reduction

water undergoes Markovnikov addition across the C=C bond, with no rearrangement

1) $Hg(OAc)_2$, H_2O/THF
2) $NaBH_4$

3-methylbut-1-ene → 3-methylbutan-2-ol (21-21)

There are two aspects of this reaction to take note of.

- The product of oxymercuration-reduction is the same that would be expected from Markovnikov's rule—i.e., the OH group forms a bond to the carbon atom that can better stabilize a positive charge.
- No rearrangement takes place with oxymercuration-reduction.

Both of these aspects can be understood from the mechanism, shown in Equation 21-22.

Mechanism for the Reaction in Equation 21-21

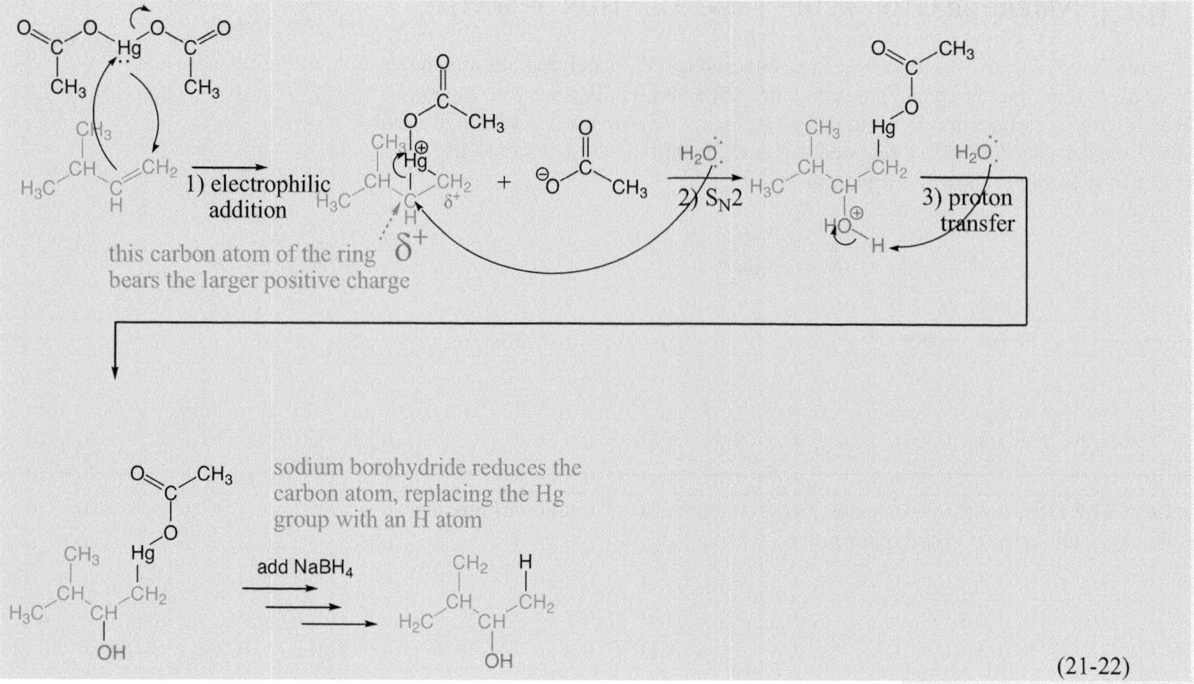

1) electrophilic addition

this carbon atom of the ring bears the larger positive charge

δ^+

2) S_N2

3) proton transfer

sodium borohydride reduces the carbon atom, replacing the Hg group with an H atom

add $NaBH_4$

(21-22)

Notice that the first three steps of the mechanism are identical to those in the formation of a halohydrin, shown previously in Equation 21-19. In the first step, the mercury atom is electron-poor, given that it is bonded to two highly electronegative oxygen atoms. It is therefore attacked by the electron-rich double bond, and simultaneously a lone pair of electrons on mercury forms a bond to carbon to produce the three-membered ring. The result is a **mercurinium ion intermediate**, which is analogous to the bromonium (or chloronium) ion intermediate we encountered in the previous sections. In the second step of the mechanism, water acts as a nucleophile to open the three-membered ring, and in the third step, the positively charged oxygen atom is deprotonated.

Subsequent reduction with sodium borohydride replaces the mercury-containing substituent with hydrogen. Although this may appear to be a simple nucleophilic substitution reaction with H^- as the nucleophile, it actually proceeds through a more complex mechanism that is believed to involve free radicals (species with unpaired electrons, see Chapter 25). Consequently, even though the oxymercuration steps take place with *anti* addition, the stereochemistry is scrambled during the reduction step, giving a mixture of both *syn* and *anti* addition of water.

Problem 22.9. Draw a detailed mechanism for each of the following reactions and draw the major products.

(a) 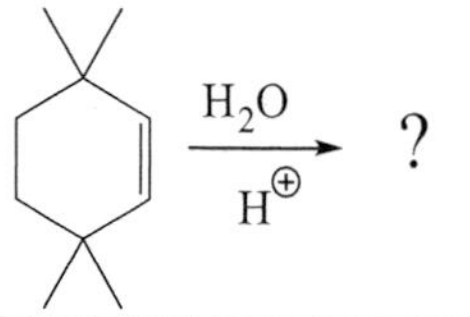 $\xrightarrow[H^{\oplus}]{H_2O}$?

(b) 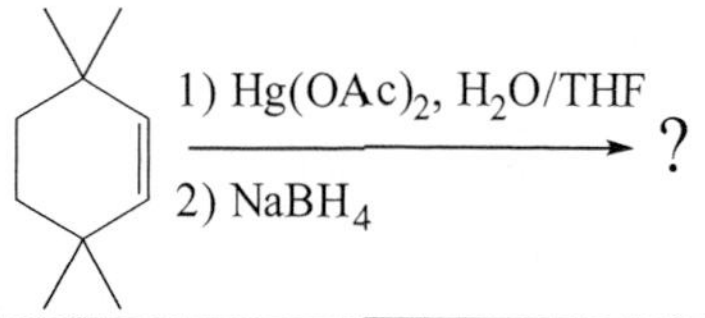 $\xrightarrow[2)\ NaBH_4]{1)\ Hg(OAc)_2,\ H_2O/THF}$?

Examining the mechanism, we can see why the addition of water follows Markovnikov's rule. In step 2, the carbon atom that is attacked by water is the one that can accommodate more of the positive charge that appears on the mercury atom—in this case, the secondary carbon instead of the primary one. This is the same carbon atom that would bear the positive charge in the carbocation intermediate produced when a proton adds to the alkene, and thus is the same carbon atom that would be attacked by water in an acid-catalyzed hydration.

We can also see why it is that rearrangement does not take place in oxymercuration-reduction, in contrast to acid-catalyzed hydration. In the acid-catalyzed hydration of an alkene, rearrangement takes place when a carbocation intermediate can undergo a 1,2-hydride shift or a 1,2-alkyl shift to produce a more stable carbocation. In oxymercuration-reduction, no carbocation intermediate is ever formed!

Problem 21.10. Draw two possible alkenes that can undergo oxymercuration-reduction to yield 2-methyl-2-pentanol as the major product.

Problem 21.11. Propose how to carry out the following transformation.

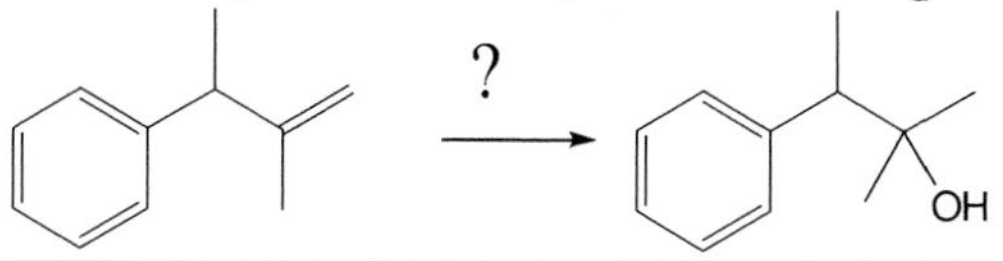

?

OH

Alkynes can also undergo Markovnikov addition of water via oxymercuration. However, just as we saw with acid-catalyzed hydration of an alkyne (Section 20.7), an unstable enol is produced initially. Subsequent tautomerization converts the enol into the more stable keto form, as shown in Equation 21-23.

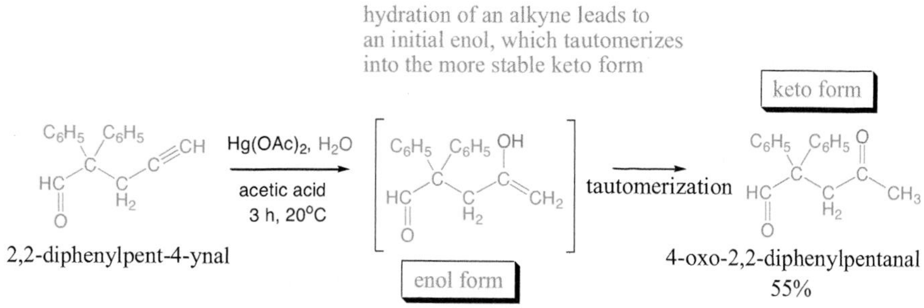

hydration of an alkyne leads to an initial enol, which tautomerizes into the more stable keto form

$Hg(OAc)_2$, H_2O / acetic acid / 3 h, 20°C

tautomerization

keto form

enol form

2,2-diphenylpent-4-ynal

4-oxo-2,2-diphenylpentanal 55%

(21-23)

Frequently, other forms of mercury(II) catalysts are used to facilitate the addition of water to an alkyne. Examples include $HgCl_2$ and $HgSO_4$, as shown below.

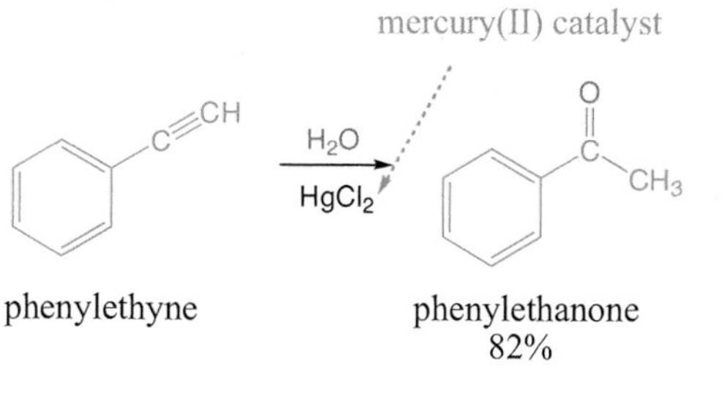

mercury(II) catalyst

H_2O / $HgCl_2$

phenylethyne

phenylethanone 82%

(21-24)

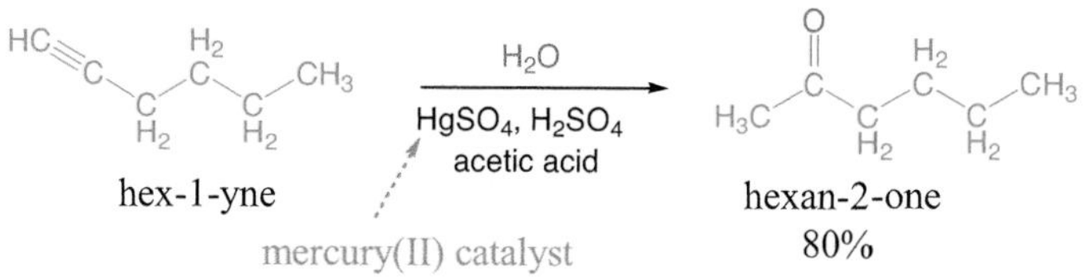

H_2O / $HgSO_4$, H_2SO_4 / acetic acid

hex-1-yne

mercury(II) catalyst

hexan-2-one 80%

(21-25)

Your Turn 21.7. Equations 21-24 and 21-25 show the overall products upon hydration of the alkynes. For each reaction, draw the initial enol that is produced, prior to tautomerization to the more stable keto form.

21-24 21-25

Internal alkynes can also be converted to ketones. However, as we saw in Chapter 20, unless the alkyne is symmetric, a mixture of isomeric ketones will be produced. This is shown in Equation 21-26.

hydration of an internal alkyne leads to a mixture of isomeric ketones

H_2O / HgO, H_2SO_4, methanol

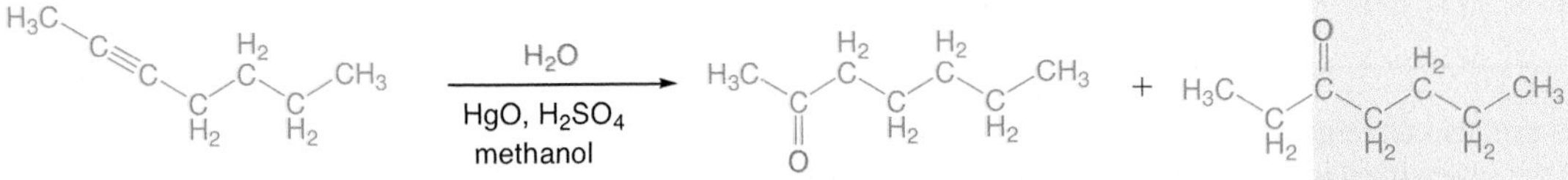

hept-2-yne → heptan-2-one ~ 67% + heptan-3-one ~ 33% (21-26)

Solved Problem 21.3. In an **alkoxymercuration-reduction** reaction, an alcohol is used as the solvent in the first step instead of water. An example is shown below. Draw the complete, detailed mechanism for this reaction and predict the major product.

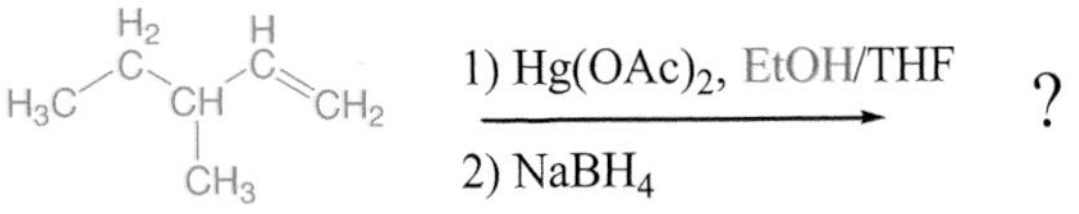

1) $Hg(OAc)_2$, EtOH/THF
2) $NaBH_4$
?

Think. How does the substitution of EtOH for water change the mechanism in Equation 21-22? What considerations should be made about *regiochemistry*? What considerations should be made about rearrangements?

Solve. The mechanism still proceeds through a cyclic mercurinium ion intermediate. Normally, H_2O acts as the nucleophile to open the ring. Here, however, this is the role of ethanol. Because the alkene is not symmetric, the alcohol can attack either carbon atom of the ring, but predominantly attacks the more highly substituted one—it bears a greater concentration of positive charge. Finally, because no carbocations are formed as intermediates, carbocation rearrangements are not a concern.

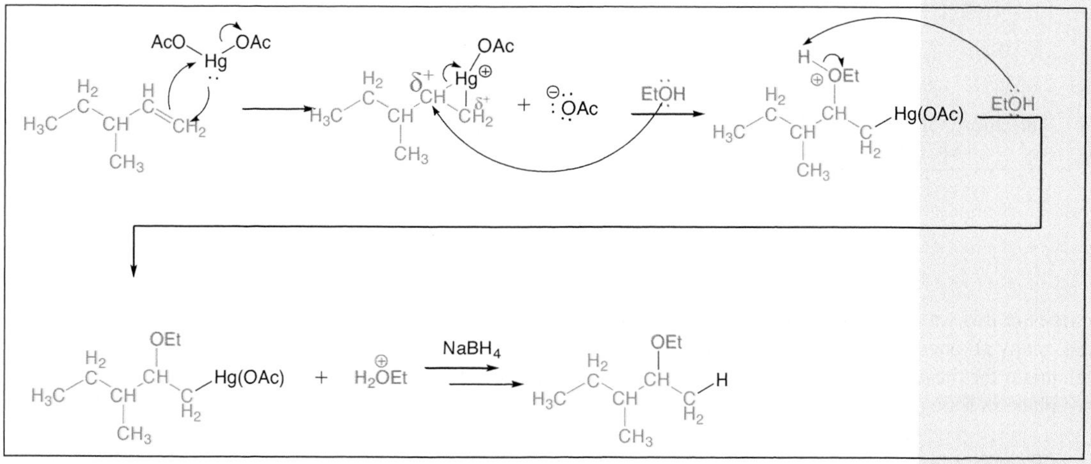

Problem 21.12. Predict the product of the following reaction.

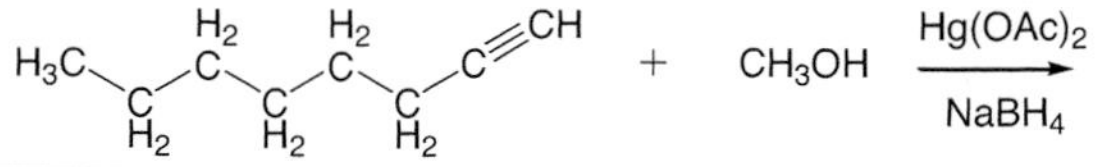

21.5. EPOXIDE FORMATION USING PEROXYACIDS

In Section 10.7, we learned of the utility of epoxides in synthesis. Namely, an epoxide can undergo nucleophilic attack to produce a 2-substituted alcohol. To produce such an epoxide, we saw in Section 10.6 that a halohydrin can be treated with a strong base under high heat. An example of such a reaction is shown in Equation 21-27.

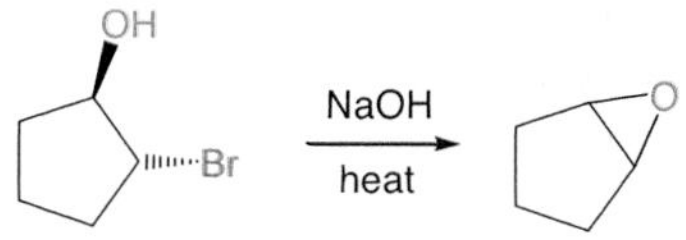

(21-27)

Unfortunately, synthesizing an epoxide in this way is often impractical. One reason is the relative severity of the conditions necessary to carry out such a reaction—i.e., a strong base and high heat. Thus, unintended reactions might take place. A second reason is that halohydrins are not very common, and therefore may not be readily available to be used as precursors.

Fortunately, an epoxide can be produced from an alkene using a **peroxyacid** (RCO_3H) such as ***meta*-chloroperbenzoic acid, MCPBA**. Examples of such **epoxidation reactions** are shown in Equations 21-28 and 21-29.

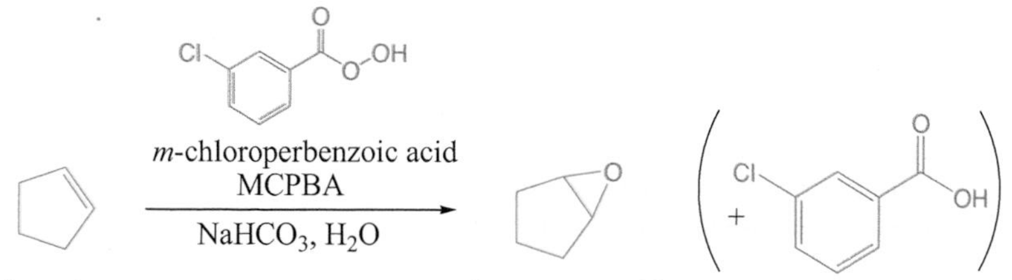

m-chloroperbenzoic acid
MCPBA
$NaHCO_3$, H_2O

cyclopentene

cyclopentene oxide
90%

(21-28)

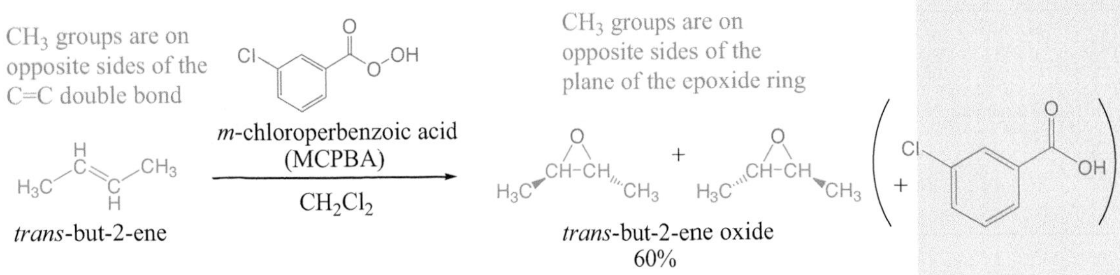

CH$_3$ groups are on opposite sides of the C=C double bond

trans-but-2-ene

m-chloroperbenzoic acid (MCPBA)

CH_2Cl_2

CH$_3$ groups are on opposite sides of the plane of the epoxide ring

trans-but-2-ene oxide
60%

(21-29)

Synthesizing epoxides in this way is advantageous, because the reaction conditions are relatively mild, and many alkenes are common or easily synthesized.

The mechanism for these epoxidation reactions is shown in Equation 21-30. Notice that it takes place in a single step—it is *concerted.*

Mechanism for the Reaction in Equation 21-29

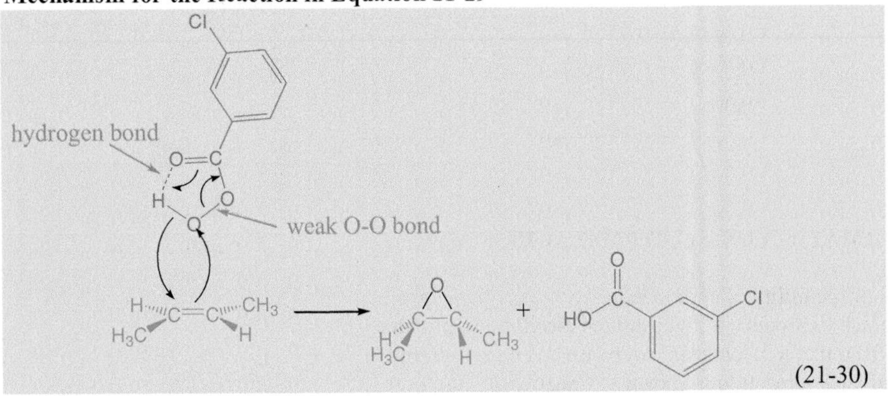

hydrogen bond

weak O-O bond

(21-30)

As we can see, the oxygen atom of the OH group is the one that is transferred to the alkene. This is driven by the fact that both of its original covalent bonds are relatively weak. The oxygen-oxygen single bond is inherently very weak. On the other hand, an O-H bond is normally quite strong, but in this case the oxygen's bond to H is weakened by the internal hydrogen bond involving the OH and the carbonyl oxygen.

Your Turn 21.8. Verify that the O-O single bond is weak by looking up its average value. Do the same for an average C-C single bond.

O-O __________ kJ/mol C-C __________ kJ/mol

With its weakened bonds, the OH's oxygen atom is highly reactive and is attacked by the π electrons from the alkene. To avoid generating a carbocation on one of the carbon atoms from the initial alkene, the pair of electrons from the OH bond is used to form an O-C bond, thereby completing the three-membered epoxide ring. The carbonyl's oxygen atom acquires the H, and the pair of electrons from the initial O-O bond goes to make a C=O bond.

Because epoxidation takes place in a single step, the stereochemical requirements presented in Section 21.1 apply. As shown previously in Equation 21-29, for example, stereochemistry is conserved—the *trans* relationship of the CH$_3$ groups about the C=C double bond in the reactants establishes a *trans* relationship about the plane of the epoxide ring in the products. Furthermore, because the products are chiral, a mixture of stereoisomers is produced.

Problem 21.13. Draw the complete, detailed mechanism for the following reaction and predict the major product, paying attention to stereochemistry.

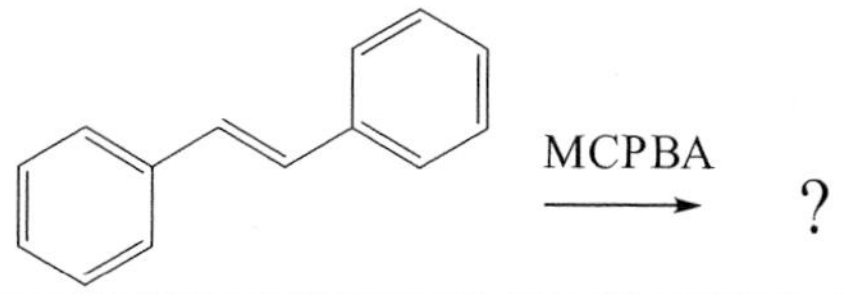

MCPBA
?

Problem 21.14. What alkene can be epoxidized using MCPBA to yield the following compound?

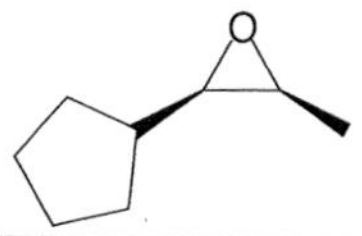

O

Typically, epoxides are not part of a target molecule in synthesis. Rather, due to the susceptibility of the ring to open upon nucleophilic attack, epoxides are more frequently used as synthetic intermediates. This is exemplified in Solved Problem 21.4.

Solved Problem 21.4. Show how to carry out the following synthesis.

OH ? OH OH

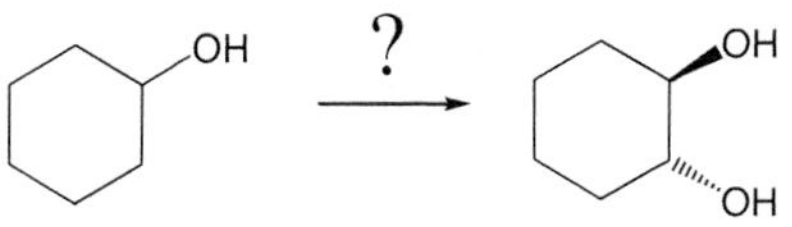

Think. What precursor can be used to produce adjacent functional groups that are *trans* to each other? What functional group can be used to produce that precursor?

Solve. Nucleophilic attack of an epoxide can produce the *trans*-1,2-diol. The epoxide can be produced by reacting an alkene with a peroxyacid. The alkene, in turn, can be produced by dehydration of the starting alcohol.

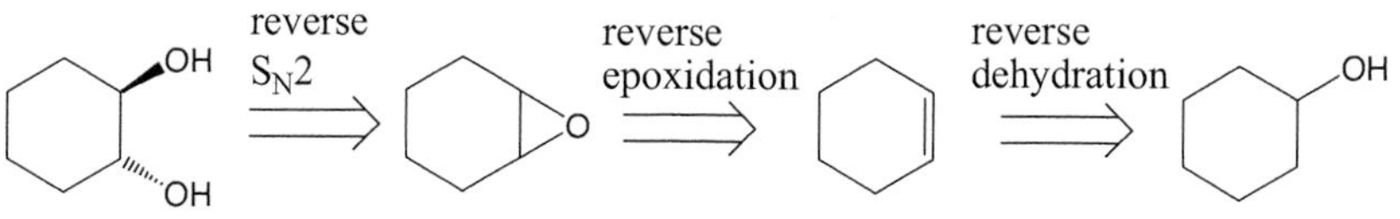

OH OH reverse S_N2 O reverse epoxidation reverse dehydration OH

In the forward direction, the synthesis would appear as follows.

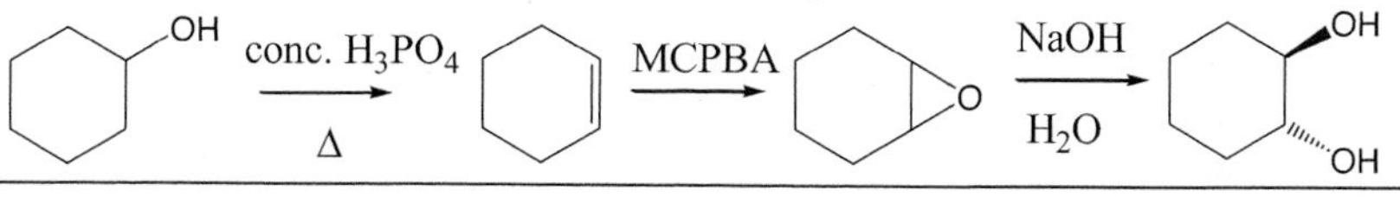

OH conc. H_3PO_4 Δ MCPBA O NaOH H_2O OH OH

Problem 21.15. Show how to carry out the following synthesis.

$H_3C-CH_2-CH_2-C{\equiv}C-CH_2-CH_2-CH_3$? $H_3C-CH_2-CH_2-CH(CH_3)-CH(OH)-CH_2-CH_2-CH_3$

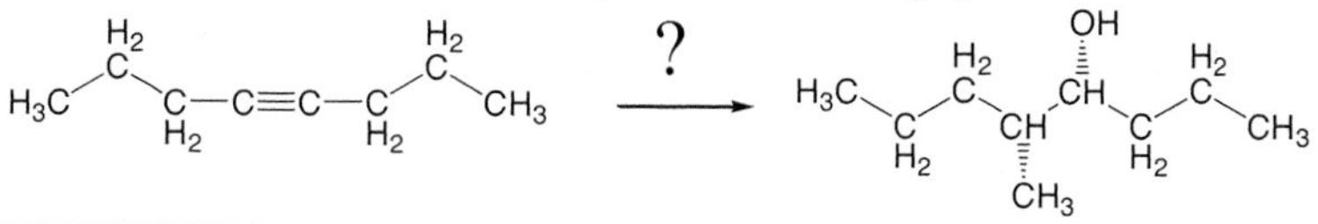

21.6. HYDROBORATION-OXIDATION: NON-MARKOVNIKOV *SYN* ADDITION OF WATER TO AN ALKENE

So far, we have seen two reactions that serve to add water across a carbon-carbon double or triple bond. One is *acid-catalyzed hydration* (Chapter 20), which proceeds through a carbocation intermediate. The second is *oxymercuration-reduction* (Section 21.4), which proceeds through a cyclic mercurinium ion intermediate, thereby avoiding carbocation rearrangements. Recall that both of these reactions add water in a *Markovnikov* fashion, in which the carbon atom that gains the OH group is the one that is better able to stabilize a positive charge (via conjugation or additional alkyl substitution). Also recall that neither of these reactions is stereospecific—a mixture of stereoisomers from both *syn* addition and *anti* addition is produced.

Hydroboration-oxidation provides a third reaction in which there is a net addition of water across a nonpolar π bond, as shown in Equations 21-31 and 21-32. In each case, the alkene first undergoes **hydroboration**, in which borane, BH_3 (either from BH_3-THF or from B_2H_6), adds across the double bond. The product is then *oxidized* with a basic solution of hydrogen peroxide, H_2O_2.

non-Markovnikov addition of H and OH

hept-1-ene → 1) BH_3-THF; 2) H_2O_2, NaOH → heptan-1-ol 92% (21-31)

H and OH with *syn* stereochemistry and non-Markovnikov regiochemistry

1-methylcyclopentene → 1) B_2H_6, THF, 0 °C, 2 h, then 20 °C, 1 h; 2) H_2O_2, NaOH, 0 °C, 2 h → *trans*-2-methylcyclopentanol 85% (21-32)

Notice the regioselectivity that is exhibited by these reactions. Specifically, in both of the above reactions, addition of OH is favored at the alkene carbon that can *least* stabilize a positive charge—a primary carbon in Equation 21-31, and a secondary carbon in Equation 21-32. This is in contrast to the Markovnikov regiochemistry exhibited by acid-catalyzed hydrolysis and by oxymercuration-reduction. Thus,

> Hydroboration-oxidation adds H and OH to an alkene with **non-Markovnikov** regiochemistry.

Notice also that hydroboration-oxidation is stereospecific. As we can see from Equation 21-32, both the H and OH groups add to the same face of the planar alkene functional group. In other words,

> In hydroboration-oxidation, an alkene undergoes *syn* addition of H and OH.

In order to understand these aspects of hydroboration-oxidation reactions, we must turn toward their mechanisms. First, let's examine the mechanism of hydroboration in Section 21.6a. Afterward, let's examine the mechanism of oxidation in Section 21.6b.

21.6a. Hydroboration: Addition of BH_3 Across a Carbon-Carbon Double Bond

Hydroboration is invaluable to organic chemistry because it is the starting point for a variety of overall reactions. We have already seen that it is the first of two sequential reactions in the non-Markovnikov hydration of alkenes. Furthermore, hydroboration can be used as a starting point for hydrogenating alkenes and alkynes, thereby reducing them to alkanes and alkenes, respectively. For these reasons, Herbert C. Brown, who discovered hydroboration, shared the 1979 Nobel Prize in chemistry.

Borane (BH_3) is the reactive species in the hydroboration of an alkene. However, borane is highly unstable because the central boron atom does not have an octet. Therefore, borane cannot be isolated. Instead, in its pure form it exists as a gaseous dimer, **diborane** (B_2H_6), where each of two hydrogen atoms comprises a bridge between the boron atoms (shown below at left)—those H atoms are involved in what are called **three-center-two-electron bonds**. Although these bonds provide some stability, diborane is highly reactive, and thus is both *toxic* and *explosive*. A more stable variation of borane is sold commercially as a 1-to-1 complex with tetrahydrofuran (shown below at right), where tetrahydrofuran acts as a Lewis base to give the boron atom its octet.

these 3-center-2-electron bonds provide some stability to the boron atom
coordination of THF to BH_3 provides some stability by giving boron an octet
H
B
O

diborane, B_2H_6

boron-THF complex (BH_3-THF)

The mechanism for the hydroboration reaction is shown in Equation 21-33. It is driven primarily by the flow of electrons from the electron-rich π bond to the electron-poor boron atom of BH_3. Similar to the mechanisms we have seen previously in this chapter, this reaction avoids the formation of a highly unstable carbocation by simultaneously forming a bond back to the second carbon atom of the double bond. Whereas in the previous reactions a lone pair was used to form that second bond to C (Section 21.1), in hydroboration that bond comes from electrons originally part of a B-H bond in BH_3. Overall, then, two bonds are broken and two bonds are formed in a *concerted* fashion—i.e., without the formation of intermediates.

Partial Mechanism for the Reaction in Equation 21-32

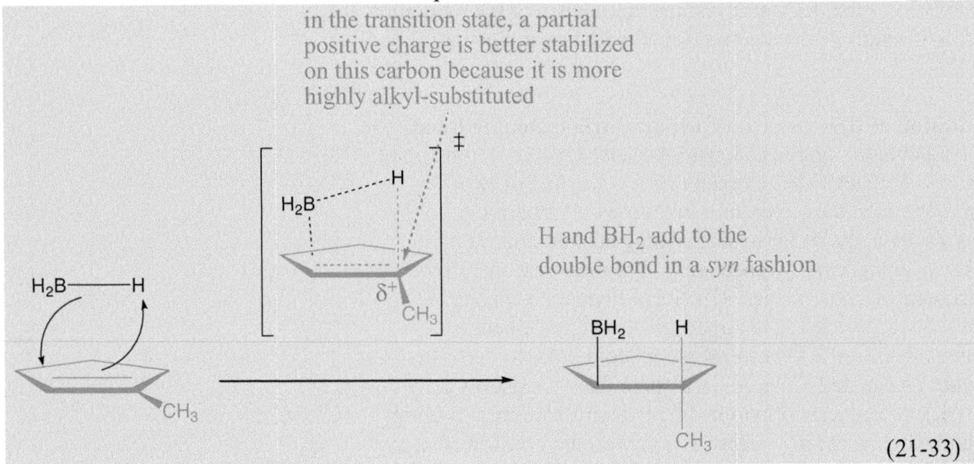
in the transition state, a partial positive charge is better stabilized on this carbon because it is more highly alkyl-substituted
‡
H₂B
H
δ+
CH₃
H and BH₂ add to the double bond in a syn fashion
H₂B
H
CH₃
BH₂
H
CH₃

(21-33)

As we can see from Equation 21-33,

> Hydroboration is *stereospecific*, with the H and BH_2 groups adding to the alkene in a *syn* fashion.

Hydroboration is also *regioselective*. The H atom primarily adds to the C with the greater number of alkyl groups, whereas the BH_2 group adds to the C with the fewer number of alkyl groups. This, too, can be explained by the fact that the reaction is concerted. With no intermediates formed along the reaction coordinate, no formal charge is generated. Charge stability is therefore much less critical than in other reactions we have seen in this chapter. Consequently, *steric hindrance* plays a large role.

> When BH_3 adds to an alkene, the larger group, BH_2, adds to the carbon atom with the fewer number of alkyl groups, in large part to minimize *steric repulsion.*

Equation 21-34 illustrates the steric repulsion that would ensue if the BH_2 group were to add to the more highly substituted alkene carbon.

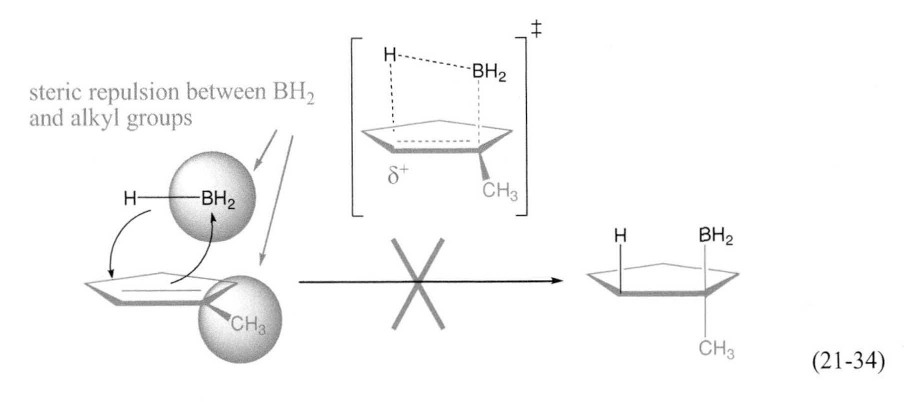
steric repulsion between BH₂ and alkyl groups
H
BH₂
CH₃
‡
H
BH₂
δ+
CH₃
H
BH₂
CH₃

(21-34)

Even though no formal charges appear, charge stability is also a factor in the regioselectivity of hydroboration. In the transition states shown in Equations 21-33 and 21-34, a *partial* positive charge appears on the carbon atom with a partial bond to hydrogen. This is because in the transition state, the C-B bond is formed to a greater extent than the C-H bond. In light of this, the transition state is most stable when the BH_2 group adds to the carbon atom with the fewer number of alkyl groups, because that allows the partial positive charge that is generated to appear on the carbon atom with the greater number of alkyl groups. The additional alkyl groups inductively stabilize that partial positive charge. Overall, then, charge stability and steric hindrance promote the same regiochemistry.

Your Turn 21.9. Borane can add to propene to produce two different products, as shown below. Complete each of the hydroboration steps by adding the curved arrows. Also, indicate the pertinent steric repulsion that is present in each reaction, similar to Equations 21-34 and 21-35, and determine which reaction is more favorable.

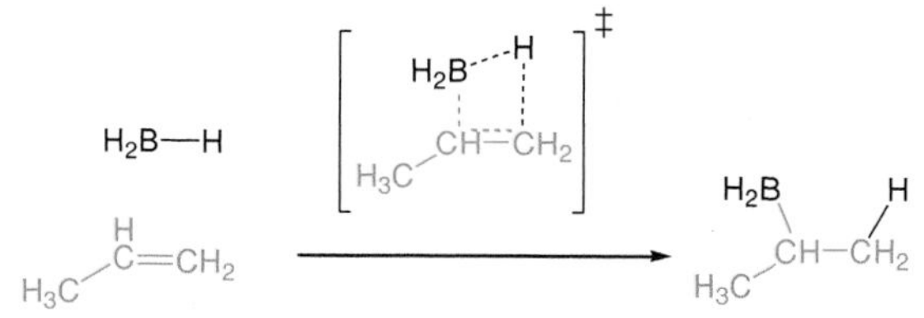

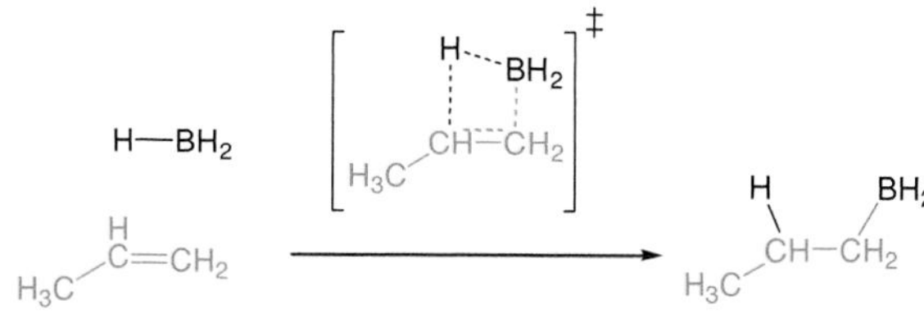

H_2B—H
H_3C–CH=CH_2
[H_2B···H, H_3C–CH···CH_2]‡
H_3C–CH(BH_2)–CH_2(H)

H—BH_2
H_3C–CH=CH_2
[H···BH_2, H_3C–CH···CH_2]‡
H_3C–CH(H)–CH_2(BH_2)

Notice that the product of hydroboration is an **alkylborane**, R-BH_2 (Equation 21-35a), which has two B-H bonds remaining. That alkylborane can therefore react with an additional unreacted alkene, as shown in Equation 21-35b. Namely, RBH-H adds across the double bond of the alkene to produce a **dialkylborane**, R_2B-H. In turn, the dialkylborane product adds across yet another equivalent of the unreacted alkene to produce a **trialkylborane**, R_3B, as shown in Equation 21-35c. As with the addition of BH_3, *each of these is a syn addition, and the hydrogen adds preferentially to the least sterically hindered alkene carbon atom.*

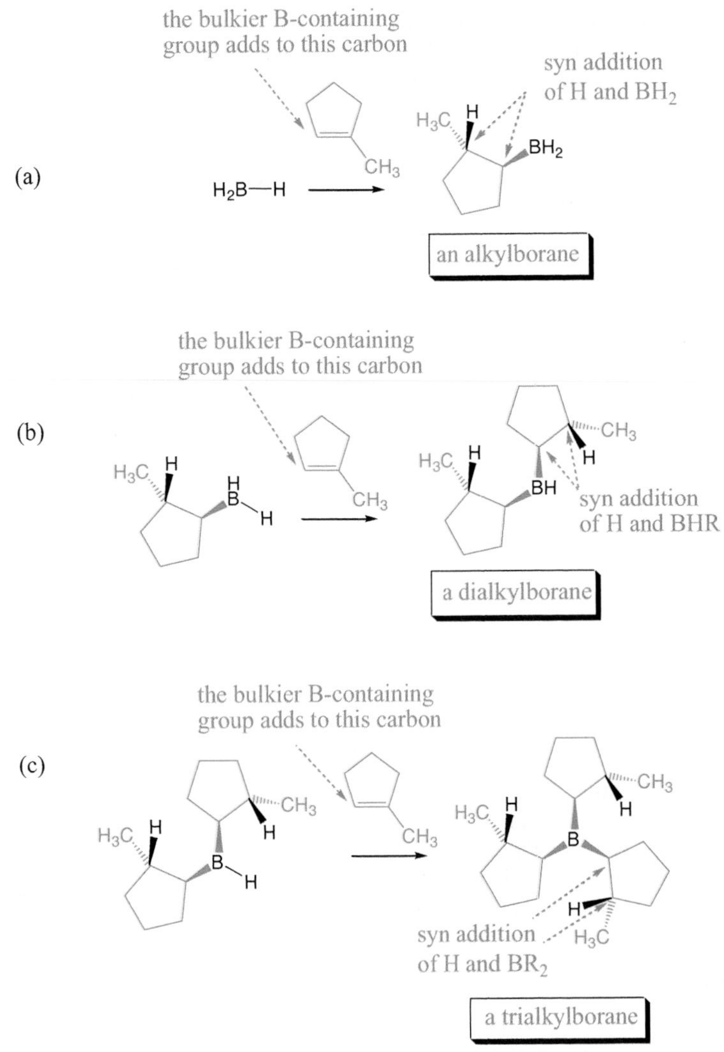

(a)

the bulkier B-containing group adds to this carbon

H_2B—H →

syn addition of H and BH_2

an alkylborane

(b)

the bulkier B-containing group adds to this carbon

syn addition of H and BHR

a dialkylborane

(c)

the bulkier B-containing group adds to this carbon

syn addition of H and BR_2

a trialkylborane

(21-35)

Problem 21.16. Draw the detailed mechanism for the formation of the monoalkylborane of the following reaction. Also, draw the trialkylborane that is ultimately produced.

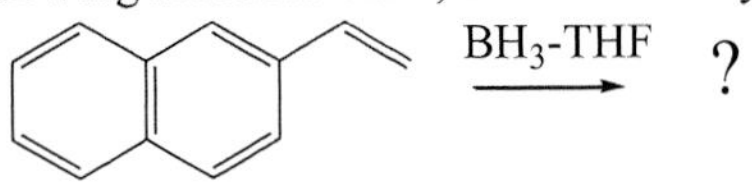

BH_3-THF → ?

21.6b. Oxidation of the Trialkyl Borane: Formation of the Alcohol

In Equations 21-31 and 21-32, we saw that after an alkene has undergone hydroboration, treatment with a basic solution of hydrogen peroxide produces the alcohol. We can now see from Equation 21-35 that the actual species that undergoes oxidation is a trialkylborane. The net reaction is shown in Equation 21-36.

each C-B bond is replaced by a C-OH bond

three equivalents of the alcohol are produced

H_2O_2, NaOH

3 ... + BO_3^{3-}

(21-36)

There are two aspects of this oxidation to take note of.

- Each boron-containing group attached to carbon is replaced by an OH group, producing three equivalents of the alcohol.
- Each OH group is *syn* to the hydrogen atom added from the previous hydroboration reaction. Thus, these substitutions take place with *retention of stereochemistry* at each carbon atom bonded to boron.

These aspects of the oxidation reaction can be understood from the mechanism, which is shown in Equation 21-36. Under basic conditions, there is an equilibrium amount of the deprotonated peroxide, HOO^-, called the **hydroperoxide ion**. The mechanism begins with coordination of HOO^- to the electron-deficient boron atom of the trialkylborane, thereby producing an unstable tetrahedral intermediate. In step 2, the breaking of a weak peroxide (O-O) bond drives a 1,2-alkyl shift that yields a **borate ester**. This pair of steps occurs twice more, comprising steps 3 – 6, resulting in a **trialkylborate ester**. In step 7, hydroxide anion (HO^-) undergoes coordination with the boron atom of the trialkylborate ester, and in step 8, heterolysis takes place to liberate an alkoxide anion (RO^-) leaving group. The OH group attached to boron is acidic, so in step 9 its proton is removed by the strongly basic alkoxide anion to produce the first equivalent of the final alcohol. This trio of steps is then repeated twice (steps 10 – 15).

Mechanism for the Reaction in Equation 21-36

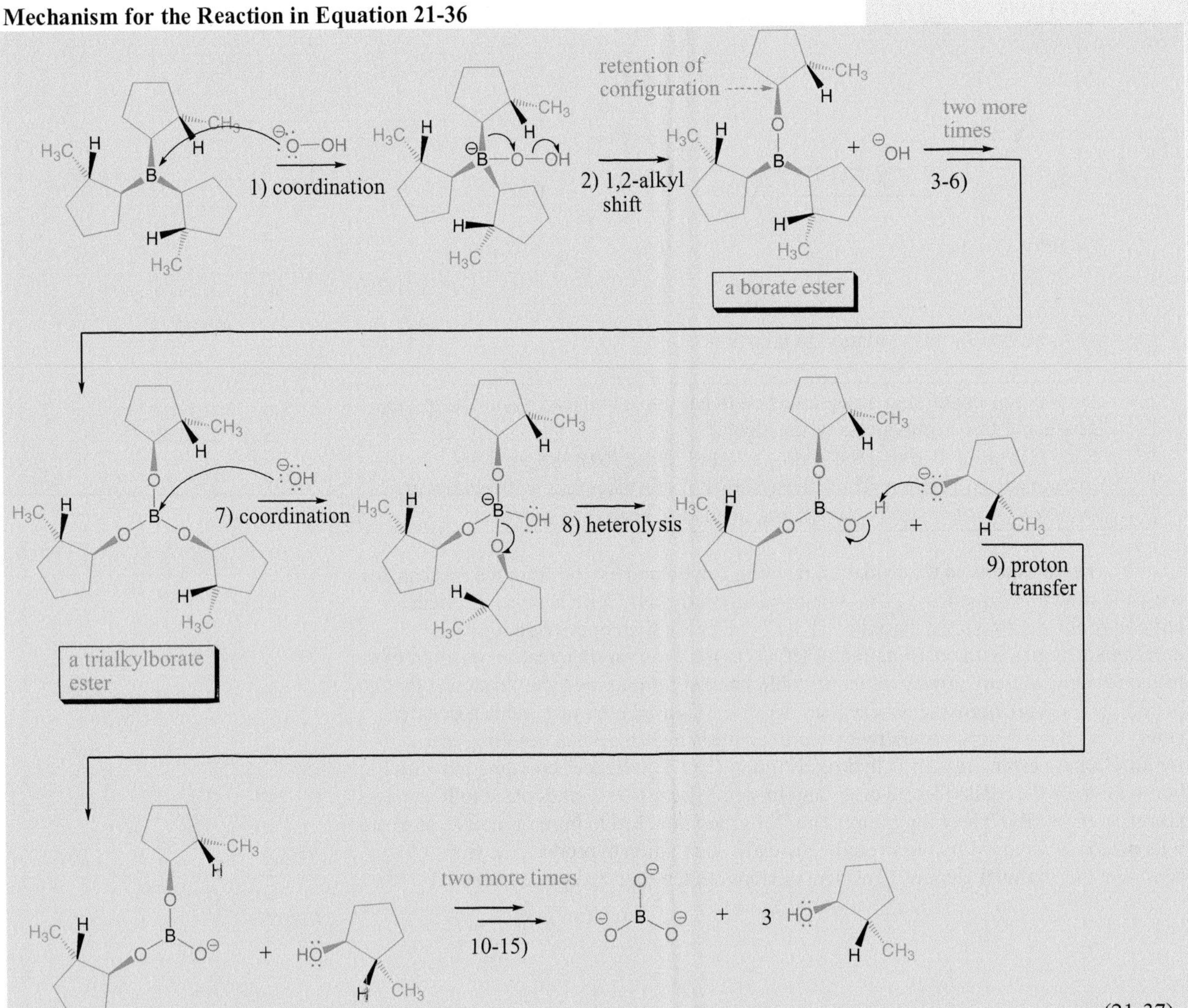

1) coordination

2) 1,2-alkyl shift

retention of configuration

a borate ester

two more times 3-6)

a trialkylborate ester

7) coordination

8) heterolysis

9) proton transfer

two more times 10-15)

(21-37)

With this mechanism, we can now see how each boron-containing group is replaced by OH with retention of stereochemistry. The critical step is step 2, where a C-B bond breaks at the same time a C-O bond forms. Because of geometric constraints during this *concerted* process, the position that the oxygen-containing group assumes about the carbon atom must be the same as that originally occupied by the boron-containing group. Thus, the configuration about that carbon atom must not change.

Your Turn 21.10. The following trialkylborane is an intermediate in a hydroboration-oxidation reaction. Draw the alcohol that is produced upon treatment with a basic solution of H_2O_2.

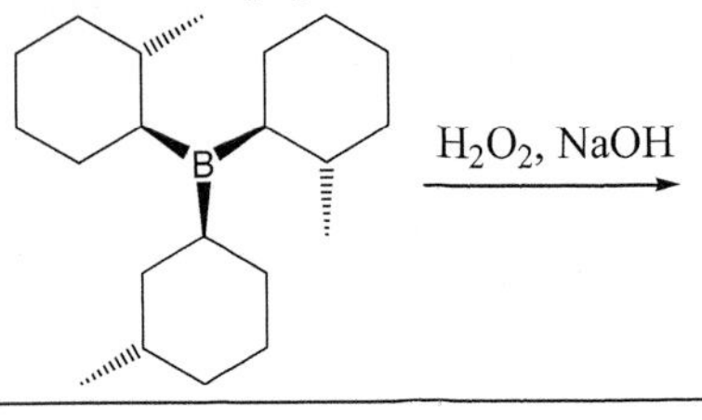

H_2O_2, NaOH

Problem 21.17. Draw the complete detailed mechanism of the reaction that takes place when the product of the reaction in Problem 21.16 is treated with a basic solution of hydrogen peroxide.

Solved Problem 21.5. Show how to carry out the following synthesis.

$H_3C-C(CH_3)=CH_2 \xrightarrow{?}$ 1-(2-methylpropyl)cyclohexan-1-ol ($(H_3C)_2CH-CH_2$ and OH on the same ring carbon)

Think. What reaction can be used to produce a new carbon-carbon bond, leaving an alcohol group on one of the carbon atoms involved in that new bond? In order to produce the appropriate precursor to that reaction, into what functional group must the alkene be converted? Which alkene carbon should gain that functional group?

Solve. A Grignard reaction involving cyclohexanone can be used to produce the new carbon-carbon bond, leaving an alcohol group on the cyclohexane ring. The required isobutyl Grignard reagent must be produced from the corresponding isobutyl halide. In order to produce that halide, we must carry out a non-Markovnikov addition to the alkene, which would place the functional group on the less substituted carbon atom. This can be accomplished by hydroboration-oxidation to produce the alcohol, following by bromination with PBr_3.

1-(2-methylpropyl)cyclohexan-1-ol $\xrightarrow{\text{reverse Grignard reaction}}$ cyclohexanone + $H_3C-CH(CH_3)-CH_2-MgBr$ $\xrightarrow{\text{reverse reduction}}$ $H_3C-CH(CH_3)-CH_2-Br$ $\xrightarrow{\text{reverse bromination}}$ $H_3C-CH(CH_3)-CH_2-OH$ $\xrightarrow{\text{reverse hydroboration-reduction}}$ $H_3C-C(CH_3)=CH_2$

In the forward direction, the synthesis would appear as follows.

$H_3C-C(CH_3)=CH_2 \xrightarrow[\text{2) NaOH, } H_2O_2]{\text{1) } BH_3\text{-THF}} H_3C-CH(CH_3)-CH_2-OH \xrightarrow{PBr_3} H_3C-CH(CH_3)-CH_2-Br \xrightarrow{Mg} H_3C-CH(CH_3)-CH_2-MgBr \xrightarrow[\text{2) } H_3O^+]{\text{1) cyclohexanone}}$ 1-(2-methylpropyl)cyclohexan-1-ol

Problem 21.18. Show how to carry out the following synthesis.

CH_3, H_3C, CH_2 ? CH_3, H_3C, CH, CH, OH

21.7. HYDROBORATION-OXIDATION OF ALKYNES

The addition of BH_3 to an alkyne takes place in much the same way as it does to an alkene, with BH_2 adding to the less sterically hindered carbon, and H adding to the more sterically hindered one (Equation 21-38). However, an alkene is produced, which itself can undergo hydroboration. Therefore, such a reaction would lead to a mixture of products, making it not very useful for synthesis.

syn addition of H and BH_2

R—C≡C—H $\xrightarrow{BH_3}$ (H)(R)C=C(H)(BH_2) $\xrightarrow{\text{alkene reacts further with } BH_3}$ mixture of products

(21-38)

Chemists avoid this problem by using a bulky dialkyl borane, such as **disiamyl borane**, instead of BH_3. An example is shown in Equation 21-39. Disiamyl borane reacts with an alkyne in the usual way, with the R_2B group adding to the less sterically hindered carbon. With the bulky R_2B group attached to the alkene, *a second addition of disiamyl borane does not occur*. Hydroboration therefore stops at the alkene.

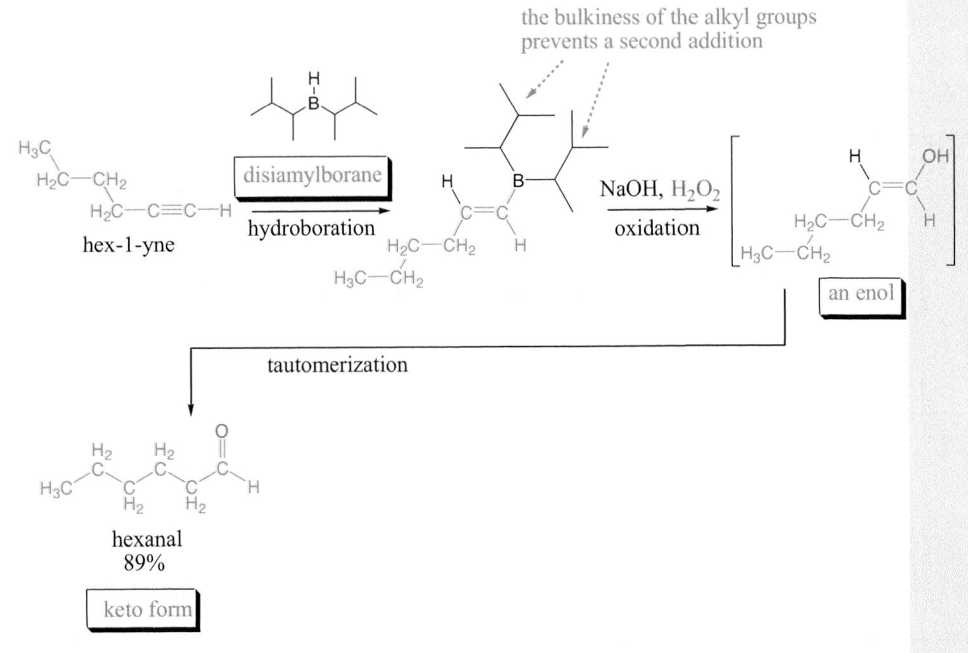

(21-39)

Subsequent oxidation with a basic solution of H_2O_2 converts the R_2B substituent on the alkene into an OH group, similar to Equation 21-36. In this case, however, the product is an *enol*, which tautomerizes into the more stable keto form.

As we can see from Equation 21-39, hydroboration-oxidation is a useful tool to convert a *terminal alkyne* into an aldehyde. This reaction can also be used to convert an internal alkyne into a ketone, but a mixture of products results unless the alkyne is symmetric.

Problem 21.19. An alkyne A is treated with disiamylborane followed by a basic solution of H_2O_2. The overall product is an aldehyde, as shown below. (a) Draw the structure of the initial alkyne A. (b) Draw the structure of the intermediate B.

$$A \xrightarrow[\text{THF}]{(C_5H_{11})_2BH} B \xrightarrow{HO^{\ominus},\ H_2O_2}$$

H

21.8. *SYN*-HYDROXYLATION OF ALKENES AND ALKYNES USING OsO_4 OR $KMnO_4$

When an alkene is treated with osmium tetroxide (OsO_4) followed by H_2O_2, the product is a *cis*-1,2-diol. An example is shown in Equation 21-40. The alkene is said to have undergone ***syn* hydroxylation**.

OH groups add across the C=C double bond in a *syn* fashion

$$\text{(E)-butenoic acid} \xrightarrow[H_2O_2,\ (CH_3)_3COH,\ 0\ ^\circ C,\ 16\ h]{OsO_4} \text{(2S,3R)- and (2R,3S)-1,2-dihydroxybutanoic acid, 53\%}$$

(21-40)

The mechanism for this reaction is shown in Equation 21-41. The first step is the addition of OsO_4 across the C=C double bond in a *syn* fashion, producing an **osmate ester**. This step is driven in part by the flow of electrons from the electron-rich C=C double bond to the electron-poor osmium atom. (Although the electrons from the alkene do not form a bond to the osmium atom directly, the osmium atom gains a lone pair of electrons.)

In steps 2 and 3, the osmate ester is hydrolyzed—the O-O bonds are replaced by O-H bonds. This hydrolysis produces the *cis*-1,2-diol and a reduced form of the osmium. Hydrogen peroxide, H_2O_2, is an oxidizing agent and oxidizes the reduced form back to OsO_4. Note that during the course of the reaction, OsO_4 is not consumed overall, so it is characterized as a *catalyst*.

Partial Mechanism for the Reaction in Equation 21-40

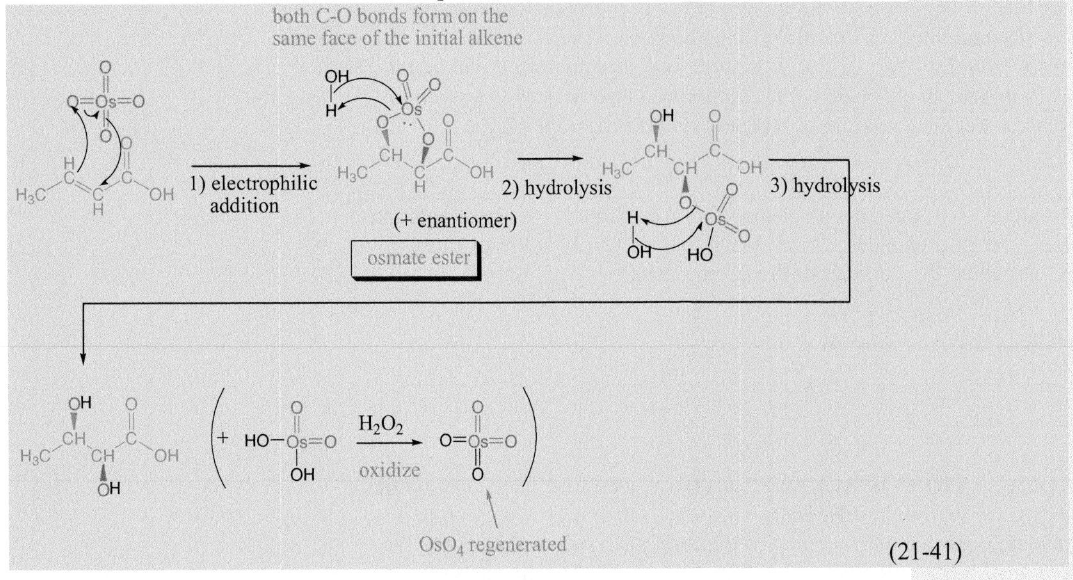

(21-41)

This reaction gives the *cis*-1,2-diol in relatively good yield, but osmium tetroxide is both toxic and expensive. Fortunately, the same reaction can be achieved using potassium permanganate ($KMnO_4$) in basic solution, as Equation 21-42 illustrates.

OH groups add across the C=C double bond in a *syn* fashion

$KMnO_4$, $HO^{\ominus}$

cold

cyclopentene

cis-cyclopentane-1,2-diol
31%

(21-42)

The mechanism for this reaction is believed to be similar to the one that involves OsO_4. Namely, the key step is the *syn* addition of MnO_4^- across the C=C double bond, making a **manganate ester**, as shown in Your Turn 21.10. This similarity of the mechanisms should be no surprise, given the structural similarities between MnO_4^- and OsO_4.

Your Turn 21.10. The manganate ester that is produced as an intermediate in Equation 21-42 is shown below. Supply the curved arrows that are necessary to depict the formation of that manganate ester from the starting materials shown below at left.

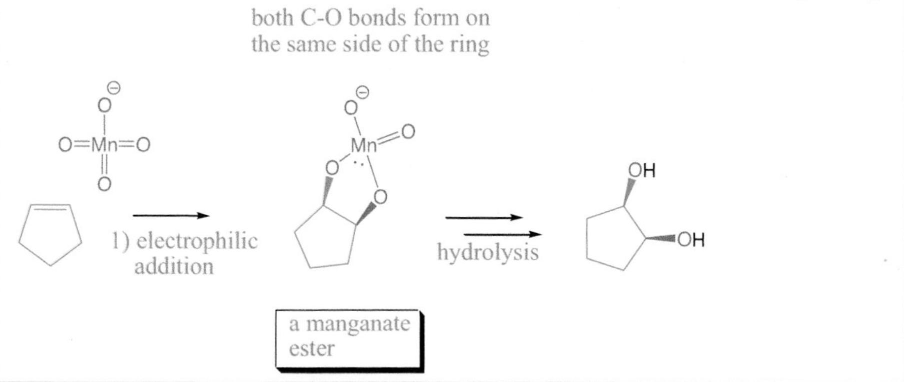

both C-O bonds form on the same side of the ring

1) electrophilic addition

hydrolysis

a manganate ester

Although $KMnO_4$ is less expensive and safer to use than OsO_4, it has some disadvantages. First, the yields are significantly lower, typically around 50% or less. Second, unless care is taken to keep the solution cold and basic, the diol product can be further oxidized by $KMnO_4$ (this will be discussed in the next section).

The C≡C triple bond of an alkyne reacts with $KMnO_4$ as well. However, instead of producing a 1,2-diol, this reaction generates an α-dicarbonyl, as shown in Equation 21-43.

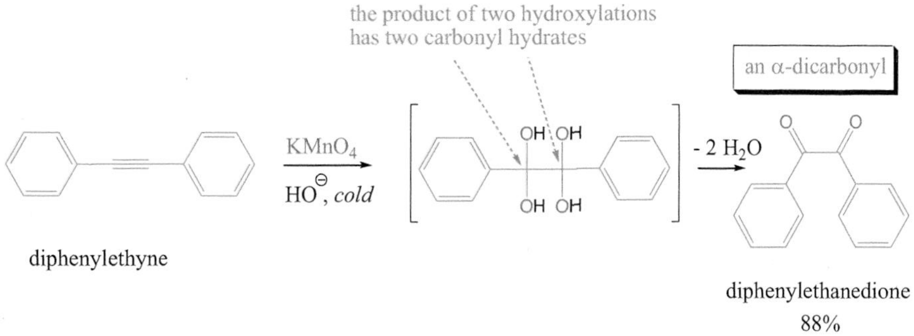

the product of two hydroxylations has two carbonyl hydrates

an α-dicarbonyl

$KMnO_4$, $HO^{\ominus}$, *cold*

$- 2\ H_2O$

diphenylethyne

diphenylethanedione
88%

(21-43)

As indicated above, we can envision the alkyne having undergone two *syn*-hydroxylations to yield a 1,1,2,2-tetraol intermediate. Recall from Chapter 16 that a *gem*-diol is equivalent to a hydrated carbonyl; loss of two equivalents of H_2O from that intermediate would give the dicarbonyl product.

Problem 21.20. Which of the following diols can be produced from an alkene using either OsO_4 or $KMnO_4$? For each one that can be, draw the alkene that can be used to produce it.

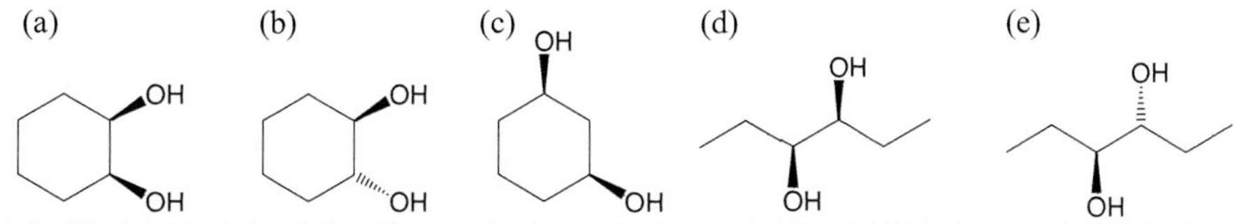

(a) (b) (c) (d) (e)

21.9. OXIDATIVE CLEAVAGE OF ALKENES AND ALKYNES

The bulk of the reactions we have examined in this chapter and Chapter 20 have been ones in which alkenes and alkynes undergo functional group conversions, leaving the structure of the carbon backbone intact. This section introduces a variety of reactions that serve to break the carbon-carbon bond of an alkene or alkyne, altering the carbon backbone in the process. One characteristic such reactions have in common is that during the course of the reaction, the alkene or alkyne undergoes oxidation. Thus, these reactions are called **oxidative cleavage** reactions. A second characteristic these reactions have in common is that each carbon atom initially part of the alkene or alkyne functional group becomes part of a carbonyl group in the products. This is illustrated in Equations 21-44 and 21-45. We will see, however, that depending upon the reagents that are used and the conditions of the reaction, those carbonyl groups can be part of ketones, aldehydes, carboxylic acids, or carbon dioxide.

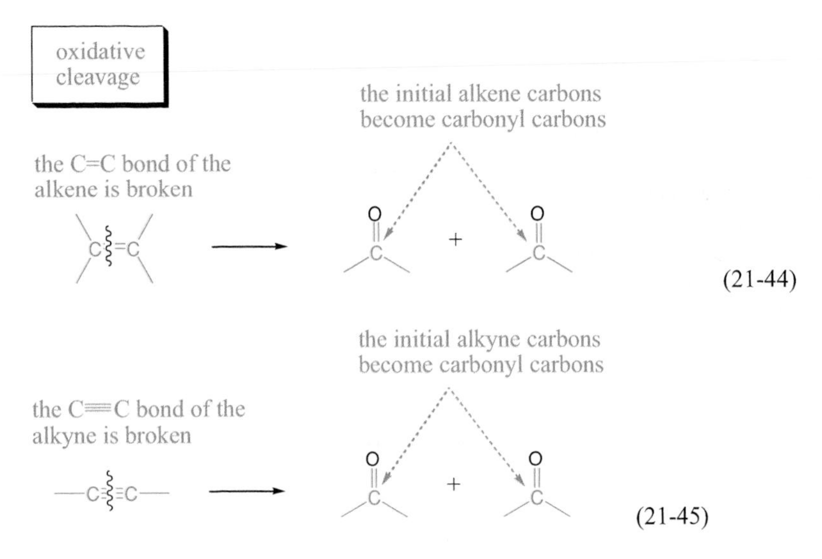

We will examine oxidative cleavage reactions involving three different reagents. Section 21.9a will discuss oxidative cleavage involving potassium permanganate, $KMnO_4$. Section 21.9b will discuss such reactions involving periodic acid, HIO_4. Finally, Section 21.9c will discuss ozonolysis, which involves ozone, O_3.

21.9a. Oxidative Cleavage Involving $KMnO_4$

In the previous section, we saw that the C=C double bond of an alkene undergoes *syn*-hydroxylation when treated with cold, basic $KMnO_4$. However, when the $KMnO_4$ solution is concentrated and the reaction mixture is heated, *oxidative cleavage* of the C=C bond takes place. An example is shown in Equation 21-46.

the alkene is cleaved

1) $KMnO_4$, conc. $HO^{\ominus}$, H_2O, 50° C
2) HCl

1-methylcyclohexene → 6-oxoheptanoic acid 61% (21-46)

The mechanism for this reaction is shown in Equation 21-47. Just as in the hydroxylation reaction (Your Turn 21.10), in step 1 MnO_4^- adds across the double bond in a *syn* fashion, yielding a manganate ester. The added heat, however, provides enough energy to break the C-C bond in step 2 via a cyclic rearrangement of six electrons, eliminating MnO_2. At this stage, the initial alkene carbons have already become carbonyl carbons—one has become part of a ketone, and the other has become part of an aldehyde. Recall that under these oxidation conditions, however, the aldehyde group reacts further to produce a carboxylic acid (Section 19.7b).

Mechanism for the Reaction in Equation 21-46

in the presence of $KMnO_4$, aldehydes are oxidized to carboxylic acids

1) electrophilic addition

2) elimination

a manganate ester

(21-47)

Equation 21-48 presents an example where one of the alkene carbons is a CH_2 group. As we can see, in such cases, cleavage of the C=C double bond initially produces formaldehyde, $H_2C{=}O$, as one of the carbonyl-containing products. Under the oxidative conditions with $KMnO_4$, formaldehyde is oxidized to carbon dioxide.

phenylethene

1) $KMnO_4$, conc. $HO^{\ominus}$, H_2O, 70° C

2) HCl

$[KMnO_4]$

benzoic acid 50%

CO_2 carbon dioxide

formaldehyde is oxidized to carbon dioxide

(21-48)

Alkynes are also susceptible to oxidative cleavage with $KMnO_4$. Unlike what we saw with the oxidative cleavage of alkenes, however, only carboxylic acids and carbon dioxide can be produced upon oxidative cleavage of an alkyne, as shown in Equation 21-49. Ketones cannot be formed under these conditions because in the C≡C triple bond, each alkyne carbon atom is bonded to the other triply bonded carbon and at most one alkyl group. Therefore, after cleavage of the C≡C triple bond, each of the initial alkyne carbon atoms can be bonded to at most one other carbon atom.

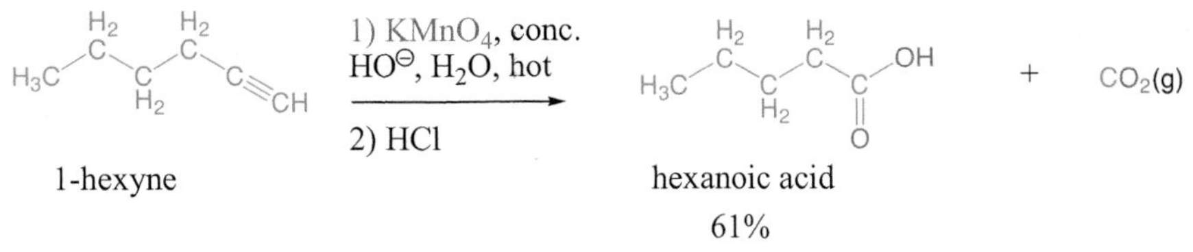

1-hexyne $\xrightarrow[\text{2) HCl}]{\text{1) KMnO}_4\text{, conc. HO}^\ominus\text{, H}_2\text{O, hot}}$ hexanoic acid (61%) + $CO_2(g)$ (21-49)

Solved problem 21.6. A hydrocarbon with formula is C_8H_{14} is treated with hot, concentrated $KMnO_4$. Bubbling is observed and the following compounds are recovered. What is a possible structure for the original hydrocarbon?

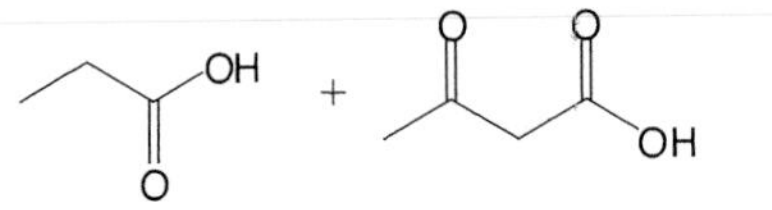

Think. Are the number of carbon atoms the same in the product compounds as in the reactant? What could give rise to the bubbling? What functional group is the precursor to a carboxylic acid under oxidative cleavage conditions?

Solve. Notice that there are a total of seven carbon atoms in the two compounds that were recovered, whereas there are eight carbons in the original hydrocarbon. The other carbon atom is lost in the form of CO_2 which bubbles out of solution.

Thinking backwards, the two carboxylic acid functional groups must have come from the initial formation of aldehydes, and CO_2 must have come from formaldehyde ($H_2C{=}O$), as shown below.

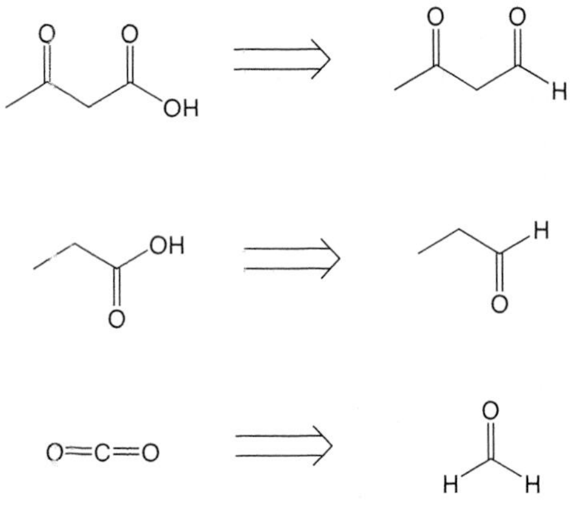

O=C=O ⟹ $H_2C{=}O$

Thinking backwards again, we know that each pair of C=O bonds must have come from the cleavage of a C=C double bond. Therefore, a possible structure for the original hydrocarbon is as follows:

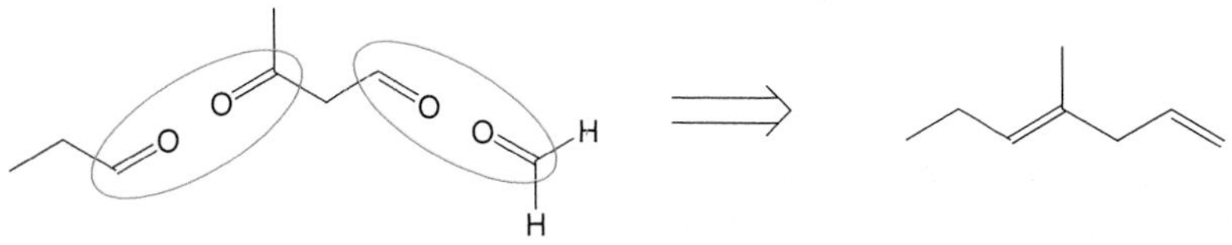

Problem 21.21. What is another possible structure for the original hydrocarbon in Solved Problem 21.6?

21.9b. Oxidative Cleavage Involving HIO_4

Similar to the oxidative cleavage involving $KMnO_4$ discussed in the previous section, an alkene can be cleaved oxidatively by treatment with OsO_4, followed by treatment with **periodic acid**, HIO_4. An example is shown in Equation 21-50.

the alkene is cleaved

aldehyde is NOT oxidized to the carboxylic acid

1) OsO_4, ether, H_2O
2) HIO_4 ether, H_2O

1-methylcyclohexene → 6-oxoheptanal

(21-50)

Unlike oxidative cleavage involving $KMnO_4$, however,

> Aldehydes that are produced upon oxidative cleavage involving HIO_4 are NOT oxidized further to either a carboxylic acid or carbon dioxide.

A partial mechanism for this reaction is provided in Equation 21-51.

Partial Mechanism for the Reaction in Equation 21-50

syn-hydroxylation with OsO_4

OH
OH
HIO_4
O OH
O—I=O
O
O
+ HIO_3

a *cis*-1,2-diol

a periodate ester

(21-51)

The first several steps comprise the *syn*-hydroxylation mechanism we saw in Section 21-8, producing a *cis*-1,2-diol. Then, after the addition of HIO_4, a cyclic **periodate ester** is produced, which undergoes a spontaneous rearrangement of six electrons to cleave the carbon-carbon single bond and produce the overall products.

Oxidative cleavage using periodic acid need not begin with the alkene, but instead can begin with the diol. However, it is important to realize that because of the fact that a cyclic periodate ester is a key intermediate (Equation 21-51), not all diols can be cleaved via this reaction.

> Only 1,2-diols in which the OH groups can be *syn* to each other can be cleaved by periodic acid.

Examples are shown in Equations 21-52 and 21-53.

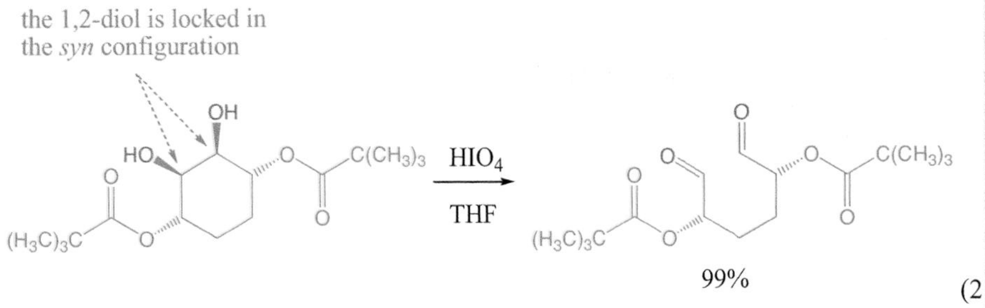

the 1,2-diol is locked in the *syn* configuration

HIO_4 / THF

99%

(21-52)

rotation about the carbon-carbon single bond allows the OH groups to be *syn* to each other

HIO_4 / ether, THF

98%

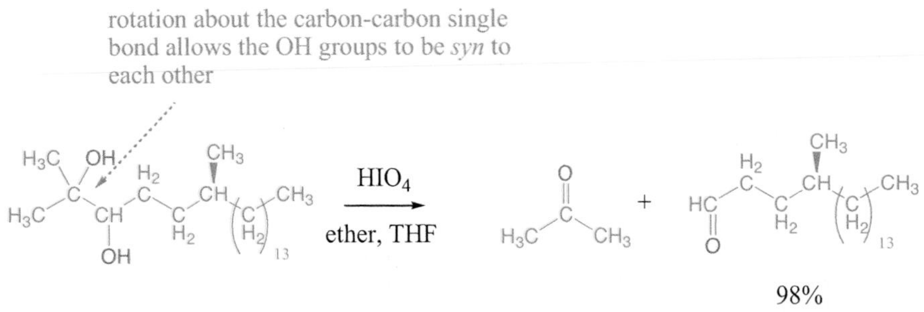

(21-53)

In Equation 21-52, the ring locks the 1,2-diol in the *syn* configuration. In Equation 21-53, rotation about the carbon-carbon single bond allows the two OH groups to become *syn* to each other.

21.9c. Oxidative Cleavage Involving Ozone: Ozonolysis

The third type of oxidative cleavage we will examine involves **ozone**, O_3, in a process called **ozonolysis**. An example is shown in Equation 21-54, in which 1-methylcyclohexene is treated with ozone, followed by dimethylsulfide, CH_3SCH_3. (Note that zinc metal in acetic acid could be used instead of dimethylsulfide.) The double bond is cleaved to yield precisely the same product as does oxidative cleavage involving periodic acid, shown previously in Equation 22-50.

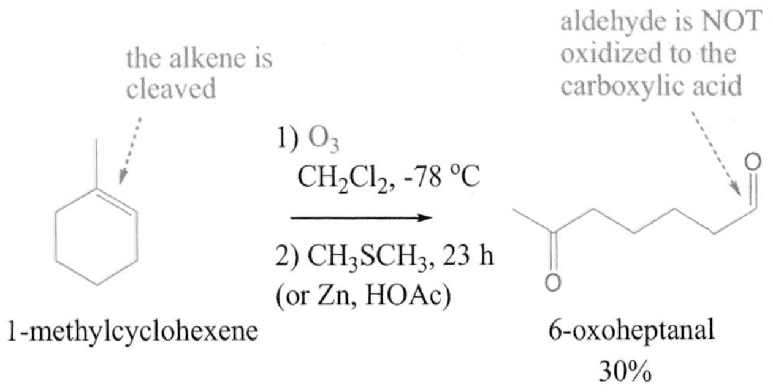

the alkene is cleaved

aldehyde is NOT oxidized to the carboxylic acid

1) O_3, CH_2Cl_2, -78 °C
2) CH_3SCH_3, 23 h (or Zn, HOAc)

1-methylcyclohexene

6-oxoheptanal 30%

(21-54)

The mechanism for this reaction is shown in Equation 21-55.

Mechanism for the Reaction in Equation 21-54

carbon-carbon bond is broken

1) electrophilic addition

2)

a molozonide

3) nucleophilic addition

an ozonide

4)

dimethyl sulfide reduces H_2O_2 to prevent oxidation of the aldehyde

5) S_N2

(21-55)

This mechanism is relatively complex, but there are some key aspects we can examine. In step 1, ozone undergoes electrophilic addition to the alkene to produce a **molozonide**, much like OsO_4 adds to an alkene to produce an osmate ester (Equation 21-41), or MnO_4^- adds to an alkene to produce a manganate ester (Equation 21-47). In step 2, six electrons undergo a cyclic rearrangement, breaking the carbon-carbon single bond. Step 3 is essentially driven by the nucleophilic addition of the negatively charged oxygen atom to the relatively electron-poor carbonyl carbon, producing an **ozonide**. In step 4, the ozonide opens, and gains a proton from water, producing a strongly nucleophilic hydroxide ion. In this step, one of the carbonyl-containing groups that appears in the overall product is produced. The second carbonyl-containing group that appears in the overall product is produced in step 5, which is an S_N2 step.

Notice that hydrogen peroxide is also produced in step 5. This is why dimethyl sulfide is added to the mixture. If a significant concentration of hydrogen peroxide accumulates, the aldehyde could be oxidized to a carboxylic acid. Dimethyl sulfide, however, is a reducing agent, and removes hydrogen peroxide by reducing it to water. Similarly, reduction of the hydrogen peroxide could be accomplished by zinc metal in acetic acid, as indicated previously in Equation 21-54.

Alternatively, oxidation of an aldehyde product might be desired in an ozonolysis reaction. To ensure that such an oxidation takes place, hydrogen peroxide can be added, as indicated in Equation 21-56.

the alkene is cleaved

1) O_3
CH_2Cl_2, -78 °C
2) H_2O_2

hydrogen peroxide oxidizes the initial aldehyde to the carboxylic acid

1-methylcyclohexene

6-oxoheptanoic acid

(21-56)

Problem 21.22. Draw the molozonide, the ozonide, and the products that are formed in each of the following reactions.

(a) 1) O_3 2) H_2O_2 ?

(b) 1) O_3 2) Zn, HOAc ?

21.10. FUNCTIONAL GROUP CHEMISTRY

Throughout this chapter and the last, we have examined primarily reactions in which a key step is electrophilic addition to a nonpolar π bond—i.e., alkenes and alkynes. In addition, we briefly examined a reaction involving 1,2-diols. This section provides a brief overview of the reactivity of such functional groups.

As usual, aspects that have been discussed in previous *Functional Group Chemistry* sections appear gray. New aspects that have been introduced in Chapters 20 and 21 appear green.

21.10a. Alkenes

An alkene is relatively electron-rich, so it tends to react with electrophiles, which are relatively electron-poor species. Strong Brønsted acids such as HCl, HBr, HI, or H_3O^+ have electrophilic protons that can add to an alkene to produce a carbocation intermediate that is later attacked by a nucleophile. Thus, these acids can add across the double bond to produce an alkyl halide or an alcohol.

If the electrophile has a pair of electrons that can form a bond to carbon, the addition of the electrophile proceeds through a cyclic transition state. The reaction proceeds through a three-membered transition state when the electrophile is a carbene, molecular halogen (Br_2 or Cl_2), a mercury(II) ion, or a peroxyacid. It proceeds through a four-membered ring in the addition of BH_3, and it proceeds through a five-membered ring in the addition of OsO_4, $KMnO_4$, or O_3.

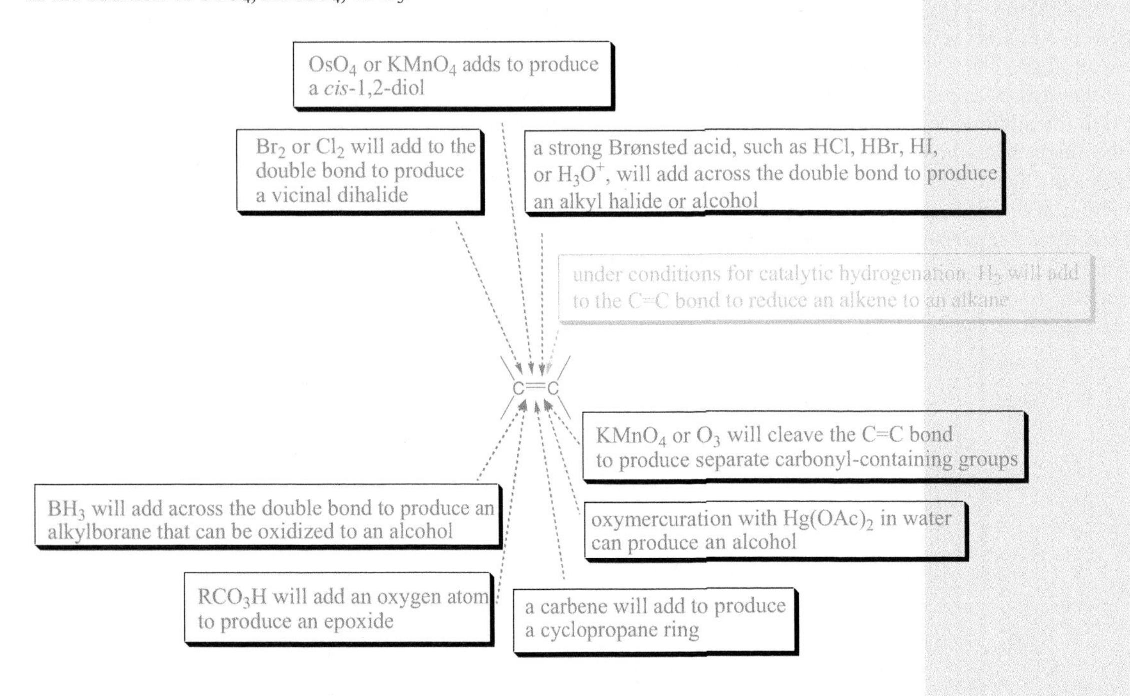
OsO4 or KMnO4 adds to produce a cis-1,2-diol
Br2 or Cl2 will add to the double bond to produce a vicinal dihalide
a strong Brønsted acid, such as HCl, HBr, HI, or H3O+, will add across the double bond to produce an alkyl halide or alcohol
under conditions for catalytic hydrogenation, H2 will add to the C=C bond to reduce an alkene to an alkane
C=C
KMnO4 or O3 will cleave the C=C bond to produce separate carbonyl-containing groups
BH3 will add across the double bond to produce an alkylborane that can be oxidized to an alcohol
oxymercuration with Hg(OAc)2 in water can produce an alcohol
RCO3H will add an oxygen atom to produce an epoxide
a carbene will add to produce a cyclopropane ring

21.10b. Alkynes

Like an alkene, an alkyne is relatively electron-rich, so it will undergo reaction with many of the same electrophiles as alkenes do. However, there are some key differences. The major difference to point out is that when an electrophile adds to the triple bond of an alkyne, a C=C double bond remains, in contrast to the single bond that remains after electrophilic addition to an alkene. Therefore, barring further reaction, the product is a vinyl-substituted compound. If the immediate product is a vinyl alcohol (i.e., an enol), keto-enol tautomerization takes place to produce the more stable ketone or aldehyde. This is the case, for example, in the addition of H_3O^+, $Hg(OAc)_2$, and BH_3.

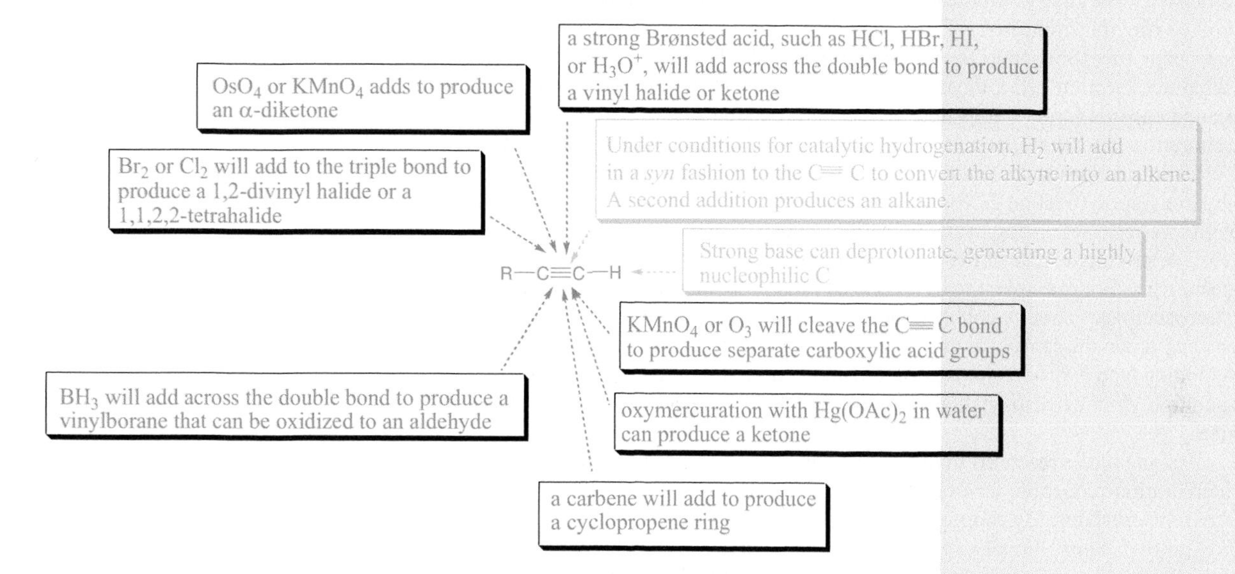

21.10c. Alcohols

The only new reaction involving alcohols is the reaction of a *cis*-1,2-diol with periodic acid. The carbon-carbon bond is cleaved, producing two separate carbonyl-containing groups, each of which could be a ketone or aldehyde.

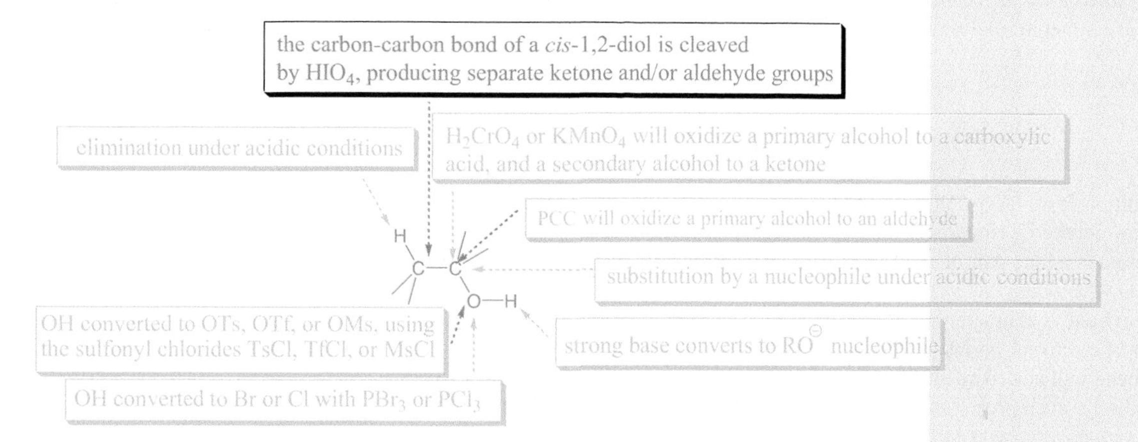

21.11. WRAPPING UP AND LOOKING AHEAD

The focus of this chapter has been on reactions in which an electrophile adds to an alkene or alkyne, without proceeding through a carbocation intermediate. For this to occur, the reaction instead proceeds through a cyclic transition state, ultimately leading to two new bonds that join both of the alkene or alkyne carbons to one or more atoms of the electrophile. One of those new bonds utilizes a pair of electrons that is originally a π bond of the alkene or alkyne. The other new bond utilizes a pair of electrons originally from the electrophile.

One of the main differences among the reactions discussed in this chapter is the number of atoms comprising the ring of the cyclic transition state in the electrophilic addition step. The first several reactions we examined proceed through a three-membered ring transition state. Those include: Addition of a carbene to produce a cyclopropane ring (Section 21.2); addition of molecular halogens to produce 1,2-dihalides (Section 21.3); oxymercuration-reduction to produce an alcohol (Section 21.4); and epoxide formation using a peroxyacid (Section 21.5). By contrast, hydroboration-oxidation (Sections 21.6 and 21.7) proceeds through a four-membered-ring cyclic transitions state, and the remaining reactions we examined—*syn*-hydroxylation (Section 21.8) and oxidative cleavage (Section 21.9)—proceed through five-membered-ring cyclic transition states.

A striking feature of the reactions in this chapter is their tendency to be stereospecific. For example, the formation of cyclopropane rings and epoxides conserves the stereochemistry about a double bond—groups that are on the same side of the initial alkene end up on the same side of the ring in the product. Halogenation takes place with *anti*-addition, and hydroboration-oxidation and hydroxylation take place with *syn*-addition. In the hydroxylation of an alkene, two hydroxyl groups add in a *syn* fashion.

Some of the reactions in this chapter are also highly regioselective. In oxymercuration-reduction, for example, water adds across an alkene or alkyne in a Markovnikov fashion. By contrast, in hydroboration-reduction, water adds in a non-Markovnikov fashion. Finally, in the conversion of an alkene to a halohydrin, the halogen atom adds preferentially to the less alkyl-substituted carbon, whereas the OH group adds to the more alkyl-substituted one.

This was the second of two chapters dealing with electrophilic addition reactions. The next two chapters maintain the theme of electrophilic reactions, but instead of addition reactions, those chapters will deal with substitution reactions. As we will see, the electron-rich species in such substitution reactions are not alkenes or alkynes, but are rather aromatic rings.

CHAPTER SUMMARY AND KEY TERMS

- Addition of an electrophile to an alkene or alkyne tends to proceed through a three-membered ring transition state if the electron-poor atom of the electrophile possesses a lone pair of electrons. Thus, no carbocation is produced. (Section 21.1)
- A **carbene** is characterized by an uncharged carbon atom that possesses a lone pair of electrons, and is produced *in situ* from an appropriate precursor. A carbene will add to an alkene, via a three-membered ring transition state, to produce a cyclopropyl ring. This reaction preserves the *cis/trans* relationships of the groups attached to the alkene carbons. (Section 21.2)
- In a non-nucleophilic solvent (such as carbon tetrachloride), Br_2 or Cl_2 will add to an alkene to produce a 1,2-dihalide. Such a reaction takes place with *anti*-addition of the halogen, signifying the initial production of a **bromonium** or **chloronium ion intermediate**. (Section 21.3a)

- In water, treatment of an alkene with a molecular halogen produces a **halohydrin**, in which a halogen atom and an OH group add in an *anti* fashion to the alkene carbon atoms. (Section 21.3b)
- **Oxymercuration-reduction** proceeds through a **mercurinium ion intermediate**, and results in the addition of water to an alkene or alkyne with Markovnikov regiochemistry. (Section 21.4)
- Treatment of an alkene with a **peroxyacid** produces an epoxide. Such a reaction preserves the *cis/trans* relationships of the groups attached to the alkene. (Section 21.5)
- In a **hydroboration-reduction reaction**, water adds to an alkene in a *syn* fashion, with non-Markovnikov regiochemistry, to produce an alcohol. (Section 21.6)
  - The hydroboration step involves the addition of BH_3 to the alkene to produce an alkylborane, and proceeds through a four-membered ring transition state. (Section 21.6a)
  - The oxidation step converts the alkylborane to the alcohol, with retention of stereochemistry. (Section 21.6b)
- A single hydroboration-oxidation of an alkyne will produce an enol that tautomerizes into ketone or aldehyde. To ensure that only an alkyne undergoes only a single hydroboration, a bulky dialkylborane is used, such as **disiamylborane**. (Section 21.7)
- An alkene or alkyne will undergo ***syn*-hydroxylation** when treated with potassium permanganate ($KMnO_4$) or osmium tetroxide (OsO_4). In such reactions, an OH group adds to each alkene or alkyne carbon in a *syn* fashion. (Section 21.8)
- **Oxidative cleavage** of an alkene will sever the C=C bond, producing two separate carbonyl-containing groups. (Section 21.9)
  - If $KMnO_4$ is used to carry out oxidative cleavage of an alkene, then each aldehyde that is initially produced is further oxidized to a carboxylic acid or to carbon dioxide. (Section 21.9a)
  - If HIO_4 is used to carry out oxidative cleavage following *syn*-hydroxylation, then the aldehydes that are initially produced are *not* further oxidized. (Section 21.9b)
  - If **oxonolysis** is used to carry out oxidative cleavage under oxidizing conditions, any aldehyde that is initially produced is further oxidized to the carboxylic acid or to carbon dioxide. If reducing conditions are used, no further oxidation takes place. (Section 21.9c)

REACTION TABLES

Table 21-1. Functional group transformations

Starting Functional Group	Typical Reagent Required	Functional Group Formed	Comments	Discussed in Section(s)
C=C Alkene	X_2 (X=Cl, Br) → CCl_4	X–C–C–X Vicinal dihalide	*Anti*-addition	21.3a
–C≡C– Alkyne	X_2 (X=Cl, Br) → CCl_4	CX_2–CX_2	2 equivalents of halogen	21.3a

		1,1,2,2-tetrahalide		
 Alkene	X_2 (X=Cl, Br), H_2O	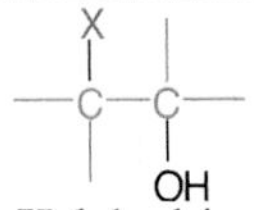 Halohydrin	OH bonds to more highly substituted carbon	21.3b
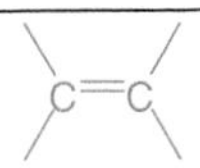 Alkene	1) $Hg(OAc)_2$, H_2O 2) $NaBH_4$	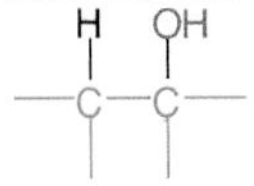 Alcohol	Markovnikov addition of water; no carbocation rearrangements	21.4
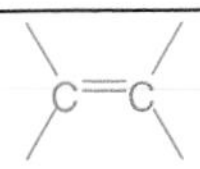 Alkene	1) B_2H_6 or BH_3:THF 2) $OH^{\ominus}$, H_2O_2	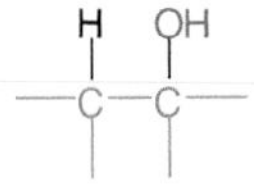 Alcohol	Non-Markovnikov addition of water	21.6
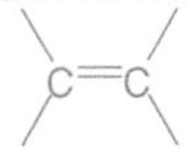 Alkene	OsO_4, H_2O; H_2O_2	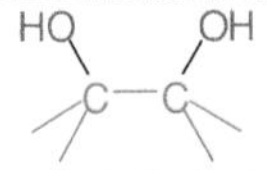 *Cis*-1,2-diol	*Syn* addition of OsO_4	21.8
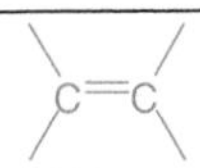 Alkene	$KMnO_4$, $HO^{\ominus}$; *cold*	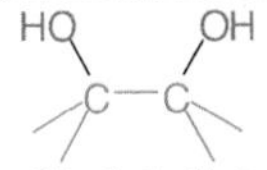 *Cis*-1,2-diol	*Syn* addition of MnO_4^-	21.8
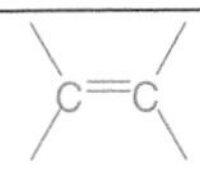 Alkene	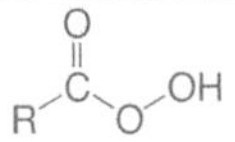 RC(=O)OOH	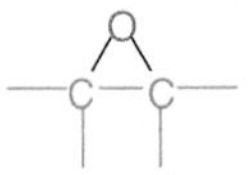 Epoxide	Conservation of *cis/trans* configuration	21.5
Alkyne	1) $Hg(OAc)_2$, H_2O 2) $NaBH_4$	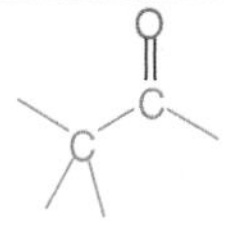 Ketone	Markovnikov addition of water	21.4
Alkyne	1) B_2H_6 or BH_3:THF 2) $OH^{\ominus}$, H_2O_2	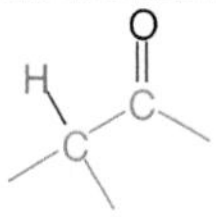 Ketone or Aldehyde	Non-Markovnikov addition of water	21.7

Table 22-2. Electrophilic addition reactions that alter the carbon skeleton

Starting Functional Group	Typical Reagent Required	Functional Group Formed	Comments	Discussed in Section(s)
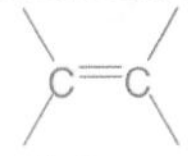 Alkene	CH_2N_2; heat or light	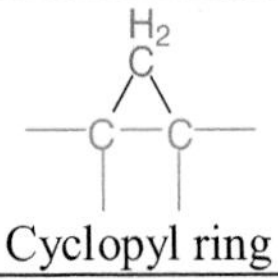 Cyclopyl ring	*Syn* addition; retention of *cis/trans* configuration	21.2
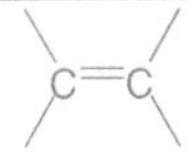 Alkene	$CHCl_3$; $(CH_3)_3CONa$	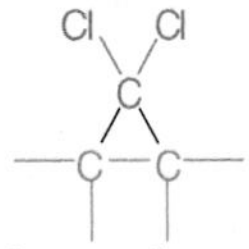 Dichlorocyclopropane	*Syn* addition; retention of *cis/trans* configuration	21.2

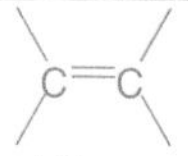 Alkene	conc. $KMnO_4$ → $HO^{\ominus}$, *hot*	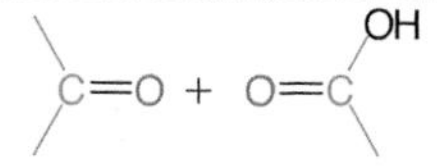 C=O + O=C(OH) Ketone or carboxylic acid	Aldehyde products oxidized to carboxylic acids	21.9a
 —C≡C— Alkyne	conc. $KMnO_4$ → $HO^{\ominus}$, *hot*	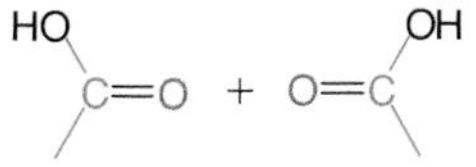 HO–C=O + O=C–OH Carboxylic acids		21.9a
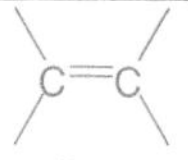 Alkene	1) O_3 → 2) $(CH_3)_2S$ or Zn, HOAc	 C=O + O=C(H) Ketone/aldehyde	Reducing conditions in 2nd step	21.9c
 Alkene	1) O_3 → 2) H_2O_2	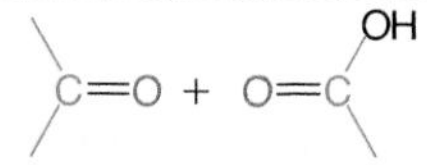 C=O + O=C(OH) Ketone or carboxylic acid	Oxidizing conditions in 2nd step	21.9c
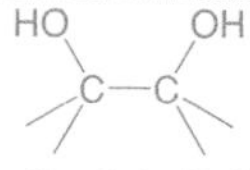 HO–C–C–OH *Cis*-1,2-diol	HIO_4 →	 C=O + O=C(H) Ketone/aldehyde		21.9b

PROBLEMS

23. Br_2 undergoes electrophilic addition to maleic anhydride as shown below. However, its reaction is much slower than with cyclopentene. Explain why.

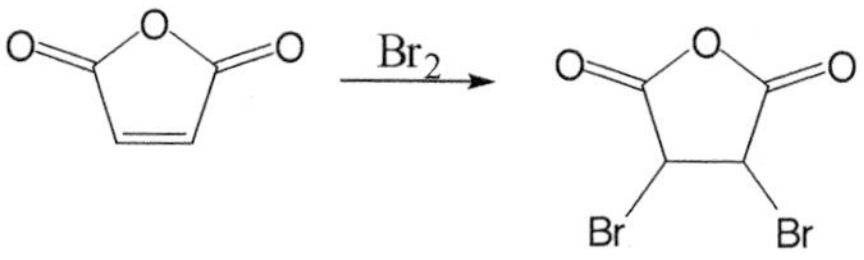

24. The electrophilic addition of Br_2 to several alkenes was examined, and the relative reaction rates are shown below. Explain.

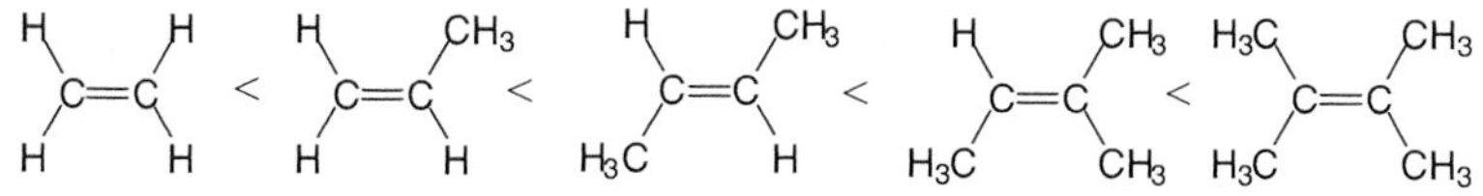

$H_2C=CH_2$ < $H(CH_3)C=CH_2$ < $(H_3C)HC=CH(CH_3)$ < $(H_3C)HC=C(CH_3)_2$ < $(H_3C)_2C=C(CH_3)_2$

increasing reaction rate with Br_2 →

25. Predict the major product(s) for each of the following reactions
    a. 4-chloro-1-butene + HBr →
    b. 1-chloro-1-butene + HBr →
    c. 4,4-dimethylcyclopentene + H_2O, H^+ →
    d. (R)-1,6-dimethylcyclohexene + diazomethane, hν →
    e. 1,5-hexadiene + 2 Cl_2 →
    f. 2-methyl-2-butene + Br_2, H_2O →
    g. Propyne + 2 HCl →
    h. 3-ethyl-1-pentyne + 2 Br_2 →
    i. Cyclopentylethene $\xrightarrow{H_3O^+}$

j. Cyclopentylethene $\xrightarrow[\text{2) NaBH}_4\text{/OH}^-]{\text{1) Hg(OAc)}_2\text{/H}_2\text{O}}$

k. Cyclopentylethene $\xrightarrow[\text{2) NaOH / H}_2\text{O}_2]{\text{1) BH}_3}$

26. For each of the following reactions, draw the complete mechanism and use the mechanism to predict the major product(s). Include stereochemistry where appropriate.

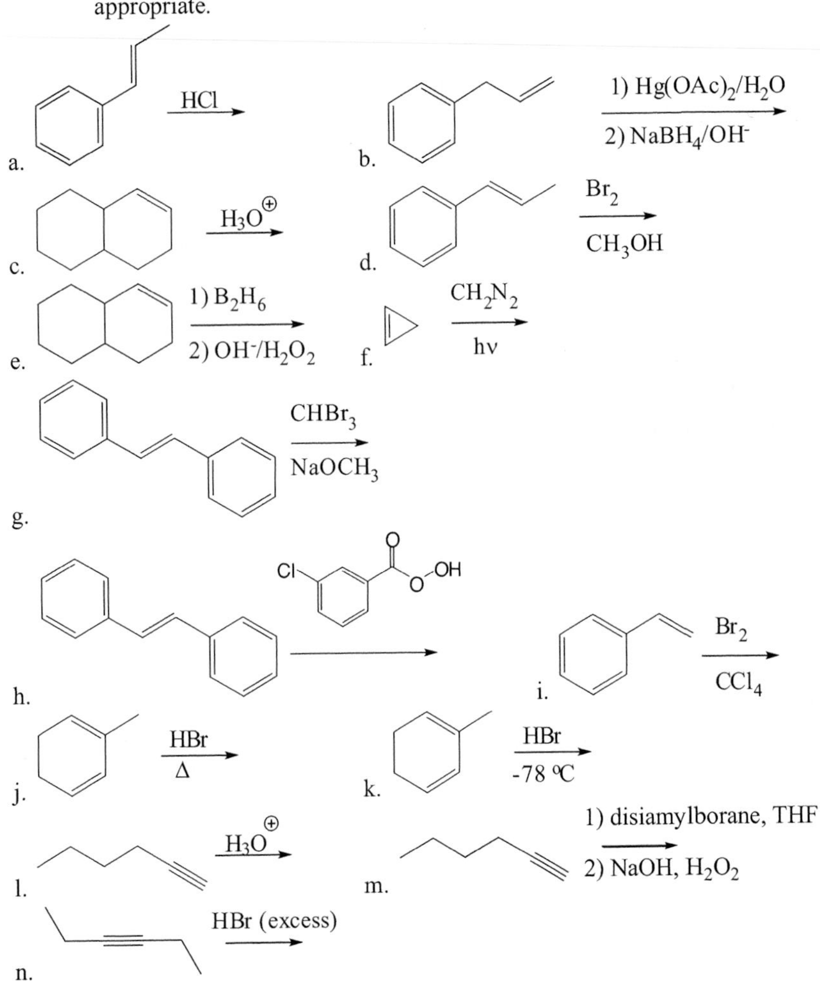

27. Show how each of the following can be synthesized from an alkene.

(a) H Br / Br H

(b)

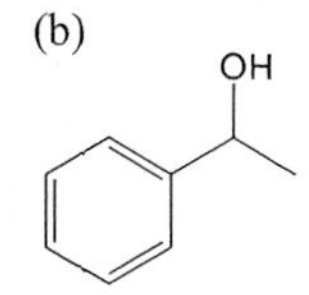

(c)

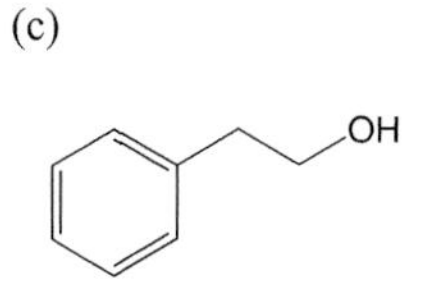

(d)

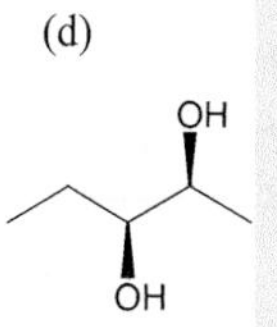

(e)

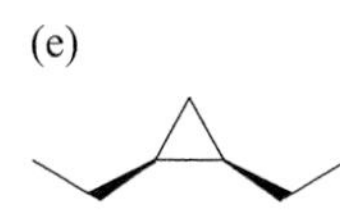

(f)

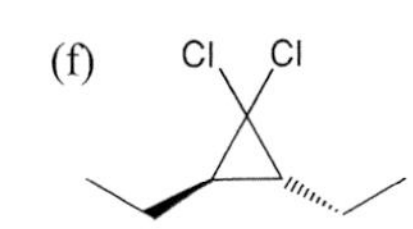

(g)

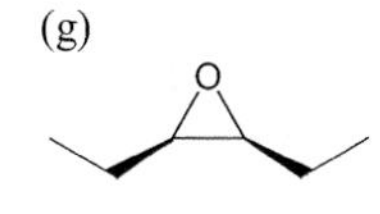

(h)

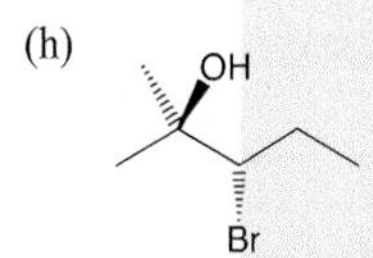

28. Show how each of the following can be synthesized from an alkyne.

(a) (b)

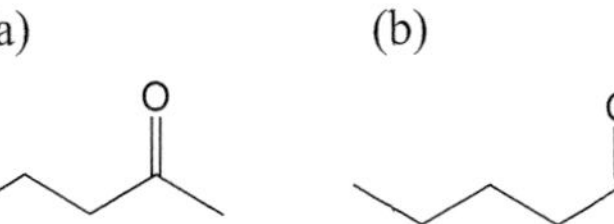

(c) O / O

(d)

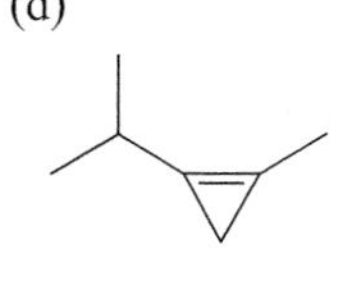

(e)

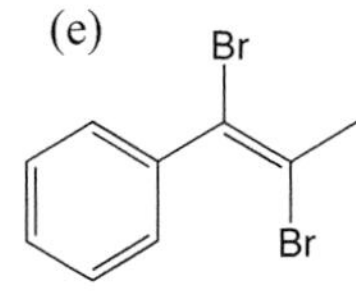

(f) Br Br / Br Br

29. Supply the missing compounds in the synthesis scheme below.

MCPBA → [A] 1) CH_3CH_2Li 2) H_3O^+ → [B] PBr_3 → [C] 1) PPh_3 2) BuLi → [D]

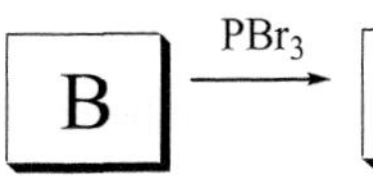

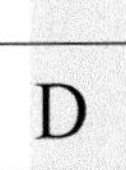

1) disiamylborane 2) NaOH, H_2O_2 → [E] [D] → [F] CH_2N_2, hν → [G]

30. Supply the missing compounds in the synthesis scheme below.

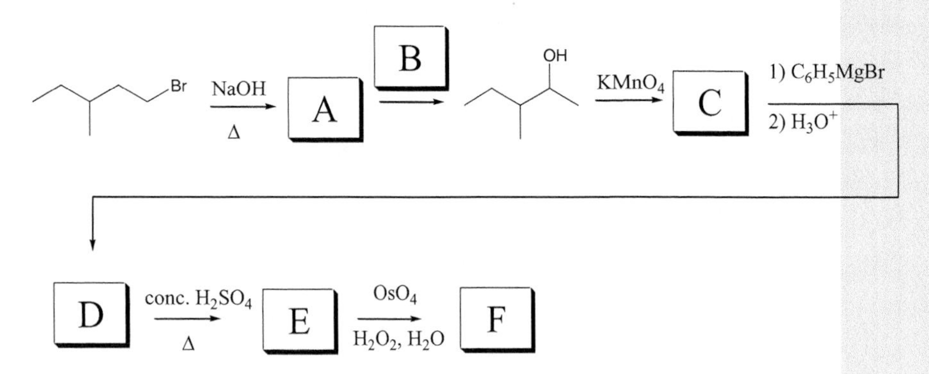

31. For each of the following reactions, draw a complete, detailed mechanism and predict the major products, paying attention to regiochemistry and stereochemistry.

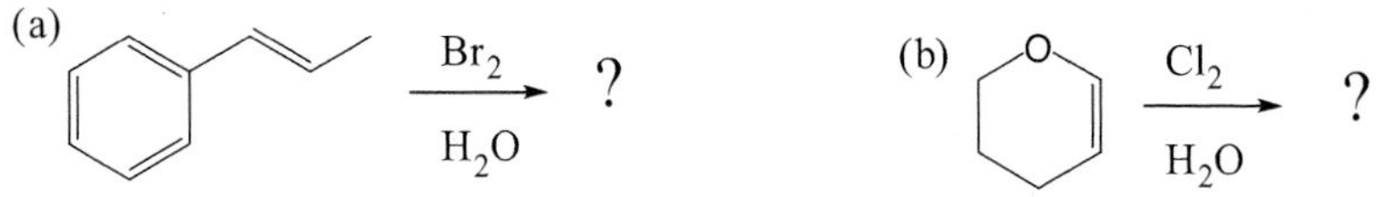

(a) $\xrightarrow[H_2O]{Br_2}$?

(b) $\xrightarrow[H_2O]{Cl_2}$?

32. Predict the product of the following reaction.

1,3-butadiene $\xrightarrow[\text{2) NaOH, } H_2O_2]{\text{1) } BH_3\text{:THF (excess)}}$?

33. Bromination can occur in a 1,4 fashion across conjugated double bonds, as in 1,3-hexadiene shown below.

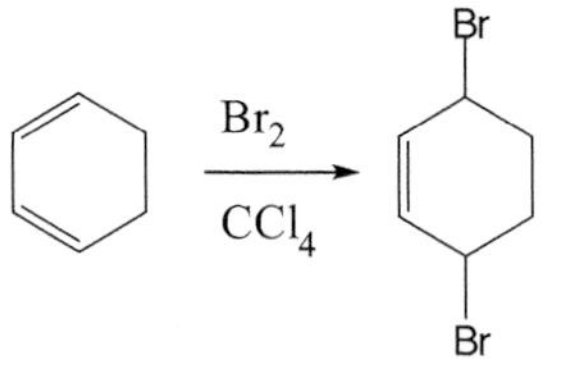

$\xrightarrow[CCl_4]{Br_2}$

Br

Br

One mechanism that has been proposed involves a 5-membered ring bromonium ion intermediate.

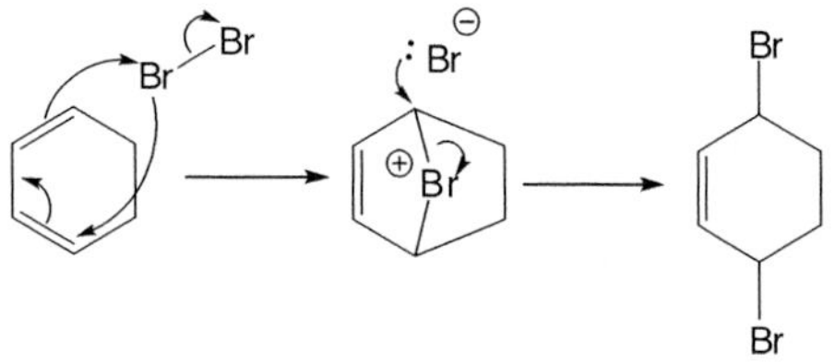

Br Br ⊖ Br ⊕ Br Br Br

(a) According to this mechanism, what should the stereochemistry be for the products? All cis, all trans, or a mixture of both? (b) Observations from experiment show that both cis and trans products are formed. Does this support or discredit the proposed mechanism above?

34. Propose a mechanism for the following reaction that accounts for the observed stereochemistry.

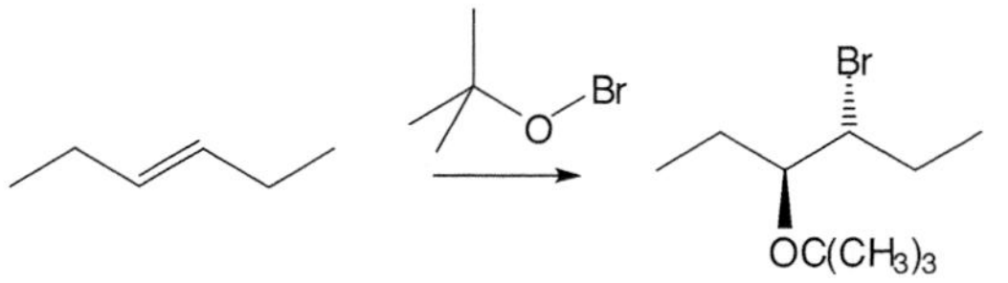

35. When cylohexene is treated with *m*-chloroperpenzoic acid, *trans*-cyclohexan-1,2-diol is produced. Propose a mechanism for this reaction, accounting for the observed stereochemistry. (Hint: Recall what a peroxyacid does to an alkene.)

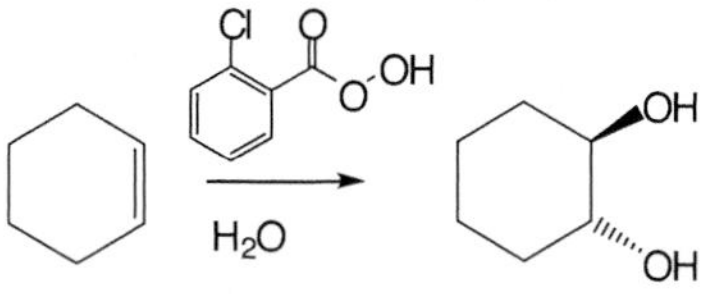

36. The high reactivity of carbenes can facilitate the synthesis of some unusual compounds. Show how each of the following can be synthesized from acyclic compounds.

a. 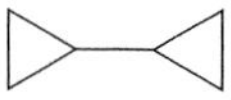 b.

37. Dichloromethane (CH_2Cl_2) can be treated with butyllithium, $CH_3CH_2CH_2CH_2$-Li, to make a carbene *in situ*, parallel to the way a carbene is generated from trichloromethane ($CHCl_3$) using HO^-. (a) Show the mechanism for the generation of a carbene from CH_2Cl_2. (b) Why is butyllithium used instead of HO^-? (c) The following reaction leads to a mixture of four products. Draw all four products.

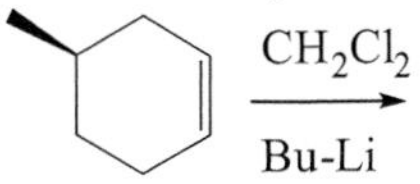

38. Propose syntheses of 2,2-dibromohexane and 1,2-dibromohexane beginning with 1-hexyne.

39. Not surprisingly, alkynes behave quite similarly to alkenes with regard to carbene addition. For example, as shown below, a carbene can add to an alkyne to yield a cyclopropene.

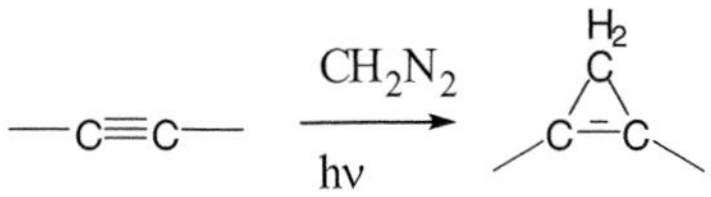

However, alkynes behave differently from alkenes when treated with a peroxyacid. Whereas an alkene would be converted into an epoxide by the addition of an oxygen atom, this addition product is not observed for alkynes under normal conditions. Suggest why. (Hint: Pay special attention to the lone pairs.)

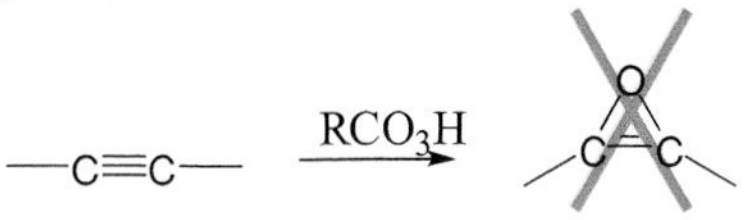

40. A student attempted to brominate the double bond in hex-3-en-1-ol, but ended up with the following cyclic ether instead. Propose a mechanism for the formation of this product.

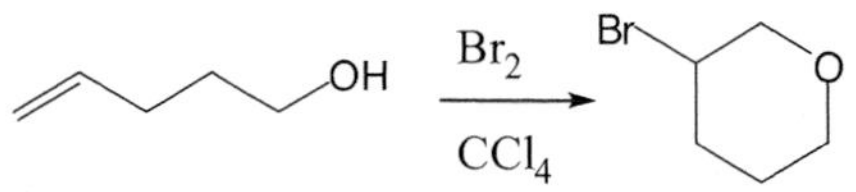

Br_2 / CCl_4

41. Iodine monochloride (ICl) is a mixed halogen that adds to an alkene via the same mechanism by which bromination takes place. With that in mind, propose a mechanism for the following reaction, and use that mechanism to predict the products, paying attention to both *regiochemistry* and *stereochemistry*. (Hint: In ICl, one atom is more electrophilic than the other.)

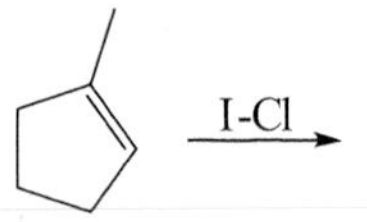

I-Cl

42. Oxidative cleavage can be used in a sequence of other reactions to alter the ring size of a compound. With this in mind, suggest how you would carry out the following transformation using any reagents necessary.

?

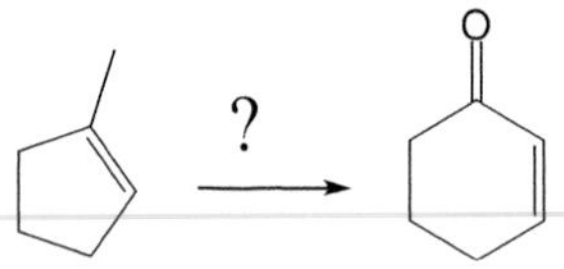

43. Outline a synthesis for each of the following compounds, given the restrictions provided. Begin designing your synthesis by performing a retrosynthetic analysis.
    a. 2-bromo-3-methylbutane from 2-bromo-2-methylbutane. You may use any reagents necessary.
    b. 2-phenyl-1-methlcyclohexanol from 1-methylcyclohexanol. You may use any reagents necessary.
    c. 2,3-dibromo-2,3-dimethylbutane using acetone and triphenylphosphine as your only carbon-containing compounds.

44. Show how to synthesize each of the following compounds beginning with phenylethyne. You may use any other reagents necessary.

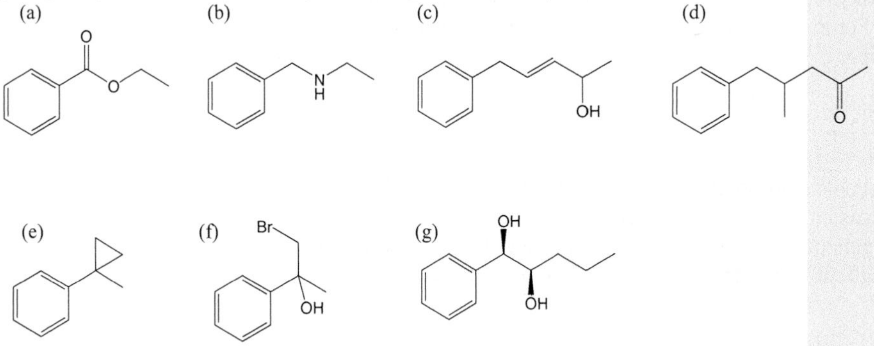

(a) (b) (c) (d)

(e) (f) (g)

45. An unknown compound, whose formula is C_6H_{10}, is known to react with one molar equivalent of Br_2 in carbon tetrachloride. When the compound was treated with a hot, basic solution of potassium permanganate, a product was formed whose IR spectrum exhibits a broad absorption of medium intensity from 2,500 cm^{-1} to 3,300 cm^{-1}, and a sharp, intense absorption near 1,700 cm^{-1}. The ^{1}H-NMR, and ^{13}C-NMR spectra of the product are shown (note: The

multiplet at 39 ppm is from the solvent, $CDCl_3$). Draw the structure of the starting compound.

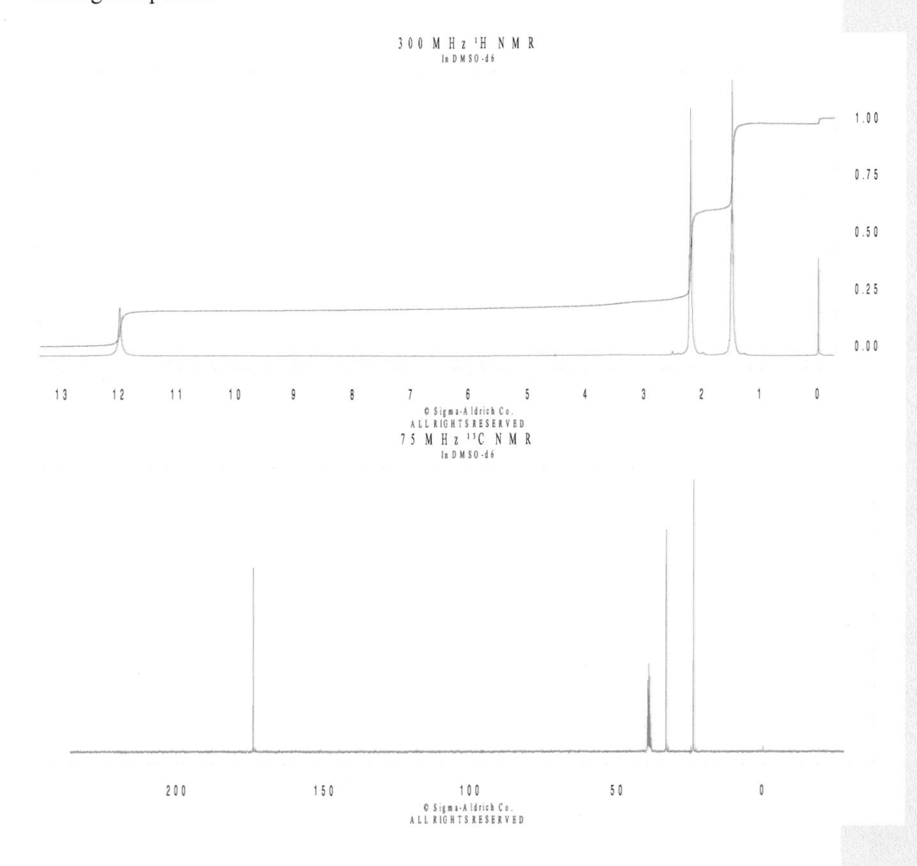

46. Treatment of pent-4-ynoic acid with mercury(II) acetate produces a compound whose formula is $C_5H_6O_2$. The IR, ^{1}H-NMR, and ^{13}C-NMR spectra are shown. Draw the product, and propose a mechanism for its formation.

O
HO
$\xrightarrow[CH_2Cl_2]{Hg(OAc)_2}$ $C_5H_6O_2$

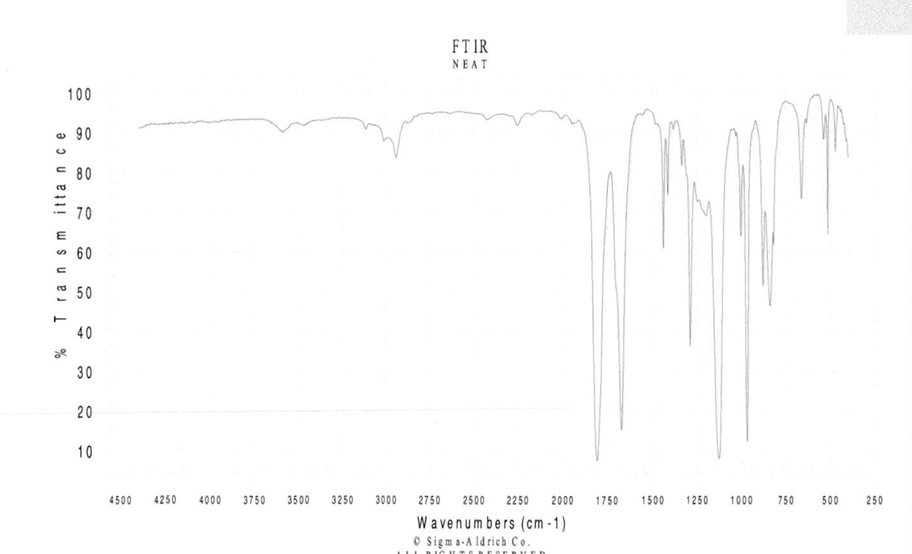
FTIR
NEAT
% Transmittance
100
90
80
70
60
50
40
30
20
10
4500 4250 4000 3750 3500 3250 3000 2750 2500 2250 2000 1750 1500 1250 1000 750 500 250
Wavenumbers (cm-1)
© Sigma-Aldrich Co.
ALL RIGHTS RESERVED
300 MHz ¹H NMR
In CDCl3

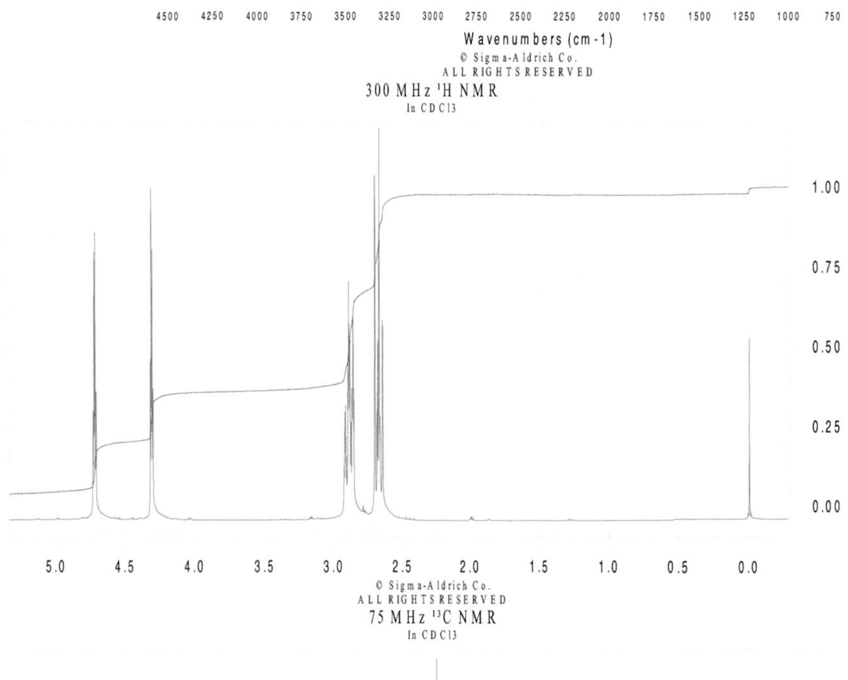
1.00
0.75
0.50
0.25
0.00
5.0 4.5 4.0 3.5 3.0 2.5 2.0 1.5 1.0 0.5 0.0
© Sigma-Aldrich Co.
ALL RIGHTS RESERVED
75 MHz ¹³C NMR
In CDCl3

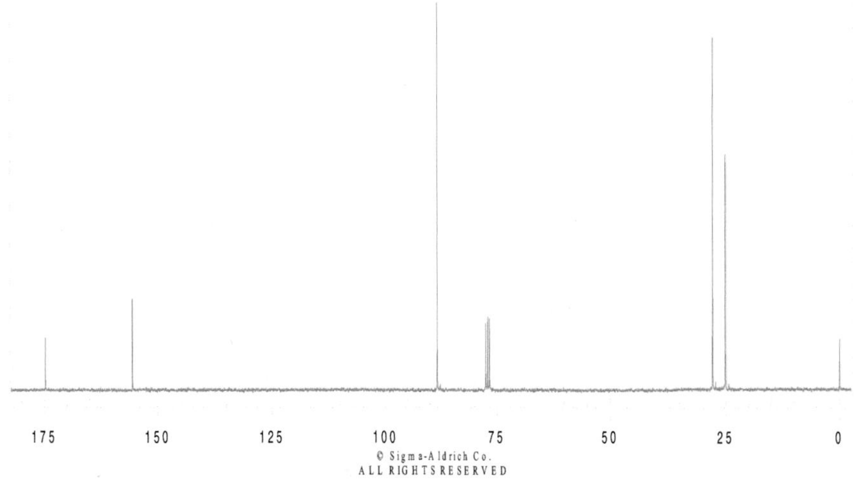
175 150 125 100 75 50 25 0
© Sigma-Aldrich Co.
ALL RIGHTS RESERVED

47. When benzene is treated with diazomethane and irradiated with light, 1,3,5-cycloheptatriene is produced. Propose a mechanism for this reaction.

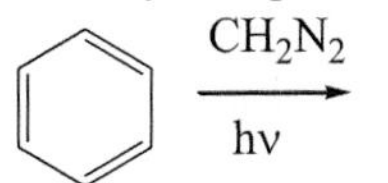

Chapter 22. Electrophilic Aromatic Substitution. 1: Substitution on Benzene and Symmetric Benzene Rings

Introduction

Benzene's representation as a Lewis structure (or, Kekulè structure) contains three conjugated double bonds arranged in a ring. We might therefore expect benzene to undergo electrophilic addition as we saw with various alkenes and alkynes in Chapters 20 and 21. However, it does not. For example, no reaction occurs when benzene is treated with HCl (Equation 22-1). Nor does benzene react with Cl_2 under normal conditions (Equation 22-2).

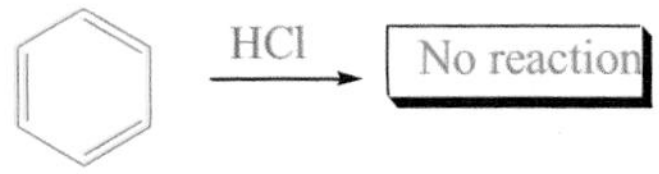

HCl → No reaction (22-1)

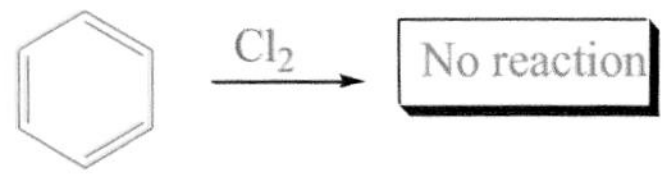

Cl_2 → No reaction (22-2)

This lack of reactivity is attributed to the stability exhibited by benzene's π system—recall from Chapter 12 that benzene is *aromatic*. Therefore, electrophilic addition reactions that *permanently* destroy benzene's aromaticity—such as those in Equations 22-1 and 22-2—are heavily disfavored.

Your Turn 22.1. Verify the above statement by drawing the electrophilic addition products for the reactions in Equations 22-1 and 22-2 in the space provided here. Show that they are indeed nonaromatic.

22-1 22-2

When iron or iron (III) chloride, $FeCl_3$, is added to the reaction mixture, however, benzene does react with Cl_2. Importantly, the reaction that takes place is *not* an addition reaction. Instead, it is a *substitution*, as is shown in Equation 22-3, in which a hydrogen atom is replaced by a chlorine atom. Because of the involvement of an aromatic species, such a reaction is called **electrophilic aromatic substitution**.

benzene $\xrightarrow[\text{Fe or FeCl}_3]{Cl_2}$ chlorobenzene + HCl

(22-3)

In this chapter we will examine the general mechanism for this and other electrophilic aromatic substitution reactions involving benzene. We will find that, although the reactions call for a variety of different reagents, they involve the same general mechanism.

Realize that aromaticity is not limited to just benzene. Other aromatic compounds we examined in Chapter 12 can also undergo electrophilic aromatic substitution, as we introduce in Section 22.8. However, because reactions involving these other aromatic compounds can be significantly more complex, requiring consideration of reaction rates and regiochemistry, much of their discussion will be reserved for Chapter 23.

CHAPTER OBJECTIVES

Upon completion of this chapter you should be able to…

- Explain why aromatic species are resistant to electrophilic addition reactions.
- Draw the general mechanism for **electrophilic aromatic substitution**; describe the characteristics and the importance of the **arenium ion intermediate**.
- Explain why electrophilic aromatic substitution takes place under *kinetic control.*
- Draw the detailed mechanism for **halogenation** of benzene; provide examples of **Lewis acid catalysts** and describe their role in the mechanism.
- Draw the detailed mechanism for a **Friedel-Crafts alkylation** and a **Friedel-Crafts acylation** reaction. List the limitations of each kind of reaction.
- Draw the detailed mechanism for a **nitration** reaction; describe the role of sulfuric acid.
- Draw the detailed mechanism for a **sulfonation** reaction; describe the role of SO_3 in **fuming sulfuric acid**, and explain why sulfonation is *reversible.*
- Recognize aromatic compounds other than benzene that can participate in electrophilic aromatic substitution; describe the complications that can arise in such reaction.
- Explain the potential complication of **ipso attack** in electrophilic aromatic substitution, as well as the reasons why most electrophilic aromatic substitution reactions do *not* proceed by ipso attack.
- Show how to synthesize a primary alkylarene using a Friedel-Crafts acylation reaction.
- Show how to synthesize aromatic carboxylic acids by employing $KMnO_4$ oxidations of carbon side chains on aromatic rings.
- Show how to synthesize aromatic amines via nitration.
- Devise syntheses that incorporate substitution reactions on aryldiazonium ions; recognize which of these reactions are classified as **Sandmeyer reactions**.

22.1. THE GENERAL MECHANISM OF ELECTROPHILIC AROMATIC SUBSTITUTION

Just as with alkenes and alkynes, the π system of benzene is relatively electron-rich. In contrast, an electrophile is relatively electron-poor, and may generically be represented as "E^+." (The positive charge emphasizes the electron-poor nature of the electrophile.) Therefore, when benzene encounters an electrophile, the two species can form a new bond, using a pair of π electrons from benzene. This is an electrophilic addition step, shown in step 1 in Equation 22-4, the general mechanism of electrophilic aromatic substitution. It is the same first step we have seen previously in the addition of a Brønsted acid across an alkene (Chapter 20). The difference is that in the addition of a Brønsted acid, the electrophile is formally a proton, H^+.

The General Mechanism for Electrophilic Aromatic Substitution

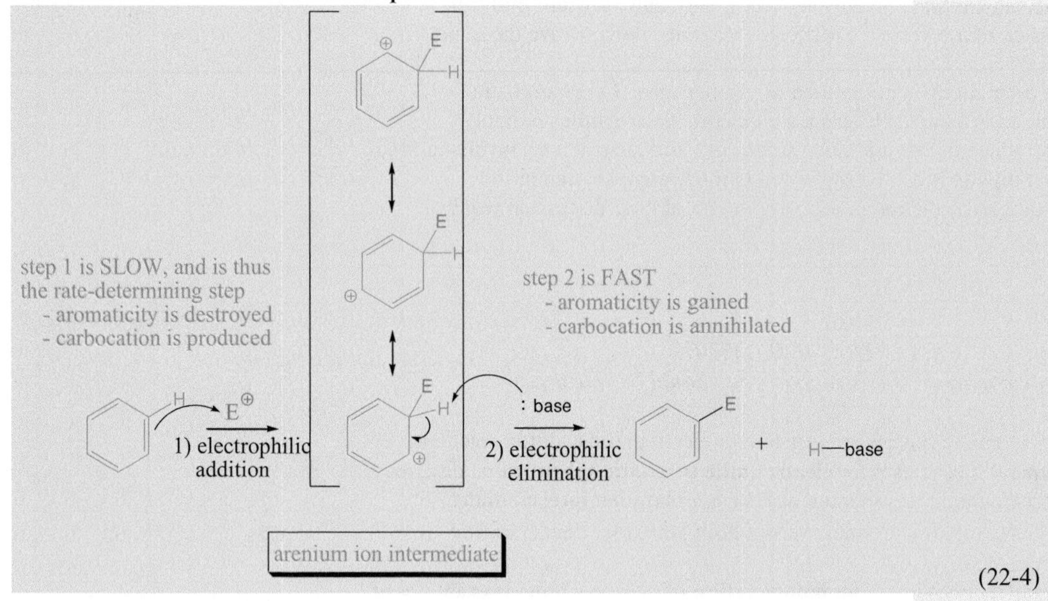

(22-4)

The product of step 1 is called an **arenium ion** or a **Wheland intermediate**. It is a carbocation intermediate consisting of five sp^2-hybridized carbon atoms and one sp^3-hybridized carbon. This intermediate participates in an electrophilic elimination step in step 2 of the mechanism. A proton (H^+) is eliminated, and is assisted by the formation of a bond to a base that is present. Overall, then, E^+ replaces H^+, converting benzene into a **substituted benzene**.

Your Turn 22.2. Label the hybridization on each carbon atom in the arenium ion intermediate below.

Notice that the arenium ion intermediate is not aromatic, and also possesses a positively charged carbon that lacks an octet. Therefore, the intermediate is much less stable than the starting compound, benzene, as illustrated in the reaction energy diagram in Figure 22-1. Consequently, the first step is highly unfavorable. By contrast, elimination of the proton from the sp^3-hybridized carbon atom in step 2 is highly favorable, because aromaticity is regained and the carbocation is annihilated.

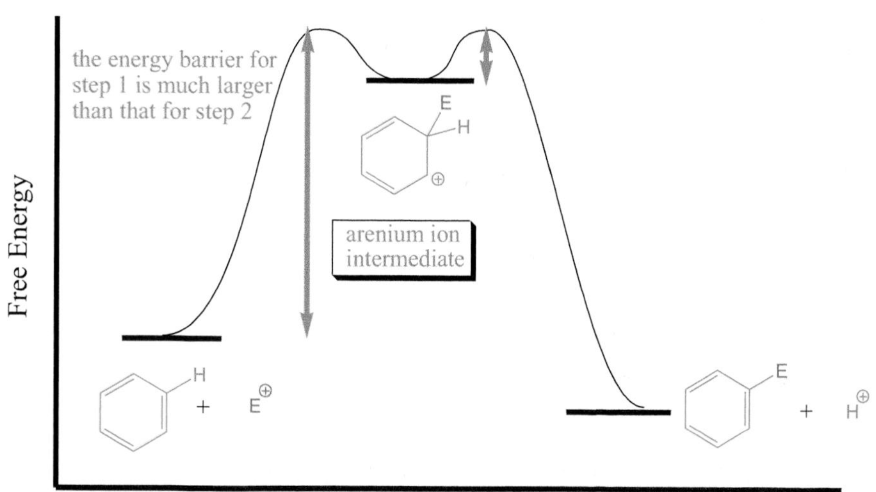

Figure 22-1. Reaction Energy Diagram for an Electrophilic Aromatic Substitution
The arenium ion intermediate is significantly less stable than either the reactants or products due to loss of aromaticity and the gain of a positively-charged carbon that lacks an octet. Therefore, the energy barrier for step 1 is much larger than that for step 2, making step 1 much slower than step 2.

Given the loss of aromaticity and the gain of a carbocation in step 1, you might wonder why electrophilic aromatic substitution takes place at all. Much of the reason has to do with the fact that the arenium ion intermediate is stabilized by the resonance delocalization of the positive charge over three different carbon atoms (Equation 22-4). Thus, the arenium ion intermediate is significantly more stable than it otherwise would be.

Your Turn 22.3. In the space provided here, draw all resonance structures and the resonance hybrid of the arenium ion intermediate from Equation 22-4.

From Figure 22-1, we can see that the energy barrier for step 1 is much larger than it is for step 2, making step 2 the much slower step. In other words,

> In electrophilic aromatic substitution, the electrophilic addition step (step 1 in Equation 22-4) is the rate-determining step.

Because benzene and the electrophile both appear as reactants in the rate-determining step, the rate of the overall reaction depends upon the concentration of each species, as indicated in Equation 22-5.

$$\text{Rate} = k\left[\text{(benzene)}\right]\left[E^{\oplus}\right] \qquad (22\text{-}5)$$

Specifically,

> The general electrophilic aromatic substitution reaction is first order with respect to the concentration of benzene, and is also first order with respect to the concentration of the electrophile.

Problem 22.1. In an electrophilic aromatic substitution reaction, suppose that the concentration of the electrophile is doubled and the concentration of benzene is tripled. What happens to the rate of the overall reaction?

As with any reaction, the reversibility of electrophilic aromatic substitution reactions can be quite important.

> In general, electrophilic aromatic substitution reactions are *irreversible* and therefore take place under *kinetic control.*

The reason for the tendency of such reactions to be irreversible stems from the conditions necessary for reaction to take place. Because step 1 in Equation 22-4 temporarily leads to the destruction of the benzene ring's aromaticity, *a very strong electrophile is required.* Consequently, electrophiles that are suitable for aromatic substitution tend to be less stable than the H^+ that is removed, making the reaction highly favorable. Moreover, removal of the H^+ in the second step is facilitated by the formation of a bond to a base, which further favors products.

Comment [JMK45]: Margin note
Electrophilic aromatic substitution typically requires a very strong electrophile.

So far, we have dealt only with the two-step electrophilic aromatic substitution mechanism in a general sense—an electrophile (E^+) first adds to the benzene ring and a proton (H^+) is then eliminated. In the sections that follow, we will focus on specific types of substitution reactions. Each of the reactions we encounter involve the same two-step electrophilic aromatic substitution mechanism, but the identity of "E^+" differs from reaction to reaction.

Realize that the high reactivity required of each of these electrophiles in general makes it difficult or impossible to add them directly as reactants. Instead,

> Electrophiles in electrophilic aromatic substitution reactions typically must be generated *in situ* from stable precursors that can be added.

Therefore, as you encounter the mechanisms for the various kinds of electrophilic aromatic substitution reactions, pay particular attention to what the actual electrophile is and how it is generated.

22.2. HALOGENATION

In the opening to this chapter, we stated that under normal conditions, benzene does not react with molecular chlorine, Cl_2 (Equation 22-2). However, in the presence of Fe or $FeCl_3$, **chlorination** occurs, whereby a chlorine atom replaces H to yield chlorobenzene (Equation 22-3). Similarly, molecular bromine, Br_2, does not react with benzene under normal conditions (Equation 22-6), but in the presence of Fe or $FeBr_3$, **bromination** takes place to produce bromobenzene (Equation 22-7).

Br_2 → no reaction

(22-6)

Br_2, Fe or $FeBr_3$, 4 h, 60 °C → bromobenzene 97% + HBr

(22-7)

The mechanism of the *bromination* of benzene is shown in Equation 22-8. Step 1 involves $FeBr_3$ acting as a Lewis acid, whereby Br_2 complexes to $FeBr_3$ in a coordination step. As indicated in Equation 22-7, $FeBr_3$ can be added directly, or it can be produced *in situ* by a reaction between Fe and Br_2. Next, in step 2, heterolysis of the bromine-bromine bond takes place *slowly*, producing Br^+ and $FeBr_4^-$. Finally, steps 3 and 4 formally comprise electrophilic aromatic substitution (i.e., the mechanism presented previously in Equation 22-4), with Br^+ as the electrophile. Notice that $FeBr_3$ is regenerated in the final step, so it is not consumed overall—it is a catalyst.

Mechanism of the Reaction in Equation 22-7

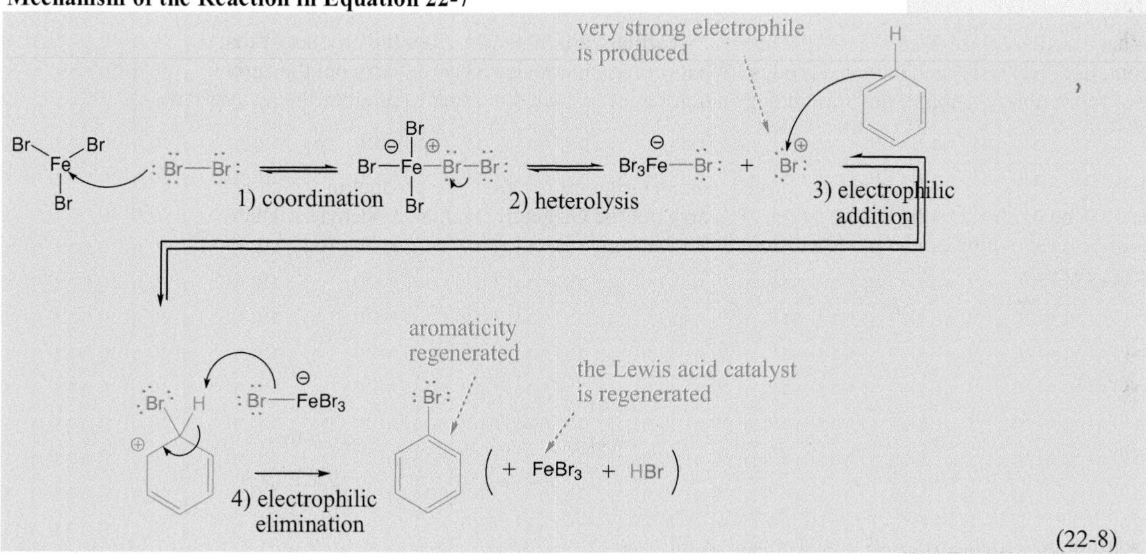

(22-8)

Your Turn 22.3. The mechanism of the chlorination of benzene is shown below, but the curved arrows have been omitted. Supply the missing curved arrows, and below each reaction arrow, write the name of the step that is taking place. Which two steps comprise the electrophilic aromatic substitution mechanism presented earlier in Equation 22-4?

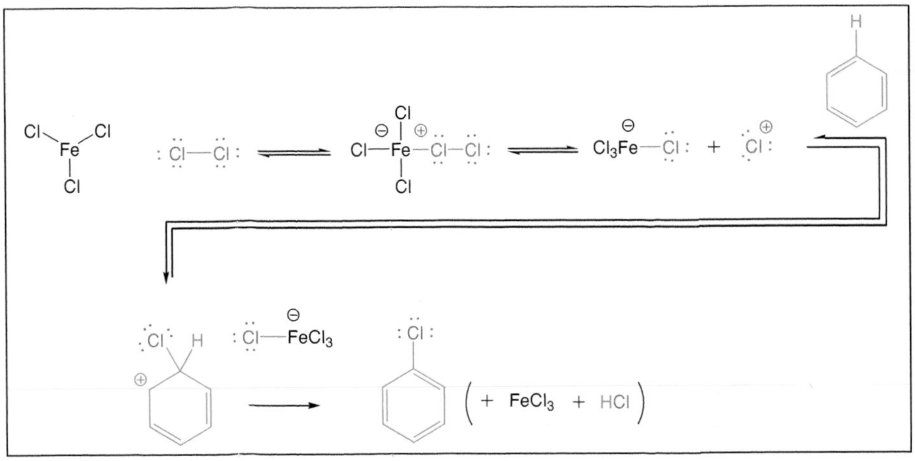

Cl–Fe(Cl)–Cl :Cl–Cl: ⇌ Cl–Fe⁻(Cl)(Cl)–Cl⁺–Cl: ⇌ Cl_3Fe^{-}–Cl: + :Cl⁺

(+ $FeCl_3$ + HCl)

Solved Problem 22.1. Show how to carry out the following synthesis using a halogenation reaction.

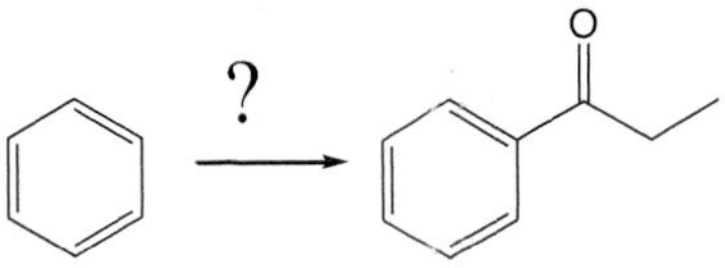

Think. What reaction can be used to form the necessary carbon-carbon bond? Does the product of that reaction contain the appropriate functional groups? What precursors are necessary to carry out the carbon-carbon bond formation reaction? How must halogenation be incorporated in order to produce the appropriate precursor?

Solve. The new carbon-carbon bond can be formed using a Grignard reaction, the product of which is an alcohol that can be oxidized to the ketone target. To carry out the Grignard reaction, a phenyl Grignard reagent must be used, which can be produced from bromobenzene. Bromobenzene can be produced by brominating benzene.

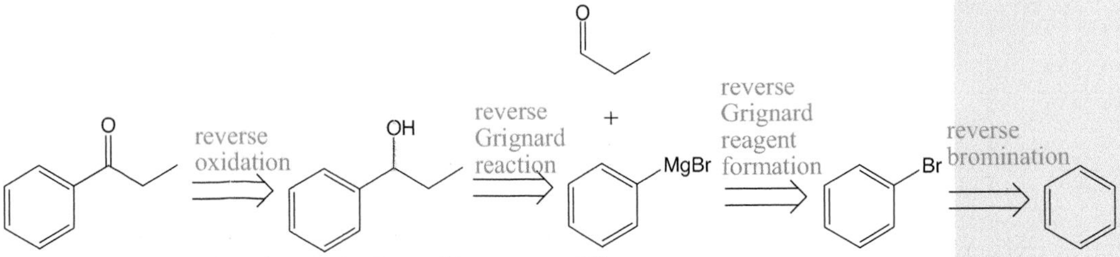

reverse oxidation ⇒ OH ⇒ reverse Grignard reaction ⇒ + MgBr ⇒ reverse Grignard reagent formation ⇒ Br ⇒ reverse bromination ⇒

In the forward direction, the synthesis would appear as follows.

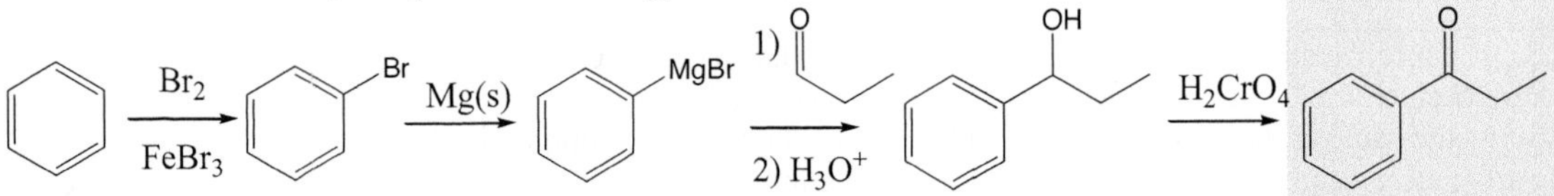

Br_2 / $FeBr_3$ → Br; Mg(s) → MgBr; 1) O, 2) H_3O^+ → OH; H_2CrO_4 → O

Problem 22.2. Show how to carry out the following synthesis using a halogenation reaction.

? → SCH_3

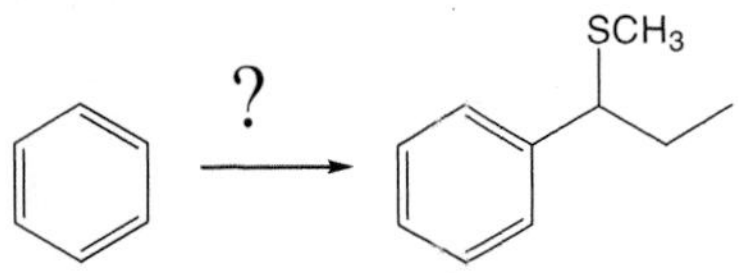

We can also envision fluorination and iodination of benzene through a similar mechanism. However, just as we saw with the addition of molecular halogens across double bonds (Chapter 21), fluorine is too reactive to be of much synthetic use, whereas iodine is too stable. Iodination, however, can be carried out in the presence of an oxidizing agent like Cu^{2+} or hydrogen peroxide (Equation 22-9). Oxidation of I_2 generates I^+, which can then enter into the electrophilic aromatic substitution mechanism.

Comment [JMK46]: Margin note
Using a strong Lewis acid catalyst, halogenation of an aromatic ring is generally limited only to bromination and chlorination.

I_2 ; $CuCl_2$ or H_2O_2 ; I

(22-9)

Problem 22.3. With the understanding that the reaction conditions in Equation 22-9 generate a small amount of I^+, draw the two-step electrophilic aromatic substitution mechanism that leads to the formation of iodobenzene.

22.3. FRIEDEL-CRAFTS ALKYLATION

In 1877, Charles Friedel and James Crafts reported that **alkylation** can take place when benzene is treated with an alkyl chloride in the presence of aluminum trichloride, $AlCl_3$, a strong Lewis acid catalyst (Equations 22-10 and 22-11). In these **Friedel-Crafts alkylation** reactions, the electrophile, E^+, is a carbocation, R^+. In Equation 22-10, the electrophile is a *t*-butyl cation, $(CH_3)_3C^+$, whereas in Equation 22-11 it appears to be the cyclohexyl cation, $C_6H_{11}^+$.

Friedel-Crafts alkylation

benzene ; CH_3 C CH_3 CH_3 Cl ; $AlCl_3$; 2 h, 0-5 °C ; CH_3 C CH_3 CH_3 ; *t*-butylbenzene ; 72%

(22-10)

benzene ; Cl ; $AlCl_3$; 3 h, 30 °C ; cyclohexylbenzene ; 93%

(22-11)

The production of such carbocation electrophiles is illustrated in Equation 22-12, the mechanism of the alkylation in Equation 22-10. The $AlCl_3$ catalyst functions in much the same way as the $FeBr_3$ catalyst does in aromatic bromination, which we saw previously in Equation 22-8. First, the alkyl halide undergoes coordination with the Al atom of $AlCl_3$. In step 2, the Cl–C bond breaks in a heterolysis step, which takes place *slowly*, yielding the carbocation electrophile. The final two steps, once again, are the electrophilic aromatic substitution steps originally shown in Equation 22-4.

Mechanism of the Reaction in Equation 22-10

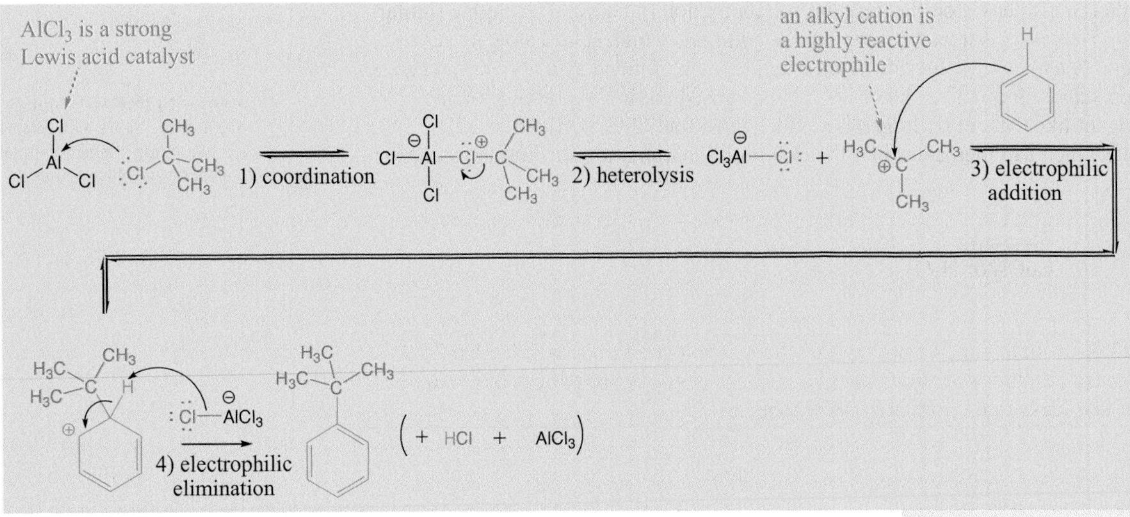

AlCl$_3$ is a strong Lewis acid catalyst

an alkyl cation is a highly reactive electrophile

1) coordination

2) heterolysis

3) electrophilic addition

4) electrophilic elimination

(+ HCl + AlCl$_3$)

(22-12)

Your Turn 22.4. The mechanism of the reaction in Equation 22-11 is shown below, but the curved arrows have been omitted. Supply the missing curved arrows, and below each reaction arrow, write the name of the elementary step taking place. Also, identify the two steps that comprise the general electrophilic aromatic substitution mechanism shown previously in Equation 22-4.

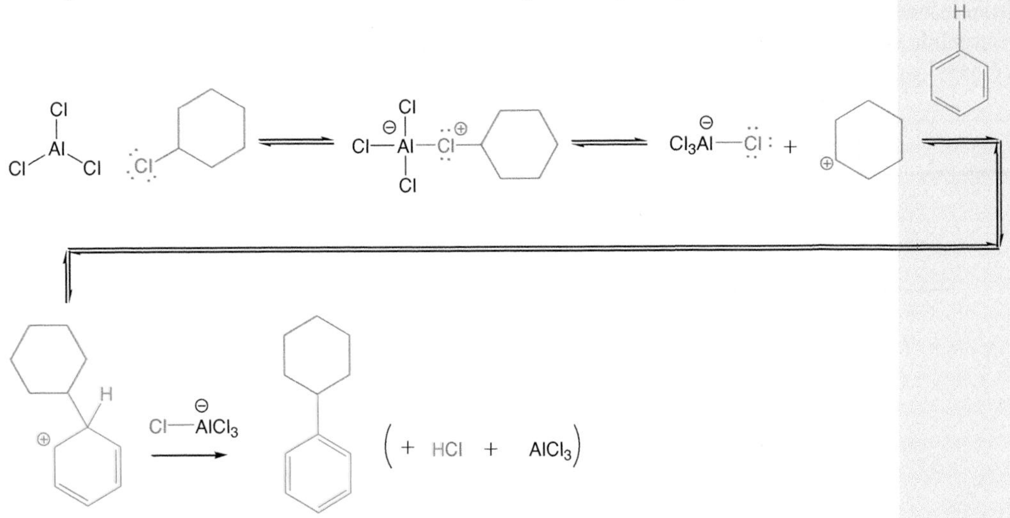

(+ HCl + AlCl$_3$)

Friedel-Crafts alkylation reactions can also take place under other conditions that generate carbocation intermediates. Examples are shown in Equations 22-13 and 22-14. In Equation 22-13, the acidic conditions convert the OH group into an excellent water leaving group. Upon the departure of that leaving group, the carbocation is produced. In Equation 22-14, on the other hand, protonation of the double bond yields a carbocation intermediate directly. Note that these are the same steps that constitute the beginnings of S$_N$1/E1 and electrophilic addition reactions, respectively.

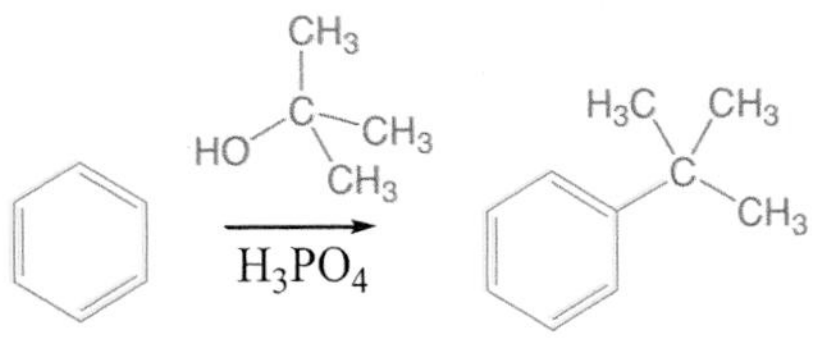

H_3PO_4

(22-13)

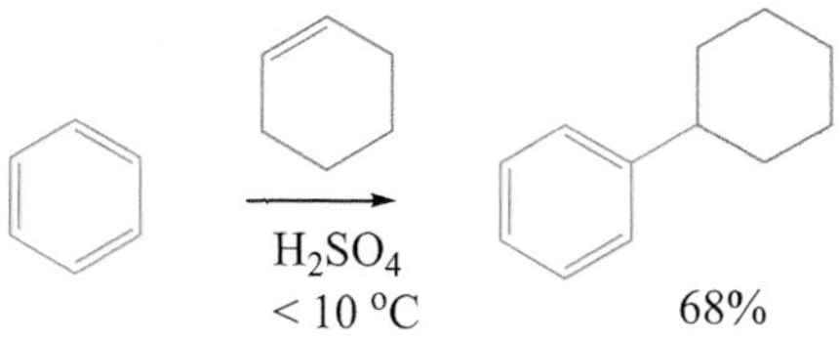

H_2SO_4
< 10 °C

68%

(22-14)

Problem 22.5. Propose a mechanism for the reaction in Equation 22-13.

Problem 22.6. Propose a mechanism for the reaction in Equation 22-14.

Solved Problem 22.2. Show how to synthesize the following compound in a single reaction, using benzene as one reagent, and (a) an alkyl halide, (b) an alkene, and (c) an alcohol as the other reagent.

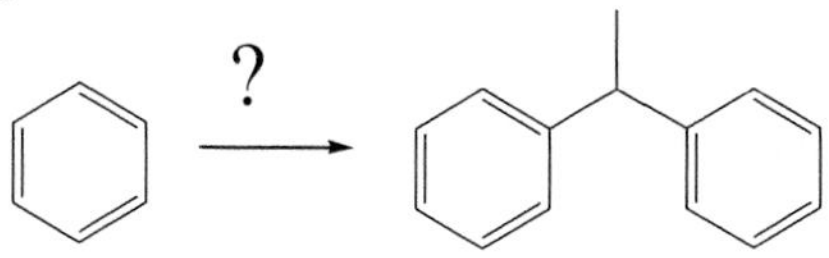

?

Think. What is the electrophile that must substitute for H^+? How can that electrophile be produced from an alkyl halide, an alkene, or an alcohol?

Solve. The electrophile that must substitute for H^+ is a carbocation, as shown below.

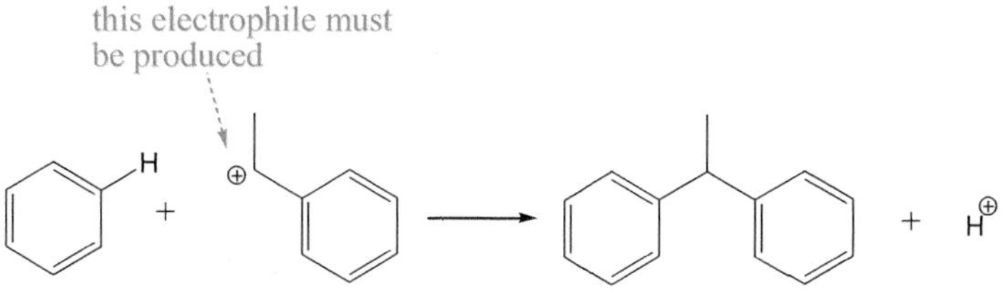

this electrophile must be produced

H + ⊕ → + H⊕

That carbocation can be produced from an alkyl halide using $AlCl_3$, a strong Lewis acid catalyst. Alternatively, it can be produced from an alkene or an alcohol under acidic conditions.

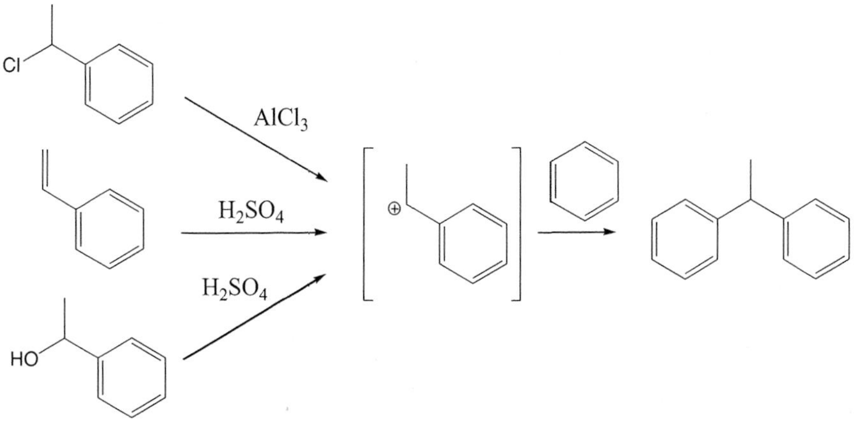

Cl

$AlCl_3$

H_2SO_4

⊕

H_2SO_4

HO

Problem 22.7. Show how you can synthesize the following alkylbenzene in a single reaction from benzene and (a) an alkyl halide, (b) an alkene, and (c) an alcohol.

22.4. LIMITATIONS ON FRIEDEL-CRAFTS ALKYLATIONS

It may seem any alkyl halide can be used to carry out a Friedel-Crafts alkylation reaction on benzene. However, there are four significant limitations we must be aware of. First, as with any reaction in which a carbocation intermediate is produced,

Friedel-Crafts alkylations are susceptible to carbocation rearrangements.

For example, propylbenzene cannot be synthesized via a Friedel-Crafts alkylation (Equation 22-15a). The attempt to do so using 1-chloropropane yields isopropylbenzene instead (Equation 22-15b).

this product would be expected if no carbocation rearrangement takes place

H_2 C CH_3 C H_2 (a)

Cl H_2 C CH_3 C H_2

$AlCl_3$

CH_3 CH CH_3 (b)

carbocation rearrangement leads to this product instead

(22-15)

The reason is that the carbocation that is initially formed—the 1-propyl cation—is a primary carbocation, and therefore rapidly rearranges to the 2-propyl cation, a secondary carbocation. Therefore, as shown in Equation 22-16, it is the 2-propyl cation that is the actual electrophile that enters the electrophilic aromatic substitution mechanism.

Partial Mechanism of the Reaction in Equation 22-15

a primary carbocation is initially produced by reaction with $AlCl_3$

a hydride shift produces the more stable 2° carbocation

H $H_2C^{\oplus}$ CH CH_3 3) electrophilic addition H C $H^{\oplus}$ C H_2 CH_3 4) 1,2-hydride shift CH_3 H_3C–CH H ⊕ Cl–$AlCl_3$ ⊖ 5) electrophilic elimination H_3C CH CH_3

(22-16)

A second limitation on the Friedel-Crafts alkylation concerns hybridization.

A Friedel-Crafts alkylation reaction does not occur readily unless the halogen atom of the alkyl halide is bonded to an sp^3-hybridized carbon.

As shown in Equations 22-17 and 22-18, for example, benzene does not undergo alkylation with aryl or vinyl halides, in which the halogen atom is bonded to an sp^2-hybridized carbon. With the increased *s*-character of an sp^2-hybridized carbon relative to an sp^3-hybridized carbon, not only is the strength of the carbon-chlorine bond greater, but so is the carbon atom's effective electronegativity (Section 3.11). Thus, the carbocation that is produced from a vinylic halide is relatively unstable. Recall that for very similar reasons, aryl and vinylic halides are resistant to nucleophilic substitution and elimination reactions (Chapter 9.6a).

the sp^2-hybridization increases the strength of the C-Cl bond, and decreases the stability of the carbocation that would be produced

Cl

$AlCl_3$

No reaction

(22-17)

Cl

H_3C C C CH_3 H

$AlCl_3$

No reaction

(22-18)

Your Turn 22.5. Verify the above statement looking in Chapter 3 to find the C-H bond strength involving an sp^3-hybridized carbon and compare it to that involving an sp^2-hybridized carbon.

sp^3 __________ sp^2 __________

Solved Problem 22.3. Show how you can synthesize 2-phenyl-2-butene beginning with benzene.

?

Think. Can the target be produced directly from a simple Friedel-Crafts alkylation? Is there another reaction that can be used to form the appropriate carbon-carbon bond?

Solve. For the target to be produced directly from a Friedel-Crafts alkylation, the precursors would be those in Equation 22-18. For reasons discussed previously, such a reaction does not occur readily. Another route must be sought.

reverse Friedel-Crafts alkylation

+

Cl

Another carbon-carbon bond formation reaction we have utilized before is the Grignard reaction. The product of a Grignard is an alcohol, which can be dehydrated to form the final product. Here we can envision a Grignard reaction between phenylmagnesium bromide and 2-butanone. The Grignard reagent can be produced from bromobenzene, which, in turn, can be synthesized using a bromination reaction.

reverse dehydration ⟹ OH ⟹ reverse Grignard ⟹ MgBr + O

reverse reduction ⟹ Br ⟹ reverse bromination ⟹

In the forward direction, the synthesis would appear as follows.

Br_2 / $FeBr_3$ → Br → Mg → MgBr → 1) 2-butanone, 2) $H^{\oplus}$ → HO → conc. H_3PO_4, heat →

Problem 22.8. Butylbenzene cannot be synthesized directly from benzene using a Friedel-Crafts alkylation. Why not? Propose an alternate synthesis of butylbenzene that does not use a Friedel-Crafts reaction.

Cl, $AlCl_3$ (crossed out) →

The third limitation of Friedel-Crafts alkylation is an outcome of the fact that electrophilic aromatic substitution on an alkylbenzene (the product) is generally faster than on benzene itself. Therefore, it is difficult to stop the reaction after a single substitution. In other words,

Friedel-Crafts alkylation reactions are susceptible to **polyalkylation**.

This is illustrated in Equation 22-19, and will be discussed in greater detail in Chapter 23.

Friedel-Crafts alkylation tends to lead to polyalkylation

Cl—R / $AlCl_3$ → R + R, R + R, R + R, R, R (22-19)

The final limitation pertains to Friedel-Crafts alkylation reactions involving substituted benzenes.

Friedel-Crafts alkylation does not readily take place on strongly *deactivated* aromatic rings.

As we will see in Chapter 23, substituents such as the nitro (NO_2) group cause the aromatic ring to be deactivated toward electrophilic aromatic substitution. Therefore, as shown in Equation 22-20, nitrobenzene does not undergo alkylation.

a nitro group *deactivates* the ring (Chapter 23)

NO_2 — Cl—R, $AlCl_3$ (crossed out) → no reaction

nitrobenzene

(22-20)

Given these limitations, Friedel-Crafts alkylation is often not the best route to generating a carbon-carbon bond to a benzene ring. Friedel-Crafts *acylation*, discussed in the next section, is another way to achieve such a carbon-carbon bond, but with fewer limitations.

22.5. FRIEDEL-CRAFTS ACYLATION

Friedel-Crafts acylation of benzene is carried out in much the same way as the alkylation reaction. The difference is that the aromatic species is treated with an *acyl chloride* (an acyl group is R-C=O), also called an *acid chloride*, instead of an alkyl chloride. The product, as shown in Equation 22-21, is an *aromatic ketone*, in which a carbon atom from benzene forms a bond to the carbon atom of the acyl group.

Friedel-Crafts acylation

an acyl chloride, also called an acid chloride

$Cl-C(=O)-CH_2-CH_3$

$AlCl_3$
3 h, 0 °C

an aromatic ketone

phenylpropanone
78%

(22-21)

The mechanism of Friedel-Crafts acylation, presented in Equation 22-22, is essentially identical to the one for Friedel-Crafts alkylation, shown previously in Equation 22-12. The strong Lewis acid catalyst, $AlCl_3$, is responsible for generating the cationic electrophile, called an **acylium ion**. In the first step, the chlorine atom of the acyl chloride undergoes coordination to the electron-deficient Al atom. In step 2, the C-Cl bond undergoes heterolysis. Step 3 is electrophilic addition of the acylium ion to the benzene ring, producing the arenium ion intermediate. Finally, in step 4, removal of the proton from the arenium ion yields the aromatic ketone product.

Mechanism of the Reaction in Equation 22-21

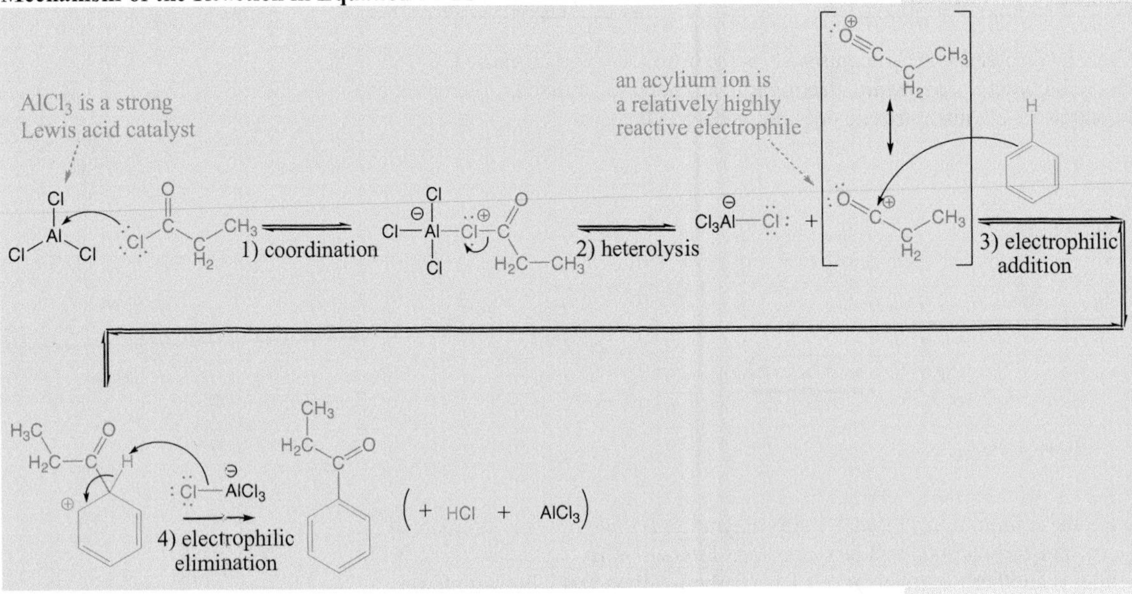

AlCl$_3$ is a strong Lewis acid catalyst

an acylium ion is a relatively highly reactive electrophile

1) coordination

2) heterolysis

3) electrophilic addition

4) electrophilic elimination

(+ HCl + AlCl$_3$)

(22-22)

Your Turn 22.6. The mechanism for the Friedel-Crafts acylation involving acetyl chloride is shown below, but most of the curved arrows have been omitted, as have the overall products. Supply the missing curved arrows, and draw the overall products. Also, write the name of each elementary step below the appropriate reaction arrow, and label the acylium ion.

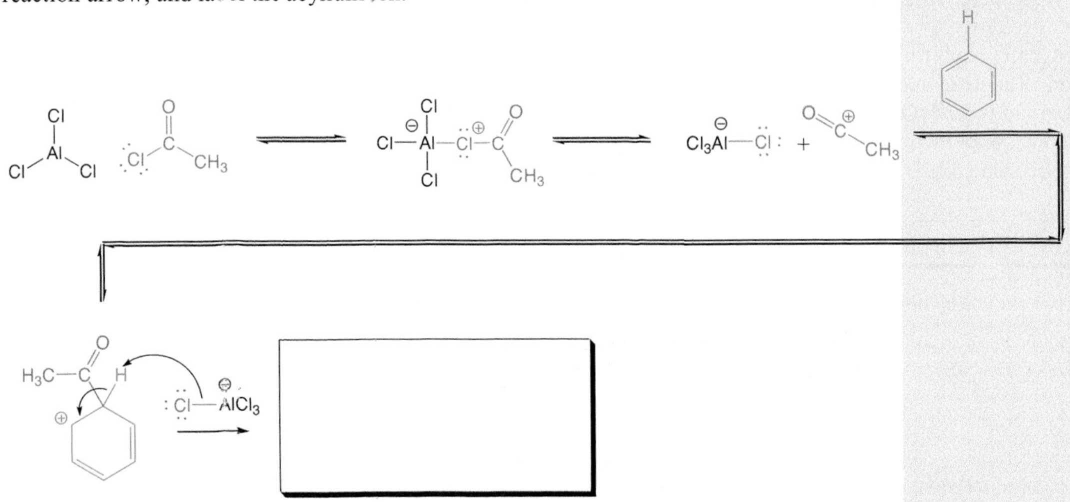

Problem 22.9. As we learned in Chapter 19, carboxylic acid chlorides behave quite similarly to carboxylic acid anhydrides. Not surprisingly, then, aromatic acylation can be carried out using an acid anhydride in the presence of AlCl$_3$, analogous to the Friedel-Crafts acylation reaction above. The example below illustrates this using acetic anhydride to produce phenylethanone. Propose a mechanism for this reaction.

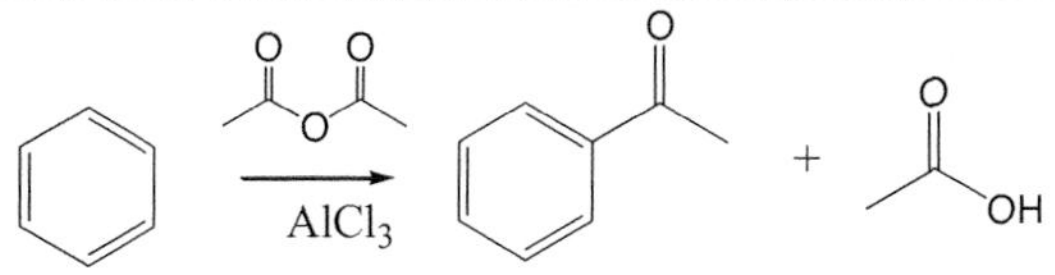

$AlCl_3$

phenylethanone

Problem 22.10. The following compound can be synthesized from benzene and a carboxylic acid anhydride in a single Friedel-Crafts reaction. What is the acid anhydride that must be used? (Hint: The two benzene rings come from two different compounds)

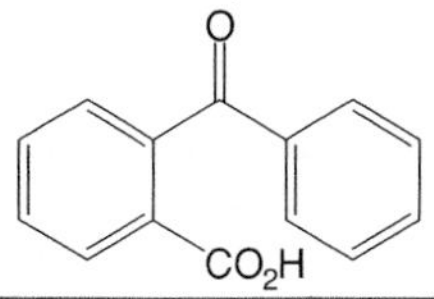

CO_2H

It might seem peculiar that Friedel-Crafts acylation can take place at all, given that in the acid chloride reactant, the chlorine atom is bonded to an sp^2-hybridized carbon. (Recall that this in fact prevents a Friedel-Crafts *alkylation* from taking place.) However, the acylium ion that is produced is *resonance stabilized* by a lone pair of electrons on the adjacent oxygen. With this additional stability, the cationic electrophile can be produced and enter into the electrophilic aromatic substitution mechanism.

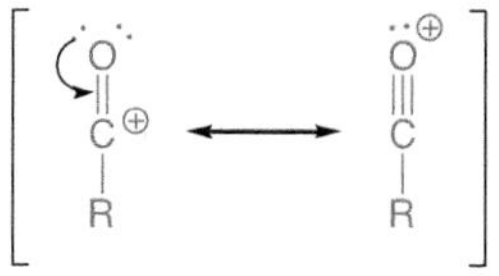

An acylium ion is resonance stabilized

Your Turn 22.7. In the space provided here, draw the resonance hybrid of a generic acylium ion.

Friedel-Crafts acylation reactions offer some key advantages over alkylations. One advantage involves carbocation rearrangements.

Friedel-Crafts acylation reactions are *not* susceptible to carbocation rearrangements, unlike Friedel-Crafts alkylation reactions.

This is because the acylium ion is a relatively stable carbocation due to resonance delocalization of the positive charge, as well as the fact that it has a resonance structure in which all atoms have their octet. A carbocation rearrangement would generally lead to an isolated positive charge that is less stable.

Another advantage that Friedel-Crafts acylation reactions have is that an aromatic ketone—the product of acylation—undergoes electrophilic aromatic substitution *more slowly* than does benzene itself. Therefore,

Friedel-Crafts acylation reactions tend to stop after just a single substitution.

This will be explained in greater detail in Chapter 23.

Friedel-Crafts acylation reactions do have some limitations, however. One limitation is in fact identical to a limitation of Friedel-Crafts alkylation reactions.

Friedel-Crafts acylation reactions usually cannot be carried out on aromatic rings with deactivating substituents.

For example, as indicated in Equation 22-23, nitrobenzene does not undergo acylation because the nitro group (NO_2) is a deactivating substituent. (This will be discussed in greater detail in Chapter 23.)

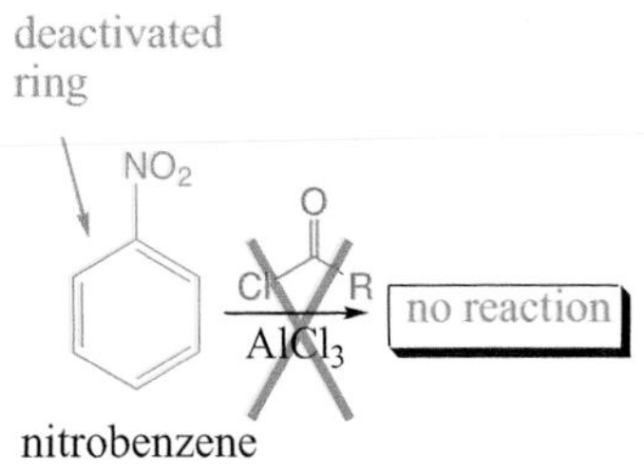

deactivated ring

NO_2

Cl–C(=O)–R, $AlCl_3$ (crossed out) → no reaction

nitrobenzene

(22-23)

A second limitation pertains to the identity of the acyl chloride.

Friedel-Crafts acylation cannot be used as a means of *formylation*, whereby H is replaced by a formyl group, HC=O.

This is because the acid chloride necessary to carry out this reaction, methanoyl chloride (Cl-CH=O), is not stable under normal conditions. A variety of other formylation reactions have been developed, however, but will not be discussed here.

Solved Problem 22.4. Show how to carry out the following synthesis, beginning with benzene and any alcohol.

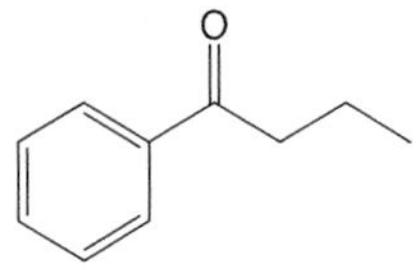

phenylbutanone

Think. To produce the target from a Friedel-Crafts acylation reaction, what precursors are necessary? How can those precursors be produced from the starting material?

Solve. In a Friedel-Crafts acylation, an aromatic carbon forms a bond to an acyl carbon. We begin our retrosynthetic analysis by disconnecting that bond to arrive at the appropriate precursors—an aromatic ring and an acyl chloride. The acyl chloride can be produced by chlorinating the corresponding carboxylic acid, which can in turn be produced by oxidizing a primary alcohol.

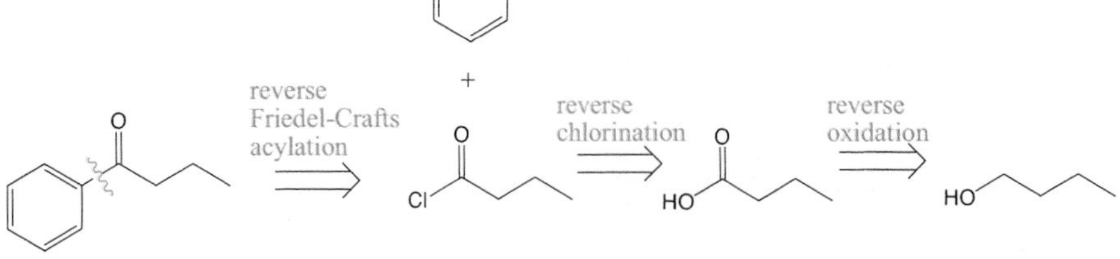

reverse Friedel-Crafts acylation ⟹ benzene + Cl–C(=O)–CH2CH2CH3; reverse chlorination ⟹ HO–C(=O)–CH2CH2CH3; reverse oxidation ⟹ HO–CH2CH2CH2CH3

In the forward direction, the synthesis would appear as follows.

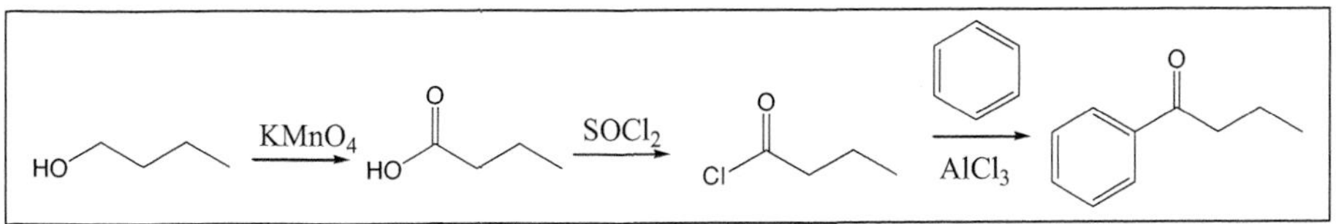

HO–butyl $\xrightarrow{KMnO_4}$ HO(C=O)propyl $\xrightarrow{SOCl_2}$ Cl(C=O)propyl $\xrightarrow[AlCl_3]{\text{benzene}}$ phenyl propyl ketone

Problem 22.11. Show how to synthesize benzophenone from benzene and any alcohol.

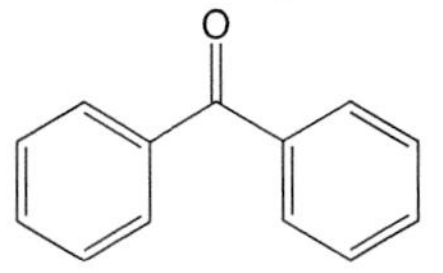

benzophenone

22.6. NITRATION

When benzene is treated with concentrated nitric acid (HNO_3), a hydrogen atom on the ring is replaced by a nitro (NO_2) group, producing nitrobenzene (Equation 22-24). Benzene is said to have undergone **nitration**.

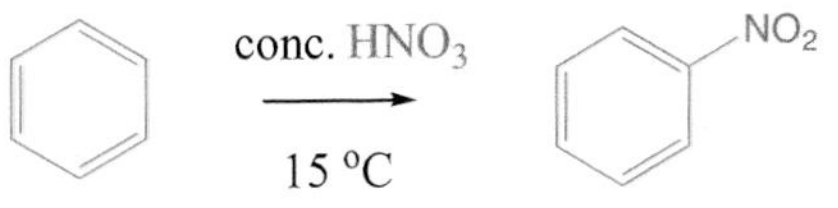

benzene $\xrightarrow[15\ ^{\circ}C]{\text{conc. } HNO_3}$ nitrobenzene (NO_2)

nitrobenzene 83%

(22-24)

The mechanism of this reaction is presented in Equation 22-25. Steps 1 and 2 of the mechanism are responsible for generating the powerful NO_2^+ electrophile. First, HNO_3 is protonated to create a good water leaving group. Next, the water leaving group departs spontaneously via heterolysis. During the heterolysis step, an additional N=O double bond is formed, using a lone pair of electrons from an oxygen atom. This aids the elimination of the water leaving group by preventing the N atom from losing its octet—this is an example of *anchimeric assistance* by the oxygen atom donating the lone pair of electrons. Once the NO_2^+ electrophile is created, it enters into the two-step electrophilic aromatic substitution mechanism, steps 3 and 4.

Mechanism of the Reaction in Equation 22-24

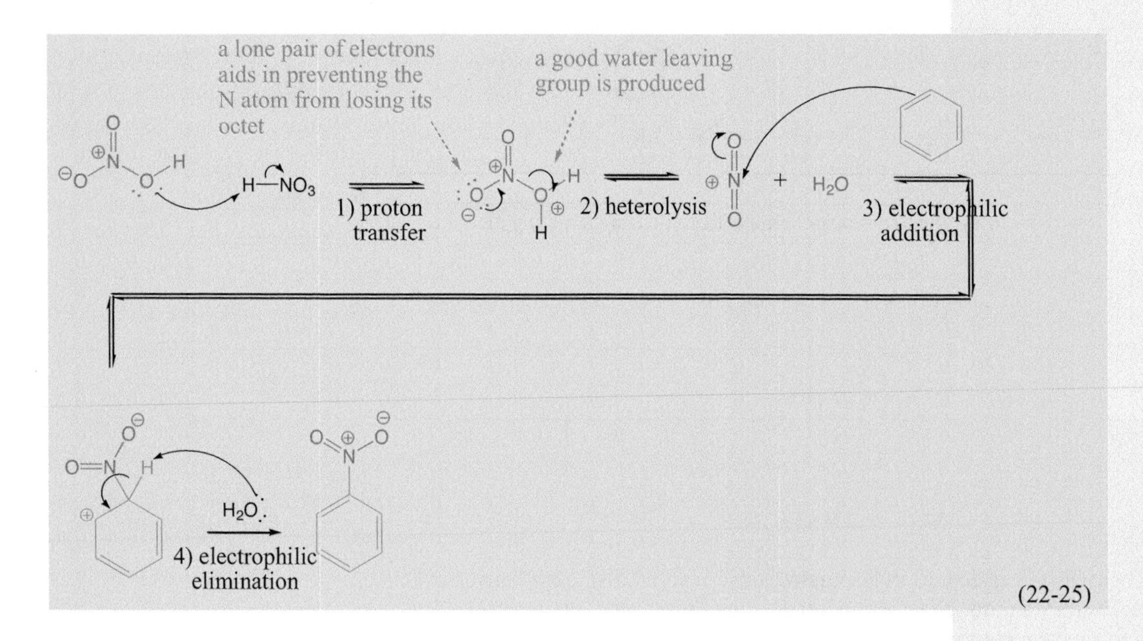

(22-25)

With concentrated nitric acid alone, the amount of NO_2^+ present is small—about 4%—so nitration of benzene tends to proceed relatively slowly. Furthermore, nitration of the nitrobenzene product takes place more slowly than nitration of benzene itself (the reasons why will be discussed in Chapter 23), making it easy to stop the reaction after just a single nitration.

Under more extreme conditions, a second nitration can occur. This can be accomplished simply by increasing the temperature at which the reaction is carried out, as shown in Equation 22-26.

a second nitration of benzene can be carried out by heating the reaction

conc. HNO_3

65 °C

O_2N NO_2

1,3-dinitrobenzene
89%

(22-26)

Your Turn 22.8. The mechanism for the second nitration of the reaction in Equation 22-26 is shown below, but the curved arrows have been omitted. Supply the missing curved arrows, and write the name of each elementary step below the corresponding reaction arrow.

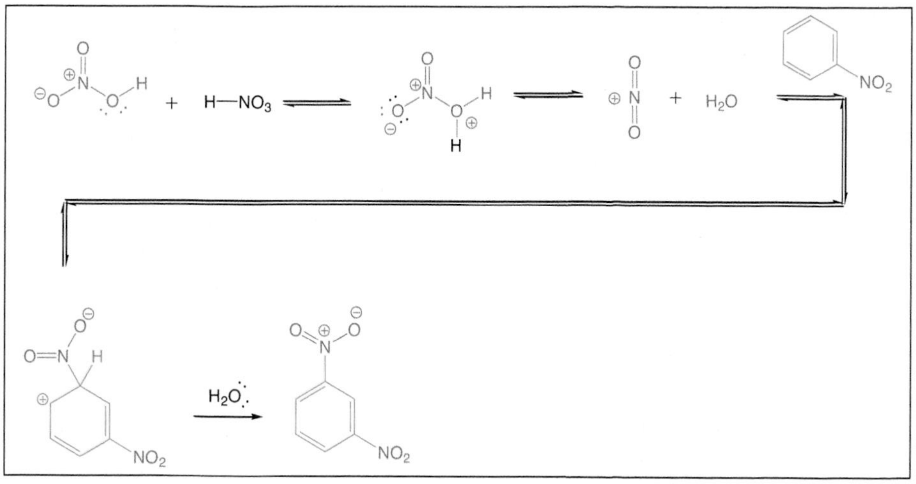

+ H—NO3 ⇌ ⇌ ⊕N + H2O

NO2

H2O: →

NO2 NO2

Alternatively, dinitration of benzene can take place at more mild temperatures by adding concentrated sulfuric acid, as indicated in Equation 22-27. Sulfuric acid, being much more acidic than HNO_3, generates a substantially higher concentration of the active electrophile, NO_2^+. This, in turn, speeds up the rate of the rate-determining step and, hence, the rate of the overall reaction.

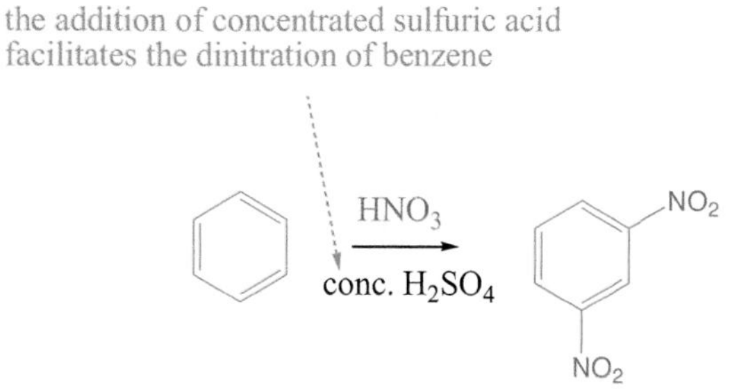

the addition of concentrated sulfuric acid facilitates the dinitration of benzene

HNO_3 / conc. H_2SO_4

NO2 NO2

(22-27)

22.7. SULFONATION

Treatment of benzene with concentrated sulfuric acid yields benzene sulfonic acid (Equation 22-28), whereby a **sulfonyl group**, SO_3H, has replaced H on the ring. This substitution reaction is called **sulfonation**.

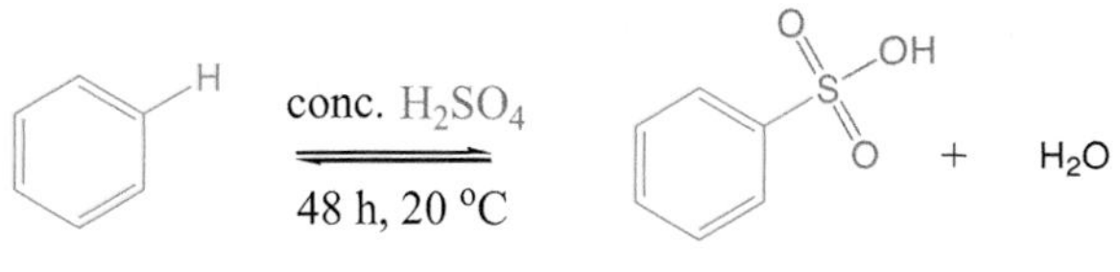

conc. H_2SO_4 / 48 h, 20 °C

+ H_2O

benzenesulfonic acid
66%

(22-28)

Just like nitration, sulfonation is easy to stop after a single substitution. This is because the product of sulfonation—benzenesulfonic acid—undergoes electrophilic aromatic substitution slower than does benzene itself. (The reasons why will be discussed in greater detail in Chapter 23.)

Under these reaction conditions, sulfur trioxide (SO_3) is believed to be the electrophile involved in the electrophilic addition step of electrophilic aromatic substitution. This is illustrated in the mechanism presented in Equation 22-29.

Mechanism of the Reaction in Equation 22-28

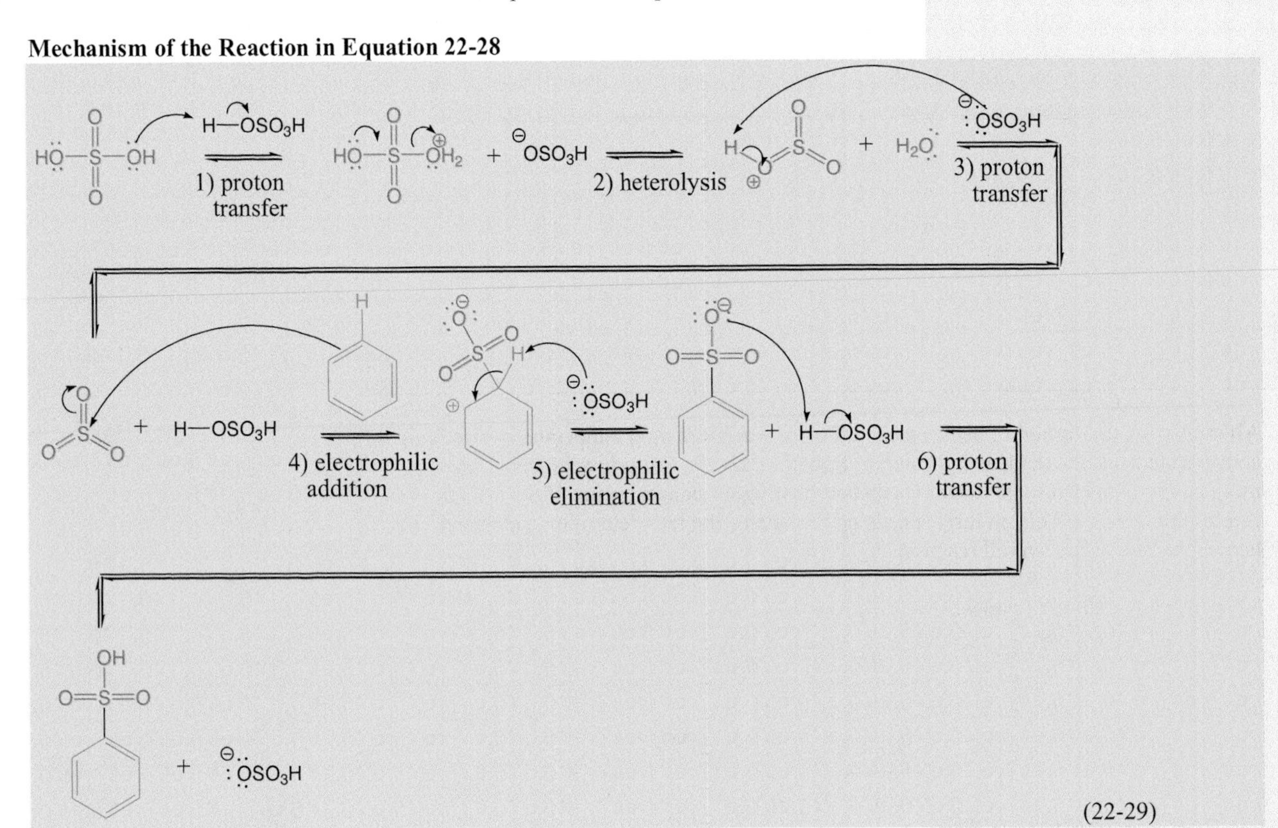

(22-29)

Concentrated H_2SO_4 contains a small amount of SO_3 at equilibrium. It is produced in much the same way as NO_2^+ is generated in concentrated HNO_3 (Equation 22-25). Protonation of an OH group in step 1 generates a very good water leaving group, which subsequently leaves in step 2 to produce HSO_3^+. Deprotonation in step 3 then yields SO_3, which enters into the two-step electrophilic aromatic substitution mechanism—steps 4 and 5. Finally, in step 6, a proton transfer produces the overall uncharged product.

Evidence for the involvement of SO_3 comes from the fact that sulfonation is much more rapid with **fuming sulfuric acid** than it is with sulfuric acid alone. Fuming sulfuric acid is simply concentrated sulfuric acid infused with SO_3. As shown in Equation 22-30, when benzene is treated with fuming sulfuric acid, disulfonation occurs.

fuming sulfuric acid

disulfonation occurs when benzene is treated with fuming sulfuric acid

conc. H_2SO_4 / SO_3, 4 h, < 90 °C

1,3-benzenedisulfonic acid 90%

(22-30)

Your Turn 22.9. The mechanism for the *second* sulfonation reaction in Equation 22-30 is shown below, but the curved arrows have been omitted. Supply the missing curved arrows, and write the name of each elementary step below the corresponding reaction arrow.

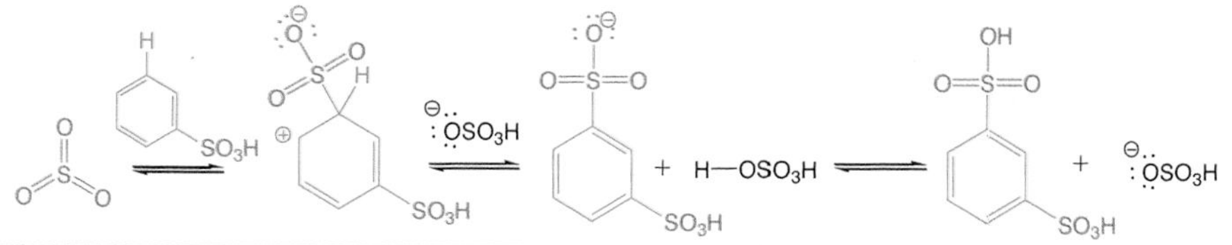

As mentioned previously, electrophilic aromatic substitution reactions are generally irreversible. Sulfonation, however, is not.

> Sulfonation of an aromatic ring is *reversible*.

The reverse of a sulfonation reaction, whereby the sulfonyl group is replaced by an H, is accomplished by heating benzene sulfonic acid in acidic water—this is simply the reverse of Equation 22-28. An example of such a **desulfonation** reaction is shown in Equation 22-31, illustrating that the SO_3H group can be removed without affecting other substituents that may be on the ring. For this reason, sulfonation can be used as a *protecting group* at a specific site on the benzene ring. This will be discussed more fully in Chapter 23.

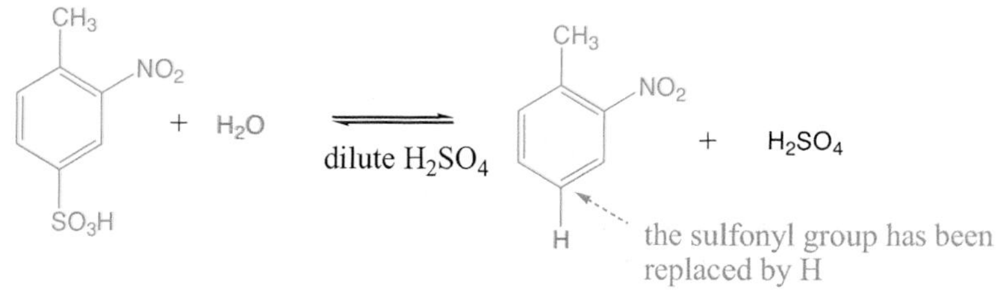

dilute H_2SO_4

the sulfonyl group has been replaced by H

(22-31)

A useful variation on the sulfonation reaction is **halosulfonation**. As shown in Equation 22-32, treatment of chlorosulfuric acid with benzene yields benzenesulfonyl chloride. If toluene is used instead of benzene (Equation 22-33), the product is *p*-toluenesulfonyl chloride (tosyl chloride), which, as we saw previously in Chapters 9 and 19, is employed to convert a poor hydroxide leaving group into a very good tosylate (TsO) leaving group.

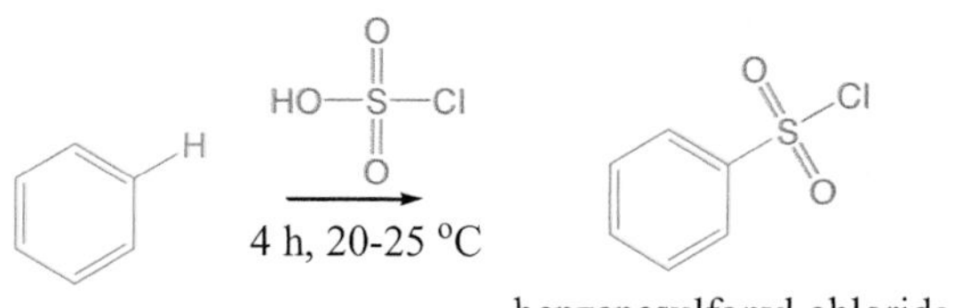

4 h, 20-25 °C

benzenesulfonyl chloride
77%

(22-32)

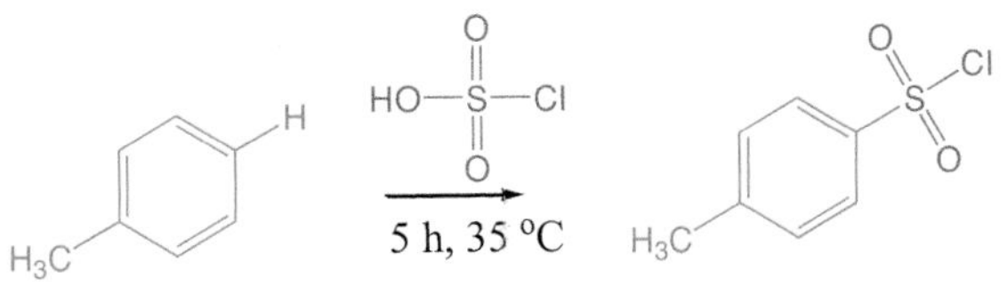

HO—S(=O)(=O)—Cl

5 h, 35 °C

p-toluenesulfonyl chloride
(tosyl chloride)
81%

(22-33)

22.8. AN INTRODUCTION TO ELECTROPHILIC AROMATIC SUBSTITUTION ON OTHER AROMATIC COMPOUNDS

In the examples we have seen in this chapter thus far, we have focused primarily on electrophilic aromatic substitution reactions involving benzene itself. However, substituted benzenes can also undergo electrophilic aromatic substitution, given that they, too, are aromatic. For example, as illustrated in Equation 22-34, *p*-dimethylbenzene undergoes bromination to yield 2-bromo-1,4-dimethylbenzene.

Br_2

Fe, CCl_4
16 h, 25 °C

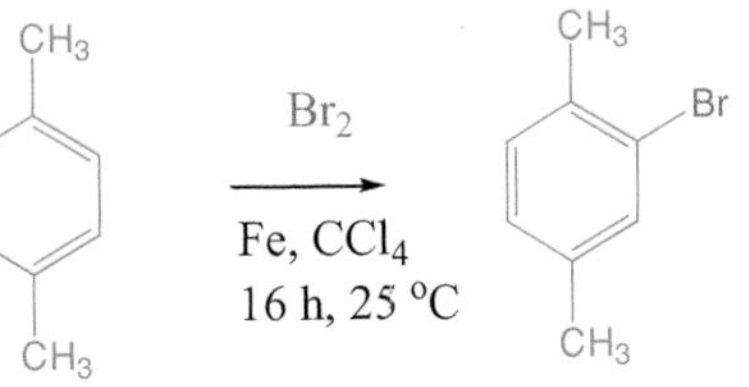

p-dimethylbenzene

2-bromo-1,4-dimethylbenzene
61%

(22-34)

The bulk of our discussion involving substituted benzenes will be saved for Chapter 23, because the substituents that are on the ring bring into play issues of reaction rates and regiochemistry. As we will learn in Chapter 23, for instance, the reaction in Equation 22-34 is faster than bromination of benzene itself.

Regiochemistry is *not* a concern for the specific reaction in Equation 22-34, because all four protons on *p*-dimethylbenzene are equivalent; substitution of any one of them leads to the same product.

Your Turn 22.10. Equation 22-34 shows the product of substitution of the upper-right proton of the ring. Draw the product that would be produced if substitution of one of the other aromatic protons were to take place instead, and compare each of these products to the one in Equation 22-34.

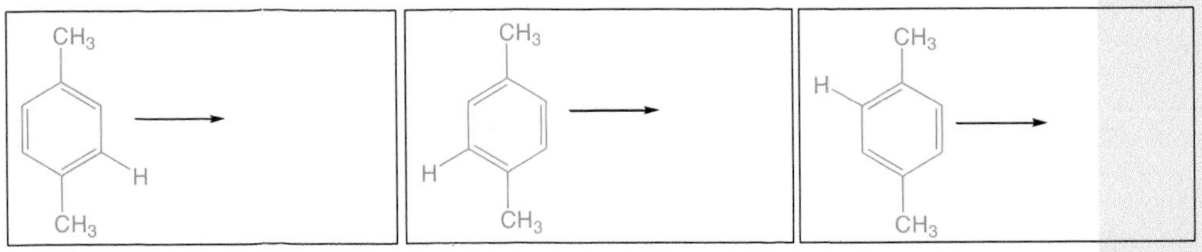

Regiochemistry is a concern, however, for toluene (methylbenzene), as shown in Equation 22-35. Toluene has three chemically distinct hydrogens. Therefore, a single bromination leads to a mixture of three isomeric products—i.e., the *ortho*, *meta*, and *para* isomers. In Chapter 23, we will see that, depending upon the substituent(s) already on the benzene ring, certain isomeric products can be heavily favored over others.

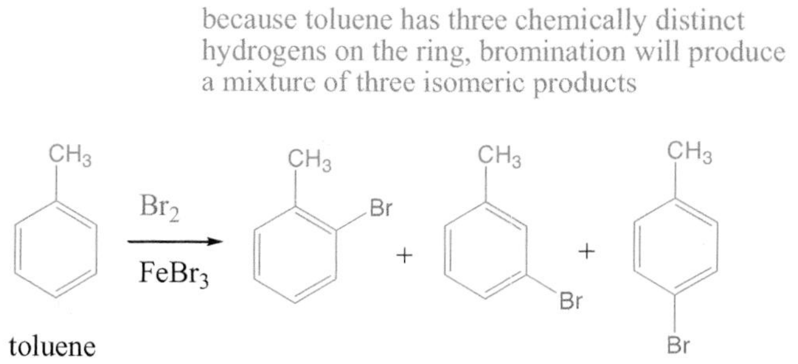

because toluene has three chemically distinct hydrogens on the ring, bromination will produce a mixture of three isomeric products

CH3 $\xrightarrow[FeBr_3]{Br_2}$ CH3, Br + CH3, Br + CH3, Br

toluene

(22-35)

Problem 22.12. Draw a complete, detailed mechanism for the formation of *each* product in Equation 22-35.

Solved Problem 22.5. An isomer of trimethylbenzene is treated with Br_2 in the presence of $FeBr_3$. Only a single product is formed. Which isomer of trimethylbenzene was the reactant?

Think. What is the net effect of the reaction conditions on the benzene ring? What are the various isomers of trimethylbenzene? How many distinct H atoms does each one have?

Solve. These are the reaction conditions for bromination of the ring, which replaces a H for Br. The following are the possible isomers of trimethylbenzene.

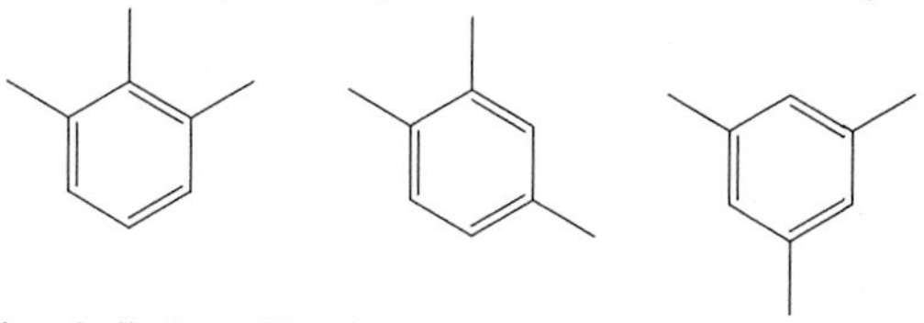

The first has 2 distinct H's, the second has 3 and the third has 1. Therefore, the reactant must be the third isomer; replacement of any H with Br yields the same product.

Problem 22.13. An isomer of tetramethylbenzene undergoes nitration to yield a single product. Based on this information, which isomer of tetramethylbenzene could the starting material have been?

As we saw in Chapter 12, rings other than the benzene ring can be aromatic. They, too, can undergo electrophilic aromatic substitution. One example is naphthalene, which, as shown in Equation 22-36, can undergo nitration. Not surprisingly, because naphthalene has two chemically distinct hydrogen atoms, a single nitration yields a mixture of isomeric nitro-substituted products. Once again, we will learn in Chapter 23 why one of those products should be favored over the other.

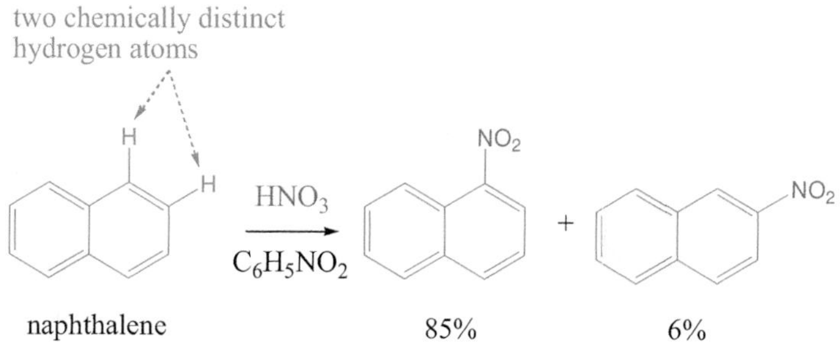

two chemically distinct hydrogen atoms

H, H $\xrightarrow[C_6H_5NO_2]{HNO_3}$ NO2 + NO2

naphthalene   85%   6%

(22-36)

Problem 22.14. Draw the complete, detailed mechanism for the formation of *each* product in Equation 22-36.

Problem 22.15. The following reaction leads to a single product only. Explain why. Predict the product of the reaction and draw the complete, detailed mechanism for its formation.

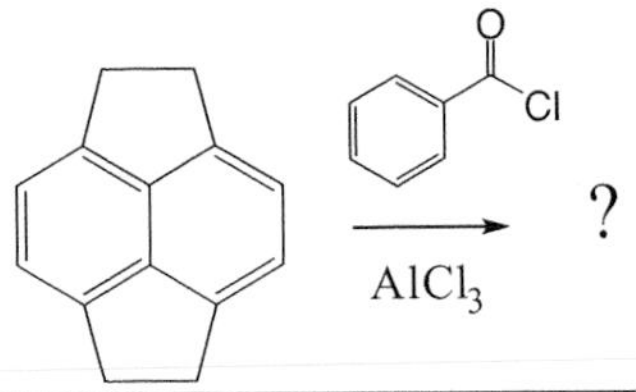

O
Cl
?
$AlCl_3$

The same situation arises with *heterocyclic* aromatic compounds like pyridine or furan. Just like in substituted benzenes and polycyclic aromatics, the presence of the hetero atom—N or O, in this case—introduces concerns of reaction kinetics and regiochemistry that will be saved for Chapter 23.

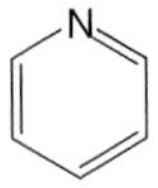

N
O
pyridine
furan 

Problem 22.16. Suppose that pyridine were to undergo a single nitration. What are the possible products formed? Draw the complete, detailed mechanism for the formation of one of them.

Problem 22.17. Suppose that furan were to undergo a single nitration. What are the possible products formed? Draw the complete, detailed mechanism for the formation of one of them.

22.9. IPSO ATTACK

So far we have only considered electrophilic aromatic substitution reactions in which an electrophile (E^+) replaces a proton (H^+) on an aromatic ring. Indeed, when benzene itself is the aromatic species, this is the only substitution that is possible, given that all six carbon atoms of the ring are bonded to hydrogen. In the previous section, however, we introduced electrophilic aromatic substitution on substituted aromatic species like toluene (Equation 22-35). Although in that particular reaction H^+ is still the substituent on the ring that is replaced, we can envision a scenario in which the electrophile replaces a non-hydrogen substituent. A generic example is shown in Equation 22-37.

Mechanism for Ipso Attack on a Monosubstituted Benzene Ring

ipso carbon
Sub E⊕ → Sub E (arenium ion intermediate) → E + Sub⊕

(22-37)

In order for this reaction to take place, the electrophile must attack the carbon on which the substituent is located, called the **ipso carbon**; the substituted benzene is said to undergo **ipso attack**. However,

Under most situations, ipso attack is not favored.

In part, this can be attributed to the additional steric bulk typically surrounding the *ipso* position than surrounds the other positions on the ring.

Perhaps more so, it has to do with the fact that the leaving group ability of H^+ is much better than those of the various Sub^+ species. As was mentioned previously in this chapter, any base that is present aids in the departure of H^+ from the arenium ion intermediate. Departure of a leaving group other than H^+ does not lead to the same kind of stabilization; rather, the leaving group abilities of other substituents depend more on their *intrinsic* abilities to stabilize the positive charge that develops.

In light of the fact that *ipso* attack is not very common, we will not discuss it in depth here, though some examples are provided as end-of-chapter problems. We will, however, call attention to one *ipso* electrophilic aromatic substitution reaction we saw previously—**desulfonation**—discussed in Section 22.7. This reaction (Equation 22-38) is simply the reverse of sulfonation. It takes place in part because the leaving group is sulfur trioxide (SO_3), which is an uncharged molecule.

CH_3, CH_3, SO_3H —(H_2O, dil. H_2SO_4)→ CH_3, CH_3, H

(22-38)

Problem 22.18. Draw the complete, detailed mechanism for the reaction in Equation 23-36.

Ipso attack is further complicated by the fact that it can lead to reactions other than simple electrophilic aromatic substitution reactions. For a more complete discussion of the outcomes of *ipso* attack, see March's Advanced Organic Chemistry.

22.10. ORGANIC SYNTHESIS: CONSIDERATIONS OF CARBOCATION REARRANGEMENTS AND THE SYNTHESIS OF PRIMARY ALKYLBENZENES

In Section 22.4, we learned that one of the limitations of Friedel-Crafts alkylations arises from carbocation rearrangements. As we saw in Equation 22-15, for example, 1-propylbenzene cannot be synthesized from a Friedel-Crafts alkylation because rearrangement of the primary carbocation intermediate that is produced yields 2-propylbenzene as the overall product instead.

To circumvent this problem, we can make use of Friedel-Crafts *acylation*; the acylation reaction brings about the formation of a carbon-carbon bond to the aromatic ring, but does not suffer from issues of carbocation rearrangements (Section 22.5). Because the immediate product of an acylation reaction is an aromatic ketone, reduction of the carbonyl group is necessary to produce an alkylbenzene. An example using the Clemmensen reduction (Chapter 17) is shown in Equation 22-39.

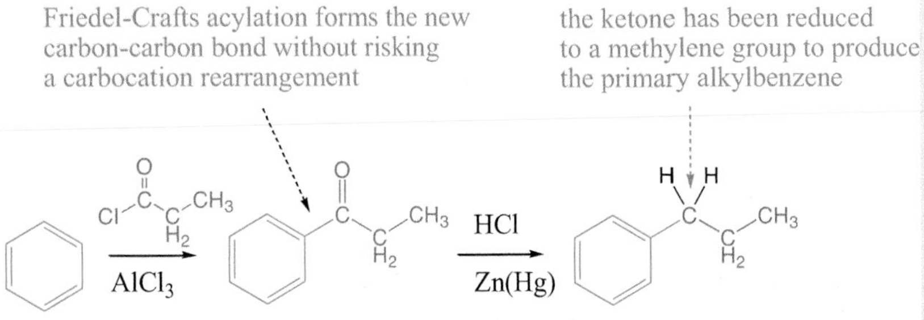

Friedel-Crafts acylation forms the new carbon-carbon bond without risking a carbocation rearrangement

the ketone has been reduced to a methylene group to produce the primary alkylbenzene

$AlCl_3$ HCl Zn(Hg)

(22-39)

Solved Problem 22.6. Show how you would carry out the following synthesis, using benzene as the only aromatic starting compound.

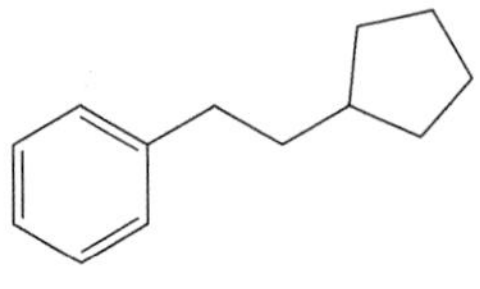

Think. The product is an alkylbenzene. Can a Friedel-Crafts alkylation be used to form the carbon-carbon bond to benzene? If not, why not? How can a Friedel-Crafts acylation reaction be incorporated into this synthesis?

Solve. A Fridel-Crafts alkylation reaction would require a primary carbocation intermediate, as shown below. This is not feasible, because such a primary carbocation intermediate, if produced, would undergo rearrangement.

a primary carbocation, if produced, would undergo rearrangement

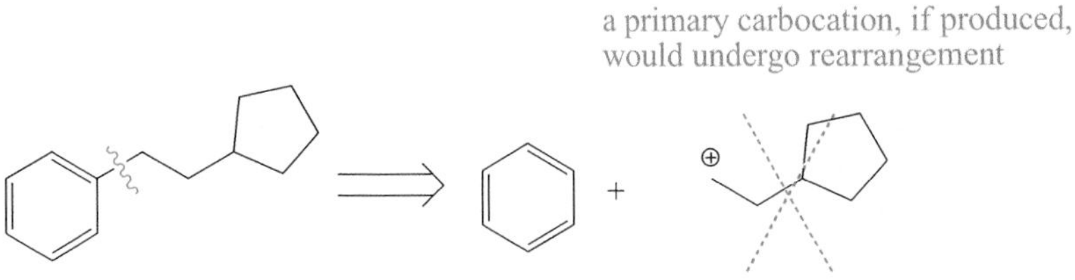

Instead, we could incorporate a Friedel-Crafts acylation reaction to produce the new carbon-carbon bond. The aromatic ketone product could then be reduced using a Clemmensen reduction.

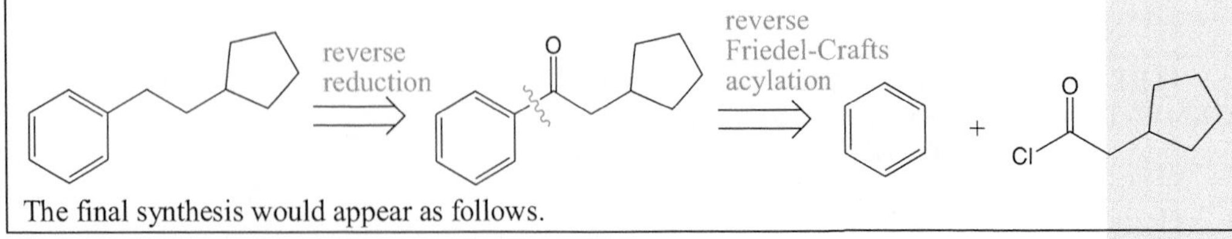

reverse reduction

reverse Friedel-Crafts acylation

The final synthesis would appear as follows.

+ Cl
O
$AlCl_3$
O
HCl
Fe

Problem 22.19. Show how to carry out the same synthesis as in the above Solved Problem, but without using the Clemmensen reduction.

Problem 22.20. Show how you would carry out the following synthesis, using benzene as the only aromatic starting compound.

22.11. ORGANIC SYNTHESIS: USEFUL REACTIONS USED IN CONJUNCTION WITH ELECTROPHILIC AROMATIC SUBSTITUTION REACTIONS

The reactions that are presented in this section are not electrophilic aromatic substitution reactions. However, we do find that they are quite useful in synthesis schemes that also involve electrophilic aromatic substitution reactions. These "useful" reactions are discussed in some detail, and their connection to electrophilic aromatic substitution reactions is also illustrated.

22.11a. Oxidation of Carbon Side-Chains: Synthesis of Benzoic Acids

Using the reactions we have encountered thus far, it is possible to attach a carboxyl group ($-CO_2H$) to a benzene ring to produce benzoic acid. As shown in Equation 22-40, benzene can be brominated, and the resulting bromobenzene can undergo dissolving metal reduction to produce a Grignard reagent. Bubbling carbon dioxide through the mixture will lead to a Grignard reaction to produce the carboxylate, which is protonated via an acid workup.

bromination of the benzene ring
dissolved metal reduction
Grignard reaction
Br_2
$FeBr_3$
Br
Mg(s)
MgBr
1) $CO_2(g)$
2) H^+
CO_2H

(22-40)

An alternative way to produce benzoic acid begins with any of a variety of monosubstituted benzenes in which a carbon atom from the substituent is directly bonded to the ring, as shown in Equations 22-41a through 22-41e. Oxidation of these substituted benzenes using $KMnO_4$ heated in a basic solution produces benzoic acid. Notice that several of such precursors could be produced using a Friedel-Crafts reaction.

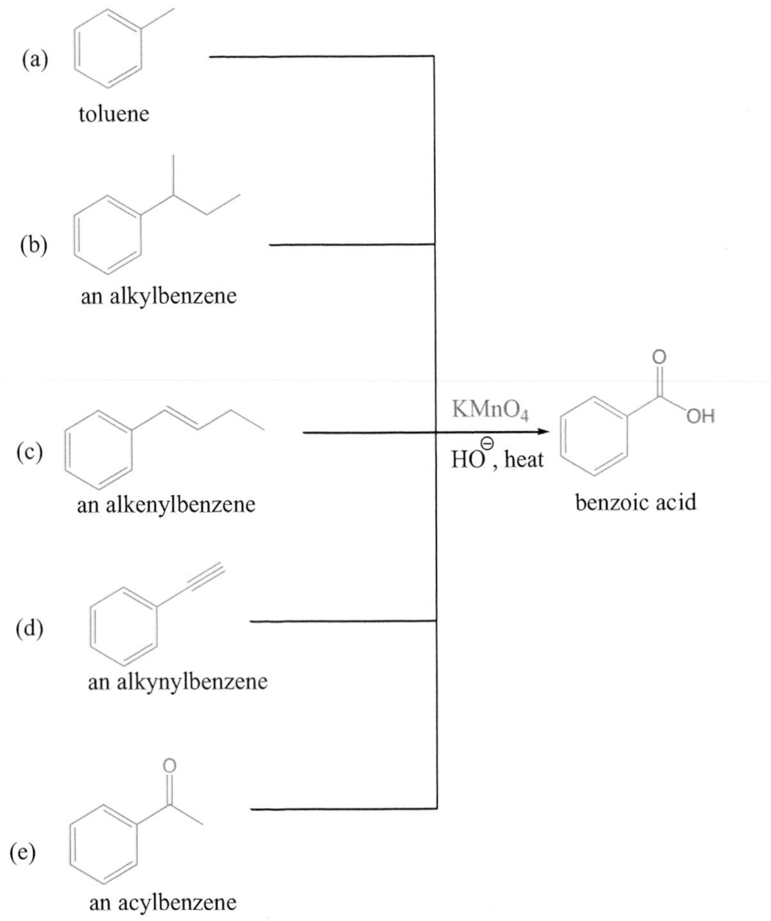

(a) toluene

(b) an alkylbenzene

(c) an alkenylbenzene

(d) an alkynylbenzene

(e) an acylbenzene

$\xrightarrow[HO^{\ominus}, \text{ heat}]{KMnO_4}$ benzoic acid

(22-41)

These oxidation reactions are believed proceed through *free radical intermediates*, species that will be discussed in detail in Chapter 25. There, we will see that the carbon atom bonded directly to the benzene ring—the **benzylic carbon**—is particularly reactive under these conditions. This is why the product of each of the reactions in Equation 22-41 is the same, essentially independent of the groups that are bonded to the benzylic carbon.

We do find, however, that this permanganate oxidation fails when the benzylic carbon is *quaternary*—i.e., bonded to four alkyl groups. As shown in Equation 22-42, for example, 2-methyl-2-phenylpropane is not oxidized to benzoic acid.

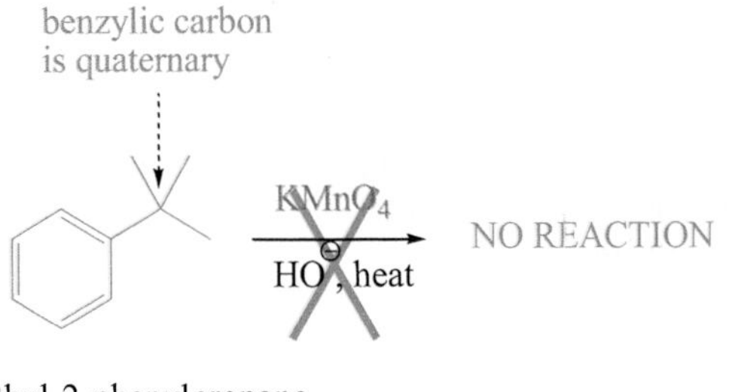

benzylic carbon is quaternary

2-methyl-2-phenylpropane $\xrightarrow[HO^{\ominus}, \text{ heat}]{KMnO_4}$ NO REACTION

(22-42)

In a synthesis, the benzoic acid product need not be part of the target molecule. Instead, as Solved Problem 22.7 highlights, the carboxylic acid functional group can be transformed into other functional groups, such as esters.

Solved problem 22.7. Propose a synthesis of ethyl benzoate from benzene and any other compounds containing 2 or fewer carbon atoms.

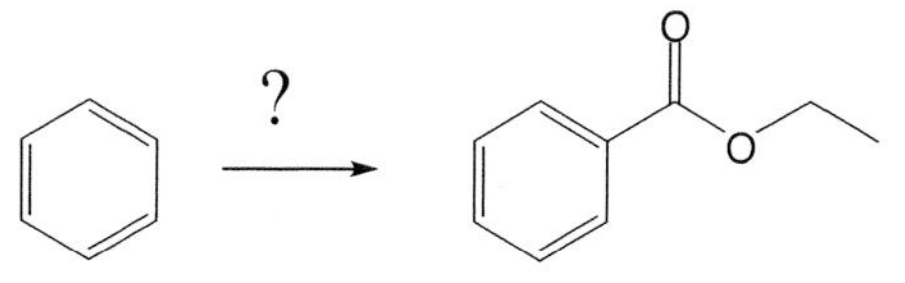

Think. How can an ester be synthesized from a precursor with fewer carbons? How can the appropriate precursor(s) be synthesized using compounds with 2 or fewer carbons?

Solve. In Chapter 19 we learned that an ester can be synthesized from a carboxylic acid and an alcohol. Here, the alcohol that is required is ethanol, which contains two carbon atoms. The carboxylic acid that is required is benzoic acid, which can be generated from $KMnO_4$ oxidation of any of a variety of substituted benzenes, as shown in Equation 23-45. The best choice is from phenylethanone, because that is the product of Friedel-Crafts acylation. If, instead, we were to choose an alkylbenzene as an intermediate, such as toluene ($C_6H_5CH_3$), a Friedel-Crafts alkylation would be required, which runs the risk of polyalkylation (Section 23.3).

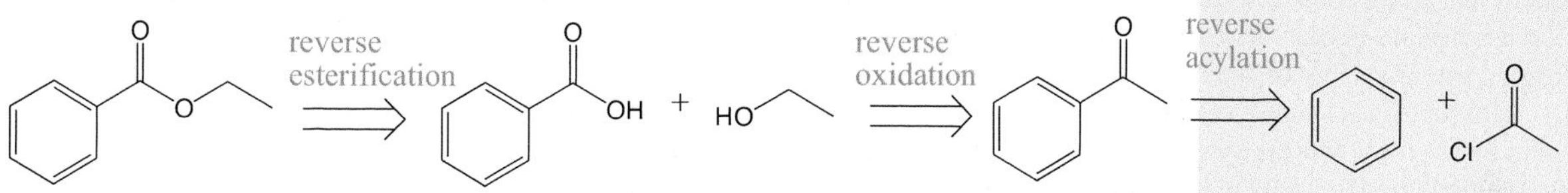

reverse esterification ⟹ OH + HO ⟹ reverse oxidation ⟹ reverse acylation + Cl

In the forward direction, the synthesis would appear as follows.

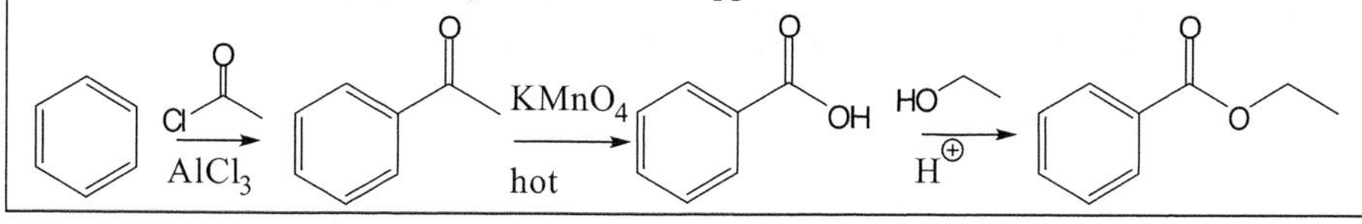

Cl, $AlCl_3$ → $KMnO_4$, hot → OH, HO, $H^{\oplus}$ → O

Problem 22.21. Show how you could synthesize phenyl benzoate using benzene as the only aromatic starting compound.

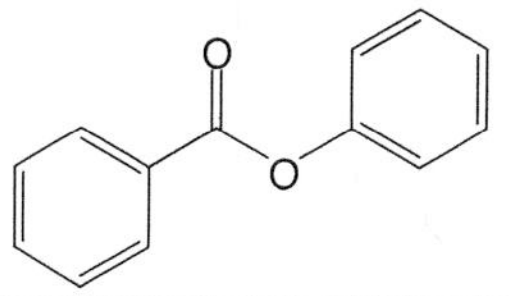

O

22.11b. Reduction of Nitrobenzenes to Aromatic Amines

An amino group ($-NH_2$) cannot be attached to a benzene ring using only electrophilic aromatic substitution reactions. However, the *nitration* of benzene (Equation 22-24) serves to attach a nitrogen atom to a benzene ring, producing a nitro-substituted benzene. That nitro group can be reduced to an amine, either by catalytic hydrogenation (Equation 22-43a) or by treatment with a metal (e.g., Fe or Sn) under acidic conditions (Equation 22-43b). The conditions for the latter resemble those of the Clemmensen reduction we encountered in Chapter 17, in which the carbonyl group of a ketone or aldehyde is reduced to a methylene (CH_2) group by treatment with a Zn(Hg) amalgam in HCl.

catalytic hydrogenation

conc. HNO_3 → NO_2 → H_2, Pd, 80 °C, EtOH → 98% (a)

HCl, Fe → 80% (b)

dissolved metal reduction

(23-43)

The reduction of a nitro substituent to an amino group is useful, in and of itself, as a functional group transformation. In particular, as we will see in the next section, aromatic amines are precursors to arenediazonium salts ($Ar\text{-}N_2^+$), which can be transformed into a variety of functionalized aromatic species.

Moreover, as we will see in Chapter 23, reduction of a nitro group to an amino group can be useful when the synthesis of di- and trisubstituted benzenes calls for specific regiochemistry. This is because an NH_2 group influences the regiochemistry of electrophilic aromatic substitution differently from how an NO_2 group does.

Solved Problem 22.8. Show how to synthesize *N*-phenylbenzamide, using benzene as the only aromatic starting compound.

N-phenylbenzamide

Think. What precursors, with fewer carbons, are appropriate for producing an *N*-substituted amide? How can each of those precursors be produced from benzene?

Solve. An *N*-substituted amide can be produced from an amine and an acid chloride—in this case, aniline and benzoyl chloride. Aniline can be produced by nitration of benzene, followed by reduction of the nitrobenzene product. Benzoyl chloride can be produced by chlorinating benzoic acid, which, in turn, can be produced by acylation of benzene, followed by $KMnO_4$ oxidation.

reverse acyl substitution

reverse reduction

reverse nitration

reverse acylation

reverse chlorination

reverse oxidation

Problem 22.22. Show how to synthesize each of the following compounds, using benzene as the only aromatic starting compound.

(a)

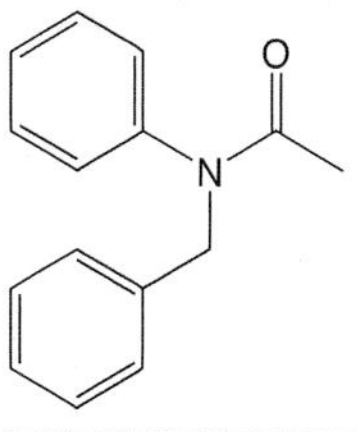

(b)

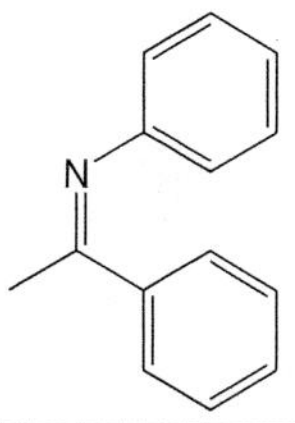

22.11c. The Benzenediazonium Ion and the Sandmeyer Reactions

When aniline is treated with sodium nitrite ($NaNO_2$) under acidic conditions, followed by copper (I) bromide (CuBr), bromobenzene is produced (Equation 22-44).

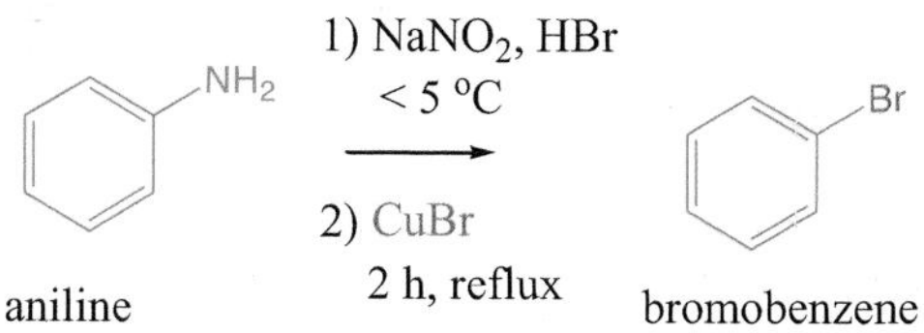

aniline

1) $NaNO_2$, HBr
< 5 °C

2) CuBr
2 h, reflux

bromobenzene

50%

(22-44)

Overall, a bromine atom replaces the amino group, but the mechanism is not a simple electrophilic aromatic substitution. As shown in Equation 22-45, the first of the two reactions is a multistep mechanism, which ultimately produces a **benzenediazonium ion**.

Mechanism for the First Reaction in Equation 22-44

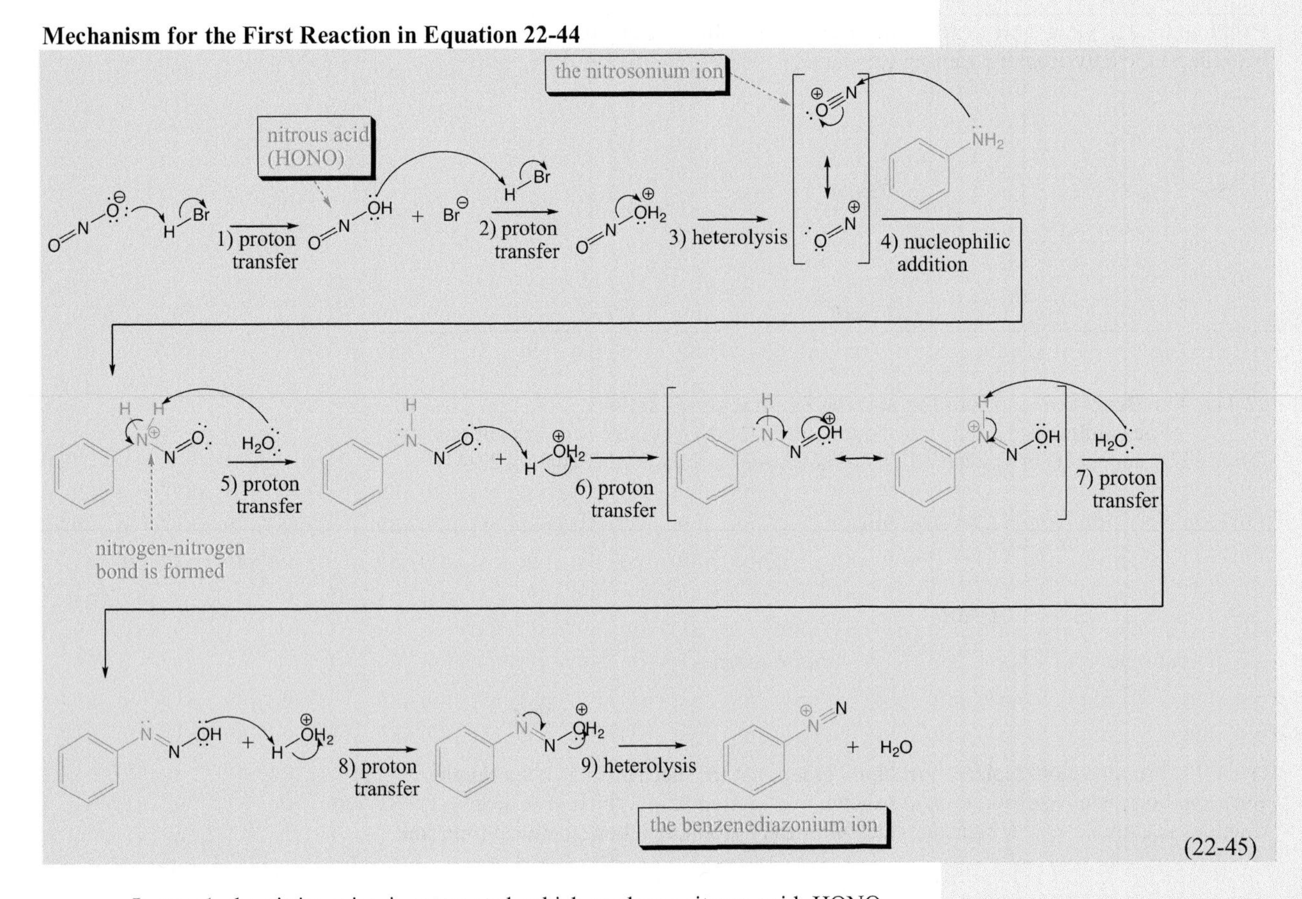

(22-45)

In step 1, the nitrite anion is protonated, which produces nitrous acid, HONO. Protonation in step 2 converts a poor hydroxide leaving group into an excellent water leaving group, which departs in step 3 to produce a nitrosonium ion, NO^+. The aromatic amine attacks the nitrosonium ion in step 4, in which a nitrogen-nitrogen bond is formed. Steps 5 – 8 are proton transfers the serve to remove hydrogen atoms from the initial amino nitrogen, and to produce a water leaving group on the adjacent nitrogen. Finally, in step 9, the water leaving group departs, producing the benzenediazonium ion.

Notice that the benzenediazonium ion possesses an N_2^+ group, which can behave as an excellent $N_2(g)$ leaving group. Thus, the ion is highly reactive, and must be kept below about 10 °C to prevent decomposition.

On the other hand, the high reactivity of the benzenediazonium ion is very beneficial if we wish to carry out a substitution reaction, simply by choosing the appropriate nucleophile. Examples are shown in Equations 22-46a through 22-46g. Some of these reactions require the presence of a Cu^{+1} catalyst—collectively, they are known as the **Sandmeyer reactions**, after the Swiss chemist Traugott Sandmeyer.

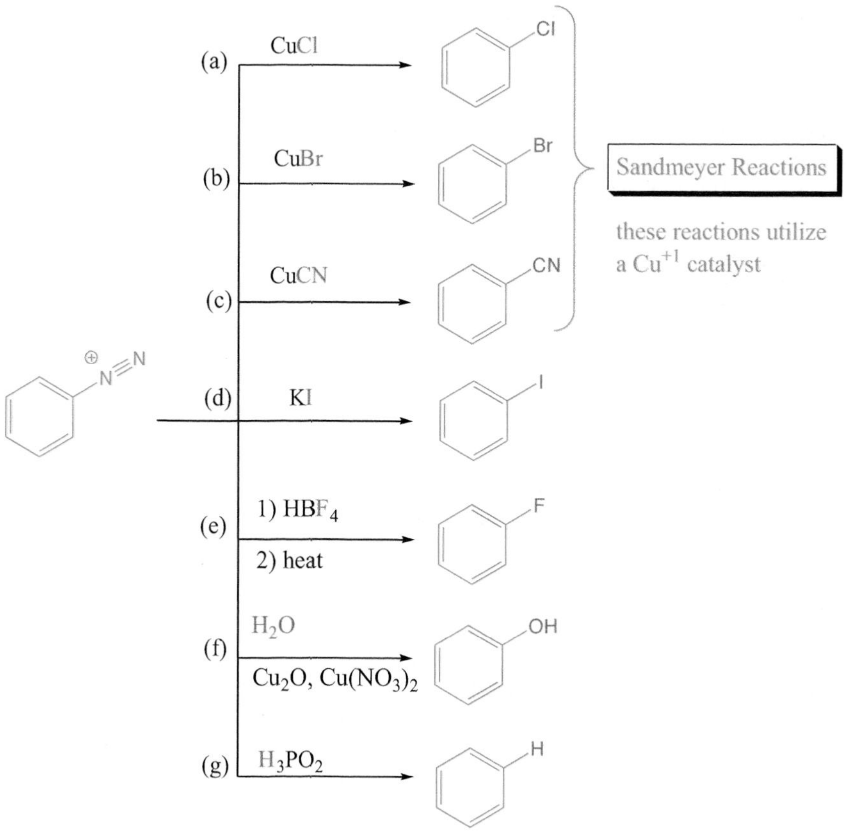

(a) CuCl → chlorobenzene
(b) CuBr → bromobenzene
(c) CuCN → benzonitrile

Sandmeyer Reactions: these reactions utilize a Cu^{+1} catalyst

(d) KI → iodobenzene
(e) 1) HBF_4 2) heat → fluorobenzene
(f) H_2O, Cu_2O, $Cu(NO_3)_2$ → phenol
(g) H_3PO_2 → benzene

(22-46)

Even though these reactions involve nucleophiles and an excellent leaving group, they do not universally proceed by ionic mechanisms such as the S_N1 or S_N2 mechanism. Instead, some are believed to involve *radical intermediates*, which contain unpaired electrons (Chapter 26). Because of the complex nature of these reactions, their mechanisms will not be discussed here.

Problem 22.23. Show how you would synthesize each of these compounds from an aromatic amine.

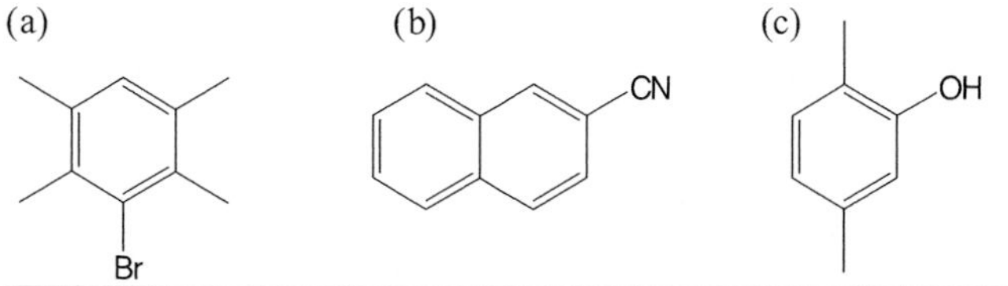

(a) (b) (c)

Br CN OH

Problem 22.24. How would you synthesize deuterobenzene from aniline?

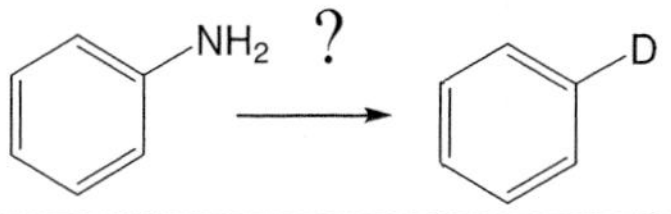

NH_2 ? → D

Notice that some of the products in Equation 22-46 can be produced using electrophilic aromatic substitution reactions we have seen previously in this chapter. For example, bromobenzene and chlorobenzene can be produced using halogenation reactions (Section 22.2). However, the benzenediazonium ion intermediate provides much more flexibility in synthesis, allowing us to synthesize compounds that cannot be synthesized directly via electrophilic aromatic substitution. Recall, for example, that difficulties arise with iodination and fluorination of benzene via electrophilic aromatic substitution. Beginning with the arenediazonium ion, however, iodobenzene (Equation 22-46d) and fluorobenzene (Equation 22-46e) can be synthesized rather straightforwardly. Similarly, cyanobenzene and phenol cannot be produced directly from benzene via electrophilic aromatic substitution, but can be produced by incorporating the benzenediazonium ion as a synthetic intermediate. This is exemplified by Solved Problem 22.9.

Solved Problem 22.9. Show how to synthesize cyanobenzene from benzene.

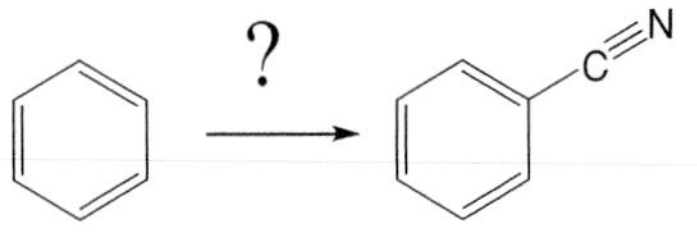

?

C≡N

cyanobenzene

Think. Can a cyano group replace H on a benzene ring directly? If not, what precursor is required? Can that precursor be synthesized from benzene using electrophilic aromatic substitution?

Solve. We have not encountered a reaction in which a cyano group replaces an H on benzene in a direct fashion. However, cyanobenzene can be made directly from a benzenediazonium ion precursor, $C_6H_5–N_2^+$. The precursor to the benzenediazonium ion is an aromatic amine, which, in turn, can be made by reducing nitrobenzene. Lastly, nitrobenzene can be made directly from benzene via nitration.

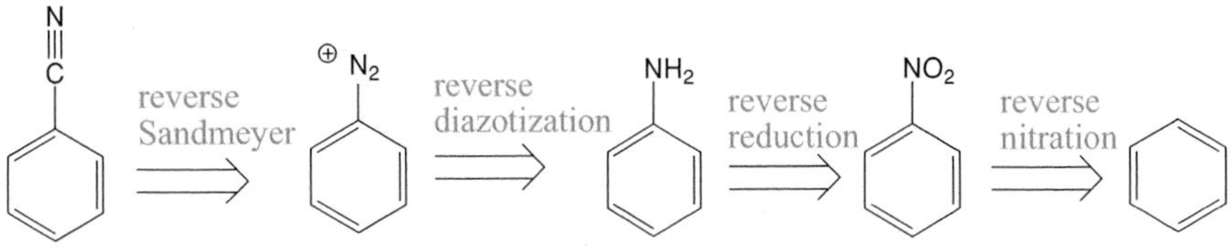

N≡C — reverse Sandmeyer ⟹ ⊕ N_2 — reverse diazotization ⟹ NH_2 — reverse reduction ⟹ NO_2 — reverse nitration ⟹ benzene

In the forward direction, the synthesis would appear as follows:

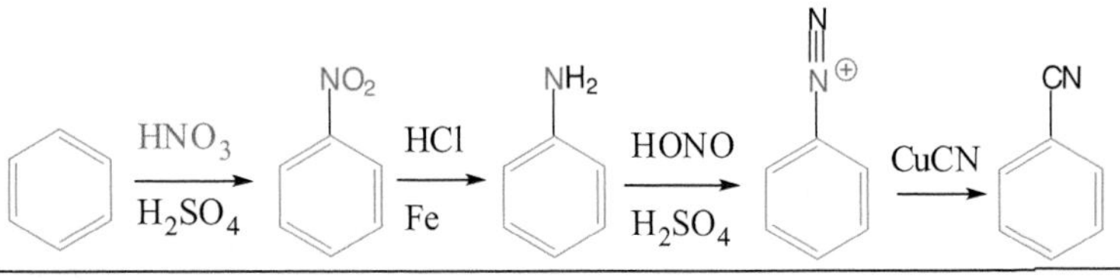

$$\xrightarrow[H_2SO_4]{HNO_3} NO_2 \xrightarrow[Fe]{HCl} NH_2 \xrightarrow[H_2SO_4]{HONO} N^{\oplus}{\equiv}N \xrightarrow{CuCN} CN$$

Problem 22.25. Show how to carry out the following synthesis, using any reagents necessary.

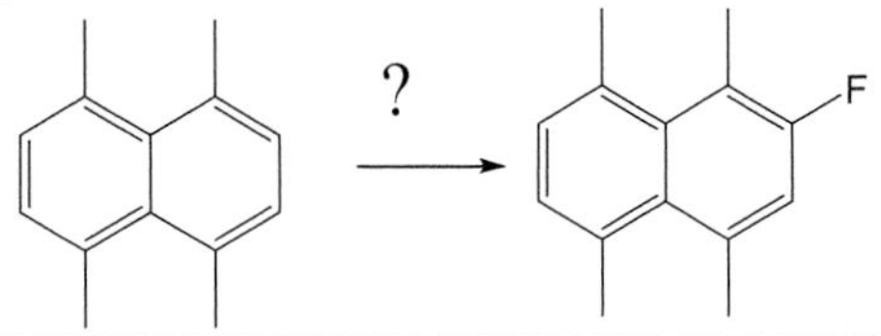

?

F

22.12. WRAPPING UP AND LOOKING AHEAD

This chapter introduced a variety of reactions in which a hydrogen atom on an aromatic ring is replaced by another group. The mechanisms for these reactions have two steps in common—addition of an electrophile (E^+) to the aromatic ring, producing an arenium ion intermediate, followed by elimination of a proton (H^+) to regenerate the aromatic ring. Thus, these reactions comprise the class of reactions called *electrophilic aromatic substitution reactions*.

Because electrophilic aromatic substitution reactions involve the temporary destruction of the aromaticity of the ring, they require very strong electrophiles. Such electrophiles are in general too reactive to be isolated, so they cannot be added directly to the reaction mixture. Rather, they must be produced *in situ* from appropriate precursors. Thus, the mechanisms for the various electrophilic aromatic substitution reactions differ not only in the identity of the electrophile, but also in the mechanism that describes how the electrophile is produced.

Some electrophilic aromatic substitution reactions have significant limitations that must be considered in a synthesis. Friedel-Crafts alkylations, for example, are susceptible to carbocation rearrangements, preventing the direct formation of a primary alkylbenzene. However, such a product can be produced by first carrying out a Friedel-Crafts acylation, followed by a reduction of the resulting ketone to a methylene group.

Some "useful" reactions were also introduced: Oxidation of carbon side-chains on a benzene ring; reduction of nitrobenzenes to aromatic amines; and the production and reaction of benzenediazonium ions. Even though these reactions do not proceed by an electrophilic aromatic substitution mechanism, they are often used in conjunction with reactions that do. For example, a carboxylic acid group can be added to a benzene ring by first alkylating or acylating the ring, and then oxidizing the new carbon side-chain. An aromatic amine is produced by first nitrating the aromatic ring, and then reducing the nitro group to an amino group. Moreover, the aromatic amine that is produced can be converted to a benzenediazonium ion, which is a precursor to a wide variety of substitution products.

The scope of this chapter was limited almost exclusively to aromatic rings that possess only one chemically distinct hydrogen atom. Therefore, only one substitution product is possible. In Chapter 23, we will focus on aromatic substitution reactions in which multiple isomeric products are possible. We will find that for such reactions, the product mixture is usually dominated by one or two of those products. Predicting which products those are involves careful consideration of the rates of the reactions that lead to each product.

REACTION TABLES

Table 22-1. Functional group transformations

Starting Functional Group	Typical Reagent Required	Functional Group Formed	Comments	Discussed in Section(s)
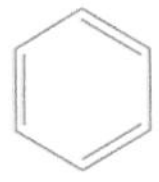 Arene	Br_2, $FeBr_3$	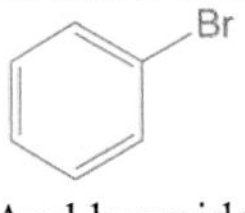 Br Aryl bromide	Electrophilic aromatic substitution	22.2
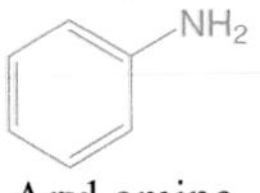 NH_2 Aryl amine	1) $NaNO_2$, H_2SO_4 2) CuBr	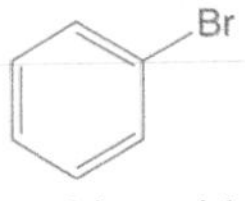 Br Aryl bromide	Proceeds through a diazonium ion	22.11c
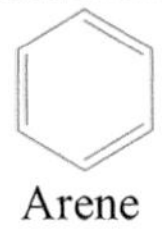 Arene	Cl_2, $FeBr_3$	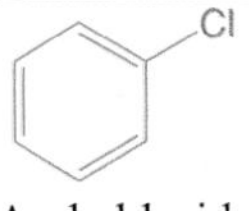 Cl Aryl chloride	Electrophilic aromatic substitution	22.2
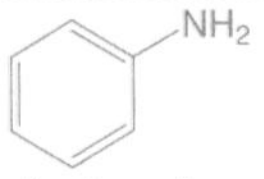 NH_2 Aryl amine	1) $NaNO_2$, H_2SO_4 2) CuCl	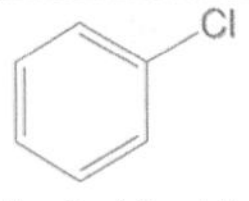 Cl Aryl chloride	Proceeds through a diazonium ion	22.11c
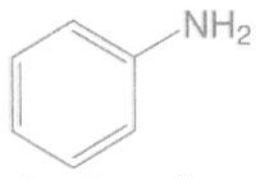 NH_2 Aryl amine	1) $NaNO_2$, H_2SO_4 2) KI	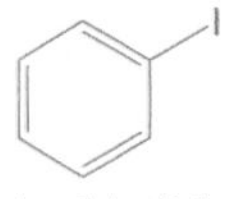 I Aryl iodide	Proceeds through a diazonium ion	22.11c
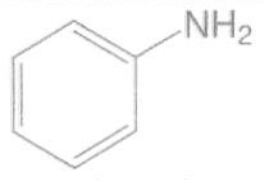 NH_2 Aryl amine	1) $NaNO_2$, H_2SO_4 2) HBF_4, then heat	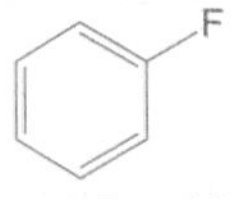 F Aryl fluoride	Proceeds through a diazonium ion	22.11c
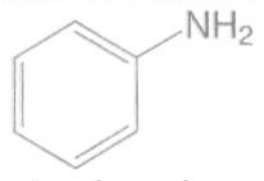 NH_2 Aryl amine	1) $NaNO_2$, H_2SO_4 2) H_2O, Cu^+	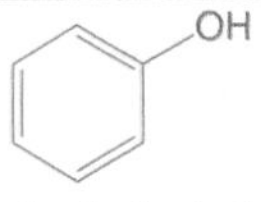 OH Aryl alcohol	Proceeds through a diazonium ion	22.11c
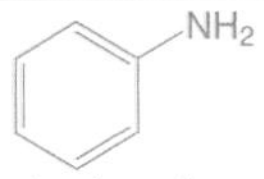 NH_2 Aryl amine	1) $NaNO_2$, H_2SO_4 2) H_3PO_2	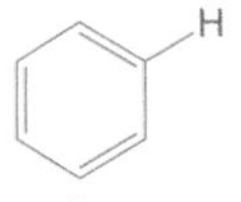 H Arene	Proceeds through a diazonium ion	22.11c
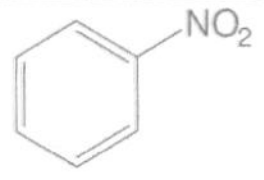 NO_2 Nitroarene	HCl, Fe	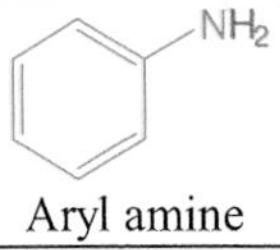 NH_2 Aryl amine	Reduction	22.11b
 Arene	HNO_3, H_2SO_4	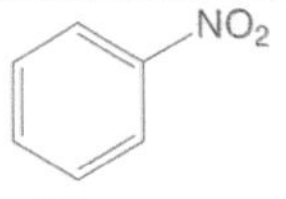 NO_2 Nitroarene	Electrophilic aromatic substitution	22.6
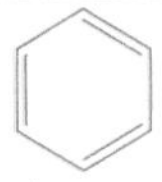 Arene	SO_3, H_2SO_4	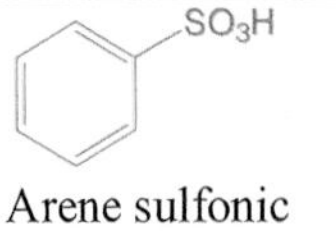 SO_3H Arene sulfonic acid	Electrophilic aromatic substitution	22.7

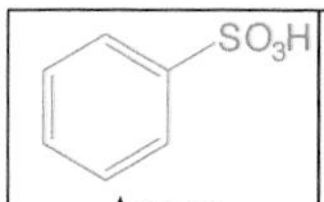 Arene sulfonic acid (SO_3H)	H_2O, dil. H_2SO_4	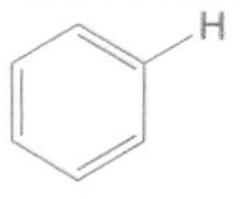 Arene (H)	Electrophilic aromatic substitution	22.7

Table 22-2. Reactions that alter the carbon skeleton

Starting Functional Group	Typical Reagent Required	Functional Group Formed	Comments	Discussed in Chapter(s)
 Arene	R-Cl, $AlCl_3$	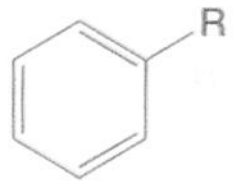 Alkylarene (R)	Electrophilic aromatic substitution	22.3 and 22.3
 Arene	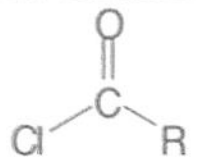 Cl-C(=O)-R, $AlCl_3$	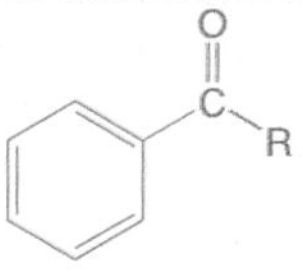 Acylarene (C(=O)R)	Electrophilic aromatic substitution	22.5
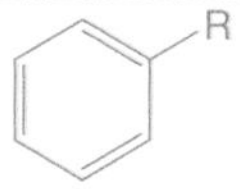 Alkylarene (R)	$KMnO_4$, heat	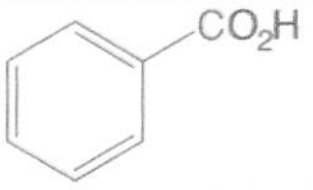 Aromatic carboxylic acid (CO_2H)	Oxidation	22.11a
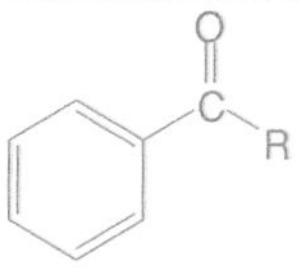 Acylarene (C(=O)R)	$KMnO_4$, heat	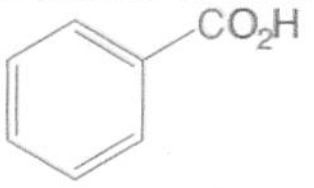 Aromatic carboxylic acid (CO_2H)	Oxidation	22.11a
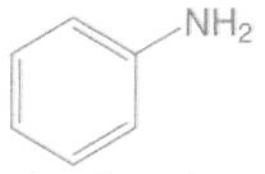 Aryl amine (NH_2)	1) $NaNO_2$, H_2SO_4 2) CuCN	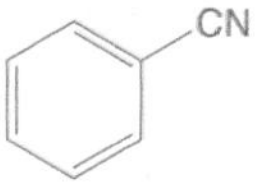 Aryl nitrile (CN)	Proceeds through a diazonium ion	22.11c

CHAPTER SUMMARY AND KEY TERMS

- The general mechanism for an **electrophilic aromatic substitution reaction** consists of two steps. First, an electrophile (E^+) adds to an aromatic ring to produce an **arenium ion intermediate**, also called a **Wheland intermediate**. Second, a proton (H^+) is eliminated, resulting in a substituted aromatic ring. (Section 22.1)
- The reaction requires the temporary destruction of aromaticity, so the electrophiles must be powerful. Therefore, such electrophiles must be generated *in situ*. Moreover, electrophilic aromatic substitution reactions are in general irreversible. (Section 22.1)

- The first step of electrophilic aromatic substitution—addition of the electrophile—is slow, so it is the rate-determining step of the reaction. Thus, the reaction is first order with respect both to the aromatic ring and to the electrophile. (Section 22.1)
- **Halogenation** of an aromatic ring typically requires a molecular halogen, Br_2 or Cl_2, in the presence of a strong **Lewis acid catalyst**, such as $FeBr_3$ or $FeCl_3$. These catalysts aid in the production of the electrophile, Br^+ or Cl^+. (Section 22.2)
- **Friedel-Crafts alkylation** of an aromatic ring requires an alkyl halide in the presence of a strong Lewis acid catalyst, such as $AlCl_3$. These catalysts aid in the production of the electrophile, a carbocation (R^+). (Section 22.3)
- Friedel-Crafts alkylation reactions are subject to a number of limitations. (Section 22.4)
    - They are susceptible to carbocation rearrangements, so they cannot be used to produce primary alkylbenzenes.
    - The halogen atom of the alkyl halide must be bonded to an sp^3-hybridized carbon atom.
    - Friedel-Crafts alkylations are susceptible to **polyalkylation.**
    - They do not readily take place if the aromatic ring is strongly *deactivated.*
- A **Friedel-Crafts acylation reaction** requires an acid halide (or acyl halide) in the presence of a strong Lewis acid catalyst. The catalyst is responsible for the production of the electrophile, an **acylium ion**, $R\text{–}C^+\equiv O$. Such reactions are not susceptible to carbocation rearrangements, and are not susceptible to multiple substitutions, but they still have some limitations. (Section 22.5)
    - They generally cannot be carried out on aromatic rings that are *deactivated.*
    - They cannot be used as a means of *formylation*, whereby H on an aromatic ring is replaced by a formyl group, HC=O.
- **Nitration** of an aromatic ring requires concentrated nitric acid (HNO_3), which produces the **nitrosonium ion** (NO^+) as the electrophile. The addition of concentrated sulfuric acid (H_2SO_4) increases the concentration of the nitrosonium ion, and therefore increases the rate of the electrophilic aromatic substitution reaction. (Section 22.6)
- **Sulfonation** of an aromatic ring requires concentrated sulfuric acid to produce sulfur trioxide (SO_3) as the electrophile. The rate of sulfonation is greater with **fuming sulfuric acid**, which is enriched with SO_3. (Section 22.7)
- Sulfonation is *reversible.* A sulfonic acid group on an aromatic ring can be replaced by H upon treatment with acidified water. (Section 22.7)
- Aromatic rings other than benzene can participate in electrophilic aromatic substitution. However, if the aromatic ring has more than one chemically distinct aromatic proton, substitution will lead to a mixture of isomers. (Section 22.8)
- In an electrophilic aromatic substitution reaction involving a substituted aromatic ring, **ipso attack** can occur, whereby substitution takes place at the aromatic carbon atom bonded to a substituent. Generally, such reactions are not as favorable as substitution of an aromatic proton, but one example includes *desulfonation.* (Sections 22.7 and 22.9)
- Although a primary alkylbenzene cannot be produced directly from a Friedel-Crafts alkylation, it can be produced using a Friedel-Crafts acylation, followed by a reduction of the ketone's carbonyl group to a methylene (CH_2) group. (Section 22.10a)
- A variety of carbon side-chains of an aromatic ring can be oxidized to a carboxylic acid by heating the aromatic compound in the presence of basic $KMnO_4$. (Section 22.11a)

- An aromatic amine can be produced by reducing a nitro-substituted aromatic ring, using either catalytic hydrogenation (e.g., $H_2(g)$, Pd) or dissolving metal reduction (e.g., Fe, HCl). (Section 22.11b)
- A **benzenediazonium ion** ($C_6H_5{-}N_2^+$) is produced when an amino-substituted benzene is treated with sodium nitrite ($NaNO_2$) under acidic conditions. The benzenediazonium ion can undergo a variety of substitution reactions readily, owing to the excellent $N_2(g)$ leaving group it possesses. Reactions involving a Cu^{+1} catalyst are called the **Sandmeyer reactions**. (Section 22.11c)

PROBLEMS

26. For each reaction, draw the complete, detailed mechanism and the major product(s).

(a) $H_3C{-}CH_2{-}Cl$, $AlCl_3$ → ?

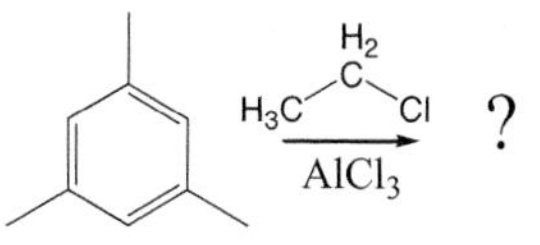

(b) Cl_2, $FeCl_3$ → ?

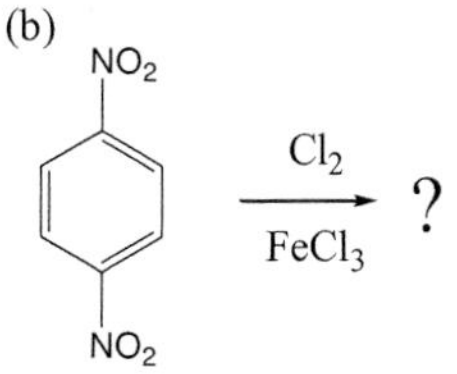

(c) $H_3C{-}C(=O){-}Cl$, $AlCl_3$ → ?

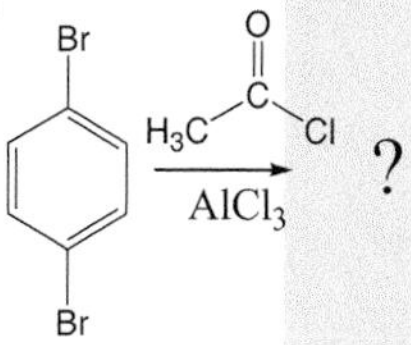

(d) conc. HNO_3 → ?

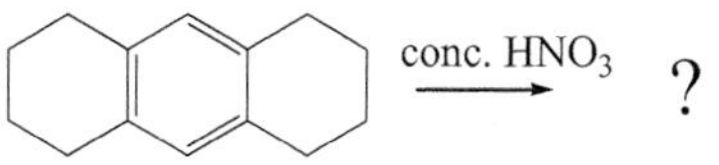

(e) conc. HNO_3, H_2SO_4, Δ → ?

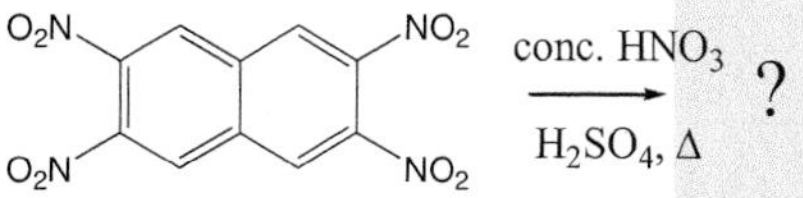

27. Supply the reagents necessary to carry out each of the following reactions.

(a) ?

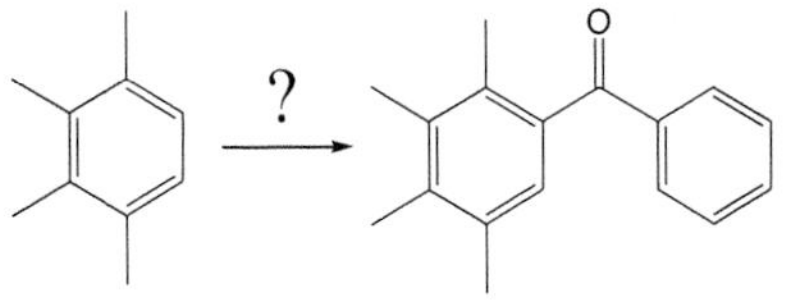

(b) O_2N NO_2 NO_2 ? Br O_2N NO_2 NO_2

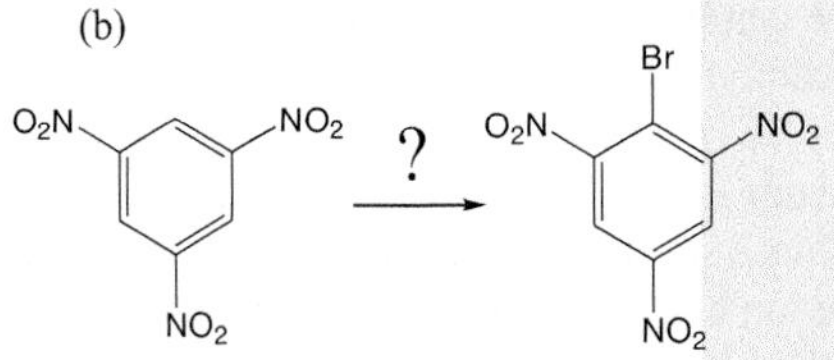

(c) SO_3H ?

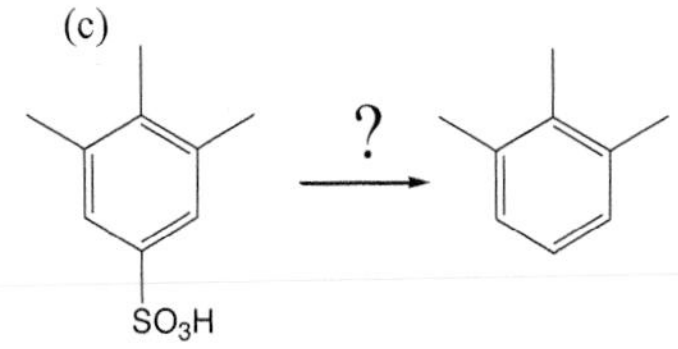

(d) Br Cl Cl Br ? NO_2 Br Cl Cl Br

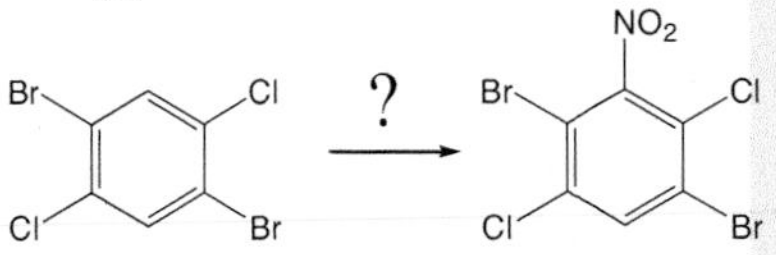

(e) Br Cl Cl Br ? NH_2 Br Cl Cl Br

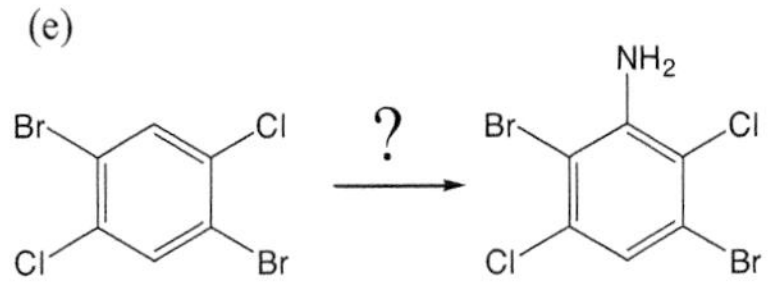

(f) Br Cl Cl Br ? CO_2H Br Cl Cl Br

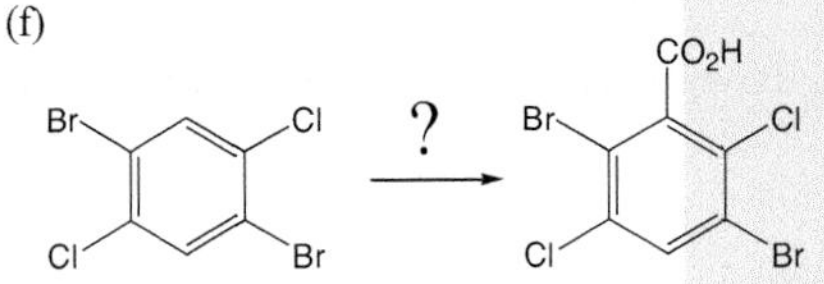

(g) ?

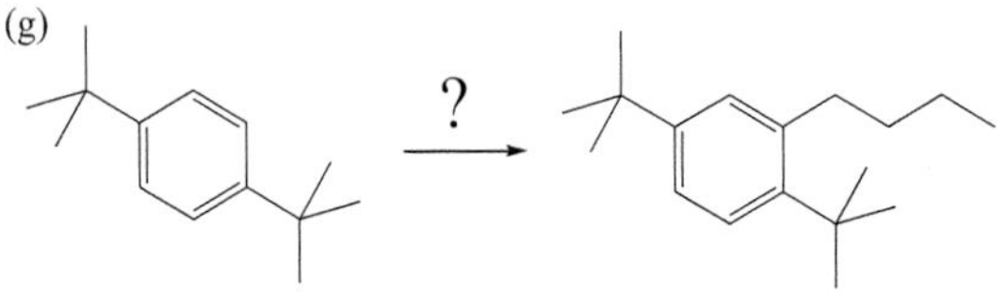

28. Supply the missing compounds in the following synthesis scheme.

benzene $\xrightarrow[FeBr_3]{Br_2}$ A $\xrightarrow{Mg(s)}$ B $\xrightarrow[2)\ H_3O^+]{1)\ \text{(ethylene oxide)}}$ C $\xrightarrow{PCC}$ D

C $\xrightarrow{PBr_3}$ E $\xrightarrow[2)\ Bu\text{-}Li]{1)\ PPh_3}$ F $\xrightarrow{D}$ G

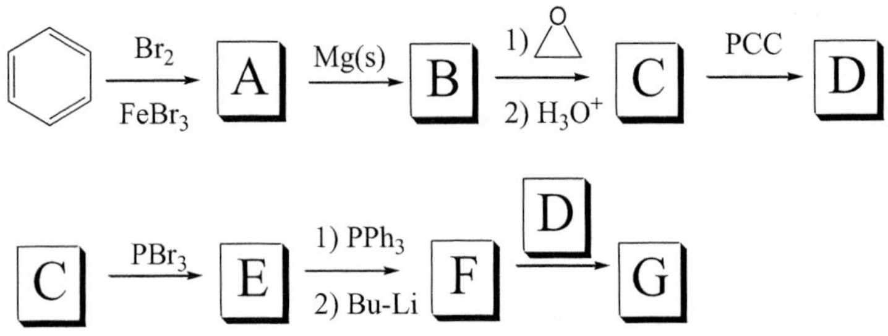

29. Supply the missing compounds in the following synthesis scheme.

benzene $\xrightarrow[AlCl_3]{\text{(acetyl chloride)}}$ A $\xrightarrow[2)\ H_3O^+]{1)\ Cl_2\ \text{(excess), NaOH}}$ B $\xrightarrow{SOCl_2}$ C

benzene $\xrightarrow{\text{conc. } HNO_3}$ D $\xrightarrow[HCl]{Fe}$ E $\xrightarrow{C}$ F $\xrightarrow[2)\ H_3O^+]{1)\ LiAlH_4}$ G

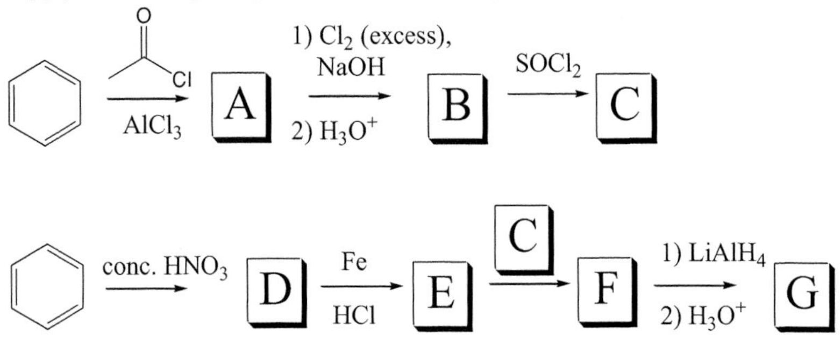

30. Supply the missing compounds in the following synthesis scheme.

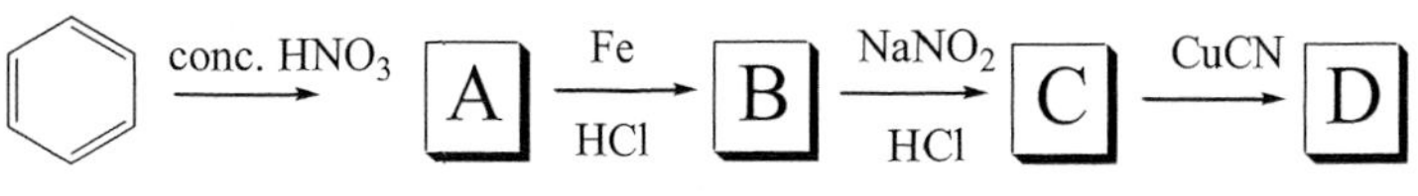

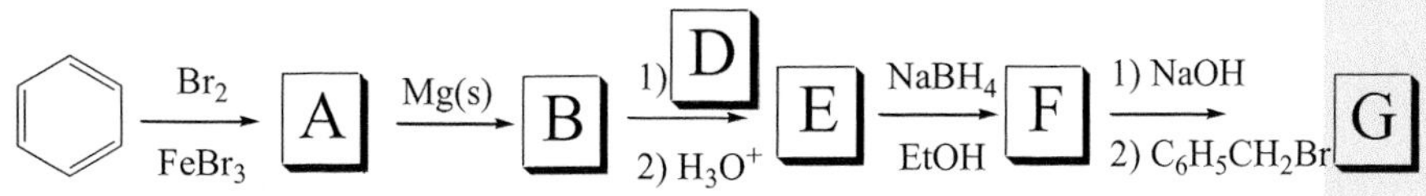

conc. HNO_3 → A → (Fe, HCl) B → ($NaNO_2$, HCl) C → (CuCN) D

(Br_2, $FeBr_3$) → A → (Mg(s)) B → (1) D, 2) H_3O^+) E → ($NaBH_4$, EtOH) F → (1) NaOH, 2) $C_6H_5CH_2Br$) G

31. Propose a mechanism for the following isotopic exchange reaction

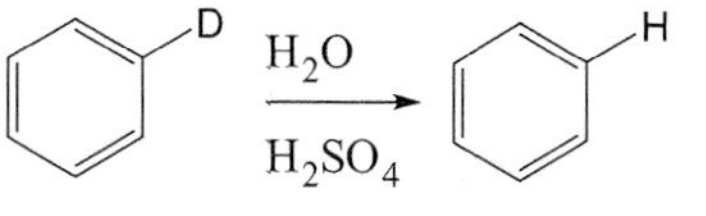

D → (H_2O, H_2SO_4) → H

32. In the acid-catalyzed aromatic alkylation involving 1-methylcyclohexene and benzene, two isomeric products are possible, but the only one that is formed is shown below. Draw the complete mechanism that leads to each product, and explain why only one isomer is formed.

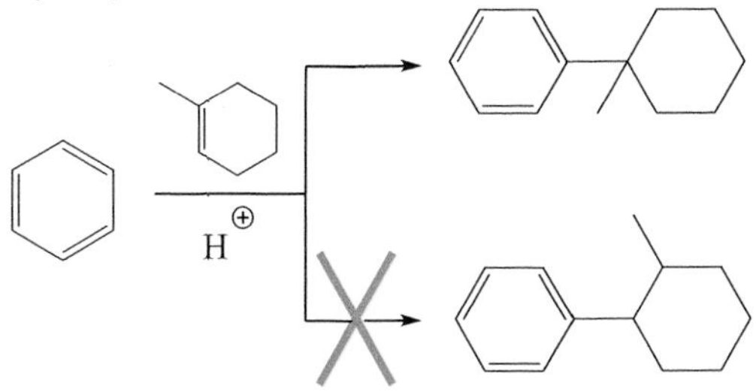

$H^{\oplus}$

33. When benzene is treated with sulfur dichloride (SCl_2) in the presence of a Friedel-Crafts catalyst like $AlCl_3$, diphenyl sulfide is produced, as shown below. Propose a mechanism for this reaction.

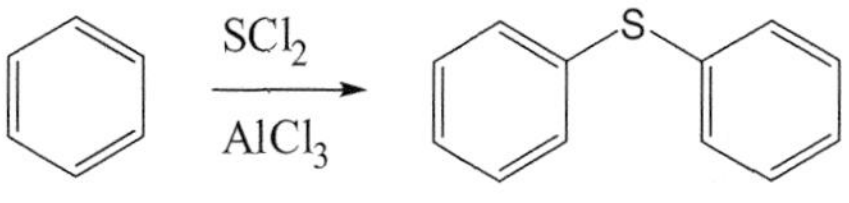

SCl_2, $AlCl_3$ → S

diphenyl sulfide

34. When diphenyl ether is reacted under the same conditions as in the previous problem, a compound is produced whose ^{13}C-NMR spectrum shows 6 signals. Draw that product.

35. When the following acid chloride is treated with $AlCl_3$, a product is formed whose ^{1}H-NMR and IR spectra are shown below. Draw the product and propose a complete, detailed mechanism for the first of the two reactions.

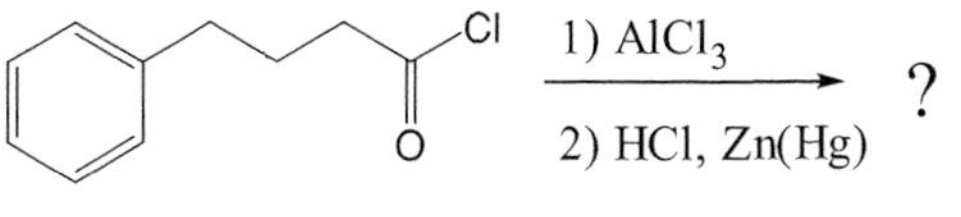

Cl, O → (1) $AlCl_3$, 2) HCl, Zn(Hg)) → ?

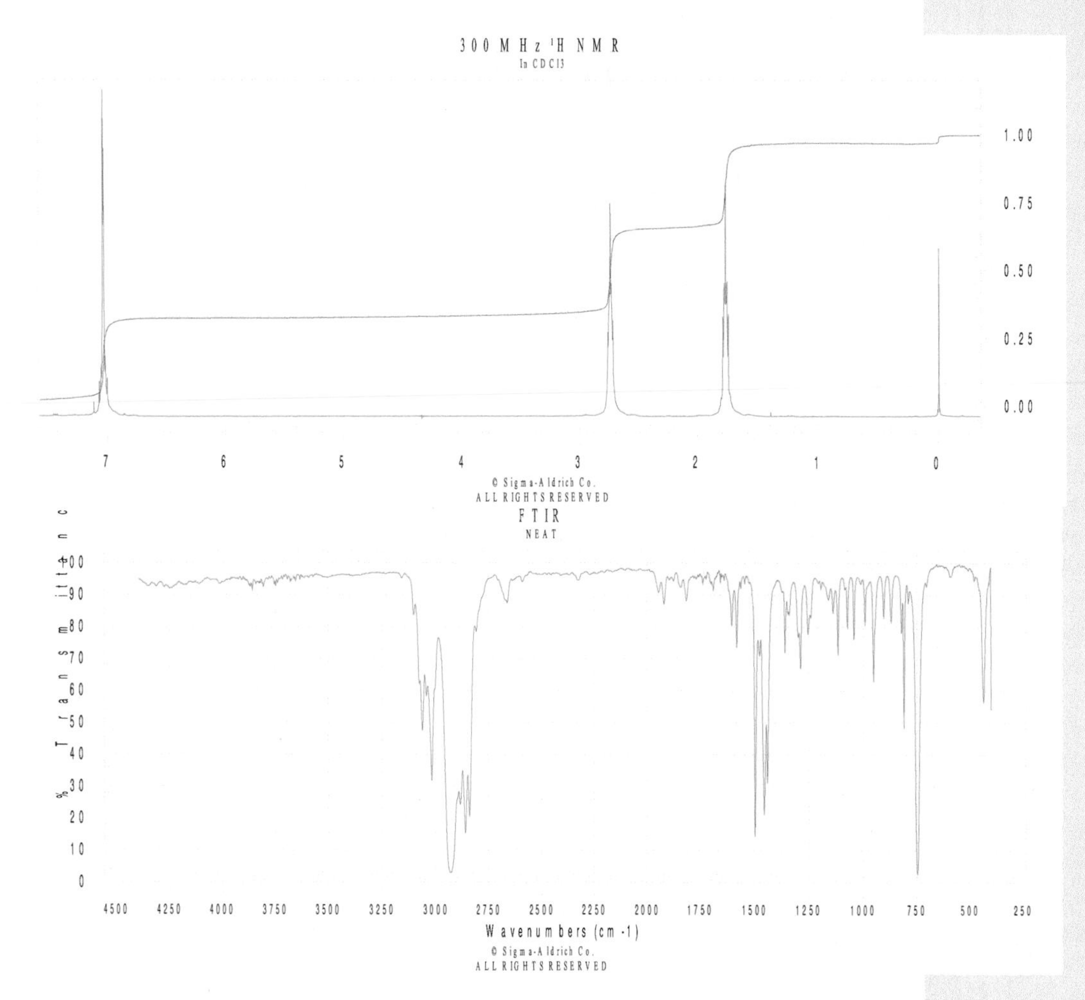

36. The following compound is treated with a dilute aqueous solution of sulfuric acid. The product's molecular formula is $C_{12}H_{16}$. The only signals it exhibits in the ¹H-NMR spectrum are at around 8 ppm and around 1.2 ppm. Draw the product and the complete, detailed mechanism that leads to its formation.

$\xrightarrow{\text{dil. } H_2SO_4}$?

37. Propose a complete, detailed mechanism for the following reaction.

$\xrightarrow[H^{\oplus}]{(CH_3)_3COH}$

38. Compounds A, B, and C are isomers of xylene (dimethylbenzene). Compound A undergoes nitration to give a single product. Compound B undergoes nitration to give two products, and compound C undergoes nitration to give three products. Identify which compound is the *ortho* isomer, which compound is the *meta* isomer, and which compound is the *para* isomer.

39. When 2,4,6-trihydroxybenzene is treated with ethanenitrle (CH_3CN) in HCl in the presence of a $ZnCl_2$ catalyst, an aromatic imine is formed. Propose a mechanism for this reaction.

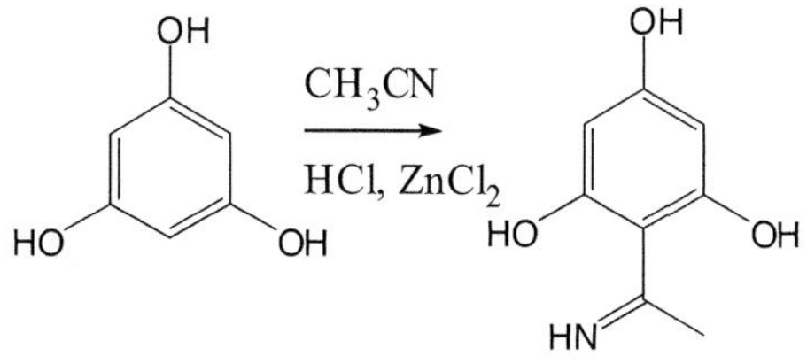

OH, HO, OH — CH_3CN / HCl, $ZnCl_2$ → OH, HO, OH, HN

40. Propose a mechanism for the Pictet-Spengler reaction, an example of which is shown below. Note, a key intermediate is provided.

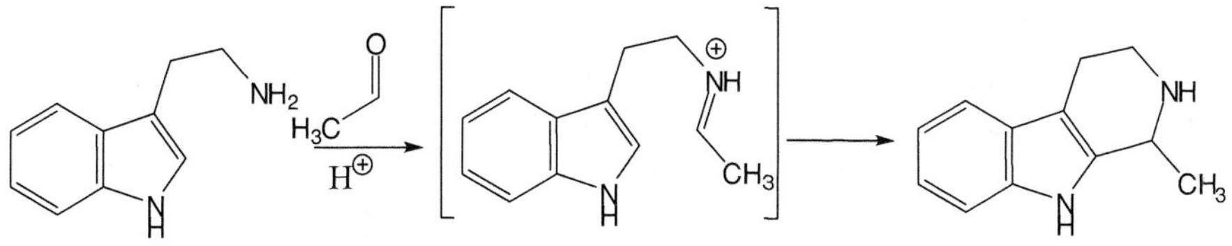

NH_2, N H, O, H_3C — $H^{\oplus}$ → [⊕ NH, CH_3, N H] → NH, N H, CH_3

41. Propose a mechanism for the following reaction. Note, the reaction does not take place without the presence of $AlCl_3$.

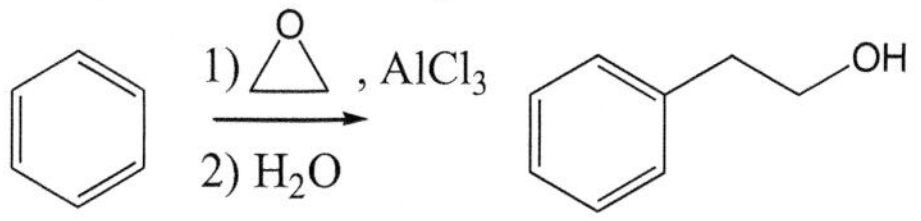

1) O (epoxide), $AlCl_3$ 2) H_2O → OH

42. Propose a mechanism for the following reaction.

O — HBr / acetic acid, Δ → $+ H_2O$

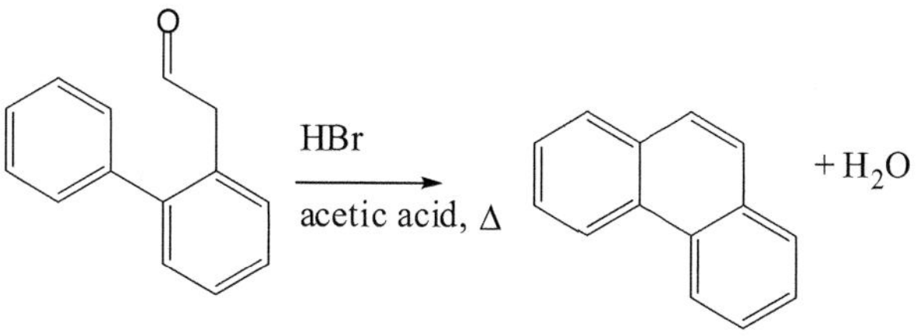

43. (a) Predict the product of the following set of reactions. (b) Draw the complete, detailed mechanism for the formation of the intermediate that is not shown.

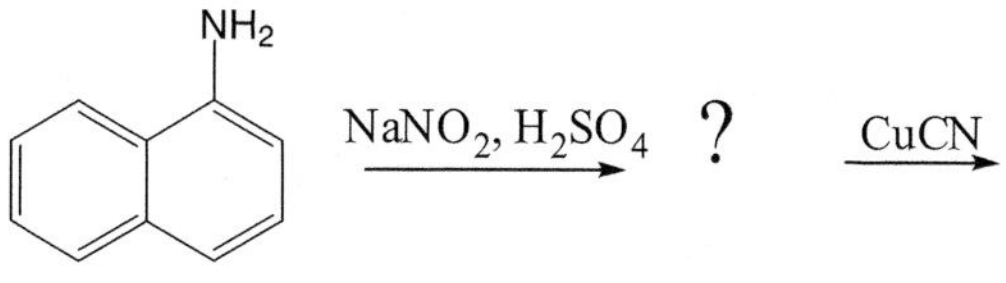

NH_2 — $NaNO_2$, H_2SO_4 → ? — CuCN →

44. The product of the following set of reactions exhibits 5 signals in its ^{1}H-NMR spectrum. Draw a complete, detailed mechanism for the formation of that product.

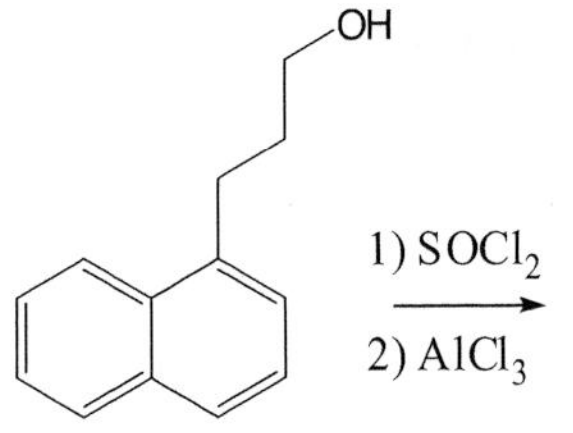

OH

1) $SOCl_2$

2) $AlCl_3$

45. Two isomeric products can be produced from the following reaction. (a) Draw the complete, detailed mechanism showing the formation of each of those products. (b) Which of those products will be formed in the greatest abundance?

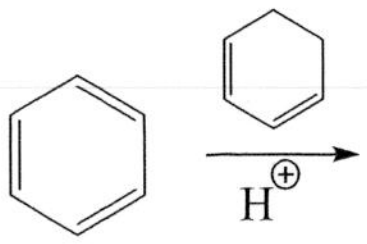

$H^{\oplus}$

46. When benzene is treated with dichloromethane in the presence of aluminum trichloride, a product is formed whose IR, ^{1}H-NMR, and ^{13}C-NMR spectra are shown below. Draw the product, and propose a mechanism for this reaction.

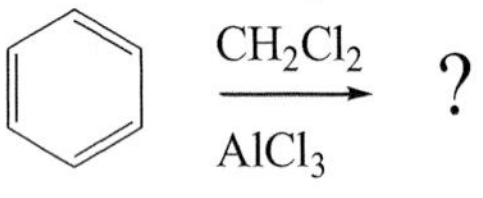

CH_2Cl_2

$AlCl_3$

?

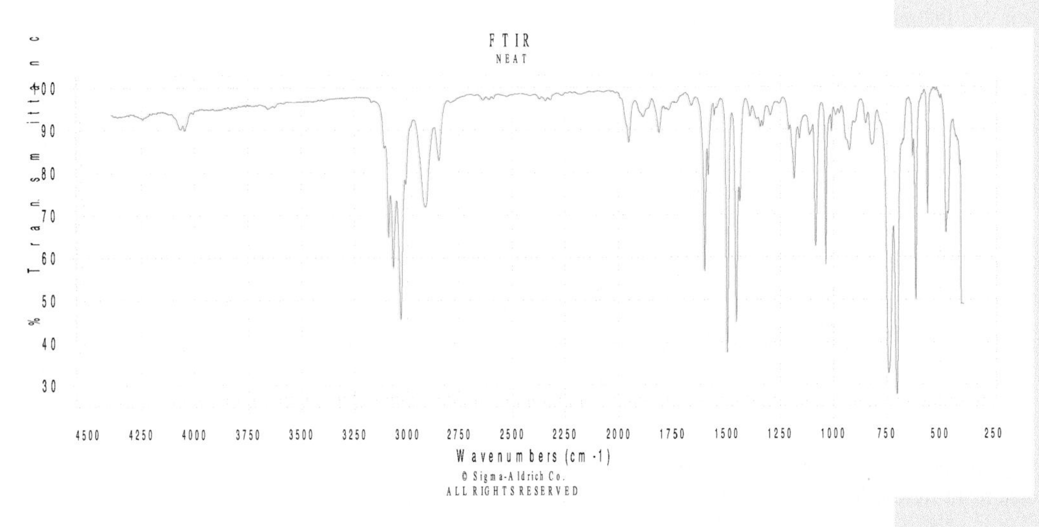

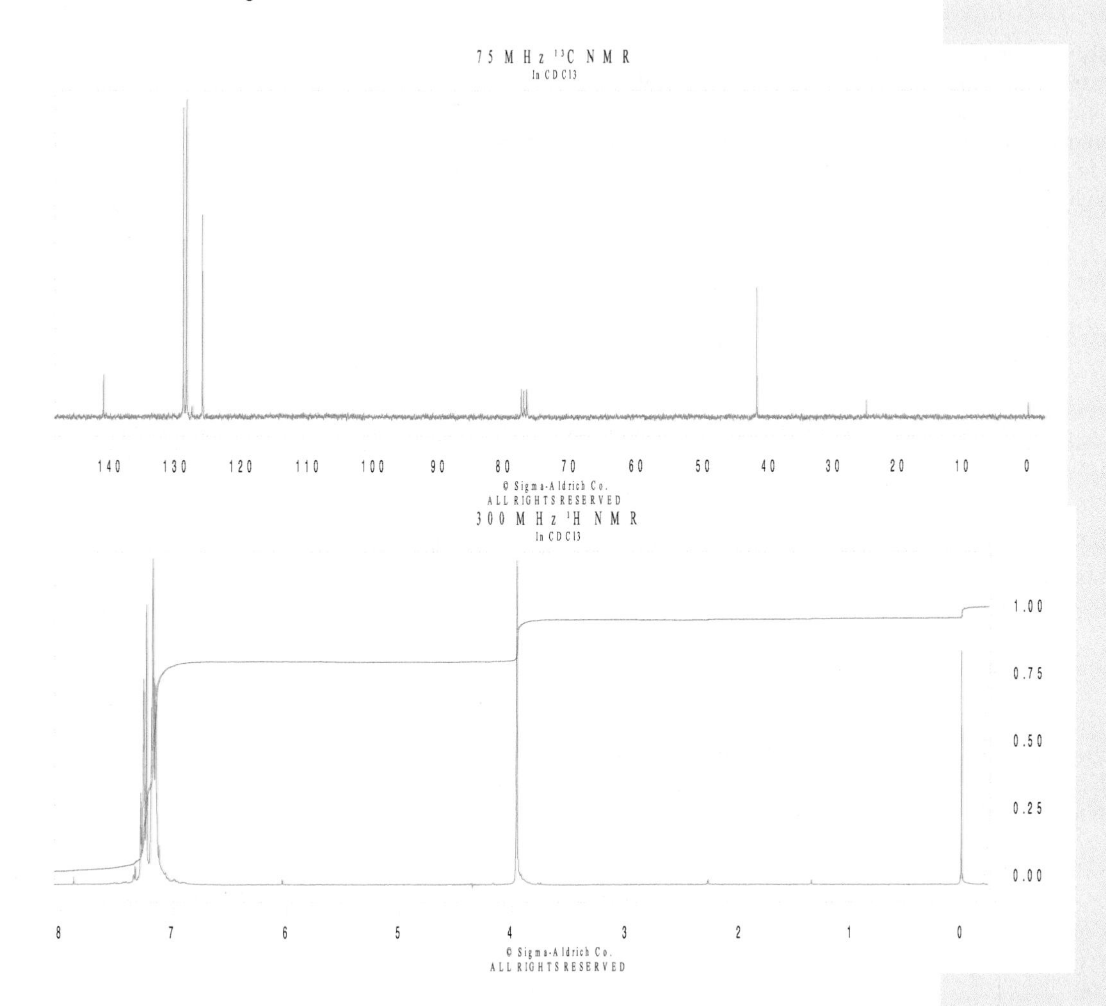

47. Halogenation using the mixed halogen ICl can feasibly lead to two different products, as shown below. Draw the complete, detailed mechanism for the formation of each product. Which do you think is the major product? Why?

I-Cl, Fe → (Cl-substituted benzene) + (I-substituted benzene)

48. Draw the complete, detailed mechanism for the following reaction. Will the product be chiral? Explain.

(benzene) + (Br-substituted alkane) → $AlCl_3$

49. Previously we mentioned that formylation of benzene (i.e., replacement of H by HC=O) cannot be carried out through a standard Friedel-Crafts acylation, because methanoyl chloride (formyl chloride) cannot be added directly. The **Gatterman-Koch synthesis** circumvents this problem by making methanoyl chloride *in situ*, using a gaseous mixture of carbon monoxide and hydrochloric acid at high pressures.

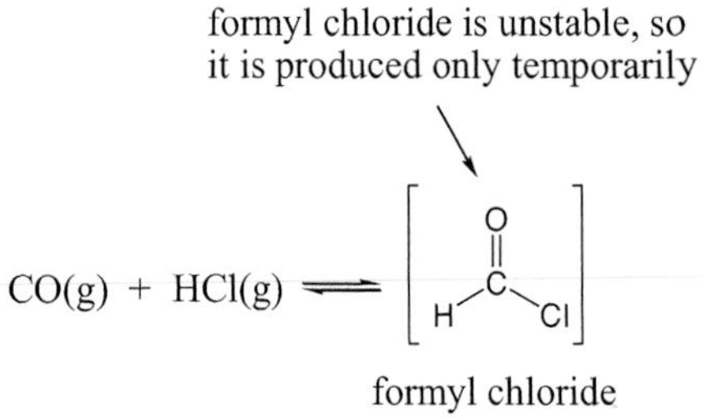

formyl chloride is unstable, so it is produced only temporarily

$$CO(g) + HCl(g) \rightleftharpoons [HC(=O)Cl]$$

formyl chloride

With this in mind, draw the detailed mechanism for the electrophilic aromatic substitution that takes place in the following reaction.

$$\text{benzene} + CO(g) + HCl(g) \xrightarrow{AlCl_3} ?$$

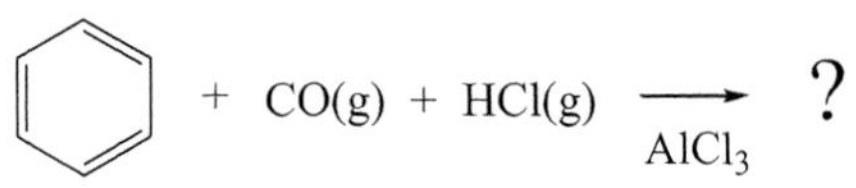

50. In the following reaction, electrophilic aromatic substitution take place via *ipso* attack. Notice that although there are two alkyl groups that can be replaced, substitution is observed only at the carbon bonded to the t-butyl group. Explain why.

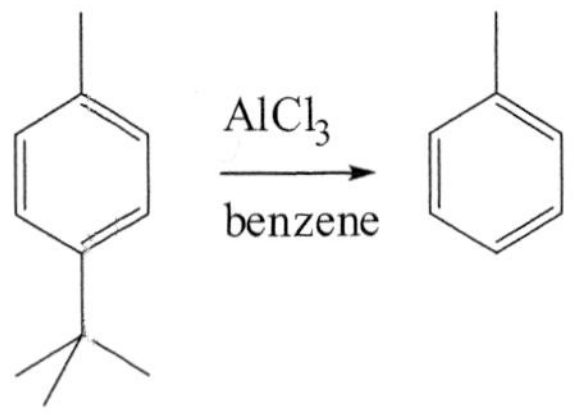

$$\text{4-}tert\text{-butyltoluene} \xrightarrow[\text{benzene}]{AlCl_3} \text{toluene}$$

51. The following reaction is an example of a *de-iodination* reaction. It takes place via an *ipso* attack. Without $AlCl_3$ present, no reaction occurs. Draw a complete, detailed mechanism for this reaction.

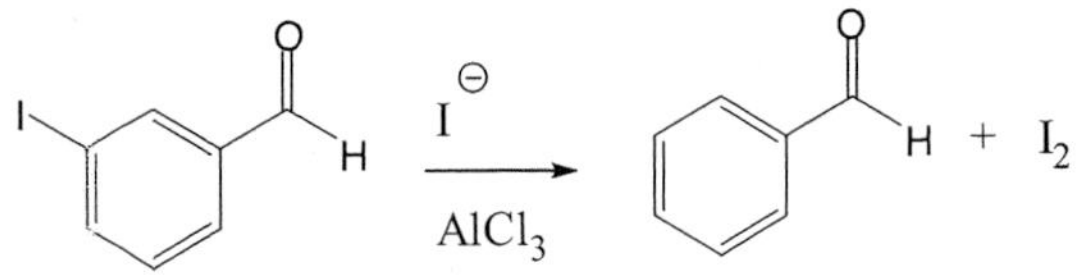

$$\text{3-iodobenzaldehyde} + I^{\ominus} \xrightarrow{AlCl_3} \text{benzaldehyde} + I_2$$

52. In the previous problem, an example of a *de-iodination* reaction is provided. Halogens other than iodine may be replaced on a benzene ring, but the reactions rates are slower; rates of substitution are observed to be: Ar-F < Ar-Cl < Ar-Br < Ar-I. Explain.

53. When benzene is treated with Br_2 in CCl_4, no reaction occurs. However, when anthracene is treated with Br_2 in CCl_4, addition of Br_2 occurs, as shown below. Explain why.

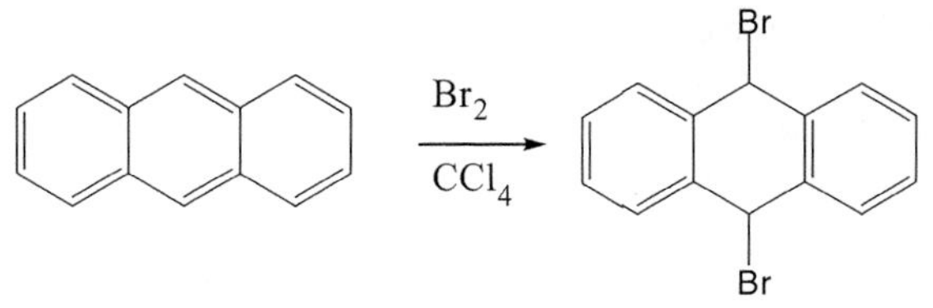

Br_2, CCl_4

Br

Br

54. Predict the product of the following reaction.

N

$H^{\oplus}$

?

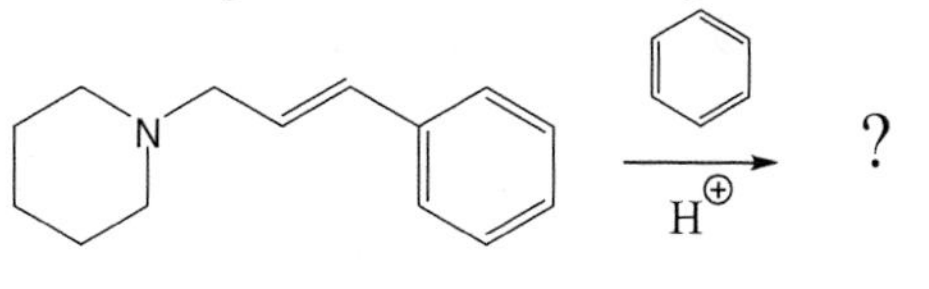

55. Draw the complete, detailed mechanism for the following reaction.

O

CH_3

N

$H^{\oplus}$

O

CH_3

N

H

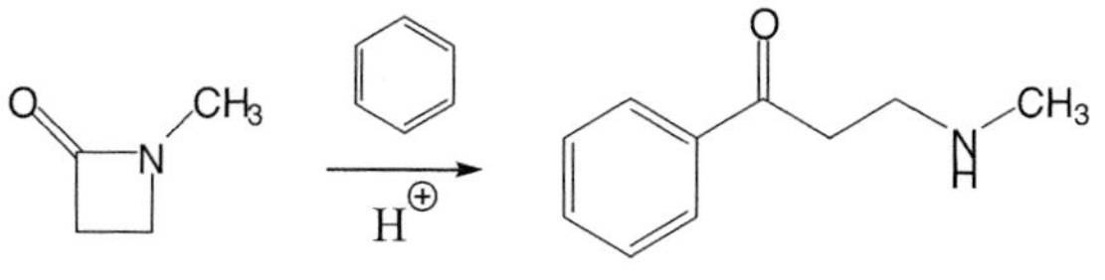

Chapter 23. Electrophilic Aromatic Substitution. 2: Substitution Involving Mono- and Disubstituted Benzene and Other Aromatic Rings

Introduction

In Chapter 22 we examined a variety of *electrophilic aromatic substitution* reactions, but did not consider the details surrounding the specific nature of the aromatic ring. Most of the focus was on substitution involving benzene (C_6H_6), which has no substituents. Electrophilic aromatic substitution on a **mono-substituted benzene** (C_6H_5-Sub), however, raises additional concerns.

One of those concerns is with *regiochemistry*. In benzene itself, all six hydrogen atoms are equivalent, so substitution of any one of them leads to precisely the same product. In contrast, as we saw in Section 22.8, a monosubstituted benzene possesses three chemically distinct hydrogens—the *ortho*, *meta*, and *para* hydrogens. Substitution therefore leads to three different possible products—*ortho*, *meta*, and *para* disubstituted benzenes (Equation 22-1)—depending upon which hydrogen is the one that is replaced. (*Notice the convention that is used to denote a generic disubstituted benzene without designating the specific isomer.*)

ortho meta para

Sub → ($E^{\oplus}$) Sub/E (ortho) + Sub/E (meta) + Sub/E (para) ⟺ Sub/E

a generic monosubstituted benzene

a generic disubstituted benzene

(23-1)

As we will see in this chapter, the substituent that is already on the benzene ring prior to substitution dictates the regiochemistry of the reaction. Some substituents are designated as *ortho/para* directors, because they lead to product mixtures consisting primarily of the *ortho-* and *para*-disubstituted products. Other substituents are designated as *meta* directors, because they promote the formation of the *meta*-disubstituted product.

A second concern with monosubstituted benzenes is the effect the substituent has on the *rate* of electrophilic aromatic substitution. Some substituents slow down the reaction rate and are therefore called *deactivating groups*. Other substituents cause the reaction rate to speed up, and are therefore called *activating groups*.

One of the main goals of this chapter is to provide a solid understanding of the factors that control both regiochemistry and kinetics of electrophilic aromatic substitution. Ultimately, you will be able to apply this knowledge toward designing efficient syntheses involving electrophilic aromatic substitution reactions.

CHAPTER OBJECTIVES

Upon completion of this chapter you should be able to…

- Identify a substituent as an *ortho/para-* or *meta*-directing group based on the electrophilic aromatic substitution product ratio when such a substituent is attached to a benzene ring.
- Explain why a substituent tends to be an *ortho/para*-director if the atom that attaches it to an aromatic ring has a lone pair of electrons.
- Explain why electron-donating groups tend to be *ortho/para*-directors, whereas electron-withdrawing groups tend to be *meta*-directors.
- Describe how steric effects tend to alter the regiochemistry of an electrophilic aromatic substitution reaction.
- Characterize an aromatic ring as being activated or deactivated, based on the rate of electrophilic aromatic substitution relative to benzene, and explain why *ortho/para*-directors tend to be activating, whereas *meta*-directors tend to be deactivating.
- Account for the effects that reaction conditions can have on a substituent's *ortho/meta/para*-directing capabilities, as well as its activating/deactivating capabilities.
- Predict the major product of electrophilic aromatic substitution on disubstituted benzene rings, as well as on aromatic rings other than benzene.
- Draw the mechanisms of nucleophilic aromatic substitution reactions, and recognize the conditions that favor such reactions.
- Devise effective syntheses that call for successive electrophilic aromatic substitution reactions.
- Incorporate protecting and blocking groups into a synthesis involving electrophilic aromatic substitution.

23.1. REGIOCHEMISTRY OF ELECTROPHILIC AROMATIC SUBSTITUTION: IDENTIFYING *ORTHO/PARA*- AND *META*-DIRECTORS

Phenol is a monosubstituted benzene, so when it undergoes nitration, the *ortho*, *meta*, and *para*-disubstituted products can be formed. As shown in Equation 23-2, however, the *ortho*- and *para*-disubstituted products dominate the product mixture. The hydroxyl (–OH) group is therefore designated as an ***ortho/para*-director.**

the *ortho* and *para* products dominate the product mixture, so OH is designated as an *ortho/para* director

phenol —HNO_3, AcOH, 60 °C→ *ortho* (NO_2 at ortho) + *meta* (NO_2 at meta) + *para* (NO_2 at para)

product ratio: *ortho* 50%, *meta* ~ 0%, *para* 50% (23-2)

By contrast, as shown in Equation 23-3, when nitrobenzene undergoes nitration, *meta*-dinitrobenzene is the major product. Thus, the NO_2 group initially attached to the ring is classified as a ***meta*-director**.

the *meta* product dominates the product mixture, so NO_2 is designated as a *meta* director

nitrobenzene —HNO_3, H_2SO_4, 30 min, 0 °C; 24 h, 25 °C→ *ortho* + *meta* + *para* dinitrobenzene

product ratio: *ortho* 7%, *meta* 91%, *para* 2% (23-3)

The results from these and other nitration reactions are summarized in Table 23-1. As we can see, the OH group and other *ortho/para*-directing substituents appear at the left of the Table, whereas the NO_2 group and other *meta*-directing substituents appear at the right. To help illustrate which type of director each substituent is, the sum of the relative percentages of the *ortho* and *para* products ("O+P") is also provided in the table.

Table 23-1: Product Distribution of Nitration of Various Monosubstituted Benzenes

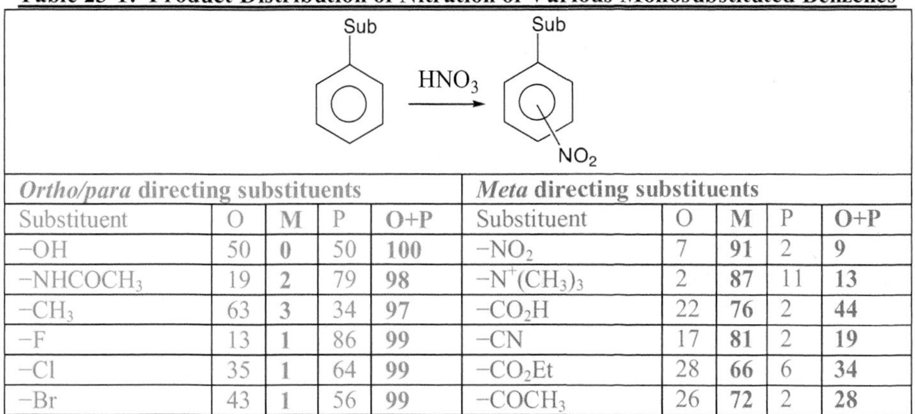

Ortho/para directing substituents					*Meta* directing substituents				
Substituent	O	M	P	O+P	Substituent	O	M	P	O+P
–OH	50	**0**	50	**100**	$-NO_2$	7	**91**	2	**9**
$-NHCOCH_3$	19	**2**	79	**98**	$-N^+(CH_3)_3$	2	**87**	11	**13**
$-CH_3$	63	**3**	34	**97**	$-CO_2H$	22	**76**	2	**44**
–F	13	**1**	86	**99**	–CN	17	**81**	2	**19**
–Cl	35	**1**	64	**99**	$-CO_2Et$	28	**66**	6	**34**
–Br	43	**1**	56	**99**	$-COCH_3$	26	**72**	2	**28**

Your Turn 23.1. The iodo (–I) and formyl (–CHO) groups are not listed in Table 23.1. The relative amounts of *ortho* and *meta* nitration products are given below for each substituent. (a) Supply the missing information pertaining to the relative amount of the *para* isomers that are produced, as well as the sum of the amounts of *ortho* and *para* products. (b) Based on that information, label each substituent as either an *ortho/para*-director or a *meta*-director.

Sub	O	M	P	O+P	Type of director
–I	45	**1**			
–CHO	19	**72**			

In the next few sections, we will examine why these substituents have the effects on regiochemistry that they do. We will look at three prototypical substituents in particular: the OH, CH_3, and NO_2 groups. What we learn from examining these groups can be extended to other similar groups as well.

Problem 23.1. Based on the information from Table 23.1, predict the major product(s) for each reaction below. Draw the complete, detailed mechanism that leads to the formation of each major product.

(a) OH; H_3C-CH_2-Cl, $AlCl_3$ → ?

(b) NO_2; Cl_2, $FeCl_3$ → ?

(c) CH_3; $H_3C-C(=O)-Cl$, $AlCl_3$ → ?

(d) $C(=O)CH_3$; Br_2, $FeBr_3$ → ?

23.2. NITRATION OF PHENOL: WHY IS A HYDROXYL GROUP AN *ORTHO/PARA*-DIRECTOR?

From Table 23-1, we can see that the OH group of phenol ($HO-C_6H_5$) directs essentially 100% of incoming electrophiles to the *ortho* and *para* positions, making it an *ortho/para*-director. To begin to understand why, recall from Section 22.1 that electrophilic aromatic substitution reactions run under *kinetic control*. Therefore,

> The relative amounts of *ortho*, *meta*, and *para*-disubstituted products that are produced in an electrophilic aromatic substitution reaction are proportional to the rates at which they are produced.

For example, given that phenol leads to a distribution of products that is 50% *ortho*, ~0% *meta*, and 50% *para*, we know that the rate of formation of the *ortho* product is about the same as that of the *para* product, whereas the formation of the *meta* product is orders of magnitude slower.

Recall also that of the two steps that formally comprise electrophilic aromatic substitution, the first step is the *rate-determining step* (Section 22.1). That step is the one that is substantially endothermic, producing the unstable arenium ion intermediate (see again Figure 22-1). Therefore, we can say that for the reaction in Equation 23-2, the rates of formation of the *ortho* and *para* arenium ions are about the same, and the formation of the *meta* arenium ion is orders of magnitude lower. Figure 23-1 shows how these ideas translate into energy diagrams for the production of the *ortho* and *meta* intermediates. Namely, the energy barrier to forming the *ortho* arenium ion is smaller than the barrier to forming the *meta* one.

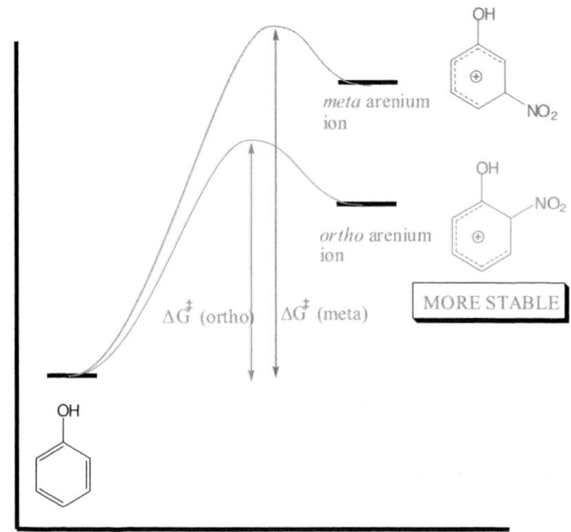

Figure 23-1. Energy Diagrams for the Rate-Determining Step in the Nitration of Phenol
Nitration at the *ortho* position is represented by the red curve, and nitration at the *meta* position is represented by the blue curve. Because the ortho product is produced in greater abundance than the meta product, we can say that $\Delta G^{\ddagger}$ leading to the *ortho* intermediate is smaller. The *Hammond postulate* thus allows us to say that the *ortho* arenium ion is more stable than the *meta* arenium ion.

Because the *ortho* and *meta* intermediates are produced by the same elementary step, we can invoke the *Hammond postulate* to say that the relative sizes of the energy barriers are a result of the *ortho* arenium ion being more stable than the *meta* one. Thus, we arrive at an important tool to help us predict the outcome of an electrophilic aromatic substitution.

> In general, the major product of electrophilic aromatic substitution is the one that is produced from the most stable arenium ion intermediate.

Problem 23.2. Consider the following arenium ion intermediates that are formed in the nitration of fluorobenzene. Using Table 23-1, determine which one is formed the fastest? Which is formed the slowest? Which is the most stable? The least stable?

The relative stabilities of the isomeric arenium ion intermediates are governed in large part by differences in charge stability. We can see how this applies to the *ortho* and *meta* intermediates in the nitration of phenol, whose resonance structures are shown in Equations 23-4 and 23-5.

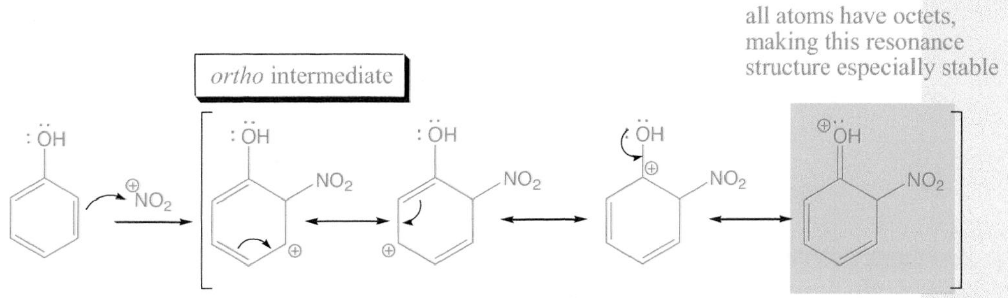

all atoms have octets, making this resonance structure especially stable

ortho intermediate

(23-4)

the lone pairs on oxygen cannot participate in resonance

meta intermediate

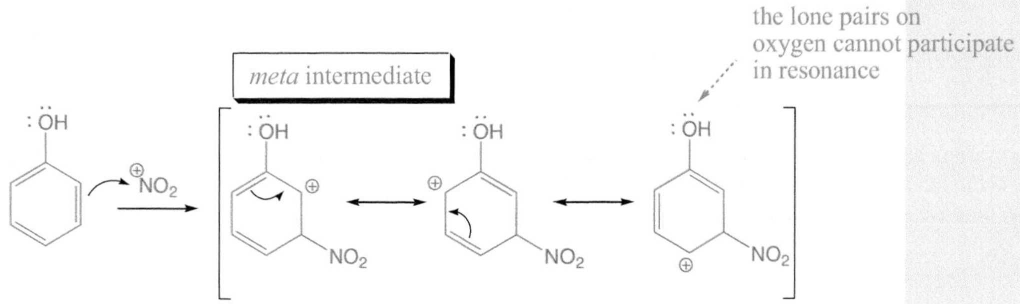

(23-5)

In particular, the positive charge that develops is better stabilized in the *ortho* intermediate than it is in the *meta* intermediate, for two reasons. First, the *ortho* intermediate has four resonance structures, serving to distribute the positive charge over four different atoms; the *meta* intermediate has only three. As indicated above, the additional resonance structure of the *ortho* intermediate arises from the fact that a lone pair of electrons from the OH oxygen can participate in resonance. This is not true in the *meta* intermediate. Second, the additional resonance structure that the *ortho* arenium ion has (highlighted in green) is substantially more stable than the other three. It is the only resonance structure in which *all atoms have their octet*. Therefore, the additional stability provided by that single resonance structure is extremely important.

Your Turn 23.2. In Equations 23-4 and 23-5, circle all atoms that do *not* have an octet.

Similar reasoning allows us to rationalize why nitration of phenol at the *para* position is also much faster than at the *meta* position, thereby making the OH group an *ortho/para*-director (see the Solved Problem below). The *para* arenium ion intermediate has four resonance structures, including one in which the positive charge is on the oxygen atom. As with the *ortho* arenium ion, all atoms in that resonance structure have their octet.

Solved Problem 23.1. (a) Draw a diagram similar to Figure 23-1 that illustrates the formation of the *para* and *meta* intermediates during the nitration of phenol. (b) Which of those two arenium ions is more stable and why?

Think. Which of the isomeric products—*meta* or *para*—is formed faster? What does that say about the stability of the respective intermediates? What role is played by resonance delocalization of the charge?

Solve. From Table 23-1, we can see that the *para* arenium ion is formed faster than the *meta*, meaning that the *para* intermediate is more stable. This gives rise to the figure below.

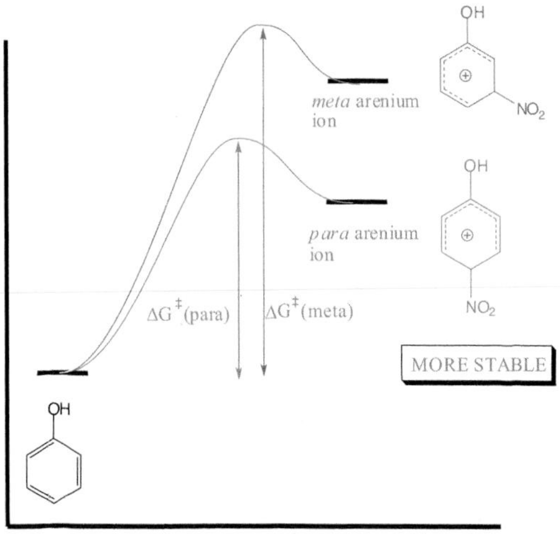

meta arenium ion

para arenium ion

$\Delta G^{\ddagger}$(para) $\Delta G^{\ddagger}$(meta)

MORE STABLE

Whereas the *meta* intermediate has only three resonance structures, the *para* intermediate has four, similar to the *ortho* intermediate. Furthermore, the one highlighted in green is the most important one, because all of its atoms have their octets.

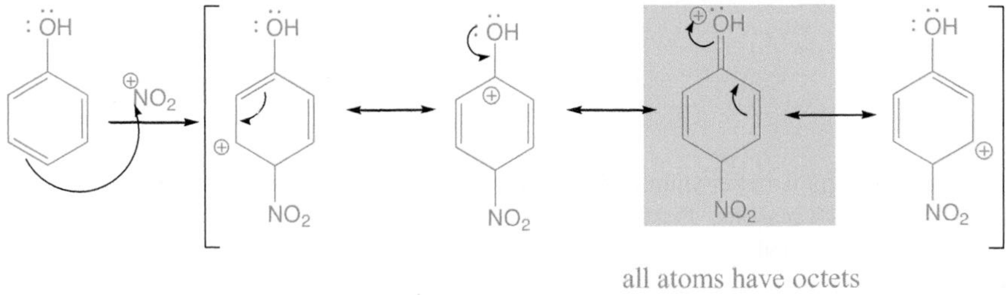

all atoms have octets

Problem 23.3. Draw a plot similar to Figure 23-1 that illustrates the formation of the *ortho* and *meta* intermediates during the nitration of fluorobenzene. Using arguments of resonance, explain the relative stabilities of the two isomeric intermediates.

As we look carefully at Table 23-1, we can begin to see a useful trend:

Substituents that are bonded to the benzene ring by an atom possessing a lone pair of electrons tend to be *ortho/para*-directors.

In addition to the OH group, this is also true for the $NHCOCH_3$, F, Cl, and Br groups. The reason is that the lone pair of electrons, as we saw in the case of phenol, is vital in providing the fourth—and most important—resonance structure in the arenium ion intermediate upon electrophilic attack at either the *ortho* or *para* positions.

Problem 23.4. For each reaction below, draw the mechanism that leads to the *ortho-*, *meta-*, and *para*-disubstituted products, and identify the major products.

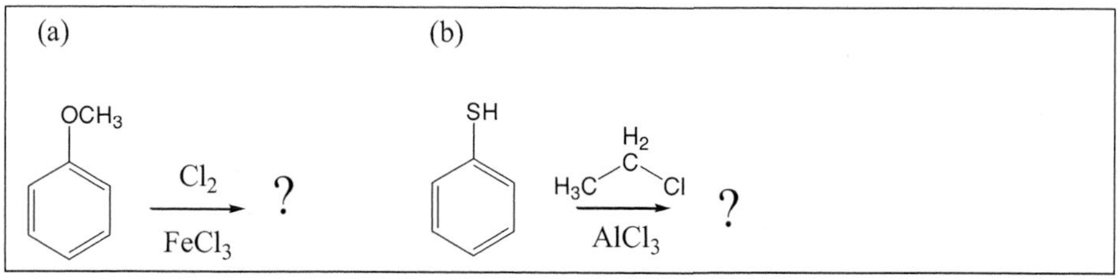

(a) OCH_3 — Cl_2 / $FeCl_3$ → ?

(b) SH — $H_3C{-}CH_2{-}Cl$ / $AlCl_3$ → ?

23.3. NITRATION OF TOLUENE: WHY IS CH_3 AN *ORTHO/PARA*-DIRECTOR?

Table 23-1 indicates that nitration of toluene also yields a product mixture that is predominantly the *ortho* and *para* disubstituted products. The CH_3 group is thus an *ortho/para*-director. However, unlike the situation with phenol, the CH_3 group is bonded to the ring by an atom that does *not* possess a lone pair of electrons—i.e., by an uncharged carbon atom. Therefore, the reason cannot be due to the presence of an additional resonance structure in the arenium ion intermediate. What can it be?

Because the dominant overall products are the *ortho* and *para* isomers, we know that the *ortho* and *para* arenium ion intermediates must be more stable than the *meta* arenium ion. By drawing all of the resonance structures, as is done for the *ortho* and *meta* intermediates in Equations 23-6 and 23-7, we can see why.

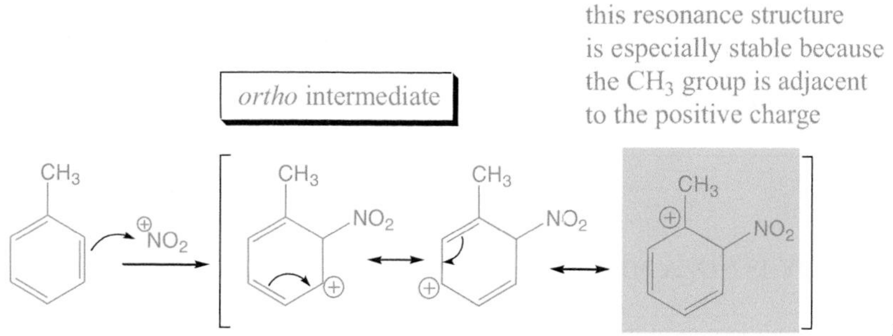

ortho intermediate

this resonance structure is especially stable because the CH_3 group is adjacent to the positive charge

(23-6)

meta intermediate

none of the resonance structures has the CH_3 group adjacent to the positive charge

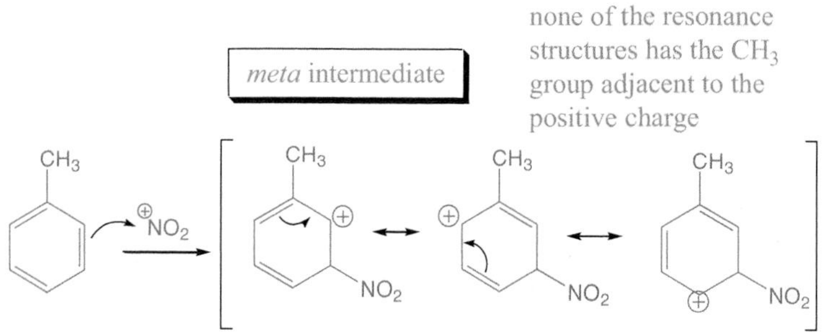

(23-7)

There are three resonance structures in each of the isomeric intermediates. If the NO_2^+ electrophile adds *ortho* to the methyl group (Equation 23-6), then two of the resonance structures have the positive charge on a secondary carbon, and the third (highlighted in green) has the positive charge on a tertiary one. The latter resonance structure is the most stable of the three, because, as we learned in Chapter 6, a tertiary carbocation is more stable than a secondary carbocation. If, instead, the NO_2^+ electrophile adds *meta* to the methyl group (Equation 23-7), then all three of the intermediate's resonance structures have the formal positive charge on a secondary carbon. Without contribution from a resonance structure with a tertiary carbocation, the *meta* arenium ion is not as stable as the *ortho* one.

Similar to what we saw with the nitration of phenol, the arguments that hold for the *ortho* intermediate also hold for the *para* intermediate (see Your Turn 23.3). Thus, in the nitration of toluene, the *para* intermediate is more stable than the *meta* intermediate.

Your Turn 23.3. Shown below are the resonance structures for the arenium ion intermediate produced during the nitration of toluene. Circle and label the one that is the most stable.

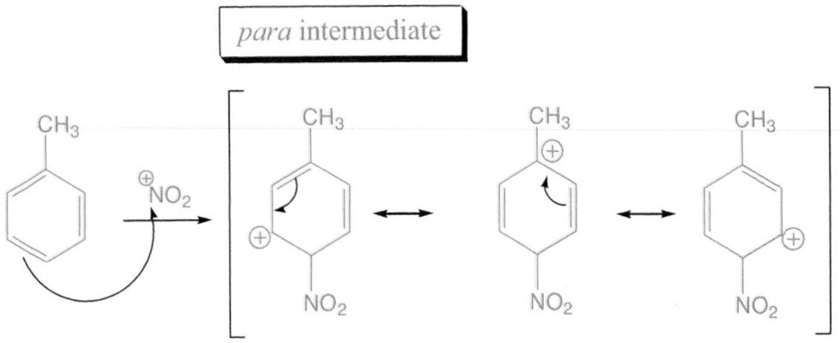

para intermediate

CH_3 $\overset{\oplus}{N}O_2$ → [CH_3 / NO_2 ↔ CH_3 / NO_2 ↔ CH_3 / NO_2]

Even though the above discussion uses the CH_3 group as a specific example, all alkyl groups stabilize carbocations in the same way. Therefore,

All alkyl groups are *ortho/para*-directors.

Problem 23.5. Draw all possible products that can be produced in the nitration of ethylbenzene. Which are the major products? Explain.

23.4. NITRATION OF NITROBENZENE: WHY IS NO_2 A *META*-DIRECTOR?

According to Table 23-1, when nitrobenzene undergoes nitration, the major product is *meta*-dinitrobenzene. Therefore, the NO_2 group initially attached to the benzene ring is a *meta*-director. Why should this be so?

To answer this question, we once again turn toward examining the stabilities of the various arenium ion intermediates. This is done for the *ortho* and *meta* intermediates in Equations 23-8 and 23-9, respectively.

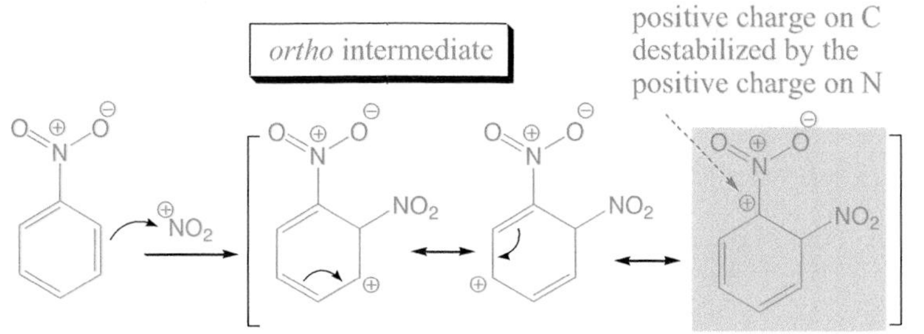

ortho intermediate

positive charge on C destabilized by the positive charge on N

(23-8)

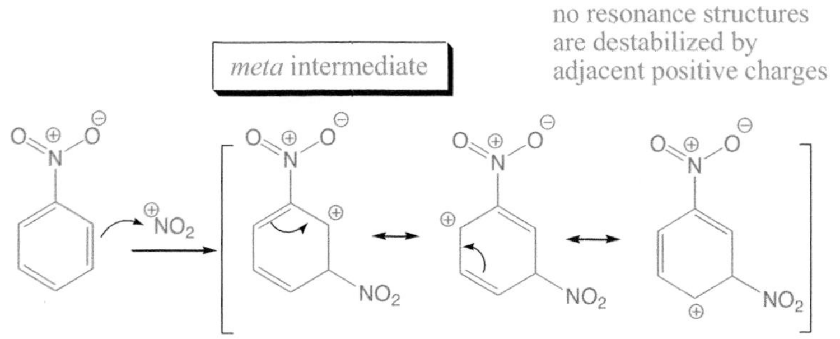

meta intermediate

no resonance structures are destabilized by adjacent positive charges

(23-9)

Although each arenium ion has three resonance structures, the *ortho* intermediate is significantly less stable than the *meta* intermediate. This is because the *ortho* intermediate has a resonance structure (highlighted in red) in which two positive charges are adjacent to each other, making that resonance structure much less stable than the other two. By contrast, none of the three resonance structures of the *meta* intermediate exhibits adjacent like charges. Because of the decreased stability in the *ortho* intermediate, formation of the *ortho* disubstituted product is *slower* than the formation of the *meta* disubstituted product.

Your Turn 23.4. Nitration of nitrobenzene at the *para* carbon proceeds through an arenium ion intermediate that has three resonance structures, as shown below. Circle and label the least stable resonance structure.

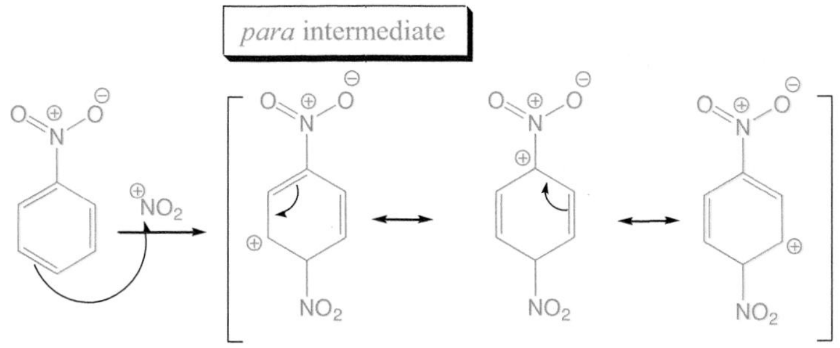

para intermediate

Solved Problem 23.2. The trifluoromethyl group (CF_3) is not listed in Table 23-1. Predict whether this would be an *ortho/para*-director or a *meta*-director.

Think. Which of the arenium ions exhibit resonance structures in which the positive charge on the ring is directly adjacent to the CF_3 substituent? What effect does the CF_3 group have on an adjacent positive charge—stabilizing or destabilizing?

Solve. The *ortho* and *meta* arenium ions are shown below with all of their resonance structures.

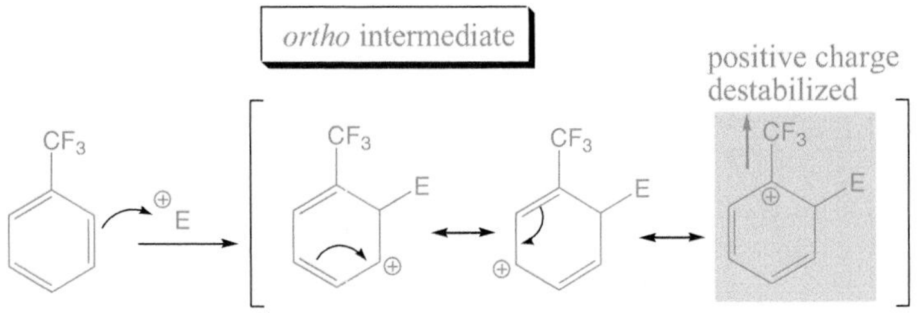

ortho intermediate

positive charge destabilized

CF_3 E CF_3 E CF_3 E CF_3 E

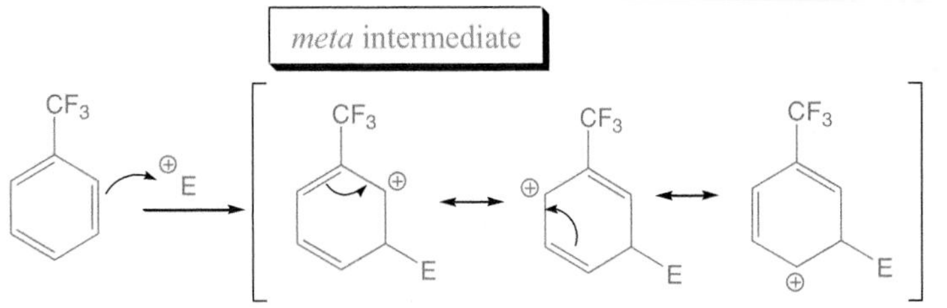

meta intermediate

CF_3 E CF_3 E CF_3 E CF_3 E

Notice that the *ortho* isomer has a resonance structure in which the positive charge is adjacent to the CF_3 group. That resonance structure is highlighted. Because CF_3 is electron withdrawing, it destabilizes the adjacent positive charge. Overall, then, the *ortho* intermediate is less stable than the *meta* intermediate. Analysis of the *para* intermediate in the same way shows that the *para* intermediate is also less stable than the *meta* intermediate. Hence the CF_3 group is a *meta*-director.

Problem 23.6. Verify the statement in the above Solved Problem that the *para* intermediate is less stable than the *meta* intermediate. Begin by drawing all resonance structures of the *para* intermediate, and note the relative stability of each structure.

23.5. STERIC EFFECTS ON REGIOCHEMISTRY

Thus far we have examined the impacts that resonance and inductive effects in an arenium ion intermediate have on the outcome of electrophilic aromatic substitution reactions. However, *steric effects* can also play a significant role. We can see this clearly from Table 23-2, which lists the relative percentages of the *ortho*, *meta*, and *para* isomers produced upon nitration of various alkylbenzenes.

Table 23-2: Steric Effects in the Nitration of Alkylbenzenes

R-benzene $\xrightarrow[H_2SO_4]{HNO_3}$ R-benzene with NO_2

Alkyl group	increasing steric bulk / increasing % para ↓	% Ortho	% Meta	% Para
—CH_3		63	3	34
—CH_2CH_3		45	7	49
—$CH(CH_3)_2$		30	8	62
—$C(CH_3)_3$		16	11	73

All of the alkyl groups shown are *ortho/para*-directors, meaning that the *meta* product is least favored in each case. However, the specific identity of the alkyl group can have a dramatic effect on the relative amounts of the *ortho* and *para* products. In particular,

> With increasing bulkiness of the alkyl group, the *para* product is increasingly favored over the *ortho* product.

As shown below, that bulkiness introduces steric hindrance upon the addition of the electrophile to the *ortho* carbon. By contrast, the electrophile is not sterically hindered when it attacks the *para* carbon.

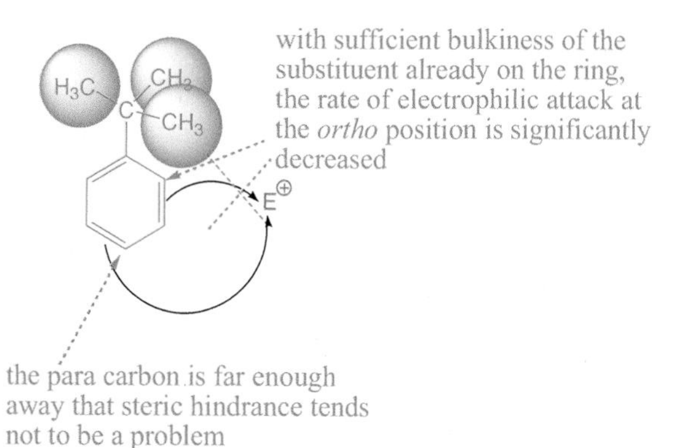

H_3C
CH_3
C
CH_3
with sufficient bulkiness of the substituent already on the ring, the rate of electrophilic attack at the *ortho* position is significantly decreased
$E^{\oplus}$
the para carbon is far enough away that steric hindrance tends not to be a problem

Problem 23.7. Draw all possible substitution products from the following reaction. Which isomer will be formed in least abundance? Do you think the relative amount of the *para* product will be greater or less than that produced upon nitration of *t*-butylbenzene? Explain.

$C_6H_5CH_2C(CH_3)_3 \xrightarrow[H_2SO_4]{HNO_3}$?

The size of the attacking electrophile (E^+) can also play a role in the regiochemistry of electrophilic aromatic substitution, as illustrated by the halogenation of bromobenzene. Chlorination of bromobenzene leads to a product mixture that is 42% *ortho* and 53% *para* (Equation 23-10). Bromination, on the other hand, leads to a distribution that is 13% *ortho* and 85% *para* (Equation 23-11). This is attributed to bromine being a much bulkier electrophile, so steric repulsion is magnified when it attacks at the *ortho* position.

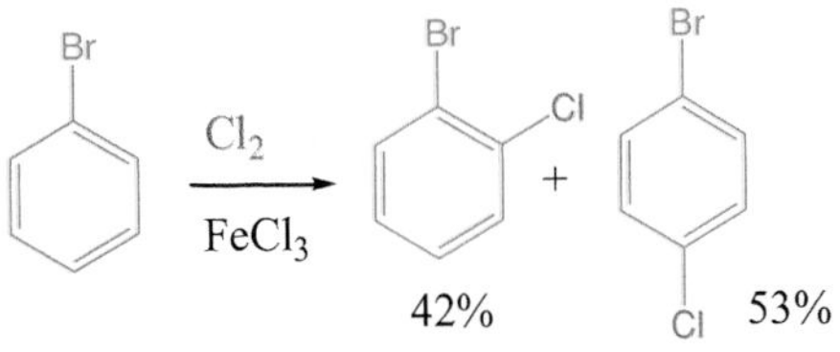

Br, Cl_2, $FeCl_3$, Br, Cl, +, Br, 42%, Cl 53%

(23-10)

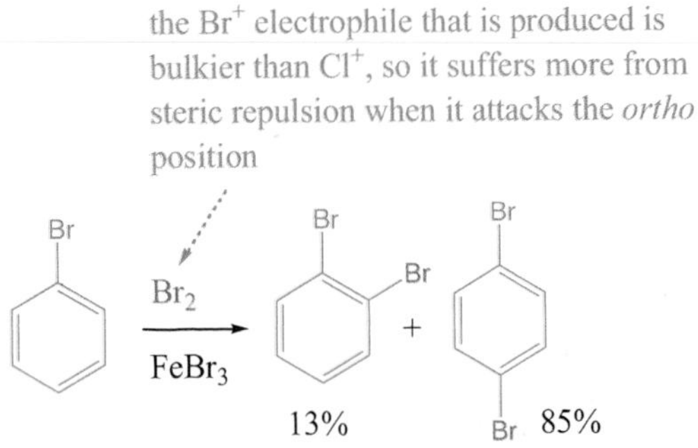

the Br^+ electrophile that is produced is bulkier than Cl^+, so it suffers more from steric repulsion when it attacks the *ortho* position

Br, Br_2, $FeBr_3$, Br, Br, +, Br, 13%, Br 85%

(23-11)

Problem 23.8. Which of the following do you think will produce the *para* product in the greater amount? Explain.

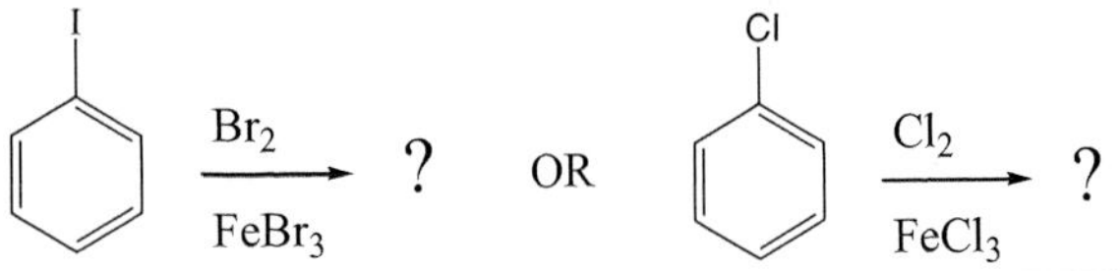

I, Br_2, $FeBr_3$, ? OR Cl, Cl_2, $FeCl_3$, ?

23.6. ACTIVATION AND DEACTIVATION OF BENZENE TOWARD ELECTROPHILIC AROMATIC SUBSTITUTION

The discussion to this point in the chapter has focused on how a substituent affects the rates of formation of the *ortho*, *meta*, and *para* products, relative to one another, for a single electrophilic aromatic substitution reaction. Those relative rates correspond to the relative abundance of the three isomers in the product mixture, consistent with the fact that electrophilic aromatic substitution generally takes place under kinetic control.

We have yet to discuss how substituents affect the *overall* rate of electrophilic aromatic substitution reaction—that is, the rate of disappearance of the aromatic reactant. Let's begin by examining Table 23-3, which contains the relative overall rates of nitration for a variety of monosubstituted benzenes.

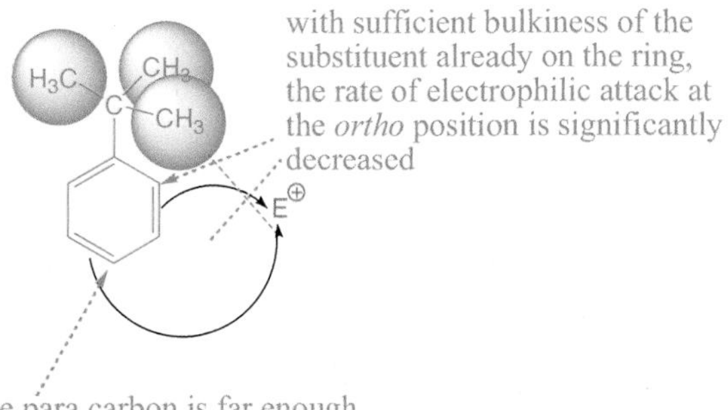

Table 23-3: Relative Rates of Nitration of Monosubstituted Benzenes

Sub-benzene $\xrightarrow[H_2SO_4]{HNO_3}$ Sub-nitrobenzene (NO_2)

Substituent	Relative Rate	Type of group
$-NH_2$	N/A[a]	Strongly activating
$-OH$	1,000	Strongly activating
$-CH_3$	25	Weakly activating
$-H$ (benzene)	1 (reference)	–
$-I$	0.18	Weakly deactivating
$-Cl$	0.033	Weakly deactivating
$-CO_2Et$	0.0037	Moderately deactivating
$-NO_2$	6×10^{-8}	Strongly deactivating
$-N^+(CH_3)_3$	1.2×10^{-8}	Strongly deactivating

[a]Aromatic amines are susceptible to oxidation under nitration conditions. The NH_2 group is determined to be a strongly activating group using other electrophilic aromatic substitution reactions.

As we can see, phenol ($HO{-}C_6H_5$) undergoes nitration about 1000 times faster than benzene itself. Consequently, the OH group is classified as an **activating group**—we say that the group *activates the benzene ring* toward electrophilic aromatic substitution. By contrast, the nitro (NO_2) group is classified as a **deactivating group**, because nitrobenzene ($O_2N{-}C_6H_5$) undergoes nitration over 10 million times *slower* than does benzene itself. In other words, relative to H, the NO_2 group *deactivates the benzene ring* toward electrophilic aromatic substitution.

Why is the OH group so strongly activating? As we saw previously (see Figure 23-1), when the electrophile adds to the *ortho* or *para* position on phenol's ring, a lone pair of electrons from OH's oxygen atom participates in resonance in the arenium ion intermediate. This lowers the energy barrier leading to the formation of the arenium ion, as shown in Figure 23-2, and hence increases the arenium ion's rate of formation.

Problem 23.9. Using Table 23-3, estimate the relative rate of nitration of bromobenzene under the same conditions as the other entries. How should it be classified with regard to its activating/deactivating ability?

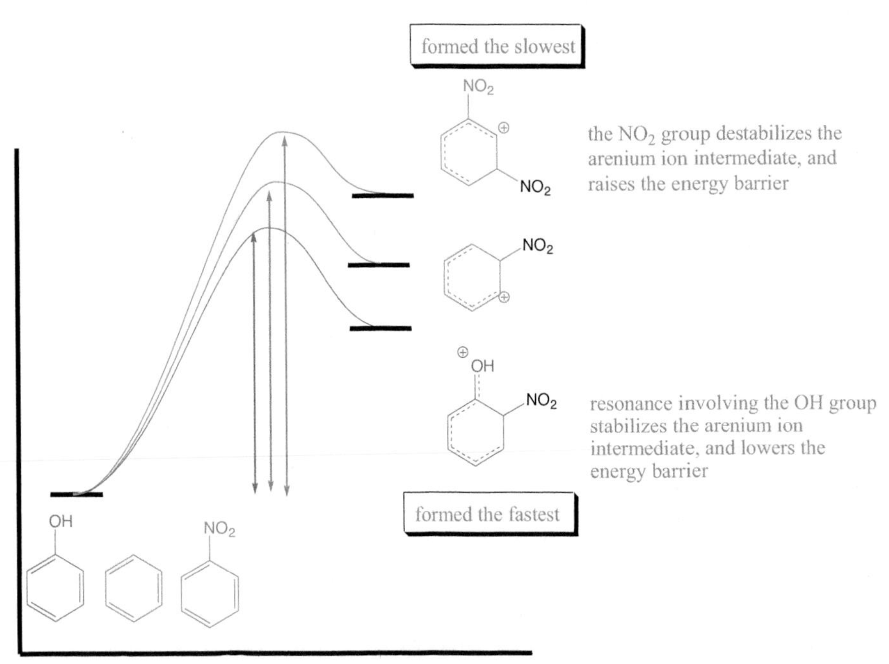

Figure 23-2. Activation and Deactivation of a Benzene Ring
Free energy diagram for the addition of NO_2^+ to benzene (green curve), phenol (blue curve), and nitrobenzene (red curve). The OH group in phenol stabilizes the arenium ion intermediate through the involvement of its oxygen atom's lone pair of electrons in resonance. Hence the OH group increases the rate of formation of the arenium ion intermediate, making it an *activating group*. A nitro group, on the other hand, destabilizes the arenium ion intermediate. Hence the nitro group slows down the rate of formation of the arenium ion, making it a *deactivating group*.

Conversely, the NO_2 group of nitrobenzene destabilizes the arenium ion intermediate that is formed. This increases the energy barrier to the formation of the arenium ion (Figure 23-2), which slows down the overall reaction rate. Thus, the NO_2 group is designated a *deactivating group*.

Solved Problem 23.3. Explain why toluene undergoes electrophilic aromatic substitution faster than benzene does, thereby making CH_3 an *activating group*.

Think. Are toluene's arenium ion intermediates more stable or less stable than that of benzene? How does that affect the energy barriers for the formation of toluene's arenium ions and hence the rates?

Solve. The CH_3 group is inductively electron donating and hence stabilizes the arenium ion intermediate. This lowers the activation energy for formation of the intermediates, which increases the rate of their formation. Hence a CH_3 group increases the overall substitution rates.

arenium ion
inductively stabilized

CH_3

E

Problem 23.10. Determine whether the benzene ring in trifluoromethylbenzene (C_6H_5-CF_3) is activated or deactivated.

Table 23-4 organizes substituents according to their *ortho/para-* or *meta-*directing ability as well as their activating/deactivating ability. Examining the characteristics of the various groups in this way, we can see a very clear trend.

- Activating groups are in general *ortho/para-*directors.
- Deactivating groups are in general *meta-*directors.

This is because both the regiochemistry and the extent of activation of the benzene ring derive from essentially the same phenomena. Substituents that are electron-donating, either via resonance or inductive effects, stabilize the arenium ion intermediate and increase the overall reaction rate. Thus, they are activating. Moreover, these groups stabilize the *ortho* and *para* intermediates better than they do the *meta* intermediate, and are therefore *ortho/para-*directors. By the same token, substituents that destabilize the arenium ion intermediate are deactivating groups. These groups destabilize the *ortho* and *para* intermediates more than they do the *meta*, making them *meta-*directors.

One exception can be seen in Table 23-4, involving halogen atoms.

Halogen substituents are deactivating groups, but are *ortho/para-*directors.

They are *ortho/para-*directors because, like the OH group, a halogen atom possesses a lone pair of electrons. Consequently, a halogen atom substituent stabilizes the arenium ion intermediate via resonance, but only when an electrophile attacks at either the *ortho* or *para* position. Conversely, halogens are deactivators because they are inductively electron-withdrawing groups.

Table 23-4: Comparison of the Activating/Deactivating and the *Ortho/Meta/Para*-Directing Nature of Substituents

Substituent	Activating/deactivating nature	Ortho/para or meta directing
$-N^{\oplus}(=O)O^{\ominus}$	Strongly deactivating	*Meta*-directing
$-N^{\oplus}H_3$ $-N^{\oplus}R_3$	Strongly deactivating	*Meta*-directing
$-C(=O)H$ $-C(=O)R$	Strongly deactivating	*Meta*-directing
$-C(=O)OH$ $-C(=O)OR$	Strongly deactivating	*Meta*-directing
$-C{\equiv}N$	Strongly deactivating	*Meta*-directing
$-S(=O)_2OH$	Strongly deactivating	*Meta*-directing
$-Cl$ $-Br$ $-I$	Weakly deactivating	*Ortho/para*-directing
$-H$ (benzene)	–	–
$-R$	Weakly activating	*Ortho/para*-directing
$-OC(=O)H$ $-OC(=O)R$	Moderately activating	*Ortho/para*-directing
$-NHC(=O)H$ $-NHC(=O)R$	Moderately activating	*Ortho/para*-directing
$-OH$ $-OR$	Strongly activating	*Ortho/para*-directing
$-NH_2$ $-NR_2$	Strongly activating	*Ortho/para*-directing
$-O^{\ominus}$	Strongly activating	*Ortho/para*-directing

We can gain more insight into the activating/deactivating character of a substituent by examining the effect the substituent has on the electron density of the benzene ring. As examples, the electrostatic potential maps of benzene, aniline, and nitrobenzene are shown in Figure 23-3.

Aniline, which possesses an NH_2 activating group, has an aromatic ring whose electron density is *greater* than that of benzene itself (indicated by the greater amount of red). As indicated, this is due to the NH_2 group's electron donation to the ring via resonance. With the increased electron density, aniline's aromatic ring is more electron-rich than benzene itself and hence experiences greater affinity for an incoming electrophile (E^+). This serves to enhance the rate of electrophilic attack, thus increasing the overall rate of substitution.

Conversely, the aromatic ring of nitrobenzene is less electron-rich (more blue/green) than benzene itself. This is due to the electron withdrawing nature of the NO_2 group. As a result, nitrobenzene's aromatic ring attracts an incoming electrophile less strongly than does benzene, causing nitrobenzene to react slower.

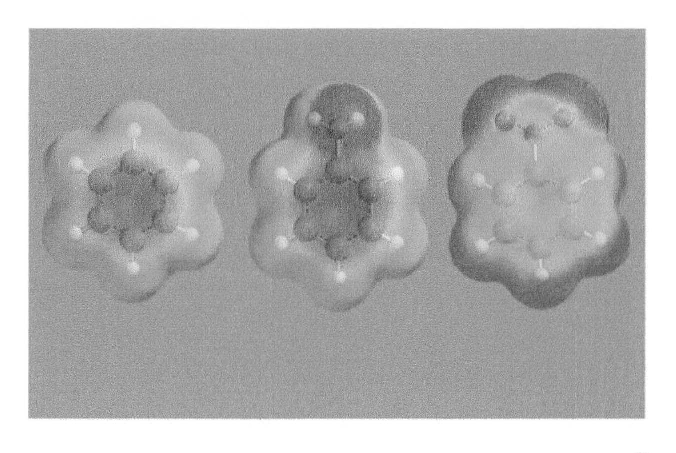

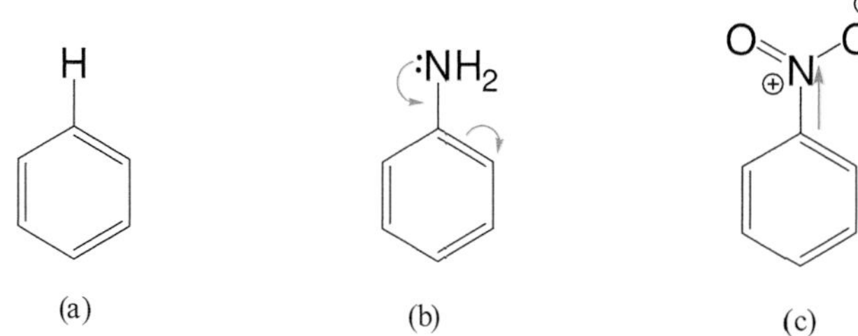

Figure 23-3. Effect of Activating and Deactivating Groups on Electron Density in the Benzene Ring
Electron density maps of (a) benzene, (b) aniline, and (c) nitrobenzene. The electron donating ability of NH_2 via resonance increases the electron density of the aromatic ring (more red) and hence activates the ring toward electrophilic aromatic substitution. Conversely, the electron withdrawing ability of the NO_2 group decreases electron density in the ring (more blue/green) and hence deactivates the ring toward electrophilic aromatic substitution.

Your Turn 23.5. The electrostatic potential maps of benzene and of a monosubstituted benzene are shown below. Determine whether the benzene ring of the latter is activated or deactivated.

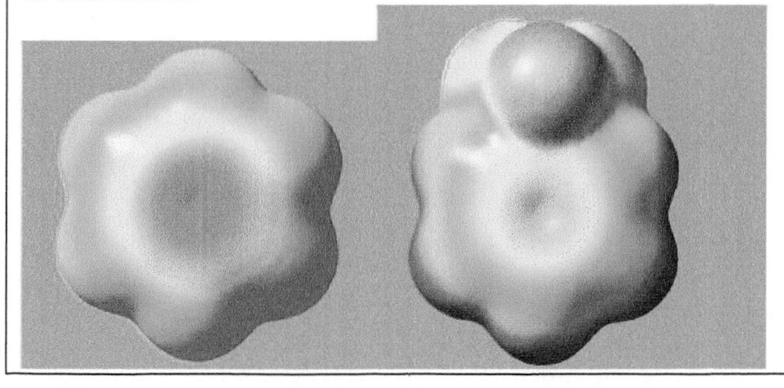

Problem 23.11. Which molecule is represented by the electrostatic potential map at the right in the above Your Turn exercise—toluene or trifluoromethylbeznene? Explain.

23.7. IMPACT OF REACTION CONDITIONS ON SUBSTITUENT EFFECTS

A substituent's effects on the regiochemistry and reaction rate of electrophilic aromatic substitution is not absolute. For some substituents, the reaction conditions also play a significant role. For example, when phenol is treated with bromine in water, it undergoes multiple brominations, even in the absence of a Lewis acid catalyst (Equation 23-12). However, when acetic acid is added to the reaction mixture, only a single bromination occurs (Equation 23-13).

three brominations occur, even without a strong Lewis acid catalyst

OH — $\xrightarrow[H_2O]{Br_2}$ — 2,4,6-tribromophenol (OH, Br, Br, Br)

97%

(23-12)

under mildly acidic conditions, only a single bromination takes place

OH — $\xrightarrow[H_2O,\ CH_3CO_2H]{Br_2}$ — para-bromophenol (OH, Br) + ortho-bromophenol (OH, Br)

(23-13)

Clearly, the nature of the substituent is affected by the pH of the solution. Phenol itself is a weak acid—its pK_a is 10.0. Therefore, in the absence of acetic acid, phenol is in equilibrium with a small amount of its conjugate base, the phenoxide anion (C_6H_5–O^-), as shown in Equation 23-14. Even though very little of the phenoxide anion is present, the O^- substituent is a *very* powerful activating group—far better than the OH group—and therefore causes a dramatic increase in the rate of electrophilic aromatic substitution. As a result, the phenoxide anion is the dominant reactant in the reaction.

the $O^{\ominus}$ substituent is a very powerful activator

OH $\underset{H_2O}{\rightleftharpoons}$ $O^{\ominus}$ $\xrightarrow{Br_2}$ $\rightarrow$ $\rightarrow$ $O^{\ominus}$ (Br, Br, Br) $\underset{H_2O}{\rightleftharpoons}$ OH (Br, Br, Br)

(23-14)

With acetic acid present, on the other hand, the pH of the solution is decreased. Due to Le Châtelier's principle, the increased concentration of H^+ substantially decreases the concentration of the phenoxide anion, effectively cutting off the channel in which the phenoxide anion is involved in electrophilic aromatic substitution. The only channel available is the one in which the electrophile attacks neutral phenol itself—a much slower reaction that can be easily stopped after just a single bromination.

Problem 23.12. Draw the complete, detailed mechanism for the reaction in Equation 23-14.

We also observe a dramatic effect of pH on the nitration of *N,N*-dimethylaniline. If *N,N*-dimethylaniline is treated with HNO_3 in acetic acid (Equation 23-15), the *ortho* and *para* nitro products are predominantly formed. This is as expected, since the lone pair on the substituent's nitrogen atom makes it *ortho/para*-directing and activating. However, if nitration is carried out in sulfuric acid, the major product is the *meta* isomer (Equation 23-16).

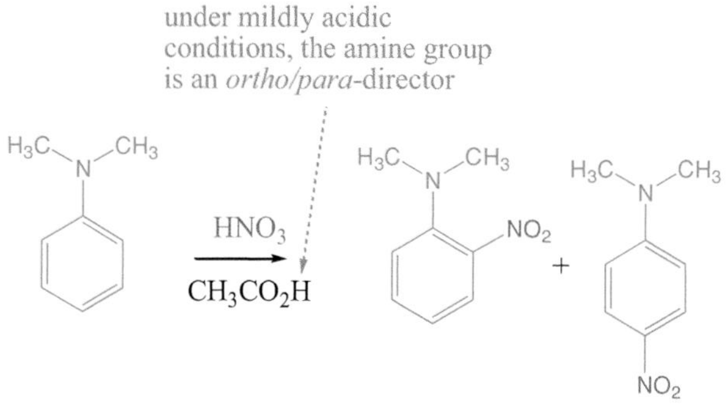

under mildly acidic conditions, the amine group is an *ortho/para*-director

HNO_3 / CH_3CO_2H

(23-15)

under strongly acidic conditions, the amine group is a *meta*-director

HNO_3 / H_2SO_4

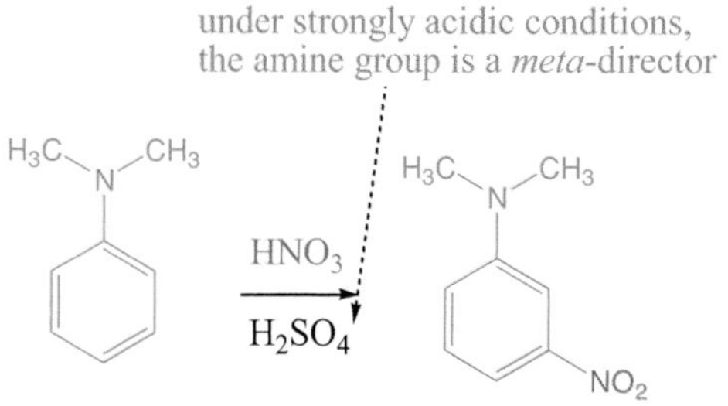

(23-16)

Because sulfuric acid is much stronger than acetic acid, it *quantitatively* protonates the amino group, generating an anilinium ion in which a +1 formal charge exists on the nitrogen atom (Equation 23-17). In this form, the substituent is highly electron-withdrawing, and is therefore a *meta*-director and a deactivator.

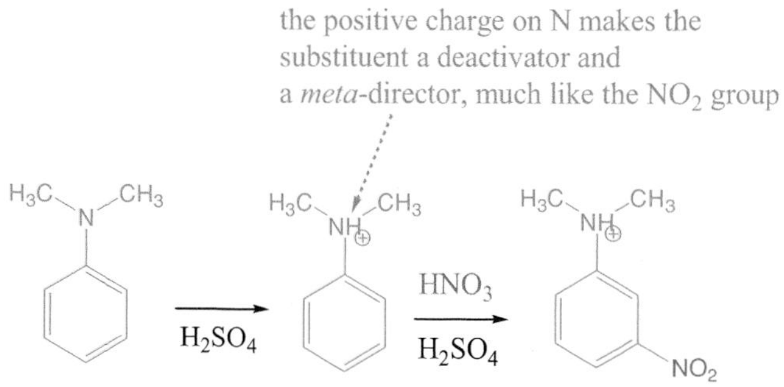

the positive charge on N makes the substituent a deactivator and a *meta*-director, much like the NO_2 group

H_2SO_4; HNO_3 / H_2SO_4

(23-17)

A similar phenomenon can occur when a strong Lewis acid is present. For example, even though aniline possesses a highly activating NH_2 group, it is incompatible with Friedel-Crafts reactions, as shown in Equation 23-18. The reason is that the amino group is a relatively strong Lewis base, and therefore readily undergoes coordination to the $AlCl_3$ Lewis acid. In that complexed form, the N atom, once again, possesses a formal positive charge, and is therefore a highly *deactivating* group that vastly decreases the reaction rate.

the positive charge on the N atom makes the substituent a deactivating group, which is incompatible with Friedel-Crafts reactions

strong Lewis base coordinates to the Lewis acid

NH_2 $\xrightarrow{AlCl_3}$ $Cl_3Al^{\ominus}$—$NH_2^{\oplus}$ $\xrightarrow{R-Cl}$ (crossed out) No reaction

(23-18)

23.8. ELECTROPHILIC AROMATIC SUBSTITUTION ON DISUBSTITUTED BENZENES

When electrophilic aromatic substitution takes place on a disubstituted benzene, effects from both of the substituents on the ring must be considered, both with regard to their activating/deactivating nature and their *ortho/meta/para*-directing capabilities. Fortunately, we often find that these effects are essentially additive.

The regiochemistry of these reactions is straightforward if the two substituents are "in agreement." For example, nitration of *p*-nitrotoluene produces almost exclusively 2,4-dinitrotoluene (Equation 23-19). The methyl group, because it is an *ortho/para*-director, favors substitution at the 2- and 6-positions on the ring (indicated by the blue arrows). Furthermore, the nitro group favors substitution at the 2- and 6-positions on the ring (indicated by red arrows) because it is a *meta*-director. With agreement like this, we observe substitution primarily at the carbon atom adjacent to the methyl group.

both substituents "agree" with regiochemistry

CH_3, NO_2 $\xrightarrow[\text{10 min, 65 °C}]{HNO_3,\ H_2SO_4}$ CH_3, NO_2, NO_2

p-nitrotoluene — 2,4-dinitrotoluene 98%

(23-19)

The situation is not quite so straightforward without this agreement among the substituents. In such situations, we can apply the following rule.

> When two substituents attached to an aromatic ring "disagree" with where to direct the incoming electrophile, regiochemistry is usually dictated by the substituent that is the stronger activating group—that is, the group that appears lower in Table 23-4.

For example, when *m*-nitrotoluene undergoes nitration (Equation 23-20), the methyl group directs substitution to the 2-, 4-, and 6-positions (indicated by the blue arrows), whereas the nitro group directs substitution to the 5-position (indicated by the red arrow). Experimentally, we observe that substitution occurs mainly at the 4- and 6-positions on the ring, suggesting that the methyl group has greater influence on regiochemistry than does the nitro group. This is consistent with the fact that the methyl group is the stronger activating substituent.

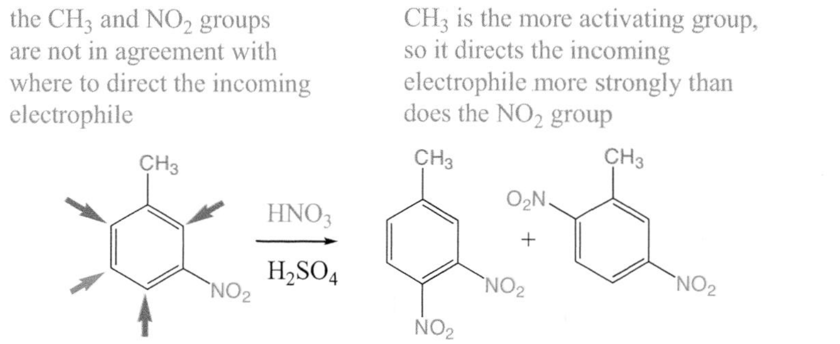

the CH_3 and NO_2 groups are not in agreement with where to direct the incoming electrophile

CH_3 is the more activating group, so it directs the incoming electrophile more strongly than does the NO_2 group

CH_3 NO_2 HNO_3 H_2SO_4 O_2N

m-nitrotoluene 3,4-dinitrotoluene 2,5-dinitrotoluene (23-20)

We can understand why the more activating group dictates the regiochemistry, by examining the resonance contributors of the various arenium ion intermediates that are possible. When the electrophile adds *meta* to the methyl group (Equation 23-21), all resonance contributors of the resulting arenium ion have about the same stability—all are secondary carbocations that are affected little by the substituents attached to the ring.

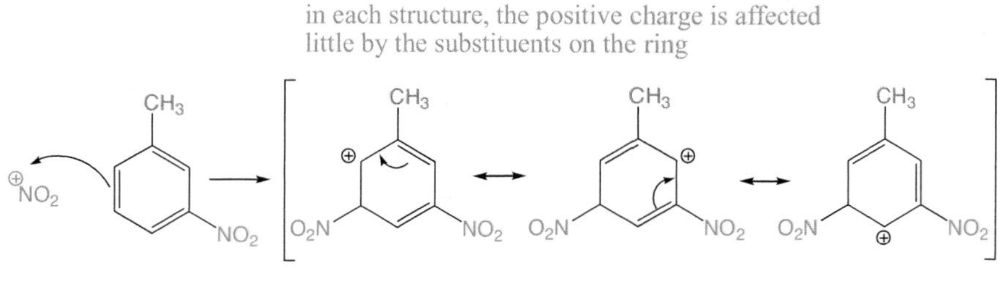

in each structure, the positive charge is affected little by the substituents on the ring

CH_3 NO_2 O_2N (23-21)

The story is somewhat different when the electrophile adds *para* to the methyl group. As we can see in Equation 23-22, the arenium ion that is produced has one resonance structure that is especially stable (highlighted in green), due to the electron-donating effects by the methyl group to the positively charged carbon. There is also one resonance structure that is particularly unstable (highlighted in red) because of the electron-withdrawing effects by the nitro group.

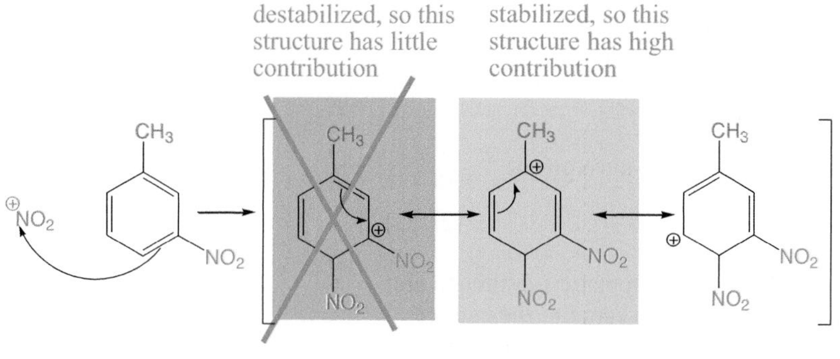

destabilized, so this structure has little contribution

stabilized, so this structure has high contribution

CH_3 NO_2 (23-22)

It is tempting to say that the destabilization in the first resonance structure counters the effects from the stabilization in the second resonance structure. However, resonance theory (Chapters 1 and 7) tells us otherwise—the greatest contribution to the resonance hybrid is from the most stable resonance structure. In other words, contribution by the destabilized resonance structures is minimized. Thus, we conclude that the arenium ion that is produced is more stable when the electrophile adds *para* to the methyl group (Equation 23-22) than it is when the electrophile adds *meta* (Equation 23-21).

Your Turn 23.6. Below are the resonance structures for the arenium ion produced when NO_2^+ adds *ortho* to the CH_3 group in *m*-nitrotoluene. Label the most stable resonance structure and the least stable resonance structure. Overall, is this arenium ion more stable or less stable than the one in Equation 23-21?

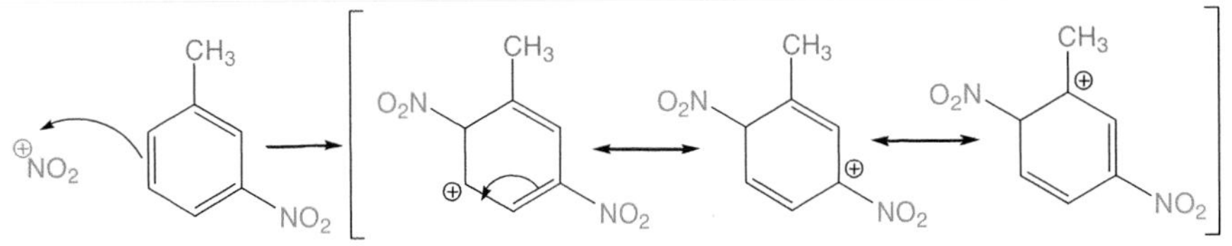

Notice in Equation 23-20 that even though the methyl group directs the incoming electrophile to the 2-, 4-, and 6-positions, substitution is favored at just the 4- and 6-positions. This is due to *steric hindrance*. The 2-position is flanked by both the CH_3 group and the NO_2 group, making that site the least accessible by the incoming electrophile. The 4- and 6-positions are more accessible because each is flanked by only one substituent—either the CH_3 group or the NO_2 group.

The situation is not as clean if the two substituents on benzene disagree with the placement of the incoming electrophile *and* have roughly the same activating/deactivating character—i.e., if they are in roughly the same location in Table 23-4. This is the case when *p*-ethyltoluene undergoes electrophilic aromatic substitution, given that the two alkyl groups have about the same activating capabilities. As indicated in Equation 23-23, a mixture of isomers is produced because the two alkyl groups are nearly equally good at directing the incoming electrophile to the position on the ring *ortho* to themselves.

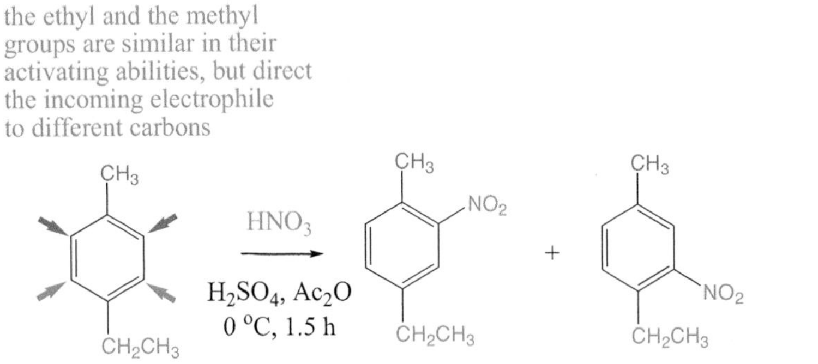

(23-23)

Substituent effects on the *overall* rate of electrophilic aromatic substitution are also additive. We can see this explicitly from Table 23-5, which contains the rates of chlorination for several methylated benzenes. In general, the rate of chlorination increases with each additional methyl group, given that each methyl group is *activating*.

Table 23-5: Relative Rates of Chlorination for Various Methylated Benzenes

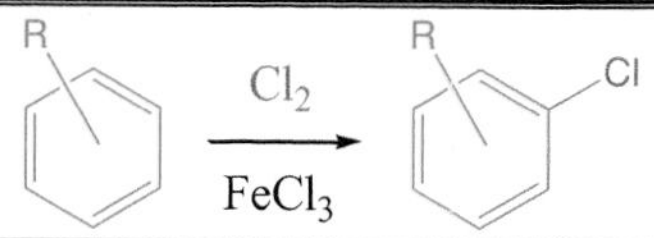

R — $\xrightarrow[FeCl_3]{Cl_2}$ — R, Cl

Aromatic species	Relative rate of chlorination
	1
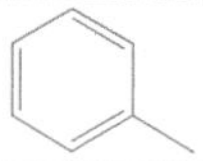	300
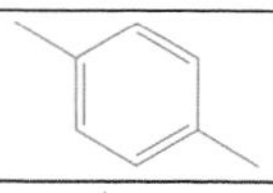	2,000
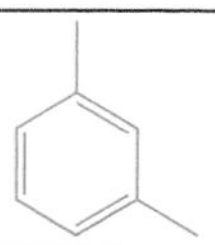	400,000
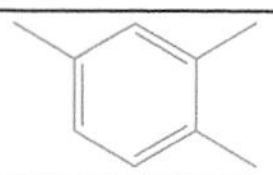	680,000
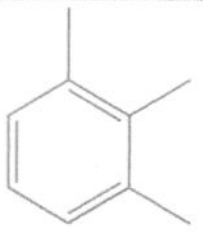	800,000
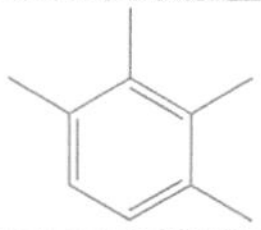	4,000,000
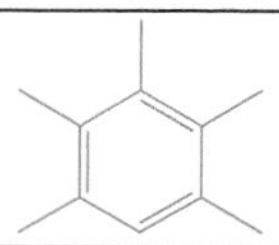	720,000,000

Solved Problem 23.4. Notice from Table 23-5 that *m*-dimethylbenzene undergoes chlorination about 20 times faster than *p*-dimethylbenzene. Explain why.

Think. In each isomer, do the methyl groups "agree" or "disagree" with where they direct the incoming electrophile? Should agreement result in a faster or slower electrophilic aromatic substitution reaction?

Solve. Each methyl group is an *ortho/para*-director. As indicated below, both methyl groups in the *meta* isomer "agree" in their placement of the incoming electrophile—i.e., at the 2-, 4-, and 6-positions. As a result, the rate is enhanced substantially. In the *para* isomer, on the other hand, the two methyl groups "disagree." Whereas one methyl group directs the electrophile to the 2- and 6-positions, the other methyl group directs the electrophile to the 3- and 5-positions.

m-dimethylbenzene *p*-dimethylbenzene

The additive effect in the activation of the ring should therefore be more substantial for the *meta* isomer than for the *para*.

Problem 23.13. For each pair of isomers, determine the one that will undergo chlorination faster. (a) *o*-dimethylbenzene or *m*-dimethylbenzene. (b) 1,2,3,4-tetramethylbenzene or 1,2,3,5-tetramethylbenzene. Explain.

23.9. ELECTROPHILIC AROMATIC SUBSTITUTION INVOLVING AROMATIC RINGS OTHER THAN BENZENE

Benzene is but one of many aromatic compounds we encounter in organic chemistry. Examples of other aromatic compounds are shown below. Naphthalene is an example of an aromatic hydrocarbon consisting of two fused rings. Furan, pyrrole, and pyridine are examples of *heterocyclic* aromatic compounds.

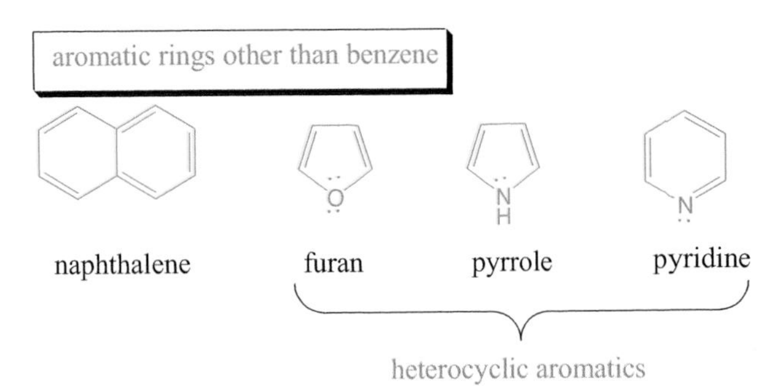

Because of the aromatic nature of these compounds, their π systems, similar to benzene's, are resistant to electrophilic addition. Permanent addition of an electrophile would destroy the aromaticity. Instead, treatment of these compounds with electrophiles tends to result in substitution in order to preserve that aromaticity.

As we will see, these compounds undergo many of the same electrophilic aromatic substitution reactions as benzene does. Unlike benzene, however, each of these compounds has at least two chemically distinct carbon atoms. In this section we will examine how this affects the *regiochemistry* and the *kinetics* of electrophilic aromatic substitution.

23.9a. Electrophilic Aromatic Substitution of Naphthalene

Naphthalene has two chemically distinct hydrogen atoms, attached to what are called the α and β positions of the ring. Hence there are two possible products of a single substitution reaction—the α-substituted product and the β-substituted product (Equation 23-24).

α-hydrogen β-hydrogen

an α-substituted naphthalene a β-substituted naphthalene

(23-24)

The general mechanisms for these reactions, presented in Equations 23-25a and 23-25b, are essentially identical to the one involving benzene. First the electron-rich aromatic species undergoes electrophilic addition with the electrophile, producing an *arenium ion intermediate*, in which the positive charge is delocalized via multiple resonance structures. Step 2 is elimination of a proton to give the overall product.

Mechanism for the Reaction in Equation 23-24

(a) 1) electrophilic addition; arenium ion intermediate; other resonance structures; : base; 2) electrophilic elimination

(b) 1) electrophilic addition; arenium ion intermediate; other resonance sructures; : base; 2) electrophilic elimination

(23-25)

Interestingly, the regiochemistry of electrophilic aromatic substitution involving naphthalene is dictated largely by whether the reaction is reversible or irreversible. As Equation 23-26 indicates, Friedel-Crafts acylation, which is an *irreversible* reaction, yields primarily the α-substituted product. On the other hand, as shown in Equation 23-27, a *reversible* substitution such as sulfonation leads to the β-substituted product as the major product.

in an *irreversible* reaction, the α-substituted product is the major product

$$\text{naphthalene} \xrightarrow[AlCl_3]{ClC(O)CH_3} \text{1-acetylnaphthalene (83\%)} \qquad (23\text{-}26)$$

in a *reversible* reaction, the β-substituted product is the major product

$$\text{naphthalene} \underset{SO_3,\ PhNO_2,\ 4\ h,\ 25\ ^{\circ}C}{\overset{\text{conc. } H_2SO_4}{\rightleftharpoons}} \text{2-naphthalenesulfonic acid } (SO_3H) \qquad (23\text{-}27)$$

In other words,

> In an electrophilic aromatic substitution reaction involving naphthalene, the α-substituted product is the kinetic product, whereas the β-substituted product is the thermodynamic product.

The fact that the α-substituted product is the kinetic product indicates that the arenium ion intermediate produced upon attack at the α carbon is more stable than the one produced upon attack at the β carbon. We can employ resonance theory to understand why. As shown in Equation 23-28, when electrophilic attack takes place at the α position, the resulting arenium ion has five resonance structures that contribute to delocalization of the positive charge. The two resonance structures highlighted in green are especially stable, because they allow the aromaticity of one ring to be preserved.

Equation 23-29 illustrates that the arenium ion produced by attack at the β position also has five resonance structures that contribute to delocalization of the positive charge. However, aromaticity is preserved in only one of those structures (highlighted in green), making the arenium ion produced from α attack more stable.

these two resonance structures are especially stable because one ring remains aromatic

(23-28)

this resonance structure is especially stable because one ring remains aromatic

(23-29)

Now let's examine why sulfonation leads primarily to the β-substituted product. Because the reaction is *reversible*, equilibrium is established, and at equilibrium the major product is the one that is the most stable. Hence the β-substituted product must be more stable than the α-substituted product. Primarily this is due to the greater *steric repulsion* involving the sulfonyl group and a hydrogen atom on the adjacent ring, as shown below.

this isomer is less stable because of the steric repulsion involving the SO_3H group and an H atom from the adjacent ring

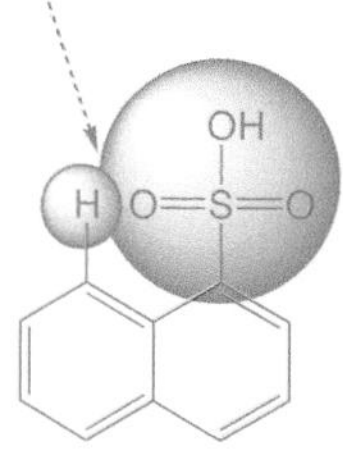

steric repulsion not as pronounced

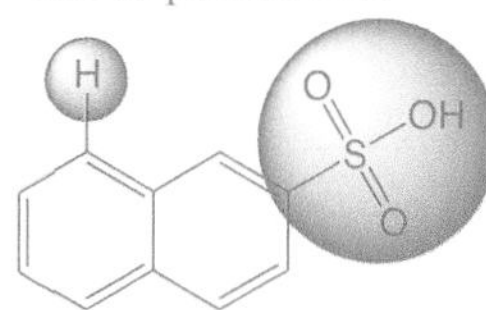

Problem 23.14. Construct a plot that contains the reaction free energy diagrams for both the α and β sulfonation of naphthalene. Pay attention to which is the more stable arenium ion intermediate and which is the more stable overall product.

Another interesting feature of naphthalene is that it undergoes electrophilic aromatic substitution faster than does benzene. That is,

The naphthalene π system is *activated* relative to benzene.

This can be demonstrated, for example, by the fact that naphthalene undergoes bromination without the presence of a Lewis acid catalyst, as shown in Equation 23-30. (Recall that a strong Lewis acid is necessary for bromination of benzene.) The fact that naphthalene is activated can be understood from the fact that the positive charge in naphthalene's arenium ion is delocalized via five resonance structures, two of which are aromatic. (This was illustrated previously in Equation 23-28.) Benzene's arenium ion, on the other hand, is stabilized by only three resonance structures, none of which are aromatic. Hence the activation energy for electrophilic aromatic substitution involving naphthalene is lower than it is for a similar reaction involving benzene.

the aromatic system of napthalene is *activated* relative to benzene, which is why bromination can take place without the presence of a catalyst

Br

Br_2

120 °C, 1 h

(no catalyst)

+ HBr

87 %

(23-30)

Electrophilic aromatic substitution on a *substituted* naphthalene is affected by the nature of the substituent, similar to what we saw with substitution on substituted benzenes. For example, chlorination of 1-methylnaphthalene yields predominantly the 1,2- and the 1,4-disubstituted products (Equation 23-31), and takes place faster than does chlorination of naphthalene itself. Just as in benzene, the methyl group is an *activating* group that provides stabilization to the arenium ion intermediate when an electrophile adds to the 2- or 4-position, but not when it adds to the 3-position.

CH_3 is an *ortho/para*-director

CH_3 Cl_2 CH_3 Cl CH_3 Cl

1-methylnaphthalene 2-chloro-1-methylnaphthalene + 4-chloro-1-methylnaphthalene

(23-31)

Realize that addition of the electrophile to the 5- or 7-position—i.e., on the ring not containing the methyl group—also leads to an arenium ion possessing an especially stable resonance structure. However, the ring containing the methyl group is more highly activated than the other ring, simply because the other ring is more distant. Consequently, the 1,5- and 1,7-disubstituted products are minor.

By the same token, when one ring of naphthalene contains a *deactivating* group, as in 2-nitronaphthalene (Equation 23-32), substitution is favored on the *other* ring. Just as we saw with unsubstituted naphthalene, the α position is more susceptible to electrophilic attack than is the β-position. Therefore, nitration of 2-nitronaphthalene, for example, leads primarily to the 1,6- and 1,7-disubstituted products.

this ring is deactivated by the NO_2 group

substitution favored at the α positions over the β positions

NO_2

2-nitronaphthalene

HNO_3

H_2SO_4

0 °C

1,6-dinitronaphthalene 42%

1,7-dinitronaphthalene 52%

(23-32)

Problem 23.15. Draw the complete, detailed mechanism for the following reaction and predict the *two* major products.

CH_3 H_3C–C(=O)–Cl ? $AlCl_3$

23.9b. Electrophilic Aromatic Substitution of Heterocyclic Aromatics

As mentioned previously, *heterocyclic* aromatic compounds can also undergo electrophilic aromatic substitution. Peculiarly, however, ring size appears to play a significant role in the reactivity, as we can see with the nitration of pyrrole (Equation 23-33) and of pyridine (Equation 23-34).

this aromatic ring is activated, so it reacts under mild conditions

substitution primarily at the 2-position

pyrrole $\xrightarrow[Ac_2O,\ -50\ ^{\circ}C,\ 3\ h]{HNO_3}$ 2-nitropyrrole 55%

4 3 2 5 N H 1 NO_2

(23-33)

this aromatic ring is deactivated, so extreme conditions are necessary for the reaction to take place

substitution primarily at the 3-position

pyridine $\xrightarrow[H_2SO_4,\ KNO_3,\ 300\ ^{\circ}C]{HNO_3}$ 3-nitropyrrole 20%

4 NO_2 5 3 6 2 N 1

(23-34)

As we can see, pyrrole undergoes nitration under very mild conditions—even milder than is required for the nitration of benzene. By contrast, nitration of pyridine requires extreme conditions. In other words, pyrrole's ring is *activated*, whereas pyridine's ring is *deactivated*.

Another difference between these two reactions is in their regiochemistry. Notice that whereas pyrrole favors substitution at the 2-position, pyridine favors substitution at the 3-position.

To understand these differences, let's examine the possible arenium ion intermediates produced upon electrophilic attack. Those that are possible from pyrrole—i.e., the 2-substituted and the 3-substituted arenium ions—are shown in Equations 23-35a and 23-35b.

Comment [JMK47]: Margin note.

(pyrrole) = activated

(pyridine) = de-activated

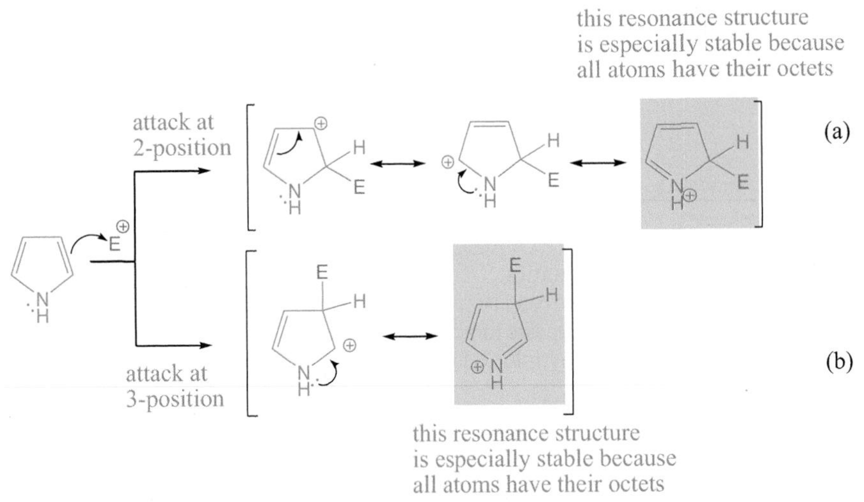

this resonance structure
is especially stable because
all atoms have their octets

attack at
2-position

(a)

(b)

attack at
3-position

this resonance structure
is especially stable because
all atoms have their octets

(23-35)

For each intermediate, notice that the positive charge is delocalized via resonance, and that one resonance structure—the one highlighted in green—is especially stable, because every atom has an octet. However, the two intermediates differ in the number of resonance structures—whereas the 2-substituted arenium ion has a total of three resonance structures, the 3-substituted ion has only two. Thus, the 2-substituted intermediate is more stable than the 3-substituted one. According to the *Hammond postulate*, the energy barrier leading to the former is smaller than the energy barrier leading to the latter, and substitution at the 2-position is favored.

Moreover, because the intermediate has a resonance structure in which all atoms have their octets fulfilled, pyrrole's arenium ion is more stable than the one produced from benzene. Hence electrophilic aromatic substitution proceeds more rapidly for pyrrole, which makes pyrrole an *activated* ring.

Why, then, does pyridine have such different behavior? Once again, let's examine the possible arenium ion intermediates produced upon electrophilic attack—in this case, the 2-, 3-, and 4-substituted arenium ions (Equation 23-36a through 23-36c).

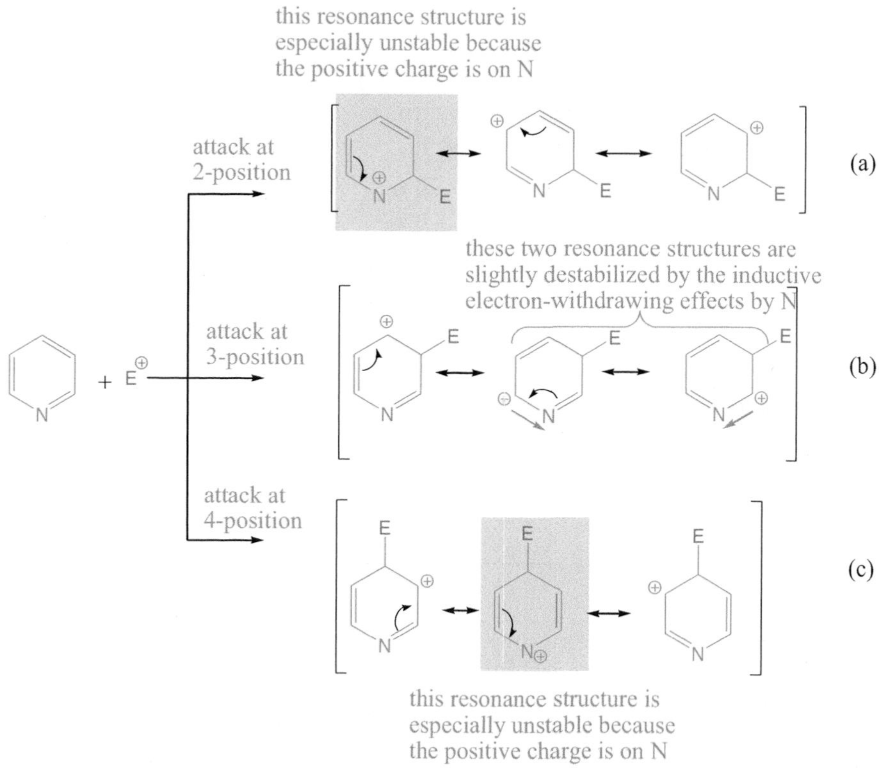

this resonance structure is especially unstable because the positive charge is on N

attack at 2-position (a)

these two resonance structures are slightly destabilized by the inductive electron-withdrawing effects by N

attack at 3-position (b)

attack at 4-position (c)

this resonance structure is especially unstable because the positive charge is on N

(23-36)

Each of the three possible arenium ions has a total of three resonance structures that serve to delocalize the positive charge. Unlike in pyrrole's arenium ion, none of the intermediates has a resonance structure in which all atoms have their octets fulfilled. Instead, two of the possible arenium ions have resonance structures that are especially *unstable*—the 2- and 4-substituted arenium ions. Those resonance structures—highlighted in pink—are particularly unstable because the positive charge is on the nitrogen atom, which has a relatively high electronegativity.

The best scenario for electrophilic attack on pyridine is at the 3-position (Equation 23-36b), where no resonance structure can be drawn in which the positive charge appears on nitrogen. Nonetheless, the 3-substituted arenium ion is less stable than benzene's arenium ion. This is because the nitrogen atom is inductively electron-withdrawing, and therefore destabilizes the nearby positive charges in the various resonance structures, as indicated. This explains why pyridine undergoes electrophilic aromatic substitution slower than does benzene.

Problem 23.16. In pyrrole's arenium ion, the resonance structure with the positive charge on the N atom was said to be especially stable. On the other hand, in pyridine's arenium ions, the resonance structure with the positive charge on N was said to be especially *unstable*. How can you reconcile this apparent contradiction?

Solved Problem 23.5. Would you expect nitration of *N*-methylpyrrole to take place faster or slower than nitration of pyrrole? Explain.

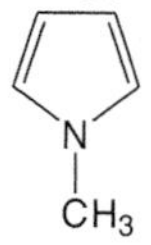

N-methylpyrrole

Think. Does the methyl group stabilize or destabilize the arenium ion intermediate?

Solve. Just like pyrrole, electrophilic aromatic substitution of *N*-methylpyrrole takes place predominantly at the 2-position, giving rise to an arenium ion intermediate whose most stable resonance structure is as follows. The electron donation of the methyl group stabilizes the positive charge on N. Because the arenium is more stable than that of pyrrole itself, nitration takes place faster.

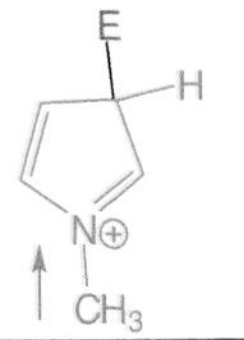

E
H
N⊕
CH_3

Problem 23.17. Draw the complete mechanism for the following reaction, and predict the major product. (Note: BF_3 acts as a Lewis acid similar to $AlCl_3$.)

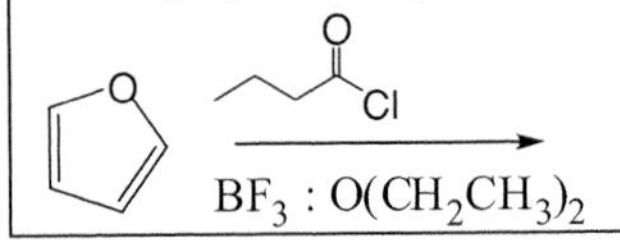

O
Cl
O
$BF_3 : O(CH_2CH_3)_2$

Problem 23.18. Bromination of thiophene takes place without the presence of a Lewis acid catalyst. (a) Explain why. (b) Draw the complete, detailed mechanism for the formation of both possible isomeric products and predict which one is the major product.

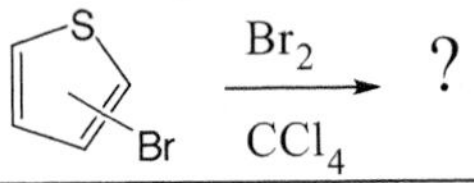

S
Br
Br_2
CCl_4
?

23.10. NUCLEOPHILIC AROMATIC SUBSTITUTION MECHANISMS

The aromatic substitution reactions we have examined in this chapter and the last proceed by mechanisms involving an electrophile attacking the aromatic ring—so-called *electrophilic aromatic substitution* reactions. In this section, we will examine two other types of aromatic substitution reactions, in which the aromatic ring is attacked by a nucleophile instead—these are examples of **nucleophilic aromatic substitution** reactions. One such reaction proceeds by a *nucleophilic addition-elimination* mechanism, and the other by a mechanism in which a *benzyne intermediate* is produced.

These reactions are fundamentally different from the ones classified as electrophilic aromatic substitution. However, nucleophilic aromatic substitution reactions are presented here because they are frequently employed in syntheses in conjunction with, or as an alternative to electrophilic aromatic substitution reactions.

23.10a. Nucleophilic Aromatic Substitution via the Addition-Elimination Mechanism

When 1-chloro-2-nitrobenzene is treated with methanamine, CH_3NH_2, *N*-methyl-2-nitroaniline is produced (Equation 23-37). Overall, chlorine is replaced by an amine group.

1-chloro-2-nitrobenzene $\xrightarrow[\text{DBU, 1 h, 80 °C}]{CH_3NH_2}$ *N*-methyl-2-nitroaniline, 90% (23-37)

The mechanism for this aromatic substitution reaction is shown in Equation 23-38.

Mechanism for the Reaction in Equation 23-37

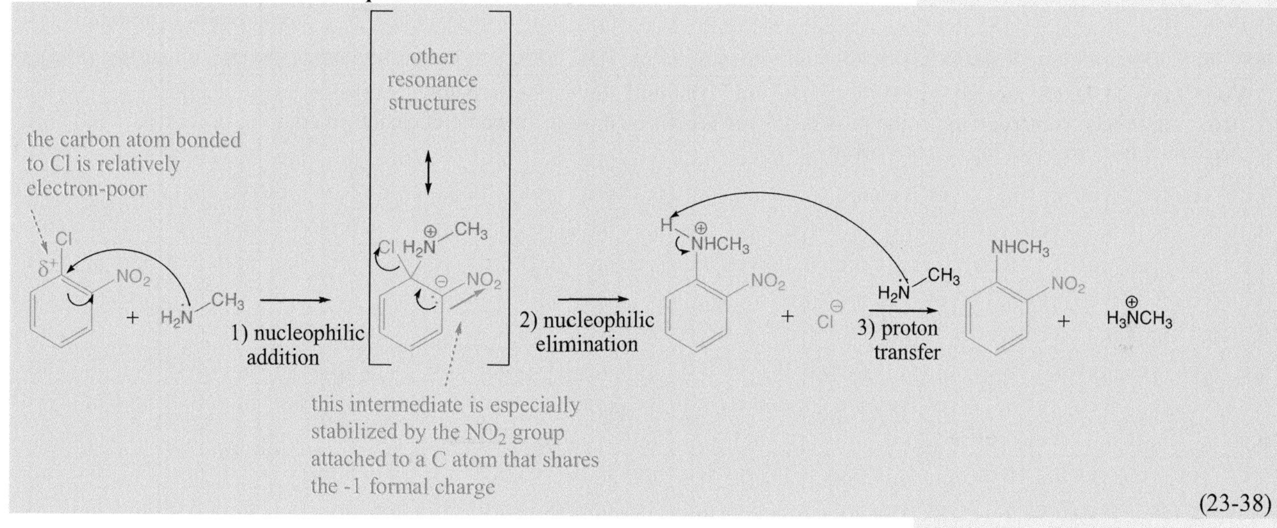

(23-38)

In step 1, the amine acts as a nucleophile, undergoing nucleophilic addition to the carbon atom bonded to chlorine. In step 2, the chlorine atom departs as a leaving group. Step 3, a proton transfer, is necessary to produce the overall uncharged product.

Notice that step 1 is favored by the electron-poor nature of the aromatic ring. Not only does the leaving group impart a partial positive charge on the carbon atom to which it is attached, thereby attracting the electron-rich nucleophile, but the product of step 1 is stabilized by the powerful electron-withdrawing nature of the nitro group. This is in contrast to electrophilic aromatic substitution, which is favored by electron-rich aromatic rings.

The importance of the electron-poor nature of the aromatic ring is evidenced by the reaction in Equation 23-29, which is a substitution that is similar to the one in Equation 23-37. Notice that with the additional electron-withdrawing nitro group on the ring, the reaction requires less heat. This is because the additional nitro group further stabilizes the negatively charged intermediate.

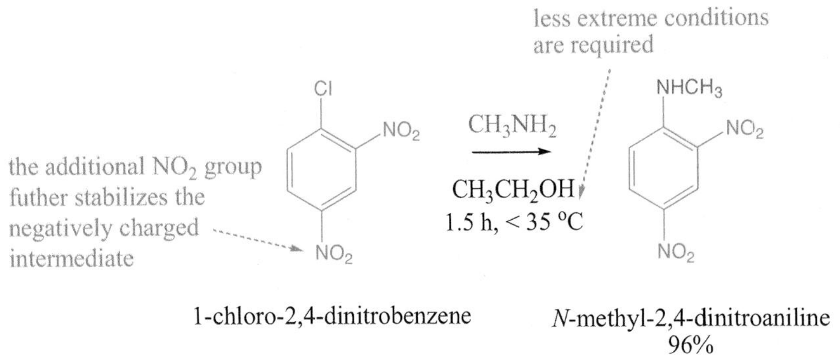

less extreme conditions are required

the additional NO_2 group futher stabilizes the negatively charged intermediate

CH_3NH_2 / CH_3CH_2OH, 1.5 h, < 35 °C

1-chloro-2,4-dinitrobenzene → N-methyl-2,4-dinitroaniline 96% (23-39)

Your Turn 23.7. The mechanism for the reaction in Equation 23-39 is shown below, but the curved arrows have been omitted. Supply the missing curved arrows, and write the name of each elementary step below its corresponding reaction arrow.

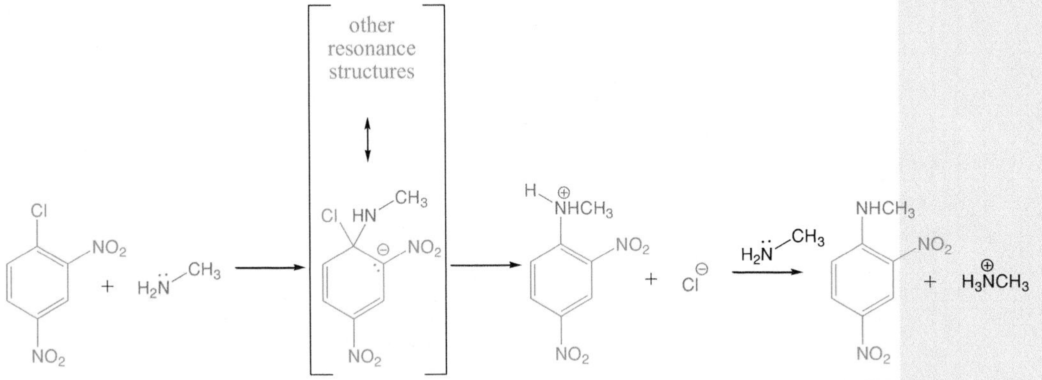

other resonance structures

Problem 23.19. Draw the detailed mechanism for the following reaction, and predict the major product. Determine whether this reaction will be faster or slower than the one in Equation 23-39.

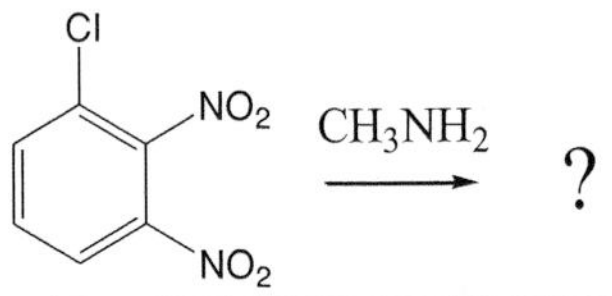

CH_3NH_2 → ?

Other support for the nucleophilic addition-elimination mechanism in Equation 23-38 comes from the trend that is observed on reaction rate involving various halogen leaving groups:

> In nucleophilic aromatic substitution reactions proceeding by the nucleophilic addition-elimination mechanism, the reaction rate increases with increasing electronegativity of the halogen leaving group: Ar–I < Ar–Br < Ar–Cl <Ar–F.

Notice that the rate increases as the leaving group ability *decreases*, so this trend is opposite to what we would expect for an S_N1 or S_N2 mechanism. It is explained, however, by the relative electron-withdrawing capabilities of halogen atoms, which increases in the order I < Br < Cl < F. Therefore, as indicated below, the stability of the negatively charged intermediate increases in the same order.

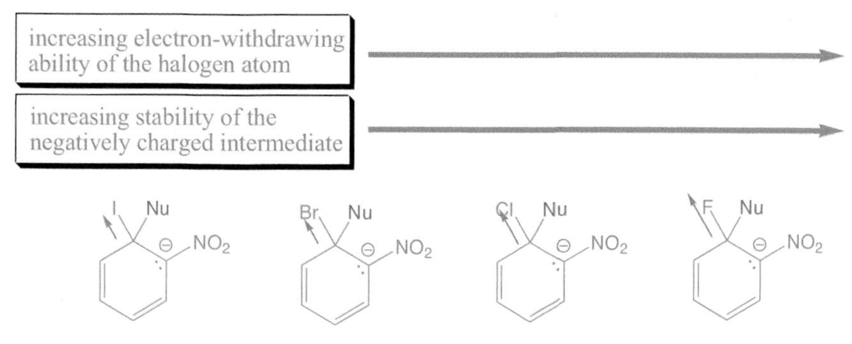

Problem 23.20. For each reaction, draw the detailed mechanism and predict the major product.

(a) Cl, NO_2, Br $\xrightarrow{CH_3NH_2}$?

(b) F, O_2N, I, NO_2 $\xrightarrow{NaOH}$?

23.10b. Nucleophilic Aromatic Substitution via a Benzyne Intermediate

Even without a strongly electron-withdrawing group attached to the ring, a halobenzene can still undergo nucleophilic substitution. For example, chlorobenzene can react with sodium hydroxide to produce phenol (Equation 23-40), or it can react with potassium amide to produce aniline (Equation 23-41). As indicated, however, these reactions typically require extreme conditions, such as the presence of a strong base, high temperatures, or both.

chlorobenzene $\xrightarrow[300\ ^{\circ}C,\ 20\ h]{NaOH\ (15\%)}$ phenol 94% (23-40)

chlorobenzene $\xrightarrow[liq.\ NH_3,\ -33\ ^{\circ}C]{KNH_2}$ aniline 60% (23-41)

We can gain insight into the mechanism for these reactions by comparing the conditions under which the two reactions above take place. Notice that when the stronger base is used (H_2N^-, Equation 23-41), the reaction can be carried out at significantly lower temperatures. Thus, the base plays a critical role in the rate-determining step.

This is illustrated in Equation 23-42, the mechanism for the reaction in Equation 23-40. Step 1 is bimolecular elimination, E2, whereby the leaving group and a neighboring proton are eliminated from the chlorobenzene substrate. The product is called a **benzyne intermediate**, because of the presence of the carbon-carbon triple bond that appears in its Lewis structure. In step 2, the benzyne intermediate undergoes nucleophilic addition to produce a deprotonated form of phenol. In step 3, that deprotonated form of phenol gains a proton from water to produce the overall uncharged product.

Mechanism for the Reaction in Equation 23-40

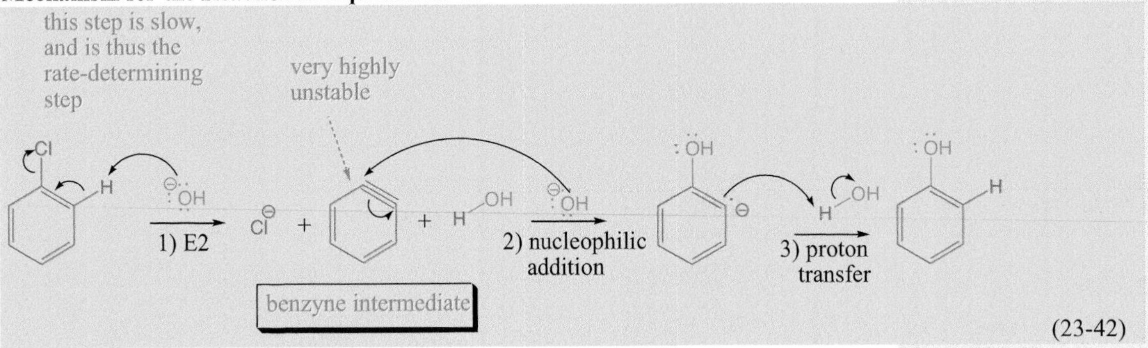

this step is slow, and is thus the rate-determining step

very highly unstable

1) E2

2) nucleophilic addition

3) proton transfer

benzyne intermediate

(23-42)

As indicated, step 1 is relatively slow, so it is the rate-determining step. The reason it is so slow is that the benzyne product is very highly unstable, stemming from the large amount of angle strain it has. The ideal bond angle for each triply-bonded carbon is 180°, but the constraints of the ring require it to be roughly 120°. Moreover, this has a major effect on the strength of the π bond that is in plane of the ring, as indicated below. For a normal π bond, adjacent *p* orbitals are parallel, but in this case they are 60° apart. As a result, the overlap of those adjacent *p* orbitals is significantly decreased, making the π bond abnormally weak, and benzyne highly reactive.

The *p* orbitals in the plane of the ring intersect at 60°. Thus, they overlap little, making the resulting π bond rather weak, and benzyne highly reactive

benzyne

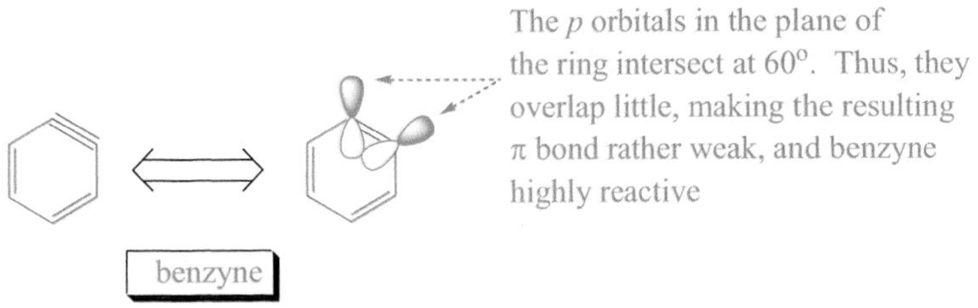

Your Turn 23.8. The mechanism to the reaction in Equation 23-41 is shown below, but the curved arrows have been omitted. Supply the missing curved arrows, and below each reaction arrow write the name of the corresponding elementary step.

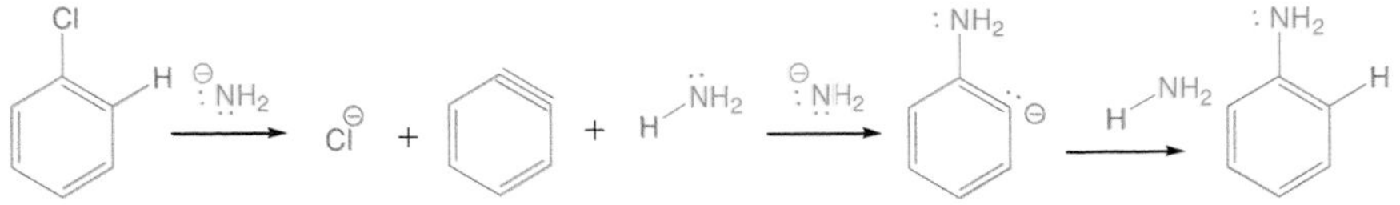

Because benzyne is highly reactive, it has not been isolated and purified. However, some experiments indirectly support its existence. One of the most compelling is a carbon-13 labeling experiment, shown in Equation 23-43. Namely, when the chlorine atom in chlorobenzene is bonded to ^{13}C, reaction with KNH_2 produces a roughly equal mixture of two isomers of aniline—in one isomer, the NH_2 group is bonded to a ^{13}C atom, and in the other isomer, it is bonded to a ^{12}C atom.

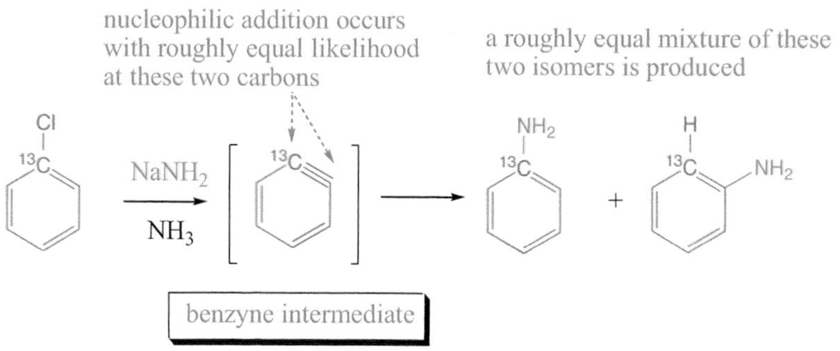

nucleophilic addition occurs with roughly equal likelihood at these two carbons

a roughly equal mixture of these two isomers is produced

Cl, 13C, NaNH$_2$, NH$_3$, 13C, NH$_2$, 13C, +, H, 13C, NH$_2$

benzyne intermediate

(23-43)

These results are explained by benzyne's symmetry about the triple bond. Thus, nucleophilic addition to benzyne occurs with essentially equal likelihood at each alkyne carbon. Addition to the alkyne ^{13}C produces one isomer, and addition to the alkyne ^{12}C produces the other.

Problem 23.21. Draw the mechanism for the formation of benzyne from bromobenzene and sodium hydroxide, as shown below.

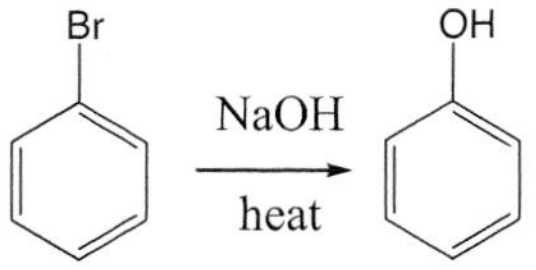

Br, NaOH, heat, OH

Suppose, instead, that the deuterium labeled bromobenzene below were used. What percentage of the product would you expect to contain the deuterium atom? Explain.

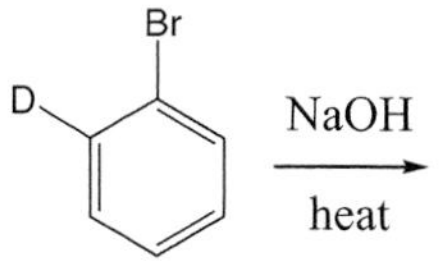

Br, D, NaOH, heat

23.11. ORGANIC SYNTHESIS: CONSIDERATIONS OF REGIOCHEMISTRY; PUTTING GROUPS ON IN THE CORRECT ORDER

As we learned in Section 23.1, a substituent that is already on the aromatic ring greatly influences the site of attack in a subsequent electrophilic aromatic substitution. Therefore, in a synthesis that requires successive substitutions, we must choose wisely the order in which the reactions are carried out. For example, suppose that we wish to synthesize *m*-chloronitrobenzene from benzene.

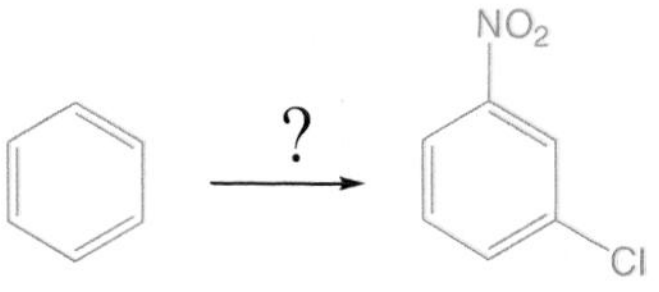

?, NO$_2$, Cl

m-chloronitrobenzene

We know that benzene can be nitrated by treating it with concentrated HNO_3 in H_2SO_4. We also know that benzene can be chlorinated by treatment with Cl_2 in $FeCl_3$. The synthesis must therefore involve both a nitration and a chlorination, but in which order?

In this case, if chlorination takes place first, we encounter a problem with regiochemistry, as shown in Equation 23-44. The product of chlorination on benzene is chlorobenzene. The chloro substituent is an *ortho/para*-director, so a subsequent nitration would yield *o*-chloronitrobenzene and *p*-chloronitrobenzene as the major products. Our target, however, is neither of these, but rather is the *meta* isomer.

an *ortho/para*-director

benzene $\xrightarrow[FeCl_3]{Cl_2}$ chlorobenzene $\xrightarrow[H_2SO_4]{HNO_3}$ *o*-chloronitrobenzene + *p*-chloronitrobenzene (23-44)

Alternatively, if nitration of benzene is carried out first (Equation 23-45), the correct isomer is indeed produced as the major product. This is because the second substitution is carried out on nitrobenzene, and the nitro group is a *meta*-director.

a *meta*-director

benzene $\xrightarrow[H_2SO_4]{HNO_3}$ nitrobenzene $\xrightarrow[FeCl_3]{Cl_2}$ *m*-chloronitrobenzene (23-45)

Solved Problem 23.6. How would you synthesize *p*-isopropylnitrobenzene from benzene?

benzene $\xrightarrow{?}$ *p*-isopropylnitrobenzene (NO_2; H_3C–CH–CH_3)

Think. Is the nitro group an *o/p*-director or an *m*-director? Is the isopropyl group an *o/p*-director or an *m*-director? Which group should be on the ring prior to the second substitution?

Solution. To obtain the target, we see that benzene must be both alkylated and nitrated. Because an alkyl group is *ortho/para*-directing and the nitro group is *meta*-directing, the order in which these substitutions is carried out is important. Given that we wish to synthesize the *para* isomer, we would like to have an *ortho/para*-directing substituent on the ring prior to the second substitution reaction. In other words, the second reaction must be a nitration on the alkylbenzene. That leaves alkylation as the first reaction. The overall synthesis would therefore appear as follows:

Problem 23.22. A student wishes to synthesize *p*-chlorobromobenzene from benzene. She knows that it requires both a chlorination and a bromination, but she is concerned about the order in which to carry out those substitutions. What would you tell her?

Another concern about the order in which substitutions are carried out arises from the fact that some substituents on the ring make certain electrophilic aromatic substitution reactions unfeasible. This is the case with Friedel-Crafts reactions, which, as we learned in Chapter 22, do not occur with highly deactivated rings. We must therefore be careful about placing a strongly deactivating group on the ring prior to carrying out a Friedel-Crafts reaction.

For example, suppose that we wish to synthesize *m*-nitroacetophenone from benzene.

benzene

m-nitroacetophenone

We can see that this synthesis requires two substitutions—a nitration and a Friedel-Crafts acylation. Because both the nitro group and the acetyl group are *meta*-directors, regiochemistry is not an issue with the order in which these substitutions are carried out. However, we do wish to avoid attempting a Friedel-Crafts reaction on nitrobenzene, given that its benzene ring is highly deactivated (Equation 23-46).

highly deactivated ring

NO REACTION

(23-46)

Instead, nitration should be the final step, leaving the Friedel-Crafts acylation as the first step. This is shown in Equation 23-47.

(23-47)

23.12. ORGANIC SYNTHESIS: INTERCONVERTING *ORTHO/PARA*- AND *META*-DIRECTORS

In the previous section, we learned that when devising a synthesis that requires successive electrophilic aromatic substitution reactions, it is important to consider the order in which the substitutions are carried out. Depending upon the *ortho/para*- and *meta*-directing capabilities of the substituents added to the ring, the wrong order could result in undesired products. In light of this, in this section we will revisit some reactions we encountered in Chapter 22, which can be used to interconvert *ortho/para*- and *meta*-directing substituents. Thus, as we will see, the regiochemistry of a substitution that takes place later in a synthesis is not automatically predetermined by the *ortho/meta/para*-directing ability of a substituent added earlier.

Recall from Section 23.11a, for example, that treatment of an alkylbenzene with a hot basic solution of $KMnO_4$ yields benzoic acid—this is shown again in Equation 23-48. Notice that the substituent in the reactant is an alkyl group, which is an *o/p*-director. By contrast, the substituent in the product is a carboxyl group, which is a *meta*-director.

ortho/para-director

meta-director

R

$KMnO_4$

$HO^{\ominus}$, heat

O

C

OH

an alkylbenzene

benzoic acid

(23-48)

We can see the usefulness of this reaction in the synthesis of *p*-nitrobenzoic acid from benzene.

a carboxyl group is
a *meta*-director

O

OH

C

?

NO_2

a nitro group is
a *meta*-director

Normally, we would run into a problem, given that both substituents—the carboxyl substituent and the nitro substituent—are *meta*-directors, in contrast to the fact that the desired product is the *para* isomer. However, we can circumvent this problem by making sure that the second electrophilic aromatic substitution takes place with an *o/p*-director already on the ring, such as an alkyl group. After the *para*-disubstituted benzene is produced, the alkyl group can be oxidized to the carboxyl group. This retrosynthetic analysis is shown below.

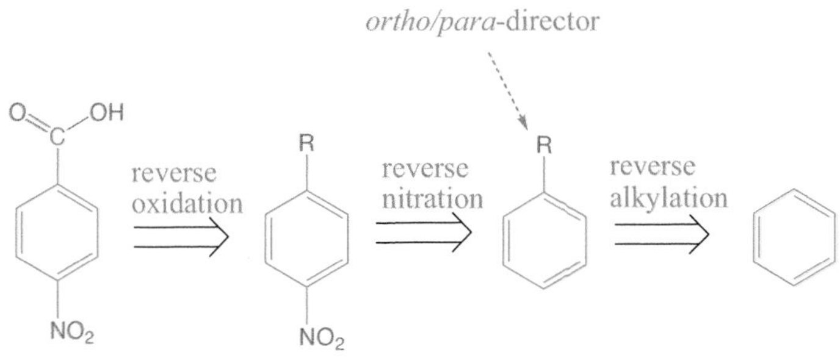

The final synthesis would then appear as Equation 23-49.

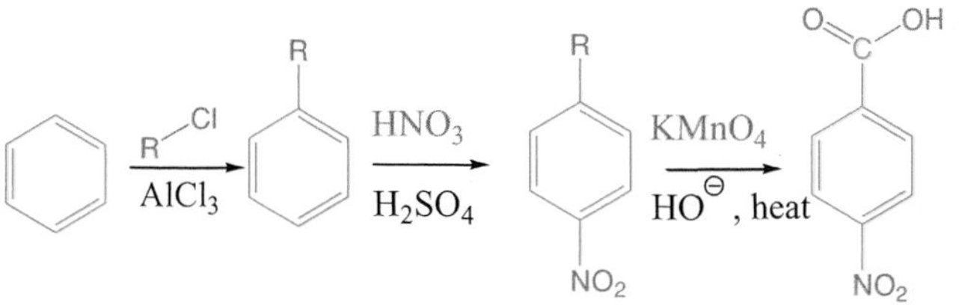

(23-49)

Problem 23.23. Show how to synthesize benzene-1,4-dicarboxylic acid from benzene, using ethanol as your only other source of carbon.

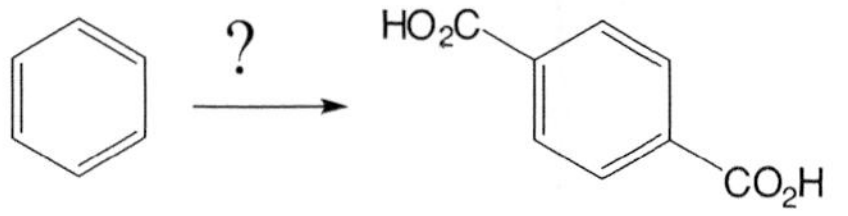

By the same token, we can achieve even greater flexibility in synthesis with the ability to convert a *meta*-director into an *ortho/para*-director. We have already encountered two types of reductions that accomplish this. One, which was discussed in Section 22.11b, is the reduction of a nitro (NO_2) group to an amine (NH_2). The second example is the reduction of a ketone's or aldehyde's carbonyl group to a methylene (CH_2) group—recall from Section 17.3 that this can be done in either acidic conditions (Clemmensen reduction), basic conditions (Wolff-Kishner reduction), or neutral conditions (Raney-nickel reduction).

The utility of these reactions can be seen in the synthesis of *m*-bromoethylbenzene from benzene.

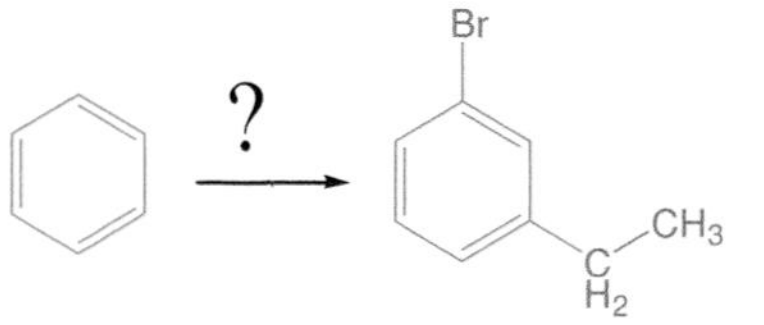

Notice that the substituents in the target are *meta* to each other, so the second of two electrophilic aromatic substitution reactions must be carried out with a *meta*-director already on the ring. However, both the bromo and the ethyl substituents are *ortho/para*-directors. This suggests that after the second substitution reaction is carried out, the *meta*-director must be converted into an *ortho/para*-director.

Thinking backwards, that *meta*-director could be an acetyl group that undergoes reduction to the ethyl group.

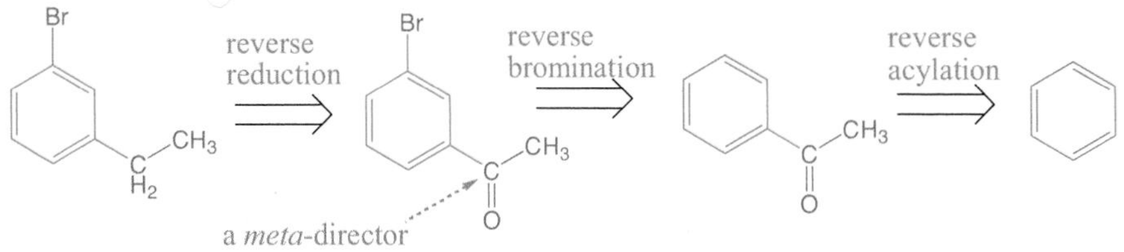

reverse reduction — a *meta*-director — reverse bromination — reverse acylation

In the forward direction, the synthesis would appear as in Equation 23-50.

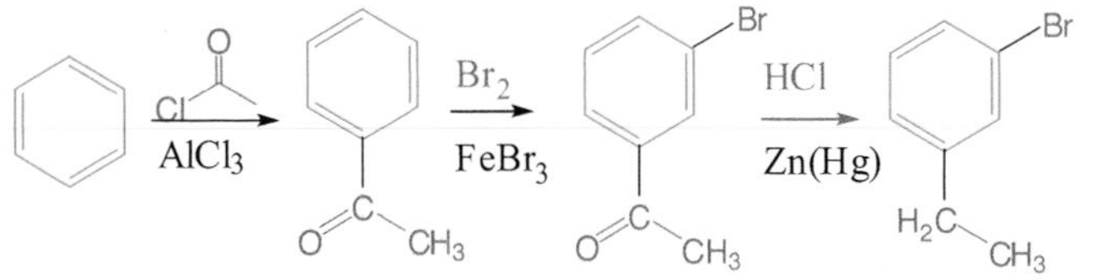

Br_2, $FeBr_3$; HCl, Zn(Hg); $AlCl_3$

(23-50)

Problem 23.24. Show how to synthesize *m*-chloroaniline from benzene.

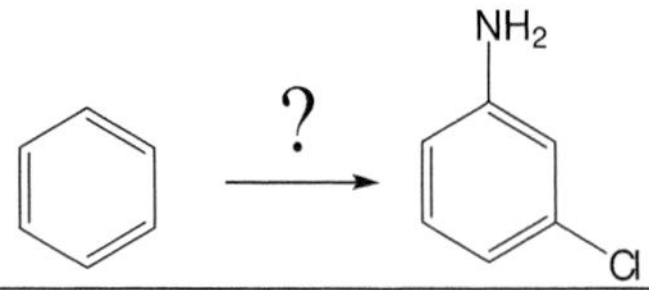

23.13. ORGANIC SYNTHESIS: CONSIDERATIONS OF PROTECTING GROUPS

In the context of electrophilic aromatic substitution, there are two ways in which to incorporate a protecting group. One is to temporarily suppress the reactivity of a substituent attached to the ring, by reversibly converting it to a different functional group. The second is to protect a particular site on the ring where substitution is not desired.

As an example of the first scenario, suppose we wish to carry out the following transformation, where aniline is acylated at the *para* position.

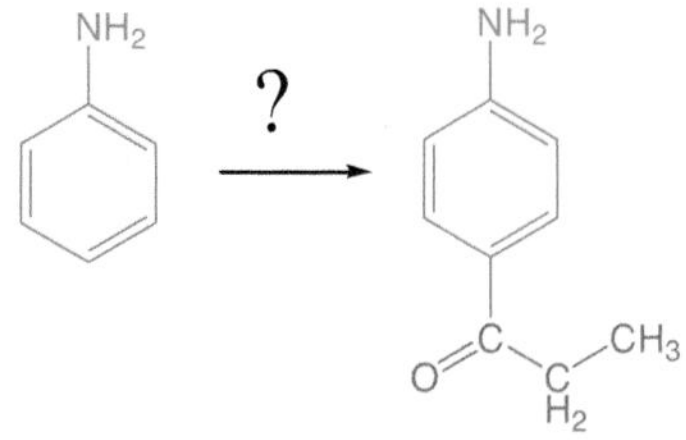

You might first think that only a simple Friedel-Crafts acylation is required, given that the NH_2 group on aniline is an *ortho/para*-director. However, as we learned in Section 23.7, the reaction conditions that are required would convert the activating amino substituent into a strongly deactivating group (Equation 23-51), thereby making a direct Friedel-Crafts acylation unfeasible.

this is a strongly deactivating group, making the Friedel-Crafts reaction unfeasible

the amine group coordinates to the strong Lewis acid

NH_2 Cl–C(=O)–CH_2–CH_3 / $AlCl_3$ → $H_2N^{\oplus}$–$AlCl_3^{\ominus}$ ✗→ NO REACTION

(23-51)

The problem here lies with the fact that the NH_2 group is a good Lewis base—its lone pair of electrons are available to form a bond to $AlCl_3$, a strong Lewis acid. To circumvent this problem, the amino group can be converted *temporarily* into a different functional group in which the lone pair of electrons is less available. The amide functional group does the trick. As we learned in Chapters 18 and 19, amides are relatively unreactive, due in large part to the resonance of N's lone pair with the adjacent carbonyl group.

Aniline is converted to the amide by treatment with an acid chloride or an acid anhydride in the *absence* of a strong Lewis acid catalyst (Equation 23-52). Notice that even in the protected form, the substituent on the ring is an *ortho/para*-director and a weak activator, due to the presence of the lone pair of electrons on N. (It would be undesirable for a protecting group to alter the regiochemistry of the reaction or to strongly deactivate the ring.) In the protected form, the acylation can then be carried out. Afterwards, the amine is deprotected by hydrolysis.

still an *ortho/para*-director

amide hydrolysis

NH_2 → (H_3C–C(=O)–O–C(=O)–CH_3) → HN–C(=O)–CH_3 (protected amine) → (Cl–C(=O)–CH_2–CH_3, $AlCl_3$) → HN–C(=O)–CH_3 / C(=O)–CH_2–CH_3 → ($HO^{\ominus}$, H_2O, heat) → NH_2 / C(=O)–CH_2–CH_3

(23-52)

Problem 23.25. Show how to carry out the following synthesis.

? → NH_2

In some instances, the reaction we wish to carry out leads to possible substitution at two or more sites on the ring. This brings about the second use of protecting groups in electrophilic aromatic substitution—we can guide the regiochemistry by protecting one of those sites. For example, suppose we are to convert phenol into *o*-bromophenol, and suppose further that the *para* product is undesired.

the *para* product is undesired

OH ? → OH Br (OH Br)

phenol o-bromophenol

The hydroxy group is an *ortho/para*-director, so simple bromination will yield a substantial amount of both the *ortho* and *para* isomers, as shown in Equation 23-53.

simple bromination will produce a mixture of both the *ortho* and *para* isomers

$$\text{phenol} \xrightarrow[CH_3CO_2H]{Br_2} \textit{o}\text{-bromophenol} + \textit{p}\text{-bromophenol} \quad (23\text{-}53)$$

One method that can be used to protect the *para* position is to place a sulfonyl group there temporarily (Equation 23-54).

$$\text{phenol} \underset{H_2SO_4}{\overset{SO_3}{\rightleftharpoons}} \text{(OH, } SO_3H\text{)} \xrightarrow[FeBr_3]{Br_2} \text{(OH, Br, } SO_3H\text{)} \underset{H^{\oplus}}{\overset{H_2O}{\rightleftharpoons}} \text{(OH, Br, H)} \quad (23\text{-}54)$$

sulfonyl group "blocks" the *para* position

deprotection

As we learned in Section 22.7, sulfonation is *reversible*, and will take place almost exclusively at the *para* position. Subsequent bromination takes place *ortho* to the hydroxyl group—the hydroxyl group dictates regiochemistry because it is the most activating group on the ring, and furthermore, there is no hydrogen atom *para* to the hydroxyl group. Effectively, then, the sulfonyl group "blocks" the para *position.* After bromination, the sulfonyl group is removed by treatment with aqueous acid.

Interestingly, an amino group can also be used as a blocking group. This is illustrated in the synthesis of *m*-chlorotoluene from *p*-methylaniline (Equation 23-55).

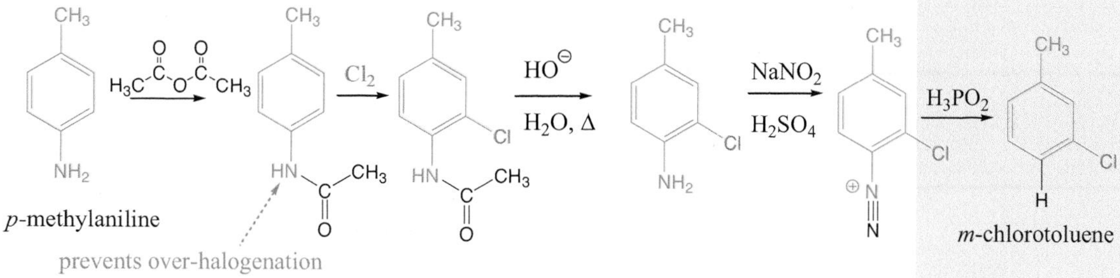

p-methylaniline

prevents over-halogenation

m-chlorotoluene

(23-55)

In the first step, the NH_2 group is converted to the amide to prevent over-halogenation—an amide group is less activating than an amine. In the second step, halogenation takes place *ortho* to the amide group, given that the amide is more activating than the methyl group. Next, the amine is deprotected by hydrolysis. Diazotization followed by treatment with H_3PO_2 converts the NH_2 group into an H (Section 22.11c). Therefore, even though the original NH_2 group is not in the final product, it was instrumental in directing the regiochemistry of chlorination.

Problem 23.26. Show how you can carry out the following synthesis without generating any of the *para* isomer.

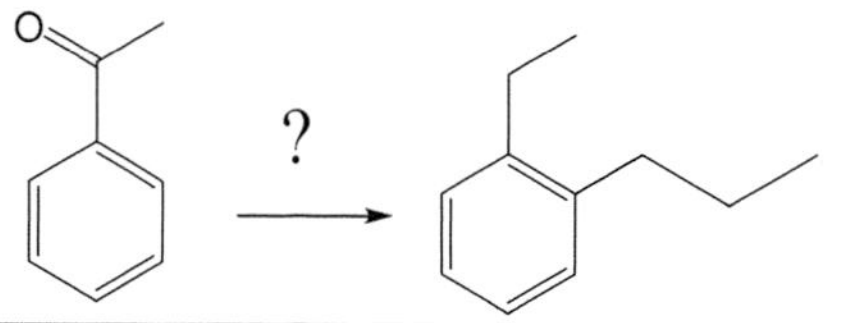

?

23.14. FUNCTIONAL GROUP CHEMISTRY

The reactions discussed in Chapters 22 and 23 have primarily involved substitution on aromatic rings, summarized in Section 23.14a. However, we have also introduced some reactions that involve transformations of functional groups to which an aromatic ring is attached, including ketones (Section 23.14b), alkenes (Section 23.14c), alkynes (Section 23.14d), and amines (Section 23.14e). As usual, aspects of functional group chemistry examined in previous chapters appear gray, whereas the new aspects appear green.

23.14a. Aromatic Rings

Substitution takes place on an aromatic ring under a variety of conditions. Typically, these reactions involve electrophilic aromatic substitution, in which a proton is replaced by a very strong electrophile. Whether that proton is one that is *ortho*, *meta*, or *para* to a substituent on the ring depends on the directing capability of the substituent. As indicated, some substitutions, such as desulfonation, replace a non-hydrogen substituent on the ring instead.

Reactions involving nucleophilic aromatic substitution can take place on an aryl halide under certain conditions.

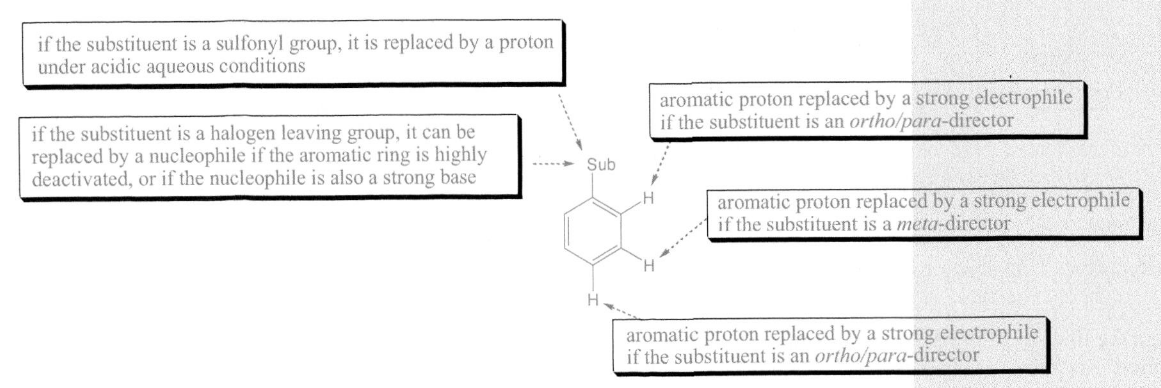

23.14b. Alkenes

The new reaction involving alkenes is the $KMnO_4$ oxidation of an aromatic alkene to a carboxylic acid.

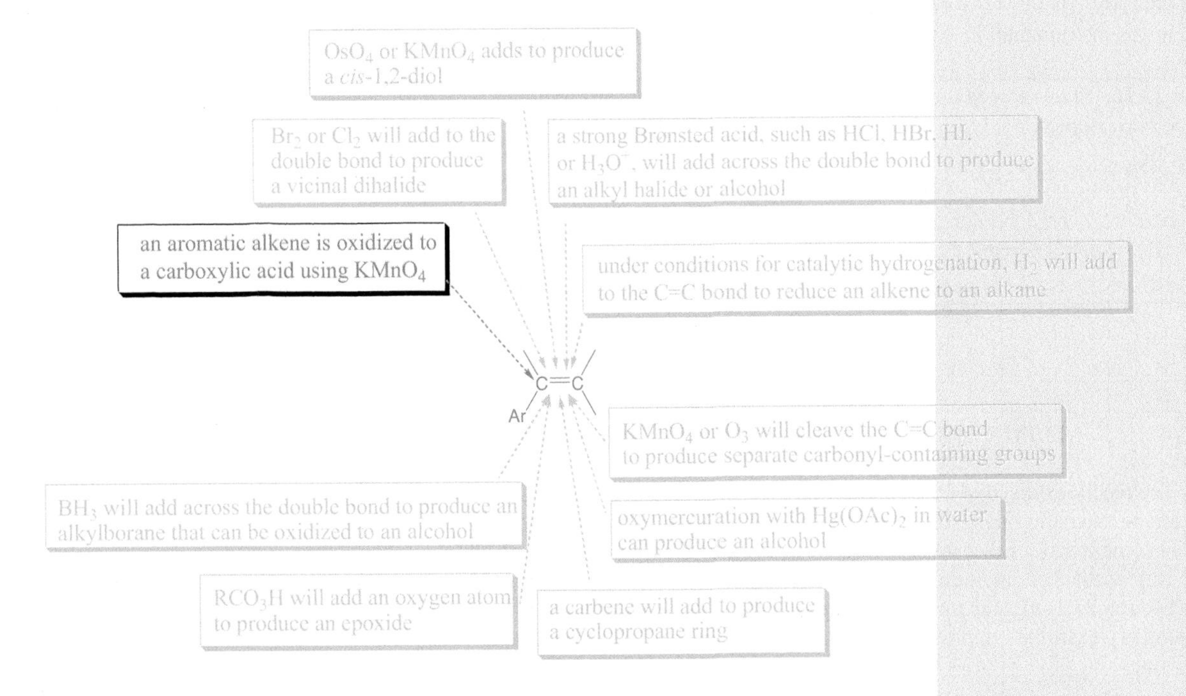

23.14c. Alkynes

The new reaction involving alkynes is the $KMnO_4$ oxidation of an aromatic alkyne to a carboxylic acid.

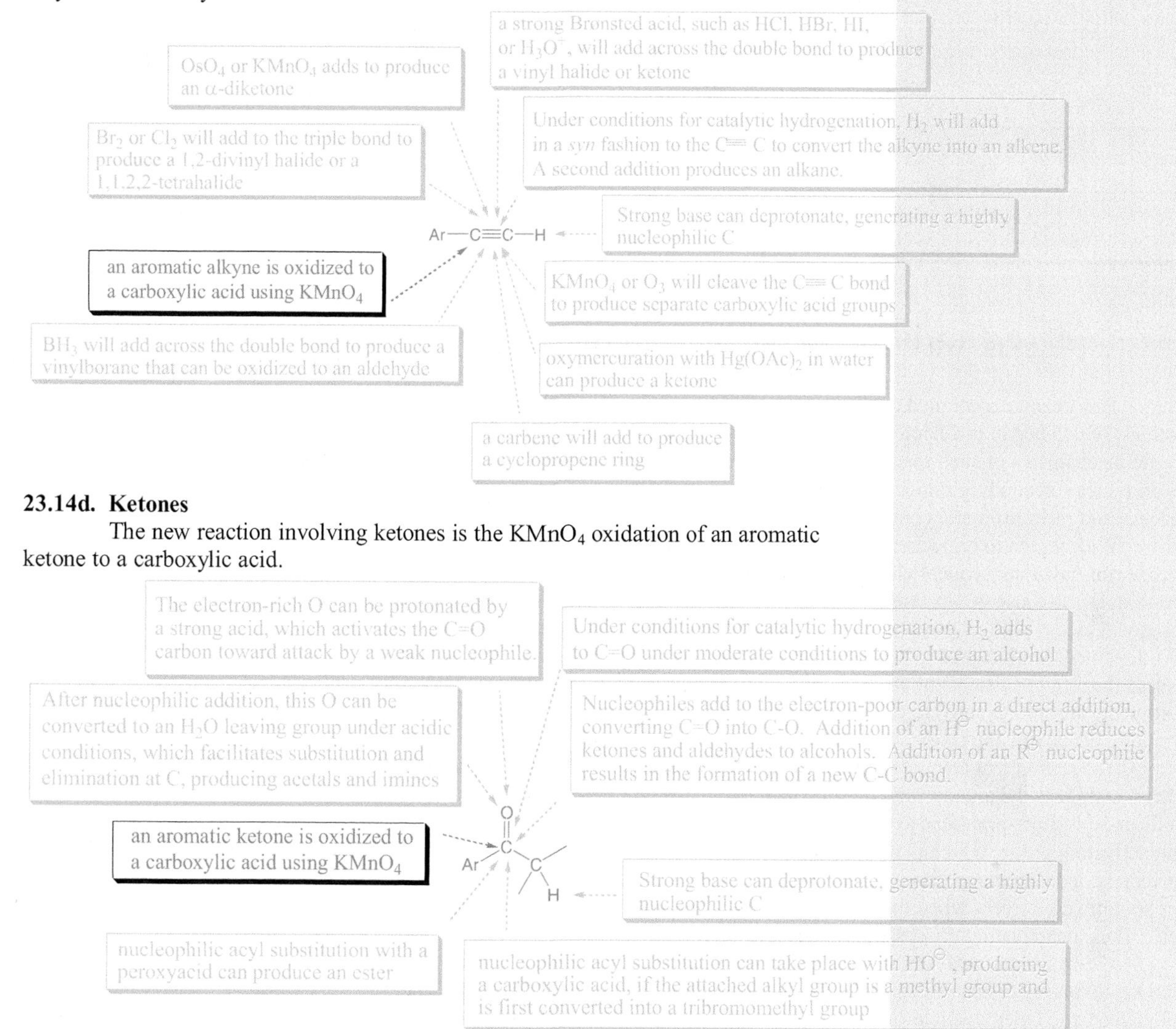

23.14d. Ketones

The new reaction involving ketones is the $KMnO_4$ oxidation of an aromatic ketone to a carboxylic acid.

23.14e. Amines

The new reaction involving amines is the conversion of an aromatic amine, $Ar\text{-}NH_2$, to an arenediazonium ion, $Ar\text{-}N_2^+$.

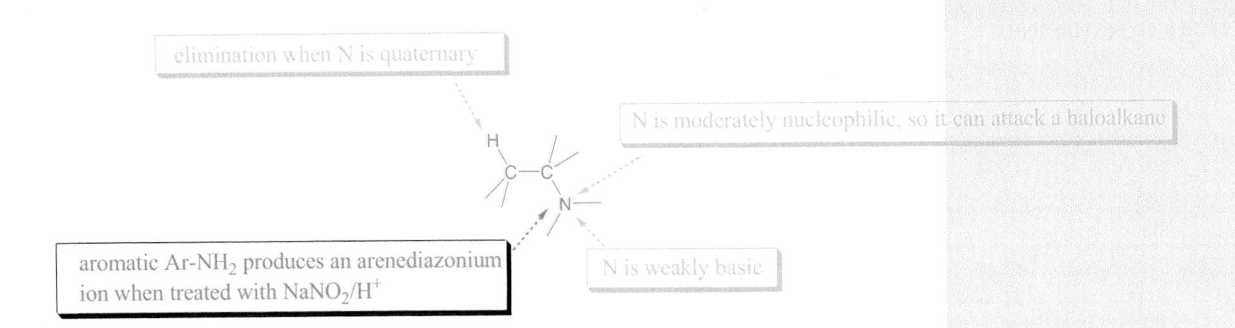

23.15. WRAPPING UP AND LOOKING AHEAD

This chapter continued the discussion of electrophilic aromatic substitution reactions, which began in Chapter 22. Whereas Chapter 22 focused primarily on the specific mechanisms of such reactions involving benzene, the main focus of this chapter was on issues surrounding regiochemistry, kinetics, and synthesis involving substituted benzenes and other aromatic compounds.

With regard to regiochemistry, we saw that certain groups already attached to a benzene ring favor subsequent electrophilic substitution at positions that are *ortho* and *para* to itself, so those groups are designated as *ortho/para*-directors. Other groups favor subsequent electrophilic substitution at positions *meta* to itself, making those groups *meta*-directors. With regard to kinetics, certain groups attached to a benzene ring tend to increase the rate of subsequent electrophilic aromatic substitution reactions, so those substituents are said to activate the aromatic ring. Other groups do the opposite, so they are said to deactivate the ring.

The reason that an activating group speeds up electrophilic aromatic substitution is that it stabilizes the arenium ion intermediate ion that is produced. Furthermore, such stabilization is more pronounced when an incoming electrophile adds either *ortho* or *para* to an activating group, which is why activating groups tend to be *ortho/para*-directors. Conversely, a deactivating group serves to destabilize the arenium ion intermediate, and does so more effectively when the incoming electrophile adds either *ortho* or *para* to itself. Thus, deactivating groups tend to be *meta*-directors.

Using similar analyses, we also examined electrophilic aromatic substitution reactions involving disubstituted benzenes and other aromatic compounds, including naphthalene and heterocyclic aromatics. For example, we saw that in disubstituted benzenes, the activating/deactivating nature of the substituents is essentially additive, and, furthermore, regiochemistry is governed by the most activating substituent present. We also saw that in the substitution of a heterocyclic aromatic, the activation of the ring and the regiochemistry of the reaction can depend heavily on the size of the ring.

Finally, we introduced two types of aromatic substitution reactions that do not proceed by the electrophilic mechanism. Rather, they are examples of nucleophilic aromatic substitution reactions. One proceeds by a nucleophilic addition-elimination mechanism, and the other proceeds through a benzyne intermediate.

Many of the reactions in the chapters to come involve the addition of species to nonpolar π bonds, reminiscent of reaction steps we have seen throughout Chapters 20 – 23. In Chapter 24, for example, we will examine the Diels-Alder reaction, in which a diene adds to an alkene. Further, in Chapter 25, we will see examples of the addition of free radicals to alkenes. Therefore, we will have opportunities to apply the knowledge we have gained from the last few chapters.

REACTION TABLES

Table 23-6. Functional group transformations

Starting Functional Group	Typical Reagent Required	Functional Group Formed	Comments	Discussed in Section(s)
X= F, Cl, Br, I (aromatic ring bearing X and EWG) Deactivate aromatic halide	$Nu^{\ominus}$ →	(aromatic ring bearing Nu and EWG)	Nucleophilic addition-elimination mechanism	23.10a
X= F, Cl, Br, I (benzene ring bearing X) Aromatic halide	$Base^{\ominus}$ →	(benzene ring bearing Base)	Proceeds through benzyne intermediate	23.10b

CHAPTER SUMMARY AND KEY TERMS

- In electrophilic aromatic substitution reactions, certain substituents attached to a benzene ring favor reaction at the *ortho* and *para* positions, and are characterized as ***ortho/para*-directors**. Others substituents favor reaction at the *meta* position, and are called ***meta*-directors**. (Section 23.1)
- A substituent attached to a benzene ring by an atom possessing a lone pair of electrons tends to be an *ortho/para*-director. When the incoming electrophile adds to a benzene carbon at the *ortho* or *para* positions, the arenium ion intermediate that is produced is stabilized by these substituents via resonance. (Section 23.2)
- Alkyl groups are *ortho/para*-directors, because they stabilize *ortho* and *para* arenium ion intermediates via electron-donating effects. (Section 23.3)
- Nitro groups and other electron-withdrawing groups are *meta*-directors. They destabilize the arenium ion intermediate when the incoming electrophile adds to the *ortho* or *para* position. (Section 23.4)
- All else being equal, the greater the steric hindrance resulting from the bulkiness of a substituent or incoming electrophile, the less favored substitution is at the *ortho* position. (Section 23.5)
- In general, *ortho/para*-directors increase the rate of electrophilic aromatic substitution, and are called **activating groups**. Conversely, *meta* directors tend to slow the reaction rate, and are called **deactivating groups**. Halogen substituents are exceptions—they are *ortho/para*-directors but are deactivating groups. (Section 23.6)
- The reason that activating groups speed up an electrophilic aromatic substitution reaction is that they stabilize the arenium ion intermediate that is produced. By contrast, deactivating groups destabilize the arenium ion intermediate. (Section 23.6)
- The conditions under which an electrophilic aromatic substitution reaction takes place can alter a substituent's *ortho/meta/para*-directing capabilities, as well as its activating/deactivating capabilities. For example, the benzene ring of phenol

is much more activated under neutral conditions than it is under acidic conditions. More strikingly, whereas an amine group is an *ortho/para*-director under mildly acidic conditions, it is a *meta*-director under strongly acidic conditions. (Section 23.7)

- When multiple substituents are attached to a benzene ring, their activating/deactivating qualities are additive, and the regiochemistry tends to be governed by the most activating of those substituents. (Section 23.8)
- Aromatic rings other than benzene can also undergo electrophilic aromatic substitution. These include naphthalene, furan, pyrrole, and pyridine. Just as in substituted benzenes, the regiochemistry and relative reaction rates are governed by the stabilities of the arenium ion intermediates that are produced. (Section 23.9)
- Aromatic rings with halogen substituents can undergo **nucleophilic aromatic substitution**, whereby the halogen atom is replaced by a nucleophile.
  - Rings that are strongly deactivated (and thus electron-poor) react via a nucleophilic addition-elimination mechanism, under relatively mild conditions. (Section 23.10a)
  - Rings that are not strongly deactivated typically require strong bases, high temperatures, or both, and proceed through a **benzyne intermediate**. (Section 23.10b)
- When incorporating successive electrophilic aromatic substitution reactions in a synthesis, it is important to consider the order in which those reactions are carried out. The incorrect order could lead to undesired regiochemistry, or could preclude some reactions entirely. (Section 23.11)
- Reactions that transform an *ortho/para*-director into a *meta*-director, and vice versa, can be instrumental in synthesis. An example of the former is the $KMnO_4$ oxidation of an alkyl side chain to a carboxylic acid. An example of the latter is the reduction of a nitro group to an amine. (Section 23.12)
- The reactivity of an aromatic amine can be temporarily decreased by converting the amine group into an amide group. Additionally, the *para* position of a benzene ring can be temporarily blocked by sulfonating that position. (Section 23.13)

PROBLEMS

27. Predict the major product(s) of each of the following reactions. Draw the complete, detailed mechanism that leads to the formation of each of those products.

(a) HO_3S–benzene $\xrightarrow[H_2SO_4]{HNO_3}$?

(b) ethylbenzene $\xrightarrow[FeCl_3]{Cl_2}$?

(c) H_3CO–benzene + benzoyl chloride (Cl) $\xrightarrow{AlCl_3}$?

(d) phenyl cyclopentyl ketone $\xrightarrow[FeBr_3]{Br_2}$?

(e) isopropylbenzene $\xrightarrow{\text{conc. } HNO_3}$?

28. For each pair of aromatic compounds, determine which will undergo electrophilic aromatic substitution faster.

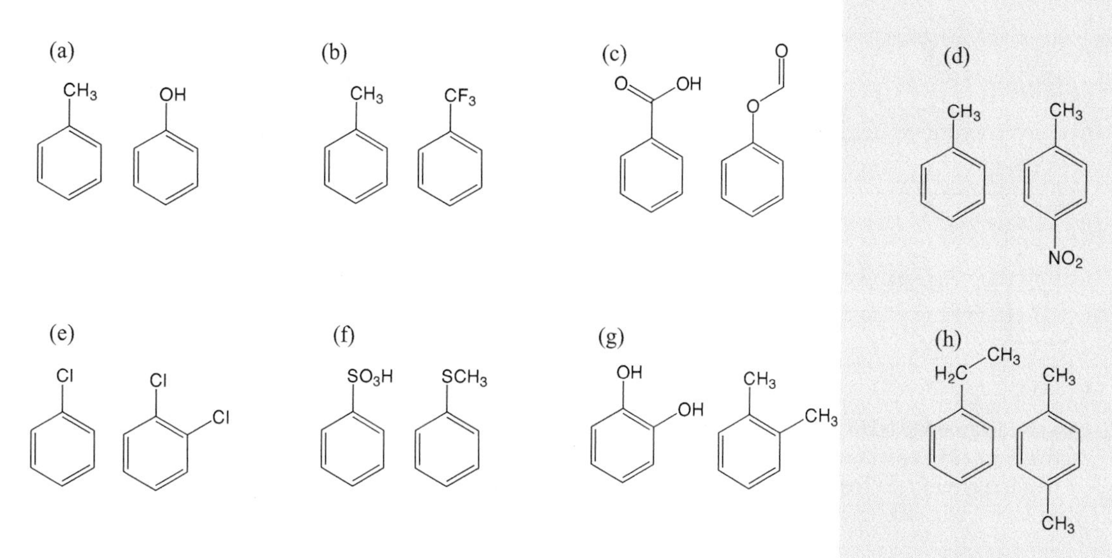

29. Draw the structures of the missing compounds in the synthesis scheme below.

Benzene $\xrightarrow[\text{AlCl}_3]{\text{propanoyl chloride}}$ A $\xrightarrow[\text{FeCl}_3]{\text{Cl}_2}$ B $\xrightarrow{CH_3\overset{\ominus}{C}H\text{-}\overset{\oplus}{P}(Ph_3)_3}$ C $\xrightarrow{\text{MCPBA}}$ D $\xrightarrow[\text{2) } H_3O^+]{\text{1) } C_6H_5MgBr}$ E $\xrightarrow[\Delta]{\text{conc. } H_3PO_4}$ F

30. Draw the structures of the missing compounds in the synthesis scheme below.

Benzene $\xrightarrow[\text{FeBr}_3]{\text{Br}_2}$ A $\xrightarrow[\text{AlCl}_3]{CH_3Cl}$ B $\xrightarrow[HO^{\ominus},\ \Delta]{\text{KMnO}_4}$ C $\xrightarrow[\text{2) } H_3O^+]{\text{1) LiAlH}_4}$ D $\xrightarrow{\text{PCC}}$ E $\xrightarrow[\text{NaOH, }\Delta]{H_3C\text{-}CO\text{-}CH_3}$ F $\xrightarrow[H_2O]{\text{KCN}}$ G $\xrightarrow[\Delta]{H_3O^+}$ H

31. Draw the structures of the missing compounds in the synthesis scheme below.

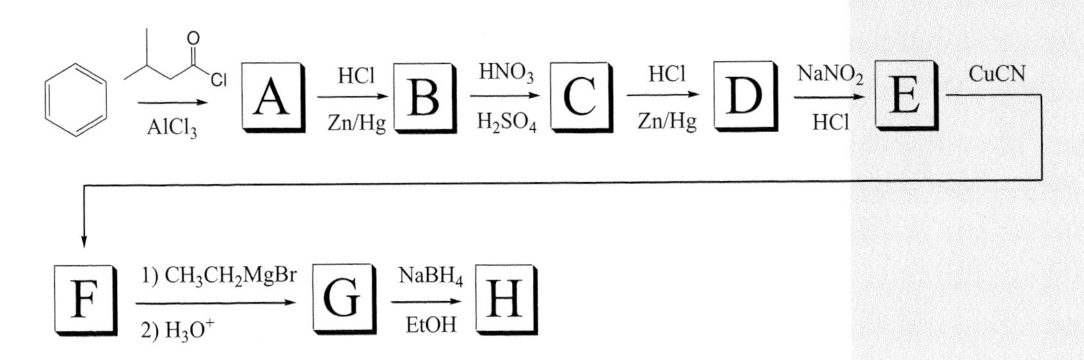

32. An amide group (–NH-CO-R) is an *ortho/para*-director and is moderately activating. (a) Explain why it is an *ortho/para*-director. (b) Explain why it is an activating group. (c) Explain why it is less activating than NH_2.

33. The OH group on phenol is considered to be an activating group. The ring in phenylmethanol, on the other hand, is deactivated. Explain.

34. When 2-methylnaphthalene undergoes electrophilic aromatic substitution, the electrophile predominantly attacks the 1-position instead of the 3-position. This suggests that the arenium ion that is formed from addition of the electrophile to the 1-position is more stable than that formed from addition of the electrophile to the 3-position. Explain why this is so. (Hint: Simple resonance theory can explain why.)

MAJOR PRODUCT

CH_3 $\xrightarrow{E^{\oplus}}$ E, CH_3 + CH_3, E

2-methylnaphthalene

S

35. As we learned in the chapter, a thiophene ring is sufficiently activated that bromination may take place without the presence of a Lewis acid catalyst. With this in mind, draw the complete mechanism for the following reaction, and predict the major product.

S $\xrightarrow[CCl_4]{Br_2}$

36. (a) For which aromatic compound do you expect nitration to take place faster—furan or thiophene? (b) For each of these compounds, at which C atom do you expect electrophilic substitution to predominantly take place? Explain your reasoning.

O S

furan thiophene

37. The electrostatic potential maps of benzene and pyridine are shown below. Is the electrostatic potential map of pyridine consistent with the ring being activated or deactivated relative to benzene? Explain.

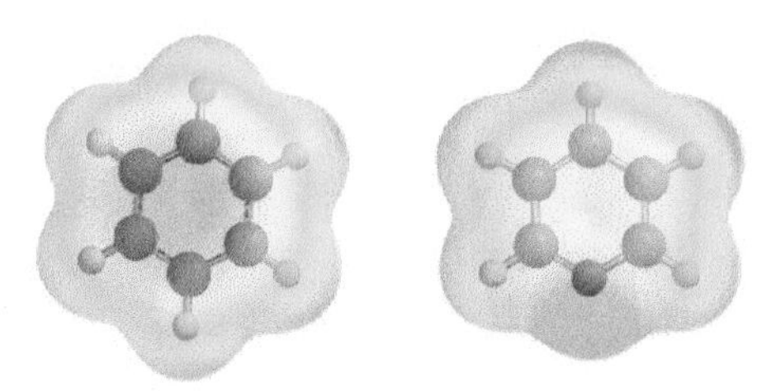

38. The electrostatic potential maps of benzene and pyrrole are shown below. Is the electrostatic potential map of pyrrole consistent with the ring being activated or deactivated relative to benzene? Explain.

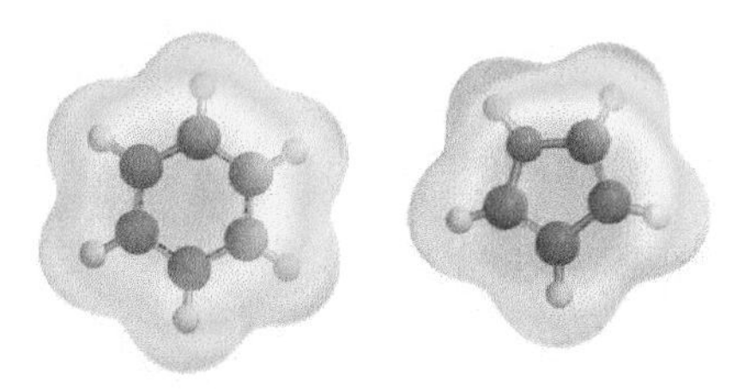

39. Predict the most likely site of attack in electrophilic substitution.

a. 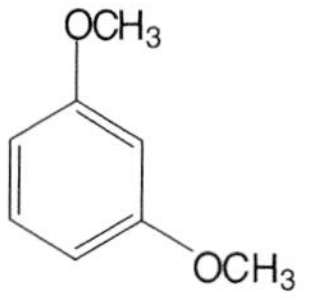 OCH_3, OCH_3

b. 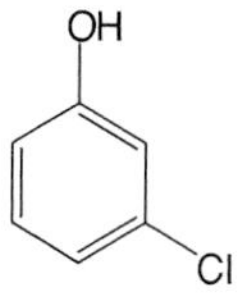 OH, Cl

c. 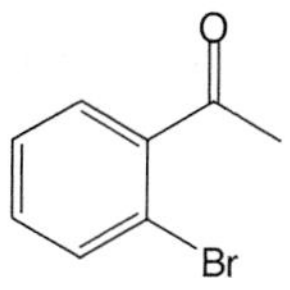 O, Br

d. 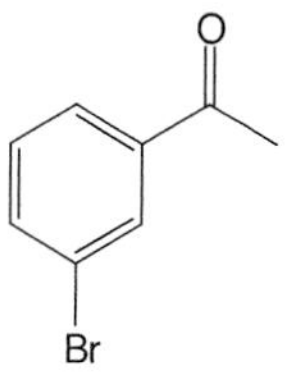 O, Br

e. 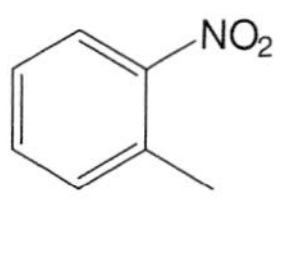 NO_2

f. 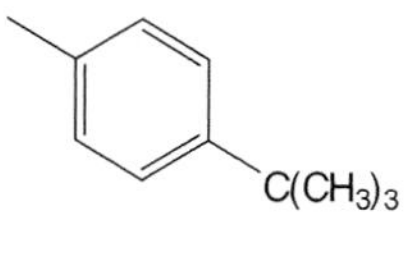 $C(CH_3)_3$

g. 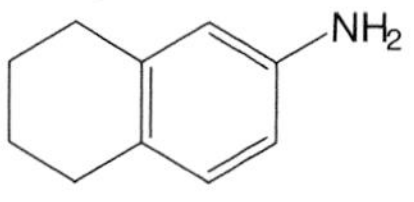 NH_2

40. In the chapter we learned that halogen atoms are one of the few substituents that are *ortho/para*-directing but are deactivating. The nitroso group (–N=O) is another of such substituents. (a) Explain why the nitroso group is *ortho/para*-directing. (b) Explain why it is deactivating.

41. Predict the most likely site of electrophilic substitution in each of the following molecules.

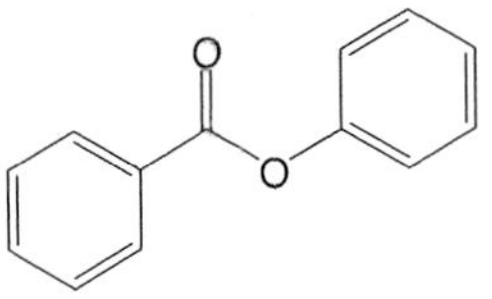

a.

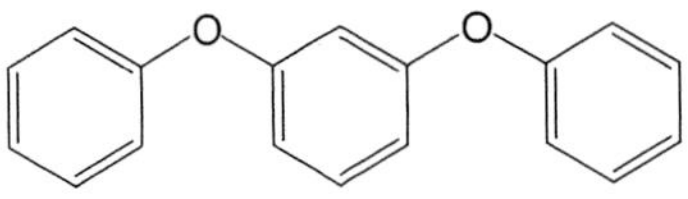

b.

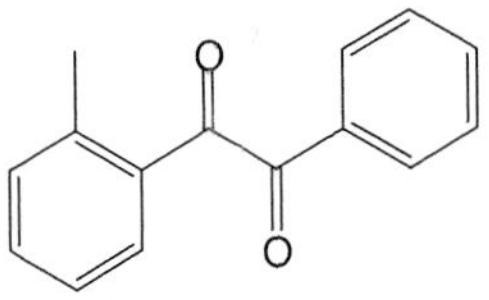

c.

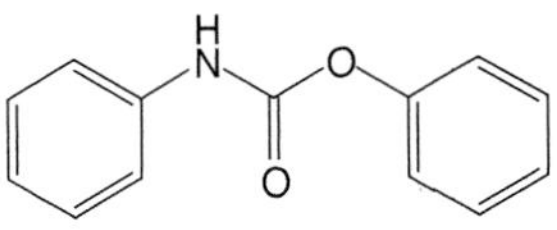

d.

42. Predict the most likely site of attack of electrophilic substitution on the compound below. (Hint: How do you determine whether the substituent is an *ortho/para*-directing group or a *meta*-directing group?)

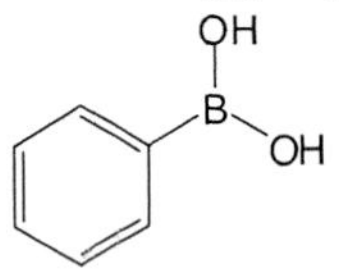

43. Show how you would carry out the following synthesis.

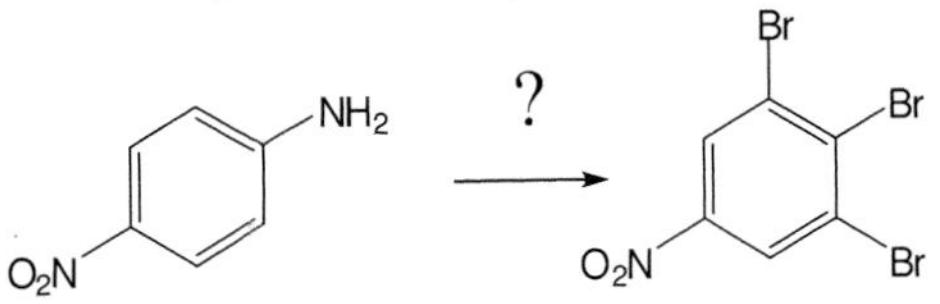

44. Draw the complete, detailed mechanism for the following reaction and predict the major product.

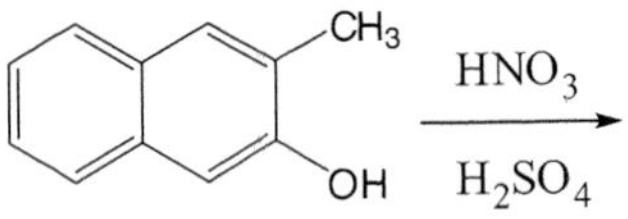

$$\xrightarrow[H_2SO_4]{HNO_3} ?$$

45. Electrophilic aromatic substitution on *N,N*-dimethylaniline is faster than on the unsubstituted aniline. In other words, the benzene ring in *N,N*-dimethylaniline is more activated than is the ring in aniline itself.

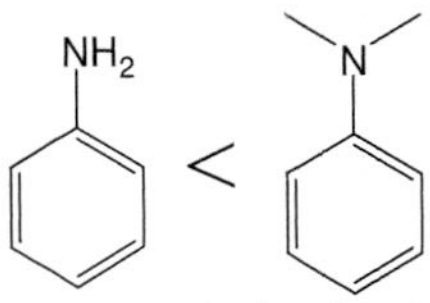

However, if the ring is methylated at the 2- and 6-positions, then the *N,N*-dimethylsubstituted compound reacts slower in electrophilic aromatic substitution than does the unsubstituted compound.

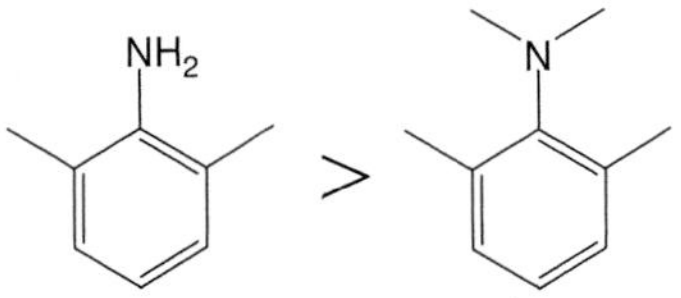

Explain both of these results.

46. The following reaction yields a compound whose molecular formula is $C_7H_6O_4$. The product's ^{1}H-NMR and ^{13}C-NMR spectra are shown. Draw the complete, detailed mechanism for this reaction.

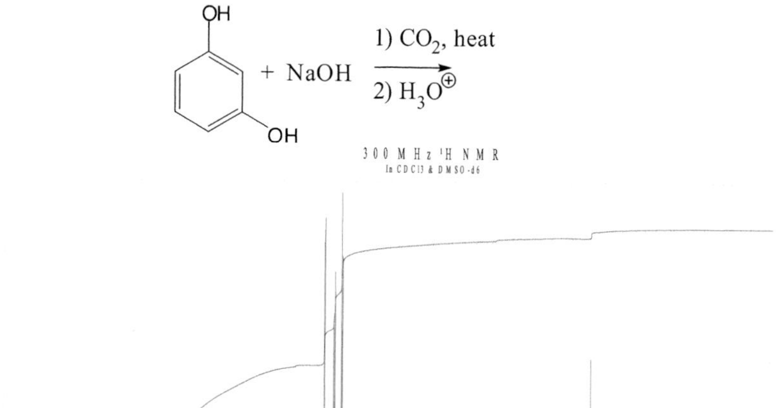

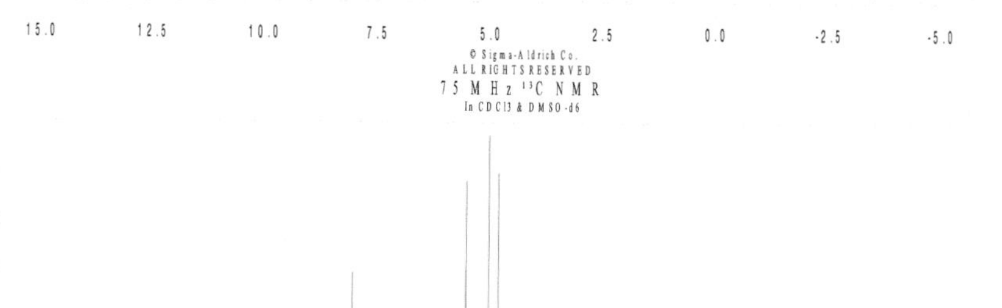

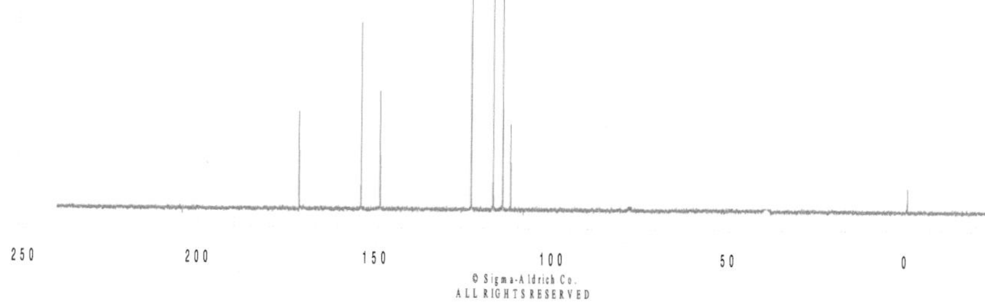

47. Draw a complete, detailed mechanism for the following reaction. A key intermediate is provided.

OH EtO O O CH₃ $\xrightarrow{H^{\oplus}}$ [O OH H₃C OH] ⟶ O O CH₃

48. Starting with benzene, show how you would synthesize each of the following.

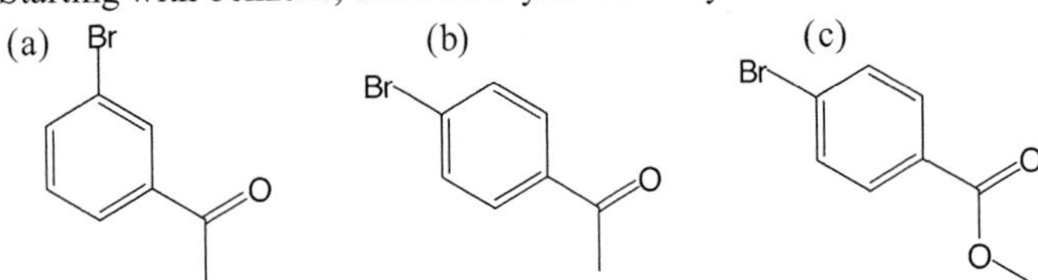

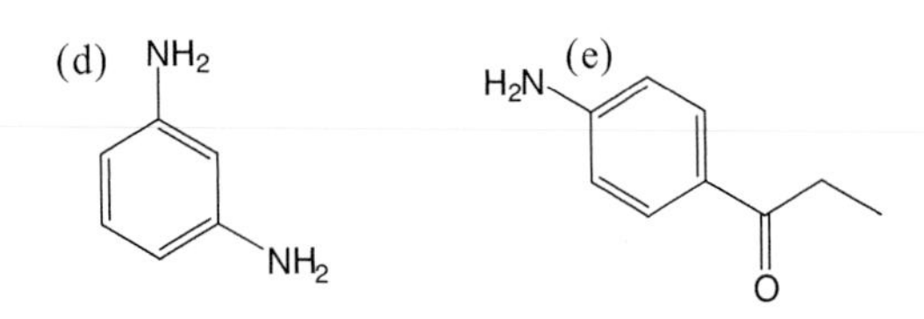

49. Draw the complete, detailed mechanism and predict the major product for each of the following reactions.

a. OH $\xrightarrow[H_2SO_4]{HNO_3}$

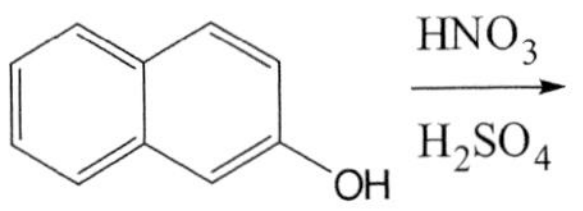

b. O Cl $\xrightarrow{AlCl_3}$

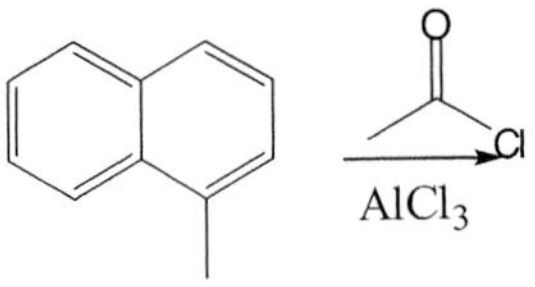

c. NO2 $\xrightarrow[FeBr_3]{Br_2}$

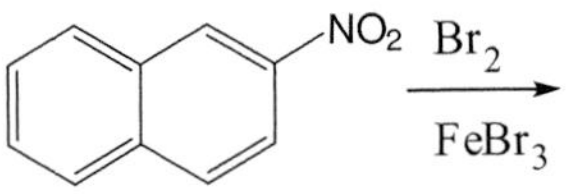

d. HN O $\xrightarrow[FeCl_3]{Cl_2}$

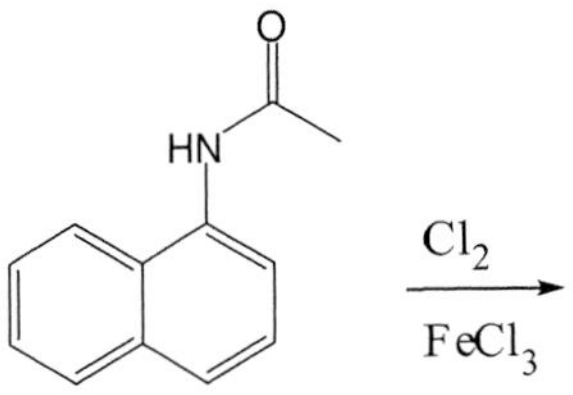

50. The phenyl group, C_6H_5, is known to be an *ortho/para*-directing group. (a) With that in mind, predict the product of the following reaction. (b) Justify why it is an *ortho/para*-director by examining the *ortho*, *meta*, and *para* arenium ion intermediates that would be formed during the course of the reaction.

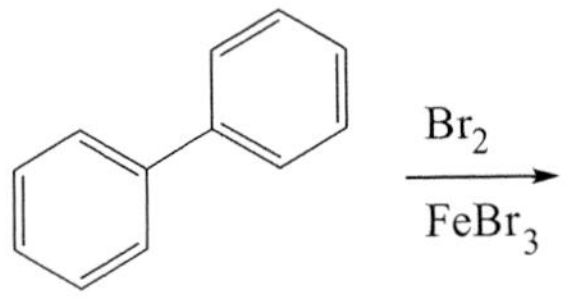

$\xrightarrow[FeBr_3]{Br_2}$

51. Draw the complete, detailed mechanism and predict the major product for each of the following reactions.

a. HN $\xrightarrow{Br_2}$

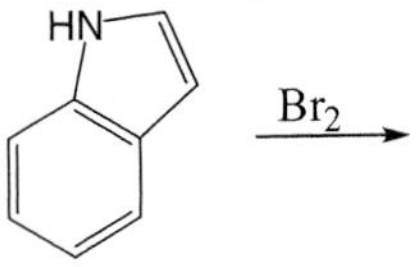

b. N $\xrightarrow[FeBr_3]{Br_2}$

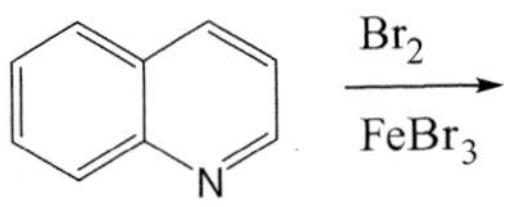

c. S $\xrightarrow[(CH_3CO)_2O]{HNO_3}$

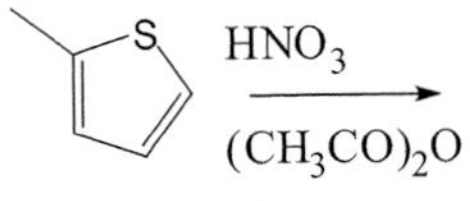

d. N N $\xrightarrow[\text{acetic acid, } \Delta]{HNO_3}$

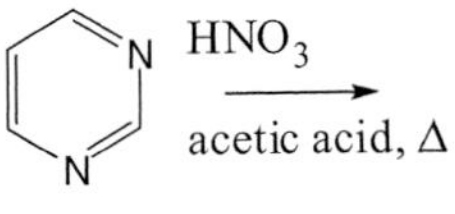

52. Predict the site on each molecule that is most likely to undergo electrophilic aromatic substitution.

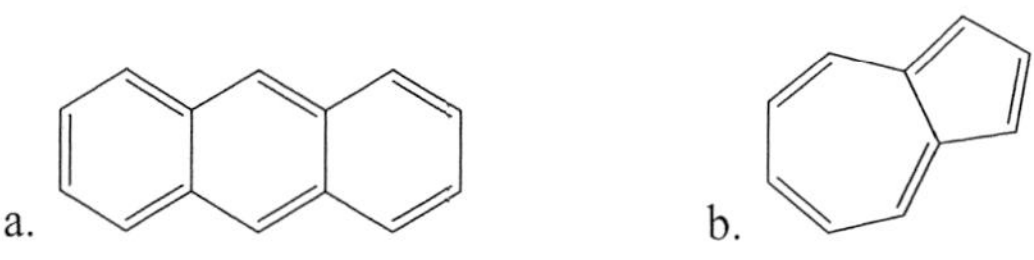

53. Draw a complete, detailed mechanism for the reaction below.

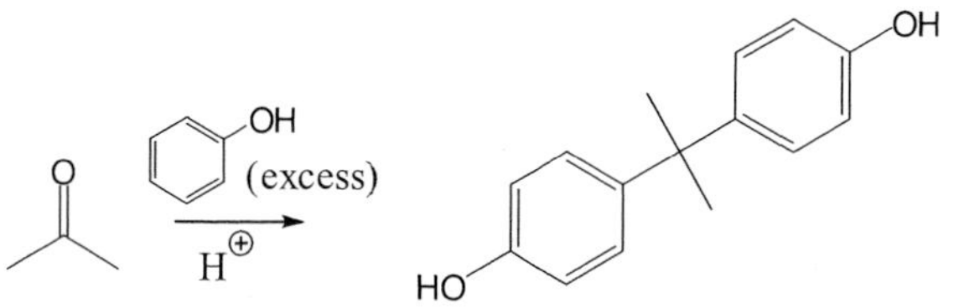

(excess)

$H^{\oplus}$

54. Show how you would synthesize the compound below, using 1-propanol and benzene as your only sources of carbon.

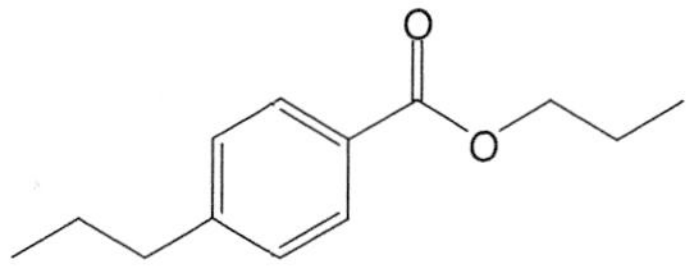

55. Show how you would synthesize each of the compounds below, using 1-butanol and benzene as your only sources of carbon.

a. 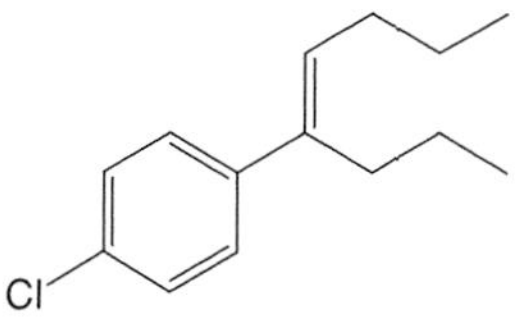 b.

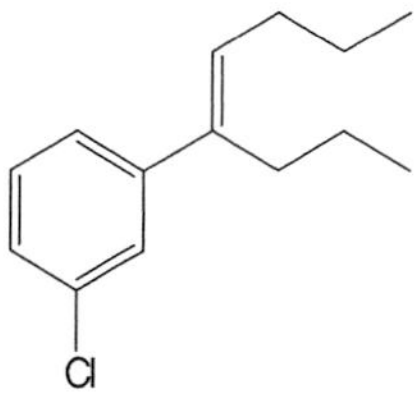

56. In the chapter, we learned that aniline becomes highly deactivated in the presence of a strong Lewis acid, due to coordination of the N atom to the Lewis acid. Thus, Friedel-Crafts reactions involving aniline are unfeasible. As shown below, this does not appear to be a problem with the N atom in pyrrole. Explain why.

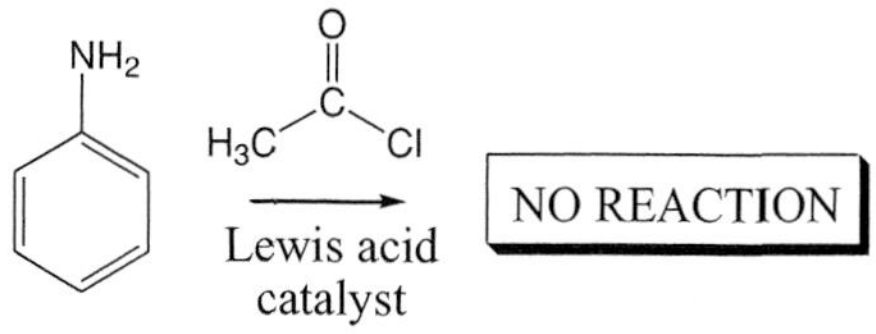

Lewis acid catalyst

NO REACTION

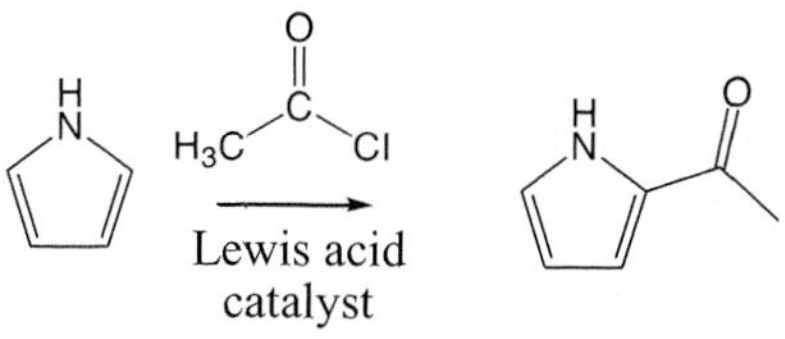

Lewis acid catalyst

Chapter 24. The Diels-Alder Reaction and Other Pericyclic Reactions

Introduction

Ethene reacts with 1,3-butadiene to form cyclohexene, as illustrated in Equation 24-1. This is the simplest example of what is called the **Diels-Alder reaction**. Because of this reaction's importance, Otto Diels and Kurt Alder—the two German chemists after whom the reaction is named—shared the 1950 Nobel prize in chemistry.

the Diels-Alder reaction

1,3-butadiene + ethene → (200 °C, 17 h, high pressure) cyclohexene 18%

new carbon-carbon bonds

(24-1)

The importance of the Diels-Alder reaction can be seen immediately by the fact that it forms two carbon-carbon bonds. (As we stressed in Chapter 11, these are the most important types of reaction in organic synthesis.) Furthermore, notice that the product of the Diels-Alder reaction is a six-membered ring, which is widely abundant in natural products. Moreover, the reaction is quite robust; it can be carried out with a variety of other functional groups present, often under mild conditions. Finally, the reaction is both *regioselective* and *stereoselective*, which provides chemists substantial control over the types of products that are formed.

As we will see, the Diels-Alder reaction's mechanism cannot be described by the elementary steps we learned in Chapters 6 and 7. Therefore, we will explore this reaction with the same systematic approach we took with the introduction of the previous elementary steps. We will begin with a look at the curved arrow notation and examples. Then we will investigate the reaction's driving force and reversibility, followed by its regiochemistry, and finally its stereochemistry.

Once we have thoroughly examined the Diels-Alder reaction, we will turn our attention to other reactions that proceed by essentially the same mechanism—ones that are characterized as *pericyclic reactions*. Among them are *electrocyclic reactions*, the *Cope rearrangement*, and the *Claisen rearrangement*. You will find that much of your knowledge gained from studying the Diels-Alder reaction is applicable to these reactions as well.

We conclude this chapter with an optional section, in which the nature of the Diels-Alder reaction is discussed from the perspective of molecular orbital theory. Such a discussion provides a deeper understanding of both the driving force and the stereoselectivity of the reaction. However, being an "optional" section, it can be skipped without undermining your understanding of material in future chapters.

CHAPTER OBJECTIVES

Upon completion of this chapter you should be able to…

- Recognize a **Diels-Alder reaction** as a **pericylic reaction,** and, more specifically, as a **[4+2] cycloaddition**.
- Identify potential **dienes** and **dienophiles** for use in a Diels-Alder reaction.
- Determine whether a cycloaddition reaction is **allowed** or **forbidden**, based on whether the reaction proceeds through an **aromatic transition state** or an **antiaromatic transition state**.
- Predict the outcome of a Diels-Alder reaction based on the diene's ability to attain an ***s-cis* conformation**.
- Describe the roles of enthalpy and entropy in the reversibility of a Diels-Alder reaction.
- Predict relative rates of Diels-Alder reactions based upon the presence of electron-donating and electron-withdrawing groups in the reactants.
- Predict the major product of a Diels-Alder reaction in terms of its *stereochemistry* and *regiochemistry*.
- Describe a **hetero Diels-Alder reaction**, and predict the products of such a reaction.
- Recognize and draw the mechanisms of pericyclic reactions other than the Diels-Alder reaction, including **electrocyclic reactions**, the **Cope rearrangement**, and the **Claisen rearrangement**.
- Employ **frontier molecular orbital theory** to predict whether a cycloaddition reaction is **thermally allowed** or **thermally forbidden**.
- Account for substituent effects and stereochemistry of Diels-Alder reactions using frontier molecular orbital theory.
- Predict which cycloaddition reactions are **photochemically allowed** and which are **photochemically forbidden**, based upon frontier orbital interactions.

24.1. CURVED ARROW NOTATION AND EXAMPLES

The mechanism for the simplest possible Diels-Alder reaction (shown earlier in Equation 24-1) is provided in Equation 24-2. This serves as the prototype for all other Diels-Alder reactions.

Mechanism for the Reaction in Equation 24-1, the Diels-Alder Reaction

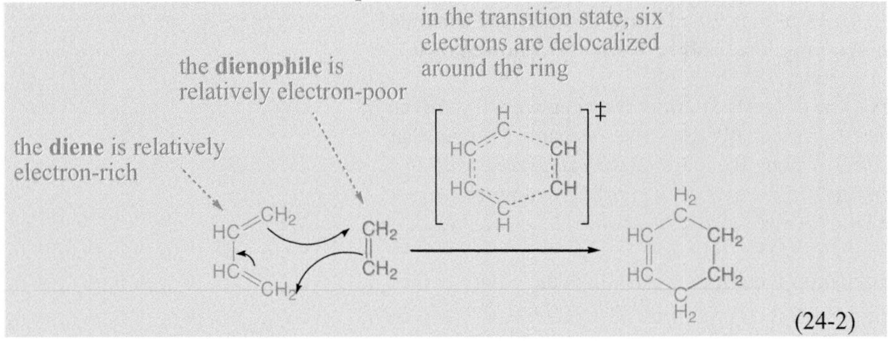

Notice that the entire reaction takes place in a single step. In other words,

> The Diels-Alder reaction is a **concerted reaction**, whereby all of the bonds that are formed and broken are done so simultaneously.

For this to occur, six electrons must flow in a cyclic fashion. Thus, the reaction proceeds through a *cyclic transition state*, so it belongs to a class of reactions called **pericyclic reactions**. More specifically, because this cyclic movement of electrons results in the formation of a ring by joining together two separate species, it is also called a **cycloaddition reaction**. (Other types of pericyclic reactions will be discussed in Section 24.8.)

Four of the six electrons involved in a Diels-Alder reaction come from a pair of *conjugated* π bonds, which is often just a **diene**. The species from which the other two electrons originate is called a **dienophile**, meaning that it is "diene loving." Notice that two electrons contributed by the dienophile are also π electrons. Consequently, a Diels-Alder reaction is often described as a **[4+2] cycloaddition**, where the numbers indicate the number of π electrons contributed by each species involved.

Comment [JMK48]: **Margin note.** In a Diels-Alder reaction, the **diene** contributes four π electrons, and the **dienophile** contributes two π electrons.

In the elementary steps we examined in Chapters 6 and 7, we saw that electrons flow from an electron-rich site to an electron-poor one. In the case of the Diels-Alder reaction, however, it may not immediately be obvious which species—the diene or the dienophile—should be viewed as electron-rich and which should be viewed as electron-poor. In fact, according to our treatment of nonpolar π bonds in Chapters 20 and 21, both species appear to be electron-rich—each has at least one alkene group, in which four electrons are concentrated in a bonding region.

However, "electron-rich" and "electron-poor" are *relative* descriptors. With this in mind, realize that the diene has four electrons in a single π system, whereas the dienophile's π system has only two. Thus,

> In a Diels-Alder reaction, the diene is relatively electron-rich, and the dienophile is relatively electron-poor.

Viewed in this way, a curved arrow is drawn from the diene to the dienophile to initiate the flow of electrons. The other two curved arrows are necessary so as to avoid breaking any octets.

The Diels-Alder reaction can take place with a variety of different molecules acting as the diene and dienophile. For example, Equation 24-3 illustrates a Diels-Alder reaction in which one of the reactants is a ring, yielding a *bicyclic* product. Equation 24-4 provides an example in which the dienophile is an alkyne—two electrons are contributed from one π bond of the triple bond, leaving the other π bond intact in the product.

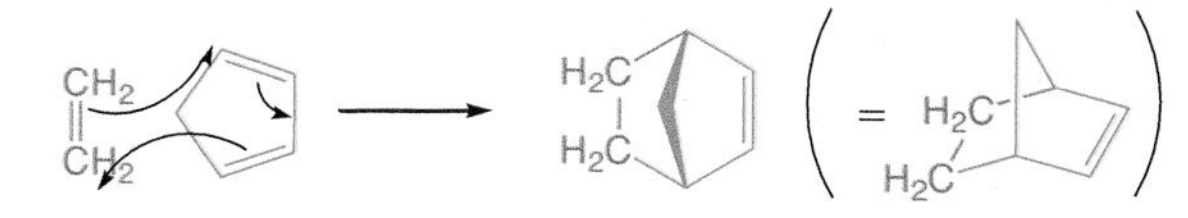

ethene cyclopentadiene bicyclo[2.2.1]hept-2-ene (24-3)

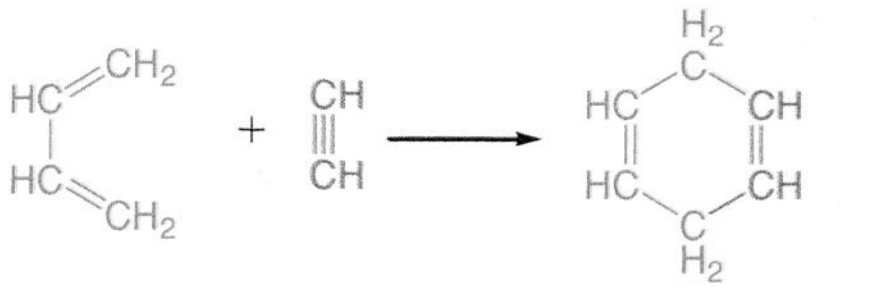

1,3-butadiene ethyne cyclohexa-1,4-diene (24-4)

Your Turn 24.1. The reaction in Equation 24-4 is repeated below. Supply the curved arrows, label the diene and dienophile, and identify which reactant is electron-rich and which is electron-poor.

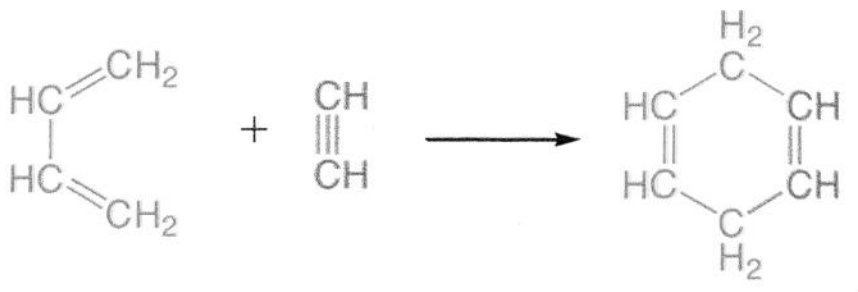

Problem 24.1. Draw the complete mechanism and the product of the following Diels-Alder reaction.

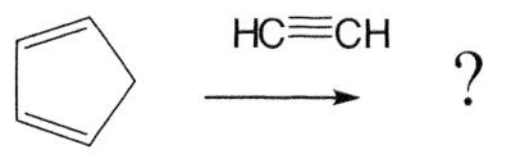

HC≡CH ?

In fact, a reaction similar to the one in Equation 24-4 provides strong evidence for the existence of benzyne. Recall from Section 23.10b that benzyne is a very reactive species and therefore cannot be isolated. However, if it is produced in the presence of a diene such as cyclopentadiene, as shown in Equation 24-5, then a Diels-Alder reaction ensues. This Diels-Alder reaction can be viewed as a benzyne "trap."

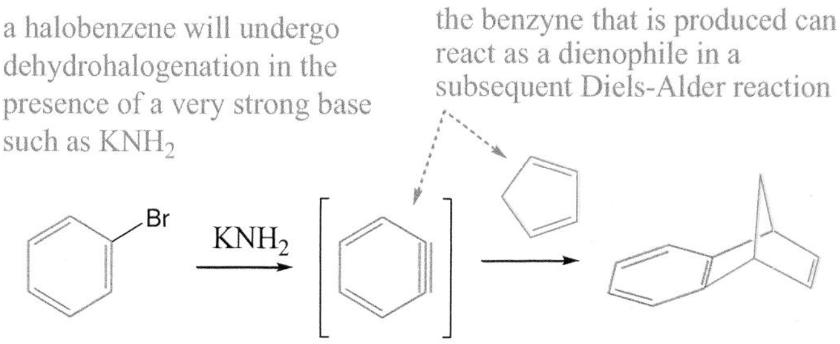

a halobenzene will undergo dehydrohalogenation in the presence of a very strong base such as KNH_2

the benzyne that is produced can react as a dienophile in a subsequent Diels-Alder reaction

Br KNH_2

benzyne intermediate (24-5)

What is consistent among all Diels-Alder reactions is the cyclic flow of six π electrons. The number of electrons is important, because in the transition state those electrons are delocalized over a complete ring. Recall from Chapter 12 that six electrons is a **Hückel number** of electrons (i.e., an odd number of pairs), and when they are delocalized over an entire ring, the species is *aromatic*. Therefore,

The Diels-Alder reaction proceeds through an **aromatic transition state**.

This provides a substantial lowering of the reaction's energy barrier, and is in large part what enables the reaction to take place under relatively mild conditions. We say that the reaction is "allowed" under normal conditions.

For comparison, let's examine two other possible cycloaddition reactions. Equation 24-6 involves two molecules of ethene, and is an example of a [2+2] cycloaddition. Equation 24-7 involves a molecule of ethene and a molecule of 1,3,5-hexatriene, and is an example of a [2+6] cycloaddition. As indicated, neither of these reactions occurs readily under normal conditions, because they would have to proceed through an **anti-aromatic transition state.** In both cases, an even number of pairs of electrons is delocalized over the entire ring—two pairs for the [2+2] cycloaddition and four pairs for the [2+6] cycloaddition. Because these reactions do not occur readily, we say that they are "forbidden."

Comment [JMK49]: Margin note. Cycloaddition reactions with **anti-aromatic transition states** do not occur readily.

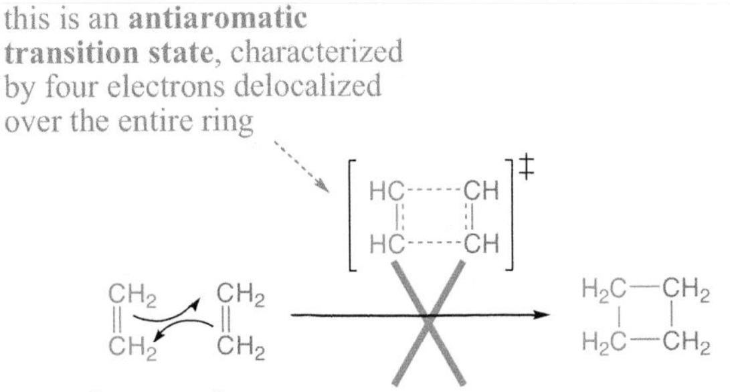

this is an **antiaromatic transition state**, characterized by four electrons delocalized over the entire ring

[HC----CH / HC----CH]‡

$CH_2{=}CH_2$ + $CH_2{=}CH_2$ ⟶ (X) $H_2C{-}CH_2$ / $H_2C{-}CH_2$

ethene ethene

(24-6)

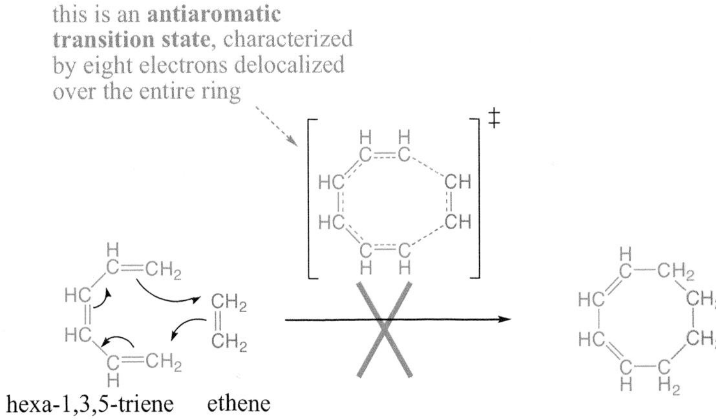

this is an **antiaromatic transition state**, characterized by eight electrons delocalized over the entire ring

hexa-1,3,5-triene ethene

(24-7)

Your Turn 24.2. The cycloaddition reaction involving two molecules of cyclopentene is shown below. Identify the transition state as being either *aromatic* or *antiaromatic*.

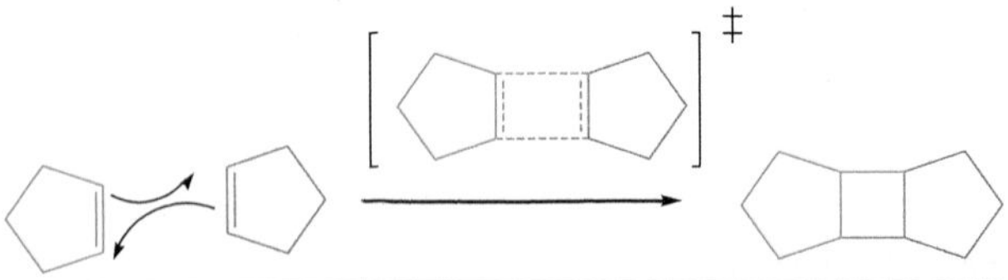

‡

Solved Problem 24.1. Is the following cycloaddition reaction allowed or forbidden?

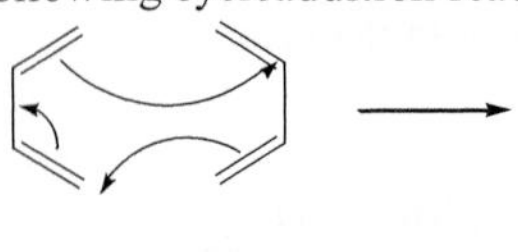

Think. In the transition state, are there electrons delocalized over an entire ring? If so, how many electrons? Is that a Hückel number or an anti-Hückel number? How does that correspond to whether the reaction is allowed or forbidden?

Solve. The transition state is shown below—it is somewhat of an average of the reactants and products.

‡

As we can see, there are electrons delocalized over an entire ring. The number of electrons that are delocalized is indicated by the curved arrow notation—each of the three curved arrows represents a movement of two electrons, for a total of six. Since six electrons is a Hückel number, the transition state is aromatic, making the reaction allowed.

Problem 24.2. Draw the transition state for the following cycloaddition reaction. Do you expect this reaction to take place readily? Why or why not?

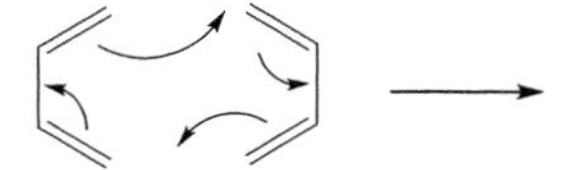

24.2. CONFORMATION OF THE DIENOPHILE

The concerted nature of the Diels-Alder reaction means that both of the new carbon-carbon σ bonds form simultaneously. Thus, both ends of the diene must be relatively close to the dienophile in the transition state. The appropriate distances are achieved only if the diene attains a geometry in which the two ends of the π system are pointing in the same direction—the so-called **s-*cis* conformation**. (The "s" indicates that the *cis* designation describes the orientation of groups about a single bond, rather than a double bond or the plane of a ring.)

with the diene in the s-*cis* conformation, the ends of the diene are at the appropriate distance from the dienophile to produce two new C-C bonds

with the diene in the s-*trans* conformation, the ends of the diene are too far from the dienophile

s-*cis* conformation

s-*trans* conformation

Otherwise, in an **s-*trans*-conformation**, the ends of the two reacting species are farther apart, which raises the energy of the transition state, and makes the Diels-Alder reaction unfeasible. In other words,

In order for a Diels-Alder reaction to take place, the diene must be in the **s-*cis* conformation.**

Attaining the s-*cis* conformation is not a problem with reactions involving cyclopentadiene as the diene (Equation 24-3), given that the ring locks the double bonds in that conformation. However, this is of minor concern if the diene is 1,3-butadiene, due to the rotation that takes place about the central single bond (Equation 24-8). The s-*cis* conformation is about 12 kJ/mol higher in energy than the s-*trans* conformation. Consequently, at equilibrium, about 3% of the molecules are in the s-*cis* conformation (Equation 24-8a), and the remainder are in the s-*trans* conformation (Equation 24-8b).

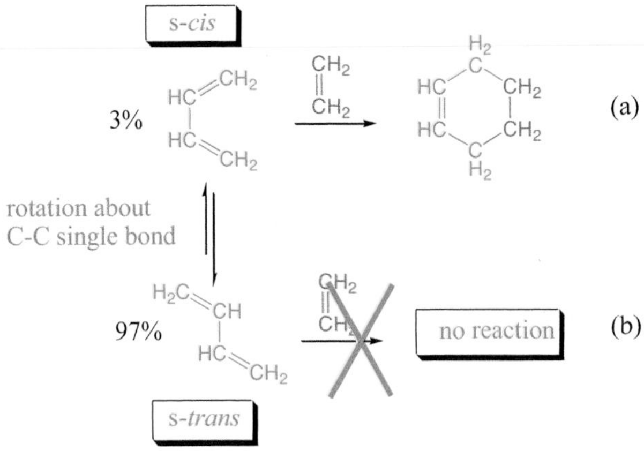

s-*cis*

3%

rotation about
C-C single bond

97%

s-*trans*

no reaction

(a)

(b)

(24-8)

As a result of this equilibrium, at any given time only about 3% of 1,3-butadiene molecules can participate in the Diels-Alder reaction. This slows the reaction substantially, and is part of the reason why the Diels-Alder reaction involving 1,3-butadiene and ethene requires such high temperatures (Equation 24-1).

Your Turn 24.3. Label which of the following is in the s-*cis* conformation, and which is in the s-*trans* conformation. Circle the one that can undergo a Diels-Alder reaction.

Evidence for the necessity of the diene being in the s-*cis* conformation comes from the fact that the reactions in Equations 24-9 and 24-10 do not occur under normal conditions; neither of the dienes in those reactions can attain the s-*cis* conformation.

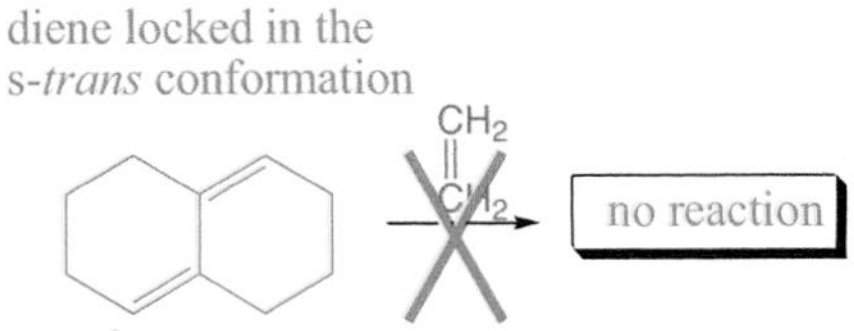

diene locked in the
s-*trans* conformation

no reaction

(24-9)

no reaction

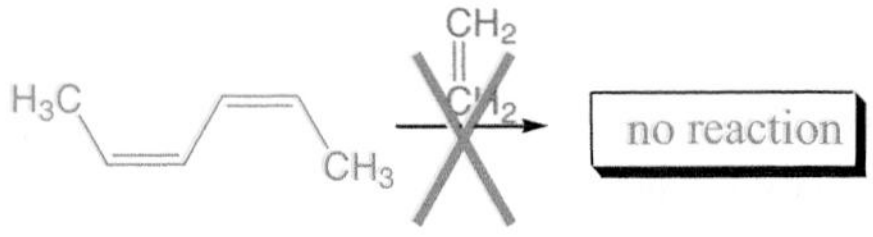

(24-10)

The diene in Equation 24-9 is locked in the s-*trans* conformation by the fused ring system. The diene in Equation 24-10, although it is not locked in the s-*trans* conformation, has severe steric strain in the s-*cis* conformation, as illustrated in Equation 24-11.

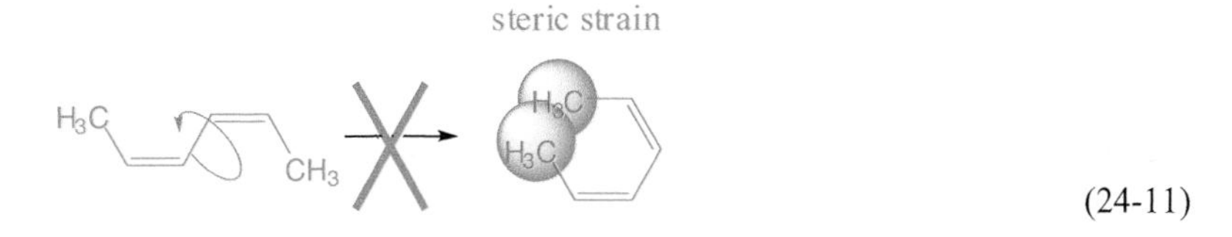

(24-11)

Solved Problem 24.2. Which molecule will react faster with ethene in a Diels-Alder reaction? Explain.

Think. Are the dienes in an s-*cis* conformation? If not, can they attain such a conformation? Which is more stable in the s-*cis* conformation?

Solve. Neither diene is in the s-*cis* conformation as written, but in each molecule, the single bond that connects the two double bonds can undergo rotation.

rotation about single bond

rotation about single bond

too much steric strain

In the s-*cis* conformation of the first molecule, no substantial strain exists. In contrast, the second molecule experiences severe steric strain of the overlapping *t*-butyl groups when in the s-*cis* conformation. Thus, the equilibrium heavily favors the s-*trans* conformation, which severely hinders the reaction. Consequently, the first diene will undergo a Diels-Alder reaction much faster than the second.

Problem 24.3. Which of the following molecules will react faster with ethene in a Diels-Alder reaction? Explain.

Problem 24.4. Although benzene contains a pair of conjugated double bonds locked in an s-*cis* conformation, benzene does not react with ethene. Draw the product of such a hypothetical reaction and explain why it does not occur.

24.3. DRIVING FORCE AND REVERSIBILITY

Under normal conditions, Diels-Alder reactions typically favor products quite heavily. For example, the prototypical Diels-Alder reaction (presented again in Equation 24-12) has a substantially negative standard free energy change (ΔG^0_{rxn} = -113 kJ/mol), and, consequently, a very large equilibrium constant (K_{eq} =3.5 x 10^{19}). Thus,

Diels-Alder reactions tend to be *irreversible* and take place under *kinetic control.*

HC(=CH2)–HC(=CH2) + CH2=CH2 ⟶ cyclohexene (HC=CH, CH2 ×4)

$\Delta G^0_{rxn} = -113$ kJ/mol

$K_{eq} = 3.5 \times 10^{19}$

(24-12)

As with any reaction, ΔG^0_{rxn} for the Diels-Alder reaction can be broken down into a ΔH^0_{rxn} term and a $T\Delta S^0_{rxn}$ term. For the Diels-Alder reaction in Equation 24-12, ΔH^0_{rxn} = -168 kJ/mol, and $T\Delta S^0_{rxn}$ = -54 kJ/mol at 25 °C. Notice that ΔH^0_{rxn} is substantially negative, which is why ΔG^0_{rxn} is negative and the products are favored.

The large negative ΔH^0 for this reaction stems primarily from how the bond energies in the product differ from those in the reactants. Notice in Equation 24-12 that three double bonds and one single bond in the reactants are converted into five single bonds and one double bond in the products. The average bond energy of a C-C single bond is 347 kJ/mol, and the average bond energy of a C=C double bond is 611 kJ/mol. Therefore, through Equation 24-13, we estimate ΔH^0_{rxn} to be -166 kJ/mol, which is close to the experimentally measured value of -168 kJ/mol.

breaking of three C=C double bonds | breaking of a C-C single bond | formation of five C-C single bonds | formation of a C=C double bond

$$\Delta H^0_{rxn} = [3(611 \text{ kJ/mol}) + 1(347 \text{ kJ/mol})] - [5(347 \text{ kJ/mol}) + 1(611 \text{ kJ/mol})] = -166 \text{ kJ/mol} \quad (24\text{-}13)$$

Notice also that the $T\Delta S^0_{rxn}$ term is negative, signifying that the products are more ordered than the reactants. This should make sense, given that the Diels-Alder reaction fuses together two separate molecules, thus decreasing the extent of disorder.

Because the entropy term has a negative sign, increasing temperature makes ΔG^0_{rxn} less negative (recall that $\Delta G^0_{rxn} = \Delta H^0_{rxn} - T\Delta S^0_{rxn}$). Usually, modest increases in temperature do not have a dramatic effect because the enthalpy term frequently dominates. However, for Diels-Alder reactions that are less exothermic, temperature becomes much more important. This is the case for the Diels-Alder reaction shown in Equation 24-14, in which cyclopentadiene behaves both as the diene and the dienophile. This reaction has a substantially smaller exothermicity (ΔH^0_{rxn} = -77 kJ/mol) than that in Equation 24-12.

+ 150 °C ΔG^0_{rxn} = -17 kJ/mol

K_{eq} = 120

cyclopentadiene dicyclopentadiene (24-14)

Your Turn 24.4. Supply the curved arrows missing from Equation 24-14.

+

At 25 °C, the $T\Delta S^0_{rxn}$ term is +42 kJ/mol, such that ΔG^0_{rxn} = -35 kJ/mol and $K_{eq} = 9 \times 10^5$. When the reaction is heated to 150 °C, the $T\Delta S^0_{rxn}$ term becomes +60 kJ/mol, such that ΔG^0_{rxn} = -17 kJ/mol, and K_{eq} = 120. Consequently, at that elevated temperature, the reaction is quite easily reversible.

Your Turn 24.5. In the space provided here, show the work to solve for ΔG^0_{rxn} at the two temperatures mentioned above (i.e., plug in for $\Delta G^0_{rxn} = \Delta H^0_{rxn} - T\Delta S^0_{rxn}$).

25 °C

150 °C

Problem 24.5. What temperature would be required in order to bring about K_{eq} = 120 for the prototypical Diels-Alder reaction in Equation 24-12? Based on this temperature, do you think that making such a reaction reversible would be practical?

24.3a. The Retro Diels-Alder Reaction

Chemists must take advantage of the reversibility of the Diels-Alder reaction in Equation 24-14 in order to prepare a fresh sample of cyclopentadiene. At room temperature, K_{eq} heavily favors products, and over about one weeks' time, cyclopentadiene *dimerizes* entirely into dicyclopentadiene. When a sample of dicyclopentadiene is heated to 150 °C or higher, not only does the reaction become much more reversible, but the low boiling cyclopentadiene (b.p. = 42 °C) is removed and collected via distillation, whereas the higher boiling dicyclopentadiene (b.p. = 170 °C) remains behind. Therefore, Le Châtelier's principle continues to drive the reaction toward the side that has cyclopentadiene—i.e., in the reverse direction.

Because this process "undoes" the Diels-Alder reaction in Equation 24-14, it is called a **retro Diels-Alder reaction**. The mechanism for this reaction is simply the reverse of a Diels-Alder mechanism. Namely, the entire reaction consists of a single step (i.e., is concerted), and that step involves the cyclic movement of six electrons. The curved arrow notation is illustrated in Equation 24-15.

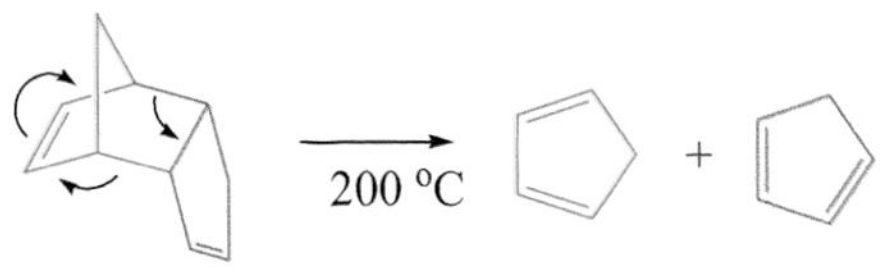

200 °C

dicyclopentadiene → cyclopentadiene + cyclopentadiene

70%

(24-15)

Your Turn 24.6. When cyclohexene is heated to very high temperatures, the reverse of the reaction in Equation 24-12 takes place, producing ethene and 1,3-butadiene. Draw the curved arrow notation for this reaction.

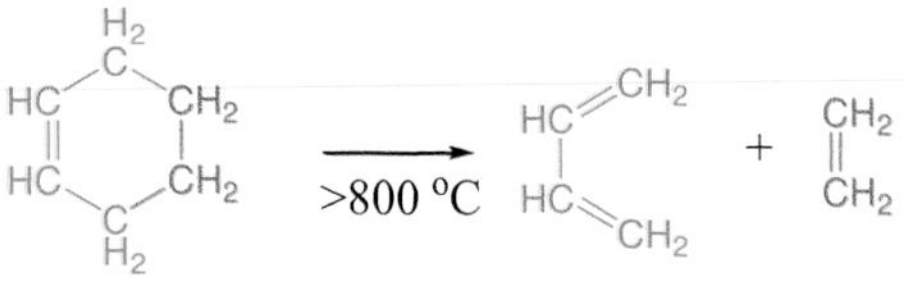

>800 °C

Problem 24.6. When the compound below is heated, a single product is produced, whose formula is C_6H_8. Draw that product, and the curved arrow notation necessary to produce it.

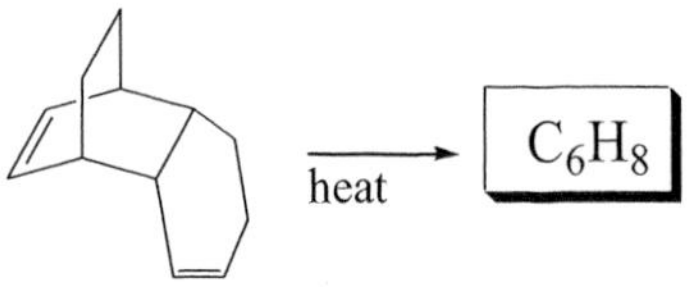

heat → C_6H_8

24.4. SUBSTITUENT EFFECTS ON THE DRIVING FORCE

The prototypical Diels-Alder reaction (Equation 24-1) between ethene and 1,3-butadiene is quite sluggish, requiring temperatures around 200 °C to proceed at a reasonable rate. Even then, the yield is quite low, at only 18%. Fortunately, Diels-Alder reactions can be facilitated by the presence of certain substituents.

- Electron-donating substituents bonded directly to the diene facilitate Diels-Alder reactions. These are the same substituents that were classified as "activating" groups in electrophilic aromatic substitution (Chapter 23).

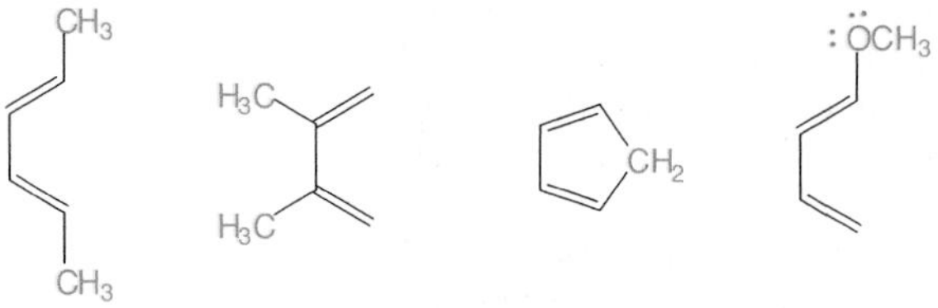

- Electron-withdrawing substituents bonded directly to the dienophile facilitate Diels-Alder reactions. These are the same substituents that were classified as "deactivating" groups in electrophilic aromatic substitution.

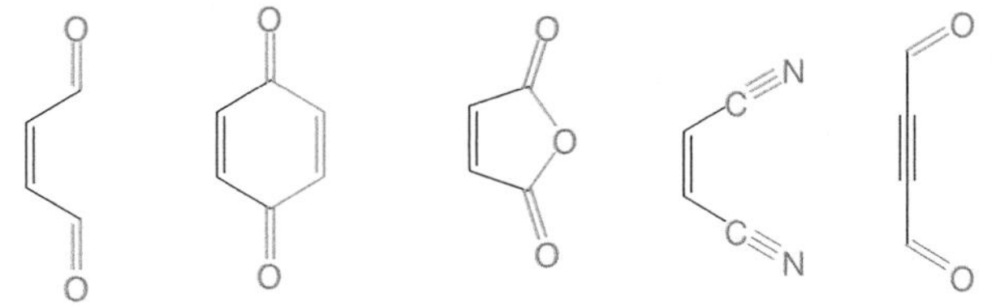

For example, the reaction in Equation 24-16 takes place at a slightly lower temperature than the one in Equation 24-1, and the yield is much higher. In that reaction, two methyl groups, which are electron-donating, are attached directly to the diene. A similar outcome is observed with the reaction in Equation 24-17, in which a nitro group, which is highly electron-withdrawing, is attached to the dienophile.

electron-donating groups on the diene facilitate a Diels-Alder reaction

CH_3 ... 185 °C, 17h

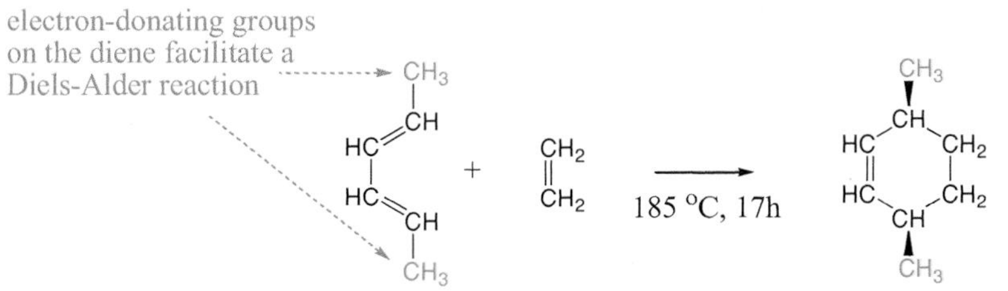

cis-3,6-dimethylcyclohexene
60%

(24-16)

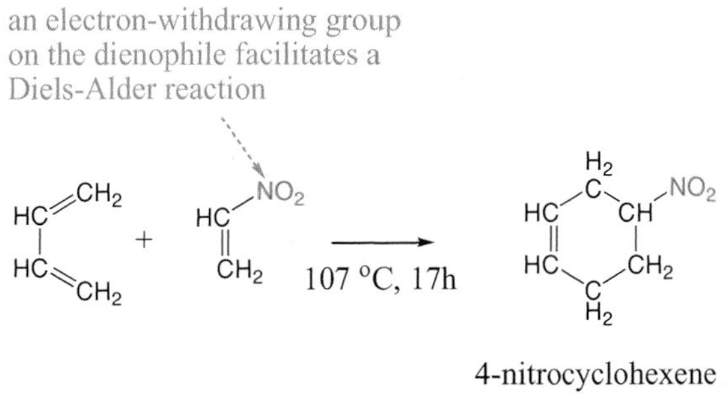

an electron-withdrawing group on the dienophile facilitates a Diels-Alder reaction

NO_2 ... 107 °C, 17h

4-nitrocyclohexene
84%

(24-17)

Effects from these electron-donating and electron-withdrawing groups can be understood from our previous picture of electron flow in a Diels-Alder reaction. Recall that even in the most fundamental Diels-Alder reaction between 1,3-butadiene and ethene, where no substituents are present, the diene is relatively electron-rich and the dienophile is relatively electron-poor. Electron-donating groups that are attached to the diene therefore increase the diene's electron density, making it even more electron-rich, and electron-withdrawing groups attached to the dienophile decrease the dienophile's electron density, making it even more electron-poor. Consequently, with either or both of these effects taking place, the driving force for the flow of electrons from the electron-rich diene to the electron-poor dienophile is enhanced.

Comment [JMK50]: **Margin note.** The driving force for a Diels-Alder reaction is increased with electron-donating groups on the diene and/or electron-withdrawing groups on the dienophile.

Solved Problem 24.3. Which of the following do you expect to react faster as a diene in a Diels-Alder reaction? Explain.

OR

Think. In a Diels-Alder reaction, is the diene considered electron-rich or electron-poor? Will electron-donating groups or electron-withdrawing groups on the diene speed up the reaction? What is the relative electron-donating/electron-withdrawing character of each substituent?

Solve. The diene is considered electron-rich in a Diels-Alder reaction, so the more electron-donating a substituent is, the faster the reaction. Both of the substituents bonded to the diene are electron donating, given that each is bonded by an atom possessing a lone pair of electrons. According to Table 23-4, the alkoxy group is more strongly activating than the amido group (due to the presence of the carbonyl group). Therefore, the diene on the right is more electron-rich than the one on the left. That on the right will react faster.

Problem 24.7. Which of the following do you expect to react faster as a dienophile in a Diels-Alder reaction? Explain.

OR

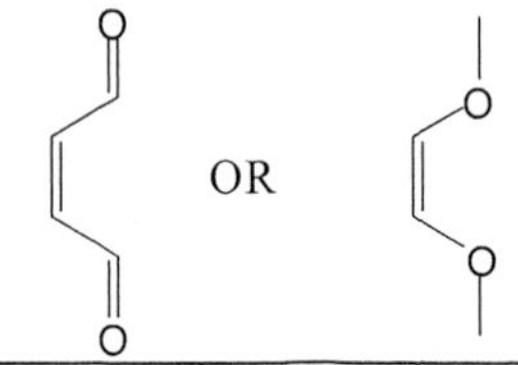

24.5. STEREOCHEMISTRY OF DIELS-ALDER REACTIONS

In the prototypical Diels-Alder reaction between 1,3-butadiene and ethene, four carbon atoms rehybridize from sp^2 to sp^3, transforming from a planar geometry to a tetrahedral geometry (see Your Turn 24.7). Therefore, depending upon the substituents that may be present, four carbon atoms can potentially become stereocenters in the products. Frequently, then, a Diels-Alder reaction produces a chiral product, and if the reactants and the environment are achiral, a racemic mixture of enantiomers must be formed.

Your Turn 24.7. In the prototypical Diels-Alder reaction below, circle the carbon atoms in the products that have been transformed from sp^2- to sp^3-hybridization and are therefore *potential* stereocenters.

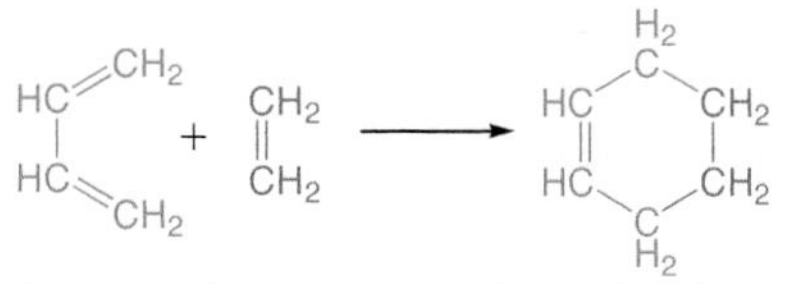

If all four of those carbon atoms could become stereocenters, then there would be 2^4=16 potential stereoisomers that could be produced. However, only a subset of those stereoisomers can actually form, because the reaction itself places certain restrictions on the stereochemistry of those carbons. For example, the diene and dienophile in Equation 24-18 yield only the *cis* configuration with respect to the ring in the products, whereas the diene and dienophile in Equation 24-19 yield only the *trans* configuration in the ring.

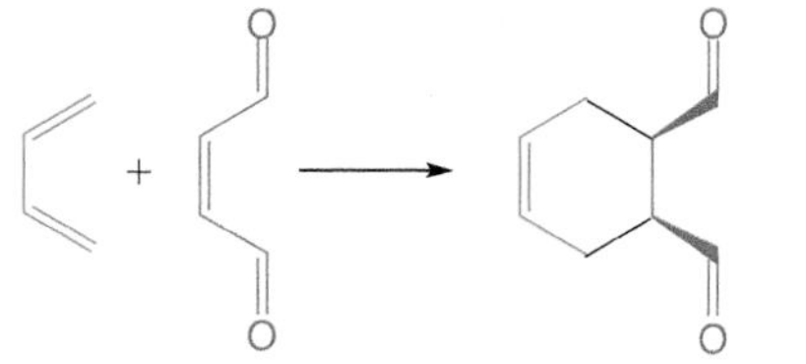

a *cis* configuraiton in the dienophile

a *cis* configuration in the ring

(24-18)

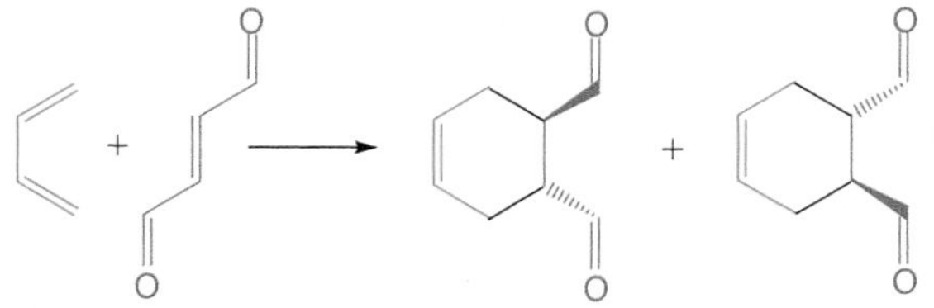

a *trans* configuraiton in the dienophile

a *trans* configuration in the ring

(24-19)

The difference is in the configuration of the substituents in the dienophile—they are *cis* to each other about the initial C=C double bond in Equation 24-18, but are *trans* to each other in Equation 24-19. In other words,

> The stereochemical configuration in the dienophile is conserved throughout the course of a Diels-Alder reaction.

Problem 24.8. Predict the product of the following Diels-alder reaction, paying attention to stereochemistry.

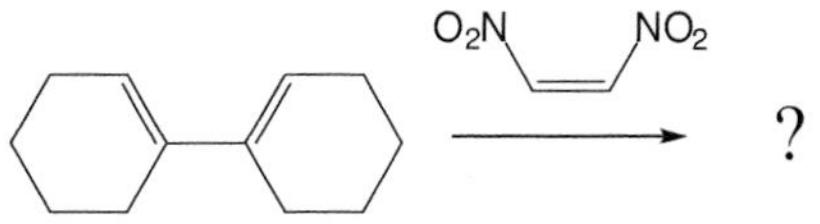

O_2N NO_2

?

Problem 24.9. Draw the dienophile that would be required to generate each of the following molecules from 1,3-butadiene in a Diels-Alder reaction.

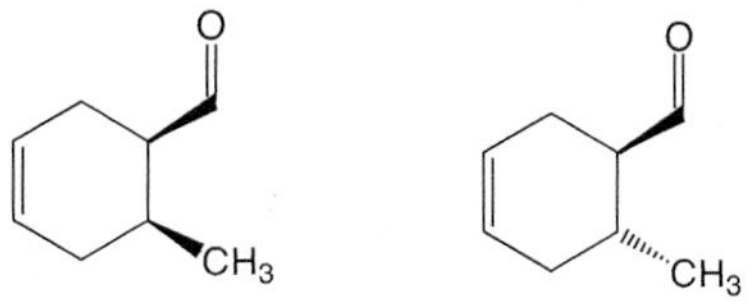

CH_3 CH_3

Similarly, the stereochemistry in the diene leads to specific stereochemical configurations in the products, as is illustrated in Equations 24-20 through 24-22.

both double bonds *trans*

CH_3 CH_3 CH_3 CH_3

a *cis* configuration in the ring

(24-20)

both double bonds *cis*

a *cis* configuration in the ring

(24-21)

trans double bond

cis double bond

CH_3 CH_3 CH_3 CH_3 CH_3 CH_3

a *trans* configuration in the ring

(24-22)

Namely,

- If the double bonds are either both *trans* (Equation 24-20) or both *cis* (Equation 24-21), then the substituents at the ends of the diene become *cis* to each other with respect to the ring in the product.
- Conversely, if one double bond is *cis* and the other is *trans*, then those two substituents become *trans* to each other in the product (Equation 24-22).

All of the stereochemical outcomes of a Diels-Alder reaction (Equations 24-18 through 24-22) are due to the fact that the reaction is concerted—the two σ bonds formed at each end of the diene and dienophile are formed *simultaneously*. Therefore, as we can see in Equations 24-23 and 24-24, the substituents about the dienophile cannot rotate relative to each other to scramble the stereochemistry. This explains our observations in Equations 24-18 and 24-19.

the new C-C bonds form simultaneously, so the relative orientation of the substituents cannot change

(24-23)

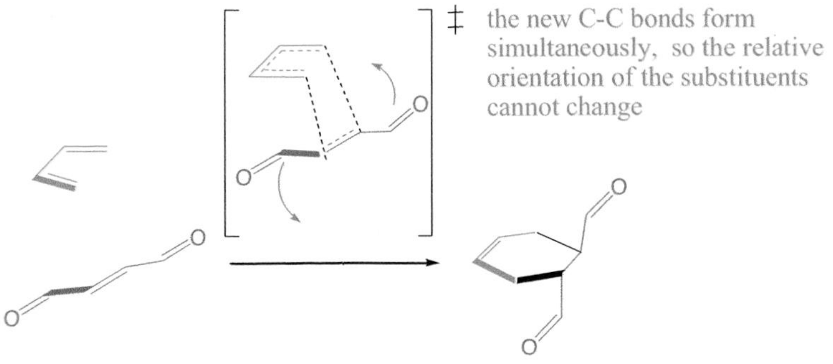

‡ the new C-C bonds form simultaneously, so the relative orientation of the substituents cannot change

(24-24)

To explain the stereochemistry we observe in Equations 25-18 through 25-20, on the other hand, we must understand that the two carbon atoms at the ends of the diene system rotate slightly as the six-membered ring relaxes into its equilibrium geometry. This is shown in Equations 24-25 and 24-26. Specifically, those carbon atoms in fact rotate in *opposite directions* during the course of the reaction—one rotates clockwise whereas the other rotates counterclockwise (if viewed from one end of the diene).

Comment [JMK51]: **Margin note.** In a Diels-Alder reaction, the C atoms at the ends of the diene rotate slightly in opposite directions.

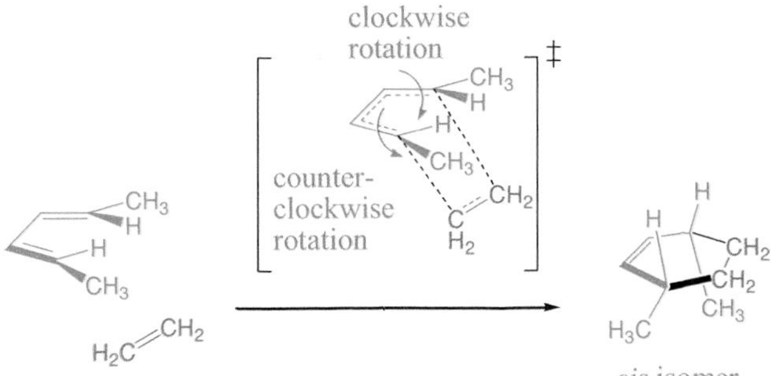

clockwise rotation

counter-clockwise rotation

cis isomer

(24-25)

clockwise rotation

counter-clockwise rotation

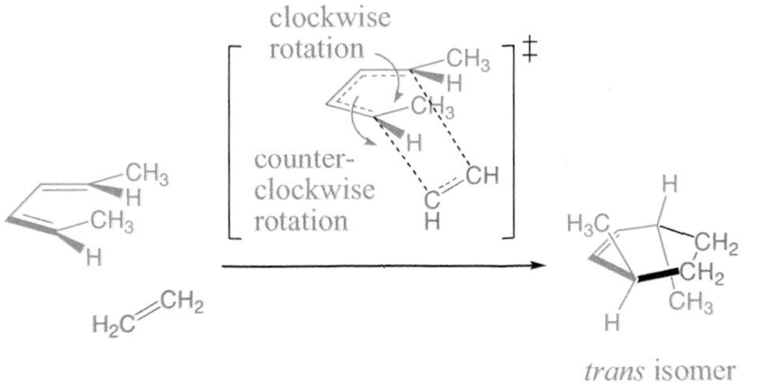

trans isomer

(24-26)

Solved Problem 24.4. Predict the product of the following Diels-Alder reaction, paying attention to stereochemistry.

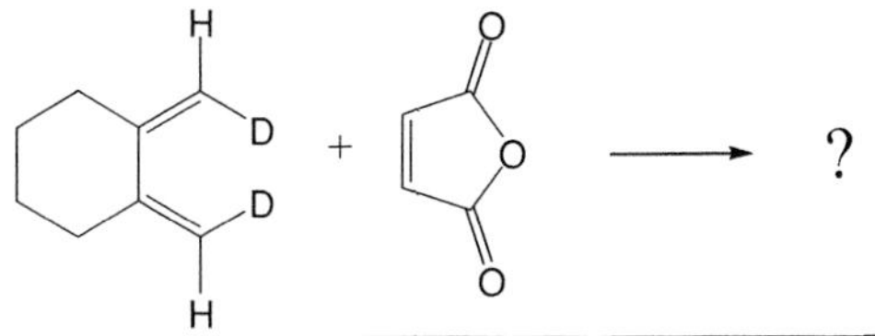

?

Think. Do the carbons at the ends of the diene become stereocenters in the products? What are the configurations about each double bond in the diene? Do the alkene carbons of the dienophile become stereocenters? What is the configuration about the carbon-carbon double bond in the dienophile?

Solve. If we draw the product without worrying about stereochemistry, we see that each end carbon in the diene does become a stereocenter, and so does each alkene carbon in the dienophile.

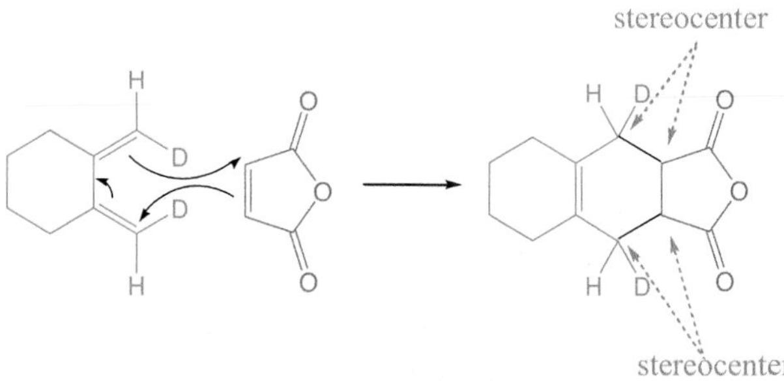

stereocenter

stereocenter

Notice that along the diene skeleton, each D-C=C-C configuration is *cis*. Likewise, each H-C=C-C configuration is *trans*. Therefore, the two D atoms will be *cis* to each other in the product, and the two H atoms will also be *cis* to each other. Also, notice that the alkene in the dienophile is in the *cis* configuration, so carbonyl groups will be *cis* to each other in the product. Overall, then, there are four stereoisomers that can be produced in this reaction.

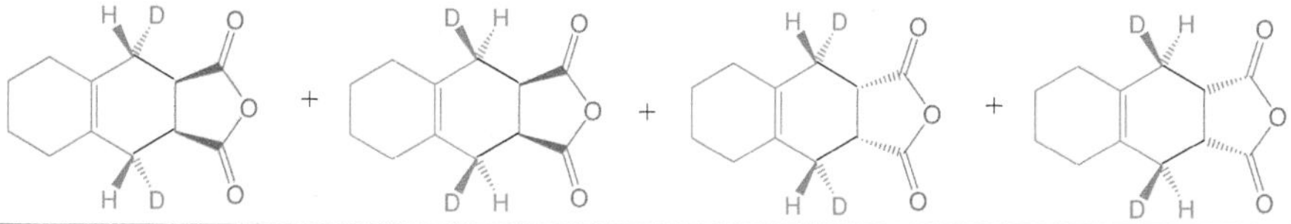

Problem 24.10. For each of the following reactions in which the dienophile is isotopically labeled, predict the Diels-Alder product, paying attention to stereochemistry.

a. + → ?

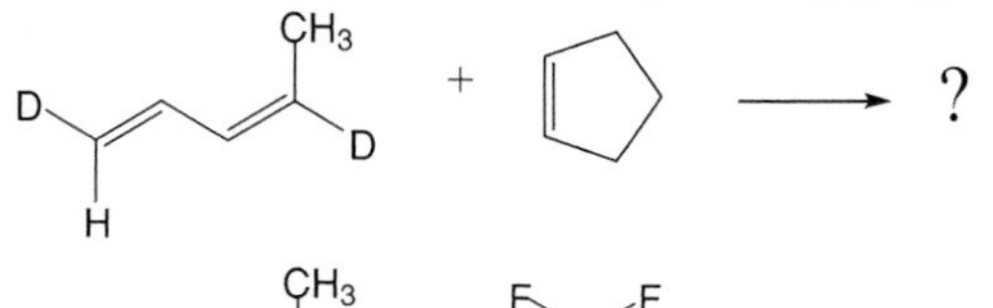

b. + → ?

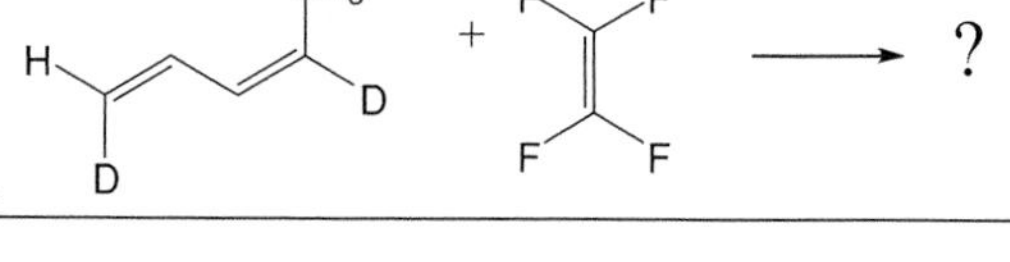

Problem 24.11. Assuming that the following is the product of a Diels-Alder reaction with ethene, draw the structure of the diene that would have been required.

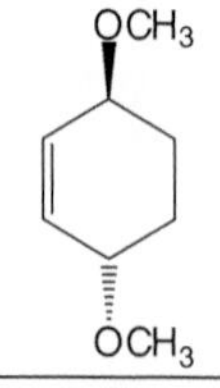

Yet another concern regarding stereochemistry involves the configurations of the carbon atoms from the diene relative to those from the dienophile. This is illustrated in Equation 24-27, in which a mixture of *diastereomers* is produced.

the endo product
is heavily favored

OCH_3 OCH_3 CO_2CH_3 CO_2CH_3 + CO_2CH_3 CO_2CH_3

exo product 3%

endo product 97%

(24-27)

As shown in Equations 24-28 and 24-29, these two products result from the two different approaches possible for the dienophile—with the substituents pointed either toward the diene or away from the diene. The approach with the dienophile's substituents toward the diene (Equation 24-28) is called an **endo approach**, and the resulting product is called the **endo product**. Conversely, the approach with the dienophile's substituents pointed away from the diene (Equation 24-29) is called the **exo approach**, and the resulting product is called the **exo product**. In essence, the endo product is the one in which the dienophile's substituents reside opposite the diene's substituents on the six-membered ring that is produced. In the exo product, on the other hand, the dienophile's substituents reside on the same side of the ring as the diene's substituents.

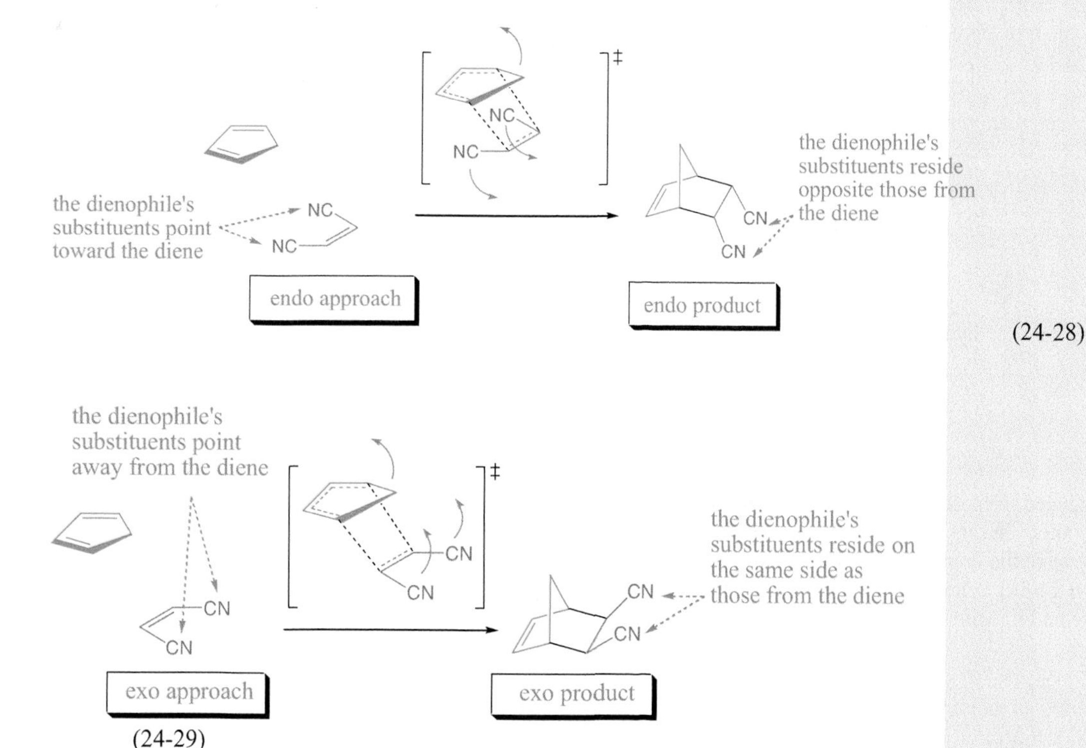

Although both *endo* and *exo* approaches are feasible, the product mixture is usually dominated by one product, according to the **endo rule**:

> In a Diels-Alder reaction, the endo approach is generally favored over the exo approach, making the endo product the major product.

Understanding the preference for the *endo* approach requires invoking molecular orbitals, and hence will be discussed in an optional section later in this chapter.

Problem 24.12. Draw the major product of the following Diels-Alder reaction, paying attention to stereochemistry.

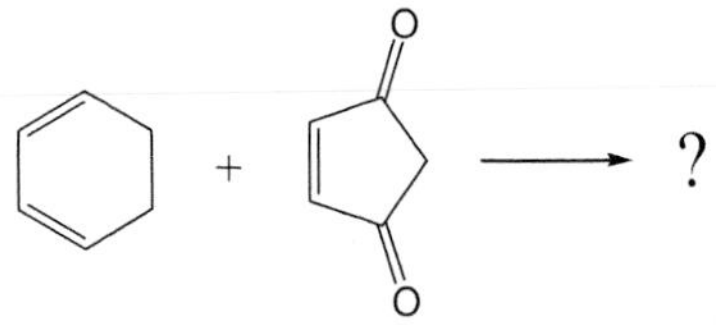

24.6. REGIOCHEMISTRY OF DIELS-ALDER REACTIONS

All of the examples of Diels-Alder reactions we have seen thus far have involved a diene or dienophile that is *symmetric*—i.e., one that possesses a plane of symmetry midway along the π system. For such reactions, regiochemistry is not a concern, because only one possible constitutional isomer can be produced. However, if both the diene and the dienophile are *asymmetric*—i.e., no plane of symmetry exists along the π system—then two constitutional isomers can be produced. An example is shown in Equation 24-30.

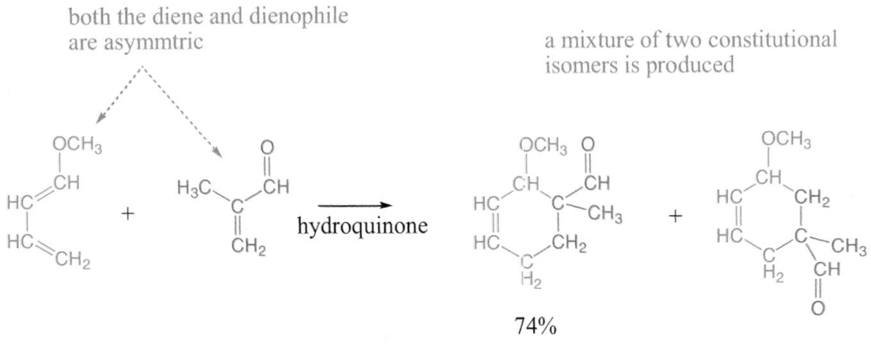

both the diene and dienophile are asymmtric

a mixture of two constitutional isomers is produced

hydroquinone

74%

(24-30)

The isomers are produced from different relative orientations of the two reactants when they approach each other. In this case, one isomer is produced from the approach in which the OCH_3 group of the diene is on the same side as the aldehyde group of the dienophile (Equation 24-31). The other isomer is produced from the approach in which those two groups are on opposite sides (Equation 24-32).

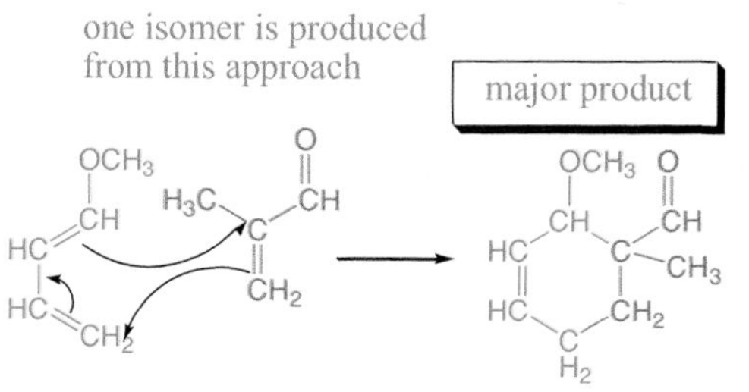

one isomer is produced from this approach

major product

(24-31)

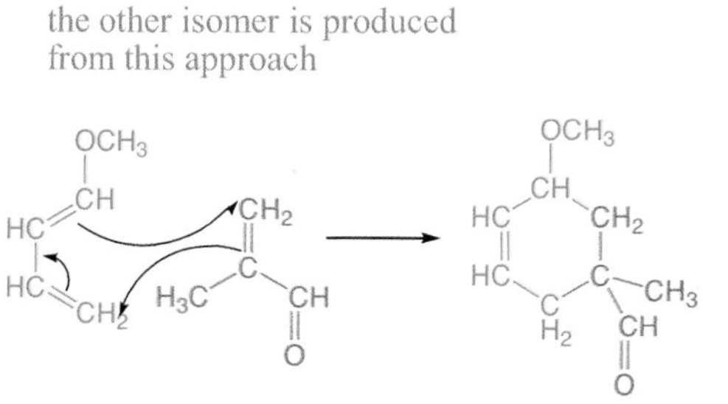

the other isomer is produced from this approach

(24-32)

Notice that the major product is produced via the approach in Equation 24-31. Thus, that approach is favored over the one in Equation 24-32. The reason can be understood by examining the distribution of charge within each reactant, established by their major resonance contributors. This is shown in Equation 24-33 for the diene, and Equation 24-34 for the dienophile.

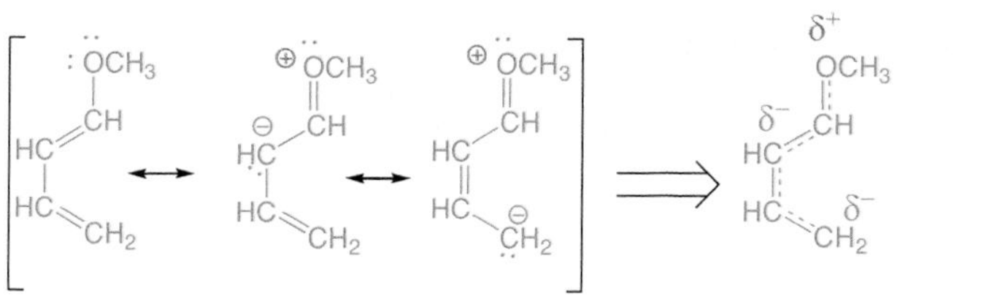

(24-33)

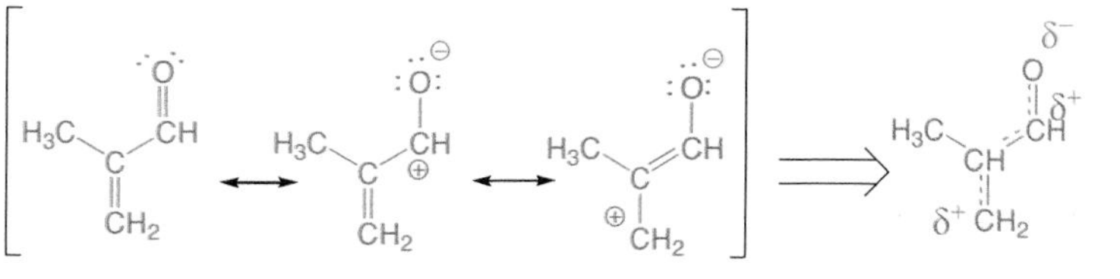

(24-34)

Your Turn 24.8. In Equations 24-33 and 24-34, supply the curved arrows necessary to convert the first resonance structure into the second, and the second one into the third.

With such charge distributions, we can see that the approach in Equation 24-31 has favorable electrostatic attraction between two carbon atoms undergoing bond formation, as shown in Equation 24-35. In contrast, the approach in Equation 24-32 leads to no such attraction among carbon atoms undergoing bond formation, illustrated by Equation 24-36. Thus, the approach in Equation 24-31 leads to the more stable transition state, and, consequently, the faster reaction.

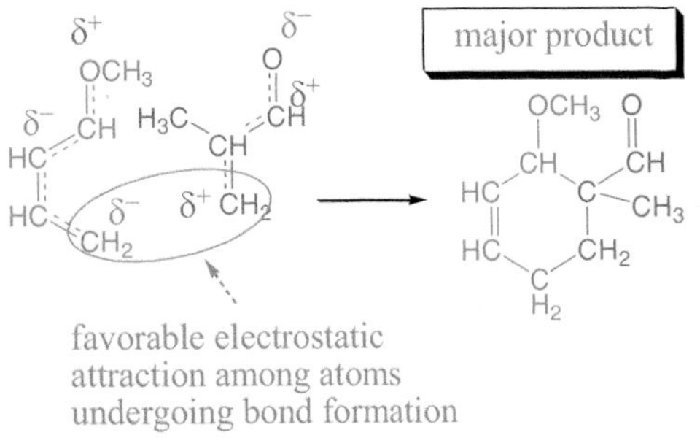

major product

favorable electrostatic attraction among atoms undergoing bond formation

(24-35)

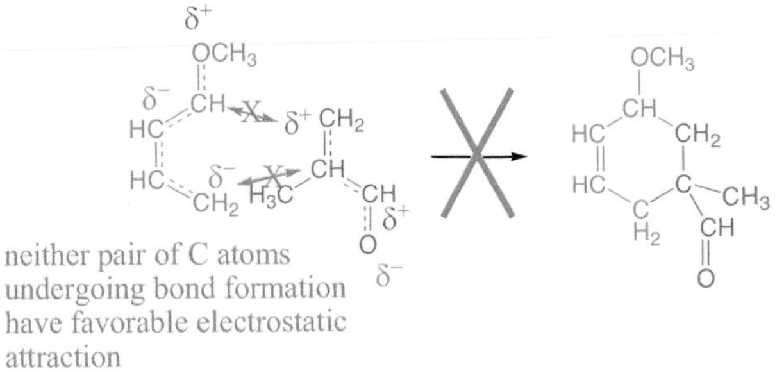

neither pair of C atoms undergoing bond formation have favorable electrostatic attraction

(24-36)

This analysis can be applied to other Diels-Alder reactions in order to predict regiochemistry. Namely,

> When the diene and the dienophile of a Diels-Alder reaction are both asymmetric, the major isomeric product is the one produced by the approach that exhibits the most favorable electrostatic attraction among atoms undergoing bond formation.

We can see how this is applied to the Diels-Alder reaction in Equation 24-37, which involves a 2-substitued diene. In this case, the constitutional isomer that is favored is the 1,4-disubstituted cyclohexene.

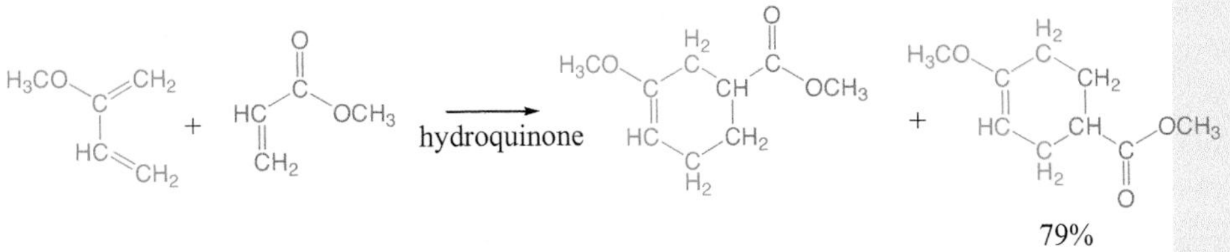

hydroquinone

79%

(24-37)

The resonance contributors and resonance hybrid of the diene are shown in Equation 24-38. Those for the dienophile are shown in Equation 24-39.

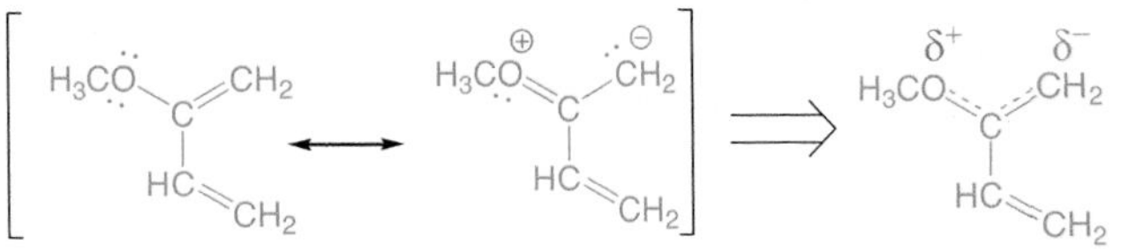

(24-38)

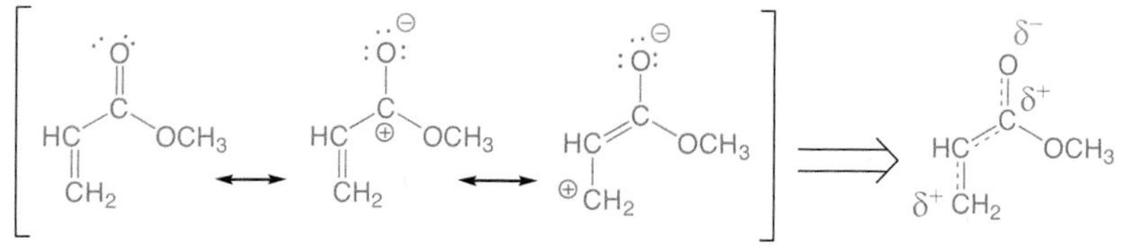

(24-39)

Your Turn 24.8. In Equations 24-38 and 24-39, supply the curved arrows necessary to convert each resonance structure into the next.

Of the two possible approaches of these reactants, the one that leads to the major product is shown in Equation 24-40. In this approach, we can see that two carbon atoms undergoing bond formation have opposite partial charges. Such is not true for the approach that leads to the minor product (see Your Turn 24.9).

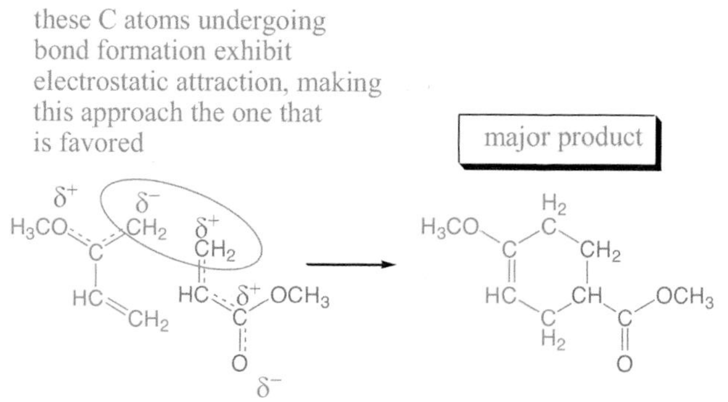

these C atoms undergoing bond formation exhibit electrostatic attraction, making this approach the one that is favored

major product

(24-40)

Your Turn 24.9. In the space provided below, draw the resonance hybrids of the diene and dienophile from Equation 24-37, exhibiting the approach that leads to the minor product. Circle each pair of carbon atoms undergoing bond formation, and next to each pair write "electrostatic attraction" or "no electrostatic attraction."

Solved Problem 24.5. Without taking into account stereochemistry, draw the major product of the following reaction.

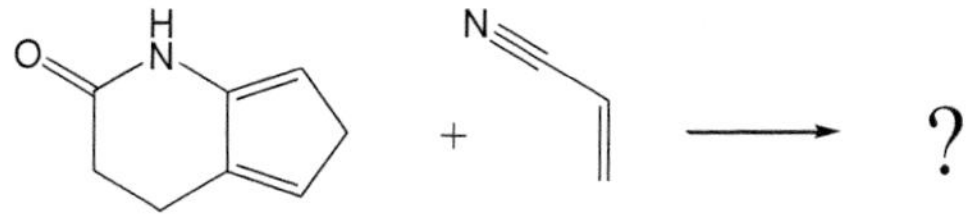

Think. Based on the symmetries of the diene and dienophile, are multiple constitutional isomers possible? What are the charge distributions along the diene and dienophile? Which approach leads to favorable electrostatic interactions among atoms undergoing bond formation?

Solve. Both the diene and dienophile are asymmetric, so two constitutional isomers can be produced. The distributions of charge in the diene and dienophile are determined by the major resonance contributors.

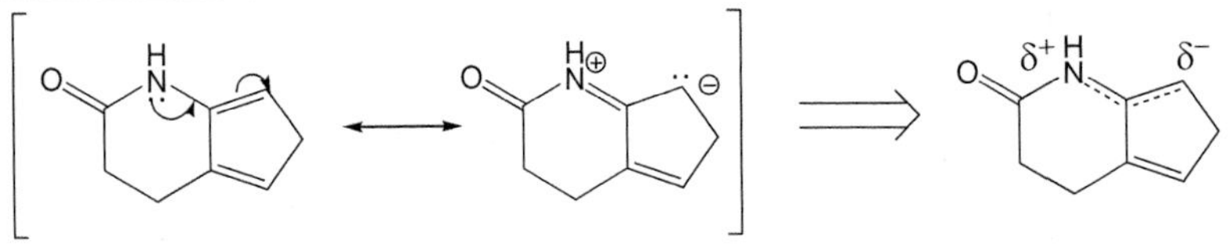

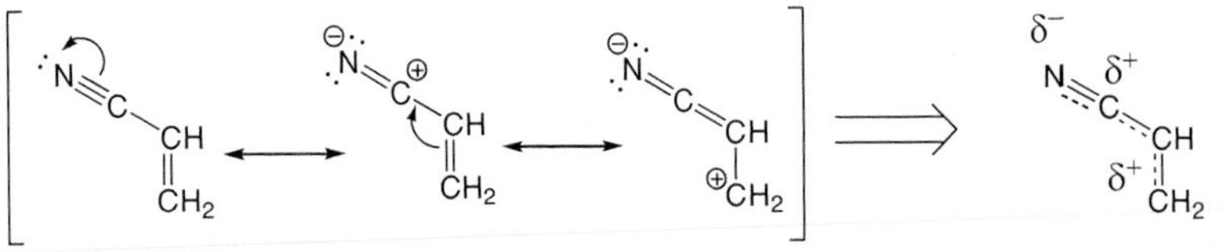

The two possible approaches of the diene and dienophile are shown below. Only in the second approach is there electrostatic attraction between carbon atoms undergoing bond formation, so that is the approach that leads to the major product.

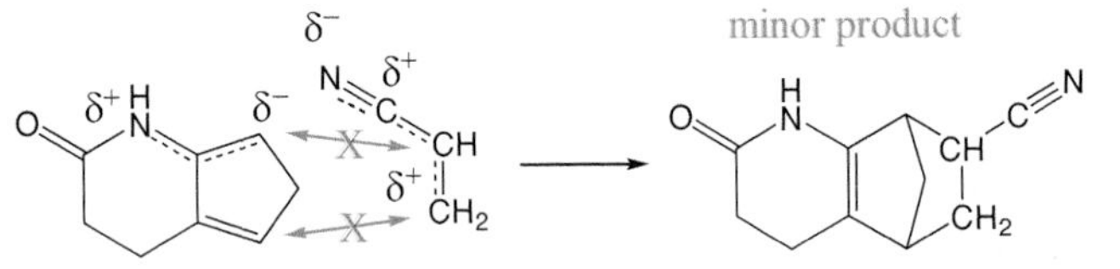

minor product

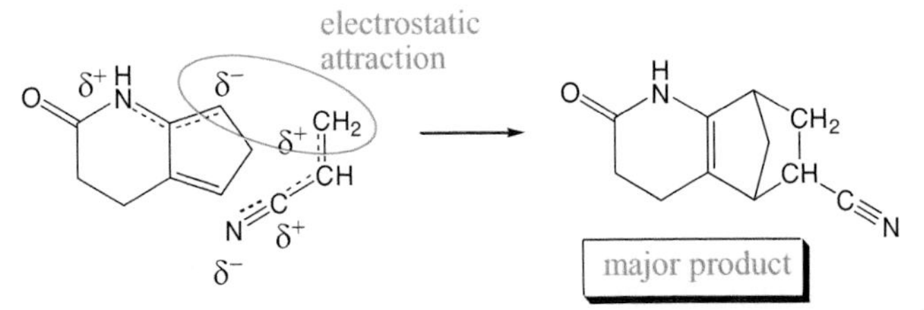

electrostatic attraction

major product

Problem 24.13. Without taking into account stereochemistry, draw the major product of the following reaction.

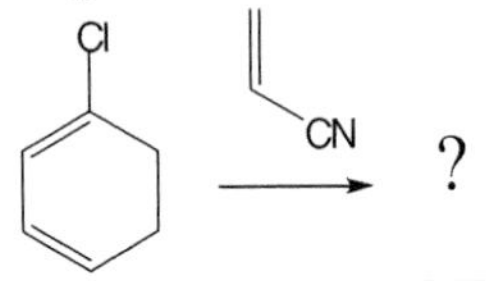

24.7. HETERO DIELS-ALDER REACTIONS

So far, all of the Diels-Alder reactions we have considered in this chapter involve only the breaking and formation of carbon-carbon bonds—these are called **carbon-only Diels-Alder reactions**. The product of such reactions, of course, is a new six-membered ring consisting of all carbon atoms. It is easy to imagine, however, a scenario in which the bonds that are broken/formed involve heteroatoms (i.e., non-carbon atoms); such reactions are called **hetero Diels-Alder reactions**.

For example, a heteroatom such as nitrogen can be part of the dienophile, as shown in Equation 24-41. Another example is illustrated in Equation 24-42, where a heteroatom can also be part of the "diene."

this N atom is incorporated into the new six-membered ring

hydroquinone, benzene
25 °C, 90 min

86%

(24-41)

hydroquinone
140 °C, 10 atm
16 h

60%

this O atom is incorporated into the new six-membered ring

(24-42)

Your Turn 24.10. Supply the curved arrows necessary for the reaction in Equations 24-42.

Hetero Diels-Alder reactions have been studied quite heavily in the last several decades, as they provide opportunities to synthesize heterocyclic compounds. An in-depth discussion of these reactions, however, is beyond the scope of this book; many of them require specific catalysts and involve intricate details of both regiochemistry and stereochemistry. Those of you who wish to learn more about hetero Diels-Alder reactions are referred to the following review: *Hetero Diels-Alder Methodology in Organic Synthesis*; Academic Press, San Diego, 1987; Weinreb, S. M.; Staib, R. R.

24.8. OTHER PERICYCLIC REACTIONS

What distinguishes the Diels-Alder reaction from other reactions we have seen previously in this book is the cyclic movement of six electrons in a concerted fashion. However, it is not the only reaction that shares this distinction. In this section we will introduce a few other pericyclic reactions that exhibit the same concerted electron movement, and hence have the same curved arrow notation as the Diels-Alder reaction.

Bear in mind, though, that each of the reactions we present here will not be covered in full. Just like the Diels-Alder reaction, each of these carries with it specific rules of regiochemistry and stereochemistry. We therefore leave in-depth studies of these reactions for an advanced course in Organic Chemistry.*

24.8a. Electrocyclic Reactions

A conjugated triene, such as *cis*-hexa-1,3,5-triene, undergoes a cyclization reaction when heated, establishing the equilibrium shown in Equation 24-43. This is an example of an *electrocyclic reaction*.

* See Anslyn, E. V.; Dougherty, D. A. *Modern Physical Organic Chemistry*, University Science, New York, 2005.

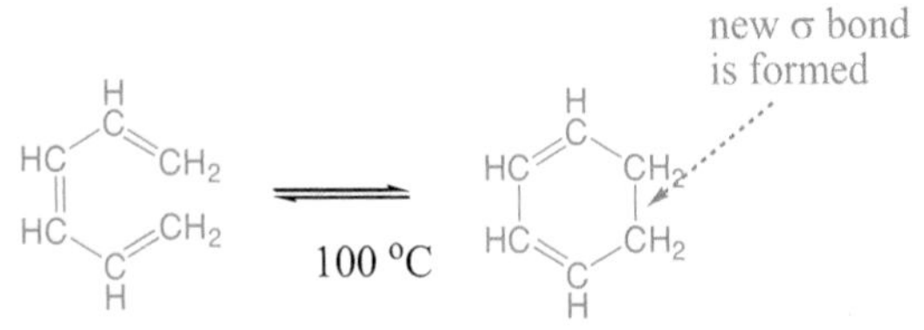

new σ bond
is formed

100 °C

(Z)-hexa-1,3,5-triene cyclohexa-1,3-diene (24-43)

An **electrocyclic reaction** is a unimolecular ring closure in which the ends of a conjugated π system are joined by a σ bond.

The mechanism for this reaction is *concerted*, and hence is described by the cyclic movement of six electrons, similar to that for a Diels-Alder reaction. This is illustrated in Equation 24-44.

Mechanism for the Reaction in Equation 24-43

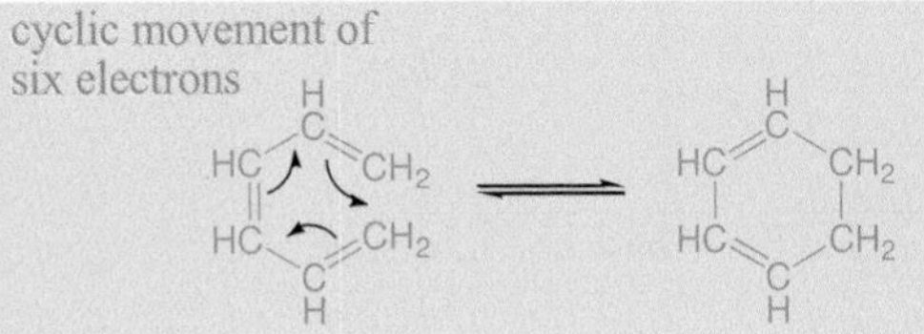

cyclic movement of
six electrons

(24-44)

The main argument in favor of a concerted mechanism is that the reaction is *stereospecific*. In Equation 24-45, for example, only the *cis* cyclohexadiene is produced; none of the *trans* isomer is produced. In Equation 24-46, exactly the opposite is true.

Comment [JMK52]: Margin note.
An electrocyclic reaction is concerted.

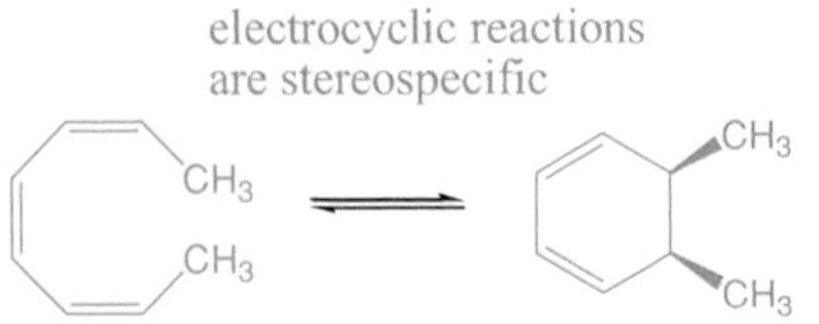

electrocyclic reactions
are stereospecific

(2Z,4Z,6Z)-octa-2,4,6-triene *cis*-5,6-dimethylcyclohexa-1,3-diene (24-45)

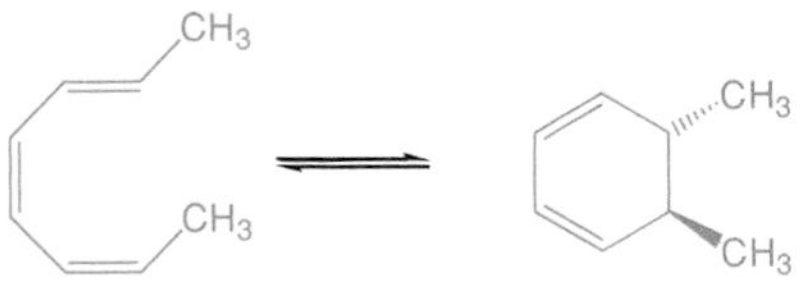

(2E,4Z,6Z)-octa-2,4,6-triene *trans*-5,6-dimethylcyclohexa-1,3-diene (24-46)

Your Turn 24.11. Supply the curved arrows necessary for both Equations 24-45 and 24-46.

24.8b. The Cope Rearrangement

When 3-methylhexa-1,5-diene is heated, it equilibrates with hepta-1,5-diene via a cyclic movement of six electrons (Equation 24-47). This is an example of a *Cope rearrangement.*

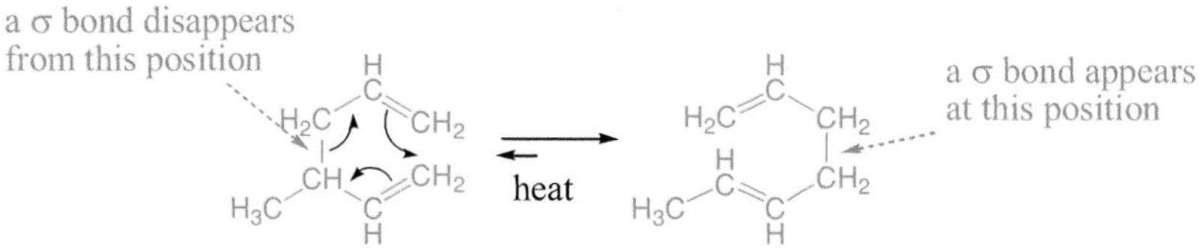

a σ bond disappears from this position

a σ bond appears at this position

heat

3-methylhexa-1,5-diene (*E*)-hepta-1,5-diene (24-47)

A **Cope rearrangement** is a unimolecular reaction that results in a shift in the position of a σ bond with respect to a π system.

Notice that in Equation 24-47, the reactant and product are constitutional isomers of each other, and can therefore be distinguished. However, the reactant and product of a cope rearrangement are not always distinguishable. This is exemplified by the cope rearrangement in Equation 24-48, in which hexa-1,5-diene is both the reactant and the product.

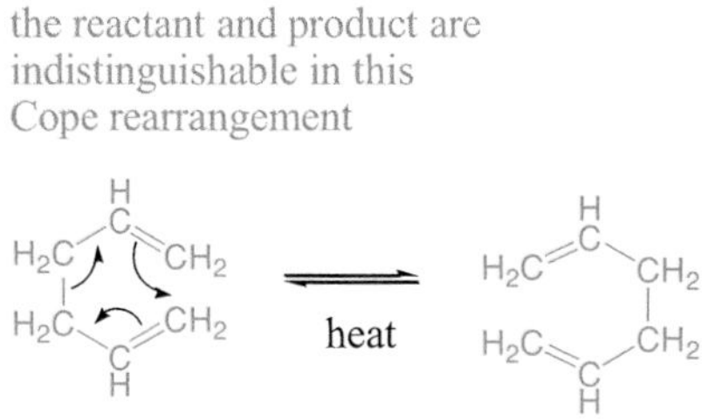

the reactant and product are indistinguishable in this Cope rearrangement

heat

hexa-1,5-diene hexa-1,5-diene (24-48)

Problem 24.14. When it is kept cold, hexa-1,5-diene exhibits three signals in its ^{13}C-NMR spectrum. When warmed, however, only two signals appear. Explain.

The Cope rearrangement has been observed with a variety of other compounds with unsaturation at the 1- and 5-positions. One particularly interesting example converts hexa-1,5-dien-3-ol into hex-5-enal, as illustrated in Equation 24-49.

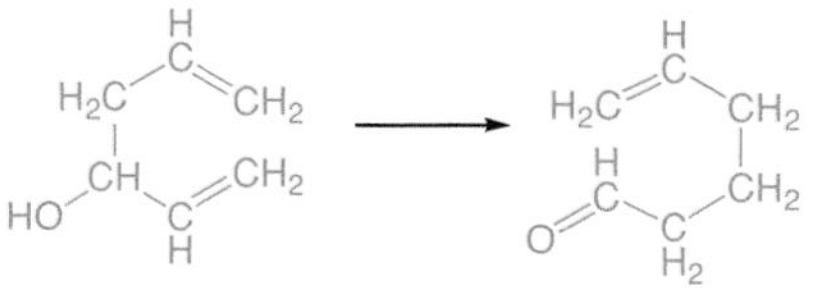

hexa-1,5-dien-3-ol hex-5-enal (24-49)

The mechanism for this reaction (Equation 24-50) begins with a Cope rearrangement, which directly produces an unstable enol. Subsequent tautomerization (Section 7.1c.2) yields the aldehyde.

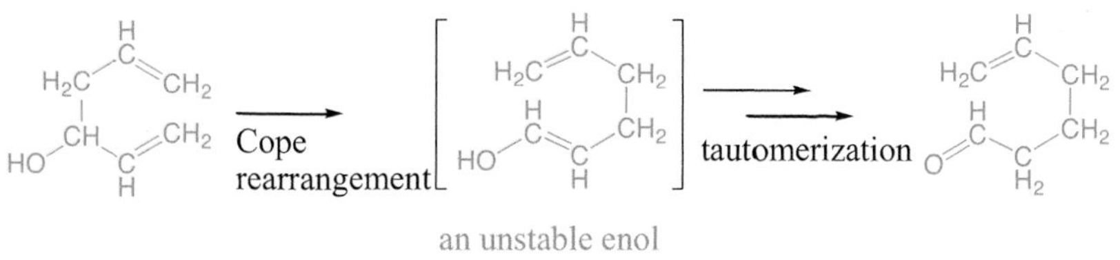

Cope rearrangement

tautomerization

an unstable enol

(24-50)

Your Turn 24.12. Supply the missing curved arrows for the Cope rearrangement in Equation 24-50.

Unlike the Cope rearrangement in Equation 24-47, the one in Equation 24-50 takes place very quickly and proceeds to products *irreversibly*. The speed of the reaction is enhanced by the involvement of the oxygen atom's lone pair in conjugation with the double bond in the enol. The irreversible nature of the reaction, on the other hand, is largely due to the fact that the keto form is substantially more stable than the enol that is initially produced.

Comment [JMK53]: Margin note. Additional conjugation in the product of a Cope rearrangement enhances the rate of the reaction.

Your Turn 24.13. In the space provided here, draw the resonance structure that helps to stabilize the enol intermediate in Equation 24-50.

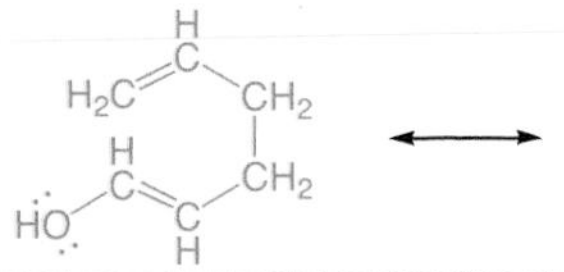

H, H_2C, C, CH_2, H, C, CH_2, HO, C, H ⟷

Solved Problem 24.6. The Cope rearrangement in Equation 24-49 takes place about 10^{10} times faster in basic solution than it does in neutral solution. Explain.

Think. What form of the 1,5-diene reactant can exist under basic conditions, but not to a significant extent under neutral conditions? What is the direct product of that species' Cope rearrangement? How does its stability compare to that of the product in Equation 24-47?

Solve. Under basic conditions, the alkoxide anion can exist in significant amounts. Cope rearrangement of that species directly produces a very stable enolate anion, as shown below. Subsequent protonation yields the overall aldehyde product.

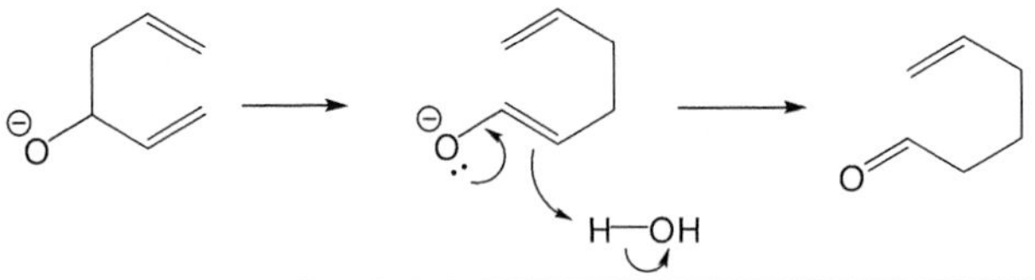

⊖O → ⊖O, H—OH → O

Problem 24.15. Which of the following 1,5-hexadienes do you think will undergo a Cope rearrangement faster? Explain.

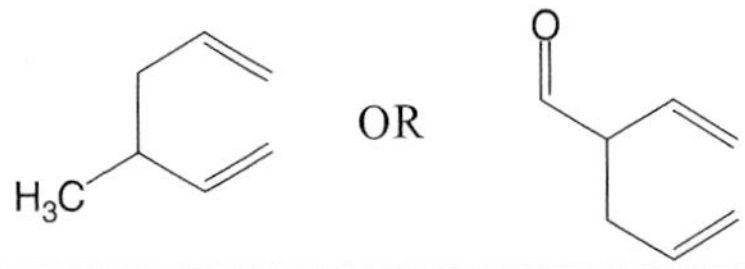

H_3C OR O

Another interesting Cope rearrangement is one that is driven by the relief of ring strain. An example is illustrated in Equation 24-51 where, during the course of the reaction, a highly strained cyclopropane ring is opened up.

Comment [JMK54]: Margin note. The rate of Cope rearrangement is enhanced by relief of ring strain.

substantial ring strain
is relieved by the opening
of the three-membered ring

1,2-divinylcyclopropane → cyclohepta-1,4-diene (24-51)

Problem 24.16. The following compound undergoes an isomerization that yields a compound with the ¹H-NMR spectrum shown. Draw the product and draw the mechanism that takes place.

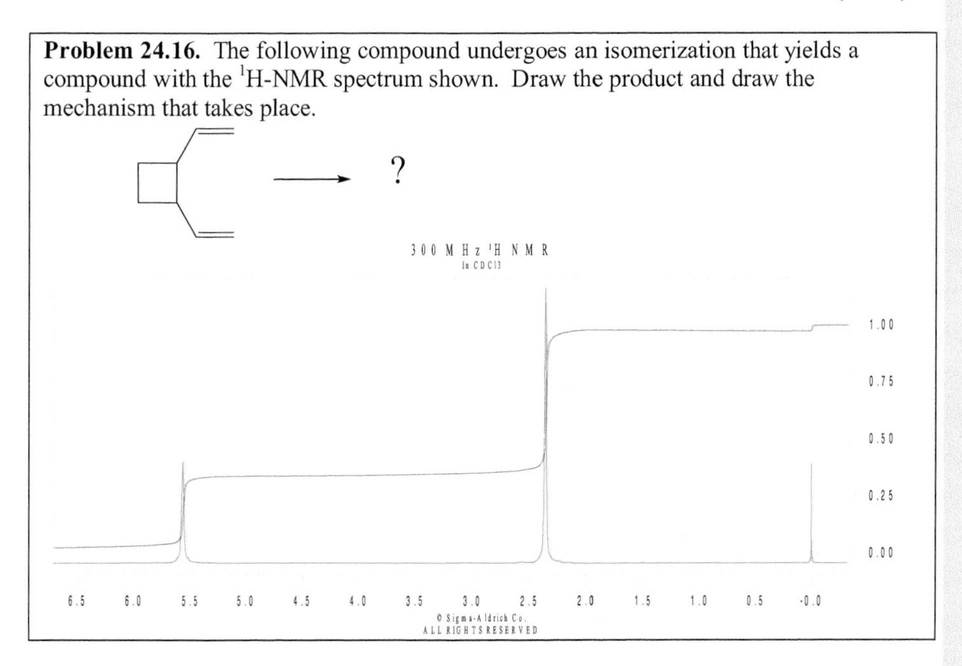

24.8c. The Claisen rearrangement

When an allyl vinyl ether is heated, a ketone or aldehyde is produced via a **Claisen rearrangement**. An example is shown in Equation 24-52.

an allylvinyl ether

3-(ethenyloxy)-1-propene → (16 h, 150 °C) pent-4-en-1-al 97% (24-52)

Like the other reactions we have examined in this chapter, the Claisen rearrangement is *concerted*, involving the cyclic movement of six electrons—the mechanism is shown in Equation 24-53.

Mechanism for the Reaction in Equation 24-52

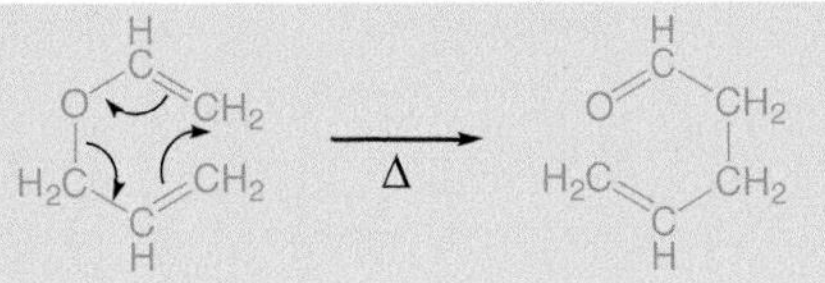

(24-53)

Notice that the Claisen rearrangement is essentially identical to a Cope rearrangement; the only difference is that the Claisen rearrangement involves an oxygen atom, whereas the Cope rearrangement involves only carbons.

Your Turn 24.14. In the space provided here, re-draw the basic Cope rearrangement mechanism in Equation 24-47 and notice the similarities to Equation 24-53.

Problem 24.17. Draw the Cope rearrangement product for each of these isotopically labeled compounds.

a) 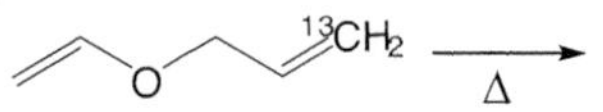 Δ b) 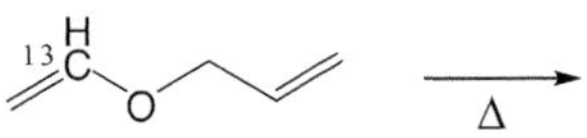 Δ

An interesting scenario arises when the vinylic portion of the allyl vinyl ether is part of an aromatic ring. The result is an *ortho*-allylphenol, as shown in Equation 24-54.

an *ortho*-allylphenol

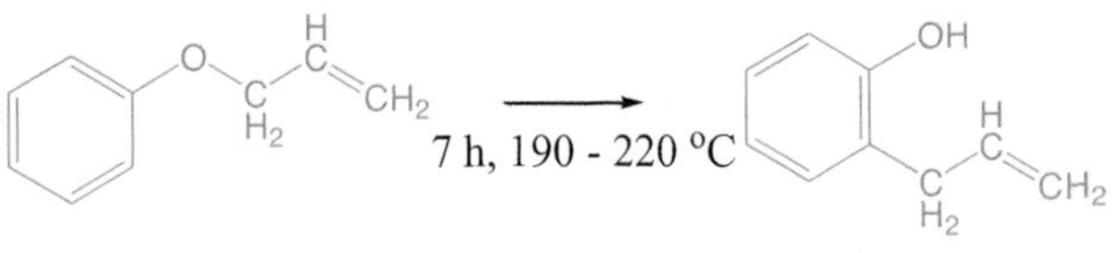

7 h, 190 - 220 °C

3-phenoxy-1-propene 2-(2-propenyl)-phenol 81%

(24-54)

The partial mechanism for this reaction is shown in Equation 24-55, which begins with the Claisen rearrangement we saw previously in Equation 24-53. Notice that the immediate product is a ketone that is no longer aromatic. Therefore, subsequent *keto-enol tautomerization* (Section 7.1c.2) is highly favored in order to regenerate that aromaticity in the form of a phenol.

Partial Mechanism for the Reaction in Equation 24-54

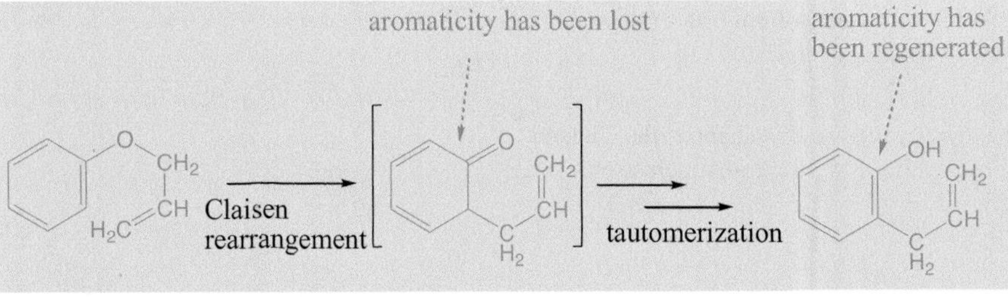

aromaticity has been lost

aromaticity has been regenerated

Claisen rearrangement

tautomerization

(24-55)

Your Turn 24.15. Supply the curved arrows for the first step in Equation 24-55.

Your Turn 24.16. In the space provided here, draw the two-step mechanism for the tautomerization in Equation 24-55.

Problem 24.18. Propose a mechanism for the reaction below, which is an example of an Overman rearrangement.

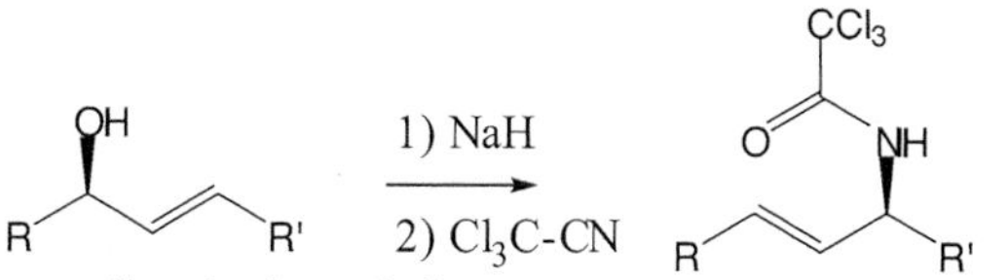

1) NaH

2) Cl_3C-CN

A key intermediate is shown below.

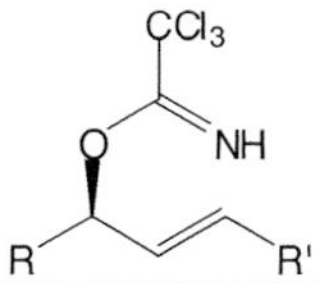

If the benzene ring is substituted at both of its *ortho* positions, as in Equation 24-56, then aromaticity cannot be regenerated after a Claisen rearrangement—regenerating the ring's aromaticity requires tautomerization, which involves deprotonation at the *ortho* position (see again Equation 24-55). Instead, a *para*-allylphenol is produced.

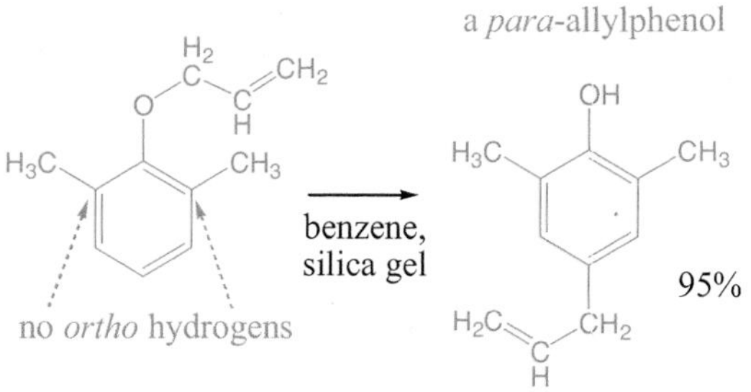

a *para*-allylphenol

benzene, silica gel

95%

no *ortho* hydrogens

(24-56)

A partial mechanism for this reaction is provided in Equation 24-57. The first step is a *Claisen rearrangement*, essentially identical to the one in Equation 24-55. Because tautomerization is not feasible after the first step, the intermediate that is formed undergoes a *Cope rearrangement.* Subsequently, tautomerization involving the *para* hydrogen can take place to regenerate the aromaticity of the ring.

Partial Mechanism for the Reaction in Equation 24-56

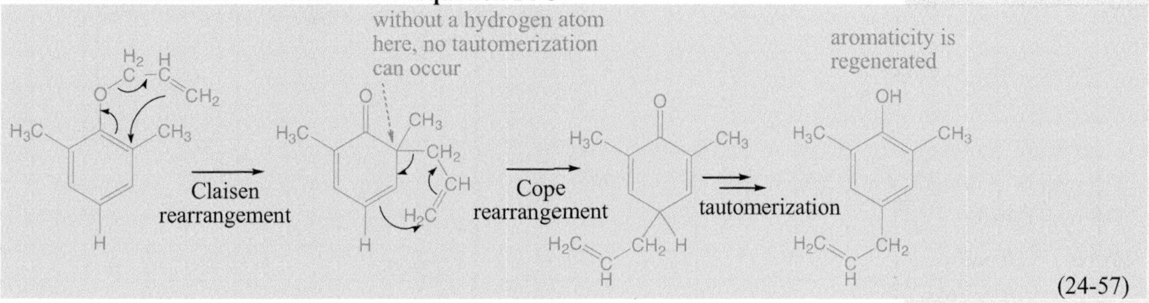

without a hydrogen atom here, no tautomerization can occur

aromaticity is regenerated

Claisen rearrangement

Cope rearrangement

tautomerization

(24-57)

Problem 24.19. Part of the evidence for the mechanism in Equation 24-57 comes from isotopic labeling experiments. Suppose that the terminal carbon of the allyl substituent in Equation 24-56 were labeled with a ^{13}C nucleus, as shown below. Which carbon would be labeled in the product?

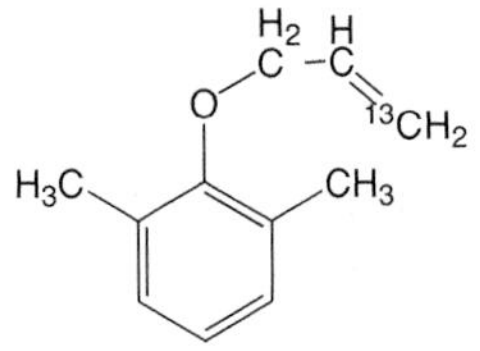

H2 H
C -C
O
13CH2
H3C
CH3

24.9. *(optional)* A MOLECULAR ORBITAL PICTURE OF THE DIELS-ALDER REACTION

Lewis structures and resonance theory can describe the Diels-Alder and other pericylic reactions quite well. However, these theories alone cannot account for some aspects of the reaction, such as the *endo rule* for stereochemistry. Furthermore, as we will see, the presence of UV light changes the outcome of the Diels-Alder reaction—this, too, cannot be accounted for by simple resonance theory.

Because of such shortcomings, this section is devoted to developing a more complete model of the Diels-Alder reaction—one that incorporates molecular orbitals. Specifically, we introduce what is called *frontier molecular orbital theory*, and see how it applies to the Diels-Alder reaction. Frontier molecular orbital theory accounts for not only the aspects of the reaction we discussed previously, but also accounts for the endo rule, as well as the impact that ultraviolet light has.

24.9a. Frontier Molecular Orbital Theory: Allowed and Forbidden Cycloaddition Reactions

In Section 24.1, we learned that the cycloaddition reaction involving 1,3-butadiene and ethene (shown again in Equation 24-58) is allowed, but the one involving two molecules of ethene (shown again in Equation 24-60) is forbidden.

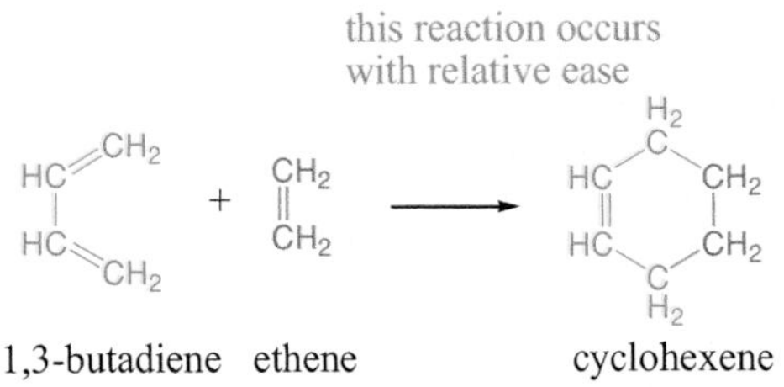

this reaction occurs
with relative ease

HC=CH2, HC=CH2 + CH2=CH2 → cyclohexene

1,3-butadiene ethene cyclohexene (24-58)

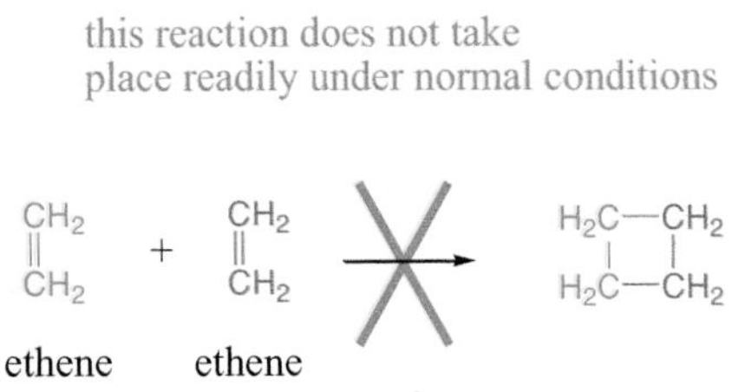

this reaction does not take
place readily under normal conditions

CH2=CH2 + CH2=CH2 ✗→ H2C—CH2, H2C—CH2

ethene ethene (24-59)

The argument previously used to explain these results is that the reaction in Equation 24-58 proceeds through an *aromatic transition state*, whereas the reaction in Equation 24-59 proceeds through an *antiaromatic* one.

Alternatively, those results can be understood by employing **frontier molecular orbital theory**. To do so, we examine the reactants' **frontier molecular orbitals**, defined as the species' *highest occupied* and *lowest unoccupied* molecular orbitals (i.e., the HOMO and LUMO, respectively), and we apply the following rules.

- If the HOMO of one reactant and the LUMO of another have the appropriate symmetry to interact, the reaction is "allowed."
- Otherwise, the reaction is "forbidden."

We focus on the frontier orbitals of the reactants for two reasons. One is that the HOMO is occupied, and the LUMO is empty—by definition, this will always be the case. Therefore, as shown in Figure 24-1a, any interaction among these orbitals must be stabilizing. As we learned in Section 3.2, two orbitals that interact must produce two new orbitals—one that has been lowered in energy (via constructive interference), and one that has been raised in energy (via destructive interference). Because the contributed electrons end up in the lower of the two new orbitals, the system is stabilized overall.

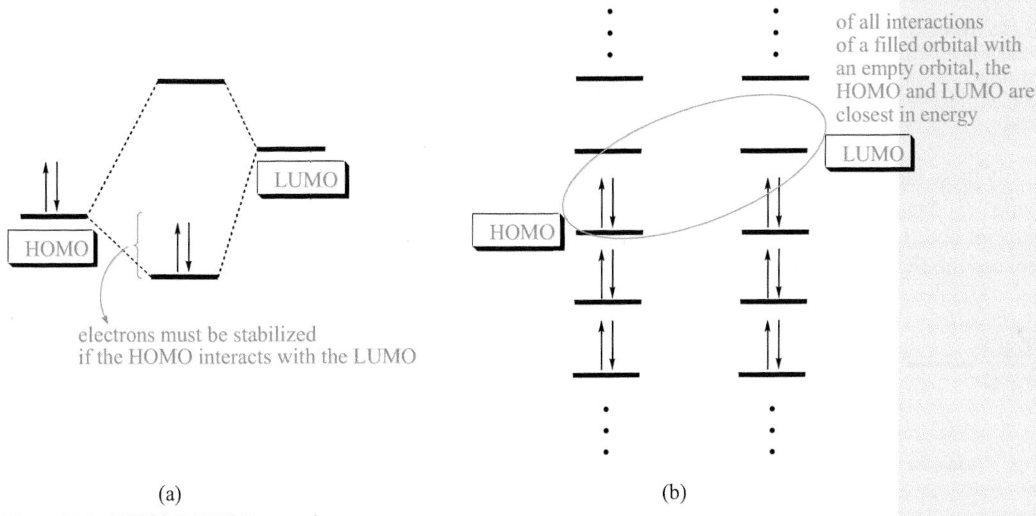

Figure 24-1. HOMO-LUMO Interactions
(a) An interaction between the HOMO of one reactant and the LUMO of another is guaranteed to provide stabilization. When the two orbitals interact, two new orbitals (center) are produced—one that is lower in energy than either the HOMO or LUMO, and one that is higher in energy. The electrons contributed by the HOMO end up in the lower of the two orbitals. (b) The similar energies of the HOMO and LUMO maximize any interaction between the two orbitals.

The second reason we focus on the frontier orbitals is that of all imaginable interactions of a filled orbital with an empty orbital, the HOMO-LUMO interaction is generally the one involving orbitals that are closest in energy. This maximizes any interaction that takes place between the orbitals (Section 3.4).

Of particular importance is the impact that a HOMO-LUMO interaction can have on the transition state of an elementary step. In a transition state, bonds are partially broken and/or partially formed, which can lead to a tremendous amount of destabilization. Without significant stabilization, the resulting energy barrier can be very large, making the reaction rate excessively small—such reactions are "forbidden." As shown in Figure 24-2, however, stabilization provided by a HOMO-LUMO interaction can provide significant stabilization to the transition state, which would lower the energy barrier and speed up the reaction. Thus, the reaction would be "allowed."

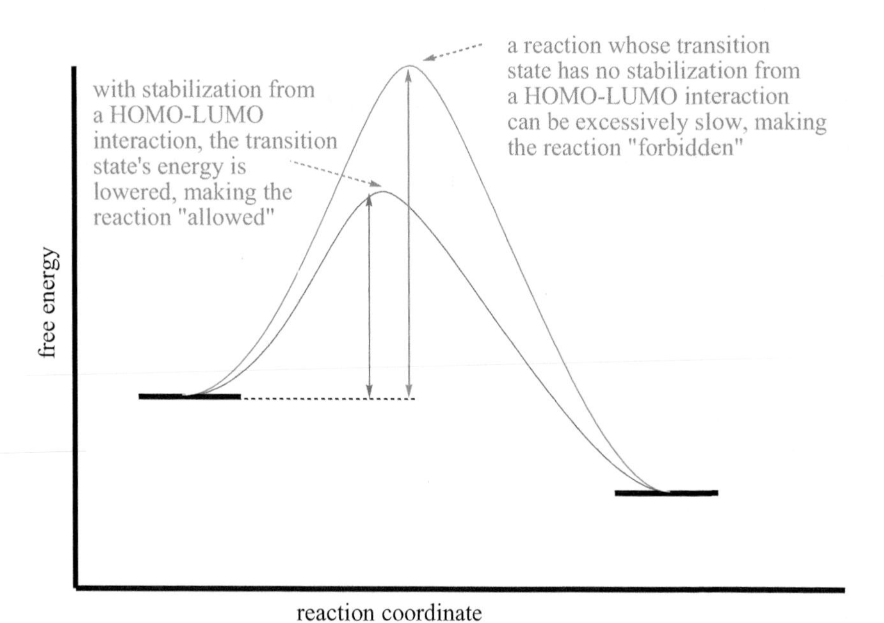

Figure 24-2. Importance of a HOMO-LUMO Interaction
Without significant stabilization in the transition state (red curve), the energy barrier can be quite large, making the reaction rate excessively slow. Such a reaction is "forbidden." With substantial stabilization in the transition state from a HOMO-LUMO interaction, however, the energy barrier is lowered, thereby increasing the reaction rate. Such a reaction is "allowed."

Let's now apply these ideas to cycloaddition reactions, beginning with the Diels-Alder reaction involving 1,3-butadiene and ethene. Figure 24-3 contains the π molecular orbital energy diagrams for both 1,3-butadiene and ethene, and highlights the frontier orbital interaction between the HOMO of 1,3-butadiene and the LUMO of ethene.

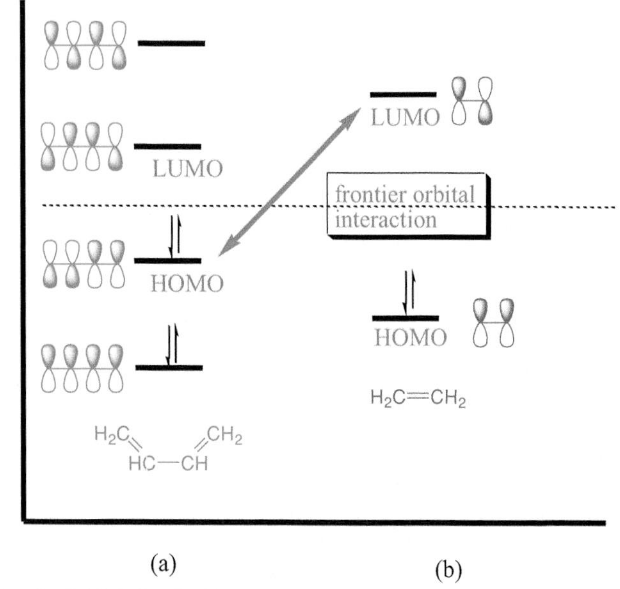

Figure 24-3. Frontier Orbitals Involved in a Diels-Alder Reaction
(a) Molecular orbital energy diagram of 1,3-butadiene. (b) Molecular orbital energy diagram of ethene. The double-headed arrow illustrated the HOMO-LUMO interaction of interest.

As indicated in Figure 24-4, as the diene and dienophile approach each other, the ends of the HOMO and LUMO π systems begin to overlap. Notice that each region of overlap results in the same type of interference—in this case, constructive interference. Thus, the frontier orbitals involved in a Diels-Alder reaction indeed have the appropriate symmetry to interact, and the reaction "allowed."

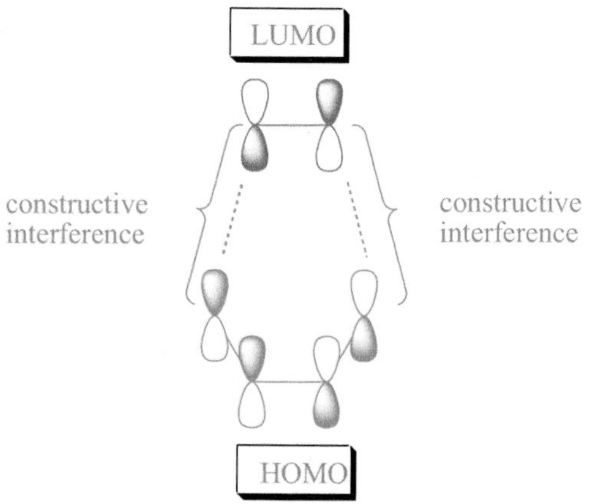

Figure 24-4. Frontier Orbital Interaction in a Diels-Alder Reaction
The HOMO of 1,3-butadiene (red) and the LUMO of ethene (blue) have the appropriate symmetry to interact. Specifically, the regions of overlap at the ends of the π systems result in the same kind of interference—in this case, constructive interference.

Your Turn 24.17. Figure 24-4 highlights one of two possible frontier orbital interactions, involving the HOMO of 1,3-butadiene and the LUMO of ethene. The figure below highlights another, involving the HOMO of ethene and the LUMO of 1,3-butadiene. Label each type of interference resulting from the indicated regions of overlap. Are they both the same, or are they different? Do the orbitals have the appropriate symmetries to interact?

LUMO

HOMO

The story is quite different for the [2+2] cycloaddition reaction involving two molecules of ethene. Figure 24-5 shows the molecular orbitals of π symmetry for each reactant, and highlights one possible frontier orbital interaction.

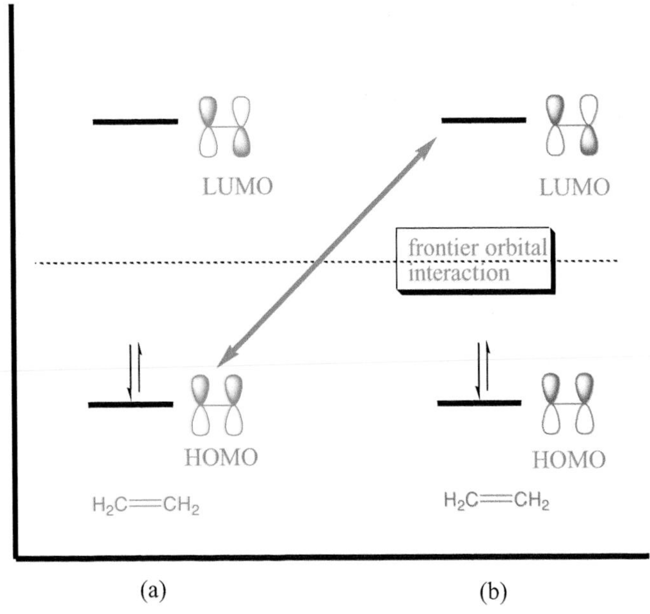

Figure 24-5. Frontier Orbitals Involved in a [2+2] Cycloaddition
(a) Molecular orbital energy diagram of one molecule of ethene. (b) Molecular orbital energy diagram of the second molecule of ethene. The green arrow indicates a HOMO-LUMO interaction.

The overlap that takes place with these orbitals is illustrated in Figure 24-6. As opposed to what we observe for the Diels-Alder reaction (Figure 24-4), symmetry prevents these orbitals from having a net interaction. Overlap on one end leads to constructive interference, but overlap on the other end leads to destructive interference. Thus, there is no net stabilization in the transition state for a [2+2] cycloaddition, and the reaction is "forbidden."

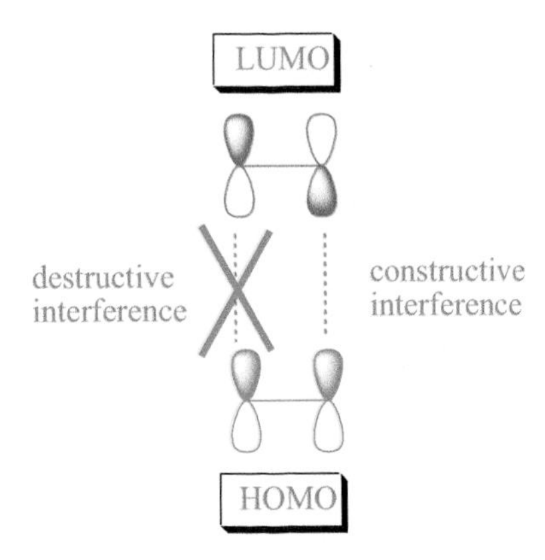

Figure 24-6. Frontier Orbital Interaction in a [2+2] Cycloaddition Reaction
The net interaction for the HOMO-LUMO interaction is zero. Whereas overlap at the right leads to constructive interference, overlap at the left leads to destructive interference. The two effects cancel each other.

Your Turn 24.18. The second HOMO-LUMO interaction in Figure 24-5 can involve the HOMO of the blue molecule and the LUMO of the red one. Overlap of those orbitals is shown below. In the boxes provided, write whether the overlap will lead to constructive or destructive interference. Do the orbitals have the appropriate symmetries to interact?

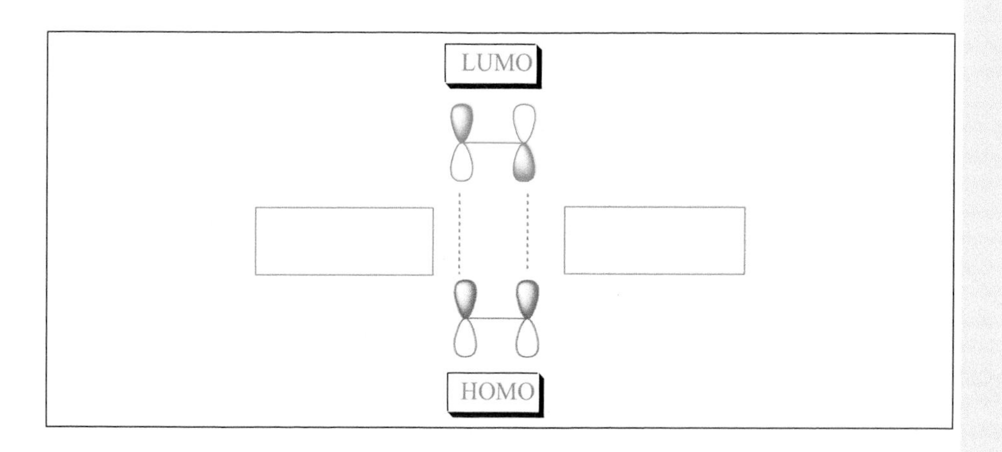

24.9b. Substituent Effects on the Driving Force

Recall that the prototypical Diels-Alder reaction involving 1,3-butadiene and ethene is rather sluggish (see again Equation 24-1). As we learned earlier in this chapter, however, Diels-Alder reactions are facilitated by electron-donating groups attached to the diene, and electron-withdrawing groups attached to the dienophile. How does frontier molecular orbital theory account for these results?

The experimental difficulties encountered with the prototypical Diels-Alder reaction can be understood by examining, once again, Figure 24-3. Notice that even though symmetry allows the frontier orbitals to interact, there is a substantial difference in energy between the HOMO of 1,3-butadiene and the LUMO of ethene. Such an energy difference limits the extent of interaction that can take place, and thus limits the resulting stabilization of the transition state.

However, electron-donating and electron-withdrawing groups can change this picture, due to the impacts such groups have on molecular orbital energies. In general,

- The energy of an orbital is *raised* with a nearby electron-donating group.
- The energy of an orbital is *lowered* with a nearby electron-withdrawing group.

These effects are understood in terms of charge repulsion among electrons. Increased electron density from a nearby electron-donating group results in increased electron-electron repulsion. Conversely, a nearby electron-withdrawing group reduces that electron-electron repulsion by removing electron density from the orbital of interest.

With this in mind, consider Figure 24-7. The energy diagram at the left shows the energies of the MOs of 1,3-butadiene and ethene, the same as previously shown in Figure 24-3. The energy diagram at the right shows how the picture changes when an electron-donating group (EDG) is attached to 1,3-butadiene, and an electron-withdrawing group (EWG) is attached to ethene. Notice specifically that the difference in energy between the HOMO of the former and the LUMO of the latter has diminished. With a smaller HOMO-LUMO energy gap, the orbitals interact to a greater extent in the transition state, which lowers the energy barrier between reactants and products.

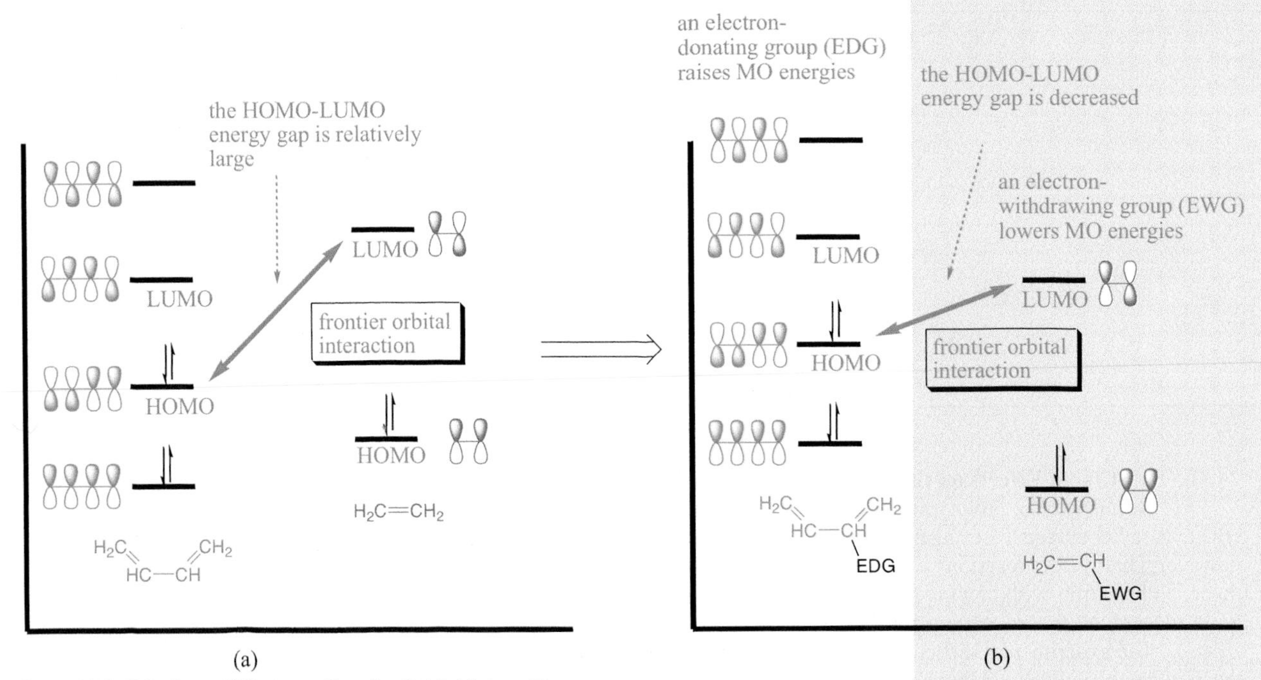

Figure 24-7. Substituent Effects on a Frontier Orbital Interaction
(a) MO energies of unsubstituted 1,3-butadiene and ethene. (b) MO energies of 1,3-butadiene with an attached electron-donating group (EDG) and ethene with an attached electron-withdrawing group (EWG). The EDG raises the MO energies of the diene, and lowers the MO energies of the dienophile, which decreases the HOMO-LUMO energy gap.

Problem 24.20. Draw a diagram similar to that in Figure 24-7b, but instead assume that an electron-withdrawing group is placed on the diene and an electron-donating group is placed on the dienophile. How does the HOMO-LUMO energy gap compare to the one in Figure 24-7a?

24.9c. The Endo Rule for Stereochemistry

As we saw previously, when both *endo* and *exo* products can be made in a Diels-Alder reaction, the *endo* products tend to be favored. Whereas simple resonance theory cannot account for these results, frontier molecular orbital theory provides us with insight.

Let's examine the Diels-Alder reaction between cyclopentadiene and propenal, which can produce both *endo* and *exo* products (Equation 24-60).

endo product *exo* product (24-60)

The π molecular orbitals of the two molecules are shown in Figure 24-8. Notice that the HOMO and LUMO of cyclopentadiene are essentially the same as those of 1,3-butadiene. (The presence of the extra CH_2 group will modify the energies only slightly, so we will ignore its effect.)

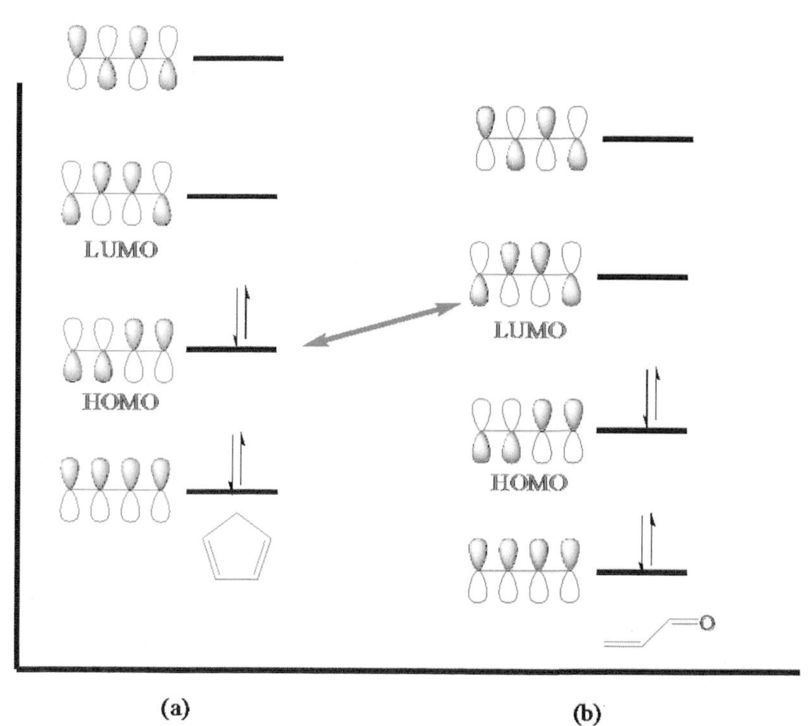

Figure 24-8. Frontier Orbitals in the Diels-Alder Reaction Involving Cyclopentadiene and Propenal
(a) π molecular orbitals of cyclopentadiene. (b) π molecular orbitals of propenal. The important HOMO-LUMO interaction between them is indicated by the arrow.

The HOMO and LUMO of propenal, on the other hand, are somewhat different from those of ethene, given that the C=O bond in propenal is *conjugated* to the C=C bond. There are therefore four π orbitals in propenal—two bonding and two antibonding—similar to 1,3-butadiene. Propenal's molecular orbitals are lower in energy due to the presence of the electron-withdrawing C=O group.

Figure 24-9 explicitly shows the interaction between the HOMO of cyclopentadiene and the LUMO of propenal, both in the *endo* approach and in the *exo* approach. Even though propenal has contribution from four *p* atomic orbitals in each of its π molecular orbitals, only the two *p* orbitals comprising the C=C double bond—i.e., those on carbon-3 and carbon-4—are directly involved in the reaction. (Those two carbon atoms are the ones that gain a σ bond during the course of the reaction.) Both the *endo* and the *exo* approach exhibit the overlap of these two *p* orbitals on the dienophile with the *p* orbitals on carbon-1 and carbon-4 of the diene—this is called the **primary orbital overlap** for this reaction.

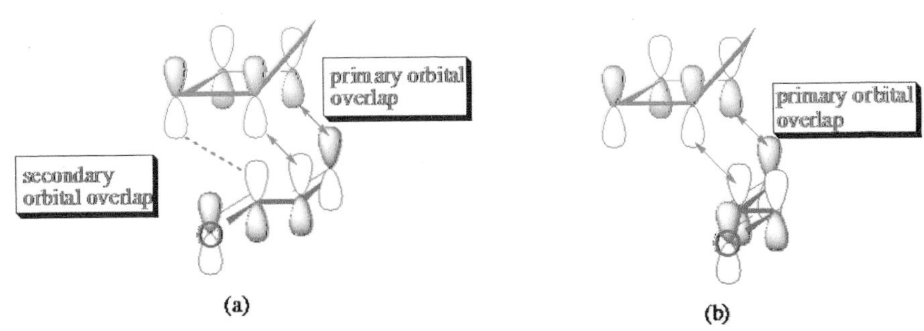

Figure 24-9. Primary and Secondary Orbital Overlap in a Diels-Alder Reaction
Interaction between the HOMO of cyclopentadiene with the LUMO of propenal (a) in the *endo* approach of propenal and (b) in the *exo* approach of propenal. Both approaches exhibit primary overlap of the orbitals used to form the two new σ bonds in the reaction, but only the *endo* approach exhibits secondary orbital overlap (dashed green line), employing an orbital on the dienophile that is not directly involved in bond formation or breaking. This lowers the energy for the transition state, thereby favoring the *endo* approach over the *exo* approach.

Notice, however, that there is additional orbital overlap exhibited in the *endo* approach, not present in the *exo* approach. In the *endo* approach, the C=O group is oriented toward the π system of the diene, allowing the *p* orbital on the carbonyl carbon to interact with an unused *p* orbital on the diene (indicated by the dashed green line). This is an example of what is called **secondary orbital overlap**. Even though the secondary overlap does not specifically lead to bond breaking or formation in the reaction, it does provide stabilization. Therefore,

> In a Diels-Alder reaction, the transition state produced via *endo* approach tends to be lower in energy than the one produced via *exo* approach. Thus, the *endo* approach tends to be favored, making the *endo* product the major product.

Your Turn 24.19. Figure 24-9b is reproduced below. Circle the two *p* orbitals that, in Figure 24-9a, are involved in secondary orbital overlap. Are those *p* orbitals closer together in Figure 24-9a or 24-9b?

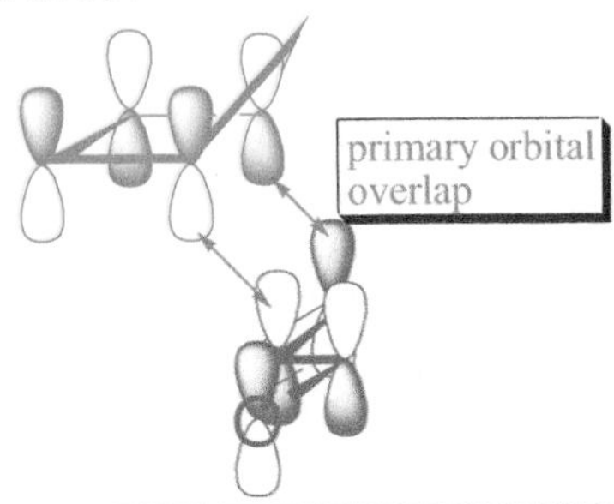

24.9d. Thermal vs. Photochemical Reactions

In all of the reactions we have considered thus far in this chapter, we have assumed that the reactants are in their ground state (i.e., lowest energy) electron configuration, where all electrons reside in the lowest energy orbitals and are paired. When all reactants are in their ground state, the reaction is said to be **thermal**. We can therefore say that the Diels-Alder reaction—a [4+2] cycloaddition reaction—is **thermally allowed**, due to the favorable frontier orbital interactions. By contrast, the [2+2] cycloaddition is **thermally forbidden**, because the frontier orbital interactions do not lead to net stabilization (see again Figures 24-4 and 24-6).

Quite interestingly, [2+2] cycloaddition reactions, such as the one between two molecules of ethene, take place readily when illuminated with ultraviolet light (Equation 24-61).

$$H_2C{=}CH_2 \xrightarrow[\text{ultraviolet light}]{} \begin{matrix} H_2C - CH_2 \\ | \quad\;\; | \\ H_2C - CH_2 \end{matrix} \qquad (24\text{-}61)$$

When ethene absorbs a photon with sufficient energy, an electron is promoted from the HOMO to the LUMO (see again Section 13.3a), thereby generating an **excited electronic state** (Figure 24-10).

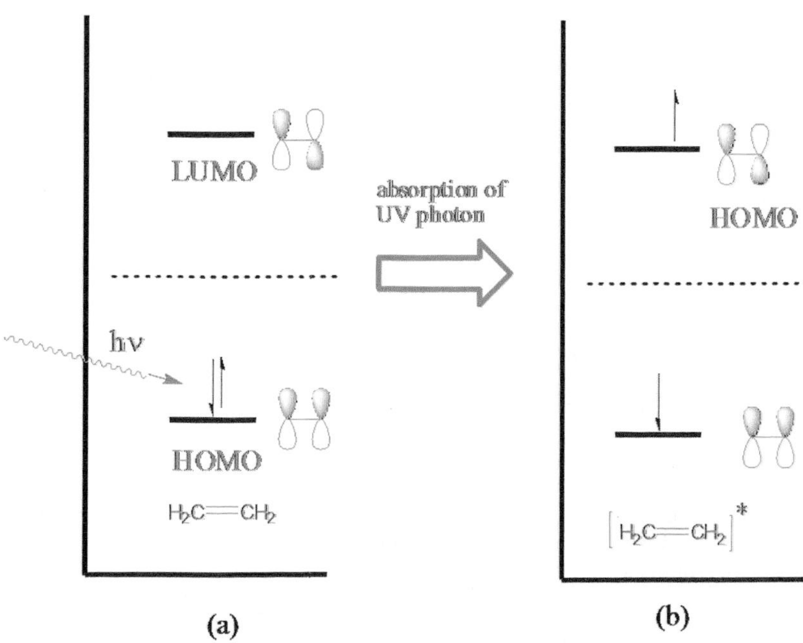

Figure 24-10. Impact of UV Photon Absorption on the Identities of the HOMO and LUMO
(a) Ground state electron configuration of ethene. (b) Excited electronic state of ethene, denoted by *. An ultraviolet photon with sufficient energy (hv) is capable of promoting an electron from ethene's HOMO to its LUMO to generate the excited state. The excited state's HOMO is the ground state's LUMO.

In that excited state, the new HOMO is the π^* molecular orbital. Therefore, when an excited molecule of ethene encounters another ethene molecule still in the ground electronic state, the frontier orbital interaction involves the π^* orbital from each species (Figure 24-11).

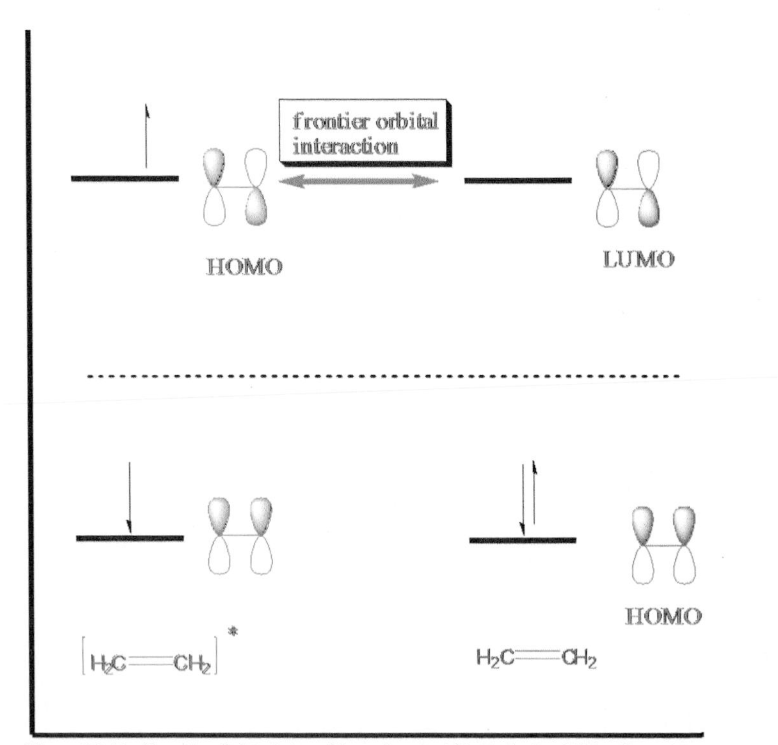

Figure 24-11. Frontier Orbitals in a Photochemical [2+2] Cycloaddition Reaction
The π molecular orbitals of ethene in an excited state are shown in red, and those of ethene in its ground state are shown in blue. The resulting frontier orbital interaction is between the π^* MO in each species.

Notice that these HOMO and LUMO orbitals do indeed have the appropriate symmetries to interact, as illustrated in Figure 24-12. Consequently, although the [2+2] cycloaddition reaction is *thermally forbidden*, it is **photochemically allowed**.

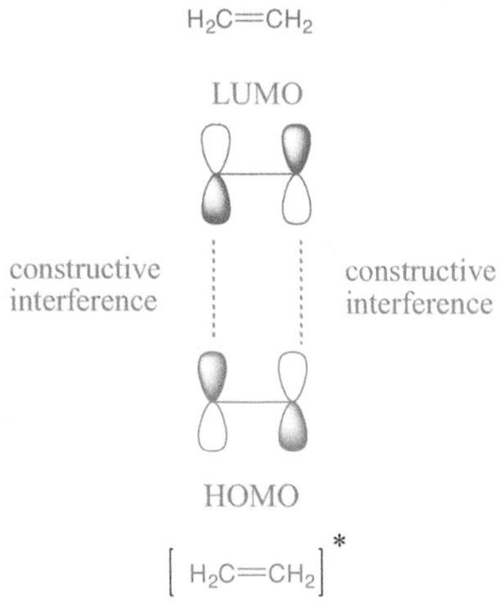

Figure 24-12. Frontier Orbital Interaction in a Photochemical [2+2] Cycloaddition Reaction
Both ends of the π systems exhibit the same type of interference—in this case, constructive interference. Therefore, the orbitals have the appropriate symmetries to interact, thus making this reaction *photochemically allowed.*

Contrary to what is observed with the [2+2] cycloaddition reaction, the Diels-Alder reaction is impeded by UV light, as indicated in Equation 24-62.

UV light impedes a Diels-Alder reaction

$HC(=CH_2)-HC(=CH_2)$ + $CH_2=CH_2$ —UV light (crossed out)→ cyclohexene ($HC=HC$, CH_2, CH_2, $C H_2$, $C H_2$)

(24-62)

When a molecule of 1,3-butadiene absorbs a photon with sufficient energy, an excited state of 1,3-butadiene is generated, in which an electron occupies the molecular orbital that was originally the LUMO (Figure 24-13).

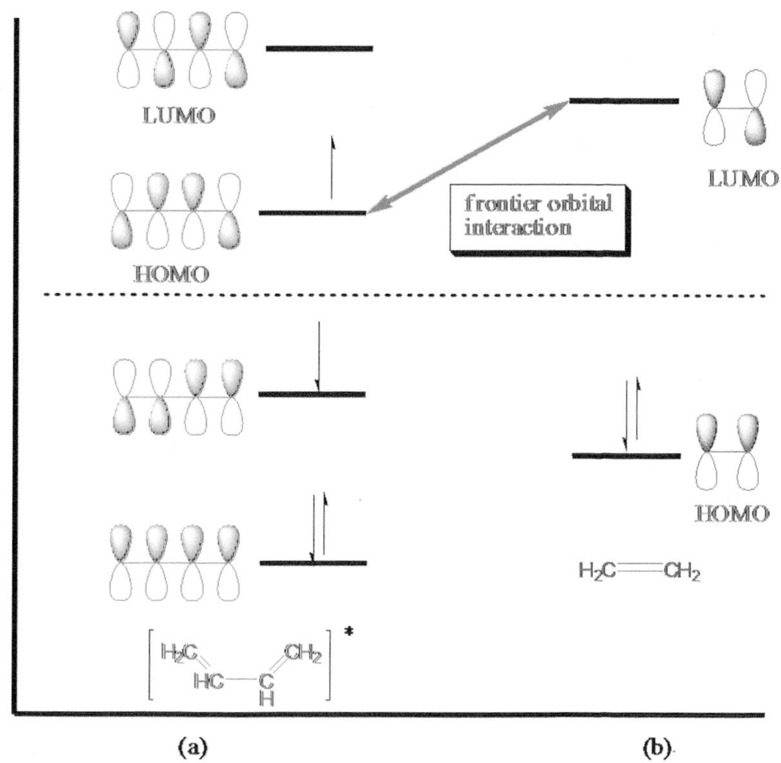

Figure 24-13. Frontier Orbitals in a Photochemical Diels-Alder Reaction
The π molecular orbitals of 1,3-butadiene in an excited state are shown in red, and those of ethene in its ground state are shown in blue. The double-headed green arrow indicates a potential frontier orbital interaction.

When this excited state species encounters a molecule of ethene in the ground state, the HOMO and LUMO that are highlighted no longer have the appropriate symmetries to interact (Figure 24-14), making the reaction forbidden. The Diels-Alder reaction is therefore said to be **photochemically forbidden**.

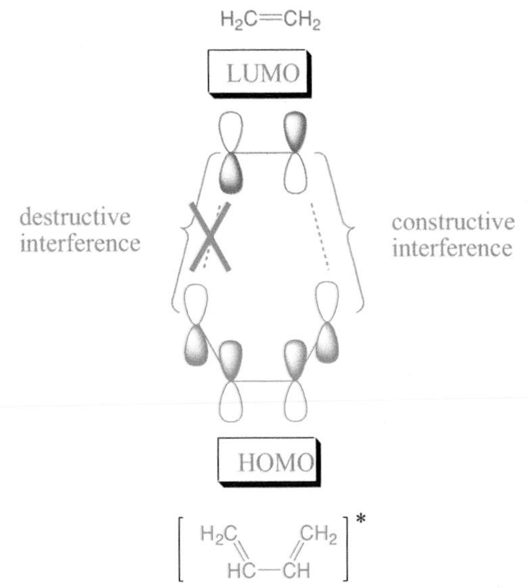

Figure 24-14. Frontier Orbital Interaction in a Photochemical Diels-Alder Reaction
Frontier orbital interaction between a molecule of 1,3-butadiene in its excited state (red) and a molecule of ethene in its ground state (blue). These orbitals do not have the appropriate symmetries to interact, because while one end exhibits constructive interference, the other exhibits destructive interference. Therefore, this reaction is said to be *photochemically forbidden*.

Your Turn 24.20. Figure 24-14 illustrates one possible frontier orbital interaction involving 1,3-butadiene in its excited state and ethene in its ground state, involving the HOMO of 1,3-butadiene and the LUMO of ethene. Below is another possible frontier orbital interaction, involving the HOMO of ethene and the LUMO of 1,3-butadiene. Next to each region of overlap, write either "constructive interference" or "destructive interference," and determine whether the orbitals have the appropriate symmetries to interact.

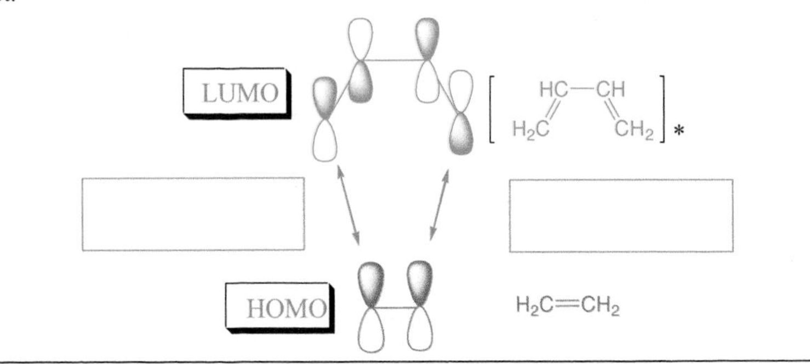

Problem 24.21. Figures 24-13 and 24-14 show that a Diels-Alder is forbidden between 1,3-butadiene in its excited state and ethene in its ground state. Using a similar analysis, determine whether a Diels-Alder reaction is allowed between 1,3-butadiene in its ground state and ethene in its excited state.

24.10. ORGANIC SYNTHESIS: THE DIELS-ALDER REACTION IN SYNTHESIS

As we have emphasized throughout this chapter, the Diels-Alder reaction is an important contribution to organic synthesis, in large part because it allows us to synthesize a six-membered carbon ring from acyclic precursors. The prototypical Diels-Alder reaction—between 1,3-butadiene and ethene—is repeated in Equation 24-63; the fundamental motif in the product is a cyclohexene ring.

an alkene functional group

a six-membered ring of carbons

(24-63)

The *alkene* functionality that is left in the product is an important feature of the Diels-Alder reaction. This allows further reaction to take place specifically at that site. For example, the C=C double bond can be hydrogenated (Section 17.5) to produce a cyclohexane ring. Or, it can undergo electrophilic addition to produce a new functional group that can be used further (Section 20.1); this is illustrated in Equation 24-64, in which the Diels-Alder product is converted into a Grignard reagent.

1) HBr 2) Mg MgBr

(24-64)

Another option is to alter the size of the ring, as shown in Equation 24-65. Oxidative cleavage (Section 21.9) opens the six-membered ring at the C=C double bond. This is followed by an intramolecular aldol condensation (Section 16.8), which forms a five-membered ring.

1) O_3 2) Zn, HOAc NaOH Δ

(24-65)

Realize, however, that the Diels-Alder reaction is not the first reaction we have encountered that allows us to produce a six-membered carbon ring. Recall from Section 16.10 that we can also do so using the Robinson annulation reaction, which is provided again in Equation 24-66. As indicated, the immediate product is an unsaturated cyclohexenone, and the carbonyl group can be selectively reduced to produce the cyclohexene ring.

NaOH Δ reduction

(24-66)

Despite the fact that a cyclohexene ring can be produced by the Robinson annulation reaction, the Diels-Alder reaction generally offers numerous advantages. One advantage is the relatively mild conditions required for a Diels-Alder reaction; by contrast, Robinson annulation requires significantly basic conditions that may interfere with other functional groups present. Furthermore, reduction of a carbonyl group to a methylene (CH_2) group in the second step in Equation 24-67 can require harsh conditions, including the presence of strong acid or strong base (see again Section 17.3).

Other advantages include the *stereoselectivity* and the *regioselectivity* of the Diels-Alder reaction. For example, in 1952, Woodward and coworkers pioneered the use of the Diels-Alder reaction as a key step in the total synthesis of cholesterol, as indicated in Equation 24-67.

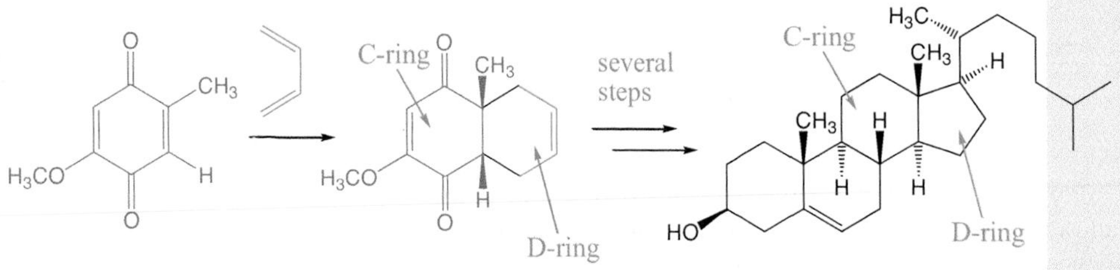

(24-67)

Notice, in particular, that the Diels-Alder reaction is employed to generate the six-membered ring that later becomes the "D-ring" in the target. It is also used to establish the initial stereochemistry of the H and CH_3 groups indicated in blue—immediately after the Diels-Alder reaction they are *cis* to each other, and through a later step in the synthesis they become *trans* to each other.

It is also interesting to note the regiochemistry of the Diels-Alder reaction in Equation 24-67. Notice that there are two portions that can act as the dienophile—the two C=C double bonds in blue on either side of the six-membered ring. Yet 1,3-butadiene selectively reacts with only one of them (the one to which the CH_3 group is attached), leaving the other one (to which the OCH_3 group is attached) available for further reaction.

Problem 24.22. In Equation 24-67, why does 1,3-butadiene react selectively with the C=C double bond containing the CH_3 group instead of the one containing the OCH_3 group?

Equation 24-67 provides a glimpse of the utility of the Diels-Alder reaction in total synthesis. For those who are interested in learning more about its use in total synthesis, see the review by Nicolaou and coworkers (*Angew. Chem. Int. Ed.* **2002**, *41*, 1668-1698).

24.11. WRAPPING UP AND LOOKING AHEAD

The focus of this chapter was on the Diels-Alder reaction, classified as a type of cycloaddition reaction. In such a reaction, a diene and a dienophile are joined together via the formation of two new σ bonds, producing a six-membered ring of carbon atoms. Like all cycloaddition reactions, the Diels-Alder reaction is a pericyclic reaction, meaning that it is concerted, and involves the cyclic movement of electrons. Thus, it is an elementary step that differs from the ones we examined in Chapters 6 and 7.

Just as we did with the other elementary steps encountered previously, we began this chapter by developing the Diels-Alder reaction in a systematic way. We first established how, in the curved arrow notation for the step, electrons flow from a relatively electron-rich diene to a relatively electron-poor dienophile. Next, we examined the driving force for the reaction in terms of free energy, enthalpy, and entropy, and we learned how, depending upon the nature of the reactants and products, a Diels-Alder reaction can be either reversible or irreversible. Finally, we learned why the Diels-Alder reaction exhibits the specific stereochemistry and regiochemistry that it does.

In addition to the Diels-Alder reaction, we took a brief look at other pericyclic reactions as well. We saw, for example, that a Diels-Alder reaction can involve the formation of bonds to atoms other than carbon, in a so-called hetero Diels-Alder reaction. Electrocyclic reactions produce a new ring via the formation of one new σ bond, whereas both the Cope and Claisen rearrangements result in a shift in the position of a σ bond.

In closing this chapter, we reexamined the Diels-Alder reaction from the perspective of molecular orbital theory. Specifically, we saw how frontier molecular orbital theory can account for the fact that Diels-Alder reactions are thermally allowed and photochemically forbidden, whereas the reverse is true for some other cycloaddition reactions. Frontier molecular orbital theory can account for other aspects of the Diels-Alder reaction as well, such as substituent effects and stereochemistry, including the endo rule.

Although the reactions we examined here required the introduction of a new elementary step, one aspect of that new step is common to the other elementary steps we examined previously—the curved arrow notation is described by the movement of *pairs* of electrons. In the next chapter, we will examine reactions that incorporate elementary steps requiring the movements of *single* electrons. Thus, those reactions involve species in which not all electrons are paired—so-called *free radicals*. As we will see, however, many aspects of reactions involving free radicals are similar to aspects of reactions we have seen thus far.

CHAPTER SUMMARY AND KEY TERMS

- The **Diels-Alder reaction** joins a conjugated **diene** and a **dienophile** (either an alkene or an alkyne), via the formation of two new σ bonds. The product is a six-membered ring of carbon atoms. (Section 24.1)
- The Diels-Alder reaction is concerted, so all bonds that are formed and broken do so simultaneously. It requires the cyclic movement of electrons, so it is classified as a **pericyclic reaction**. (Section 24.1)
- The Diels-Alder reaction is "allowed," because it is a **[4+2] cycloaddition**, proceeding through an **aromatic transition state**. Reactions that proceed through an **antiaromatic transition state**, such as the **[2+2] cycloaddition**, are "forbidden." (Section 24.1)
- In order for a Diels-Alder reaction to take place, the diene must be able to attain the ***s*-cis conformation**. Diels-Alder reactions cannot take place with the diene in the ***s*-trans conformation**. (Section 24.2)
- Enthalpy tends to heavily favor the products of a Diels-Alder reaction, whereas entropy favors products. Therefore, Diels-Alder reactions tend to be irreversible and proceed under kinetic control, but at high temperatures, some can undergo the reverse reaction—a **retro Diels-Alder reaction**. (Section 24.3)
- Diels-Alder reactions are facilitated by electron-donating groups attached to the diene, and electron-withdrawing groups attached to the dienophile. (Section 24.4)
- Diels-Alder reactions are stereospecific. (Section 24.5)
    - Substituents that are *cis* to each other about the C=C double bond of the dienophile end up *cis* to each other in the new ring that is produced. Otherwise, the substituents end up *trans* to each other in the ring.
    - Substituents attached to the dienophile end up *cis* to each other in the new ring that is produced if the double bonds of the dienophile are both *cis* or both *trans*. Otherwise, the substituents end up *trans* to each other in the ring.
    - Diels-Alder reactions tend to favor an *endo* product over an *exo* product.
- When the diene and dienophile are both asymmetric, two isomeric products can be produced. The major product is the one produced by the approach that

exhibits the most favorable electrostatic attraction among atoms undergoing bond formation. (Section 24.6)

- Diels-Alder reactions can involve the formation of new σ bonds to atoms other than carbon. These are called **hetero Diels-Alder reactions**. (Section 24.7)
- Pericyclic reactions encompass reactions other than cycloaddition reactions. (Section 24.8)
    - An **electrocyclic reaction** produces a new ring through the conversion of a π bond to a σ bond.
    - A **Cope rearrangement** results in a shift in the position of a σ bond with respect to a π system, and involves only carbon atoms.
    - A **Claisen rearrangement** is identical to a Cope rearrangement, but involves at least one atom other than carbon.
- **Frontier molecular orbital theory** considers interactions among the HOMO and LUMO of reactants—so-called **frontier molecular orbitals**.
    - The frontier orbitals in a Diels-Alder reaction have the appropriate symmetries to interact, making the reaction thermally allowed. The frontier orbitals of a [2+2] cycloaddition cannot interact, making the reaction thermally forbidden. (Section 24.9a)
    - The frontier orbital interaction of a Diels-Alder reaction is enhanced with electron-donating groups attached to the diene and/or electron-withdrawing groups attached to the dienophile. Thus, the energy barrier is lowered and the reaction rate is increased. (Section 24.9b)
    - **Secondary orbital overlap** involving the diene and dienophile favors the endo approach over the exo approach. (Section 24.9c)
    - With one of the reactants in an excited state, the frontier orbitals of a [2+2] cycloaddition have the appropriate symmetries to interact, but those of a Diels-Alder reaction do not. Thus, the former reaction is **photochemically allowed**, and the latter is **photochemically forbidden**. (Section 24.9d)

PROBLEMS

23. Below are several isomers of $C_{10}H_{14}$ with two fused 6-membered rings. (a) Identify which of those will react with ethene in a Diels-Alder reaction and which will not. (b) Draw one more isomer with two fused 6-membered rings that *will* react with ethene in a Diels-Alder reaction.

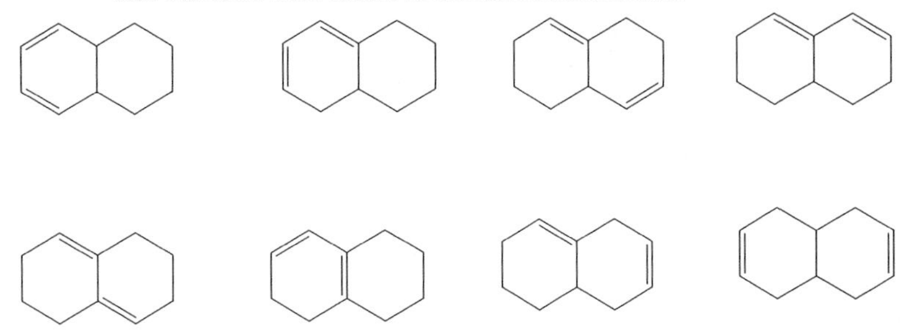

24. Rank the following compounds in order of increasing rate of reaction in a Diels-Alder reaction with ethene.

25. Rank the following in order of increasing rate of reaction in a Diels-Alder reaction with 1,3-butadiene.

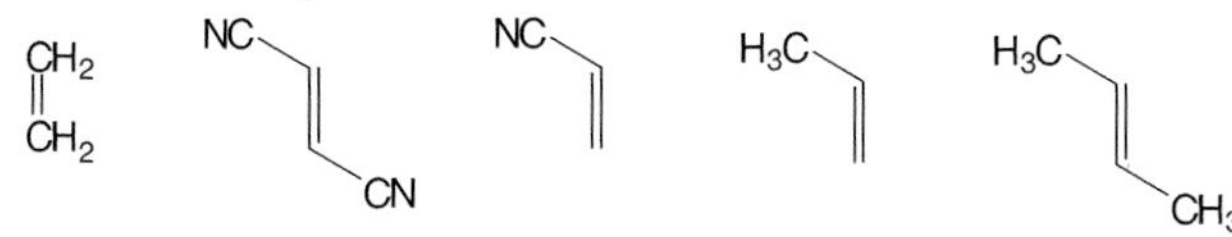

26. Consider the following dienes in a Diels-Alder reaction. Which do you think will react the fastest? Which do you think will react the slowest? Explain.

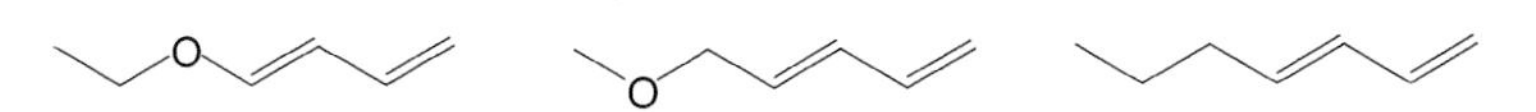

27. Which of the following will react faster as a diene in a Diels-Alder reaction? Explain.

28. Which of the following would you expect to react faster as a dienophile in a Diels-Alder reaction? Explain.

O_2N O_2N

29. Which of the following would you expect to react faster as a dienophile in a Diels-Alder reaction? Explain.

HO   HO

30. Anthracene readily undergoes a Diels-Alder reaction with tetracycanoethene, even though it is aromatic. (a) Draw the two possible products that can form from this reaction. (b) Explain why anthracene can readily undergo a Diels-Alder reaction, whereas benzene does not.

$$+ \quad (NC)_2C=C(CN)_2 \longrightarrow \; ?$$

31. A student, understanding that alkenes and alkynes behave similarly in many regards, attempted the following reaction—an alkyne analog of the Diels-Alder reaction. However, she obtained no product. Explain why.

$$HC\equiv C-C\equiv CH \xrightarrow{HC\equiv CH}$$

32. The following compound can be produced from either of two *different* Diels-Alder reactions. (a) Draw the reactants that can be used for each Diels-Alder reaction. (b) Which route do you suppose would be the better one? Why?

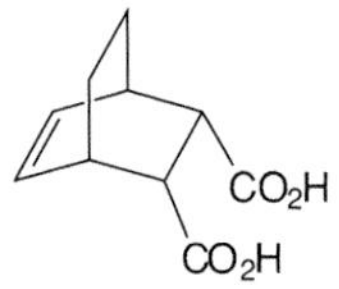

CO_2H

CO_2H

33. The compound below can be produced from two different Diels-Alder reactions. (a) Draw the reactants that would be required for each reaction. (b) Which set of reactants would be the better choice? Why?

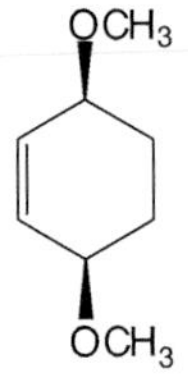

OCH_3

OCH_3

34. Draw a mechanism to account for the following reaction that scrambles the isotopic labeling.

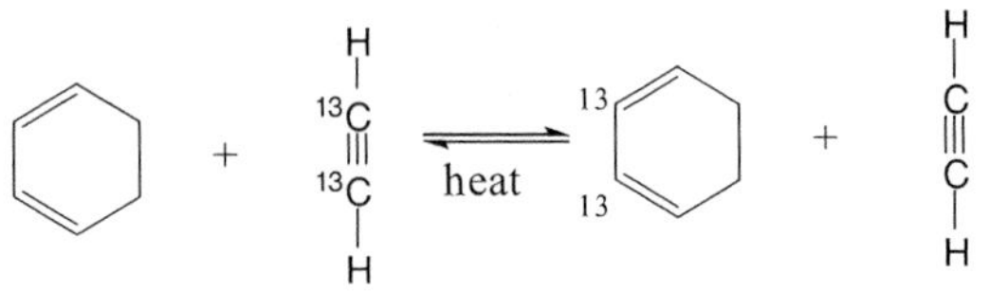

H–$^{13}C\equiv^{13}C$–H, heat, 13, 13, H–C≡C–H

35. The following is an example of a hetero Diels-Alder reaction. Draw the mechanism for the reaction and predict the product, paying attention to stereochemistry.

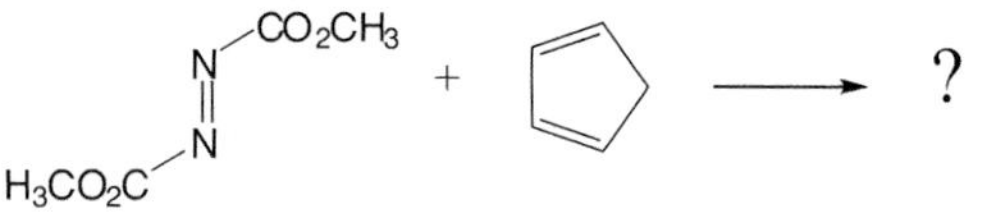

H_3CO_2C–N=N–CO_2CH_3 + → ?

36. Two constitutional isomers can be produced from the Diels-Alder reaction below. (a) Draw the mechanism for the formation of each isomer and (b) determine which isomer is the major product. (Hint: Is a benzene ring considered electron-rich or electron-poor?)

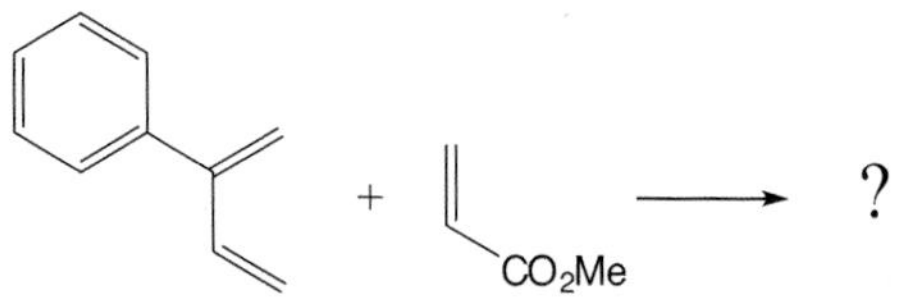

+ CO_2Me → ?

37. When *cis*-1,3,9-decatriene is heated, a reaction is observed to take place. The product of that reaction, when treated with excess Br_2 in CCl_4, yields a compound whose formula is $C_{10}H_{16}Br_2$. What is the product of the first reaction?

38. Draw the structures of the missing compounds in the following synthesis scheme.

HBr, 40 °C → A; NaCN → B; (butadiene) → C; NaOH, H_2O, heat → D; 1) CH_2N_2 2) DIBAH -78 °C → E

E; HO–CH₂CH₂–OH, H^+ → F; (furan) → G; H_2, Pd → H; H_3O^+, heat → I

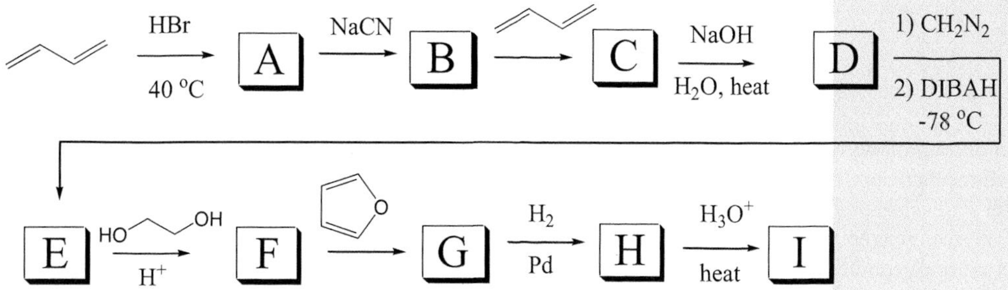

39. Draw the structures of the missing compounds in the following synthesis scheme.

(benzene) Br_2, $FeBr_3$ → A; Mg → B; 1) (ethylene oxide) 2) H_3O^+ → C; $Na_2Cr_2O_7$, H_2SO_4 → D; $SOCl_2$ → E; (benzene), $AlCl_3$ → F

F; $NaBH_4$, EtOH → G; conc. H_3PO_4, Δ → H; (1,4-dimethoxy-cyclopentadiene, OCH_3, OCH_3) → I

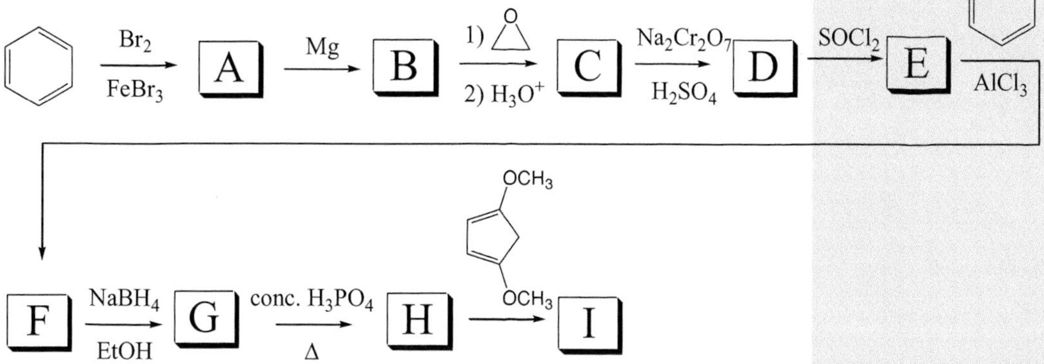

40. Show how you would synthesize each of the following compounds using ethene and 1,3-butadiene as your only sources of carbon.

(a)

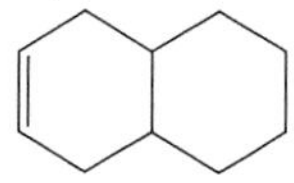

(b) HO ... OH

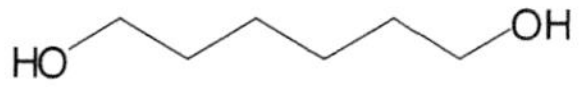

(c) HO ... O

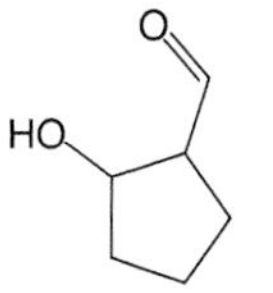

(d) ... O

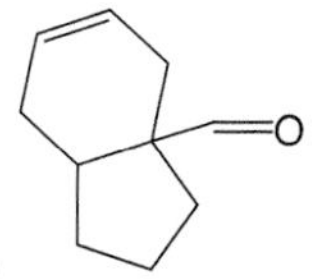

41. The following compound cannot be synthesized *directly* from a Diels-Alder reaction. (a) Why not? (Hint: Examine the reactants that would be required.) (b) What change(s) can be made to the synthesis to get around this problem?

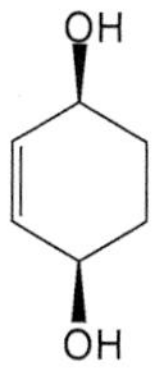

OH

OH

42. Show how you would synthesize the following compound beginning with benzene.

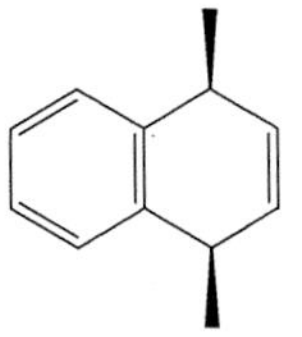

43. For each of the following reactions, (a) draw the curved arrows necessary for a concerted mechanism, (b) draw the transitions state, (c) determine whether each transition state is *aromatic* or *anti-aromatic*, and (d) based on your answer to part (c), determine whether the reaction is "allowed" or "forbidden" under normal (thermal) conditions.

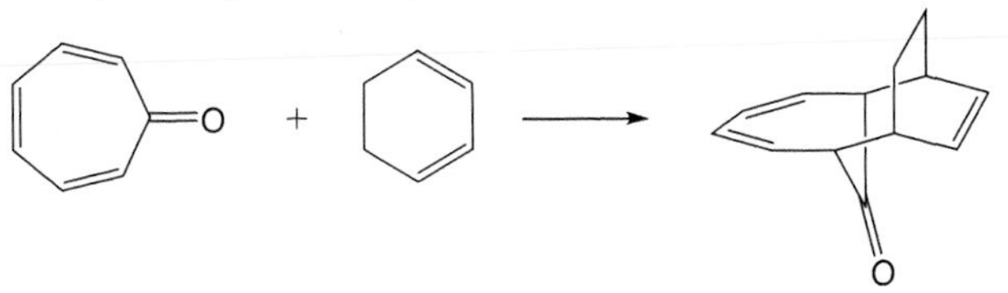

i.

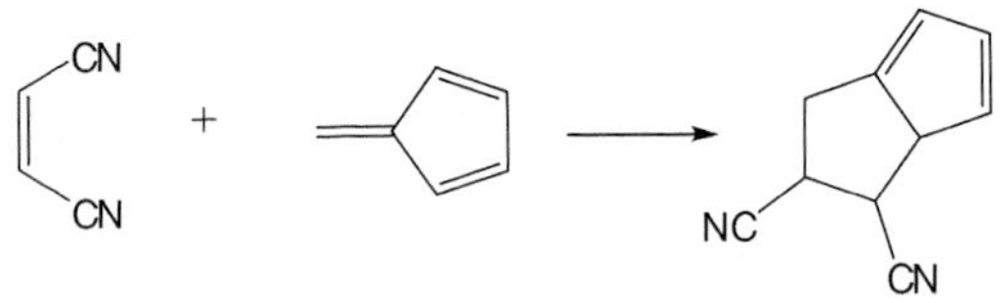

ii.

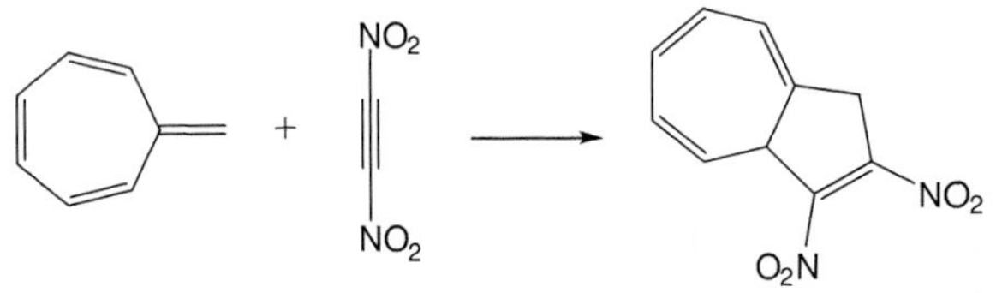

iii.

44. Draw the product of the following reaction, assuming that it takes place via an [8+2] cycloaddition.

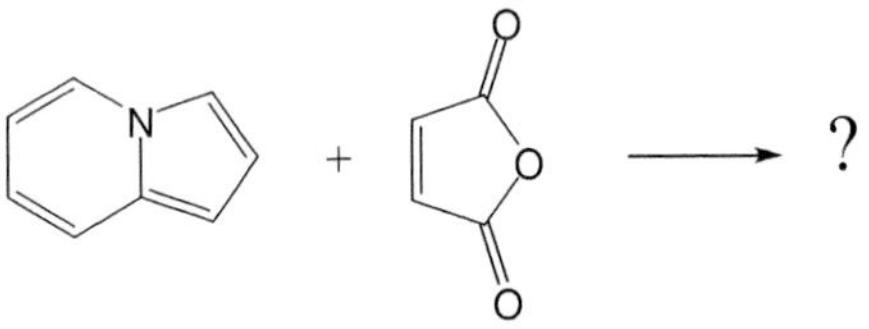

45. Draw the product of the following reaction, assuming that it takes place via a [6+4] cycloaddition.

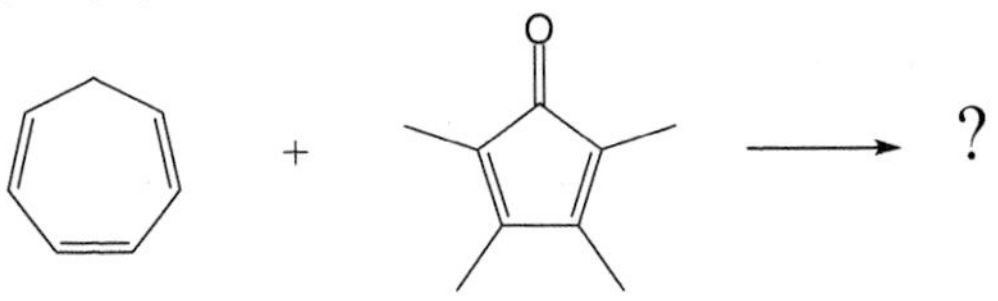

46. When biphenylene is warmed to 40 °C, it decomposes into a compound whose ^{1}H-NMR spectrum exhibits one signal—a singlet at 7.3 ppm. (a) Draw the mechanism for this reaction. (b) Draw the transition state for this reaction,

illustrating that it proceeds through an anti-aromatic transition state. (c) Explain why this reaction proceeds at mild temperatures even though it proceeds through an anti-aromatic transition state.

40 °C ?

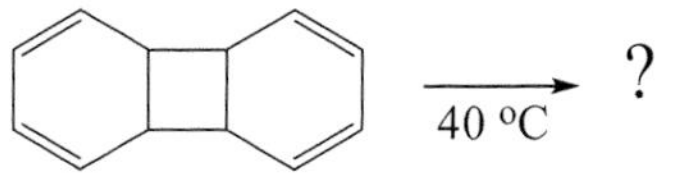

biphenylene

47. The following reaction can take place by two different mechanisms. (a) Draw both of these mechanisms and (b) describe how isotopic labeling can be used to distinguish the two mechanisms.

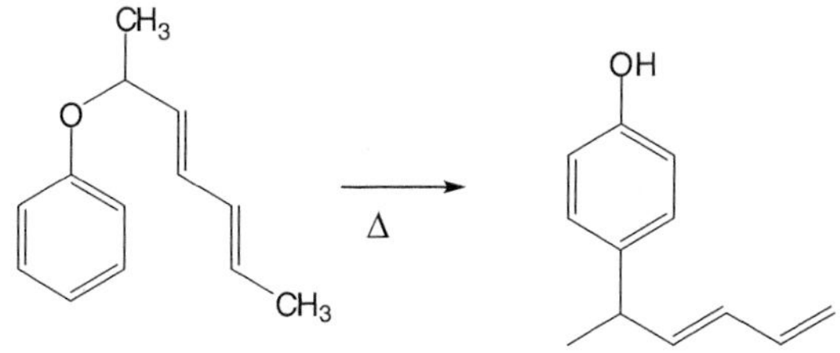

CH_3 O CH_3 Δ OH

48. For each of the following reactions, (a) draw the HOMO of one reactant and the LUMO of the other, assuming that both reactants are in their ground state and (b) illustrate the HOMO-LUMO interaction and determine if such an interaction leads to an "allowed" or "forbidden" reaction.

i. $H_2C{=}CH_2$ +

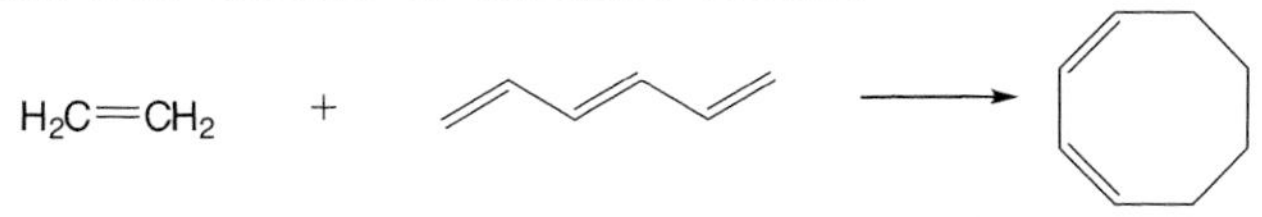

ii. +

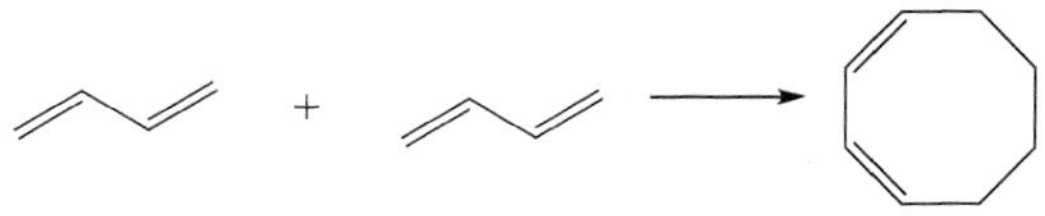

iii. +

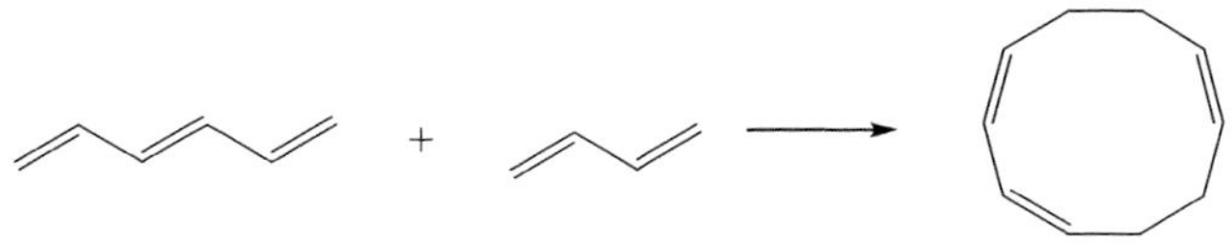

49. Repeat the previous problem, assuming that *one* of the reactants is in its lowest excited state. Based on your answers, which of the reactions are "photochemically allowed"?

50. When the compound below is heated to 700 °C, a product is collected, whose formula is C_4H_6. The ^{1}H-NMR and ^{13}C-NMR spectra of that compound are shown below. Draw the structure of that product, and draw the mechanism of the reaction that accounts for its formation.

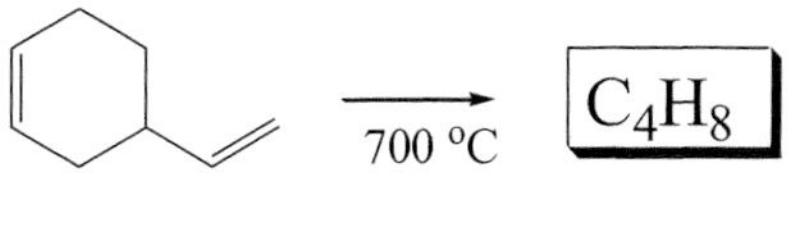

700 °C C_4H_8

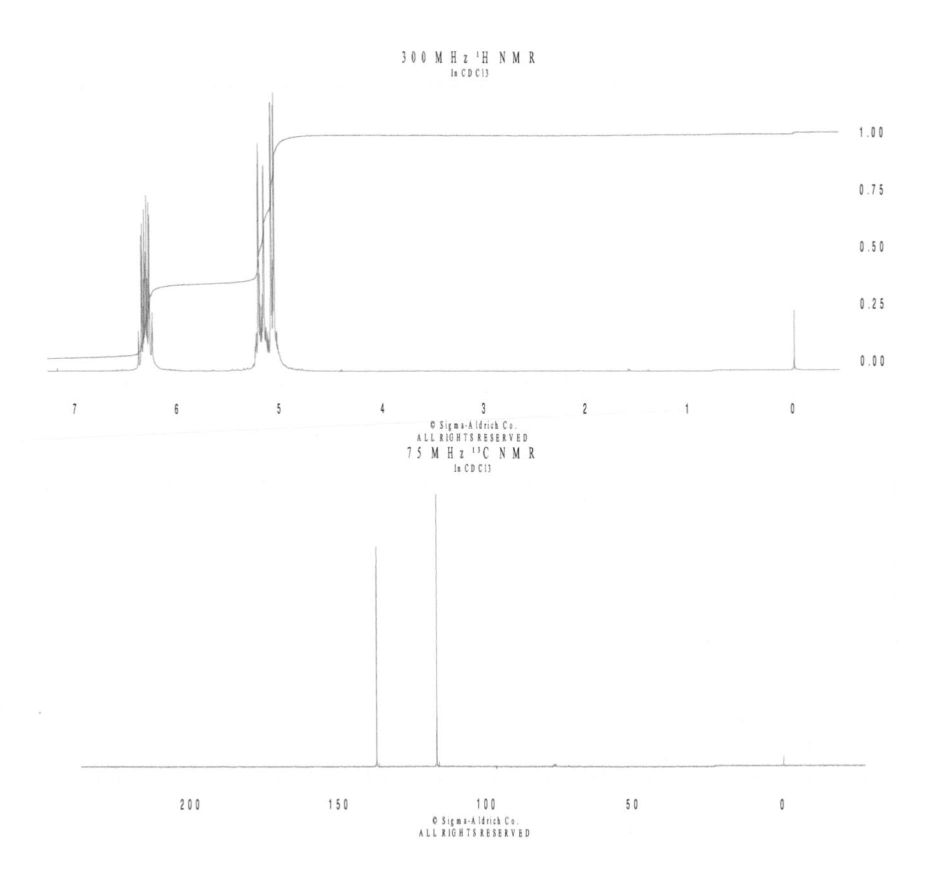

51. When the compound below is heated, ethene gas is evolved and a product is formed, whose formula is $C_{14}H_8O_2$.

heat → $C_{14}H_8O_2$

The ^{1}H-NMR and ^{13}C-NMR spectra of the product are shown below. Draw the structure of the product, and draw the mechanism that accounts for its formation. What is the main driving force that favors the products of this reaction?

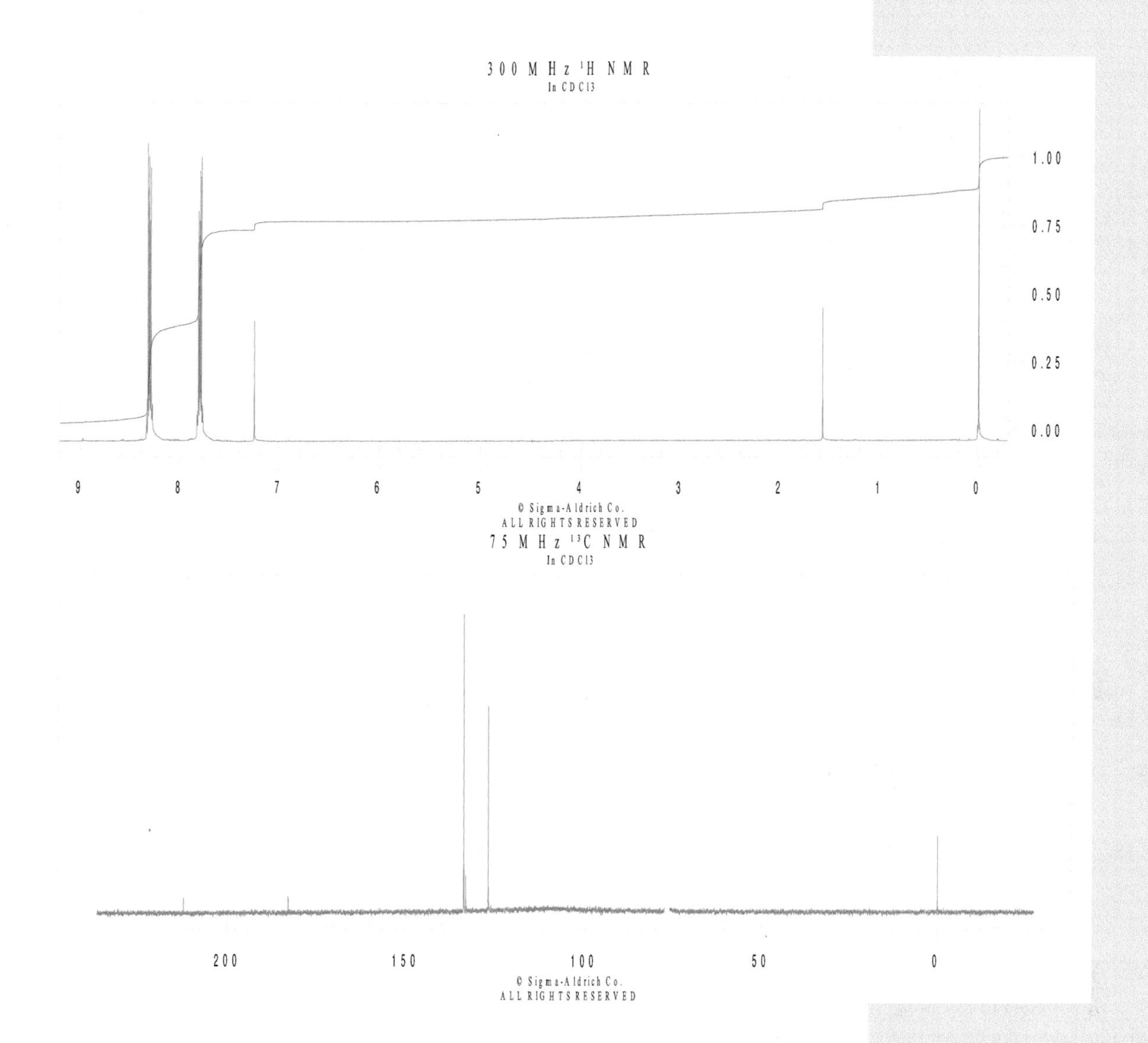
300 MHz ^{1}H NMR
In CDCl3
1.00
0.75
0.50
0.25
0.00
9 8 7 6 5 4 3 2 1 0
© Sigma-Aldrich Co.
ALL RIGHTS RESERVED
75 MHz ^{13}C NMR
In CDCl3
200 150 100 50 0
© Sigma-Aldrich Co.
ALL RIGHTS RESERVED

Chapter 25. Reactions Involving Free Radicals

Introduction

Throughout this book, our focus has been on reaction mechanisms whose individual steps are driven by the flow of electrons from a site that is electron-rich to one that is electron-poor. Thus, we have not had the opportunity to discuss the reactivity of alkanes or alkyl (i.e., R) groups. Alkanes and alkyl groups lack functional groups—they consist of only carbon and hydrogen atoms connected by relatively nonpolar single bonds—so they do not have sites that are especially electron-rich or electron-poor.

However, alkanes are not inert under all conditions. In fact, as you already know from everyday experiences, alkanes react *violently* via combustion. Methane, for example, is used as natural gas to heat our homes. Propane is used in gas grills and camp stoves, and a mixture of relatively small hydrocarbons is used as gasoline for our car engines. Clearly these reactions must proceed by mechanisms that differ from what we have encountered thus far.

Although we will not explore combustion in depth in this chapter, we will examine other, related reactions that are important to organic chemistry. These include halogenation of alkanes, alkene additions, and dissolved metal reductions. What these reactions share in common is the fact that they involve very highly reactive intermediates called *free radicals*.

> A **free radical** is a species that possesses at least one unpaired electron.

Examples include the bromine atom and the methyl radical, shown below.

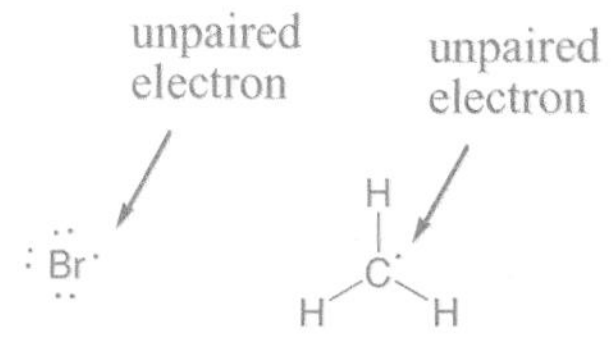

unpaired electron　　unpaired electron

$:\ddot{Br}\cdot$　　$H_3C\cdot$

bromine atom　　methyl radical

Not surprisingly, free radicals such as these behave somewhat differently from other species in which all electrons are paired—so-called **closed-shell species**. Therefore, this chapter presents a picture of how free radicals behave, and develops the picture in a systematic way. We will first discuss free radical structure and stability. Then, we will take a close look at the most common elementary steps that free radicals undergo. Finally, we will delve into the mechanisms of the useful free radical reactions mentioned above.

CHAPTER OBJECTIVES

Upon completion of this chapter you should be able to:

- Distinguish a *free radical* from a *closed-shell species*.
- Explain why free radicals are very unstable and highly reactive.
- Use single-barbed curved arrows to describe the flow of electrons in elementary steps involving free radicals.
- Determine relative stabilities of free radicals, given appropriate bond dissociation energies.
- Predict the relative stabilities of alkyl radicals, given only their Lewis structures.
- Draw all resonance structures of a given free radical.
- Describe the geometry and hybridization of a carbon atom that has an unpaired electron.
- Draw the curved arrow notation for each of the common elementary steps involving free radicals: *homolysis*, *radical coupling*, *bimolecular homolytic substitution*, and *radical addition*.
- Describe the factors that play major roles in the driving force for each of the common elementary steps involving free radicals.
- Draw the complete mechanism for a *dissolving metal reduction*, and predict the major product, including stereochemistry.
- Outline the major characteristics of a free radical *chain reaction*.
- Identify *initiation*, *propagation*, and *termination* steps of a radical chain reaction mechanism.
- Recognize common *radical initiators*, and explain their relevance in a free radical chain reaction.
- Draw the mechanism of *radical halogenation* an alkane, and predict the major product.
- Explain the difference in selectivity between free radical bromination and free radical halogenation.
- Explain the advantage of using *N*-bromosuccinimide (NBS) in the free radical bromination of an allylic carbon.
- Draw the complete mechanism of the radical addition of HBr to an alkene, and predict the major product of such a reaction, including regiochemistry.
- Incorporate free radical reactions in synthesis.

25.1. CURVED ARROW NOTATION: HOMOLYSIS

Because free radicals contain an unpaired electron, it is impossible for all of their atoms to have a complete octet. Therefore,

> Free radicals are in general very unstable and highly reactive, and thus usually cannot be isolated for any substantial amount of time.

Once a radical is produced, it will typically react very quickly with other species present, including the solvent.

By and large, radicals are produced from neutral, closed-shell precursors via *homolytic bond dissociation*, or *homolysis*.

> **Homolytic bond dissociation**, or **homolysis**, is the breaking of a covalent bond, whereby the electrons comprising that bond are distributed equally to the atoms that are disconnected.

A bromine radical (Br•), for example, can be produced from molecular bromine, Br_2, by homolysis of the Br–Br bond (Equation 25-1). Homolysis of a C–H bond in methane (Equation 25-2), on the other hand, will produce a methyl radical (H_3C•) and a hydrogen radical (H•).

homolysis of the Br-Br bond → two radicals are produced

$$Br{-}Br \xrightarrow{\Delta} Br\cdot + \cdot Br \quad (25\text{-}1)$$

homolysis of the C-H bond → two radicals are produced

$$H_3C{-}H \xrightarrow{h\nu} H_3C\cdot + \cdot H \quad (25\text{-}2)$$

Notice that the *curved arrow notation* describing homolysis differs from that which describes other elementary steps we encountered in previous chapters. Specifically, the use of *single-barbed arrows* is required.

> A **single-barbed arrow** (⇀) represents the movement of a *single electron*.

Therefore, the curved arrow notation in Equations 25-1 and 25-2 explicitly illustrates that one electron from the covalent bond moves to one atom and the second electron moves to the other atom. In contrast, with previous elementary steps we have examined, which involve only closed-shell species, electrons move as *pairs*; hence the use of the *double-barbed arrow* (→).

Your Turn 25.1. The homolysis of Cl_2 produces to chlorine radicals, as shown below. Add the appropriate curved arrows to indicate this homolysis.

$$Cl{-}Cl \longrightarrow Cl\cdot + \cdot Cl$$

Problem 25.1. Draw the curved arrow notation and products for the homolysis of each of the following bonds.
a) the C-C bond in ethane
b) a C-H bond in ethane
c) the C-Br bond in 2-bromopropane
d) a C-H bond in benzene

To gain a feel for how unstable free radicals are, it would help to revisit the energy diagram of the type we encountered in Chapter 1. As shown in Figure 25-1, it requires 435 kJ/mol to break a C–H bond in CH_4, and thereby produce a hydrogen radical (H•) and a methyl radical (H_3C•). This corresponds to a vanishingly small equilibrium constant of less than 10^{-70}.

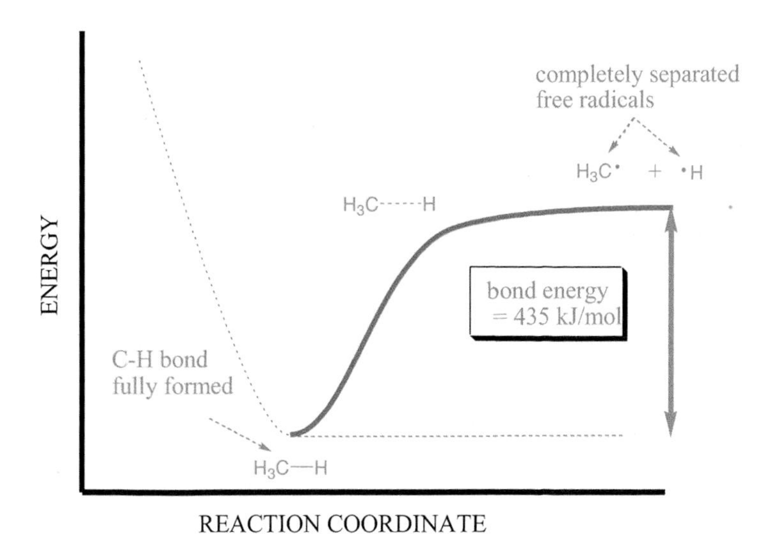

Figure 25-1. Reaction Energy Diagram for the Homolysis of a C–H Bond in CH_4
The homolytic bond dissociation energy of 435 kJ/mol is the difference in energy between the energy minimum and the energy of the separated free radicals at the right of the figure.

Because of the large energy required for homolysis, the concentration of free radicals in solution is essentially zero under normal conditions for most species. To produce any reasonable concentration of free radicals, energy must be supplied in the form of heat or ultraviolet (UV) light. Therefore, indicators such as $\xrightarrow{\Delta}$ or $\xrightarrow{h\nu}$ provide a clue that radicals are being produced, as illustrated previously in Equations 25-1 and 25-2.

Comment [JMK55]: Margin note.
Radicals are produced by heat or light.

For a molecule that has only one type of covalent bond, such as Br_2 or CH_4, only one set of homolysis products are possible. For other molecules that have more than one type of covalent bond, more than one set of homolysis products is possible. For example, bromomethane (CH_3Br) has three C–H bonds and one C–Br bond. As shown in Equation 25-3, homolysis of a C–H bond produces the H• and $BrCH_2$• radicals, whereas homolysis of the C–Br bond produces the Br• and H_3C• radicals.

homolysis of a C-H bond

the weakest bond in the molecule

$H-CH_2-Br \xrightarrow{h\nu} H\bullet + \bullet CH_2Br$ (a)

$\xrightarrow{h\nu} H_3C\bullet + \bullet Br$ (b)

homolysis of the C-Br bond

(25-3)

However, as indicated, homolysis leads almost exclusively to the latter products. This is because the C–Br bond is the weakest bond in the molecule. The bond dissociation energy of the C–Br bond in bromomethane is 297 kJ/mol, significantly less than the bond dissociation energy of bromomethane's C–H bond, which is 406 kJ/mol. Therefore, the C–Br bond is the one that is easiest to break.

This reasoning can in general be used to predict the favored products of homolysis.

> The major products of homolysis derive from breaking the weakest bond in the molecule—i.e., the bond with the smallest bond dissociation energy.

In light of this, it can be very helpful to know the bond dissociation energies for specific bonds in a variety of molecules, which are provided in Tables 25-1, 25-2, and 25-3. Notice that Table 25-1 contains bond dissociation energies of bonds involving hydrogen, Table 25-2 contains bond dissociation energies of C–C bonds, and Table 25-3 contains bond dissociation energies of bonds involving carbon and a heteroatom, or two heteroatoms.

Table 25-1. Homolytic Bond Dissociation Energies Involving Bonds to Hydrogen[a]

Bond	Homolytic Bond Dissociation Energy (kJ/mol)	Bond	Homolytic Bond Dissociation Energy (kJ/mol)
H–H	435	$H-CH_3$	435
H–F	569	$H-CH_2CH_3$	410
H–Cl	431	$H-CH(CH_3)_2$	395
H–Br	366	$H-C(CH_3)_3$	381
H–I	297	$H-CH{=}CH_2$	433
H–OH	498	$H-C{\equiv}CH$	522
$H-OCH_3$	427	$H-CH_2-CH{=}CH_2$	356
$H-OC_6H_5$	356	$H-CH_2-C_6H_5$	356
H–SH	377	$H-CH_2Br$	406
		$H-CH_2OH$	385

a: Adapted from Lowry and Richardson

Table 25-2. Homolytic Bond Dissociation Energies Involving C–C Bonds[a]

Bond	Homolytic Bond Dissociation Energy (kJ/mol)	Bond	Homolytic Bond Dissociation Energy (kJ/mol)
H_3C-CH_3	368	$H_3C-C(=O)-CH_3$	343
$H_3C-CH_2CH_3$	356	$H_3C-CH_2-C(=O)-CH_3$	331
$CH_3-H_2C-CH=CH_2$	372	$H_3C-C\equiv N$	510
$CH_3-H_2C-C_6H_5$	377	$H_2C=CH-C(=O)-CH_3$	372
$H_2C=HC-CH=CH_2$	418	$H_3C-C(=O)-C(=O)-CH_3$	347
$HC\equiv C-C\equiv CH$	628	$H_3C-CH=CH_2$	385
$H_5C_6-C_6H_5$	418	$H_3C-C_6H_5$	389
$H_2C=HC-C_6H_5$	414	$H_3C-CH_2-C_6H_5$	301
		$H_3C-CH_2-CH=CH_2$	301

a: Adapted from Lowry and Richardson

Table 25-3. Homolytic Bond Dissociation Energies Involving Carbon-Heteroatom Bonds and Heteroatom-Heteroatom Bonds[a]

Bond	Homolytic Bond Dissociation Energy (kJ/mol)	Bond	Homolytic Bond Dissociation Energy (kJ/mol)
$F-CH_3$	451	$HO-CH_3$	383
$Cl-CH_3$	355	$HO-C_6H_5$	464
$Cl-CH_2CH_3$	343	H_2N-CH_3	331
$Cl-CH(CH_3)_2$	339	$HO-OH$	213
$Cl-C(CH_3)_3$	334	CH_3O-OCH_3	151
$Cl-CH=CH_2$	376	$H_3C-C(=O)-O-O-C(=O)-CH_3$	123
$Cl-C\equiv CH$	464	$F-F$	159
$Cl-CH_2-CH=CH_2$	293	$Cl-Cl$	243
$Cl-CH_2-C_6H_5$	284	$Br-Br$	192
$Br-CH_3$	297	$I-I$	151
$I-CH_3$	234		

a: Adapted from Lowry and Richardson

Solved Problem 25.1. Predict the major homolysis products of ethane.

$$CH_3CH_3 \xrightarrow[h\nu]{} ?$$

Think. What are the distinct types of bonds in the molecule? Which is the weakest? What are the products upon homolysis of that bond?

Solve. There are two distinct types of bond. One is $H-CH_2CH_3$, and the other one is H_3C-CH_3. The first one's bond dissociation energy is 410 kJ/mol (Table 25-3), and the second one's is 368 kJ/mol (Table 25-1). Therefore, the second is the weaker bond, and its homolysis leads to the major products.

$$H_3C{-}CH_3 \xrightarrow[h\nu]{} H_3C\bullet + \bullet CH_3$$

Problem 25.2. Predict the major homolysis products of methanol.

$$CH_3OH \xrightarrow[h\nu]{} ?$$

25.2. STRUCTURE AND STABILITY OF ALKYL RADICALS

Although free radicals are in general very unstable, we can assign different *relative* stabilities to various radicals, based on the energy required to produce them via homolysis (Tables 25-1 through 25-3). For example, Equations 25-4a through 25-4d provide the C–Cl homolysis reactions of a variety of chloroalkanes, yielding the Cl• atom and an alkyl radical (R•) as the products.

(a) $H_3C{-}Cl \xrightarrow[h\nu]{} H_3C\bullet + \bullet Cl$ (methyl radical) 355 kJ/mol

(b) $H_3C{-}CH_2{-}Cl \xrightarrow[h\nu]{} H_3C{-}\dot{C}H_2 + \bullet Cl$ (primary radical) 343 kJ/mol

(c) $H_3C{-}CH(CH_3){-}Cl \xrightarrow[h\nu]{} H_3C{-}\dot{C}H(CH_3) + \bullet Cl$ (secondary radical) 339 kJ/mol

(d) $H_3C{-}C(CH_3)_2{-}Cl \xrightarrow[h\nu]{} H_3C{-}C\bullet(CH_3)_2 + \bullet Cl$ (tertiary radical) 334 kJ/mol

(25-4)

The free energy diagrams for these homolysis reactions are shown in Figure 25-2.

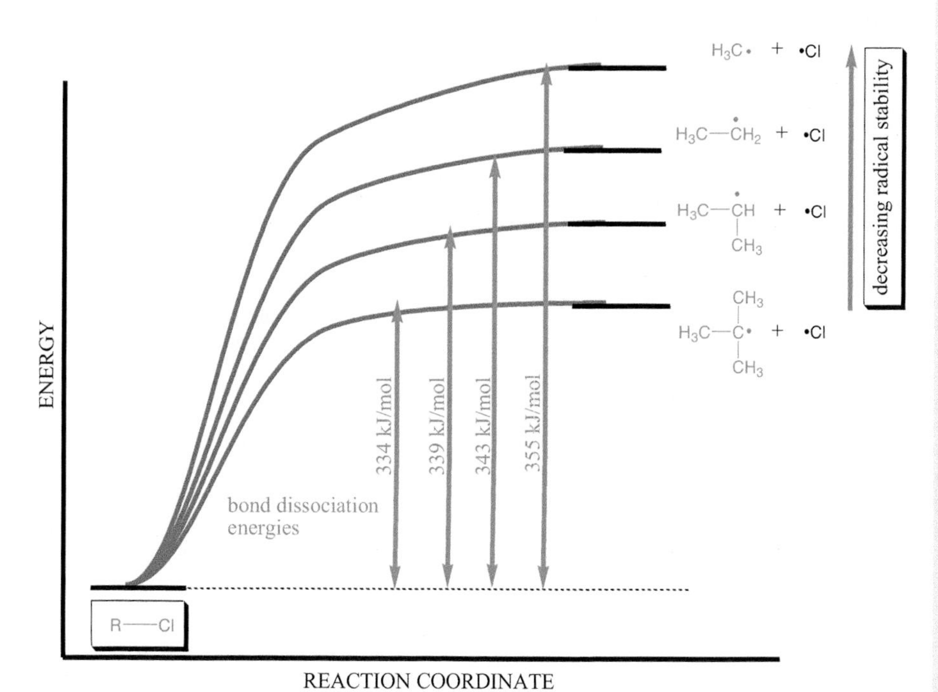

Figure 25-2. Relative Stabilities of Alkyl Radicals
Reaction energy diagrams for C−Cl homolysis in a variety of chloroalkanes. Alkyl radical stability increases in the order $H_3C\bullet < H_3CCH_2\bullet < (CH_3)_2CH\bullet < (CH_3)_3C\bullet$.

Because a Cl• radical is produced in all four reactions, any difference in product energy must come from different stabilities of the alkyl radicals that are produced. For example, it requires 12 kJ/mol additional energy to produce a methyl radical than it does to produce an ethyl radical (355 kJ/mol vs. 343 kJ/mol), so $\bullet CH_3$ appears 12 kJ/mol higher in energy than $\bullet CH_2CH_3$ in Figure 25-2. In other words, $\bullet CH_3$ is 12 kJ/mol less stable than $\bullet CH_2CH_3$. In turn, $\bullet CH_2CH_3$ is 4 kJ/mol less stable than $\bullet CH(CH_3)_2$, which is 5 kJ/mol less stable than $\bullet C(CH_3)_3$.

Your Turn 25.2. The figure below represents homolysis for the H-Cl and H-Br bonds, but is incomplete. Write the homolytic bond dissociation energies in the boxes provided at the bottom of the figure. Also, write the Br• and Cl• products in the appropriate boxes at the top of the figure. Which radical is more stable, Br• or Cl•?

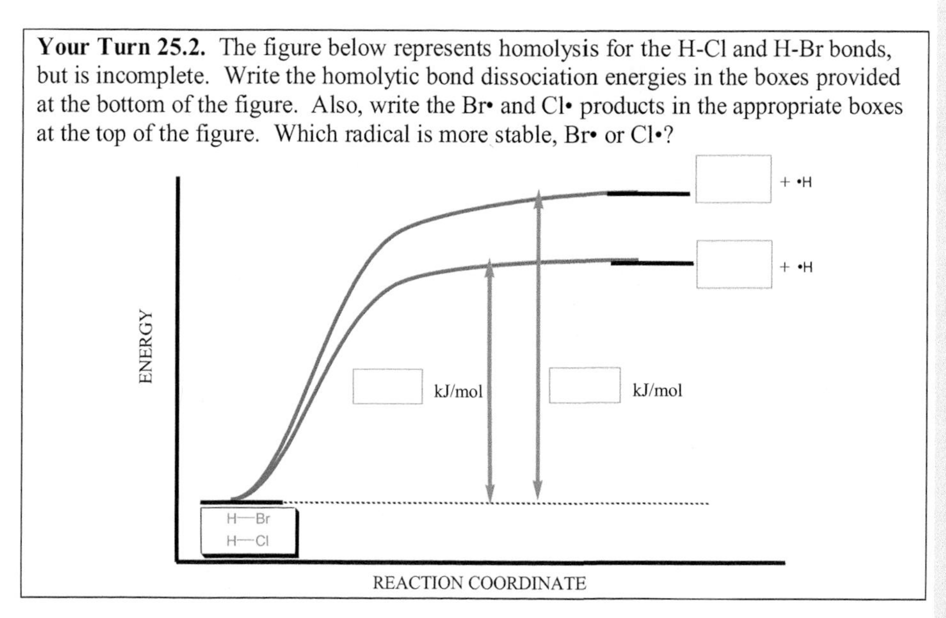

Notice that these relative stabilities establish the following trend.

> Alkyl radical stability increases in the order:
> methyl < primary (1°) < secondary (2°) < tertiary (3°)

This order of alkyl radical stability is identical to that of *carbocation* (R^+) stability (Section 6.6e). This suggests that the carbon atom that has the unpaired electron can be viewed as *electron-poor*, in much the same way as a carbon atom bearing a positive charge in a carbocation. With this in mind, each additional alkyl group inductively stabilizes a free radical due to its electron-donating capability, as indicated below.

Comment [JMK56]: Margin note. Alkyl groups stabilize carbon radicals.

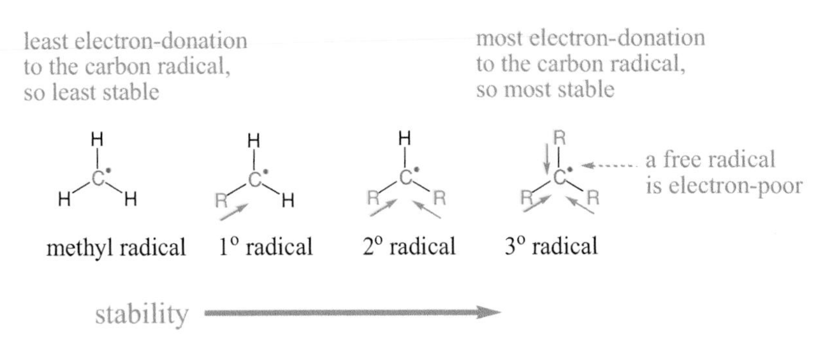

> **Problem 25.3.** Homolysis of a C-H bond can occur at three distinct locations on 1,3,5-trimethylcyclohexane to yield three different free radicals. Draw each of those radicals and rank them in order from least to most stable.

Hybridization also impacts the stability of an alkyl radical. Notice in Table 25-3 that C–Cl bond dissociation energies for ethane, ethene, and ethyne are 343 kJ/mol, 376 kJ/mol, and 464 kJ/mol, respectively. This tells us that the ethyl radical ($\bullet CH_2CH_3$) is more stable than the vinyl radical ($\bullet CH{=}CH_2$), which, in turn, is more stable than the ethynyl radical ($\bullet C{\equiv}CH$). Thus,

> Alkyl radical stability decreases as the hybridization of the carbon atom possessing the unpaired electron goes from sp^3 to sp^2 to *sp*—i.e., with increasing *s*-character of the carbon atom.

This is because as a carbon atom's *s*-character increases, so does its effective electronegativity (Section 3.11). Just as its ability to accommodate a positive charge decreases (Section 6.6c), so, too, does its ability to accommodate an unpaired electron.

The similarities between alkyl radicals and carbocations are further seen with allyl and benzyl radicals. Recall that the allyl cation and the benzyl cation are more stable than ordinary primary carbocations. This is due to resonance delocalization of the positive charge, as illustrated in Equations 25-5 and 25-6.

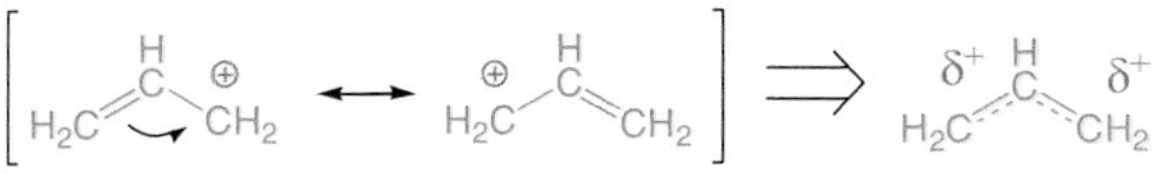

allyl cation (25-5)

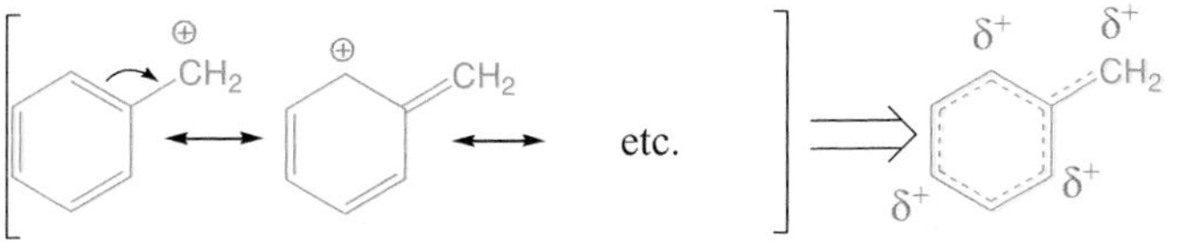

benzyl cation (25-6)

Your Turn 25.3. Complete Equation 25-5 by drawing in the two missing resonance structures.

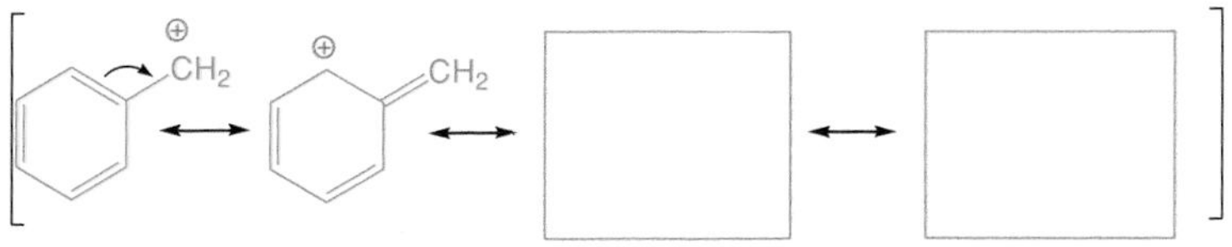

benzyl cation

Similarly, the allyl radical (CH_2=CH–CH_2•) and the benzyl radical (C_6H_5–CH_2•) are more stable than ordinary primary alkyl radicals. We can see this from the fact that the C–Cl bonds in CH_2=CH–CH_2–Cl and C_6H_5–CH_2–Cl are weaker than that in chloroethane by 50 kJ/mol and 59 kJ/mol, respectively.

Comment [JMK57]: Margin note. Allyl and benzyl radicals are substantially more stable than alkyl radicals.

Problem 25.4. Draw a plot similar to that in Figure 25-2 and Your Turn 25.2, illustrating the relative stabilities the ethane radical (CH_3–CH_3) and the allyl radical.

Equations 25-7 and 25-8 illustrate that the additional stabilization of the allyl and benzyl radicals is also due to resonance. Notice in particular that even though the curved arrow notation is different from that used to indicate resonance in the cations, the unpaired electron in each radical is shared among the same carbon atoms as in the respective carbocations.

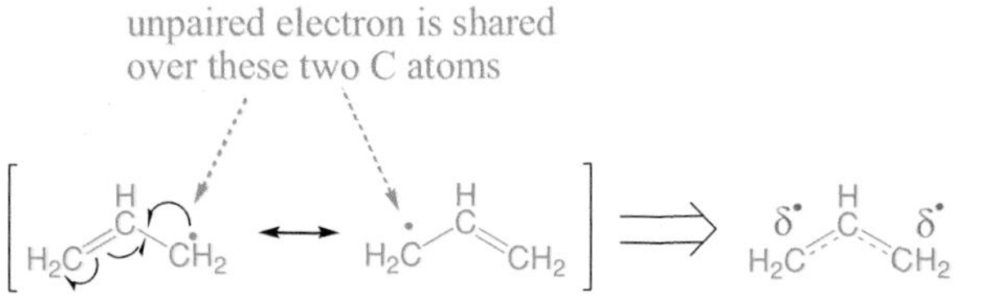

unpaired electron is shared over these two C atoms

(25-7)

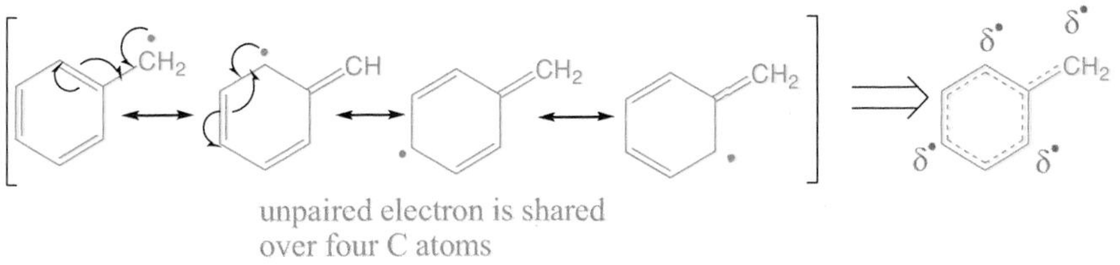

unpaired electron is shared over four C atoms

(25-8)

Your Turn 25.4. Equation 25-8 is missing the curved arrow notation that shows how the third resonance structure is converted to the fourth. Supply that curved arrow notation in the structure below at the left.

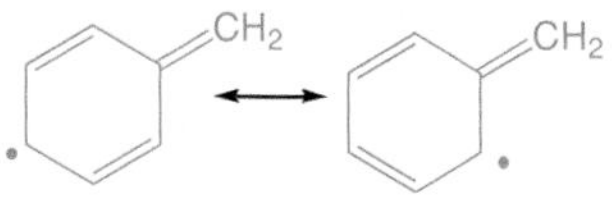

The *resonance hybrids* of the allyl and benzyl radicals (Equations 25-7 and 25-8) are ways to illustrate the delocalization of the unpaired electron about the entire species. Another way to depict this is through **electron spin density plots** like those in Figure 25-3. In such plots, *electron spin density* (i.e., unpaired electron character) is represented by the blue color—the deeper the blue color, the greater the spin density. Notice how well the electron spin density plots agree with the resonance hybrids.

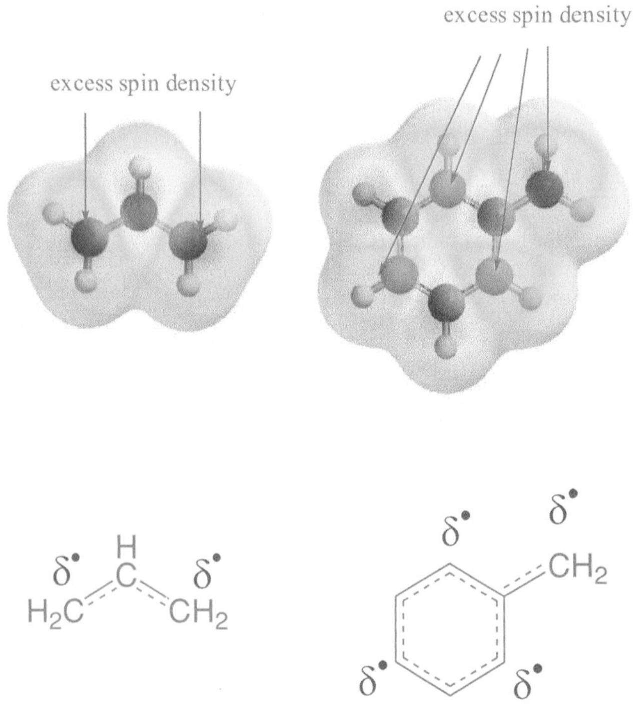

Figure 25-3. Electron spin density plots
The electron spin density plot of the allyl radical is shown at the top left, and that of the benzyl radical is shown at the top right. The deeper the blue color, the greater the electron spin density. Spin density in the allyl radical is delocalized over the two terminal carbon atoms. Spin density in the benzyl radical is delocalized over four carbon atoms.

Problem 25.5. Which carbon atom in the benzyl radical possesses the greatest spin density? Why does that carbon bear the most spin density? (Hint: It would help to examine the resonance structures of the benzyl radical.)

Solved Problem 25.2. Which is the weakest C–C single bond in the following molecule?

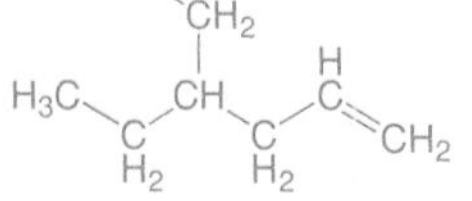

Think. What are the distinct types of C–C bond? What are the products upon homolysis of each of those bonds? Can the stabilities of the product radicals be differentiated based on resonance and/or alkyl substitution?

Solve. There are four distinct C–C bonds, labeled a – d below. The corresponding homolysis products are shown at the right.

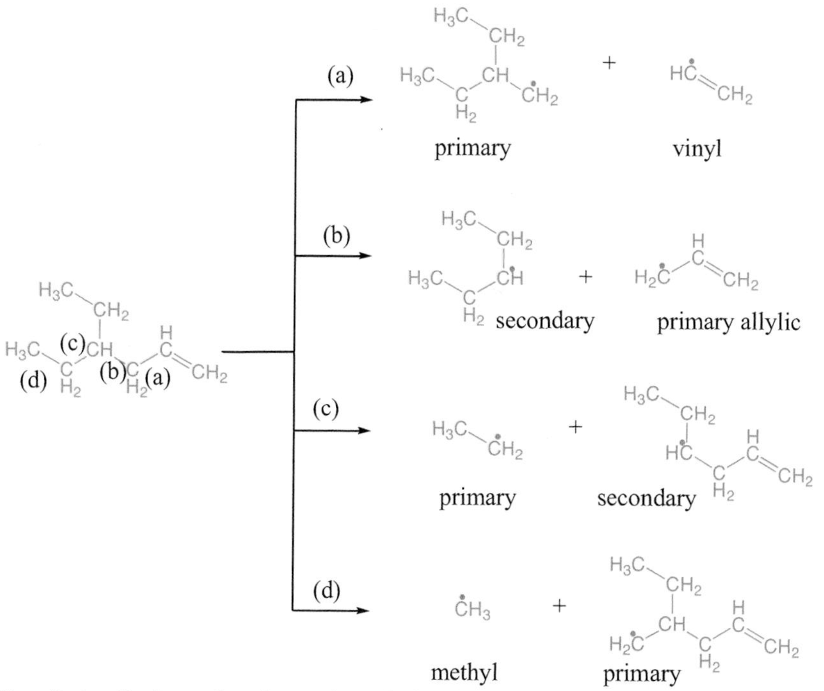

(a) primary + vinyl

(b) secondary + primary allylic

(c) primary + secondary

(d) methyl + primary

The alkyl radicals produced upon homolysis of bonds (b) and (c) have the greatest alkyl substitution on the carbon atom with the unpaired electron—one is a primary radical, and the other is a secondary. However, the primary alkyl radical produced upon homolysis of bond (b) is stabilized substantially by resonance. Thus, homolysis of bond (b) gives the most stable products, making bond (b) the weakest of the C–C bonds.

Problem 25.6. Which is the weakest C–H bond in the following molecule?

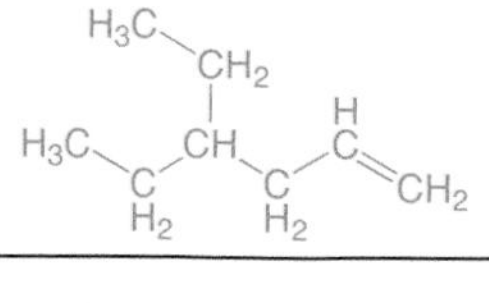

Problem 25.7. For each of the following molecules, indicate which C-H bond is the weakest. Which do you think is the weaker of those two C-H bonds? Explain.

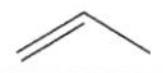

Problem 25.8. Predict the most likely homolysis product when a *mixture* of cyclohexene, HBr, and hydrogen peroxide (H_2O_2) is heated.

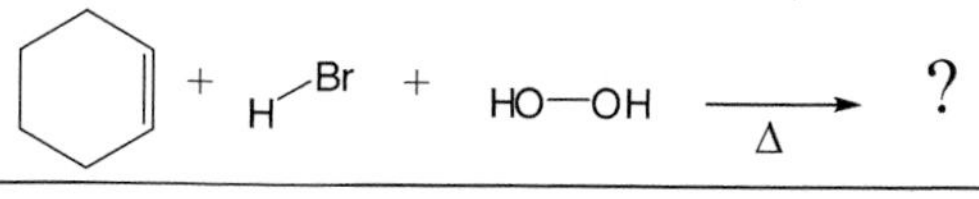

$$\text{cyclohexene} + H{-}Br + HO{-}OH \xrightarrow{\Delta} ?$$

Yet another similarity between alkyl radicals and carbocations is their structures. A prime example is the comparison of the methyl cation to the methyl radical (Figure 25-4)—both species are *entirely planar*. Therefore, just like the positively charged carbon of a carbocation,

> A carbon atom that has an unpaired electron is sp^2-hybridized.

Because each sp^2-hybridized orbital is used to make a bond to hydrogen, the unpaired electron must reside in the carbon atom's unhybridized *p* orbital. By comparison, that *p* orbital of H_3C^+ is empty.

a methyl radical and a methyl cation are both planar, so each one's carbon atom is sp^2-hybridized, possessing a single unhybridized *p* orbital

the unhybridized *p* orbital in the methyl radical contains the unpaired electron

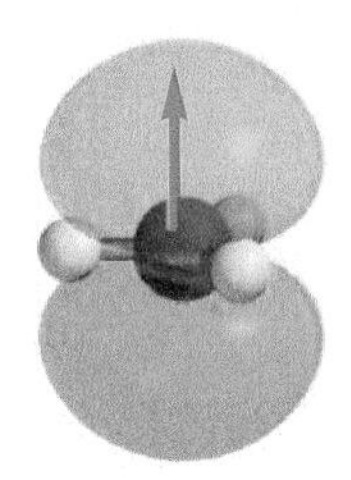

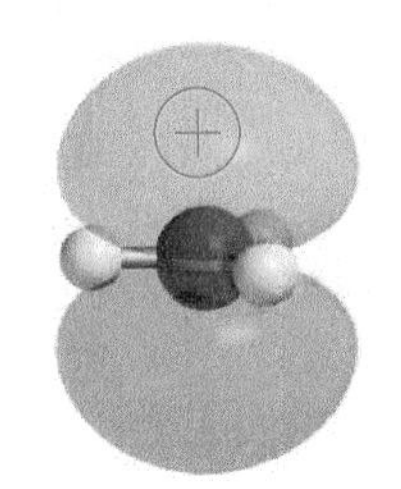

in a methyl cation, the unhybridized *p* orbital is empty

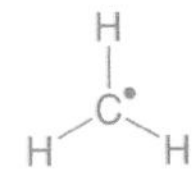

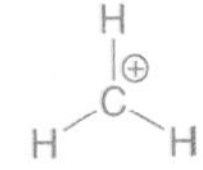

Figure 25-4. Structural Similarities Between the Methyl Radical and Methyl Cation
The three-dimensional structure of the methyl radical is shown at the left, and that of the methyl cation is shown at the right. Both structures are entirely planar, indicating that the C atom is sp^2-hybridized. The single unpaired electron in $H_3C•$ must therefore reside in an unhybridized *p* orbital. That *p* orbital of the methyl cation is empty.

25.3. OBSERVING FREE RADICALS: ELECTRON SPIN RESONANCE (ESR)

The primary technique used to gain structural information about radicals is called **electron spin resonance (ESR)** spectroscopy, which is also called electron paramagnetic resonance (EPR) spectroscopy. The theory behind ESR spectroscopy is very similar to that of NMR spectroscopy (Chapter 14). Just like a proton (^1H) or carbon-13 (^{13}C) nucleus, each electron can contribute a spin of +½ or -½ atomic units to the spin of the entire molecular species, depending on whether it is in the α or β state. If all electrons are paired, then the molecular species has no net electron spin, and cannot be observed by ESR spectroscopy. However, a free radical has an unpaired electron, so the species does indeed have a net electron spin.

When a free radical is placed in a strong magnetic field, the α and β states of the unpaired electron are separated in energy by an amount ΔE_{spin}, analogous to what happens to ^1H and ^{13}C nuclei. Transitions between the two spin states are induced when photons having an energy equal to ΔE_{spin} are absorbed. These transitions appear as photons having an energy equal to ΔE_{spin} are absorbed. These transitions appear as signals in the ESR spectrum, much the same way as transitions between nuclear spin states appear in an NMR spectrum. A main difference between the two types of spectra is in the frequencies used to induce spin transitions. Whereas NMR spectroscopy employs radiofrequency radiation in the range of 90 – 900 MHz, microwave frequencies of 10 GHz are common for ESR spectroscopy.

Another aspect of ESR spectroscopy that is similar to NMR spectroscopy is signal splitting. Recall that in ^{1}H-NMR spectroscopy, the signal of a proton coupled to *N* equivalent protons is split into *N*+1 peaks—the so-called *N*+1 rule. Likewise, the signal of an unpaired electron can be split when the electron is coupled to nearby protons. This can be seen in the ESR spectrum of the methyl radical ($H_3C\bullet$), shown in Figure 25-5.

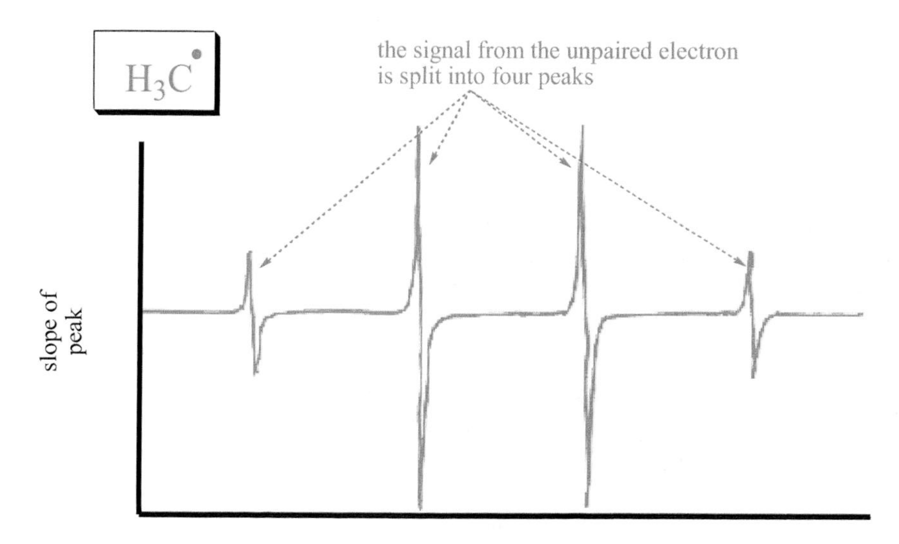

Figure 25-5. Electron Spin Resonance Spectrum of the Methyl Radical ($H_3C\bullet$)
The signal from the single unpaired electron is split into different peaks by the neighboring H atoms. Because the signal is split by three equivalent H atoms, four peaks appear, according to the *N*+1 rule. The peaks appear in the usual 1:3:3:1 ratio of intensities.

Because the methyl radical has a single unpaired electron, the spectrum must exhibit just one signal. However, because that electron is coupled to three equivalent protons, the signal is split into four peaks, according to the *N*+1 rule. As expected, those peaks appear as a 1:3:3:1 ratio of intensities.

Notice that the features in an ESR spectrum are more complex than those in NMR spectra. This is because in ESR spectroscopy, the *slope* of a peak is plotted as a function of frequency. This is done to enhance ESR's detection capability, given that free radicals are usually encountered in very low concentrations in solution (they are highly unstable).

Although ESR spectroscopy is quite a powerful tool used to study free radicals, any further discussion on this topic is beyond the scope of this book. If you are interested in learning more about this technique, refer to *Electron Spin Resonance: Elementary Theory and Practical Applications* by John Wertz (1st ed., Springer, 1986).

25.4. COMMON ELEMENTARY STEPS THAT FREE RADICALS UNDERGO

Just as there are a small number of common elementary steps involving closed-shell species (Chapters 6 and 7), so, too, are there relatively few elementary steps that are common for free radicals. In this section, we will examine those steps in detail,

With the chemical intuition we gain about these elementary steps, we will be better equipped to tackle the mechanisms of the synthetically useful reactions later in this chapter, which are nothing more than specific sequences of these elementary steps.

25.4a. Radical Coupling

Perhaps the simplest of steps that a free radical can undergo is *radical coupling*, an example of which is shown in Equation 25-9.

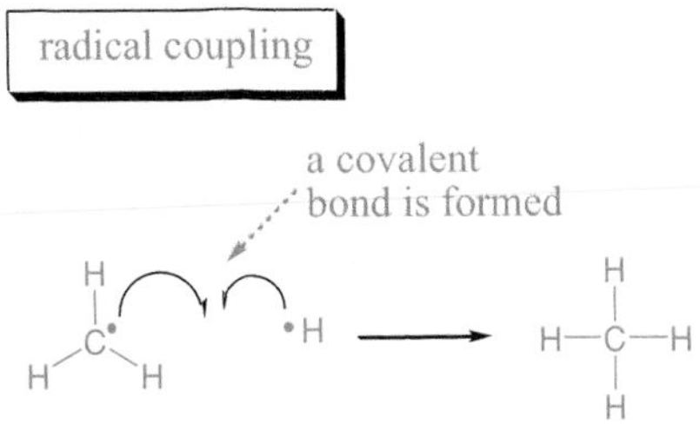

radical coupling

a covalent bond is formed

$$H_3C\cdot + \cdot H \longrightarrow CH_4 \quad (25\text{-}9)$$

As we can see, such a step involves two free radicals. In this case, the unpaired electron on carbon joins with the unpaired electron on hydrogen to form a new C–H bond. This is indicated by the two single-barbed arrows pointing to the bond-forming region (just as with double-barbed arrows, the atoms are assumed to follow their own electrons). In general,

> In a **radical coupling** step, an unpaired electron from one atom joins with an unpaired electron from a second atom, forming a new covalent bond that connects the two atoms together.

Your Turn 25.5. A radical coupling step involving two $H_3C\bullet$ radicals is shown below. Supply the missing curved arrows.

$$H_3C\bullet \; + \; \bullet CH_3 \longrightarrow H_3C{-}CH_3$$

Radical coupling is essentially the reverse of homolysis—whereas homolysis produces two new free radicals by breaking a covalent bond, radical coupling annihilates two free radicals by forming a new covalent bond. Therefore, whereas homolysis is typically very highly unfavorable,

> Radical coupling is usually very highly favorable, making it *irreversible.*

Problem 25.9. Two triphenylmethyl radicals will undergo radical coupling *reversibly* to produce hexaphenylethane. Explain why this is an exception to the general rule above.

$$2\ Ph_3C\bullet \rightleftharpoons Ph_3C{-}CPh_3$$

Because radical coupling is the reverse of homolysis, the free energy diagram for a radical coupling step is precisely the reverse of that for homolysis. For example, the free energy diagram for the radical coupling of a methyl and a hydrogen radical, shown in Figure 25-6, is the reverse of CH_4 homolysis, shown previously in Figure 25-1.

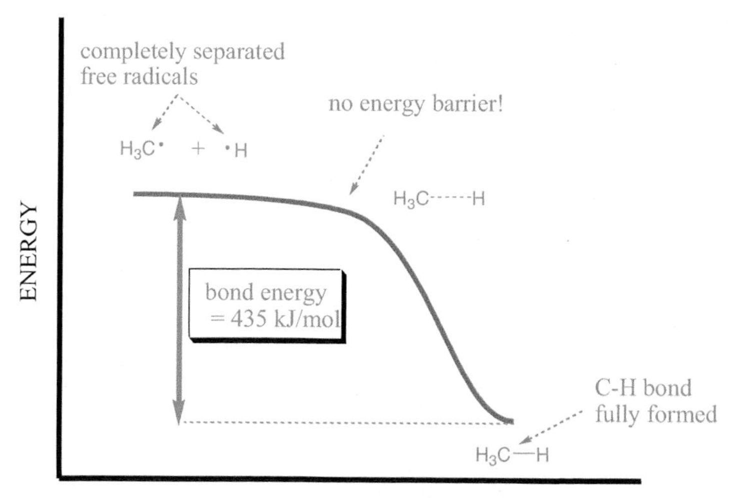

Figure 25-6. Reaction Energy Diagram for Radical Coupling
The completely separated methyl and hydrogen radicals appear at the right, and the fully formed C–H bond appears at the right. This energy diagram is essentially the mirror image of the one for homolysis, shown previously in Figure 25-1. Notice that unlike other reaction steps we have seen, radical coupling proceeds with no energy barrier between reactants and products.

Notice that at every distance of separation between the two radicals, shortening that distance (i.e., moving to the right in the figure) results in a lower energy. In other words,

> Radical coupling proceeds with no energy barrier!

In this regard, free radical coupling is distinct from every other elementary step we have seen. This is a testament to how reactive and unstable free radicals are.

25.4b. Bimolecular Homolytic Substitution (S_H2)

As we saw in the previous section, a radical coupling step involves the reaction of one free radical with a second. However, it is also possible for a free radical to react with a *closed-shell species*. One example is the **bimolecular homolytic substitution** (**S_H2**) step. An example is illustrated in Equation 25-10, which involves a Br• radical and a molecule of methane, CH_4.

this bond is broken

a new H-Br bond is formed

$$CH_4 + \cdot Br \longrightarrow \cdot CH_3 + H{-}Br \qquad (25\text{-}10)$$

The curved arrow notation explicitly shows that the C–H bond is broken, and one of the two electrons from that bond ends up on the carbon atom. The other electron from that bond joins with the bromine radical to form a new H–Br bond. Thus, a hydrogen atom is transferred from the carbon atom to the bromine atom. For this reason, the S_H2 step in Equation 25-10 is more specifically called a **hydrogen atom abstraction**.

Your Turn 25.6. Supply the missing curved arrows for the following hydrogen atom abstraction step.

$$H_3C{-}CH_2{-}H + {\bullet}Cl \longrightarrow H_3C{-}\dot{C}H_2 + H{-}Cl$$

An example of an S_H2 step that is *not* a hydrogen atom abstraction is shown in Equation 25-11. In this case, a chlorine radical, Cl•, is abstracted from a molecule of Cl_2.

$$H_2\dot{C}{-}H + Cl{-}Cl \longrightarrow H{-}CH_2{-}Cl + {\bullet}Cl \qquad (25\text{-}11)$$

Notice that although the curved arrow notation for an S_H2 step differs from that of an S_N2 step, the dynamics of the two steps are essentially the same. Recall that for an S_N2 step, a nucleophile forms a new bond to an atom attached to a leaving group, thus breaking the bond to the leaving group. The leaving group typically leaves in the form of an anion. Analogously,

> In an S_H2 step, a free radical forms a new bond to an atom, causing another bond to that atom to break. In the process, a new free radical is displaced from that atom.

Problem 25.10. Draw the three possible S_H2 steps, including curved arrows, that can occur between Cl• and ethane. (Hint: Which atom(s) can be attacked? Which bond(s) can be broken?)

$$C_2H_6 + {\bullet}Cl \longrightarrow ?$$

Because an S_H2 step involves the formation of one bond and the breaking of another, the driving force for this step comes from the difference in their bond dissociation energies. In Equation 25-11, for example, a Cl–Cl bond (243 kJ/mol) is broken and a C–Cl bond is formed (349 kJ/mol). The products are therefore favored by 106 kJ/mol, which corresponds to a very large equilibrium constant of about 10^{18}.

By contrast, the S_H2 step in Equation 25-10 heavily favors reactants. In that step, an H–Br bond (366 kJ/mol) is formed at the expense of breaking a stronger C–H bond (435 kJ/mol). Thus, the reactants are more stable by 69 kJ/mol, which corresponds to a very small equilibrium constant of about 10^{-12}.

Frequently, there are multiple possible S_H2 steps that can be drawn when a free radical reacts with a closed-shell species. For example, Equations 25-12 through 25-14 show three possible outcomes when a Cl• radical attacks neopentane. Equation 25-12 is a hydrogen atom abstraction, whereby the Cl• radical forms a bond to H, and displaces an alkyl radical. In Equations 25-13 and 25-14, Cl• forms a new bond to a methyl carbon. In Equation 25-13, H• is displaced, whereas in Equation 25-14, an alkyl radical is displaced.

$$H_3C{-}C(CH_3)_2{-}CH_2{-}H + \cdot Cl \longrightarrow H_3C{-}C(CH_3)_2{-}\dot{C}H_2 + H{-}Cl \qquad \Delta H^0 \sim -20 \text{ kJ/mol} \tag{25-12}$$

$$H_3C{-}C(CH_3)_2{-}CH_2{-}H + \cdot Cl \not\longrightarrow H_3C{-}C(CH_3)_2{-}CH_2{-}Cl + \cdot H \qquad \Delta H^0 \sim +60 \text{ kJ/mol} \tag{25-13}$$

$$H_3C{-}C(CH_3)_2{-}CH_3 + \cdot Cl \not\longrightarrow H_3C{-}\dot{C}(CH_3){-}CH_3 + H_3C{-}Cl \qquad \Delta H^0 \sim -20 \text{ kJ/mol} \tag{25-14}$$

Despite the multiple possible outcomes, notice that the hydrogen atom abstraction in Equation 25-12 is the S_H2 step that is favored, essentially to the exclusion of the others. Even the S_H2 step in Equation 25-14, whose ΔH^0_{rxn} is similar to that for the step in Equation 25-12, does not take place to any substantial amount. Largely, this has to do with steric hindrance, much the same way as steric hindrance impacts S_N2 reactions. As indicated below, when a free radical attacks a carbon atom, it encounters significant steric hindrance. By contrast, a hydrogen atom, residing on the exterior of a molecule, remains easily accessible.

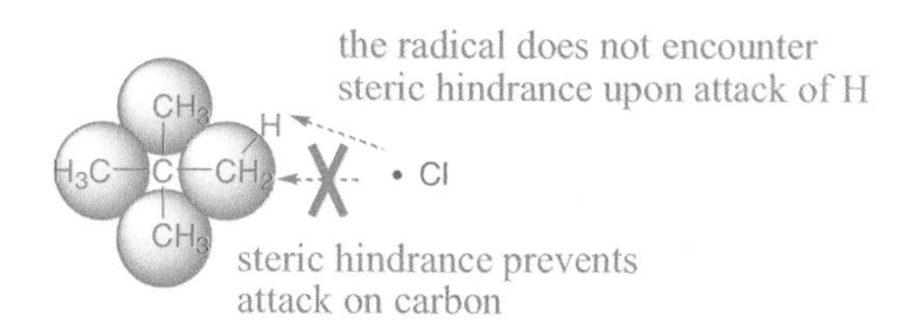

Hydrogen is not the only type of atom that resides on the exterior of a molecule. Halogen atoms do as well, and therefore tend not to cause significant steric hindrance during an S_H2 attack. What halogen atoms and hydrogen atoms have in common is that they form only one bond to other atoms—they are **monovalent** atoms.

With this in mind, the major lesson from the above example can be summarized as follows.

> When multiple possible outcomes are possible for an S_H2 step, the one that is favored tends to be the one in which a *monovalent* atom (i.e., H, F, Cl, Br, or I) is attacked by the free radical.

In many cases, a molecule involved in an S_H2 step has multiple distinct monovalent atoms that can be attacked by a free radical. In such cases, we can apply the following rule of thumb.

> If more than one monovalent atom can be attacked in an S_H2 step, the atom that is predominantly attacked is the one that is attached by the weakest bond.

For example, propane has two distinct H atoms that can be attacked by Cl•, as shown in Equations 25-15 and 25-16. In Equation 25-15, the hydrogen that is attacked is bonded to a secondary carbon, and 395 kJ/mol is required to break that bond. In Equation 25-16, the hydrogen is bonded to a primary carbon, so the bond energy is 410 kJ/mol. As indicated, the S_H2 step in Equation 25-15 is favored because it involves breaking the weaker of the two C–H bonds.

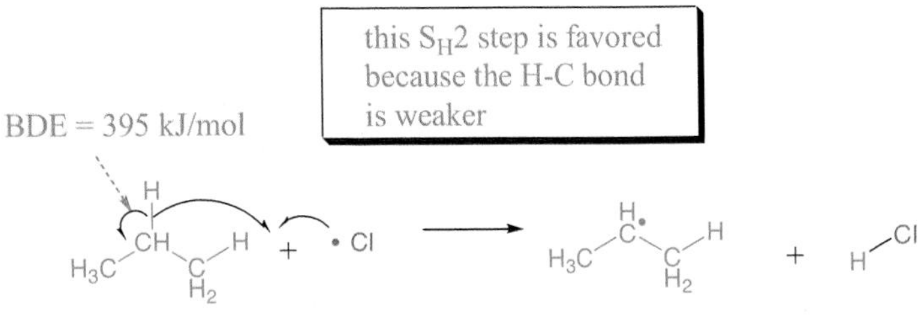

this S_H2 step is favored because the H-C bond is weaker

BDE = 395 kJ/mol

(25-15)

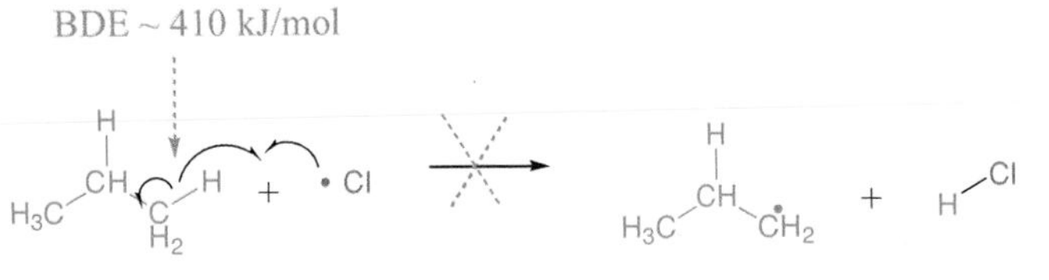

BDE ~ 410 kJ/mol

(25-16)

Solved Problem 25.3. Predict the major product of the following S_H2 step. Include the curved arrow notation.

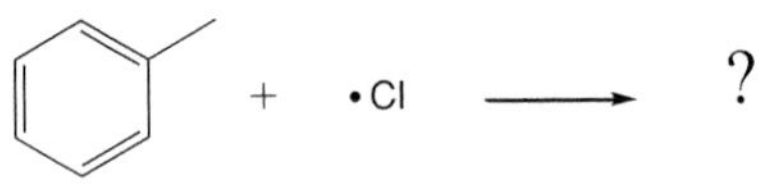

Think. What types of atoms are typically attacked in an S_H2 step? How many distinct types of that atom are in toluene? Which of those atoms is involved in the weakest bond?

Solve. Typically, S_H2 steps involve abstraction of a hydrogen or halogen atom. In toluene, there are two types of H atoms—those at the benzylic position and those on the ring itself. Benzylic C–H bonds (BDE = 356 kJ/mol) are weaker and therefore more easily broken than phenyl C–H bonds (BDE ≈ 433 kJ/mol). Therefore the most likely S_H2 step will occur at the benzylic carbon.

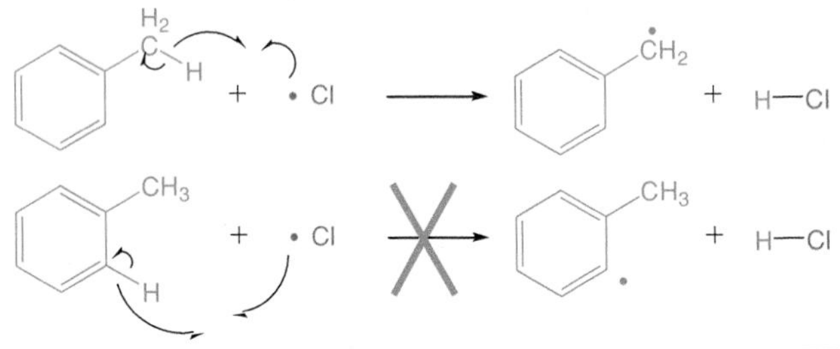

Problem 25.11. Predict the outcome of the following S_H2 step. Include the curved arrow notation.

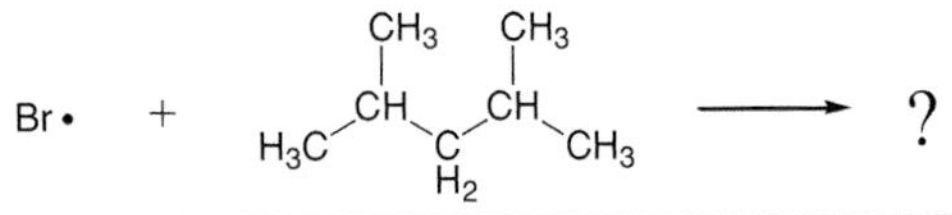

25.4c. Radical Addition to an Alkene or Alkyne

Recall from Chapter 20 that a C=C double bond of an alkene is relatively *electron-rich*. Therefore, when an alkene encounters an *electron-poor* free radical, **radical addition** step can take place, such as the one in Equation 25-17. Likewise, as shown in Equation 25-18, a free radical can add to the C≡C triple bond of an alkyne.

radical addition

an alkene is electron-rich

a free radical is electron-poor

$$(H_3C)_2C{=}C(CH_3)_2 + \cdot Br \longrightarrow (H_3C)_2\dot{C}{-}C(CH_3)_2{-}Br \qquad (25\text{-}17)$$

an alkyne is electron-rich

a free radical is electron-poor

$$C_6H_5{-}C{\equiv}C{-}C_6H_5 + \cdot SC_6H_5 \longrightarrow C_6H_5{-}\dot{C}{=}C(SC_6H_5){-}C_6H_5 \qquad (25\text{-}18)$$

As we can see, in such a step, one electron from the multiple bond of an alkene or alkyne joins with the unpaired electron from the free radical, and a second electron from the multiple bond ends up as an unpaired electron on carbon. Thus,

> In a radical addition step, one carbon atom from an alkene or alkyne forms a new bond to a free radical, and the second alkene or alkyne carbon gains an unpaired electron.

Your Turn 25.7. Supply the curved arrows necessary for the radical addition step shown below.

$$\text{cyclohexylidenecyclohexane} + \cdot Cl \longrightarrow \text{(1-chlorocyclohexyl)cyclohexyl radical}$$

Bond energies are a very important driving force for a radical addition step, just as we saw for the S_H2 step in the previous section. Notice that during the course of a radical addition step, a σ bond is gained and a π bond lost. Typically, σ bonds are stronger than π bonds, so the product is usually highly favored over the reactants. For the reaction in Equation 25-17, for example, a C-Br bond (293 kJ/mol) is formed at the expense of a C-C π bond (about 280 kJ/mol*), making the products favored by about 13 kJ/mol.

Notice that the alkene and alkyne in Equations 25-17 and 25-18 are symmetric, so the addition of the free radical to either of the multiply-bonded carbon atoms produces the same product. However, if the alkene or alkyne is asymmetric, then the multiply-bonded carbons would be distinct, and one of two constitutional isomers could be produced, depending upon which carbon atom gains the new bond to the free radical. This is illustrated in Equations 25-19 and 25-20, in which Br• adds to propene.

* Computed as the difference in energy between an average C=C double bond (619 kJ/mol) and an average C-C single bond (339 kJ/mol).

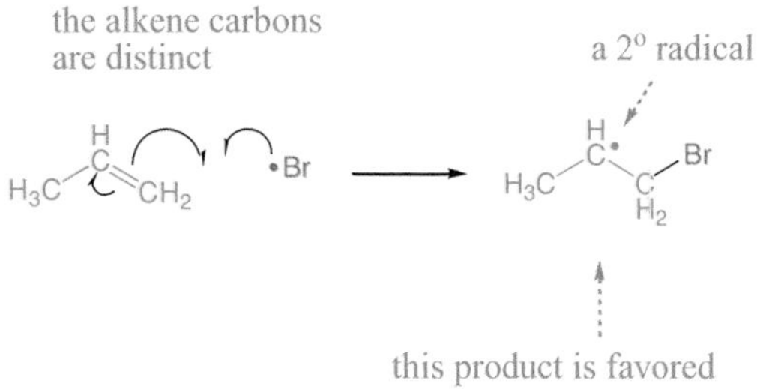

the alkene carbons
are distinct

a 2° radical

(25-19)

this product is favored

a 1° radical

(25-20)

In Equation 25-19, the Br• radical adds to the terminal carbon, leaving an unpaired electron on the central carbon. In Equation 25-20, on the other hand, the Br• radical adds to the central carbon, leaving the unpaired electron on a terminal carbon.

As indicated in Equation 25-20, addition of the Br• radical to the central carbon does not occur to any appreciable extent. This is in large part because the secondary radical that is produced in Equation 25-19 is more stable than the primary radical formed in Equation 25-20. In general,

> The addition of a free radical to an alkene or alkyne takes place so as to produce the most stable free radical product.

You will recognize that this general rule is analogous to a form of Markovnikov's rule (Section 20.2), in which the addition of a proton (H^+) to an alkene or alkyne takes place so as to produce the most stable carbocation intermediate.

Solved Problem 25.4. Draw the curved arrow notation and the most likely product for the following radical addition step.

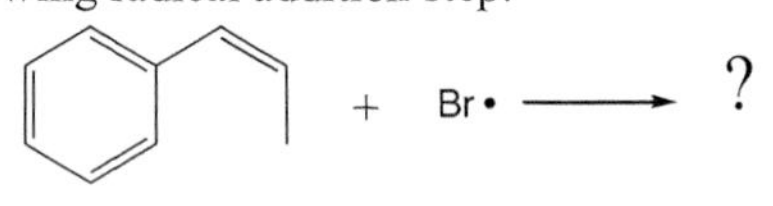

+ Br• ⟶ ?

Think. Which π bond do you think would be preferentially attacked? What are the possible products from attack of that C=C bond? Which is the most stable?

Solve. Although there are π bonds shown on the benzene ring, they will not be involved in an addition reaction here because aromaticity would be destroyed. Therefore, attack will take place at one of the vinyl carbon atoms. Both possible products are shown below.

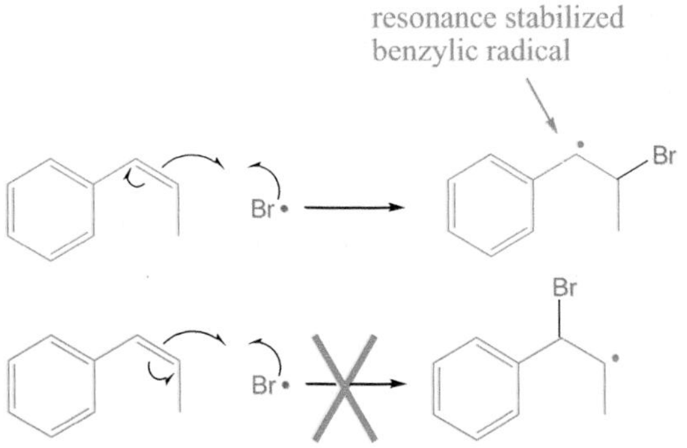

resonance stabilized
benzylic radical

The first of the two possible steps is favored because its radical product is resonance stabilized, which is not observed in the product of the second possible step.

Problem 25.12. There are four different possible products from the following radical addition step. Draw the curved arrow notation for each one along with the product that is formed. Which do you think is the most likely one formed? Why?

$$+ \quad \bullet OH \longrightarrow \quad ?$$

25.5. DISSOLVING METAL REDUCTIONS: HYDROGENATION OF ALKENES AND ALKYNES

Now that we have examined the common elementary steps that free radicals undergo, we are ready to delve into a variety of synthetically useful reactions involving free radicals. There are essentially two types of free radical reactions in organic chemistry—those that proceed through a *chain reaction* mechanism and those that do not. Because they are more straightforward, we will begin with reactions that do *not* involve chain reactions—namely, two types of hydrogenation reactions that are categorized as **dissolving metal reductions**. Later in this chapter, we will explore chain reactions.

Hydrogenation via a dissolving metal reduction takes place under conditions that differ from catalytic hydrogenation, discussed previously in Section 17.5. Recall that in catalytic hydrogenation, a solid metal catalyst such as Pt(s), Pd(s), or Ni(s) is used. Thus, the catalyst is in a different phase from the reactants dissolved in solution. Hence catalytic hydrogenation is an example of **heterogeneous catalysis**.

In contrast, as the name suggests, in a *dissolving metal reduction*, a metal such as Na(s) or Li(s) is *dissolved* in solution along with the reactants. When this takes place in a solvent such as liquid ammonia, NH_3(l), for example, the metal donates an electron, and the ammonia solvent stabilizes it via extensive solvation. The result is what is called a **solvated electron**, as depicted in Equation 25-21.

$$Na\cdot \xrightarrow[NH_3(l)]{} Na^{\oplus} + e^{\ominus}\text{ (solvated)} \qquad (25\text{-}21)$$

In light of this,

> The active radical species in a dissolving metal reduction involving NH_3(l)/Na(s) is simply an electron that does not formally belong to any atoms.

In the discussion that follows, we will see examples of how this solvated electron is involved in the reduction of multiple bonds. Section 25.5a discusses the reduction of alkynes to *trans*-alkenes, and Section 25.5b discusses the Birch reduction of benzene rings.

25.5a. *Anti*-Hydrogenation: Synthesis of *trans*-alkenes

When oct-4-yne is treated with sodium metal dissolved in liquid ammonia (-78 °C), the triple bond is reduced to a double bond (Equation 25-22).

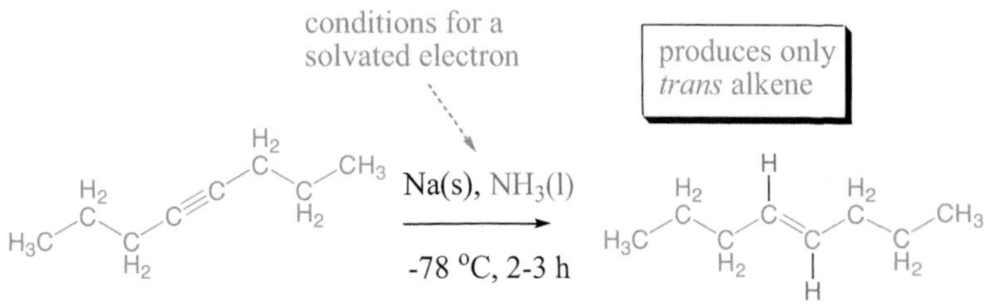

conditions for a solvated electron

produces only *trans* alkene

oct-4-yne $\xrightarrow[-78\ ^{o}C,\ 2\text{-}3\ h]{Na(s),\ NH_3(l)}$ (*E*)-oct-4-ene > 80% (25-22)

Notice that the reaction is stereospecific.

A dissolving metal reduction of an alkyne produces only the *(E)*-alkene.

Overall, this is an ***anti*-hydrogenation** reaction in which two hydrogen atoms add to the triple bond in a *trans* fashion. This reaction is therefore a complement to catalytic hydrogenation (Section 17.5), which forms exclusively the *cis* product.

Your Turn 25.8. Draw the product of the following reaction, in which oct-4-yne undergoes catalytic hydrogenation.

oct-4-yne $\xrightarrow[Pd,\ BaSO_4]{H_2(g)}$

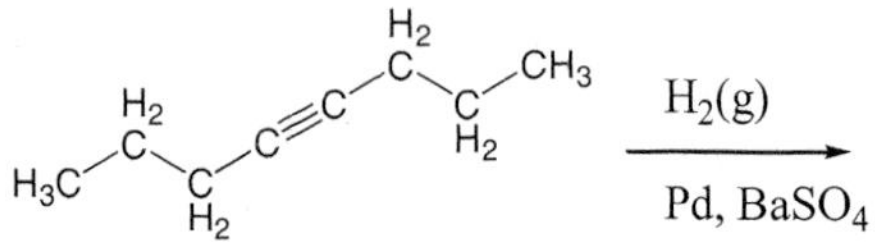

The mechanism for the above dissolving metal reduction is shown in Equation 25-23. Initially, a solvated electron is present, which, as was noted previously, is produced upon dissolving solid sodium in liquid ammonia. In step 1 of this mechanism, one such solvated electron adds to an alkyne carbon. Thus, the triple bond is converted into a double bond, and one of the initial alkyne carbons gains an unpaired electron. The carbanion that is produced is a very strong base, and deprotonates ammonia in step 2. This produces an uncharged alkyl radical, which, in step 3, undergoes radical coupling with a second solvated electron. Finally, in step 4, the carbanion that is produced deprotonates a second molecule of ammonia, yielding the overall product.

Mechanism of the Reaction in Equation 25-22

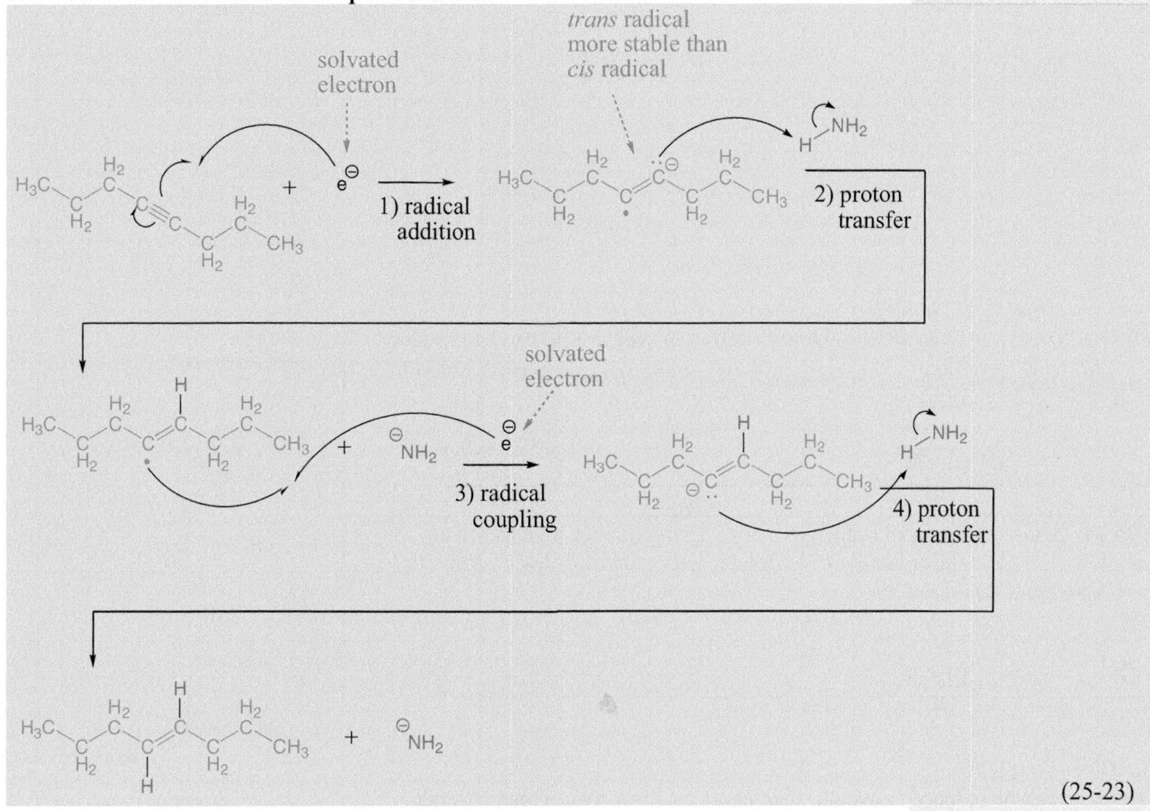

(25-23)

The stereochemistry of this reaction is established in the first step—the addition of a solvated electron to the C≡C triple bond. Although both the *cis* and *trans* forms of the vinyl radical can be produced, the two radicals are in rapid equilibrium, as shown below. The *trans* form has less steric strain, so it is more stable, and hence leads to the major product.

steric strain makes this
configuration less stable

Such an equilibrium is analogous to nitrogen inversion (Section 5.4d), in which the two pyramidal configurations of an uncharged nitrogen atom equilibrate. Unlike nitrogen inversion, which proceeds through a planar transition state, the equilibrium involving the vinyl radical proceeds through a linear transition state.

Dissolving metal reductions are much more sluggish with alkenes than alkynes. This is in part because the negative charges that develop in the mechanism are less stable on alkene carbons than they are on alkyne carbons—alkene carbons have less *s*-character, and thus a smaller effective electronegativity (Section 3.11). Therefore, dissolving metal reductions can be carried out selectively.

A dissolving metal reduction will selectively reduce an alkyne over an alkene.

An example is shown in Equation 25-24. As you can imagine, this can be very useful in synthesis.

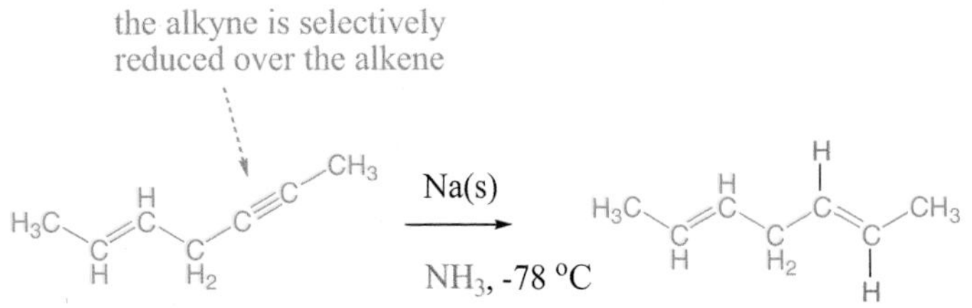

the alkyne is selectively reduced over the alkene

H_3C–CH=CH–CH_2–C≡C–CH_3 $\xrightarrow[NH_3,\ -78\ ^\circ C]{Na(s)}$ H_3C–CH=CH–CH_2–CH=CH–CH_3

(25-24)

Problem 25.13. Draw the alkyne from which the following compound can be produced via a dissolving metal reduction.

? $\xrightarrow[NH_3(l),\ -78\ ^\circ C]{Li(s)}$

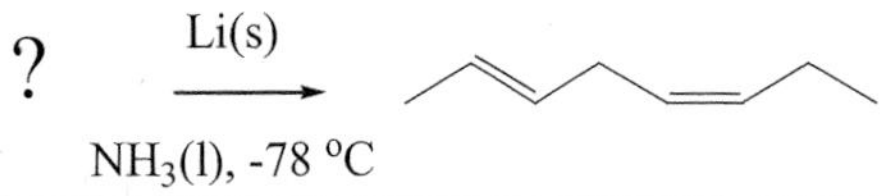

Problem 25.14. A dissolving metal reduction can be used to reduce a ketone to an alcohol, as shown below in the reduction of acetone to 2-propanol. Draw a complete, detailed mechanism for this reaction.

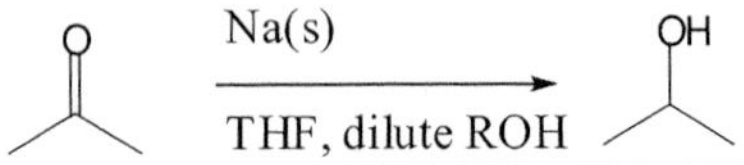

O $\xrightarrow[THF,\ dilute\ ROH]{Na(s)}$ OH

25.5b. The Birch Reduction

Benzene can be reduced to cyclohexane using catalytic hydrogenation under high temperature and pressure (Equation 25-25). Such conditions are necessary because aromaticity makes benzene's π systems quite stable.

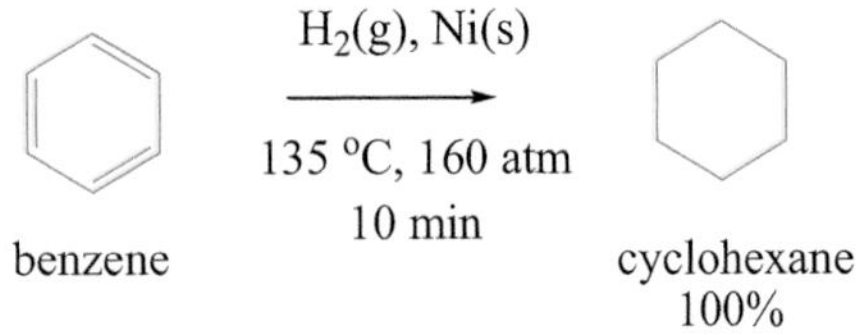

benzene $\xrightarrow[135\ ^\circ C,\ 160\ atm,\ 10\ min]{H_2(g),\ Ni(s)}$ cyclohexane 100%

(25-25)

Under these conditions, it is not practical to stop the reaction at an intermediate stage of reduction—i.e., at a diene or an alkene. This is because the second and third reductions, which involve alkenes that are no longer aromatic, are faster than the first.

A **Birch reduction** (Equation 25-26), on the other hand, reduces benzene to cyclohexa-1,4-diene. Not only does the reaction stop after just a single hydrogenation, but reduction takes place *regioselectively*, yielding only the 1,4-diene.

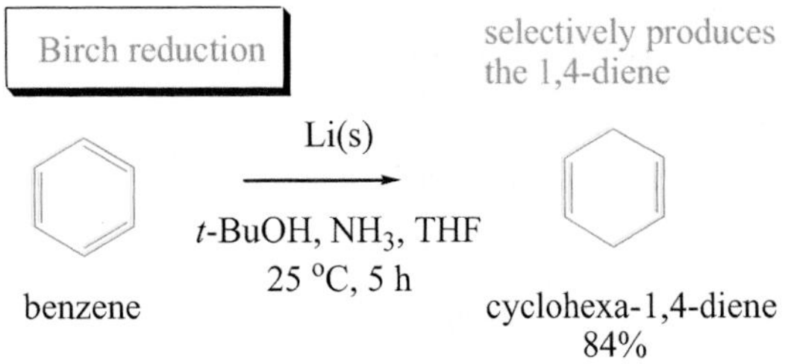

Birch reduction

selectively produces the 1,4-diene

benzene $\xrightarrow[t\text{-BuOH},\ NH_3,\ THF,\ 25\ ^\circ C,\ 5\ h]{Li(s)}$ cyclohexa-1,4-diene 84%

(25-26)

The conditions for a Birch reduction are very similar to those for the dissolving metal reductions we saw in the previous section. The difference is that a small amount of an alcohol (typically *t*-butyl alcohol, $(CH_3)_3COH$) is used as the proton source. Not surprisingly, then, the mechanism for the Birch reduction, shown in Equation 25-27, is similar to that for the dissolving metal reduction of an alkyne, shown previously in Equation 25-23.

Mechanism for the Birch reduction in Equation 25-26

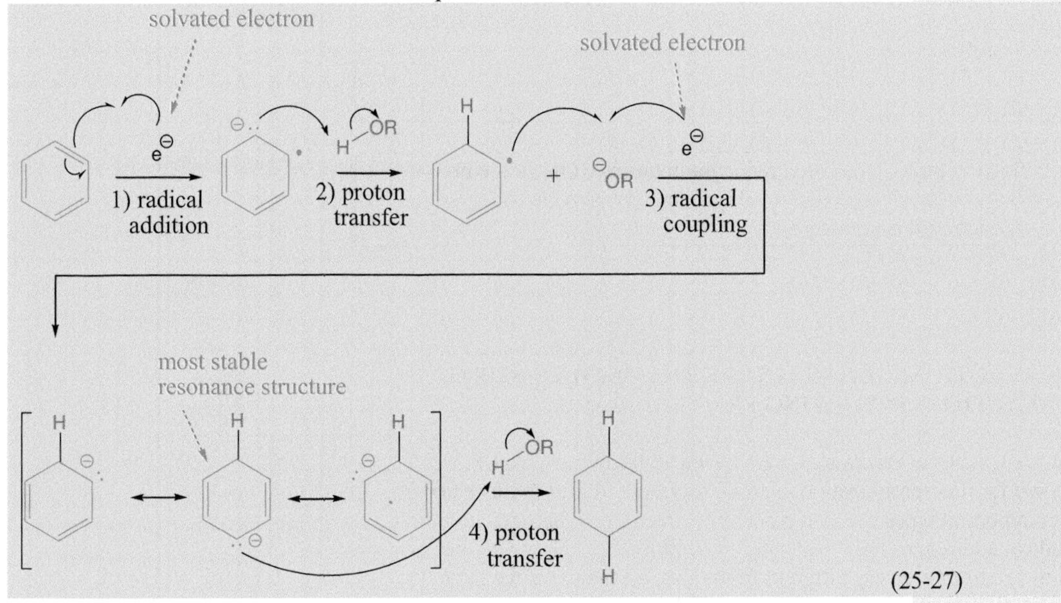

(25-27)

Step 1 is radical addition of a solvated electron to a C=C double bond of the benzene ring. The radical anion intermediate that is produced is strongly basic and thus deprotonates the alcohol in step 2 to produce an uncharged alkyl radical. Radical coupling takes place in step 3, this time producing a closed-shell carbanion species in which the negative charge is delocalized over three carbon atoms. That carbanion then deprotonates a second molecule of the alcohol to produce the overall product.

Notice that in the final step of the mechanism, protonation can occur at any of the three carbon atoms sharing the negative charge. However, protonation takes place almost exclusively at the one indicated. Why this is so is not entirely clear, but is probably because that resonance structure is the most stable of the three. In that resonance structure, the negative charge is adjacent to two sp^2-hybridized carbon atoms, each of which has a relatively high effective electronegativity (Section 3.11). This allows some electron density to be drawn away from the carbon atom bearing the negative charge. By contrast, in the other two resonance structures, the negative charge is adjacent to only one sp^2-hybridized carbon, so there is less inductive stabilization.

Problem 25.15. Benzoic acid undergoes the Birch reduction to yield a carboxyl-substituted 1,4-cyclohexadiene. However, there are two possible products, depending upon the location of the carboxyl group relative to the C=C double bonds. (a) Draw the mechanism that leads to the formation of *each* of these products, and predict which one is the major product. (b) Do you think that the Birch reduction of benzoic acid will occur faster or slower than of benzene itself? (Hint: Is a carboxyl group an electron-donating or an electron-withdrawing group?)

CO_2H

Li(s), ROH / NH_3(l) → ?

Problem 25.16. Why do you think that a Birch reduction requires ROH as the proton source whereas a dissolving metal reduction of an alkyne uses the solvent, NH_3, as the proton source? (Hint: Which acid is stronger?)

25.6. CHAIN REACTIONS: CHARACTERISTIC MECHANISMS OF REACTIONS INVOLVING FREE RADICALS

In addition to the types of reactions we have seen so far in this chapter, free radicals are well known for their participation in *chain reactions*. Later in this chapter, we will examine two important types of chain reactions—free radical halogenation in Section 25.8, and radical addition of HBr to alkenes in Section 25.9. However, because some aspects of chain reactions are very different from other mechanisms we have examined, we will first discuss chain reactions in a general sense.

A defining characteristic of a **free radical chain reaction** is the involvement of a free radical intermediate that is often responsible for producing *many thousands* of product molecules. To do so, this requires a *cyclic process*, depicted in Figure 25-7.

Comment [JMK58]: **Margin note.** In a chain reaction, a single radical can catalyze an overall reaction thousands of times.

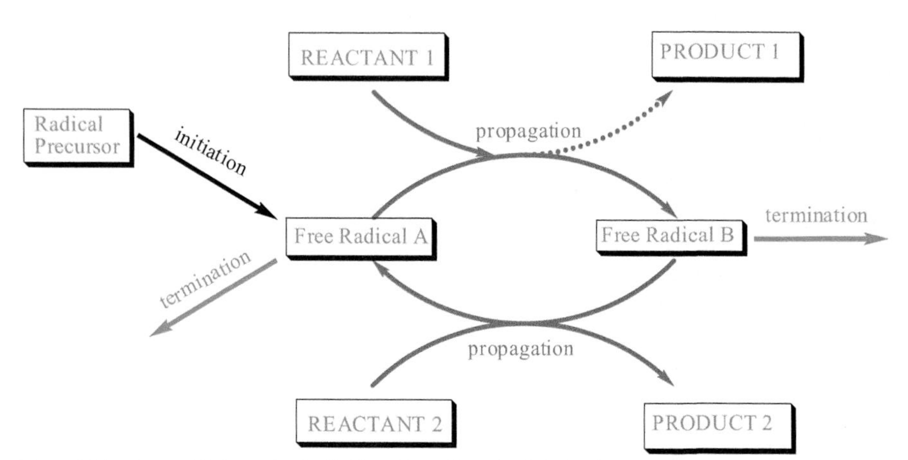

Figure 25-7. General Schematic of a Radical Chain Reaction Mechanism
The chain reaction itself is depicted by the blue arrows, which illustrate the reactants being converted to products through a cyclic process involving free radicals. These are chain propagation steps. An initiation step (black arrow) generates free radicals for the process, whereas termination steps (red arrows) remove free radicals from the process.

That cyclic process is depicted by the set of blue arrows in the figure. An initial free radical, "free radical A," reacts with a molecule of the *overall* reactants ("Reactant 1") to produce a second free radical, "free radical B." Depending upon the specific mechanism, this step may or may not also produce a molecule of the reaction's *overall* product, "Product 1"—hence the reason for the dashed blue arrow. Free radical B then reacts with a different reactant molecule ("Reactant 2") to regenerate free radical A, and in the process "Product 2" is formed.

Throughout this cyclic process, radical A is not consumed. Therefore, once it is regenerated, it is free to participate in the process again and again. Each time the free radical completes a cycle, an additional molecule of each overall product is produced. Consequently, these steps are called **propagation steps**, and the set of steps that completes the entire cycle is called the **propagation cycle**. At any given time during the course of the reaction, a large number of these propagation cycles can take place simultaneously.

Recall from Section 25.1 that under normal conditions, the concentration of free radicals in solution is essentially zero. Therefore, for a propagation cycle to begin, there must be a step that produces the initial free radical A. This is called an **initiation step**, and is depicted in Figure 25-7 by a black arrow. As indicated, a closed-shell precursor is typically required to produce the initial radical.

Comment [JMK59]: Margin note. Initiation steps are responsible for generating the initial radical that enters the propagation cycle.

Finally, due to their very high reactivity, radicals A and B can react with species other than those labeled "reactants" in Figure 25-7. As indicated by the red arrows, these steps remove radicals A and B from the propagation cycle. Without those free radicals, the propagation cycle must end. Such steps are therefore called **termination steps**.

Comment [JMK60]: Margin note. Termination steps remove radicals from the propagation cycle.

Although Figure 25-7 helps give you a conceptual understanding of free radical chain reactions, mechanisms for such reactions are typically written with each step on a separate line. For example, the general mechanism depicted above would appear as shown in Equations 25-28a through 25-28e.

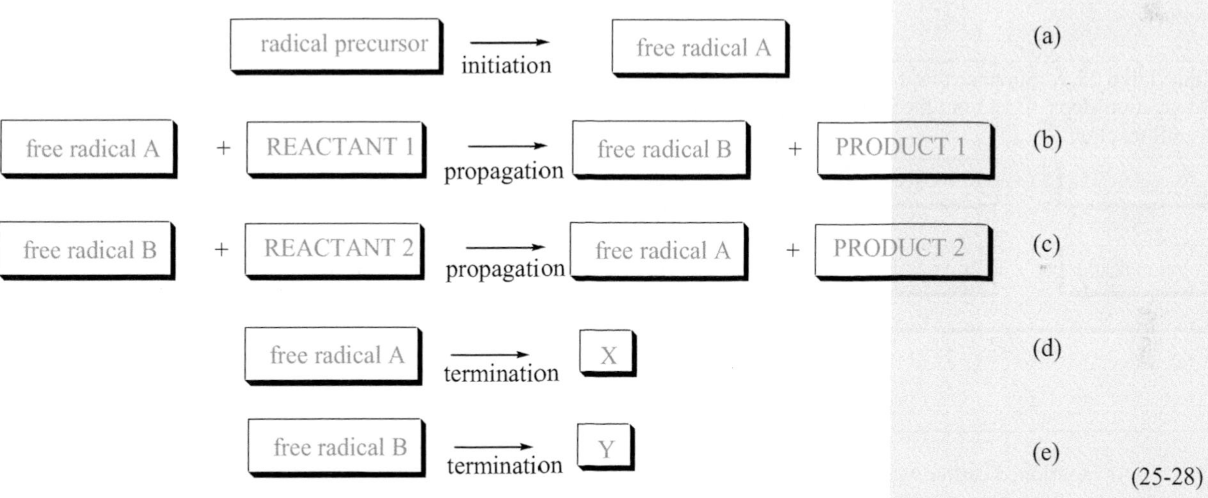

(25-28)

Just as indicated in Figure 25-7, the step in Equation 25-28a shows that free radical A is produced from a radical precursor in an initiation step. One propagation step is shown in Equation 25-28b, illustrating that free radical A reacts with REACTANT 1 to produce free radical B and PRODUCT 1. The second propagation step, Equation 25-28c, shows that free radical B reacts with REACTANT 2 to produce free radical A and PRODUCT 2. Two termination steps are shown in Equations 25-28d and 25-28e, where X and Y represent generic byproducts.

Although the mechanism in Equation 25-28 contains several different reactants and several different products, not all of them contribute to the overall reaction. In general,

The overall reaction of a free radical mechanism is obtained by summing the propagation steps only.

The initiation step is not included because its product is a free radical that is typically highly reactive, and therefore not isolable. The termination steps are not included because they occur very infrequently—the most abundant species in solution will be the overall reactants, and will therefore be the species with which the free radical intermediates will most likely react.

Applying this idea to the mechanism in Equation 25-28, we obtain the overall reaction by summing steps (b) and (c) only, as shown below.

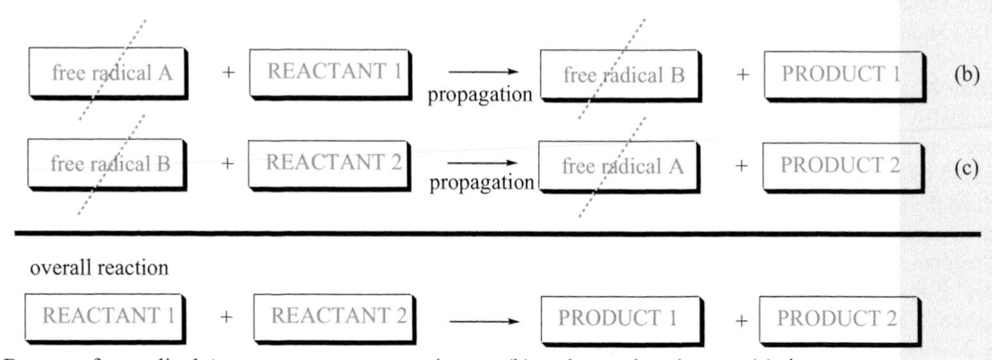

Because free radical A appears as a reactant in step (b) and a product in step (c), it cancels when taking the sum. Similarly, free radical B is cancelled, because it appears as a product in step (b) and a reactant in step (a). This leaves REACTANT 1 and REACTANT 2 as overall reactants, and PRODUCT 1 and PRODUCT 2 as overall products.

Your Turn 25.9. Suppose that a free radical chain reaction consists of the following propagation steps. Cross out the redundant species and sum the steps to obtain the overall reaction.

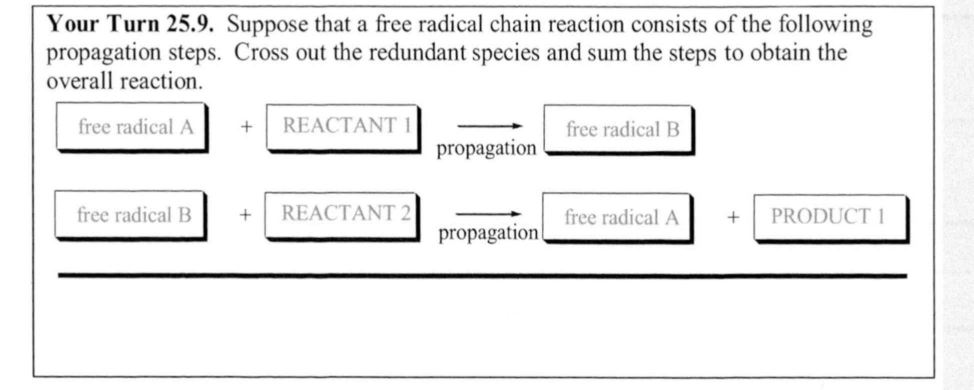

As mentioned earlier, we will see how these basic ideas of chain reactions are applied to specific reactions in Sections 25.8 and 25.9. Before we do, however, we will discuss the idea of radical initiation to greater depth in the next section.

25.7. RADICAL INITIATORS

Recall from Figure 25-7 that a radical chain reaction is initiated by a radical *precursor*. What types of reagents are used as these **radical initiators**? What are the steps that are involved to generate the initial radicals used in the propagation cycle of a chain reaction?

One of the most common ways to initiate free radicals is through *homolysis* of a closed-shell species. Precursors that are particularly useful are those that contain a weak bond, thus making homolysis relatively easy. Popular choices include molecular halogens (Cl_2, Br_2, and I_2), as well as peroxides (RO–OR), an example of which is shown in Equation 25-29.

Comment [JMK61]: Margin note. Radical initiators typically have a weak covalent bond.

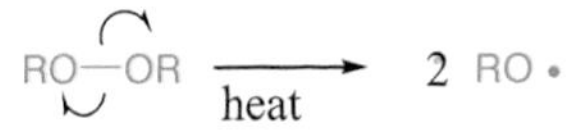

RO—OR —heat→ 2 RO•

(25-29)

Your turn 25.10. Verify that the above mentioned precursors have weak bonds by comparing their bond energies to that of a typical C–H bond.

Cl–Cl ________ Br–Br ________ I–I ___________

HO–OH ______________ H_3C–H ________

Molecular oxygen, O_2, can also be used as a radical initiator. Interestingly, it does not require homolysis, because it is a *diradical* itself—that is, O_2 has two unpaired electrons. Therefore, as shown in Equation 25-30, O_2 can react with a closed-shell species to generate a free radical that can enter a chain reaction.

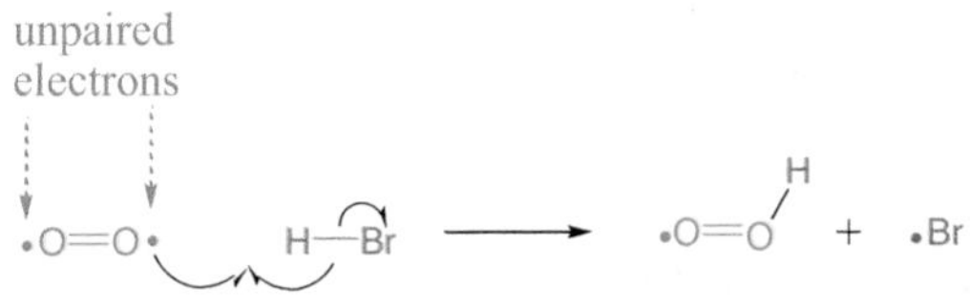

unpaired electrons

•O=O• + H—Br ⟶ •O=O–H + •Br

(25-30)

A particularly popular free radical initiator is **2,2'-azobisisobutyronitrile (AIBN)**, because it contains an excellent N_2 leaving group in the middle of the molecule. When heated to only 40 °C (Equation 25-31), a molecule of AIBN decomposes to form two cyanopropyl radicals. Moreover, N_2 is a gas, so it permanently leaves the reaction mixture, making radical initiation effectively irreversible.

N_2 is very stable, and is also a gas that leaves the reaction mixture, making radical intiation effectively irreversible

weak bond

40 °C

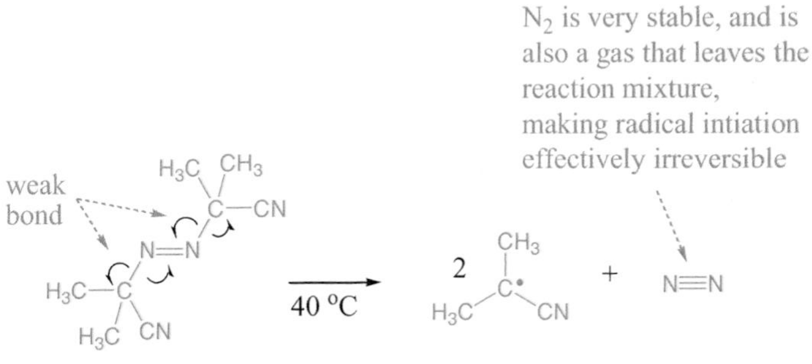

2,2'-azobisisobutylnitrile (AIBN) ⟶ 2 $(CH_3)_2$C•CN + N≡N

(25-31)

Problem 25.17. Azobenzene is shown below. Which do you think would serve as a better radical initiator—azobenzene or AIBN? Explain.

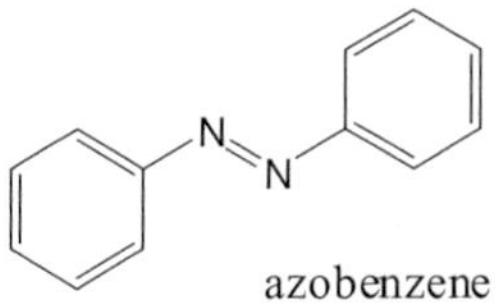

azobenzene

Another popular precursor used to initiate a chain reaction is ***N*-bromosuccinimide, NBS** (Equation 25-32), given that the N–Br bond is relatively weak (194 kJ/mol).

weak bond

N-bromosuccinamide (NBS) → N• + •Br (25-32)

Problem 25.18. The *average* N-B bond is about 243 kJ/mol. Yet that for NBS is 194 kJ/mol. Explain why.

Having some familiarity with radical initiators, as well as the general aspects of the free radical chain reaction mechanism, we are ready to examine from specific free radical chain reactions. In the next section, we will examine free radical halogenation, and in Section 25.9, we will examine the free radical addition of HBr to an alkene.

25.8. HALOGENATION OF ALKANES: SYNTHESIS OF ALKYL HALIDES

When an alkane such as cyclohexane is treated with a molecular halogen such as Cl_2, no reaction occurs (Equation 25-28). However, if the same mixture is illuminated with ultraviolet light, *halogenation* takes place, producing chlorocyclohexane and hydrogen chloride (Equation 25-29).

cyclohexane + Cl_2 → no reaction (25-33)

cyclohexane + Cl_2 →(40 - 75 °C, hν; ultraviolet light) chlorocyclohexane 93% + HCl (25-34)

As we learned in Section 25.1, the requirement of ultraviolet light suggests that free radicals are produced. Indeed, as we will see in Section 25.6a, the mechanism involves free radical intermediates, so the reaction in Equation 25-28 is more specifically called a **radical halogenation**.

Radical halogenation can take place with a variety of alkanes, as well as other molecular halogens (more will be said about this later). In general,

Radical halogenation is a substitution reaction, in which a hydrogen atom from an alkane is replaced by a halogen atom from a molecular halogen, X_2, producing a halogen halide as a byproduct.

Here, we will discuss some important aspects of radical halogenations, beginning with a close look at the mechanism. With an understanding of the mechanism, we will then examine issues pertaining to the choice of halogen, including kinetics and thermodynamics, as well as selectivity.

25.8a. The Mechanism of Radical Halogenation

The mechanism for radical halogenation is a *chain reaction* and, as such, consists of *initiation*, *propagation*, and *termination* steps. The initiation step in this reaction (Equation 25-35) is simply homolysis of the chlorine molecule, producing chlorine radicals—recall that halogen molecules are common radical initiators due to their weak covalent bond.

Comment [JMK62]: Margin note.
Free radical halogenation is a chain reaction.

Initiation Step for the Reaction in Equation 25-34

UV light brings about the homolysis of the Cl-Cl bond

$$Cl{-}Cl \xrightarrow{h\nu} Cl\cdot + Cl\cdot \quad (25\text{-}35)$$

Your Turn 25.11. Halogenation of cyclohexane can take place with Br_2 instead of Cl_2, as shown below.

$$C_6H_{12} \text{ (cyclohexane)} + Br_2 \xrightarrow{h\nu} C_6H_{11}Br \text{ (bromocyclohexane)} + HBr$$

In the space provided here, draw the initiation step, including curved arrows.

Those radicals can then enter into a propagation cycle to begin converting the overall reactants from Equation 25-34 into overall products (see again Figure 25-7). For this reaction, there are two propagation steps, shown in Equations 25-36a and 25-36b. In the first propagation step, a chlorine radical (formed by the homolysis in Equation 25-35) abstracts a hydrogen atom from cyclohexane (an overall reactant), producing a molecule of HCl (an overall product) and a cyclohexyl radical. In the second propagation step, that cyclohexyl radical abstracts a halogen atom from Cl_2 (an overall reactant), producing a molecule of chlorocyclohexane (an overall product), and leaving behind a chlorine radical.

Propagation Steps for the Reaction in Equation 25-34

$Cl\cdot$ + cyclohexane $\xrightarrow{S_H2}$ HCl + cyclohexyl radical (a)

the initial chlorine radical is regenerated

cyclohexyl radical + Cl–Cl $\xrightarrow{S_H2}$ chlorocyclohexane + $Cl\cdot$ (b)

overall reaction

cyclohexane + Cl_2 ⟶ chlorocyclohexane + HCl (c)

(25-36)

Notice that these two steps in Equations 25-36a and 25-36b do indeed have the characteristics that define a propagation cycle. First, *none of the radicals are consumed overall*—each is used in one of the steps, and is regenerated in the other. Second, the sum of the two steps, shown in Equation 25-36c, yields the overall reaction, the same as the one we saw previously in Equation 25-34.

Your Turn 25.12. In the space provided here, draw the propagation steps for the reaction in Your Turn 25.11. (Hint: They are very similar to the ones in Equation 25-36.)

There are two ways for a propagation cycle to cease. One is for the overall reactants to be completely consumed, as is the case for any chemical reaction. The second is for the radicals involved in the propagation steps to be destroyed in any of a variety of termination steps. As shown in Equations 25-37a and 25-37b, *radical coupling* between a radical from a propagation step and any other radical present in solution can destroy such radicals.

Comment [JMK63]: **Margin note.** Radical coupling involving a radical in the propagation cycle can be characterized as a termination step.

Termination Steps for the Reaction in Equation 25-34

$Cl\cdot$ $\cdot Cl$ $\xrightarrow{\text{radical coupling}}$ Cl—Cl (a)

cyclohexyl radical + $\cdot Cl$ $\xrightarrow{\text{radical coupling}}$ chlorocyclohexane (b)

(25-37)

Your Turn 25.13. In the space provided here, draw two termination steps for the reaction in Your Turn 25.11. (Hint: They are similar to the ones in Equation 25-37.)

Problem 25.19. Draw another termination step for the chain reaction in Equation 25-34, which is not shown in Equation 25-37.

Problem 25.20. For the reaction in Equation 25-34, construct a diagram similar to that in Figure 25-7, illustrating the fate of each species.

Solved Problem 25.5. Methane can undergo radical halogenation, as shown below. Draw the mechanism for this reaction, including the initiation and propagation steps, along with two termination steps.

$$CH_4 + Br_2 \xrightarrow[h\nu]{} H_3C\text{—}Br + H\text{—}Br$$

Think. For the initiation step, what is the weakest bond in the reactants that can undergo homolysis? For the propagation steps, what S_H2 step can the initial radical undergo to produce the HBr product? What S_H2 step can the resulting radical undergo to produce the CH_3Br product, and regenerate the initial radical? For the termination steps, what possible radical coupling steps can take place?

Solve. The weakest bond present is the Br–Br bond, which undergoes homolysis in an initiation step to produce two Br• radicals.

$$Br\text{—}Br \longrightarrow 2\ Br\bullet$$

In the first of two propagation steps, a Br• radical abstracts a hydrogen from CH_4 to produce one overall product, HBr, and a methyl radical, $H_3C\bullet$. In the second propagation step, the methyl radical abstracts a bromine atom from Br_2 to produce the second overall product, CH_3Br, and regenerate the initial Br• radical.

$$Br\bullet\ \ H\text{—}CH_3 \longrightarrow Br\text{—}H + \bullet CH_3$$

$$H_3C\bullet\ \ Br\text{—}Br \longrightarrow H_3C\text{—}Br + Br\bullet$$

Termination steps can be radical coupling between any two radicals that appear. Two such steps are shown below.

$$H_3C\bullet\ \ \cdot Br \longrightarrow H_3C\text{—}Br$$

$$H_3C\bullet\ \ \cdot CH_3 \longrightarrow H_3C\text{—}CH_3$$

Problem 25.21. Ethane can undergo radical halogenation, as shown below. Draw the mechanism for this reaction, including the initiation and propagation steps, along with two termination steps.

$$CH_3CH_3 + Cl_2 \xrightarrow[h\nu]{} CH_3CH_2Cl + HCl$$

25.8b. Kinetics and thermodynamics of radical halogenation

Although the mechanism of halogenation is the same regardless of the identity of the molecular halogen that is used, there are aspects that make certain of these halogenations more feasible to carry out than others. One important aspect to consider is the relative reaction rates, which exhibit a periodic table trend.

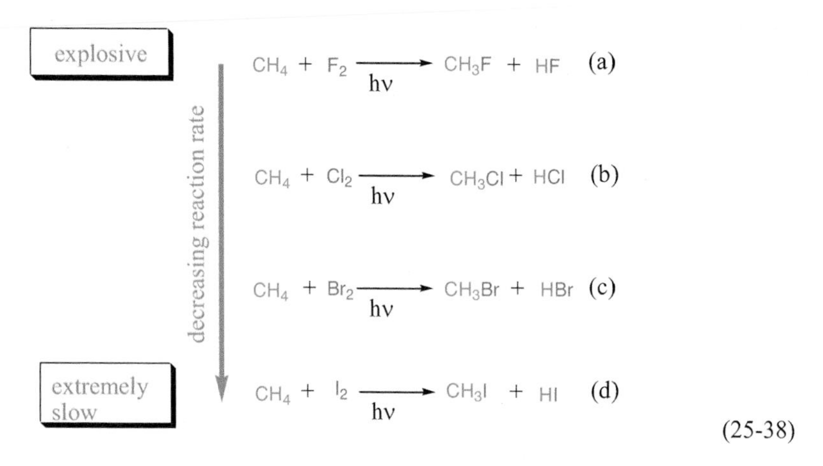

(25-38)

Namely,

The rate of free radical halogenation decreases in the order: $F_2 > Cl_2 > Br_2 < I_2$.

Fluorination is explosive, even with dilute concentrations. Chlorination is slower but is still potentially explosive. Bromination is slower still and therefore quite controllable. Iodination is very slow; the reaction must be heated in order for the reaction to proceed at a reasonable rate.

To begin to understand the reason for this trend, recall from the discussion of kinetics in Chapter 8 that a reaction's rate depends on the size of the energy barrier between reactants and products. Let's therefore construct the energy diagrams for each of the above halogenation reactions. The important steps are the two propagation steps in each reaction, because those are the steps that are directly responsible for converting the overall reactants into overall products (see again Equation 25.36). The value of ΔH^0_{rxn} for each such propagation step is listed in Table 25-4. (These values are calculated from the bond dissociation energies provided earlier in Tables 25-1 through 25-3.)

Table 25-4. Reaction enthalpies for the propagation steps of $CH_4 + X_2 \rightarrow CH_3X + HX$

	ΔH^0_{rxn} (kJ/mol)			
Reaction	X• = F•	X• = Cl•	X• = Br•	X• = I•
$X\bullet + CH_4 \longrightarrow HX + CH_3\bullet$	-134	+4	+69	+138
$CH_3\bullet + X_2 \longrightarrow CH_3X + X\bullet$	-292	-106	-101	-83
$CH_4 + X_2 \longrightarrow CH_3X + HX$	-426	-102	-32	+55

From these values, we can construct the reaction energy diagrams in Figure 25-8. The *overall* energy barrier for each reaction is governed by the first of the two propagation steps. As we can see, the size of the energy barrier decreases in the order: $I_2 > Br_2 > Cl_2 > F_2$. This is an outcome of Hammond's postulate (Section 9.3), given that ΔH^0_{rxn} of the first propagation step becomes increasingly positive (i.e., less favorable) in the same order. Moreover, this is consistent with fluorination being the fastest of the halogenation reactions and iodination being the slowest.

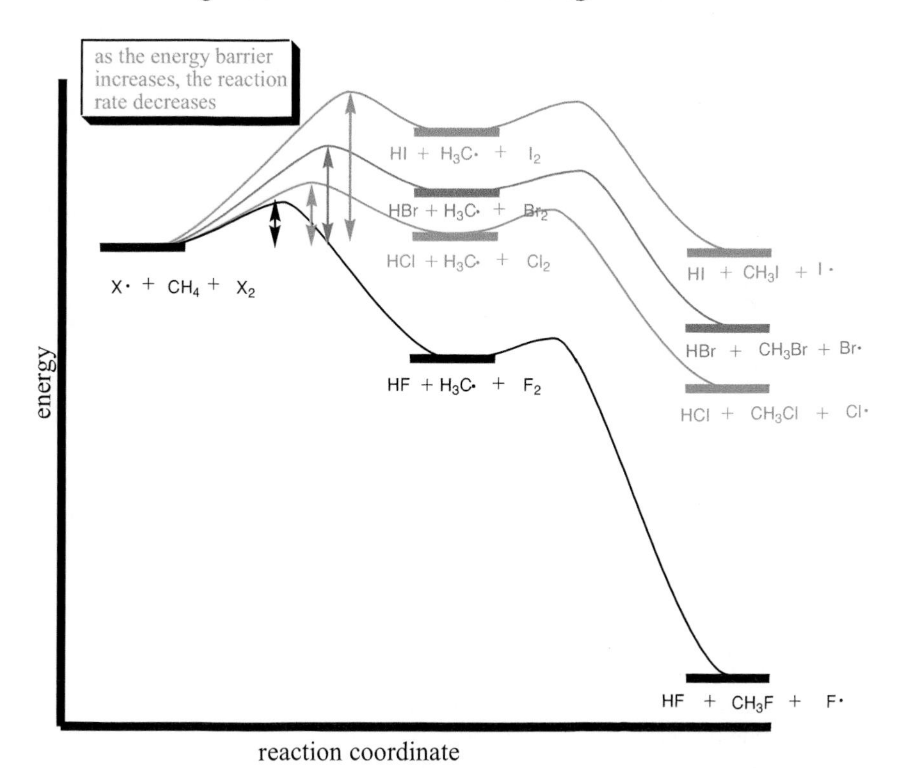

Figure 25-8. Energy Diagrams for the Halogenation of CH_4.
The black curve represents fluorination, the red curve represents chlorination, the blue curve represents bromination, and the green curve represents iodination. The overall energy barriers between reactants and products is indicated by the respective double-headed arrows. Fluorination has the smallest energy barrier, followed by chlorination, bromination, and finally iodination.

Another major factor contributing to the differences in halogenation rates is the *overall* ΔH^0_{rxn}. Notice that the fluorination reaction *overall* is very exothermic—by about 426 kJ/mol. This large amount of heat that is generated will raise the temperature of the reaction mixture, which further increases the reaction rate. Hence this large exothermicity also contributes to the fact that fluorination is explosive. By contrast, iodination is endothermic overall, which is why it must be heated to proceed.

25.8c. Selectivity of Chlorination and Bromination

As we just saw, the various halogenation reactions differ significantly in their reaction kinetics and thermodynamics. An important outcome of these differences is in the *selectivity* of halogenation reactions. Consider, for example, the chlorination and bromination reactions below.

$$H_3C{-}CH_2{-}CH_3 \xrightarrow[h\nu]{Cl_2} H_3C{-}CHCl{-}CH_3 + H_3C{-}CH_2{-}CH_2Cl \quad (25\text{-}39)$$

propane → 2-chloropropane ~60% + 1-chloropropane ~40%

$$H_3C{-}CH_2{-}CH_3 \xrightarrow[h\nu]{Br_2} H_3C{-}CHBr{-}CH_3 + H_3C{-}CH_2{-}CH_2Br \quad (25\text{-}40)$$

propane → 2-bromopropane ~99% + 1-bromopropane ~1%

In both cases, the secondary halide is favored over the primary one, but the *extent* to which it is favored is much greater for bromination than it is for chlorination. In other words,

> Free radical bromination of an alkane is much more selective than free radical chlorination.

How much more selective is bromination than chlorination? To answer this question, we can compare the actual product distribution of each reaction to what they would be if the reaction were completely nonselective (i.e., favoring all positions equally). For example, as indicated in Equation 25-39, chlorination of propane favors reaction at the secondary carbon over a primary one by a ratio of 60:40.

Now consider what that ratio would be if the reaction were completely nonselective. Notice that in propane, there are two equivalent secondary hydrogens, and six equivalent primary hydrogens. If each type of hydrogen were to react with equal likelihood, then reaction at the primary carbon would be favored by a factor of three over reaction at the secondary carbon. Therefore, that ratio of secondary product to primary product would instead be 1:3. Dividing this ratio into the one that is actually observed, 60:40, gives us the selectivity of chlorination at a secondary carbon relative to a primary.

chlorination selectivity (2°/1°) = (60:40) / (1:3) = (60:13⅓) = (4.5:1)

This tells us that if the number of primary and secondary hydrogens were the same, then the secondary product would be favored by a ratio of 4.5-to-1.

Repeating this for the bromination in Equation 25-40, we obtain:

bromination selectivity (2°:1°) = (99:1) / (1:3) = (297:1)

Comparing the two ratios for halogenation at a secondary vs. primary carbon, we can see that bromination is about 297/4.5 = 66 times more selective than is chlorination.

Product distributions from other halogenation reactions have also enabled us to determine the relative selectivities of chlorination and bromination toward the halogenation at secondary vs. tertiary carbons. These results can be combined with the ones from above to give the following relative selectivities for primary, secondary, and tertiary carbons.

Relative selectivities of halogenation at 1°, 2°, and 3° carbons
• Chlorination = 1 : 4.5 : 6 • Bromination = 1: 297 : 19,000

We have discussed what the relative selectivities are for chlorination vs. bromination, but we have yet to explain why. The reason can be understood by examining the first of the two propagation steps for halogenation, which is the one that governs which hydrogen atom is abstracted. In that step, the halogen radical, X•, can abstract a hydrogen atom from propane at either a secondary carbon (Equation 25-41) or a primary one (Equation 25-42). As we learned in Section 25.4b, abstraction from the secondary carbon is the one that is favored, producing the more stable alkyl radical. This is true regardless of whether the attacking radical is Cl• or Br•, because the H–X bond that is formed is the same in both cases.

a secondary radical is more stable than a primary one

$$H_3C{-}CH_2{-}CH_3 + \cdot X \longrightarrow H_3C{-}\dot{C}H{-}CH_3 + HX \quad (25\text{-}41)$$

$$H_3C{-}CH_2{-}CH_3 + \cdot X \longrightarrow H_3C{-}CH_2{-}\dot{C}H_2 + HX \quad (25\text{-}42)$$

However, what does depend on the identity of the attacking radical is the specific value of ΔH^0_{rxn}. If Cl• attacks, then those values for Equations 25-41 and 25-42 are -36 kJ/mol and -21 kJ/mol, respectively. If Br• attacks, then the values are +29 kJ/mol and +44 kJ/mol.

The impact that the choice of attacking radical has on the pair of reaction steps can be seen in Figure 25-9, which provides their reaction energy diagrams.

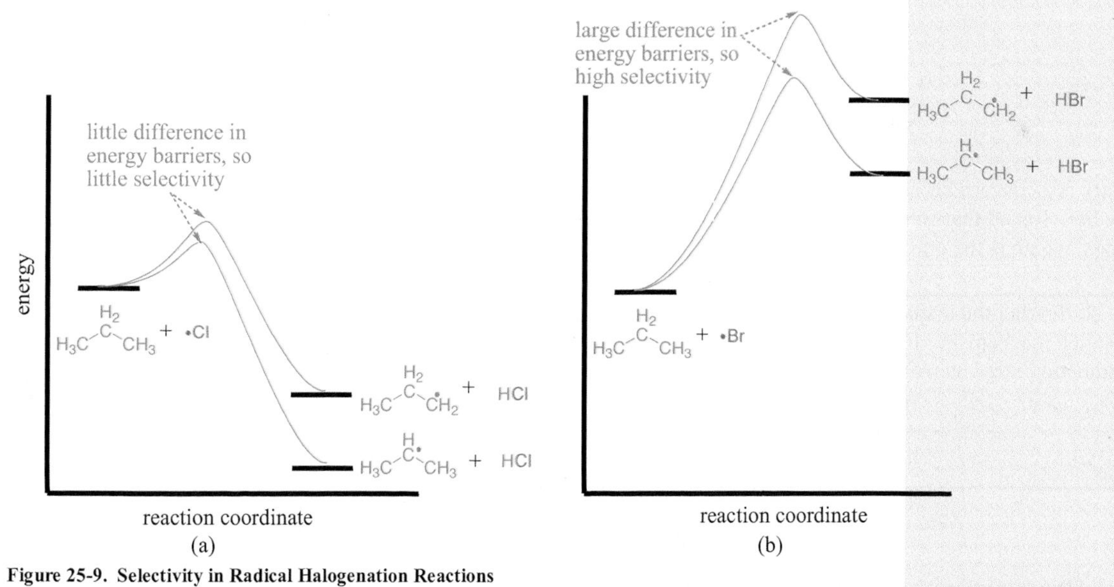

Figure 25-9. Selectivity in Radical Halogenation Reactions
(a) Hydrogen abstraction by Cl• at a secondary and primary carbon atom. (b) Hydrogen abstraction by Br• at a secondary and primary carbon. The energy barriers are similar in size in (a), so there is little selectivity in chlorination. In (b), the energy barriers are significantly different in size, so bromination occurs with high selectivity.

When the attacking radical is Cl• (Figure 25-9a), both hydrogen abstractions are significantly exothermic. Thus, according to the Hammond postulate, both abstractions should proceed through a transition state that resembles the reactants, giving rise to energy barriers that are similar in size. Consequently, both abstractions will occur with similar rates.

By contrast, when Br• is the attacking species, both hydrogen abstractions are significantly endothermic, so their transition states will resemble the products. Because the products are significantly different in energy, so, too, are the transition states, giving rise to energy barriers that are significantly different in size. Namely, hydrogen abstraction from a secondary carbon will take place much faster than it will at a primary carbon.

Solved Problem 25.6. Predict the major product of the following reaction and draw the complete, detailed mechanism. Include all initiation and propagation steps.

Br_2, hν → ?

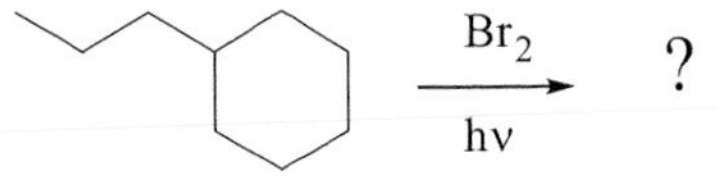

Think. What is the initial radical that is formed? By what process? How will that radical interact with the neutral molecules present? Is regiochemistry a concern?

Solve. Br_2 will undergo homolysis, as suggested by the presence of light. Therefore, the initial radical is Br•.

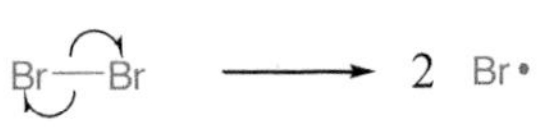

Br—Br → 2 Br•

With the alkane present, radical halogenation will occur via two propagation steps. The Br• radical abstracts a hydrogen atom to yield an alkyl radical, R•. That alkyl radical then abstracts a bromine atom from Br_2 to yield R–Br and Br•.

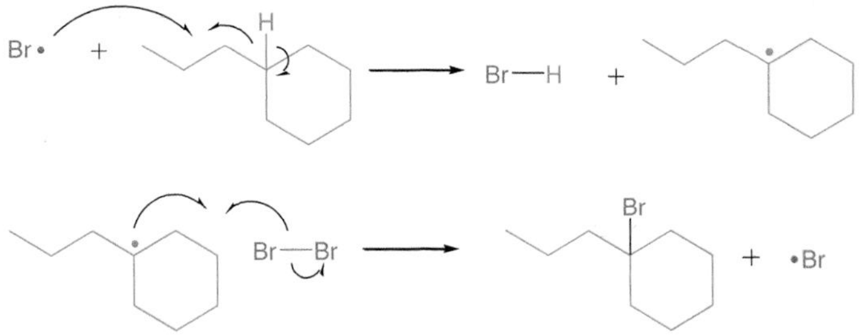

Br• + H → Br—H +

Br—Br → Br + •Br

Regiochemistry is a concern because there are multiple distinct H atoms that can be abstracted by Br•. Recall that Br• is highly selective toward hydrogen atoms attached to tertiary carbons, which is the one that is shown.

Problem 25.22. Predict the major product of the following reaction and draw the complete, detailed mechanism. Include all initiation and propagation steps. Draw two plausible termination steps as well.

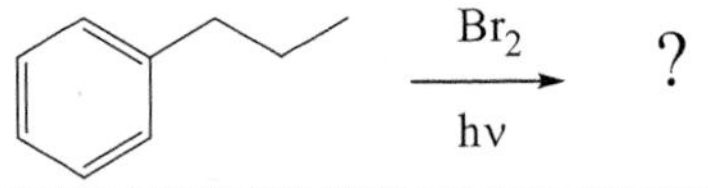

Br_2, hν → ?

25.8d. Radical Bromination Using *N*-Bromosuccinimide

If an alkene undergoes radical bromination, substitution will most likely take place at the allylic position, due to the resonance stabilization in the allylic radical that would be produced upon hydrogen abstraction. Thus, for example, radical bromination of cyclopropene would produce 3-bromocyclopentene, as shown in Equation 25-43a. However, a problem arises if we carry out such a bromination by simply treating the alkene with molecular bromine and UV light. As we learned in Chapter 21, Br_2 will also add to the C=C double bond in an *electrophilic addition* reaction (Equation 25-43b).

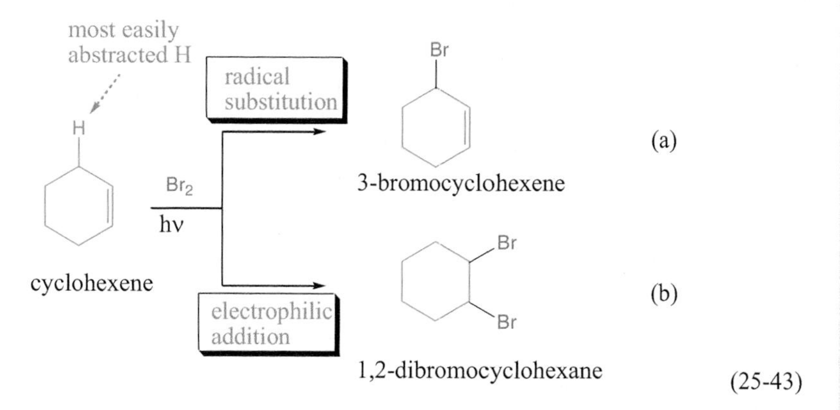

(25-43)

To avoid this problem, chemists will carry out free radical bromination using ***N*-bromosuccinimide** (**NBS**). As shown in Equation 25-44, NBS reacts with cyclohexene to give only the allylic bromide.

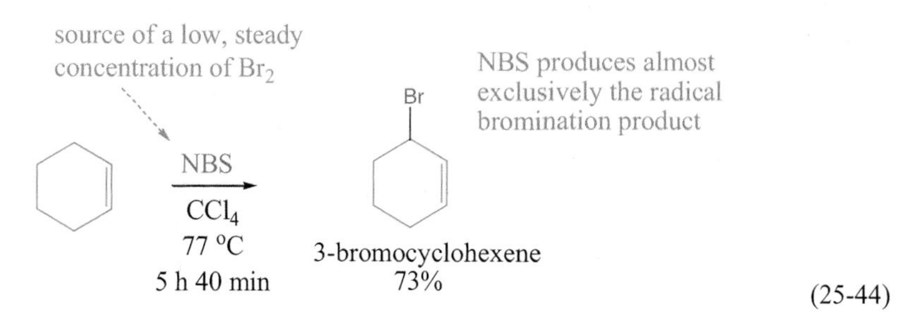

(25-44)

N-Bromosuccinimide does not alter the mechanism of radical bromination, but rather controls the rates of the competing reactions in Equation 25-43 by controlling the concentration of Br_2.

> In the presence of a compound with alkane C–H bonds, *N*-bromosuccinimide (NBS) is the source of a low, steady concentration of Br_2.

The way in which Br_2 is produced from NBS is shown in the mechanism in Equation 25-45.

Comment [JMK64]: Margin note

NBS = Br—N (succinimide ring with two C=O)

Mechanism for the Production of Br_2 from NBS

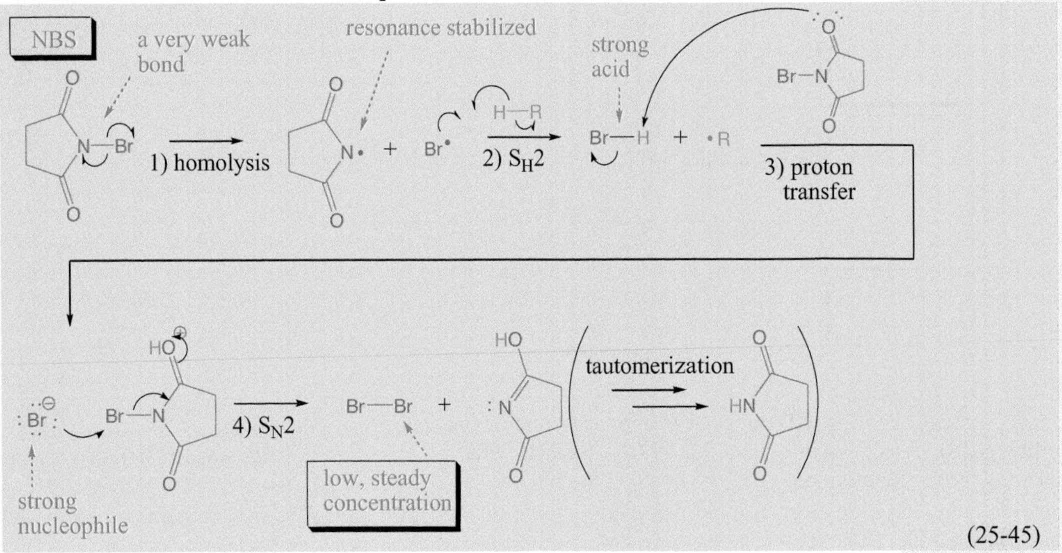

NBS — a very weak bond — resonance stabilized — 1) homolysis — $N\bullet + Br^\bullet$ — 2) S_H2 — strong acid — $Br—H + \bullet R$ — 3) proton transfer — : Br : strong nucleophile — 4) S_N2 — Br—Br + — low, steady concentration — tautomerization

(25-45)

Step 1 is homolysis of the N–Br bond to produce a bromine radical, Br•. This step requires only modest heating, because that bond is particularly weak—single bonds connecting any two heteroatoms tend to be weak, and furthermore, the resulting unpaired electron on N is resonance-delocalized over two oxygen atoms. In step 2, the newly-formed Br• radical abstracts a hydrogen atom from the alkane, producing HBr, a strong acid. Thus, in step 3, a carbonyl oxygen on NBS is protonated, which also produces Br^-, a strong nucleophile. Finally, step 4 is an S_N2 step, in which the Br^- nucleophile attacks a Br atom from a second molecule of NBS, yielding Br_2.

Your Turn 25.14. Above, it is mentioned that homolysis of NBS produces a resonance-stabilized free radical. In the space provided here, draw the additional resonance structures, and include the appropriate curved arrows.

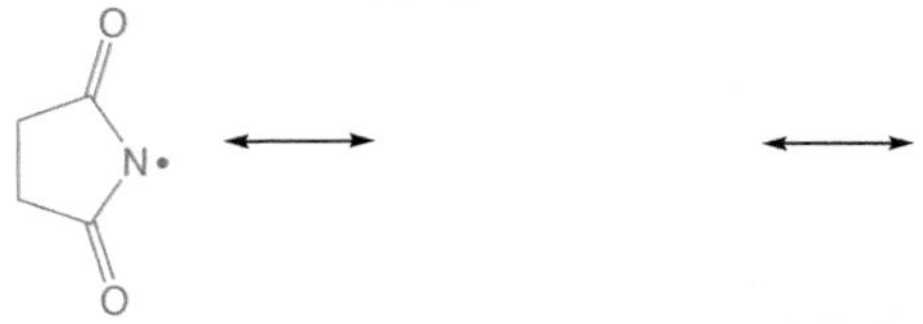

Given that NBS maintains a low concentration of Br_2, we should ask why it is that radical bromination is favored over electrophilic addition. Recall from Section 21.3 that the addition of Br_2 to an alkene proceeds through a bromonium ion intermediate, as shown below.

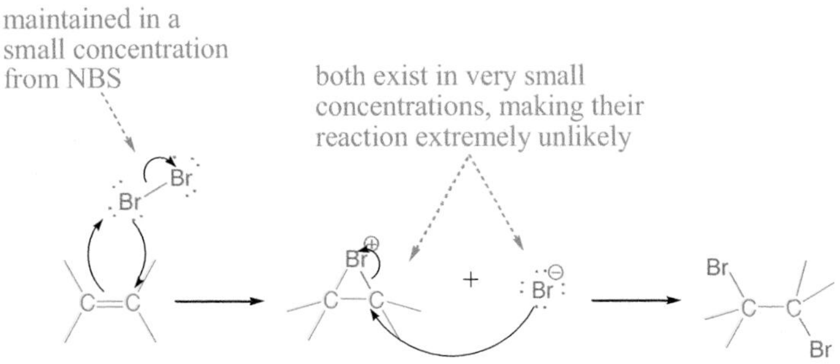

maintained in a small concentration from NBS — both exist in very small concentrations, making their reaction extremely unlikely

(25-46)

The second step requires the reaction between the bromonium ion intermediate and a bromide ion, both of which must be produced from Br_2. At any given time, only a fraction of Br_2 will have reacted to produce such species, so their concentrations must be even smaller than the initial concentration of Br_2. This makes it extremely unlikely for a bromonium ion intermediate and a bromide ion to find each other to react.

The story is somewhat different for radical bromination using NBS, whose initiation and propagation steps are shown in Equation 25-47.

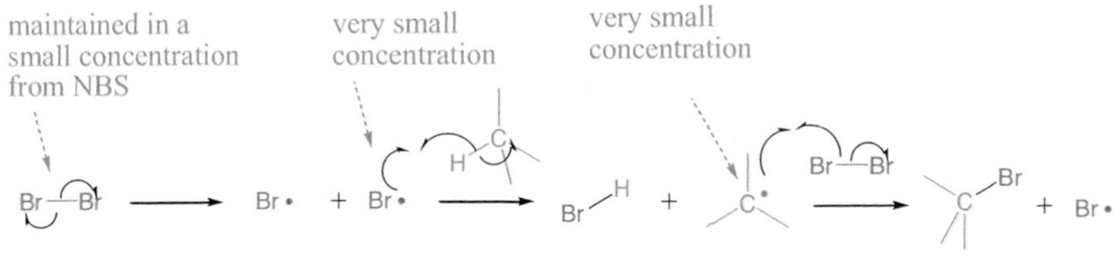

maintained in a small concentration from NBS

very small concentration

very small concentration

Br—Br ⟶ Br• + Br• ⟶ Br—H + C• ⟶ C—Br + Br•

(25-47)

Notice that none of these steps requires the reaction between two species produced from Br_2. Therefore, none of the steps has an excessively slow rate.

Problem 25.23. Predict the major product of the following reaction. Pay attention to stereochemistry.

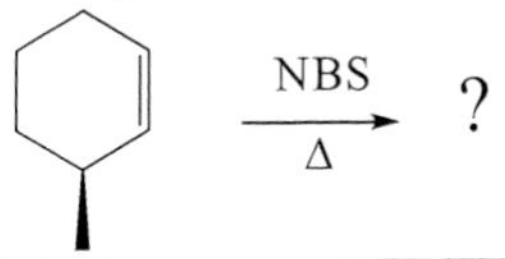

$\xrightarrow[\Delta]{\text{NBS}}$?

25.9. RADICAL ADDITION OF HBr: NON-MARKOVNIKOV ADDITION

Recall from Section 20.2 that under normal conditions, a hydrogen halide adds across the double bond of an alkene in a Markovnikov fashion. Therefore, for example, HBr will add to propene to produce 2-bromopropane, as shown in Equation 25-48—overall, the hydrogen atom adds to the least alkyl-substituted carbon, whereas the bromine atom adds to the most alkyl-substituted carbon. The reason, as discussed in Chapter 20, is that the first step of the mechanism is protonation of the C=C double bond, which proceeds through the *most stable carbocation intermediate*.

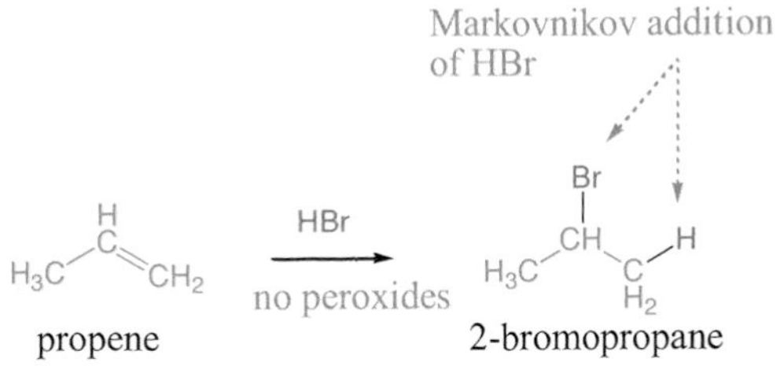

Markovnikov addition of HBr

$H_3C-CH=CH_2 \xrightarrow[\text{no peroxides}]{\text{HBr}} H_3C-CH(Br)-CH_2-H$

propene 2-bromopropane

(25-48)

Remarkably, if a small amount of peroxides is added, 1-bromopropane will be produced as the major product instead, as indicated in Equation 25-49. In such a reaction, HBr still adds across the C=C double bond, but with a regiochemistry opposite to that in Equation 25-48—the H atom adds to the more substituted carbon, and the Br atom adds to the less substituted one. This is an example a **non-Markovnikov addition**.

non-Markovnikov addition of HBr

propene $\xrightarrow[\text{peroxides}]{HBr}$ 1-bromopropane (25-49)

We recognize peroxides as *radical initiators* because of the weak O–O bond. Hence, the reaction in Equation 25-49 proceeds by a radical mechanism, which is outlined in Equation 25-50. Step 1 is heterolysis of the peroxide to produce two alkoxy radicals. In step 2, an alkoxy radical abstracts a hydrogen from HBr to produce a bromine radical. That bromine radical adds to the alkene in step 3, and the resulting alkyl radical abstracts a hydrogen atom from HBr, yielding the overall product.

Mechanism for the Reaction in Equation 25-49

RO—OR ⟶ 2 RO• (a)
1) heterolysis

RO• H—Br ⟶ RO—H + Br• (b)
2) S_H2

Br• H_2C=CH–CH_3 ⟶ $BrCH_2$–$\dot{C}H$–CH_3 (c)
3) radical addition

$BrCH_2$–$\dot{C}H$–CH_3 H—Br ⟶ $BrCH_2$–CH_2–CH_3 + Br• (d)
4) S_H2

propagation steps (c), (d)

(25-50)

This is a *chain reaction*, recognized by the fact that steps 3 and 4 comprise a propagation cycle—i.e., those are the propagation steps. Specifically, the bromine radical that reacts in step 3 is regenerated as a product in step 4. Thus, you will notice that summing those two steps yields the net reaction.

Your Turn 25.15. The propagation steps from Equation 25-50 are repeated below. Cross out the redundant species, and sum the two steps to arrive at the net reaction.

Br• H_2C=CH–CH_3 ⟶ $BrCH_2$–$\dot{C}H$–CH_3

$BrCH_2$–$\dot{C}H$–CH_3 H—Br ⟶ $BrCH_2$–CH_2–CH_3 + Br•

Notice that the initial Br• radical that is used in the propagation steps is produced by the sequence of steps 1 and 2. Hence, the first two steps in Equation 25-50 can be viewed as a set of initiation steps. As usual, a termination step is any step that removes a free radical from the propagation cycle (see Your Turn 25.16).

Your Turn 25.16. In the space provided here, draw two plausible termination steps for the reaction in Equation 25-49.

The reason that this mechanism proceeds in a non-Markovnikov fashion has entirely to do with step 3, which is the first of the two propagation steps. This is a radical addition to the C=C double bond. As we saw previously in Equations 25-19 and 25-20, this step favors the formation of the *more stable alkyl radical*—a secondary radical—which requires the Br• radical to add to the terminal carbon. If, instead, the Br• atom were to add to the central carbon, a less stable primary alkyl radical would be produced, as was previously shown in Equation 25-20.

Comment [JMK65]: **Margin note**
Radical addition of HBr across C=C proceeds through most stable alkyl radical to produce the non-Markovnikov product.

25.10. ORGANIC SYNTHESIS: RADICAL REACTIONS IN SYNTHESIS

The free radical reactions we have examined in this chapter are valuable to the field of organic synthesis, for two main reasons. First, they allow us to carry out transformations that are not practical with reactions whose mechanisms involve only closed-shell species. Second, they allow us to carry out transformations we have seen in previous chapters, but with different regioselectivity or stereoselectivity.

Free radical halogenation is an example of a transformation that is impractical with mechanisms involving only closed-shell species. For instance, without the use of radical halogenation, it is difficult to imagine how to *functionalize*—i.e., add a functional group to—the 3-position of cyclohexene, as indicated below. This is because the transformations we have seen in previous chapters would require a functional group to be present at that site already.

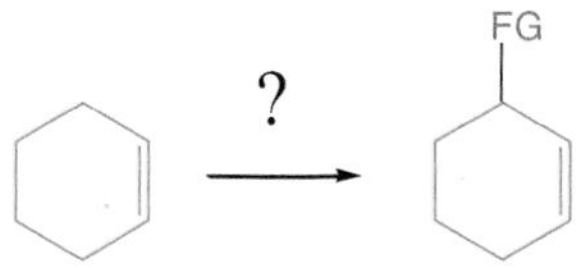

FG

?

(25-51)

However, such a transformation is easy to accomplish with bromination using NBS, which we previously saw in Equation 25-44.

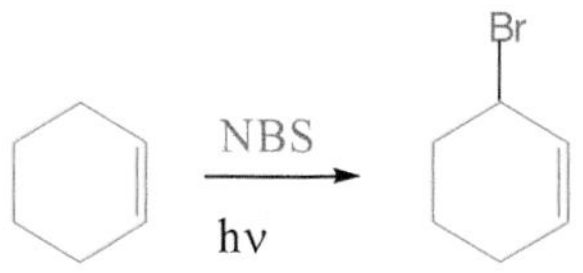

Br

NBS

hν

(25-52)

Allylic bromination such as this has been employed in the synthesis of some natural products, such as (+)-koninginin D. A key step in the synthesis is shown in Equation 25-52 (*Chem. Commun.* **1999**, 1129). Notice that under the relatively mild conditions that are used, other functional groups such as ketones and esters are not affected.

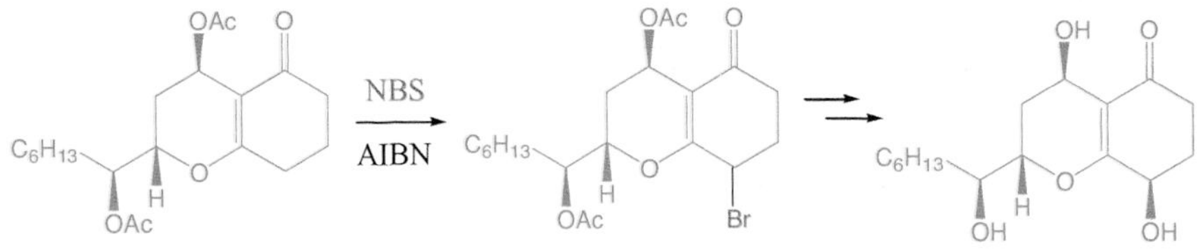

NBS
AIBN

(+)-koninginin D

(25-52)

Radical bromination with NBS is also a popular method to functionalize the benzylic position of aromatic compounds in synthesis. Equation 25-53 shows its use in a key step in synthesizing flavones (*Eur. J. Org. Chem.* **1999**, 135).

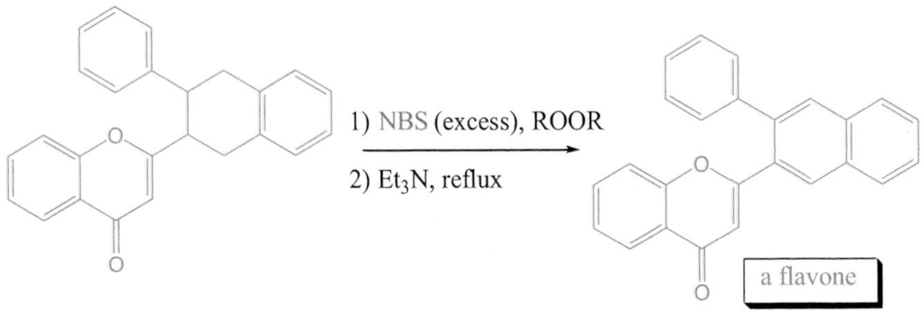

1) NBS (excess), ROOR
2) Et_3N, reflux

a flavone

(25-53)

Problem 25.24. (a) Draw the product that is immediately formed in Equation 25-53 after reaction with excess NBS. (b) What kind of reaction takes place in the second reaction in Equation 25-53?

Another important aspect of radical reactions is *regioselectivity* that can differ from that in other reactions we have encountered previously. An example is with hydrohalogenation of an alkene. Recall from Chapter 20 that HBr adds across a C=C double bond in a Markovnikov fashion, proceeding through the most stable carbocation intermediate. In this chapter, we saw that in the presence of a radical initiator such as peroxides, addition of HBr takes place in a non-Markovnikov fashion, proceeding through the most stable *radical* intermediate. The importance of this can be seen in Solved Problem 25.7.

Solved Problem 25.7. Show how you would carry out the following transformation using at least one radical chain reaction.

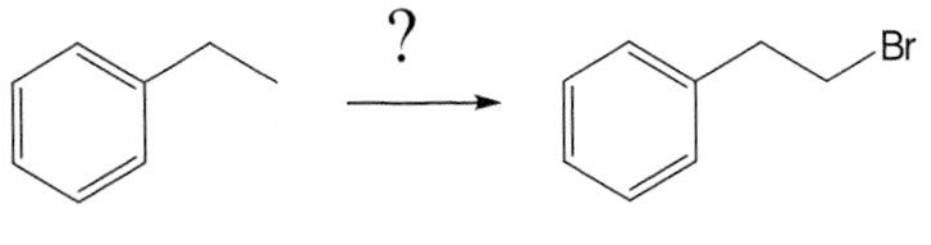

?

Think. What functional group can be used to halogenate a carbon that is two carbons away from a benzene ring? How can that functional group be introduced on a carbon that initially is not functionalized?

Solve. The alkyl bromide product can be made from phenylethene via anti-Markovnikov radical addition of HBr.

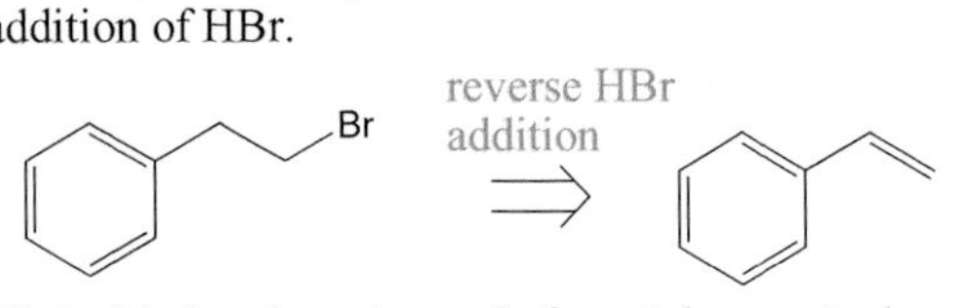

reverse HBr addition

That C=C double bond can be made from 1-bromo-1-phenylethane in an E2 reaction.

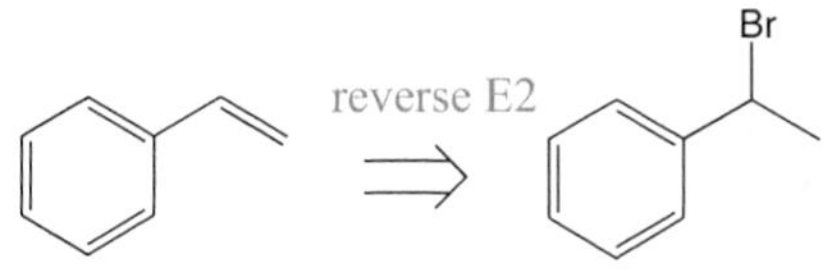

Br

reverse E2

$\Rightarrow$

That alkyl bromide can, in turn, be made from a radical halogenation of phenylethane.

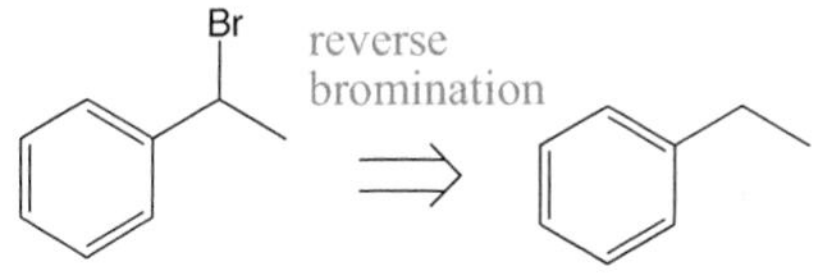

Br

reverse
bromination

$\Rightarrow$

Reversing the reactions and adding the appropriate reagents, the synthesis appears as follows.

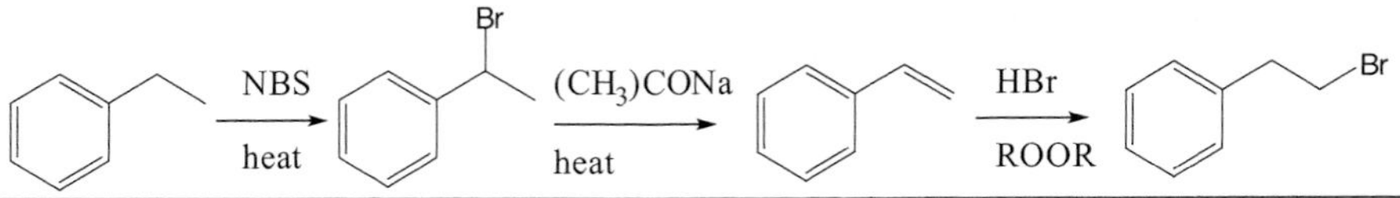

NBS / heat → (Br) → $(CH_3)CONa$ / heat → → HBr / ROOR → (Br)

Finally, free radical reactions can offer *stereoselectivity* that differs from other reactions we have seen previously. An important example of this is with dissolving metal reductions, which can reduce an alkyne to a *trans*-alkene.

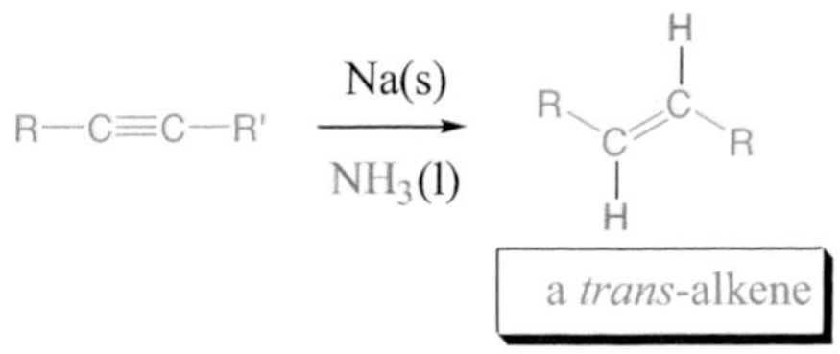

$$R{-}C{\equiv}C{-}R' \xrightarrow[NH_3(l)]{Na(s)}$$

a *trans*-alkene

(25-54)

This contrasts catalytic hydrogenation (Section 17.5), which reduces an alkyne to a *cis*-alkene.

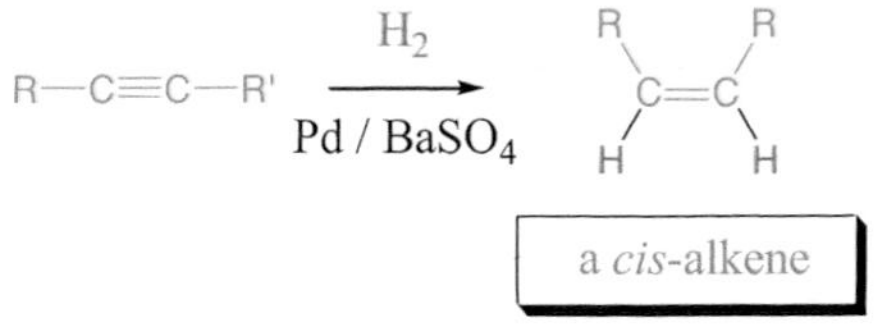

$$R{-}C{\equiv}C{-}R' \xrightarrow[Pd\ /\ BaSO_4]{H_2}$$

a *cis*-alkene

(25-55)

An application of the dissolving metal reduction of an alkyne is shown in Equation 25-56 (*J. Org. Chem.*, **1986**, *51*, 5320-5327). This is a step in the total synthesis of sphingosine, which undergoes phosphorylation *in vivo* to produce a potent signaling lipid. (Notice that in Equation 25-56, the reaction conditions also lead to the removal of a protecting group.)

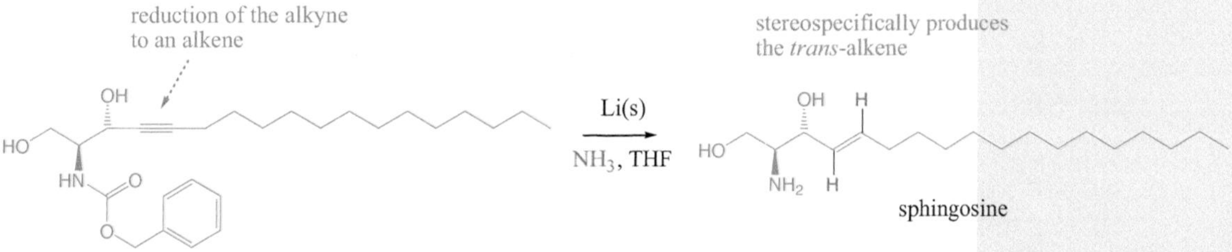

reduction of the alkyne
to an alkene

stereospecifically produces
the *trans*-alkene

Li(s) / NH_3, THF

sphingosine

(25-56)

25.11. FUNCTIONAL GROUP CHEMISTRY

Although many different types of compounds can participate in free radical reactions, this chapter focused primarily on various hydrocarbons. These include alkanes, alkenes, alkynes, and aromatic rings. As usual, new aspects of functional group chemistry appear green. Ones discussed in previous chapters appear gray.

25.11a. Alkanes

This is the first chapter in which reactions of alkanes are discussed. This is because the reactions discussed in previous chapters are primarily ones that involve elementary steps driven by the flow of electrons from an electron-rich site to an electron-poor site. Alkanes have no functional groups, and thus have no sites that are especially electron-rich or electron-poor.

Without functional groups to guide the flow of electrons, alkanes are severely limited in the kinds of useful reactions in which they can participate. Radical halogenation is one of them.

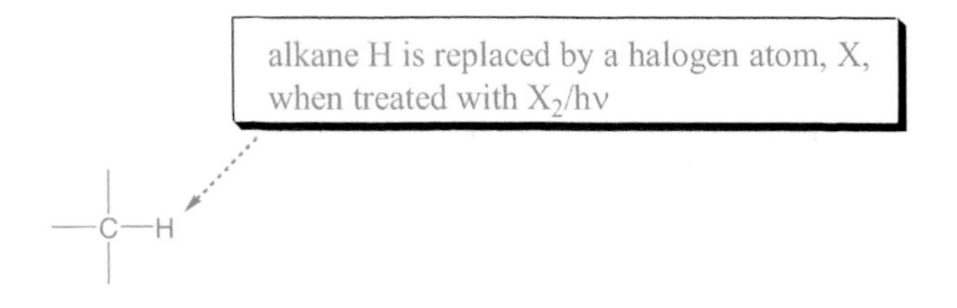
alkane H is replaced by a halogen atom, X, when treated with X_2/hν
C
H

25.11b. Alkenes

The new reactions we encountered in this chapter, involving alkenes, are the halogenation of an allylic position, and the radical addition of HBr across a carbon-carbon double bond.

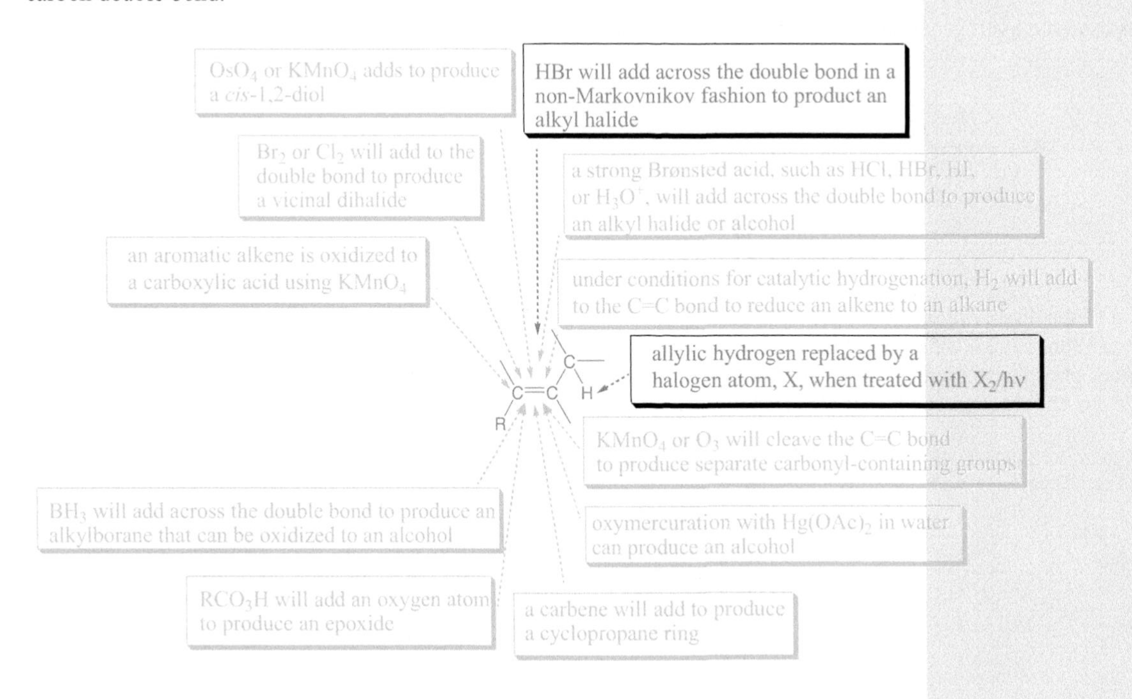
OsO_4 or $KMnO_4$ adds to produce a *cis*-1,2-diol
HBr will add across the double bond in a non-Markovnikov fashion to product an alkyl halide
Br_2 or Cl_2 will add to the double bond to produce a vicinal dihalide
a strong Brønsted acid, such as HCl, HBr, HI, or H_3O^+, will add across the double bond to produce an alkyl halide or alcohol
an aromatic alkene is oxidized to a carboxylic acid using $KMnO_4$
under conditions for catalytic hydrogenation, H_2 will add to the C=C bond to reduce an alkene to an alkane
allylic hydrogen replaced by a halogen atom, X, when treated with X_2/hν
C=C
C
H
R
$KMnO_4$ or O_3 will cleave the C=C bond to produce separate carbonyl-containing groups
BH_3 will add across the double bond to produce an alkylborane that can be oxidized to an alcohol
oxymercuration with $Hg(OAc)_2$ in water can produce an alcohol
RCO_3H will add an oxygen atom to produce an epoxide
a carbene will add to produce a cyclopropane ring

25.11c. Alkynes

The new reaction we encountered in this chapter, involving alkynes, is the dissolving metal reduction of an alkyne to produce a *trans*-alkene.

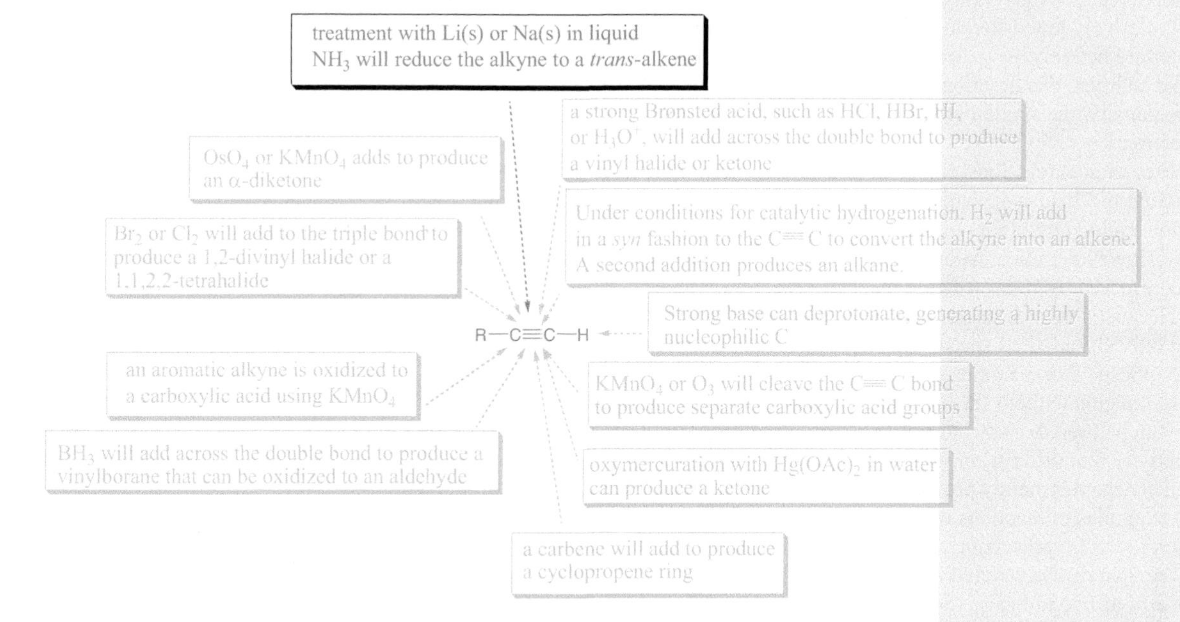

25.11d. Aromatic Rings

We encountered two new reactions in this chapter involving aromatic rings. One is the Birch reduction of the ring, and the other is the halogenation of the benzylic carbon.

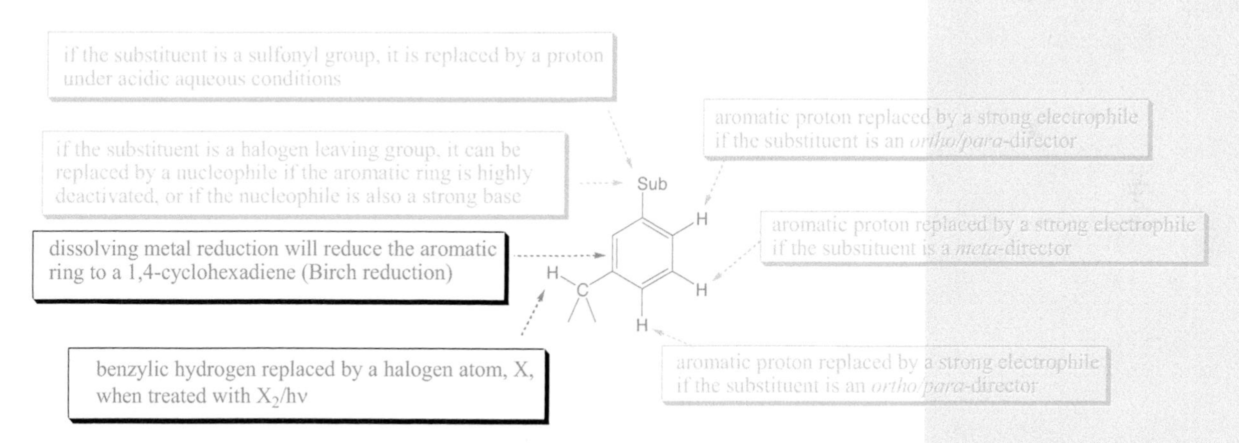

25.12. WRAPPING UP AND LOOKING AHEAD

This chapter introduced you to the chemistry of free radicals. Because a free radical, by definition, has at least one unpaired electron, an atom lacks an octet, making the radical highly unstable and very reactive. Moreover, the atom that lacks an octet is relatively electron-poor. Thus, we find many similarities between alkyl radicals and carbocations. For example, a carbon atom bearing an unpaired electron tends to have a planar geometry, analogous to the positively charged carbon atom of a carbocation. Furthermore, an alkyl radical is stabilized by resonance delocalization of the unpaired electron, as well as by alkyl groups attached to the radical carbon. Likewise, carbocations are stabilized by resonance delocalization of the positive charge, as well as by alkyl groups attached to the positively charged carbon.

Like reactions involving closed-shell species, reactions involving free radicals consist of relatively few different types of elementary steps. The ones we examined in this chapter are heterolysis, radical coupling, bimolecular homolytic substitution (S_H2), and radical addition. To describe these steps, we introduced new aspects of curved arrow notation—namely, the single-barbed arrow, which corresponds to the movement of a single electron.

Free radical reactions can be classified according to whether or not they undergo chain reaction mechanisms, characterized by the involvement of free radicals in a propagation cycle. Dissolving metal reductions involve free radicals, but are not chain reactions. However, radical halogenation of alkanes and radical hydrobromination of alkenes do proceed by chain reaction mechanisms.

Because free radical reactions involve steps that differ from mechanisms involving only closed-shell species, free radical reactions can offer several benefits to organic synthesis. For example, they enable us to functionalize alkane carbons, which is difficult to imagine without the involvement of free radicals. Furthermore, free radical reactions can be used to carry out transformations with stereoselectivity or regioselectivity that differ from reactions involving only closed-shell species.

This chapter merely provided an introduction to free radical chemistry. We will see more examples of reactions involving free radicals in Chapter 26, specifically in the application toward synthesizing polymers. However, the field of free radical chemistry is vast—more than can be covered in this book. If you are interested in learning more about the chemistry of free radicals, you are encouraged to read Togo, Hideo. *Advanced Free Radical Reactions for Organic Synthesis*, Atlanta: Elsevier Science.

REACTION TABLES

Table 25-5. Functional group transformations

Starting Functional Group	Typical Reagent Required	Functional Group Formed	Comments	Discussed in Section(s)
R—C≡C—R Alkyne	Na(s) or Li(s) → NH_3(l), -78 °C	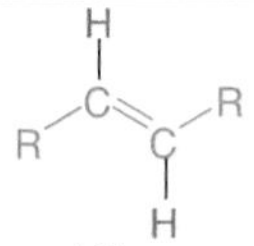 Alkene	Forms *trans* alkene only	25.5a
 Benzene	Li(s), ROH → NH_3(l)	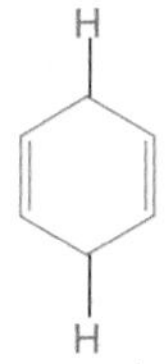 1,4-cyclohexadiene	*Birch reduction* Forms 1,4-cyclohexadiene only	25.5b
R—H Alkane	X_2 → hν	R—X Alkyl halide	X=Cl,Br	25.8
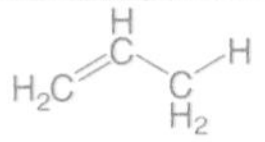 Alkene	NBS → hν	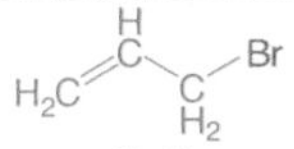 Allylic bromide	Favors allylic substitution over bromination of C=C	25.8d
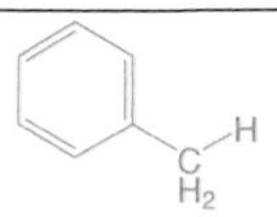 Phenyl alkane	NBS → hν	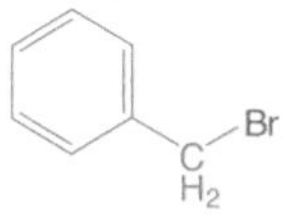 Benzylic bromide		25.8d
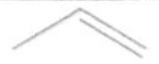 Alkene	HBr → peroxides	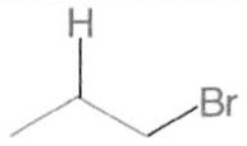 Alkyl bromide	Non-Markovnikov regiochemistry	25.9

CHAPTER SUMMARY AND KEY TERMS

- A species that possesses at least one unpaired electron is called a **free radical**, in contrast to a **closed-shell species**, in which all electrons are paired. (Introduction)
- Free radicals lack an octet, so they are very unstable and highly reactive. They are generally produced by **homolysis** of a covalent bond in a closed-shell precursor. (Section 25.1)
- Homolysis generally favors the breaking of the weakest bond. (Section 25.1)
- A **single barbed arrow** ( ) describes the movement of a single electron in an elementary step. (Section 25.1)
- Radical stability can be determined from homolytic bond dissociation energies. All else being equal, the greater the energy required to produce the radical via homolysis, the more unstable the radical is. (Section 25.2)
- The stability of a radical increases with:
    - Decreasing *s*-character on the atom with the unpaired electron.
    - Increasing resonance delocalization of the unpaired electron.
    - Additional alkyl groups attached to the atom with the unpaired electron. (Section 25.2)
- A carbon atom that has an unpaired electron tends to be sp^2-hybridized and has a planar geometry. (Section 25.2)
- Free radicals are experimentally observed using **electron spin resonance (ESR) spectroscopy**, which has many parallels to NMR spectroscopy. (Section 25.3)
- In a **radical coupling** step, an unpaired electron from each of two radicals join to produce a new covalent bond. (Section 25.4a)
    - Radical coupling is typically irreversible, and proceeds to products with no energy barrier.
- In a **bimolecular homolytic substitution (S_H2)** step, a free radical forms a bond to an atom of a closed-shell species, and displaces another free radical from that atom. (Section 25.4b)
    - In an S_H2 step, a radical favors attack of a **monovalent atom**.
    - All else being equal, the S_H2 favors attack that leads to the breaking of the weakest bond in the closed-shell species.
- In a **radical addition** step, an alkene or alkyne carbon forms a bond to a free radical, and the other alkene or alkyne carbon gains an unpaired electron. (Section 25.4c)
    - Radical addition is regioselective, favoring the most stable free radical product.
- In a **dissolving metal reduction**, a **solvated electron** behaves as the free radical species. (Section 25.5)
    - The dissolving metal reduction of an alkyne produced a *trans*-alkene.
    - The dissolving metal reduction of a benzene ring, called a **Birch reduction**, produces 1,4-cyclohexadiene.
- A **free radical chain reaction** is characterized by the involvement of free radicals in a cyclic sequence of steps, called **propagation steps**, that are responsible for converting overall reactants into overall products. (Section 25.6)
    - Throughout the sequence of propagation steps, also called the **propagation cycle**, free radicals are not consumed overall.
    - The overall reaction is obtained by summing just the propagation steps.
    - The first free radical that enters the propagation cycle is produced by an **initiation step**.
    - A **termination step** is characterized by the removal of a free radical from the propagation cycle, and is responsible for slowing the overall reaction.
- A **radical initiator** is a precursor from which a free radical is produced, and generally possesses a relatively weak covalent bond. Common ones are

molecular halogens, ***N*-bromosuccinimide (NBS)**, **2,2'-azobisisobutylnitrile (AIBN)**, and peroxides, RO–OR. (Section 25.7)

- **Radical halogenation** is a chain reaction that serves to replace an alkane hydrogen with a halogen atom, and takes place when free radicals are generated in the presence of a molecular halogen and compound containing an alkane hydrogen. (Section 25.8)
  - The identity of the molecular halogen plays a major role in the kinetics and thermodynamics of radical halogenation. Both the rate and exothermicity of halogenation decrease in the order: $F_2 > Br_2 > Cl_2 > I_2$.
  - Bromination is highly selective, whereas chlorination is only slightly selective.
  - *N*-Bromosuccinimide is commonly used to brominate an allylic carbon in order to avoid addition of Br_2 to the alkene.
- Addition of HBr to an alkene takes place with **non-Markovnikov** regioselectivity when free radicals are present. (Section 25.9)

PROBLEMS

25. The following is an example of an S_H2 step in which the radical attacks an atom that is *not* monovalent. Supply the curved arrow notation for this step.

26. The following is an example of a McLafferty rearrangement, which takes place in the gas phase in a single step. It is an important fragmentation process in mass spectrometry. Provide the curved arrow notation for this step.

27. The radical cation product in the previous problem has a single resonance structure. Draw that resonance structure, using the proper curved arrow notation.

28. In each of the following compounds, which H would most likely be abstracted by a halogen radical, X•?

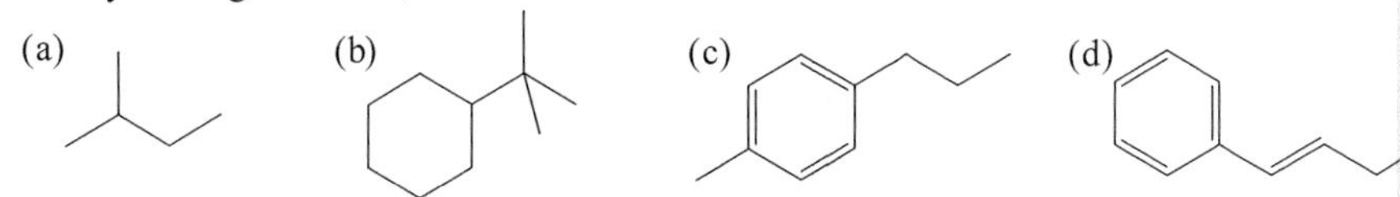

29. Upon treatment with Cl_2/hv, a compound C_9H_{12} yields only a single monochloride. What is the structure of the compound?

30. The energy barrier for rotation of a CH_2 group in an allyl radical ($H_2C{=}CH{-}CH_2\bullet$) is about 66 kJ/mol. How does this compare to the energy

barrier for rotation of a CH_3 group in propane (Chapter 3)? Explain this difference.

31. A hydrogen radical is known to abstract a hydrogen atom from an alkane in the same manner that halogen atoms do. Like halogen atoms, a hydrogen radical abstracts a hydrogen atom from a secondary carbon preferentially over a hydrogen from a primary carbon, in a 5:1 ratio. (a) Draw the two isomeric propyl radicals that are formed upon hydrogen abstraction from propane by an H radical. (b) Draw the curved arrow notation for the formation of each of those isomeric radicals. (c) Compute the percentage of each propyl radical that is formed, taking into account the different numbers of each type of H on propane.

32. At which carbon in the following molecule will radical substitution predominantly take place? Explain.

33. As we saw in the chapter, dissolving metal reductions reduce alkynes to *trans*-alkenes. However, these reactions fail when the alkyne is a terminal alkyne. Explain why. (Hint: What species appear in the mechanism?)

R—C≡CH —[Na(s); NH_3(l), -78°C]—✗→ R–CH=CH_2

34. Predict the product of each of the following reactions and provide the complete, detailed mechanism.

(a) Br_2, hν → ?

(b) NBS, hν → ?

(c) Br_2, CCl_4 → ?

(d) HBr, ROOR → ?

(e) HBr → ?

35. For each of the following reactions, draw the complete mechanism, and determine whether the product mixture will be optically active.

(a) (b)

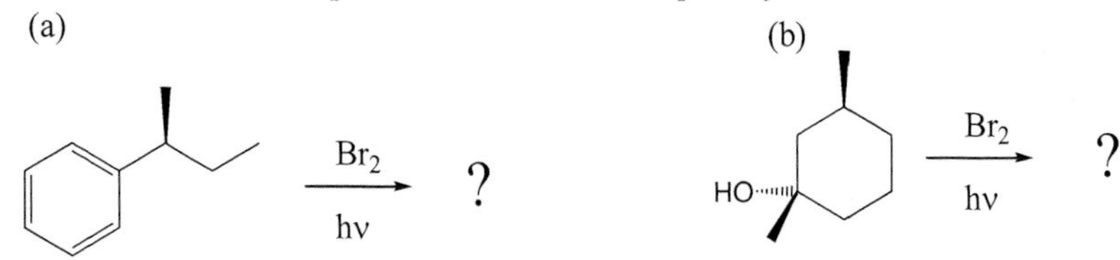

36. Similar to alkanes, hydrogen gas can undergo radical halogenation, according to the reaction below (X = F, Cl, Br, or I). Propose a mechanism for this reaction, including initiation and propagation steps, and provide two plausible termination steps.

$$H{-}H \quad + \quad X{-}X \xrightarrow[h\nu]{} 2\ H{-}X$$

37. In the halogenation of H_2, described in the previous problem, which halogen will react fastest? Defend your answer with the appropriate bond energies from Tables 25-1 through 25-3.

38. Propose a mechanism for the following reaction, which proceeds by a radical chain reaction. Include initiation and propagation steps, and provide two plausible termination steps.

$$H_2C{=}CH_2 \quad + \quad CCl_4 \xrightarrow[h\nu]{} Cl{-}CH_2{-}CH_2{-}CCl_3$$

39. When an ether is exposed to air for prolonged periods of time, it undergoes a radical chain reaction with oxygen gas to form *hydroperoxides* that are explosive. An example of an overall reaction diethyl ether is shown below. Provide a complete, detailed mechanism for this reaction, including initiation and propagation steps, and provide two plausible termination steps.

OOH

O + $O_2(g)$ ⟶ O

a hydroperoxide of diethyl ether

40. In the problem above, illustrating the formation of a hydroperoxide from diethyl ether, notice that the hydroperoxide forms at the carbon that is α to the oxygen atom and not the one that is β to it. Explain why. (hint: You may wish to write out the respective radicals that are formed upon H-abstraction)

41. The following aromatic substitution reaction has been proposed to proceed via a radical chain reaction.

I $\xrightarrow{H_2N^{\ominus}}$ H_2N + H_2N

The following mechanism has been proposed, where Ar is the aromatic ring.

$$ArI \longrightarrow ArI^{\ominus}\cdot$$

$$ArI^{\ominus}\cdot \longrightarrow Ar\cdot + I^{\ominus}$$

$$Ar\cdot + H_2N^{\ominus} \longrightarrow Ar\dot{N}^{\ominus}$$

$$Ar\dot{N}H_2^{\ominus} + ArI \longrightarrow ArNH_2 + ArI^{\ominus}\cdot$$

a) Identify each step as either *initiation, propagation*, or *termination.*
b) Add up the propagation steps to verify that the net equation is that given above.
c) Propose three possible termination steps.

42. The following are proposed steps of a radical mechanism, but are in no particular order. a) Draw in the appropriate curved arrows for each step. b)

Label each step as either *initiation*, *propagation*, or *termination*. c) Using this mechanism, write the balanced net reaction.

Cl· + △ ⟶ Cl∕\∕·

Cl—Cl —hν⟶ 2 Cl·

Cl∕\∕· + Cl· ⟶ Cl∕\∕\Cl

Cl∕\∕· + Cl∕\∕· ⟶ Cl∕\∕\∕\∕Cl

Cl∕\∕· + Cl—Cl ⟶ Cl∕\∕\Cl + Cl·

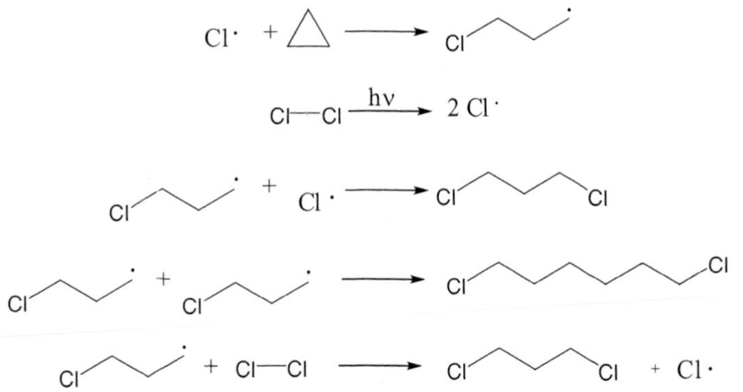

43. The following are proposed initiation and propagation steps of a radical chain reaction mechanism, but are in no particular order. (a) Draw in the appropriate curved arrows for each step. (b) Label each step as either *initiation* or *propagation.* (c) Write the balanced net reaction. (d) Provide two plausible *termination* steps, including curved arrows.

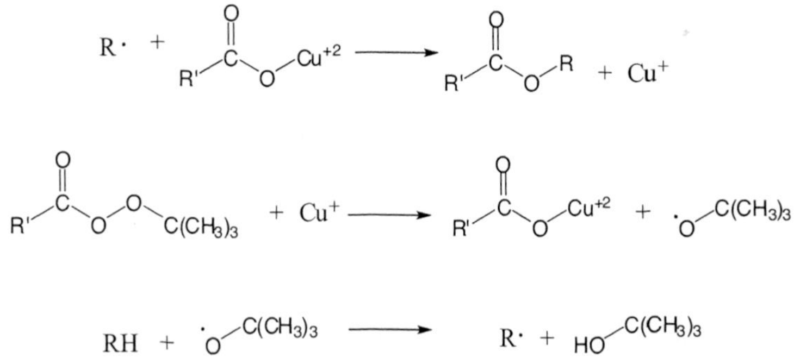

R· + R'C(=O)O–Cu^{+2} ⟶ R'C(=O)O–R + Cu^{+}

R'C(=O)O–O–$C(CH_3)_3$ + Cu^{+} ⟶ R'C(=O)O–Cu^{+2} + ·O–$C(CH_3)_3$

RH + ·O–$C(CH_3)_3$ ⟶ R· + HO–$C(CH_3)_3$

44. The following are proposed initiation and propagation steps of a radical chain reaction mechanism, but are in no particular order. (a) Draw in the appropriate curved arrows for each step. (b) Label each step as either *initiation* or

propagation. (c) Write the balanced net reaction. (d) Provide two plausible *termination* steps, including curved arrows.

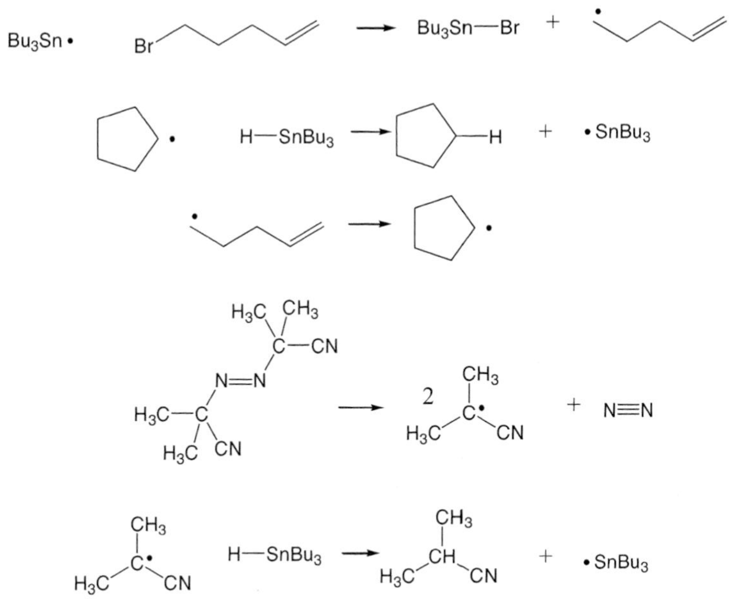

$Bu_3Sn\bullet$ Br → $Bu_3Sn—Br$ + •

• H—$SnBu_3$ → —H + •$SnBu_3$

• → •

H_3C CH_3 C—CN N=N $H_3C—C$ H_3C CN → 2 CH_3 C• H_3C CN + N≡N

CH_3 C• H_3C CN H—$SnBu_3$ → CH_3 CH H_3C CN + •$SnBu_3$

45. As we saw in the chapter, the selectivity of chlorination at 1°, 2°, and 3° carbons is about 1:4:6. Interestingly, this ratio is relatively independent of the type of solvent. If the reaction takes place in benzene, however, it is believed that Cl_2 forms a weak complex to the aromatic ring, thereby stabilizing the chlorine molecule. Does this lead to a greater selectivity or a lesser selectivity in chlorination? Explain.

46. Propose a chain reaction mechanism for the following elimination of HI to form an alkene, illustrating reasonable initiation, propagation, and termination steps. Based on this mechanism, calculate the ΔH^0_{rxn} for each propagation step and for the net reaction.

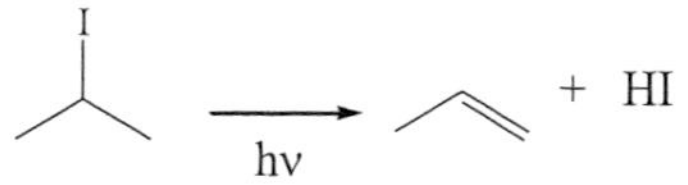

I → (hν) + HI

47. Propose a chain reaction mechanism for the decomposition of dimethyl ether to form methane and formaldehyde.

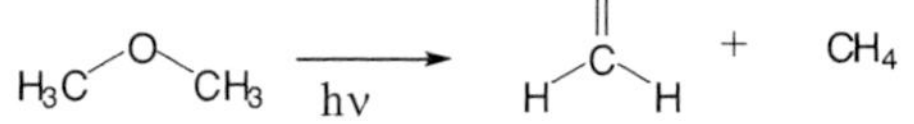

H_3C O CH_3 → (hν) O C H H + CH_4

48. The following reaction proceeds by a chain reaction mechanism. Propose initiation and propagation steps, and provide two plausible termination steps.

O + Cl—≡N → (C_6H_5 O O C_6H_5 O O) CN O Cl

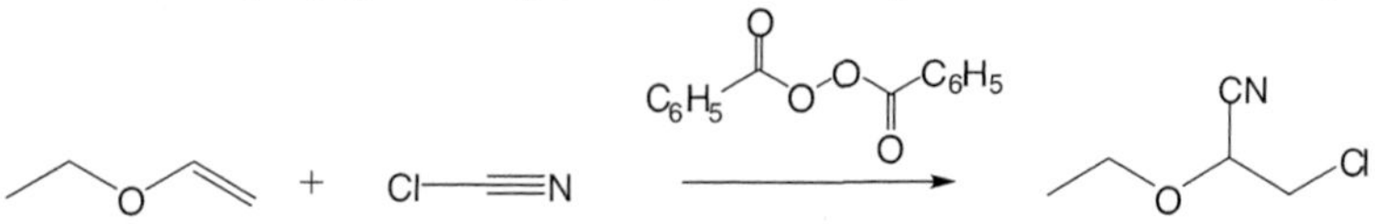

49. Both bicyclo[2.2.1]heptane and bicyclo[3.3.1]nonane are saturated hydrocarbons composed of only secondary and tertiary carbons. Earlier in this chapter, we learned that radical substitution in general takes place preferentially at a tertiary

carbon. Indeed, when bicyclo[3.3.1]nonane is treated with the bromotrichloromethane under irradiation, substitution takes place 100% at the tertiary carbon. However, under the same conditions, no substitution at the tertiary carbon is observed in bicyclo[2.2.1]heptane. Explain. (Hint: It may help to build molecular models of each of these compounds)

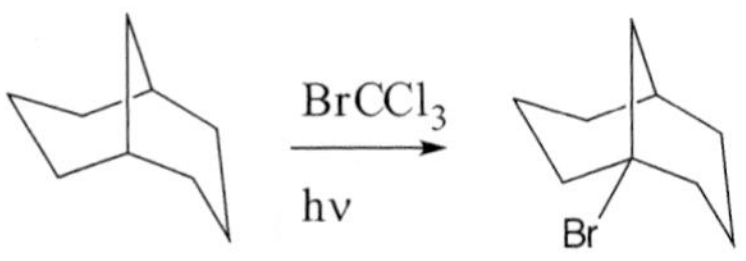

$BrCCl_3$, hν

Br

bicyclo[3.3.1]nonane 100%

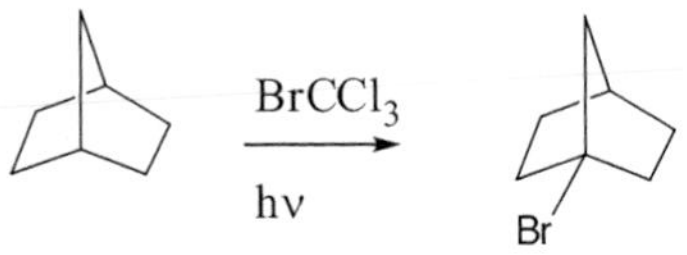

$BrCCl_3$, hν

Br

bicyclo[2.2.1]heptane 0%

50. Propose a mechanism for the chain reaction in the previous problem, including initiation and propagation steps. Provide two plausible termination steps.

51. As shown below, acyl peroxides can be used as a means to initiate alkyl radicals. Propose a mechanism for this reaction.

O O R R O O → 2 R· + 2 CO_2

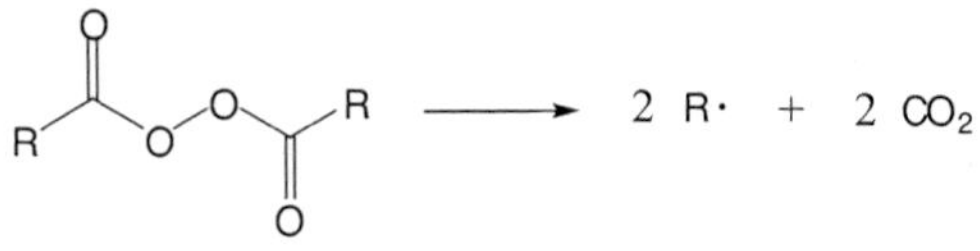

52. Radical halogenation in general yields a mixture of stereoisomers. However, as shown below, when a Br atom is adjacent to the site of H abstraction, retention of stereochemistry is observed. Provide a detailed mechanism for this reaction and propose a key intermediate that leads to the reaction's stereochemistry. With that key intermediate, explain why retention of stereochemistry is observed.

Br CH_3 Br_2, hν → Br Br CH_3

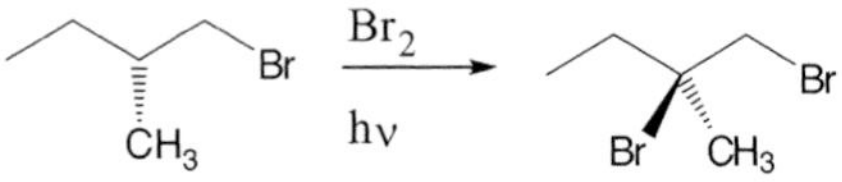

53. The following addition of HBr to 2-bromo-2-butene takes place regioselectively, with the Br preferentially adding to the alkene C already possessing a Br atom. (a) Provide a detailed mechanism for this reaction, including initiation and propagation steps. (b) Explain why this regiochemistry is observed.

Br HBr, ROOR → Br Br

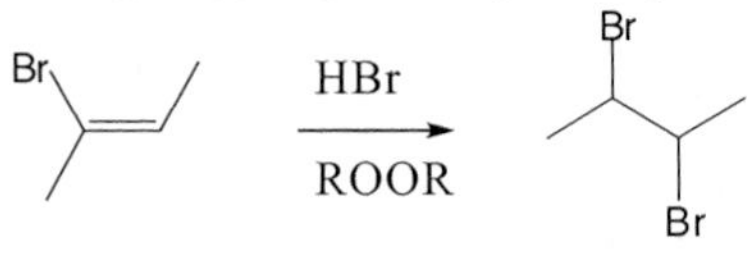

54. The following reaction conditions catalyze the conversion of *cis*-1,2-diphenylethene to *trans*-1,2-diphenylethene. Provide a detailed mechanism for this reaction.

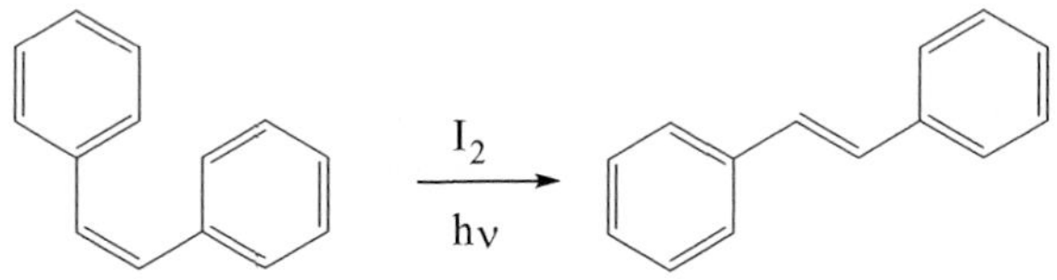

55. The radical addition of HBr can be used to cyclize a carbon chain, as shown below. Provide a detailed mechanism for this reaction. Include initiation and propagation steps, and provide two plausible termination steps.

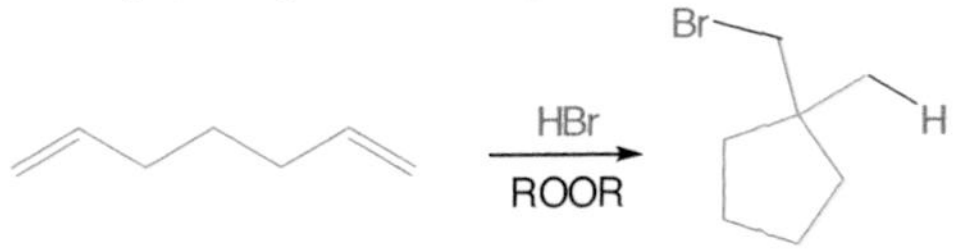

56. Provide a detailed mechanism to account for the following reaction. Include initiation and propagation steps and draw two plausible termination steps. (Hint: You may want to consult the previous problem.)

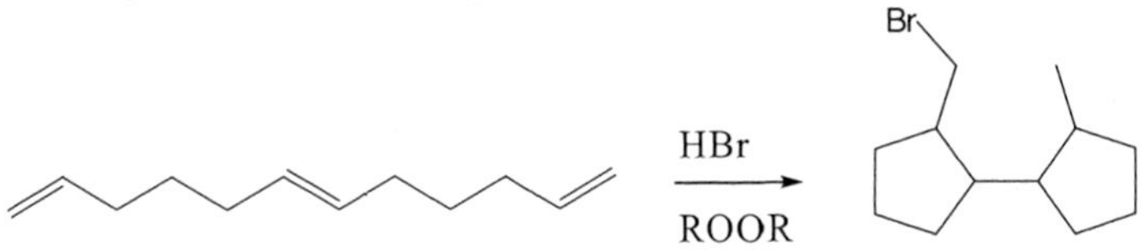

57. Suggest how you would synthesize each of the following compounds beginning with propylbenzene. You may use any other reagents necessary.

(a)

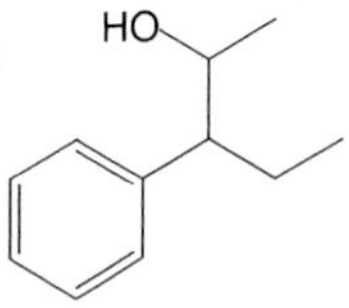

(b)

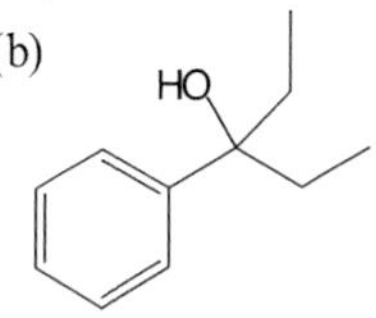

(c)

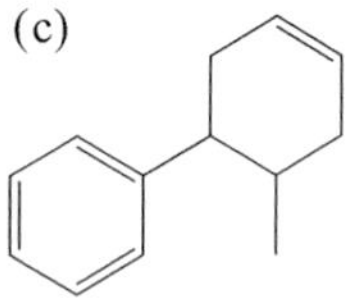

(d)

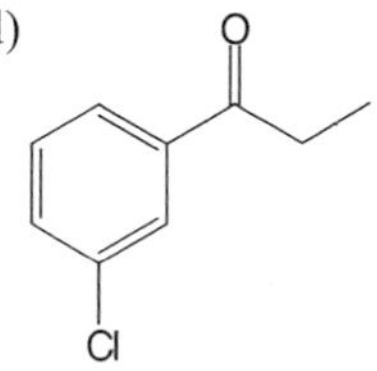

(e)

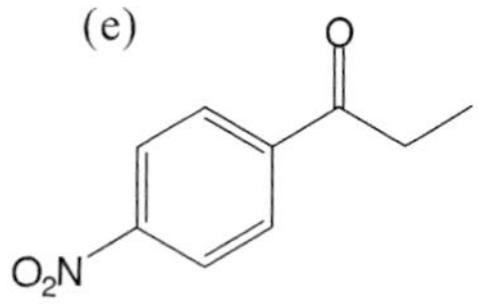

58. Supply the missing structures in the following synthesis scheme.

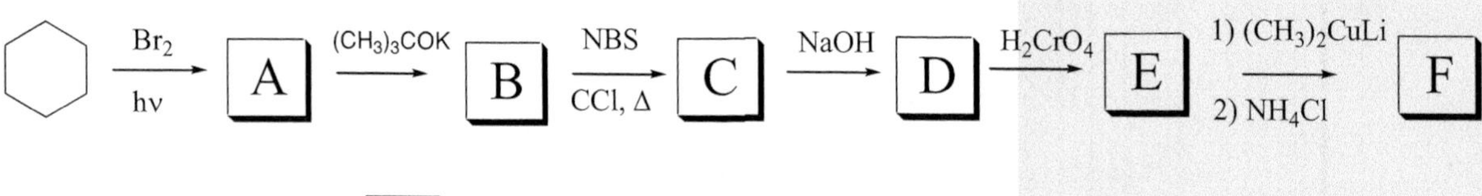

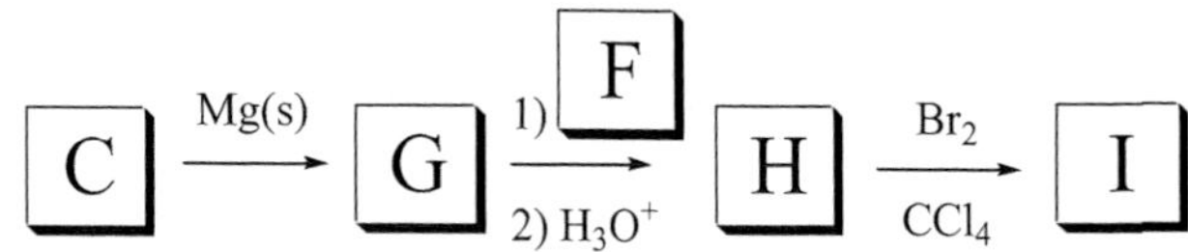

59. Supply the missing structures in the following synthesis scheme.

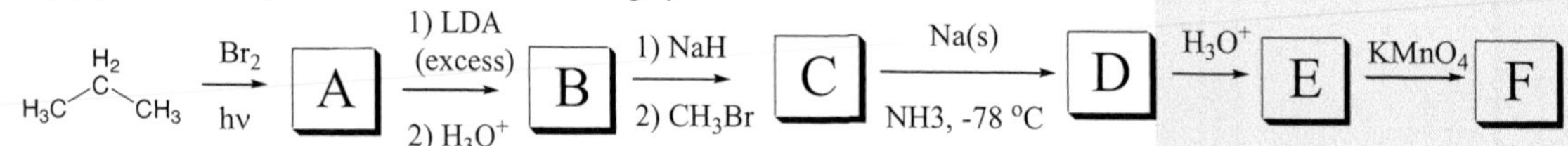

A 1) PPh_3 2) Bu-Li G F H I

60. Suggest how you would synthesize each of the following compounds beginning with 2-methylpropane. You may use any other reagents necessary.

(a) O (b) S (c) (d)

(e) (via PPh_3) (f) D D

61. Show how you would synthesize each of the following from 3-cyclopentyl-2-propyne. You may use any other reagents necessary.

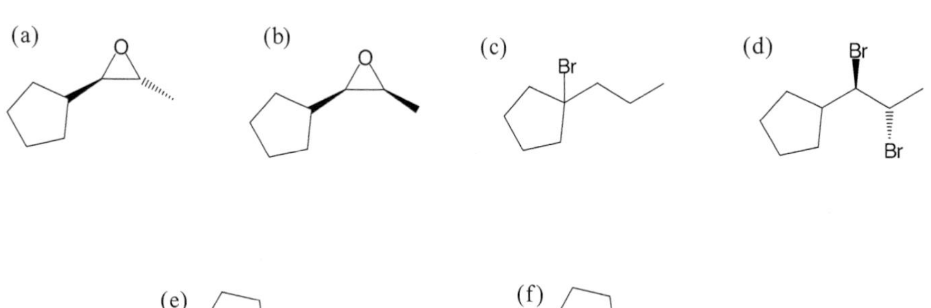

62. A student wanted to determine whether rearrangement of alkyl radicals occurs and therefore ran the following reaction.

$\xrightarrow[h\nu]{Cl_2}$?

(a) Why would the student think that radical rearrangement might take place in this reaction? To help answer this question, draw the mechanism of the radical reaction that would potentially take place. (b) The student acquired an NMR spectrum of the product, which is shown below. What should she conclude regarding alkyl rearrangements? Explain.

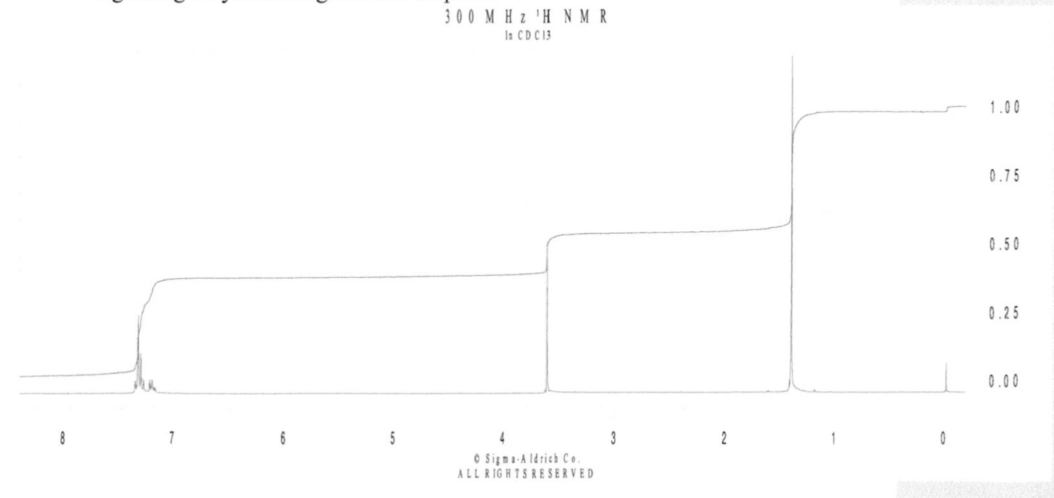

63. In the presence of di-*t*-butyl peroxide, phenol dimerizes to produce a mixture of isomeric products. Two are shown. (a) Draw a mechanism that accounts for the formation of each product. (b) Draw the structure of a third isomeric product that would be produced in the mixture.

OH $\xrightarrow{(H_3C)_3C\text{-}O\text{-}O\text{-}C(CH_3)_3}$ + OH

Interchapter 2: Fragmentation Patterns in Mass Spectrometry

INTRODUCTION

Chapter 14 provided an introduction to mass spectrometry. There, we learned that once a sample is injected into a mass spectrometer, the acquisition of a mass spectrum consists of four main stages, as shown below. First, the sample is heated, in order to produce gaseous molecules, M_{gas}. Second, the vaporized sample passes through an electron beam, where ionization takes place—when a high-energy electron collides with M_{gas}, an electron is ejected from the molecule, producing a molecular ion, M^{+}_{gas}. Third, ions are guided to the detector. Finally, the electronic signal generated by collisions of ions with the detector is converted into the ion's relative abundance, and the spectrum is produced.

① $M_{liq} \xrightarrow{\text{heater}} M_{gas}$

② $M_{gas} \xrightarrow{\text{electron beam}} M^{+}_{gas} + e^{-} + \text{fragment ions}$

③ M^{+}_{gas} + fragment ions ⟶ detector

④ detector ⟶

As we discussed in Chapter 14, in the ionization stage, collisions between the electrons and the uncharged molecules carry enough energy to break covalent bonds as well, resulting in fragmentation of the molecular ion. The fragment ions that are produced are also detected, which is why numerous mass peaks appear in a mass spectrum, even for pure samples.

With regard to interpreting a mass spectrum, our focus in Chapter 14 was primarily on determining the molar mass of the compound that produces the spectrum. Doing so largely involves identifying the M^{+} peak, as well as various M+1 and M+2 isotope peaks. Here, we will see that there is also extensive structural information that can be interpreted from a mass spectrum, based on the appearance of specific fragment peaks.

Interpreting fragment peaks requires an understanding of the chemical processes responsible for producing the corresponding fragment ions. Notably, such **fragmentation pathways** consist of elementary steps that involve free radicals. We can see that this is the case, given that the ionization process causes the loss of a single electron from a closed-shell, uncharged molecule. Thus, the molecular ion must have an unpaired electron, making it a free radical. More specifically, because it also carries a positive charge, the molecular ion is called a **radical cation**.

Because our focus in this interchapter is on gathering structural information about a compound, our discussion is divided into sections according to the functional groups involved. We will begin by discussing the fragmentation of alkanes, which contain no functional groups at all. Then we will discuss functional groups containing double bonds, including alkenes and aromatic rings. Following that, we will discuss functional groups with heteroatoms, consisting of only single bonds, including alkyl halides, amines, ethers, and alcohols. Finally, we will discuss functional groups containing carbonyl groups, including ketones, aldehydes, and carboxylic acids.

IC2.1. ALKANES

Let's begin by examining the mass spectrum of hexane, which we discussed previously in Section 14.17.

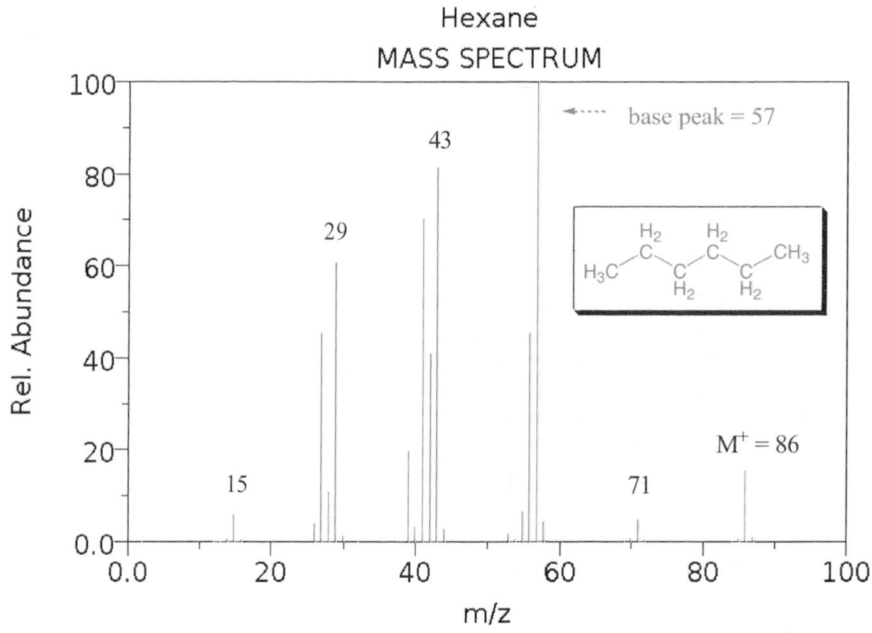

NIST Chemistry WebBook (http://webbook.nist.gov/chemistry)

Figure IC2-1. Mass Spectrum of Hexane

The M^+ peak and the base peak are indicated. The values of *m/z* for selected peaks are provided above the peaks.

The M^+ peak is identified at 86 amu, which corresponds to hexane's molar mass. Because the molecular ion is produced by loss of an electron from one of the many σ bonds, the molecular ion is ambiguously represented by placing square brackets around the parent molecule, along with a dot and a positive charge to indicate a radical cation.

loss of an electron from a σ bond

$m/z = 86$

Several key fragment peaks are also identified—at 71 amu, 57 amu, 43 amu, 29 amu, and 15 amu—which, as we saw in Section 14.17, correspond to the breaking of the various carbon-carbon bonds. For example, the base peak (i.e., the most intense mass peak) at 57 amu corresponds to the breaking of the C2-C3 bond to produce both a butyl cation and an ethyl radical (Equation IC2-1). As another example, the peak at 15 amu corresponds to the breaking of the C1-C2 bond to produce a methyl cation and a pentyl radical (Equation IC2-2)

the uncharged radical is not detected

the fragment ion is detected

ethyl radical

butyl cation
m/z= 57 amu

(IC2-1)

the fragment ion is detected

the uncharged radical is not detected

methyl cation
m/z= 15 amu

pentyl radical

(IC2-2)

Because the intensity of the peak at 57 amu is substantially more intense than the one at 15 amu, we can conclude that the fragmentation pathway in Equation IC2-1 is much more likely than the one in Equation IC2-2. Why should this be so?

The answer has to do with the stability of the fragmentation products. In each case, both a cation and an alkyl radical are produced. Notice that cation stability favors Equation IC2-1, because the positively charged carbon is more highly alkyl-substituted (Section 6.6e). By contrast, radical stability favors Equation IC2-2, because the carbon atom bearing the unpaired electron is more highly alkyl-substituted. Yet the cation stability wins out.

In general, the more stable a fragment ion is, the more likely is the fragmentation pathway that produces that fragment ion.

This rule of thumb can be very useful, particularly when distinguishing isomers. Consider 2-methylpentane, whose mass spectrum is shown in Figure IC2-2 below. The M^+ peak appears at 86 amu, the same as in the mass spectrum of hexane. However, the base peak for 2-methylpentane is at 43 amu, in contrast to the one for hexane, which is at 57 amu. The fragmentation that accounts for this base peak is shown in Equation IC2-3, and, as indicated, is favored by the fact that the cation that is produced is secondary.

secondary carbocation is more stable than a primary or methyl cation

isopropyl cation
m/z= 43 amu

propyl radical

(IC2-3)

Problem IC2.1. Notice in Figure IC2-2 that the mass peak at 71 amu is more intense than the one at 29 amu. Explain why, accounting for the fragment ions that correspond to those peaks.

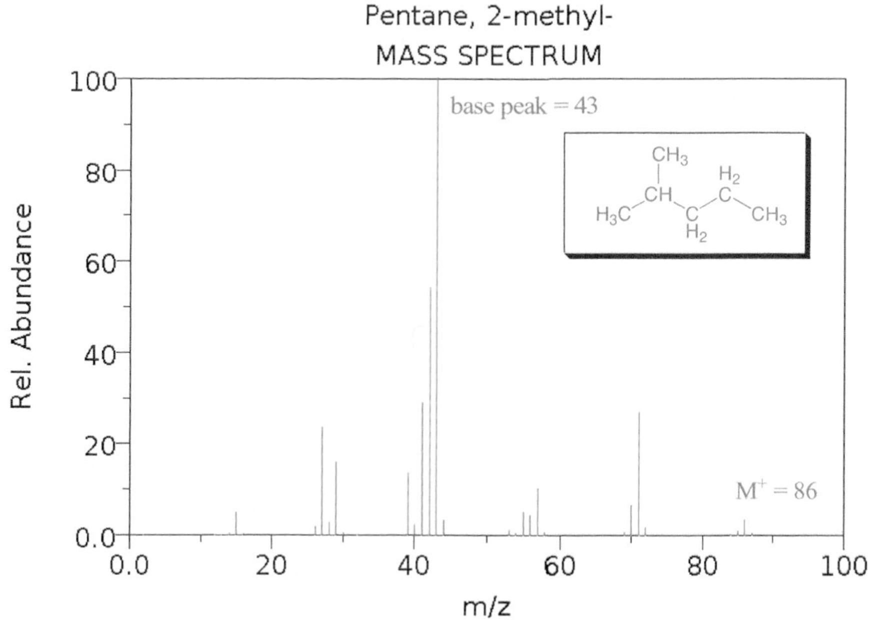

Figure IC2-2. Mass Spectrum of 2-Methylpentane
The values of *m/z* for the molecular ion and base peaks are provided above the peaks.

Another difference between the spectra in Figures IC2-1 and IC2-2 is the relative sizes of the M^+ peaks. Notice that the M^+ peak for 2-methylpentane is much smaller than the one for hexane. Thus, fragmentation is more likely for the molecular ion of 2-methylpentane, and stems from the fact that with the additional branching, more stable fragment ions can be produced. With even more branching, as in 2,2-dimethylbutane, the M^+ peak disappears essentially entirely.

With sufficient stability of a fragment ion, the M^+ peak can disappear essentially entirely from a compound's mass spectrum.

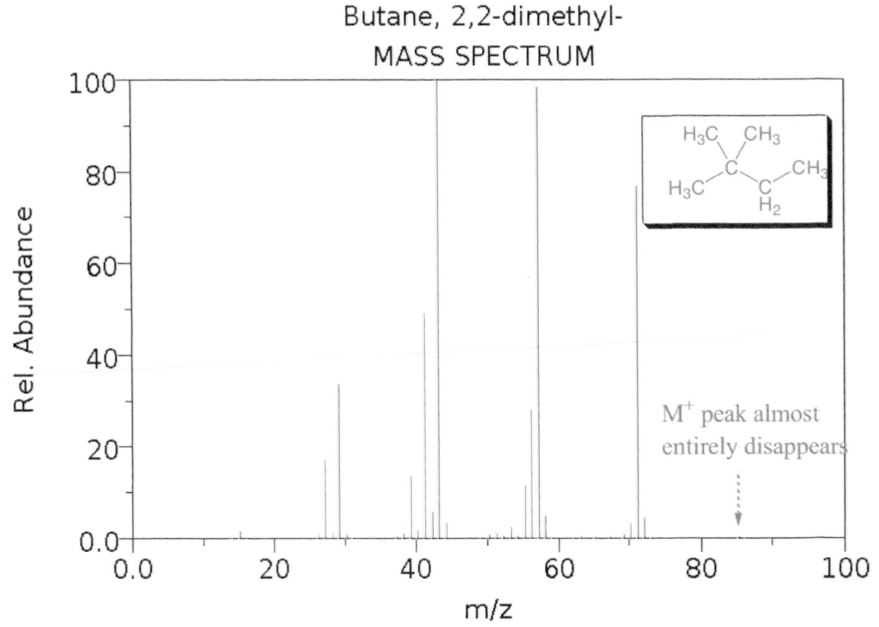

Figure IC2-3. Mass Spectrum of 2,2-Dimethylbutane
The M^+ peak is almost entirely absent from the spectrum, because, due to the significant branching of the alkyl chain, fragmentation gives rise to relatively highly stable fragment ions.

> **Problem IC2.2.** Mass spectra of butylcyclopentane and *t*-butylcyclopentane were acquired. Spectrum A exhibited significant mass peaks at 126 amu, 97 amu, 83 amu, 69 amu, 55 amu, and 41 amu. Spectrum B exhibited significant peaks at 111 amu, 69 amu, 56 amu, and 41 amu. Match each spectrum with its compound.

IC2.2. ALKENES AND AROMATIC COMPOUNDS

The previous section dealt with the fragmentation of alkanes only, which contain just carbon and hydrogen atoms joined by σ bonds. Thus, when an electron is ejected, it is often unclear as to how to represent the resulting molecular ion as a Lewis structure. The situation is much less ambiguous for alkenes and aromatic compounds, which contain π electrons. Because π electrons are relatively high in energy, one such electron is ejected in the ionization process to produce the molecular ion. An example is shown for 2-hexene in Equation IC2-4.

loss of an electron from the π bond

2-hexene → m/z = 84 amu (IC2-4)

Because of the relatively well-defined nature of an alkene's molecular ion, fragmentation pathways tend to be more clear-cut. One such pathway is as follows.

> An alkene's molecular ion tends to expel an alkyl radical from an allylic carbon, producing an allylic cation.

As we can see in Equation IC2-5, for example, the molecular ion of 2-hexene can expel an ethyl radical to produce a resonance-stabilized 2-butenyl cation. (Notice, in particular, that a unpaired electrons are involved in the curved arrow notation for this process, so single-barbed arrows are required.) The driving force for such a process is the stability that is gained by the resonance delocalization of the positive charge.

the allylic cation that is produced is resonance-stabilized

m/z = 84 amu → 2-butenyl cation m/z = 55 amu + $H_2\dot{C}$–CH_3

(IC2-5)

In fact, this fragmentation pathway is the most likely one for 2-hexene. We can see that this is the case from the fact that the allylic cation that is produced is the one that gives rise to the base peak at 55 amu in the mass spectrum (Figure IC2-4).

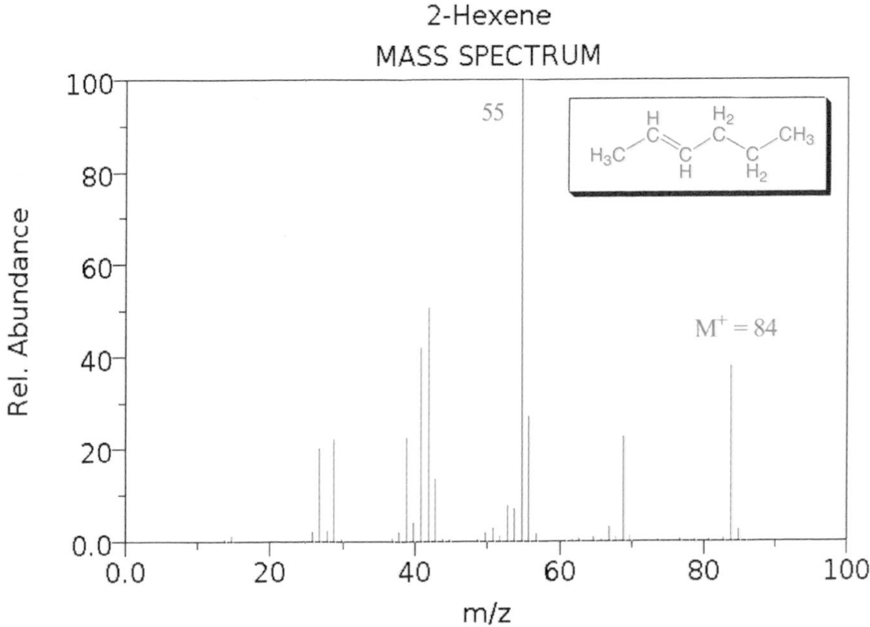

Figure IC2-4. Mass Spectrum of 2-Hexene
The M^+ peak appears at 84 amu. Loss of an ethyl radical produces a resonance-stabilized allylic cation that gives rise to the base peak at 55 amu.

Similar fragmentations are observed for aromatic compounds.

> An alkylbenzene's molecular ion tends to expel an alkyl radical from an benzylic carbon, producing a benzylic cation.

Consider butylbenzne, whose mass spectrum is shown in Figure IC2-5. The molecular ion, produced by the loss of a π electron, gives rise to the peak at 134 amu. Loss of a propyl radical from the benzylic carbon (Equation IC2-6) produces the benzylic cation, whose mass peak appears at 91 amu.

benzylic cation
$m/z = 91$ amu

(IC2-6)

Interestingly, such a benzylic cation is believe to rearrange to the more stable **tropylium ion**, as shown in Equation IC2-7. The additional stability is attributed to the fact that the tropylium ion has seven equivalent resonance structures that serve to delocalize the positive charge, while maintaining aromaticity in the ring.

rearrangement

the tropylium ion

(IC2-7)

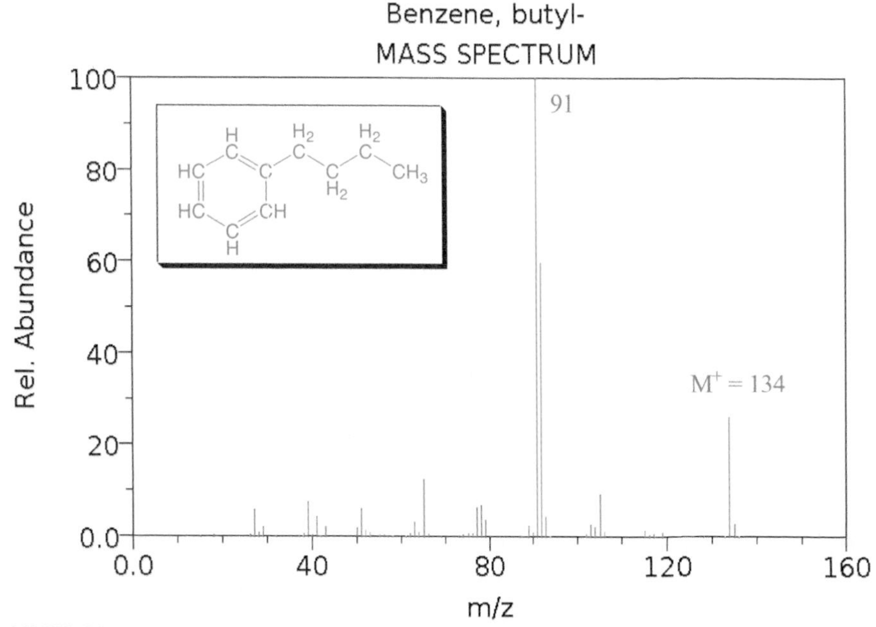

Figure IC2-5. Mass Spectrum of Butylbenzene
The M^+ peak appears at 134 amu. Loss of a propyl radical produces a resonance-stabilized benzylic cation that gives rise to the base peak at 91 amu.

Problem IC2.3. In the mass spectrum of 3-hexene, a peak appears at 69 amu. Show how the fragmentation of 3-hexene's molecular produces the ion that gives rise to this peak.

IC2.3. ALKYL HALIDES, AMINES, ETHERS, AND ALCOHOLS

Many functional groups contain *heteroatoms* (i.e., atoms other than carbon or hydrogen), which can play major roles in fragmentation pathways, and therefore help govern the fragmentation patterns observed in a mass spectrum. In the context of mass spectrometry, one of the most important features of a heteroatom is its lone pair of electrons. Being nonbonding electrons, lone pairs are typically the least tightly bound electrons in the molecule. Therefore,

> In the ionization of a molecule containing a heteroatom, a lone-pair electron is generally the most likely electron removed to produce the molecular ion, M^+.

Thus, like alkenes and aromatic compounds, the molecular ion of a compound with a heteroatom tends to have a relatively well-defined Lewis structure.

With this in mind, consider the mass spectrum of 2-chloro-2-methylbutane, shown in Figure IC2-6.

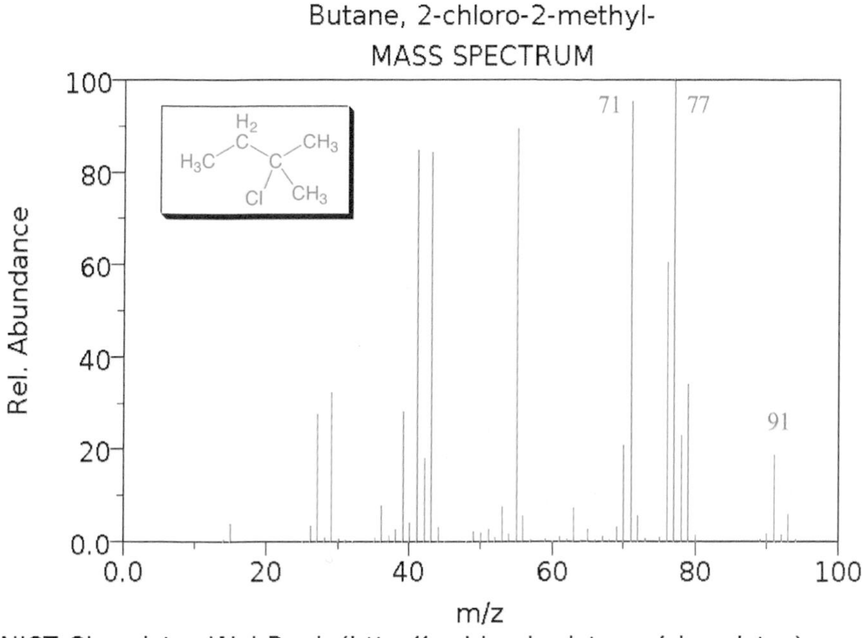

Figure IC2-6. Mass Spectrum of 2-Chloro-2-methylbutane
The M^+ peak, which would appear at 88 amu, is absent. The masses of other significant fragment ions are labeled above their corresponding peaks.

Loss of a nonbonding electron from the chlorine atom produces the molecular ion, with m/z = 106 amu, as shown in Equation IC2-8. The peak corresponding to M^+ does not appear in the spectrum, because fragmentation takes place very readily. One fragmentation pathway, shown in Equation IC2-8, is heterolysis of the C-Cl bond, producing an alkyl cation fragment with m/z = 71 amu.

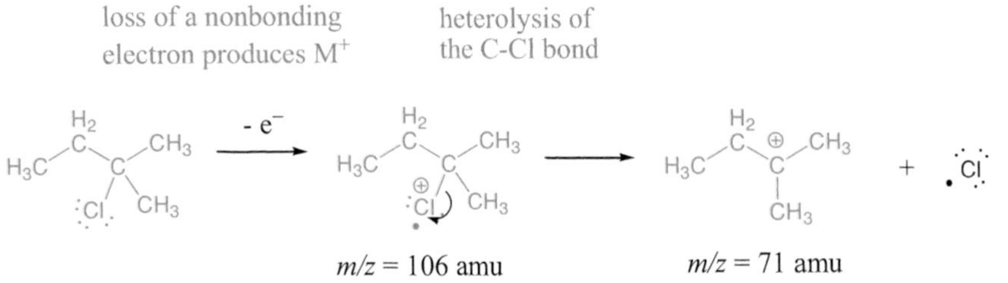

loss of a nonbonding electron produces M^+

heterolysis of the C-Cl bond

m/z = 106 amu $\quad$ m/z = 71 amu

(IC2-8)

Another common fragmentation pathway is elimination of an alkyl group from the carbon atom bonded to the heteroatom—this is an example of **α-cleavage**. There are two such α-cleavage pathways for the molecular ion of 2-chloro-2-methylbutane, as shown in Equations IC2-9 and IC2-10. These account for the mass peaks at 91 amu and 77 amu. Notice in each case that in the fragment ion, *all atoms have an octet*, which provides substantial driving force for the process.

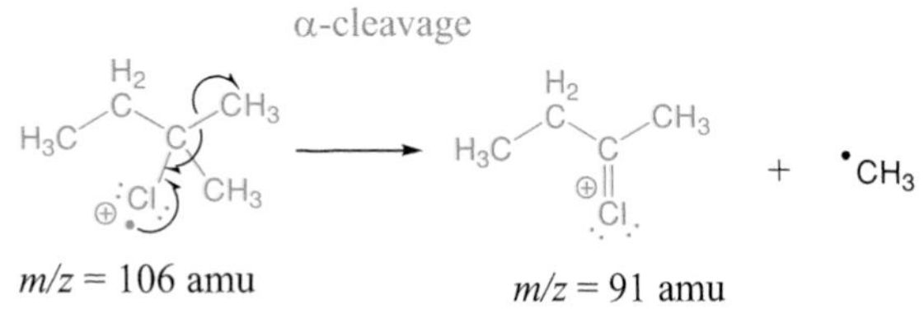

α-cleavage

m/z = 106 amu $\quad$ m/z = 91 amu

(IC2-9)

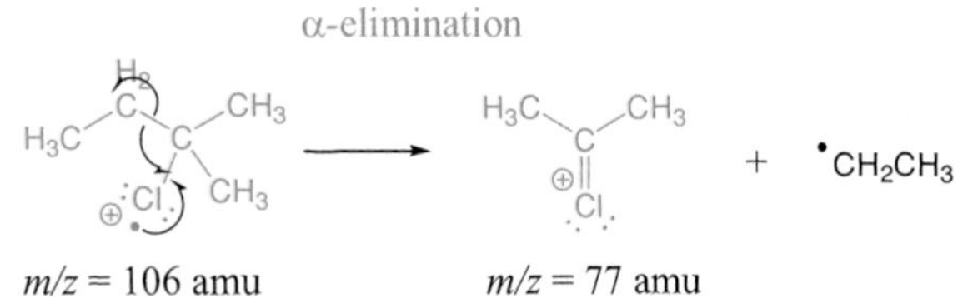

α-elimination

m/z = 106 amu $\quad$ m/z = 77 amu

(IC2-10)

These two fragmentation pathways—heterolysis and α-cleavage—are also common to other functional groups with heteroatoms, such as amines, ethers, and alcohols. However, depending on the identity of the functional group, as well as the specific structure of the compound, one such fragmentation pathway can be highly favored over the other.

For instance, α-cleavage is very common for amines, typically leading to the fragment ion that corresponds to the base peak. This is the case for *N*,*N*,2-trimethyl-2-propanamine, whose mass spectrum is shown in Figure IC2-7. The value of m/z for the molecular ion is 101 amu. As shown in Equation IC2-11, loss of a CH_3 group via α-cleavage produces the fragment ion giving rise to the base peak at m/z = 86 amu.

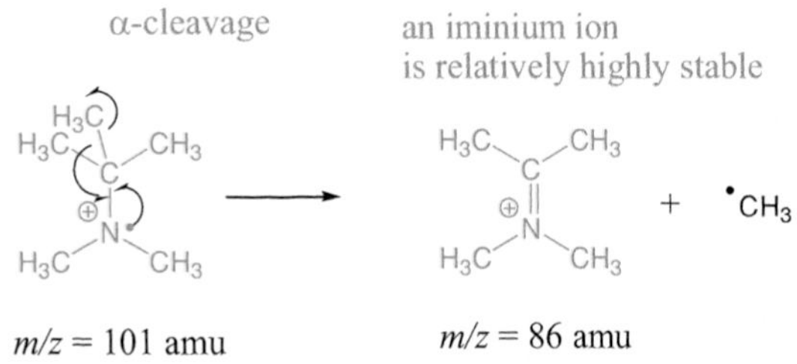

α-cleavage

an iminium ion is relatively highly stable

m/z = 101 amu $\quad$ m/z = 86 amu

(IC2-11)

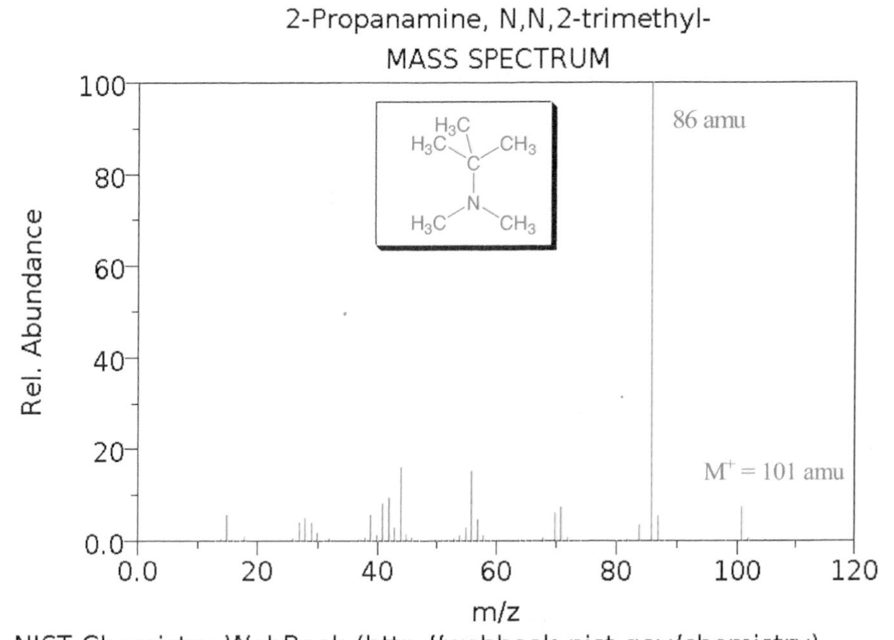

Figure IC2-7. Mass Spectrum of *N*,*N*,2-Trimethylpropanamine
The M^+ peak appears at 101 amu, is absent. The base peak at 86 amu corresponds to a fragment ion produced by α-cleavage of the molecular ion.

Ethers and alcohols exhibit α-cleavage as well, but typically not as prominently. In the mass spectrum of diisopropyl ether (Figure IC2-8), for example, fragmentation via α-cleavage gives rise to the mass peak at 87 amu, which is significantly smaller than the base peak. Likewise, in the mass spectrum of 1-pentanol (Figure IC2-9), α-cleavage gives rise to the relatively small peak at 31 amu.

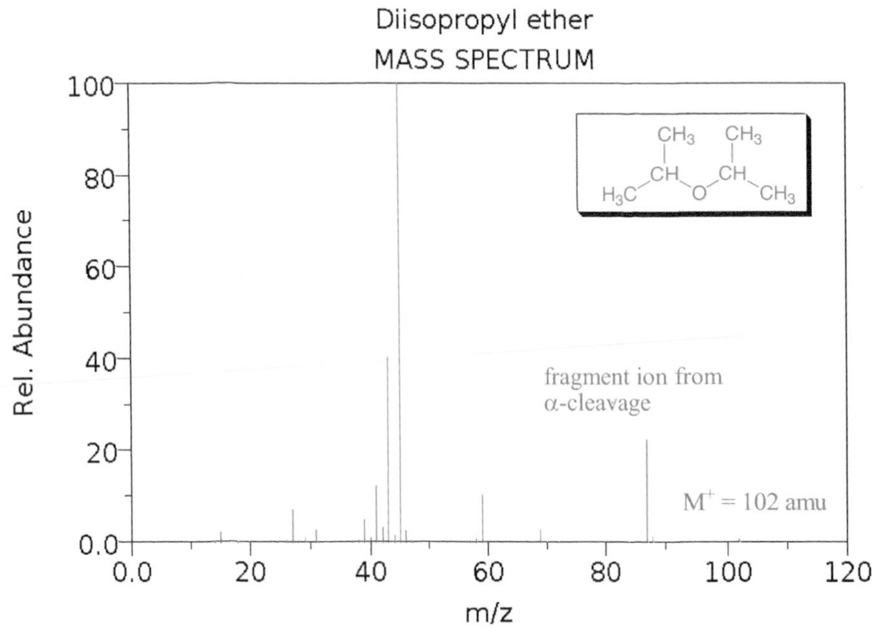

Figure IC2-8. Mass Spectrum of Diisopropyl Ether

The M^+ peak appears at 102 amu. The peak at 87 amu corresponds to a fragment ion produced by α-cleavage of the molecular ion.

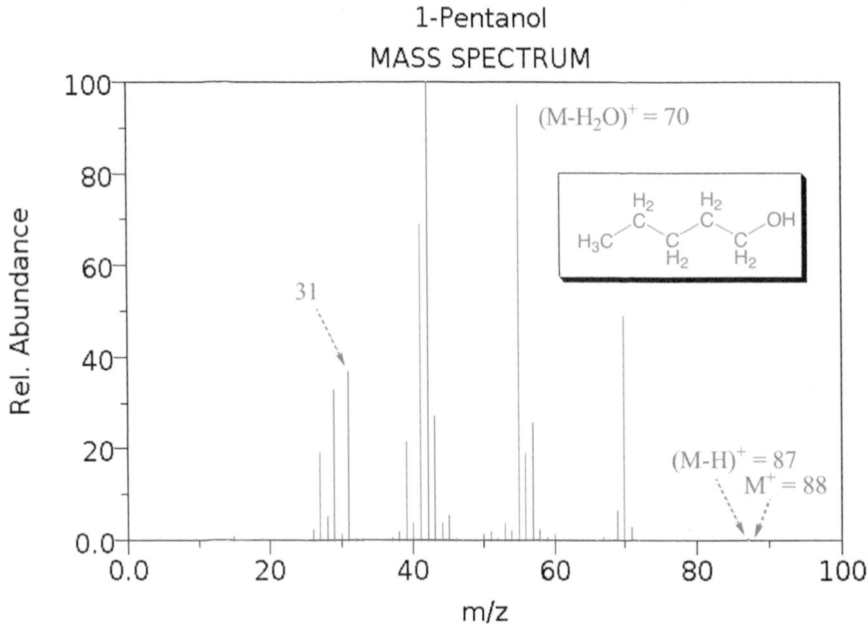

Figure IC2-9. Mass Spectrum of 1-Pentanol

The M^+ peak would appear at 88 amu, but is absent. The peak at 87 amu corresponds to a fragment ion produced by loss of a hydrogen atom. The peak at 70 amu corresponds to loss of water from the molecular ion. The peak at 31 amu corresponds to α-cleavage of the molecular ion.

Problem IC2.4. Draw the fragmentation pathway of 1-pentanol's molecular ion, which accounts for the mass peak at 31 amu.

There are two other fragmentation pathways characteristic of an alcohol as well.

An alcohol's molecular ion will typically undergo

- Loss of a hydrogen atom to give rise to an $(M-H)^+$ peak that is 1 amu lighter than the molecular ion.
- Loss of a water molecule to give rise to an $(M-H_2O)^+$ peak that is 18 amu lighter than the molecular ion.

For example, the molecular ion of 1-pentanol is 88 amu. Notice that in the mass spectrum in Figure IC2-9, there is a small $(M-H)^+$ mass peak at 87 amu, which is lighter than the molecular ion by 1 amu. Also, there is a prominent peak at 70 amu, which is lighter than the molecular ion by 18 amu, and corresponds to the $(M-H_2O)^+$ ion. The curved arrow notations for these steps are shown in Equations IC2-12 and IC2-13, respectively.

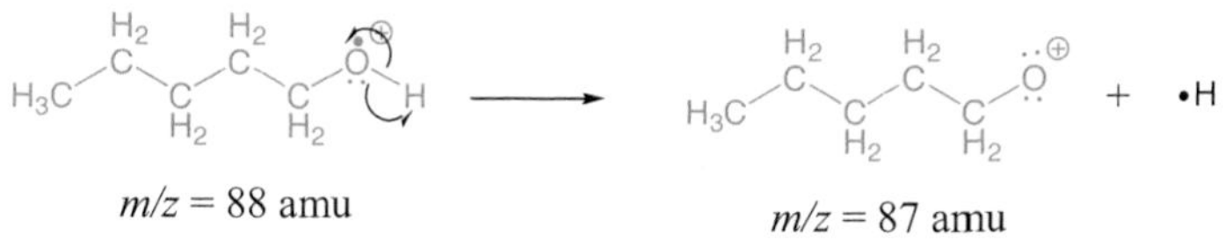

m/z = 88 amu → m/z = 87 amu + •H (IC2-12)

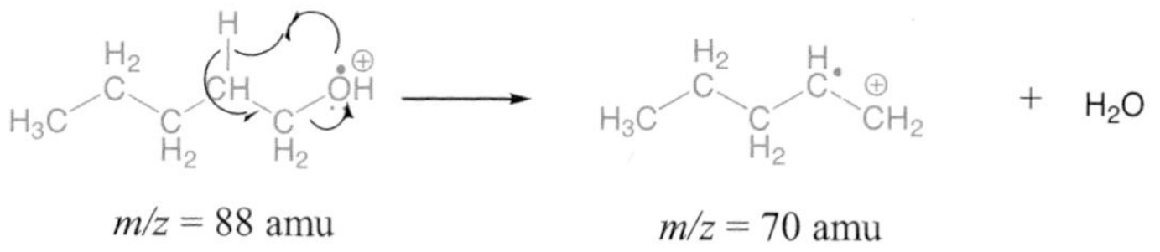

m/z = 88 amu → m/z = 70 amu + H_2O (IC2-13)

IC2.3. CARBONYL-CONTAINING COMPOUNDS

Similar to the functional groups we discussed in the previous section, carbonyl-containing groups such as ketones, aldehydes, and carboxylic acids, have an oxygen atom with lone pairs of electrons. Thus, it should be no surprise that such compounds undergo ionization and fragmentation processes similar to the ones that alkyl halides, amines, and ethers undergo. Namely,

- The molecular ion of a carbonyl-containing compound is typically produced by loss of a nonbonding electron from the carbonyl oxygen.
- A common fragmentation pathway of such a molecular ion is α-cleavage.

Consider, for example, the mass spectrum of 2-hexanone (Figure IC2-10).

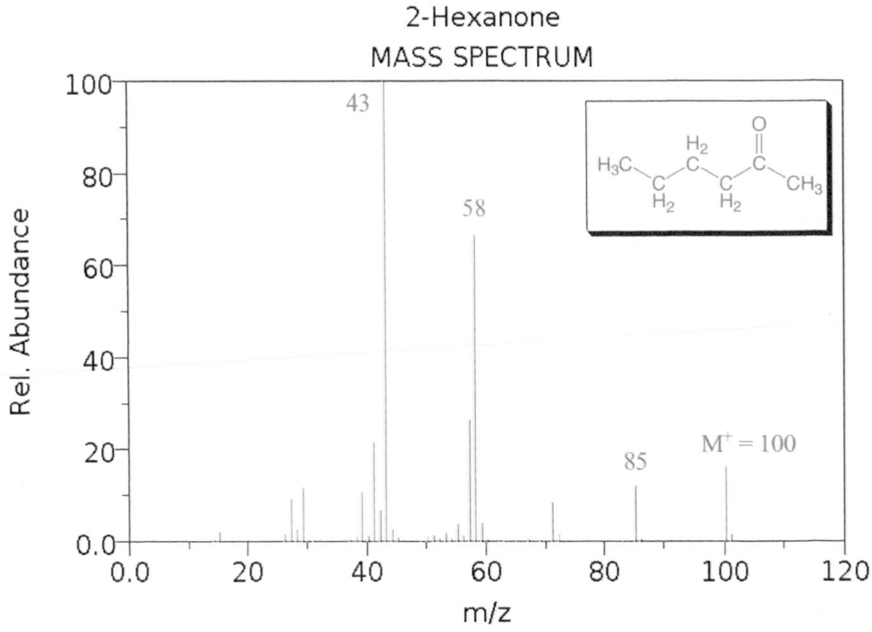

Figure IC2-10. Mass Spectrum of 2-Hexanone
The M$^+$ peak appears at 100 amu. The peaks at 43 amu and 85 amu correspond to fragment ions produced upon α-cleavage of the molecular ion. The mass peak at 58 amu corresponds to a fragment ion produced by a McLafferty rearrangement.

As shown in Equation IC2-14, 2-hexanone undergoes ionization to produce the molecular ion with m/z = 100 amu. Subsequent α-cleavage can expel a propyl radical from the carbonyl carbon to produce a relatively stable *acylium ion*, giving rise to the base peak at 43 amu. (This is the same type of ion that appears as an intermediate in a Friedel-Crafts acylation reaction, Section 22-5.) Alternatively, α-cleavage of a methyl radical produces the ion corresponding to the mass peak at 85 amu.

an acylium ion

2-hexanone —(loss of nonbonding e$^-$)→ m/z = 100 amu —(α-cleavage)→ $H_3C{-}CH_2{-}\dot{C}H_2$ + m/z = 43 amu (IC2-14)

Problem IC2.5. Show the fragmentation pathway that gives rise to the mass peak at 85 amu in the mass spectrum of 2-hehxanone.

In addition to α-cleavage, there is another fragmentation pathway characteristic of carbonyl-containing compounds.

A carbonyl-containing compound can undergo a **McLafferty rearrangement** if an alkyl group attached to the carbonyl carbon possesses a γ-carbon with at least one hydrogen atom.

Such a fragmentation pathway is named after Professor Fred W. McLafferty at Cornell University. As shown in Equation IC2-15, a hydrogen atom from the γ-carbon shifts to the carbonyl oxygen, and the bond joining the α- and β-carbons is broken. The result is the ejection of an uncharged alkene molecule. In the case of 2-hexanone's molecular ion, the McLafferty rearrangement produces an enol radical cation of acetone, giving rise to the mass peak at 58 amu.

m/z = 100 amu ⟶ H_3C–CH=CH_2 + an enol radical cation m/z = 58 amu (IC2-15)

The McLafferty rearrangement is not limited to just ketones, but is characteristic of several functional groups containing the carbonyl group, including aldehydes, carboxylic acids, esters and amides. For example, the molecular ion of pentanoic acid undergoes a McLafferty rearrangement, giving rise to the mass peak at 60 amu in Figure IC2-11.

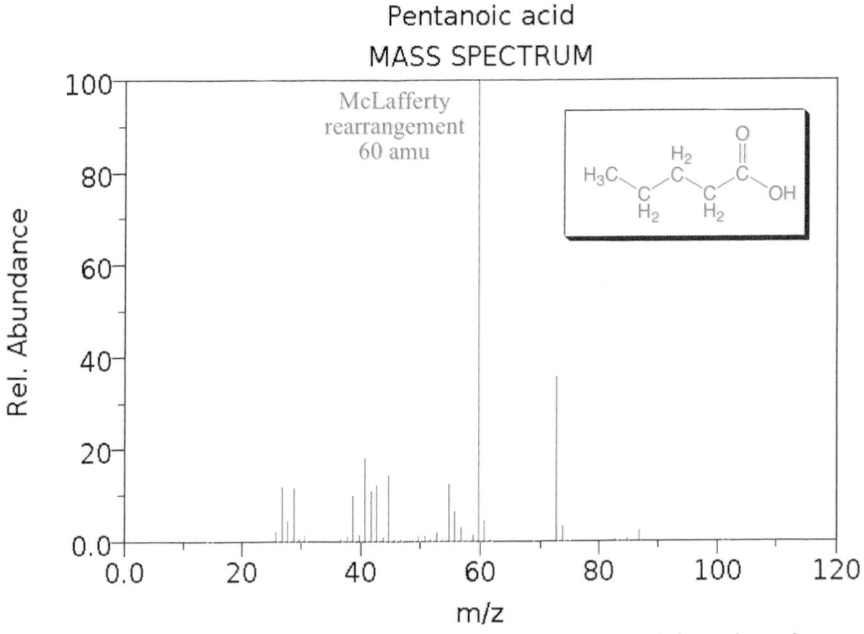

Figure IC2-11. Mass Spectrum of Pentanoic Acid
The mass peak at 60 amu corresponds to a fragment ion produced by a McLafferty rearrangement.

Problem IC2.6. The base peak in the mass spectrum of hexanamide appears at 59 amu. Draw the ion that corresponds to this mass peak, and show how it is produced from the molecular ion.

Chapter 26. Polymers

Introduction

In Chapter 25, we studied free radicals, and particularly the mechanism of chain reactions. This type of reaction allows alkanes, which are unreactive under normal laboratory conditions, to undergo halogenation. We also saw that the free-radical reaction of HBr with alkenes increases a chemist's control of regioselectivity: the reaction provides the product of non-Markovnikov addition of HBr.

In this chapter, we will examine a powerful use of free-radical chain reactions: the synthesis of large molecules called **polymers**. Polymers are large molecules formed from smaller molecules. Trademarked products such as Plexiglas, Kevlar, and Teflon are all polymers with special properties that make them desirable for specific uses, as shown in Figure 26.1.

Not available

Figure 26-1. Shown from top left are clear parts machined from Plexiglas, body armor made from Kevlar, and a non-stick skillet with a Teflon lining. Shown from bottom left is a gecko, climbing glass through the adhesion of the setae on its feet, and a close-up of setae. The gecko's setae adhere through van der Waal's attractions alone. Teflon is the only known substance which geckos cannot climb

The uses of polymers are determined principally by their physical properties, many of which depend upon the intermolecular forces present (Chapter 2) and the range of motion allowed by rotation about single bonds (Chapter 4). We will see a variety of reactions from different chapters (particularly Chapters 19 and 25) that allow chemists to synthesize polymers and subsequently alter polymer molecules to introduce desirable properties. We begin the chapter with an examination of polystyrene, a model for free-radical polymerization and a polymer you are familiar with, and then study the relationship between the structure of polymer molecules and their properties.

CHAPTER OBJECTIVES

Upon completing this chapter you should be able to:

- Recognize relationships between monomers, polymers, and repeating units.
- Provide the mechanisms for the steps in free-radical polymerization.
- Identify types of polymers by type (linear, network, crosslinked, homopolymers, copolymers) and by the functional groups present.
- Name simple polymers.
- Differentiate between chain-growth and step-growth polymerization.
- Recognize the relationships between polymer structure and physical properties such as thermal transitions and solubility.
- Understand the relationship between the structure of a polymer and its uses.
- Explain why high temperatures lead to depolymerization and degradation.

26.1. POLYSTYRENE: A SYNTHETIC POLYMER

Polystyrene is a synthetic polymer that you are familiar with. Styrofoam, for example, is a foam made from polystyrene, used in packing "peanuts" and in insulated, disposable coffee cups. Polystyrene has been available since the 1930's.

Not available

Figure 26-2. Uses of Styrofoam.
Styrofoam cups for hot beverages and styrofoam "peanuts"

Polystyrene was discovered in the nineteenth century when several chemists found that styrene, a liquid at room temperature, changed into polystyrene, a jelly-like substance:

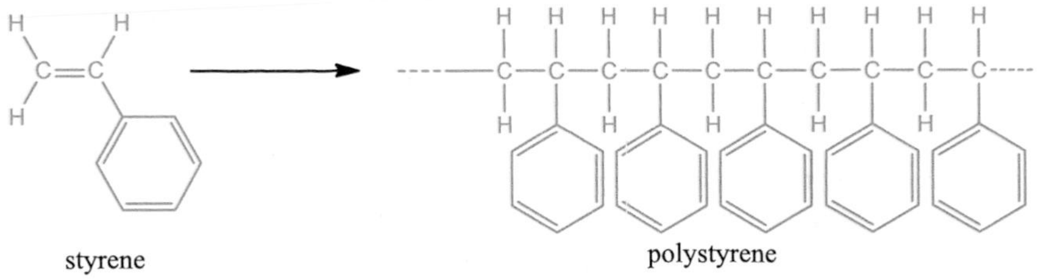

styrene → polystyrene (26-1)

Note that the dashes at either end of polystyrene represent a continuation of the structure; the product is a large molecule which is difficult to depict on a single page.

26.1a. The structure of styrene and polystyrene

In the synthesis of polystyrene, styrene is considered to be the **monomer** that produces the polymer; it is the single part (*mono* + *mer*) that produces a large molecule with many parts (*poly* + *mer*). Note that the carbons shown below in red are part of the **polymer chain** or **backbone** and the phenyl rings, shown in blue, are attached to the polymer backbone.

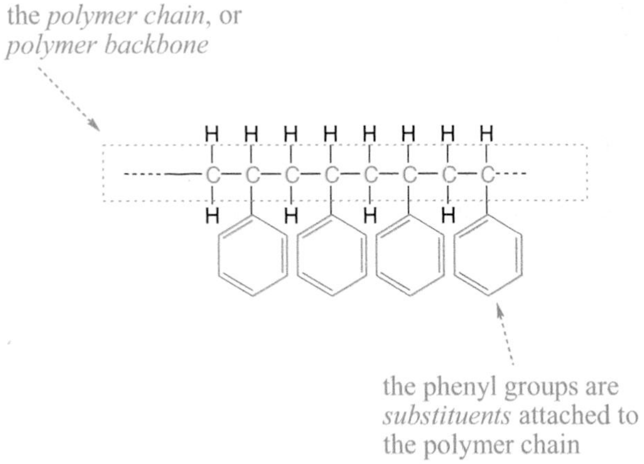

the *polymer chain*, or *polymer backbone*

the phenyl groups are *substituents* attached to the polymer chain (26-2)

The phenyl rings can be described as substituents (the phenyl ring is "substituted" for a hydrogen, the "default" atom attached to a carbon), side groups, side chains, or pendant groups. Pendant means "hanging," describing the phenyl groups that are hanging off the polymer chain.

Your turn 26.1. Below is the partial structure of polypropylene. Circle the side chains on this polymer. What adjective, similar to phenyl, can you use to describe the side chains?

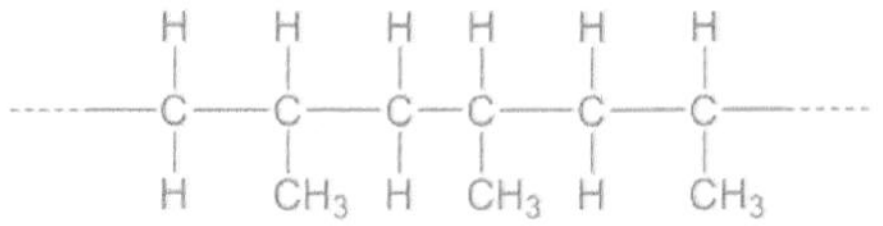

You can more clearly see the relationship between styrene and polystyrene by mentally cutting the main chain of the polymer into two-carbon units, as shown below at left. This gives you the **repeating unit** of the polymer, shown below at right.

the *repeating unit* of polystyrene

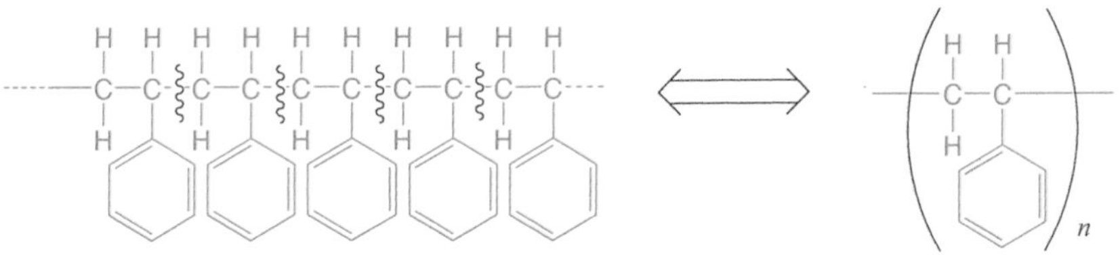

(26-3)

As you can see, all of the atoms in styrene appear in the repeating unit. However, whereas in styrene the carbon atoms attached to the benzene ring are connected by a double bond, in the repeating unit, they are connected by a single bond. As we will see later, this is because the π electrons of the C=C double bond are used to join the monomers together. Note that the value of n, the number of repeating units, is the **degree of polymerization or DP**.

The repeating unit is a group of atoms that occurs over and over (repeatedly) in a polymer. The number of repeating units determines the degree of polymerization.

Note that the monomer and the repeating unit are similar but not identical. One skill you need is to identify the relationship between monomers and repeating unit. In the case of polystyrene, the relationship is easy: the double bond between two carbons in the monomer has disappeared, and an additional single bond to each carbon has appeared. Note that this two-carbon unit with a double bond is referred to as a **vinyl group** (see Section N5d):

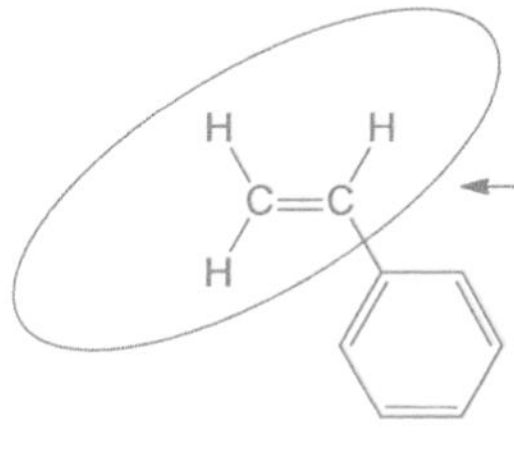

vinyl group

As there are a large number of vinyl monomers that chemists have used to make polymers, the relationship between a vinyl monomer and the subsequent polymer applies to a large number of polymers.

Solved problem 26.1. Poly(vinyl chloride) is used for plumbing materials (PVC pipe) and has the structure shown below. Based on the structure of the polymer, what is the structure of vinyl chloride?

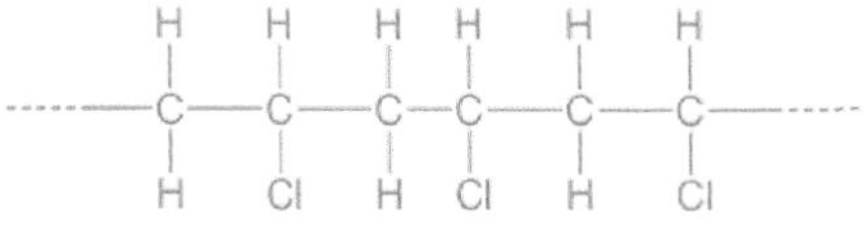

Think. How can you imagine cutting the polymer to determine the repeating unit? How is the repeating unit of a vinyl polymer related to the monomer?

Solve. The carbons in the structure make the main chain of the molecule. The chlorine atoms are substituents, or side-groups, in the same way phenyl rings are side-groups in polystyrene. The repeating pattern is shown below:

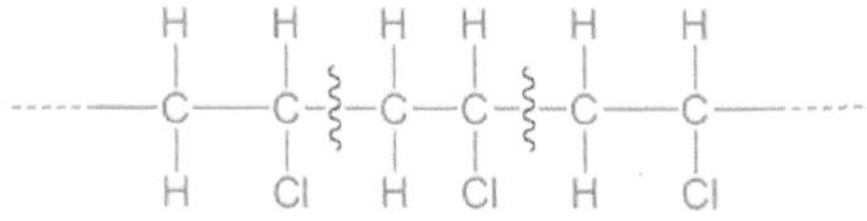

If we realize that the bonds formed between the repeating units during the chemical reaction, we will recognize that the monomer had a double bond between the carbon atoms:

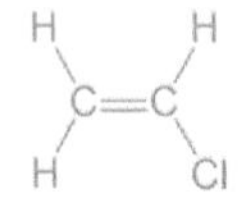

Problem 26.1. poly(methyl methacrylate), or Plexiglas, has the structure below and can be made form a vinyl monomer. What is the structure of the monomer?

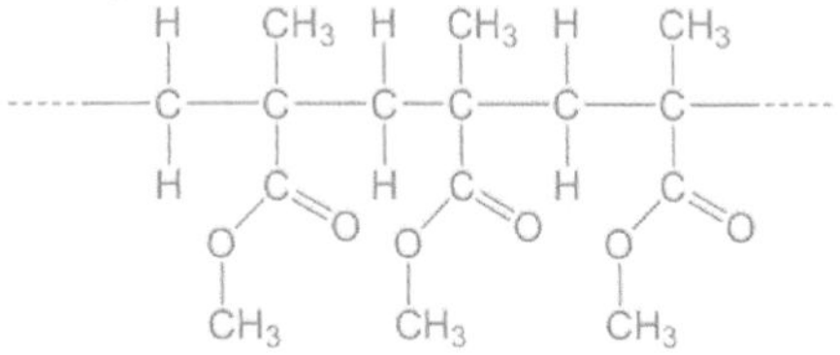

26.1b. Free-radical polymerization of styrene

Manufacturers create polystyrene from styrene by means of a free-radical chain reaction, an example of which is shown in Equation 26-4.

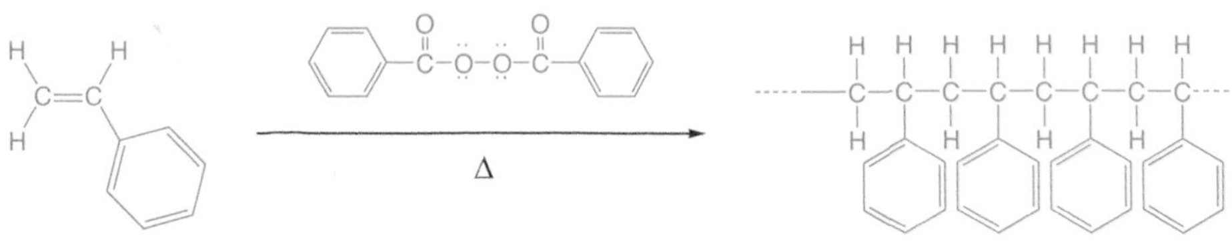

Δ

(26-4)

The mechanistic steps of this reaction are identical to those you studied in Section 25.6. The reaction begins with an **initiation** step which creates free radicals. Generally, the monomer is not capable of producing free radicals readily, so we introduce a radical initiator similar to AIBN (see Section 25.7); benzoyl peroxide is a common initiator. Because oxygen-oxygen single bonds are particularly weak (see Table 25-3), heating benzoyl peroxide results in the homolysis of the bond between the two oxygen atoms:

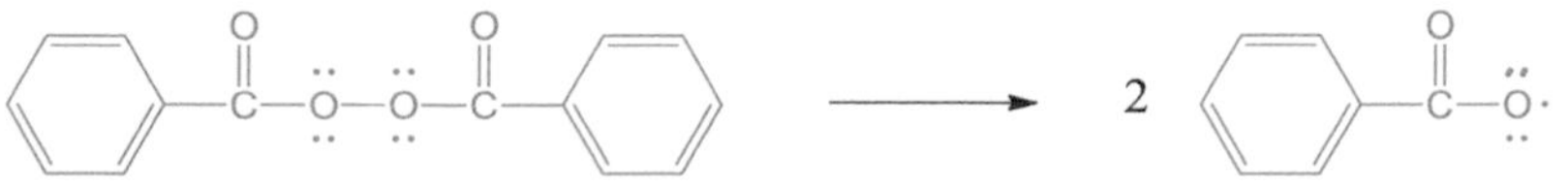

(26-5)

The two radicals that result are resonance stabilized:

Your turn 26.2. Provide the arrows that show the movement of electrons in the two previous equations.

After initiation, **propagation** occurs via radical addition (Section 25.4c). A radical from the initiator adds to a styrene molecule:

Free radical from initiator — Monomer — Reactive polymer chain

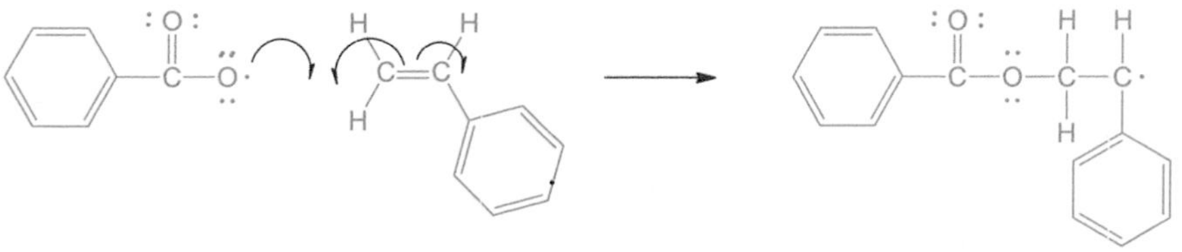

(26-6)

What occurs next explains how the polymer chain forms: the radical from the previous step adds to another molecule of styrene, increasing the length of the carbon chain:

Reactive polymer chain — Monomer — Reactive polymer chain

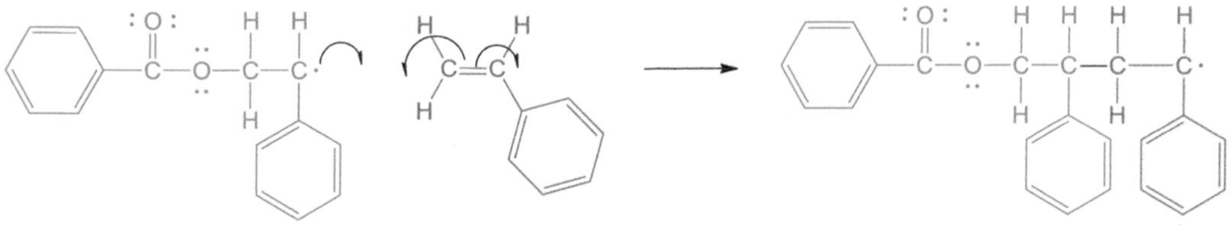

(26-7)

This radical can continue to propagate, adding to a third styrene molecule:

Reactive polymer chain — Momomer — Reactive polymer chain

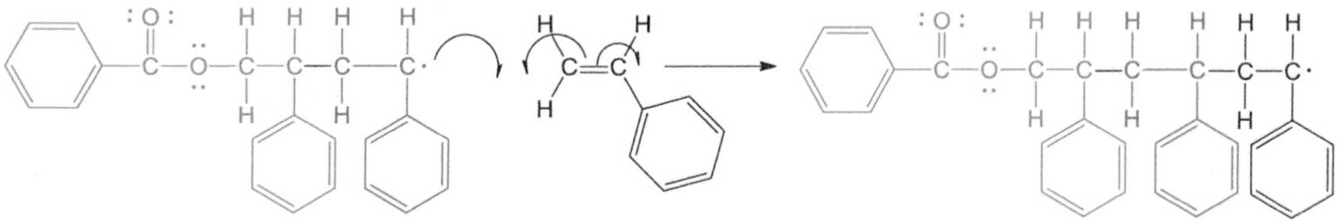

(26-8)

Your turn 26.3. Predict the product of the next step in the reaction, shown below.

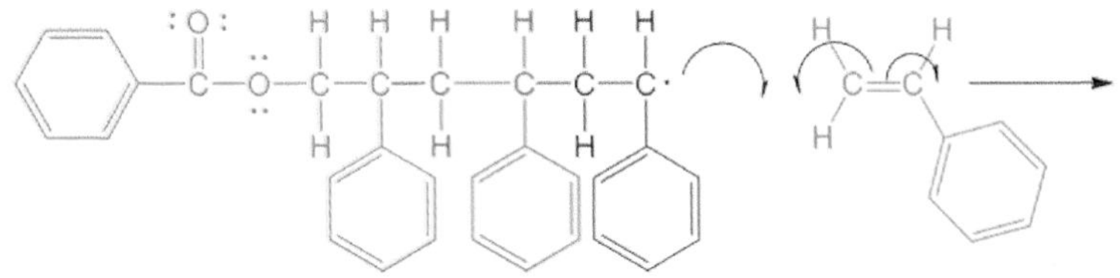

Propagation is a fast reaction. Since the reaction occurs in styrene, with no solvent, the concentration of one of the reactants is high; this increases the rate of reaction. Propagation is also product-favored and exothermic, because a σ bond replaces a π double bond. Recall that σ bonds are stronger than π bonds and consequently the formation of σ bonds is thermodynamically favored.

The propagation steps in the polymerization explain the term **chain-growth polymerization**. In chain-growth polymerization, individual sites (in this case, the initiating radicals) start the formation of a large chain. This growth of polymer chains is illustrated in Figure 26-3, in which the series of diagrams shows how propagation creates chains with time. The diagram begins with unreacted starting material in (a), proceeds to initiation in (b), and then shows how propagation and initiation continue in (c) through (e).

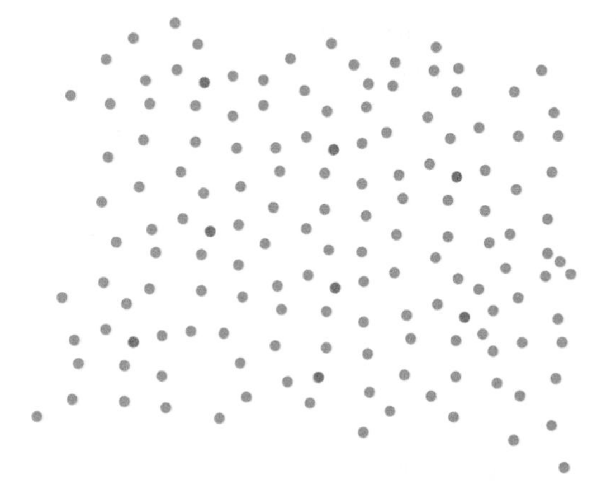

(a) A solution of styrene and benzoyl peroxide prior to heating. The red dots represent styrene molecules and the blue dots represent benzoyl peroxide molecules.

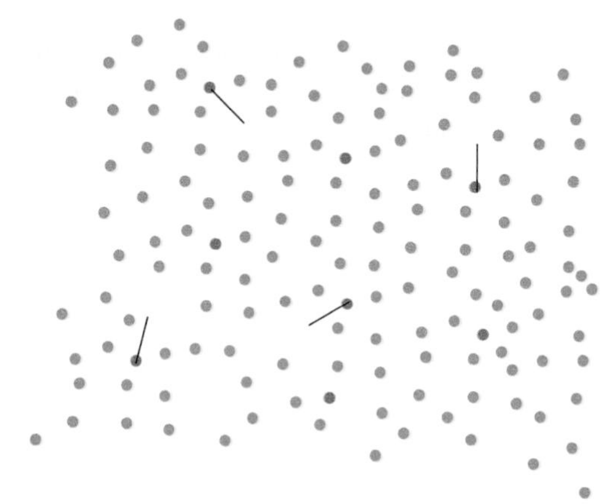

(b) During heating, the benzoyl peroxide molecules undergo homolysis and initiate propagation. The black lines represent bonds formed between an initiating radical and a styrene molecule.

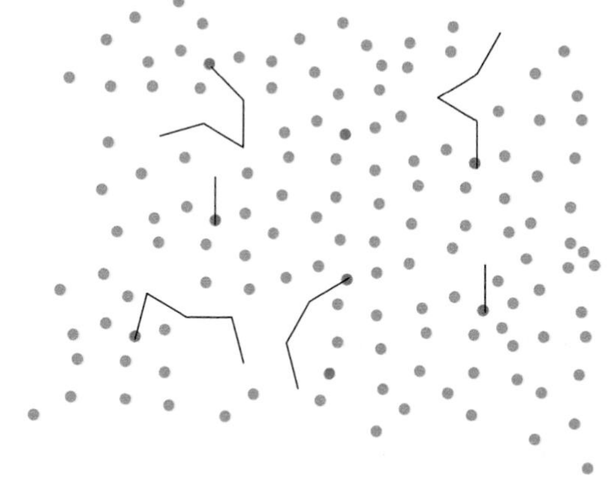

(c) Propagation continues for each of radicals, and the chain grows longer. Initiation continues, but at a slower rate than propagation.

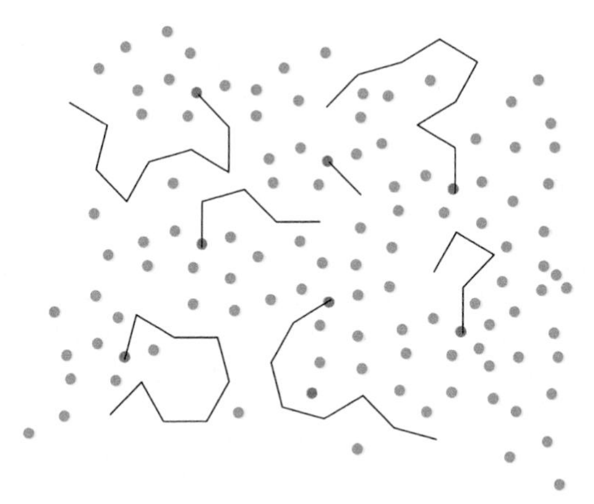

(d) Propagation continues and each chain increases in length. Benzoyl peroxide molecules that remain also initiate chain growth.

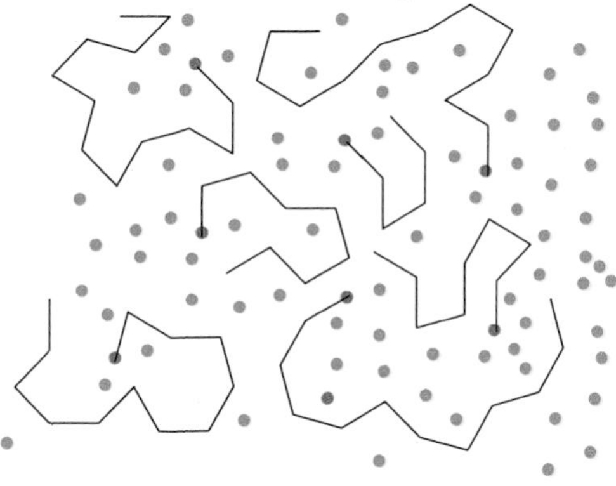

(e) Later in the reaction, initiation is minimal. Propagation continues and polymer chains grow longer.

Figure 26-3. Growth of polymer chains during polymerization of styrene

To differentiate between the two carbons in the vinyl group, the less substituted carbon in the double bond is the **tail**, and the more substituted carbon is the **head**. Note that there are two possible ways the radical can add to the vinyl group of styrene: head-to-tail or head-to-head.

head
tail
head
tail
head-to-tail addition

(26-9)

head
tail
head
tail
head-to-head addition

(26-10)

In almost all free-radical polymerizations, head-to-tail addition is favored. There are two reasons. First, the radical formed in the head-to-tail addition is generally thermodynamically favored. In the formation of polystyrene, for example, the product of head-to-tail addition is resonance stabilized, while the radical produced in head-to-head addition is not.

The second reason is kinetic: steric repulsions between the two phenyl groups (one at the end of the propagating radical and one in the monomer) make it unlikely for the occurrence of a successful collision between the two species.

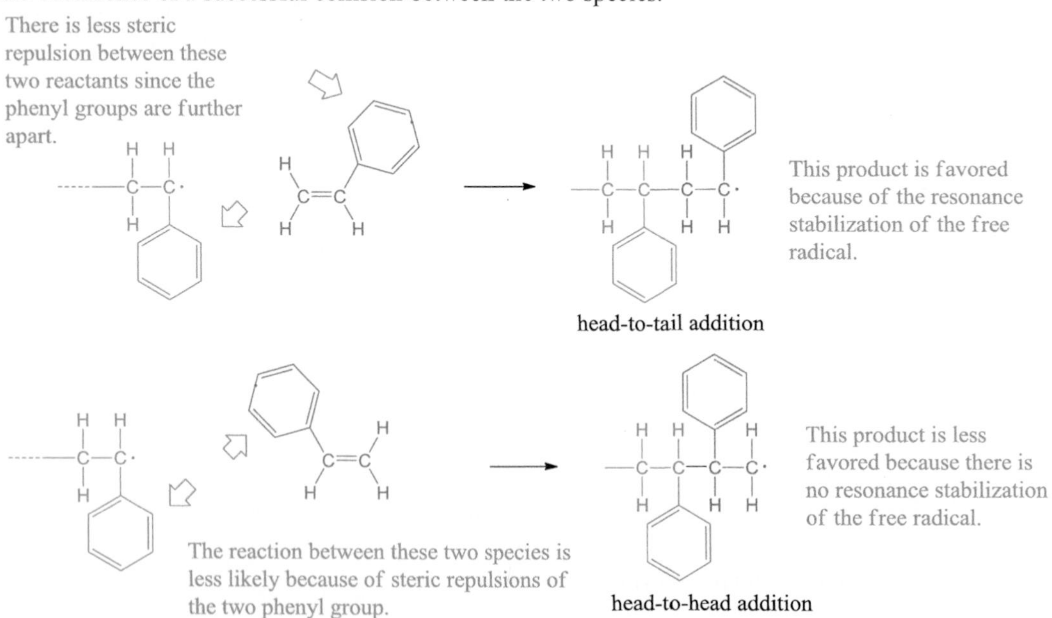

There is less steric repulsion between these two reactants since the phenyl groups are further apart.
This product is favored because of the resonance stabilization of the free radical.
head-to-tail addition
This product is less favored because there is no resonance stabilization of the free radical.
The reaction between these two species is less likely because of steric repulsions of the two phenyl group.
head-to-head addition

Figure 26-4. Head-to-tail and head-to-head addition in the polymerization of styrene

Both thermodynamics and kinetics favor head-to-tail addition.

Your turn 26.4. Use curved-arrow notation to show the movement of electrons in the head-to-tail addition of a growing chain of poly(ethyl acrylate) to a molecule of ethyl acrylate. Draw resonance structures to explain why head-to-tail addition occurs.

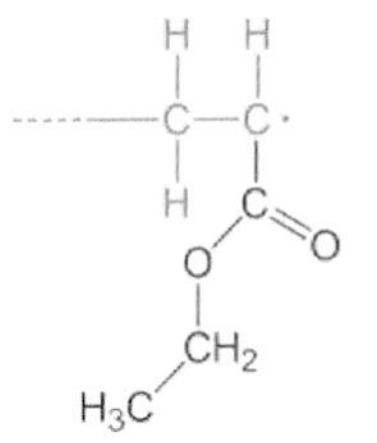

H H
C—C·
H C=O
O
CH_2
H_3C

→

Propagating chain of poly(ethyl acrylate) | ethyl acrylate | Product of head-to-tail addition

Problem 26.2. Propylene, shown below, also undergoes head to tail addition in free-radical polymerization.

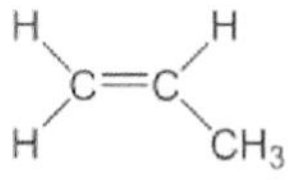

H H
C=C
H CH_3

propylene

(a) Draw the a propagating chain of polypropylene, a propylene molecule, and the product of head –to-tail addition. (In other words, an equation similar to the one in Your turn 26.4.)
(b) There are no resonance contributors that you can draw for the radical formed by head-to-tail addition. However, head-to-tail addition is still thermodynamically favored over head-to-head addition. Explain this observation.

Problem 26.3. Crotonic acid polymerizes much more slowly than acrylic acid. How do you explain the difference in reactivity?

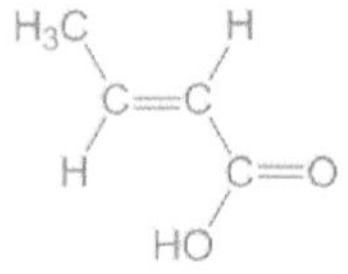

H_3C H
C=C
H C=O
HO

crotonic acid

H H
C=C
H C=O
HO

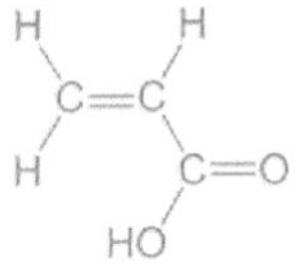

acrylic acid

Propagation could, in theory, continue until there are no remaining molecules of monomer. In reality, the growth of the chain ends when **termination** occurs. Termination can occur in two ways. The first is through radical coupling (see Section 25.4a), also called **combination**. Two radicals that are close enough to react will do so readily, since the activation energy is zero (again, see Section 25. 4a):

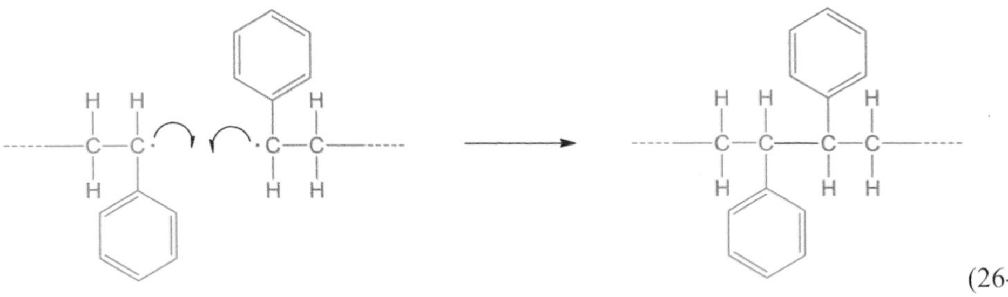

(26-11)

The second pathway for termination is **disproportionation**. Disproportionation applies to any reaction in which two identical species react to produce two different products. In the case of polystyrene, one of the radicals can abstract a hydrogen atom from another radical (see Section 25.4b). Because the hydrogen abstraction occurs at a carbon adjacent to a free radical, a double bond forms in the species that gives up the hydrogen atom. One product is a molecule that has hydrogen as its last atom; the other product contains a carbon-carbon double bond. This reaction is similar to the second step of an E1 reaction (see Section 8.2):

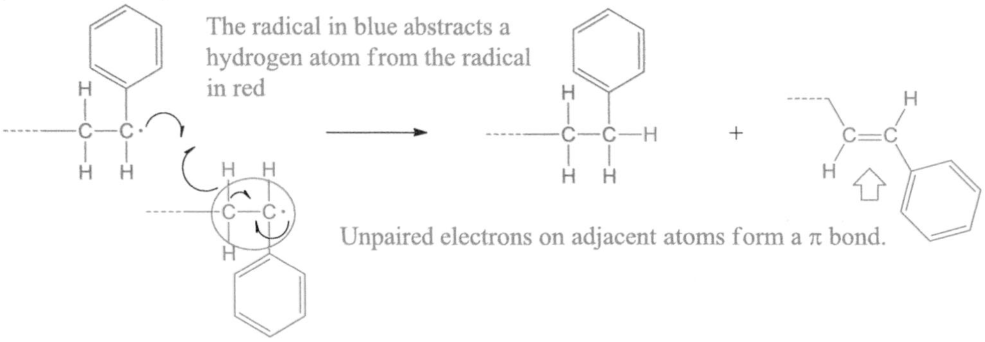

The radical in blue abstracts a hydrogen atom from the radical in red

Unpaired electrons on adjacent atoms form a π bond.

(26-12)

Free-radical polymerization can terminate by combination, which results in a single product, or in disproportionation, which results in two products.

26.1c. Other aspects of polystyrene

Most organic syntheses strive to have a single product. In the synthesis of polystyrene, however, a chemist cannot precisely control the length of chains that are produced. Consequently, polystyrene is a mixture of chains of different lengths. Analysis of the product shows that there is distribution of chain lengths, with some chains shorter or longer. Consequently, polystyrene is described with an **average molecular weight**. Chemists also refer to the **degree of polymerization**, or the number of monomer units that have been incorporated into an average chain.

For example, Figure 26-5 represents the results of gel permeation chromatography of a sample of polystyrene with an average molar mass of 24,000 g/mol, which represents an average degree of polymerization of 230, or 230 styrene molecules incorporated into a polymer chain. Commercial grade polystyrene has an average molar mass over 200,000 g/mol.

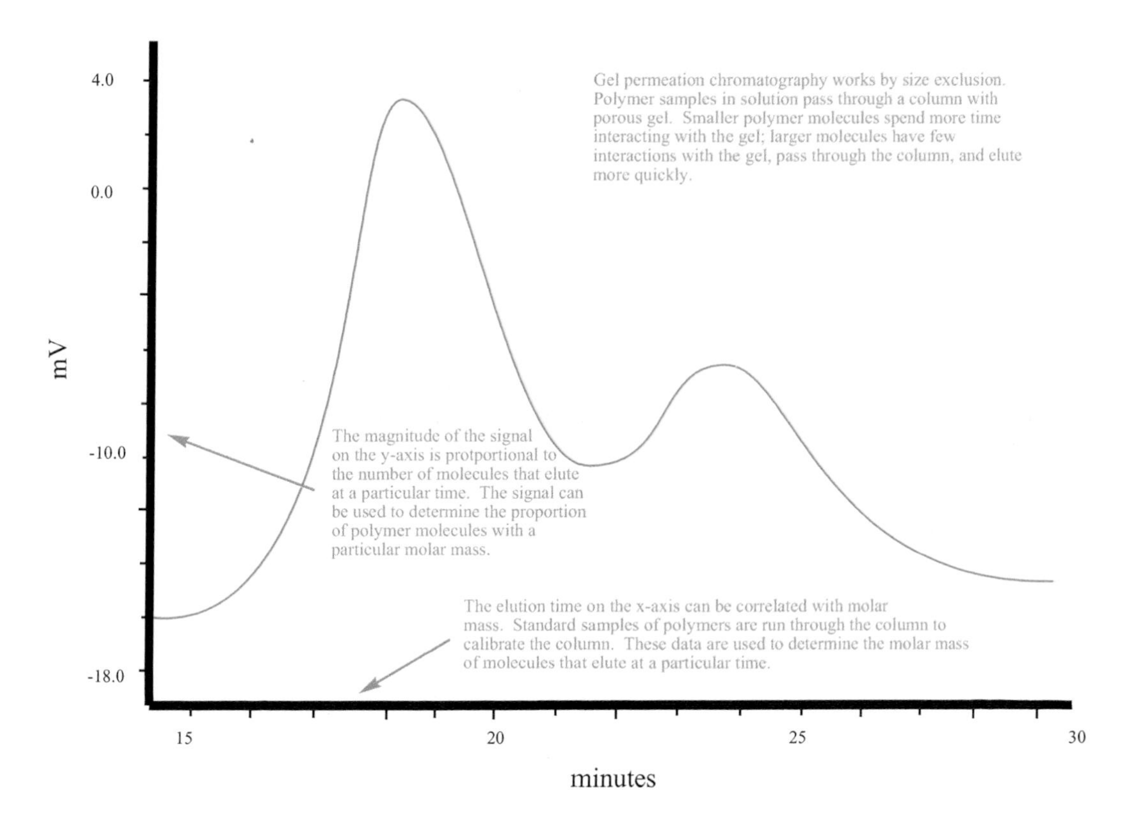

4.0
0.0
-10.0
-18.0
mV
15
20
25
30
minutes
Gel permeation chromatography works by size exclusion. Polymer samples in solution pass through a column with porous gel. Smaller polymer molecules spend more time interacting with the gel; larger molecules have few interactions with the gel, pass through the column, and elute more quickly.
The magnitude of the signal on the y-axis is protportional to the number of molecules that elute at a particular time. The signal can be used to determine the proportion of polymer molecules with a particular molar mass.
The elution time on the x-axis can be correlated with molar mass. Standard samples of polymers are run through the column to calibrate the column. These data are used to determine the molar mass of molecules that elute at a particular time.

Figure 26-5. Gel permeation chromatogram of a polystyrene sample

Because polystyrene molecules are so large, we usually use a shorthand notation in which we replace

with the following condensed formula:

The unit in parentheses is the repeating unit of the polystyrene and the average number of repeating units, *n*, is the degree of polymerization. This figure is similar to a condensed formula for decane:

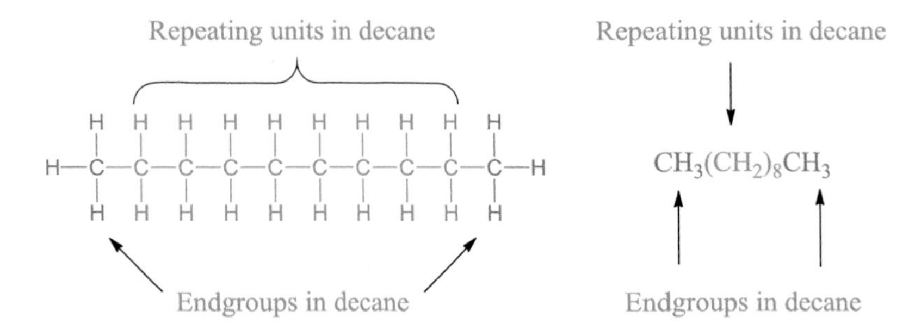
Repeating units in decane
Repeating units in decane
$CH_3(CH_2)_8CH_3$
Endgroups in decane
Endgroups in decane

Note that the structure for polystyrene does not show the endgroups of the molecule. At one end, we would expect to see a fragment from the benzoyl peroxide radical that initiated the polymerization. There are three possibilities for the other end of the polymer molecule, shown in Figure 26-6: (a) a benzoyl peroxide fragment, (b) a hydrogen atom, or (c) a carbon-carbon double bond. If two polymer chains terminate by combination, (a) will be the product. If two polymer chains terminate by disproportionation , (b) and (c) will be the products.

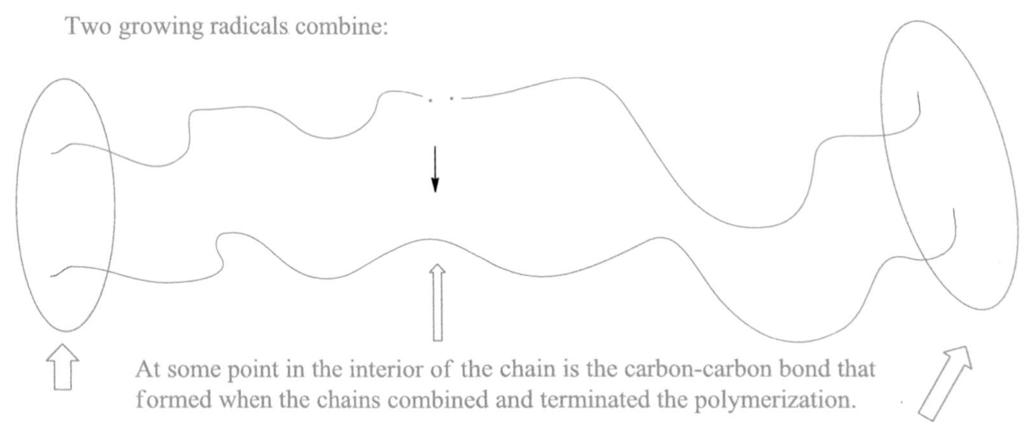
Two growing radicals combine:
At some point in the interior of the chain is the carbon-carbon bond that formed when the chains combined and terminated the polymerization.
Endgroups

The contributions of the endgroups (in blue) is small compared to the overall length of the polymer chain.

(a) The product of combination, in which two chains, each initiated by a radical from benzoyl peroxide, are joined by a carbon-carbon single bond

(b) One of the products of disproportionation, with hydrogen as the terminal atom.

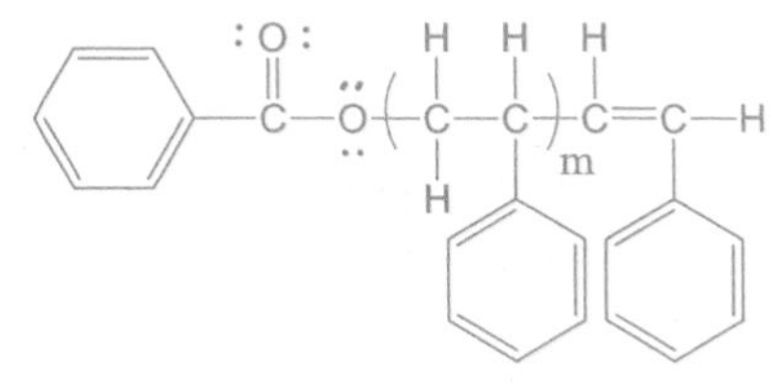

(c) A second product of disproportionation, with a carbon-carbon double bond at the end of the polymer chain.

Figure 26-6. Products of termination steps in free-radical polymerization

Because the endgroups are variable and because their contribution to the overall structure is small (2 units out of more than 19,000 in a typical molecule in commercial polystyrene), most representations of polymers omit the end groups.

> Chemists consider only the repeating unit of a polymer in their evaluation of its structure because the endgroups do not make a significant contribution to the structure or the properties of the polymer.

26.2. GENERAL ASPECTS OF POLYMERS

The terms and concepts that apply to the free-radical polymerization of styrene in Section 26.1 apply to numerous polymers and polymerizations. All polymers are created from monomers and contain repeating units; however, polymers fall into different classifications. We will examine how to classify a polymer and how to name simple polymers.

26.2a. Polymers, monomers and repeating units

In any polymer, we will find a repeating unit. The repeating unit may contain all of the atoms in the monomer, or only a portion of the atoms. For example, when Wallace Carothers synthesized nylon in 1938, he used adipic acid (1,6-hexanedioic acid) and 1,6-hexanediamine. If you examine the structures of the starting material and the product in the synthesis of nylon in Equation 26-13, you will see that all of the carbon and nitrogen atoms in the monomers have been incorporated into the repeating unit. Some oxygens and hydrogens, however, are missing.

$$HO-\overset{O}{\overset{\|}{C}}CH_2CH_2CH_2CH_2\overset{O}{\overset{\|}{C}}-OH \;+\; H_2NCH_2CH_2CH_2CH_2CH_2CH_2NH_2$$

adipic acid
1,6-hexandioic acid

1,6-hexanediamine

$$\downarrow \Delta$$

$$\left(\overset{O}{\overset{\|}{C}}CH_2CH_2CH_2CH_2\overset{O}{\overset{\|}{C}}\underset{H}{\underset{|}{N}}CH_2CH_2CH_2CH_2CH_2CH_2\underset{H}{\underset{|}{N}}\right)_n$$

nylon

(26-13)

> **Your turn 26.5.** What is the other product of the above reaction? That is, what is a plausible formula for a product that will balance this reaction?

The production of a second product is not unusual in polymerizations. The product is most frequently water, but there are other possibilities.

> **Problem 26.4.** Nylon (see Equation 26-13) can also be synthesized from adipoyl chloride and 1,6-hexanediamine, shown below. What will be the two products of the reaction?
>
> $$Cl-\overset{O}{\overset{\|}{C}}CH_2CH_2CH_2CH_2\overset{O}{\overset{\|}{C}}-Cl \;+\; H_2NCH_2CH_2CH_2CH_2CH_2CH_2NH_2 \longrightarrow$$

26.2b. Classes of polymers

Polymers can be classified according to several criteria. These include

- type of chain
- functional group(s) in the chain
- monomer(s) used to make the polymer
- number of different monomers used
- linearity of the polymer

The simplest classification is whether the main chain contains only carbon atoms or whether it contains heteroatoms as well. Polymers with only carbons in the main chain are **carbon-chain polymers**. Those with heteroatoms are **heterochain polymers**.

More specifically, polymers can be classified by functional group. For example, **poly(ethylene terephthalate)**, or **PET**, which is used to make two-liter bottles for carbonated beverages, is a **polyester** because the main chain contains multiple ester groups.

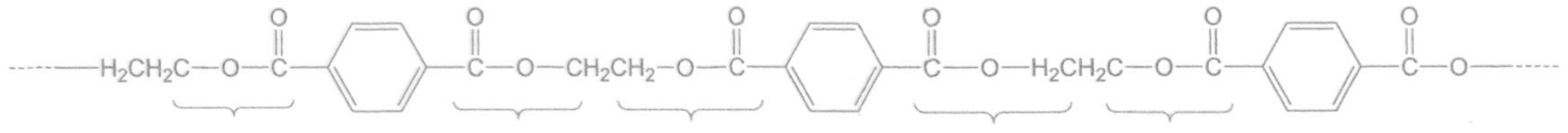

The presence of multiple ester groups make PET a polyester.

or

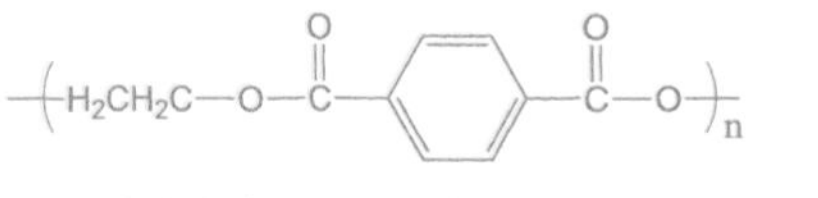

poly(ethylene terephthalate) or PET

Note that the repeating unit for PET contains two ester groups. This may not be immediately obvious from the structure. To recognize the second one, you have to imagine a second repeating unit:

The first ester group is clearly visible in the repeating unit.

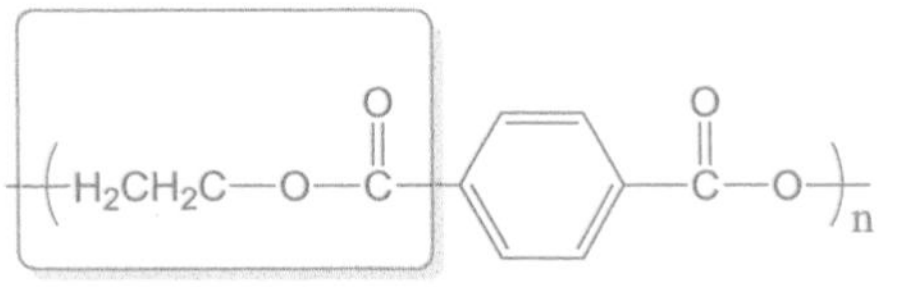

poly(ethylene terephthalate) or PET

The second ester group is not as apparent until you visualize the continuation of the polymer chain:

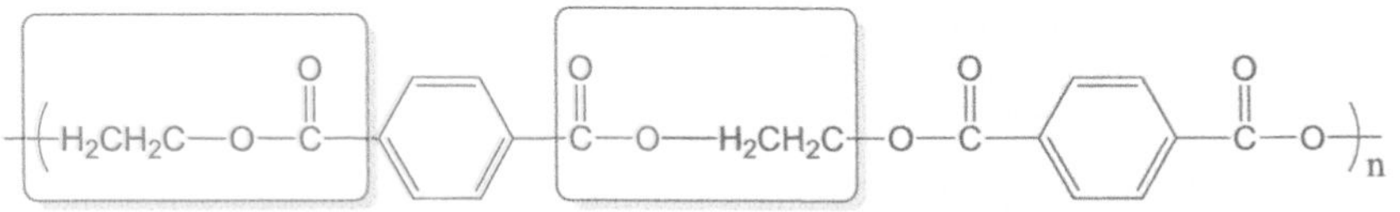

or recognize that the ethylene group on the left, along with the COO on the right, represent the second ester group:

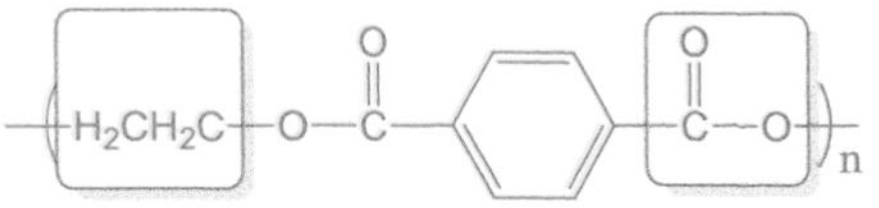

> **Your turn 26.6.** Examine the structure of nylon in Equation 26-12. Based on the functional groups in the polymer chain, what class of polymers does nylon fall into? How many times does the functional group appear in the repeating unit?

Polymers with only carbons in the backbone, or main chain, are usually described in terms of the monomer used to make them. For example, the polymers below are referred to as **polyacrylates** or **acrylics** because the monomers are considered derivatives of acrylic acid:

acrylic acid

methyl methacrylate

acrylonitrile

poly(acrylic acid)

poly(methyl methacrylate)

poly(acryonitrile)

Alkenes at one time were referred to as **olefins**. As a result, polyethylene, polypropylene, and other polymers made from akenes or dienes are still referred to as **polyolefins**:

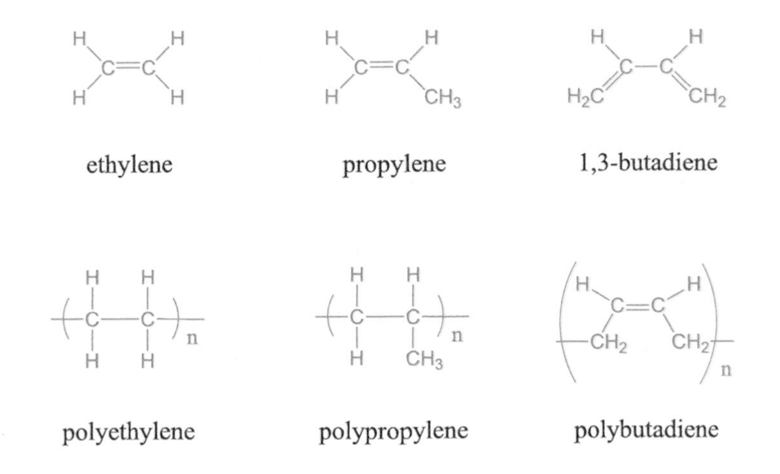

Returning to our discussion of polystyrene, we refer to polystyrene as a **homopolymer** because there is one monomer used in its synthesis.

The use of two monomers leads to the synthesis of a **copolymer**. For example, a copolymer of styrene and butadiene was important during World War II because it was a suitable replacement for natural rubber, which was in limited supply. The polymer is called styrene-butadiene rubber or SBR.

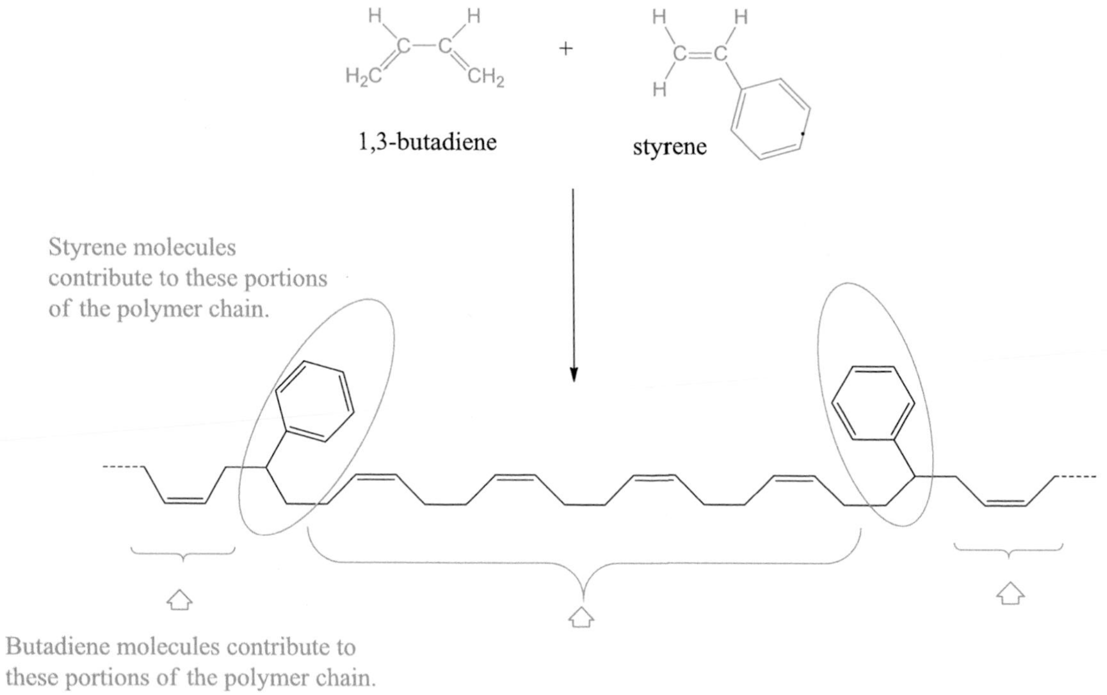

1,3-butadiene + styrene

Styrene molecules contribute to these portions of the polymer chain.

Butadiene molecules contribute to these portions of the polymer chain.

Styrene-butadiene rubber (SBR), a copolymer of 1,3-butadiene and styerne (26-14)

Note that copolymers are possible when each monomer is capable of forming a homopolymer. For example, 1,3-butadiene is capable of forming a homopolymer, as is styrene. Consequently, the reaction of the two creates a copolymer. Nylon (see Section 26.21), however, is not considered a copolymer. Although two reactants are used to synthesize nylon, neither of the reactants, adipic acid or 1,6-hexanediamine, is capable of forming polymer in the absence of the other reactant.

26.2c. Linear polymers, branched polymers, network polymers, and crosslinking

Polystyrene, nylon, and poly(ethylene terephthalate) are examples of **linear polymers**. Linear polymers are analogous to straight chain or linear alkanes, in which there are no branches. (See Section N2.) **Branched polymers** are analogous to substituted alkanes, such as 4-ethyl dodecane, in which there are carbon chains that are not part of the main chain. Low-density polyethylene (LDPE) is an example of a branched polymer.

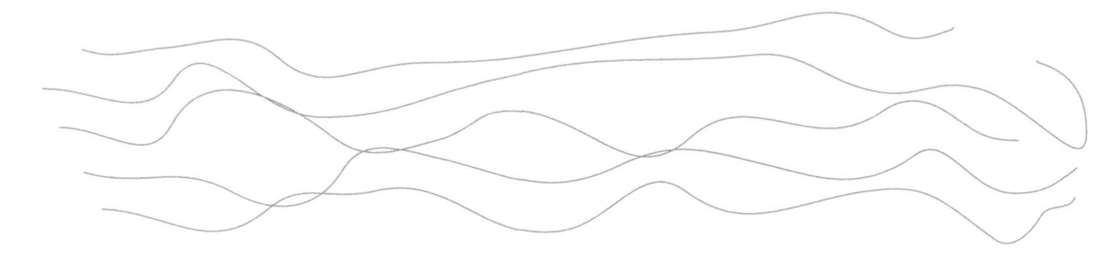

(a) A linear polymer. The lines represent carbon chains; individual atoms are not shown. Note there are no branches.

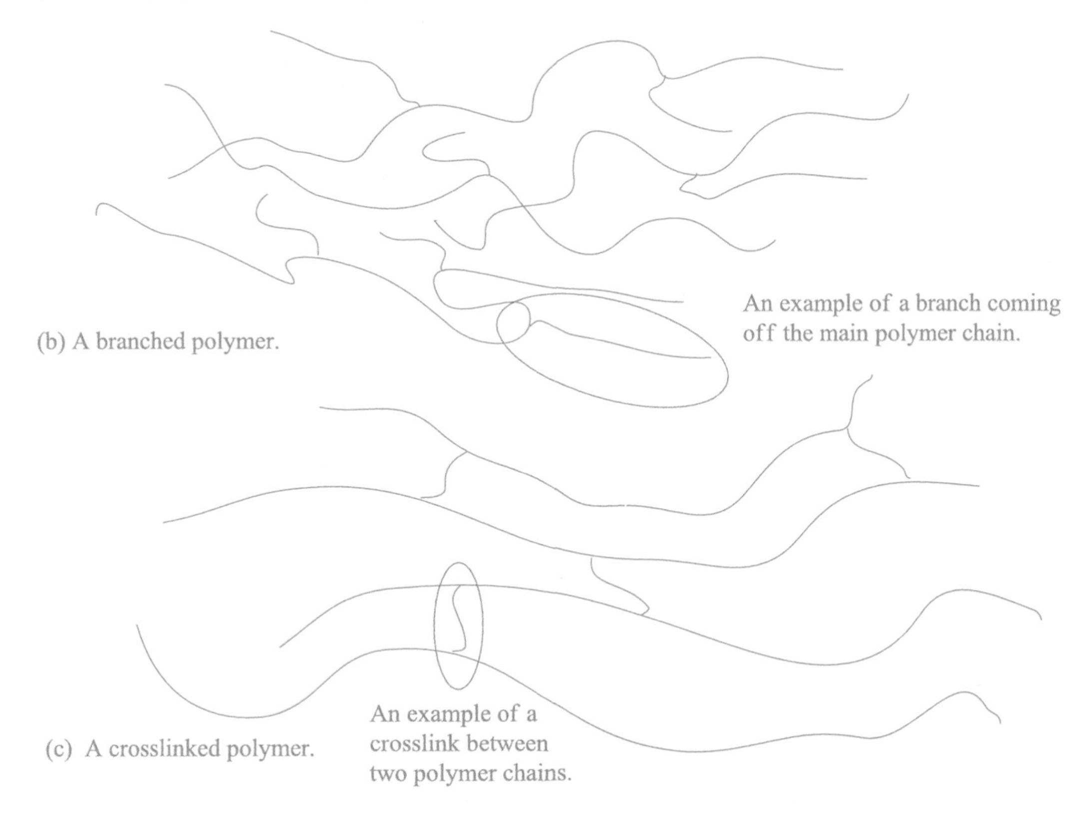
(b) A branched polymer.
An example of a branch coming off the main polymer chain.
(c) A crosslinked polymer.
An example of a crosslink between two polymer chains.

Figure 26-7. (a) A linear polymer; (b) a polymer with significant branching; (c) a crosslinked polymer

If branches connect two polymer chains, the short connections between longer polymer chains are frequently called **crosslinks**.

Historically, a significant introduction of crosslinking into a polymer was the vulcanization of rubber. In the nineteenth century, rubber found limited uses because it became brittle at low temperatures and a gooey mess at high temperatures. However, Charles Goodyear discovered that processing rubber at high temperatures with sulfur gave a material that had the desired elasticity of rubber, but did not lose its properties at extreme temperatures. This process, called vulcanization, introduced crosslinks between the rubber chains:

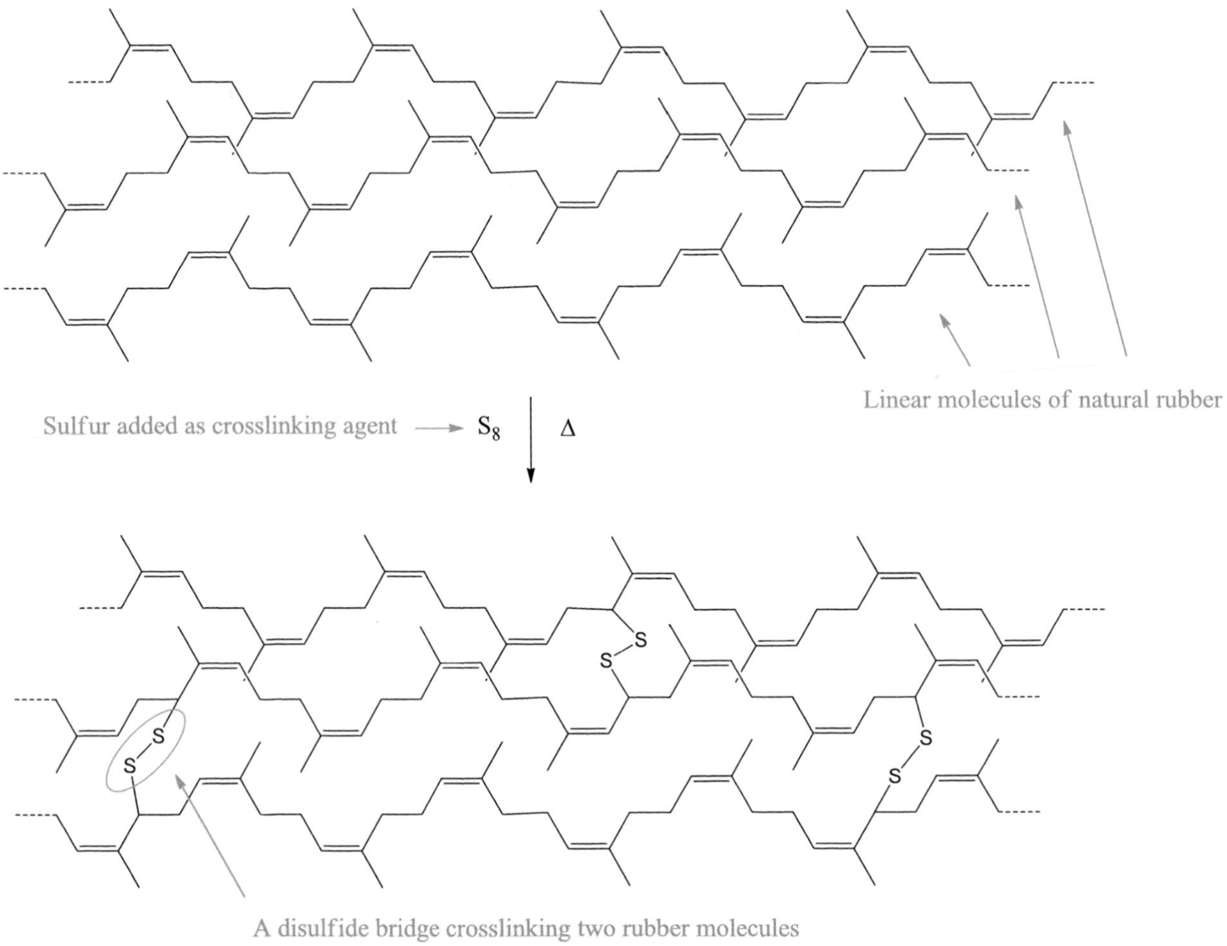

Linear molecules of natural rubber

Sulfur added as crosslinking agent → S_8 Δ

A disulfide bridge crosslinking two rubber molecules

Figure 26-8. Crosslinking in vulcanized rubber

However, some polymerizations introduce crosslinks as part of the polymerization process. One of the best known is the reaction of phenol and formaldehyde to produce the hard material known as **Bakelite**. If you compare the number of crosslinks per monomer unit in vulcanized rubber and in Bakelite, you see that Bakelite has a much higher degree of crosslinking. Consequently, Bakelite is referred to as a **network polymer** because there is no recognizable linearity in the polymer. In fact, a sample of Bakelite can actually be considered to be a single molecule.

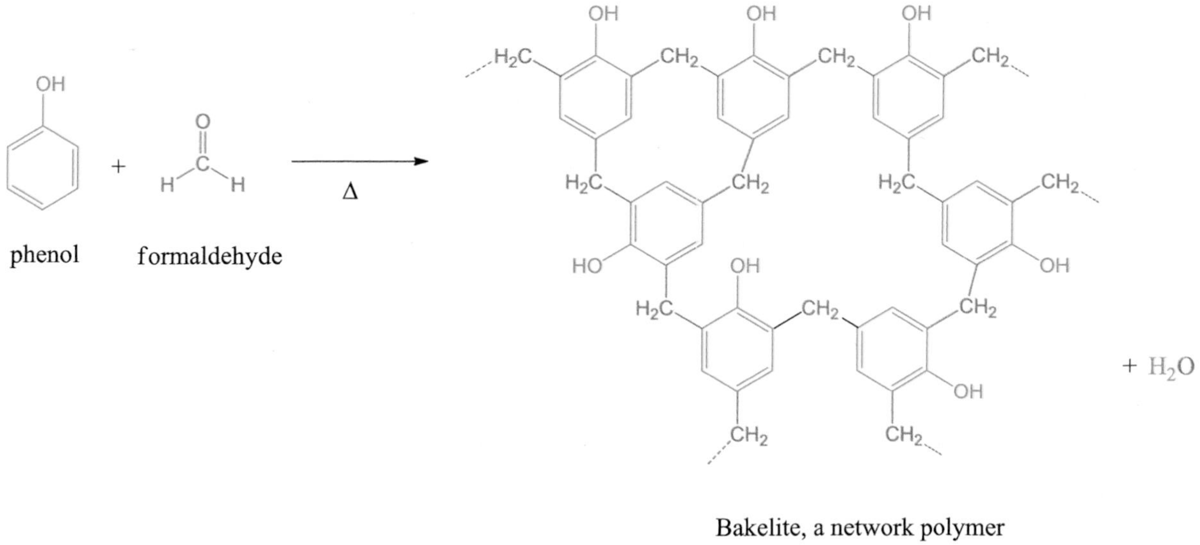

phenol formaldehyde $\xrightarrow{\Delta}$ Bakelite, a network polymer $+ H_2O$

Figure 26-9. Synthesis of Bakelite

26.2d. Polymer Nomenclature

IUPAC recommends that a polymer's name be based on its repeating unit; however, the trivial names are based on the monomer from which the polymer is made. For example, the repeating unit of the polymer below is $-CH_2-$, which leads to the IUPAC name poly(methylene). The trivial (and more common) name is polyethylene.

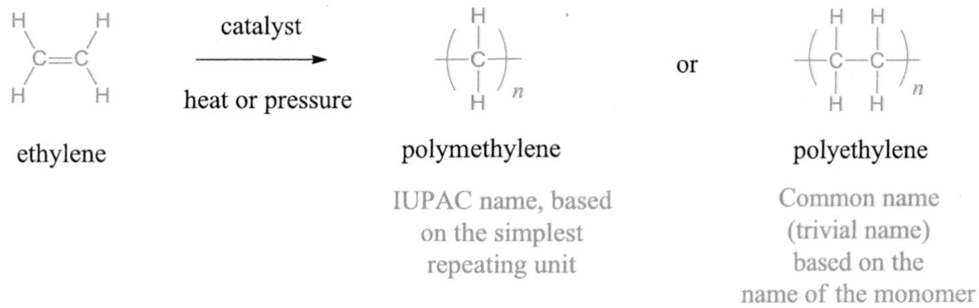

ethylene $\xrightarrow[\text{heat or pressure}]{\text{catalyst}}$ polymethylene or polyethylene

polymethylene: IUPAC name, based on the simplest repeating unit

polyethylene: Common name (trivial name) based on the name of the monomer

IUPAC allows the use of the trivial name for approximately twenty common polymers. We will use these trivial names in this text for two reasons: first, you are more likely to encounter the trivial names and, second, the trivial name helps establish the relationship between the polymer and the monomer from which it is made.

In general, the names for homopolymers use the format: polymonomer. If the monomer has a name of two or more words, then the monomer's name goes in parentheses in the name of the polymer.

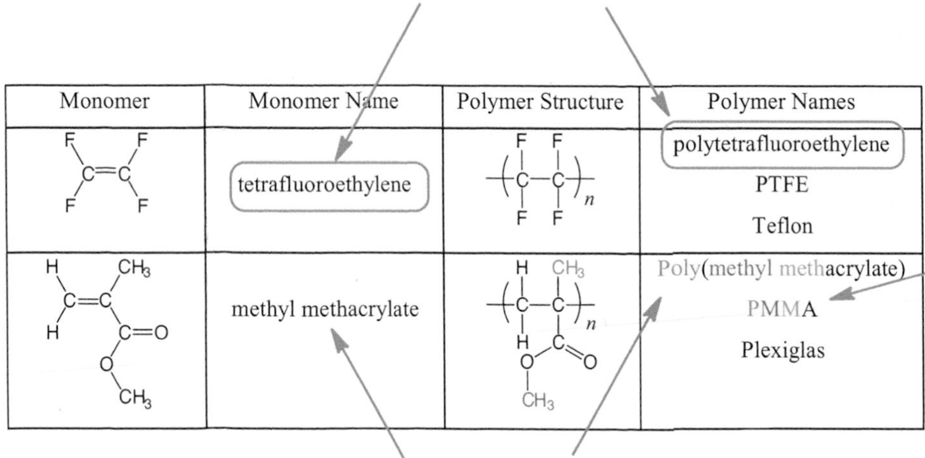

The prefix *poly* is added to the name of the monomer to create the name of the polymer
Monomer
Monomer Name
Polymer Structure
Polymer Names
tetrafluoroethylene
polytetrafluoroethylene
PTFE
Teflon
methyl methacrylate
Poly(methyl methacrylate)
PMMA
Plexiglas
The initial letters of *poly* and of the other structural features of the monomer are used to form the acronym PMMA
Because the monomer name is composed of two separate words, the name is placed in parentheses before the prefix *poly* is added.

Figurre 26.10. Relationships between names of monomers and names of polymers

In addition to trivial names, there are trademarked names for polymers such as Teflon and Plexiglas. Unfortunately, such names provide no information about the structure of the polymer. In addition, there are acronyms for many monomers. The acronyms are usually derived from the prefix *poly* and the initial letters of the different portions of the monomer.

Step-growth polymers more commonly use the name of the repeating unit as the basis for the name of the polymer. For example, the most common polyester is poly(ethylene terephthalate), or PET. In PET, the repeating unit is named as an ester of terephthalic acid and the ethylene group:

$$HO-C(=O)-C_6H_4-C(=O)-OH + HO-CH_2CH_2-OH \xrightarrow[\Delta]{\text{acid catalyst}} \left[H_2CH_2C-O-C(=O)-C_6H_4-C(=O)-O \right]_n \qquad (26\text{-}15)$$

terephthalic acid — ethylene glycol — poly(ethylene terephthalate), an ester of terephthalic acid and ethylene glycol, PET

However, not all common step-growth polymers use a recognizable system for their names. Consequently, we will restrict exercises in naming polymers to chain-growth polymers.

> Polymer names are derived from the monomer used to make the polymer or from the repeating unit in the polymer. The acronyms of polymer names begin with P (for *poly*) and contain the initial letters of the chemical structures in the monomer or repeating unit.

Problem 26.5. The derivate of acrylic acid, shown below, undergoes free-radical polymerization to make a polymer that is water-soluble. Draw the condensed formula for the polymer and provide its name and acronym.

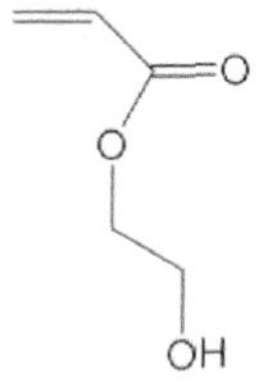

2-hydroxyethyl acrylate

26.3. POLYMERIZATIONS

Having discussed the structure of polymers, we now need to learn how to make them. In theory, any reaction that forms a bond between two molecules can be used to make a polymer. While there are a wide number of reactions that are used to make polymers, each reaction can be classified into one of two categories: *chain-growth polymerization* or *step-growth polymerization.* A study of these two types of reactions will help us understand how monomer can react to form polymer chains.

26.3a. Chain-growth polymerization

You examined the free-radical polymerization of styrene in Section 26.1b. This reaction of styrene is an example of **chain-growth polymerization**, in which monomer units add one at a time to a growing chain.

Note that most addition polymerizations are free-radical chain reactions, but there are important exceptions. However, the steps in addition polymerization are generally the same as those in free-radical polymerization. As we saw in Section 26.1b, the steps are *initiation*, *propagation*, and *termination.*

For example, styrene can also undergo anionic polymerization. In anionic polymerization of styrene, the initiator, butyllithium, forms an anion instead of a free radical:

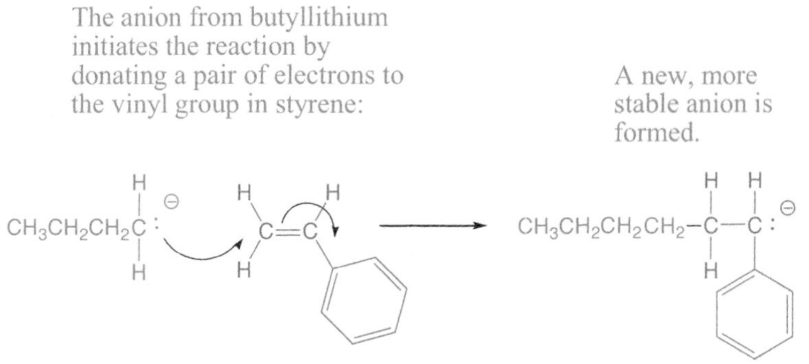

The anion from butyllithium initiates the reaction by donating a pair of electrons to the vinyl group in styrene:

A new, more stable anion is formed.

$CH_3CH_2CH_2CH_2^{\ominus}$ + $H_2C{=}CH(C_6H_5)$ ⟶ $CH_3CH_2CH_2CH_2{-}CH_2{-}CH^{\ominus}(C_6H_5)$

(26-16)

Your turn 26.7. Why is the anion on the product side of the reaction in Equation 26-16 more stable than the anion on the reactant side?

In the propagation steps, monomers still combine with the growing chain to form a reactive species similar to the reactant; these species are also anions, and not free radicals:

$$CH_3CH_2CH_2CH_2-CH_2-\overset{\ominus}{C}H(Ph) + H_2C=CH(Ph) \longrightarrow CH_3CH_2CH_2CH_2-CH_2-CH(Ph)-CH_2-\overset{\ominus}{C}H(Ph)$$

(26-15)

In this case, termination will occur with a proton transfer step. An acid is added to the reaction mixture and ends the propagation.

Your turn 26.8. Why are combination and termination not possible mechanisms for termination in the anionic polymerization of styrene?

Cationic polymerization is also possible, but is not as widely used.

Note that addition polymerization can occur with monomers that do not contain vinyl groups. For example, ethylene oxide (oxirane) undergoes an anionic polymerization that can be described as a **ring-opening polymerization**:

$$H_2C\overset{O}{—}CH_2 \xrightarrow{CaO} \left(-CH_2-CH_2-O-\right)_n$$

(26-18)

The oxide anion in calcium oxide initiates polymerization, acting as a nucleophile:

Alkoxide anion forms

Oxide anon acts as nucleophile and initiates the reaction

(26-19)

The alkoxide anion can now act as nulceophile and be the site of chain growth:

Propagation steps repeat

$$\ominus:\ddot{O}-\left(CH_2CH_2O\right)_n-CH_2CH_2\ddot{O}:^{\ominus}$$

Alkoxide anion reacts with another ethylene oxide molecule

(26-20)

Termination will occur when an acid is added to the reaction mixture. The alkoxide anion will react with the acid in a proton-transfer step:

$$^{\ominus}:\ddot{O}-\left(CH_2CH_2O\right)_n-CH_2CH_2\ddot{O}:^{\ominus} + H-B \longrightarrow {}^{\ominus}:\ddot{O}-\left(CH_2CH_2O\right)_n-CH_2CH_2OH + :B$$

(26-21)

> **Your turn 26.9.** The polymer chain that is produced in Equation 26-21 will undergo another reaction before termination of the polymerization is complete. Provide the mechanism for the reaction.

Chain-growth polymerizations all contain the three steps of initiation, propagation, and termination.

26.3b. Step-growth Polymerization

Many heterochain polymers, including nylon and PET, shown earlier, are made through step-growth polymerization. In contrast to addition polymerization, **step-growth polymerization** occurs when molecules throughout a mixture react, as opposed to reactions only at the end of growing chains. Consider the synthesis of nylon-6,6 from adipic acid and 1,6-hexanediamine. Note that the system contains two different compounds, each of which is bifunctional. The carboxylic acid group of adipic acid reacts with an amine group from 1,6-hexane diamine:

$$HO{-}\overset{O}{\overset{\|}{C}}CH_2CH_2CH_2CH_2\overset{O}{\overset{\|}{C}}{-}OH \; + \; H_2NCH_2CH_2CH_2CH_2CH_2CH_2NH_2$$

adipic acid
1,6-hexandioic acid

1,6-hexanediamine

$$\downarrow \Delta$$

$$HO{-}\overset{O}{\overset{\|}{C}}CH_2CH_2CH_2CH_2\overset{O}{\overset{\|}{C}}\underset{H}{\underset{|}{N}}CH_2CH_2CH_2CH_2CH_2CH_2\underset{H}{\underset{|}{N}}{-}H \quad + \quad HO{-}H$$

the first step in the growth of the polymer chain (26-22)

The reaction proceeds and the chain length increases:

$$HO{-}\overset{O}{\overset{\|}{C}}CH_2CH_2CH_2CH_2\overset{O}{\overset{\|}{C}}\underset{H}{\underset{|}{N}}CH_2CH_2CH_2CH_2CH_2CH_2NH_2 \quad + \quad HO{-}\overset{O}{\overset{\|}{C}}CH_2CH_2CH_2CH_2\overset{O}{\overset{\|}{C}}\underset{H}{\underset{|}{N}}CH_2CH_2CH_2CH_2CH_2CH_2NH_2$$

$$\downarrow \Delta$$

$$HO{-}\overset{O}{\overset{\|}{C}}CH_2CH_2CH_2CH_2\overset{O}{\overset{\|}{C}}\underset{H}{\underset{|}{N}}CH_2CH_2CH_2CH_2CH_2CH_2\underset{H}{\underset{|}{N}}{-}\overset{O}{\overset{\|}{C}}CH_2CH_2CH_2CH_2\overset{O}{\overset{\|}{C}}\underset{H}{\underset{|}{N}}CH_2CH_2CH_2CH_2CH_2CH_2NH_2 \quad + \quad H{-}OH \qquad (26\text{-}23)$$

Figure 26-10 shows what occurs over time.

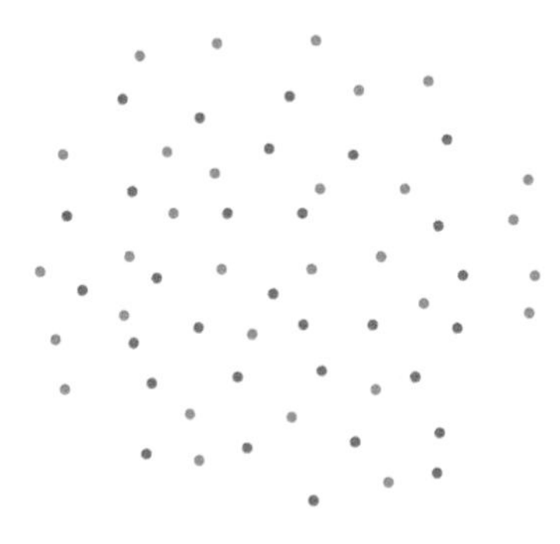

(a) A mixutre of adipic acid (AA, shown as red dots) and 1,6-hexanediamine (HD, shown as blue dots).

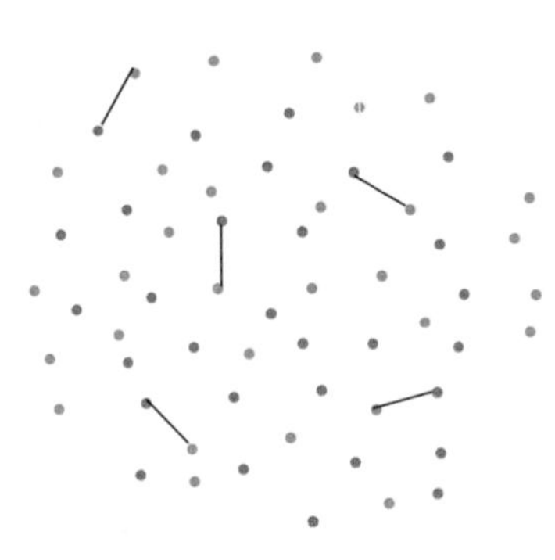

(b) When the reaction begins, a single AA reacts with a single HD.

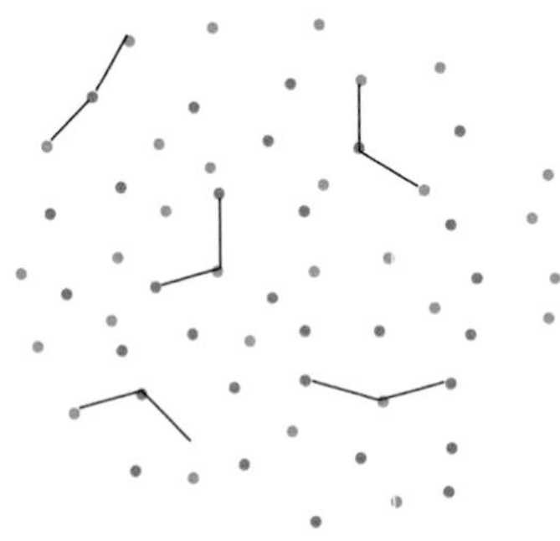

(c) The AAHD units can grow at either end, reacting with either another AA or another HD.

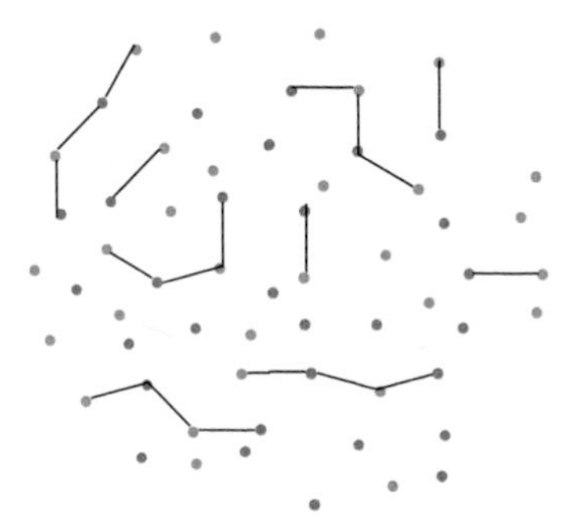

(d) The polymer chains grow step-wise, adding an AA or HD to the end of the chain. At the same time, single units of AA and HD continue to react to start new chains.

(e) Growing chains also react with each other. When this occur, the polymer chain increases in size to a greater extent than when a single AA or HD reacts. Note that ends of these large chains are still reactive. Other chains continue to grow through addition of a single AA or HD.

Figure 26-10. Growth of polymer chains during synthesis of nylon

Note that at each step, growth of the polymer chain occurs when a carboxylic acid group reacts with an amine. Early in the reaction, the size of the chain may increase by the length of a single adipic acid molecule or a single 1,6-hexanediamine molecule; however, as the reaction progresses, long chains may join together when a step occurs. Note that this step is similar to combination in chain-growth polymerization, but in step-growth polymerization, the chains are capable of further reactions.

The distinctions between step-growth polymerization and chain-growth polymerization are important. Chain-growth polymerizations are fast reactions and the products are thermodynamically favored. Step-growth polymerization is slower, and, because the reactions are reversible, removal of water or other products can be important if the polymer is to reach high molecular weight. In the synthesis of nylon, for example, the reaction is reversible and slow; heat is required to drive the reaction to completion. This method for synthesizing an amide is different from those you studied in Chapter 19.

Historically, this type of reaction was referred to as condensation polymerization, because a small molecule (in this case water) was formed as a product.

Many addition-elimination reactions can be used to make step-growth polymers. For example, the Fischer esterification (see Section 19.6) of terephthalic acid and ethylene glycol may be used to make polyesters, such as PET (see Equation 26-15):

HO—C(=O)—C₆H₄—C(=O)—OH + HO—CH₂CH₂—OH —(acid catalyst, Δ)→

terephthalic acid   ethylene glycol

$$\cdots—H_2CH_2C—O—C(=O)—C_6H_4—C(=O)—O—CH_2CH_2—O—C(=O)—C_6H_4—C(=O)—O—H_2CH_2C—O—C(=O)—C_6H_4—C(=O)—O—\cdots$$

or

$$—\!\!\left(H_2CH_2C—O—C(=O)—C_6H_4—C(=O)—O\right)_n— \quad + \quad H_2O$$

poly(ethylene terephthalate) or PET
an ester of terephthalic acid and ethylene glycol

(26-24)

Alternatively, transesterification is also useful to make PET:

$$H_3CO—C(=O)—C_6H_4—C(=O)—OCH_3 + HO—CH_2CH_2—OH \xrightarrow[\Delta]{\text{acid catalyst}} —\!\!\left(H_2CH_2C—O—C(=O)—C_6H_4—C(=O)—O\right)_n— \quad + \quad CH_3OH$$

(26-25)

In the two previous examples, water or methanol was a product of the reaction and must be removed from the product mixture to isolate the polymer. Some step-growth polymerizations do not involve the production of a second product. Polyurethanes are an example:

the isocyanate functional group   the urethane functional group

$$O=C=N—C_6H_3(CH_3)—N=C=O + HO—CH_2CH_2—OH \longrightarrow \cdots—CH_2CH_2—O—C(=O)—N(H)—C_6H_3(CH_3)—N(H)—C(=O)—O—CH_2CH_2—O—\cdots$$

tolune diisocyanate   ethylene glycol or 1,2-ethanediol   a polyurethane

or

$$—\!\!\left(C(=O)—N(H)—C_6H_3(CH_3)—N(H)—C(=O)—O—CH_2CH_2—O\right)_n—$$

(26-26)

In chain-growth polymerization, an initiator reacts with a single functional group in a molecule to create a product that reacts with another monomer; the initiator reacts with one end of the molecule and creates a reactive species at the other end of the molecule. In step-growth polymerization, two different functional groups, each on a separate molecule, react to join molecules together; the groups at either end of the new molecule are capable of further reaction.

Problem 26.6. The steps in the reaction in Equation 26-26 are the following: (1) Addition of a nucleophile to a polar double bond and (2) a proton transfer step. Provide the mechanism for this reaction.

26.4. CHEMICAL REACTIONS AFTER POLYMERIZATION

We have seen how to synthesize polymers. Just as multistep synthesis is an important aspect of organic chemistry, so are the subsequent reactions that a polymer may undergo. These reactions impart special properties to the polymers that render them more suitable for their purpose. In general, reactions usually include modifications of side-groups in a polymer; some more specific reactions have the sole purpose of cross-linking polymer chains to create network polymers.

26.4a. Modification of side-groups

Frequently, the monomer for a particular polymer is unavailable or results in a polymer with inferior properties. Changes to the polymer, particularly in the side chains, can address this problem.

26.4a1. Hydrolysis of poly(vinyl acetate) to poly(vinyl alcohol). Elmer's glue, contact lens solution, and other products contain **poly(vinyl alcohol)**, or **PVA**. Because of the large number of hydroxyl groups off the main chain, PVA is soluble in water and is used in a large number of water-based products.

However, you cannot make PVA from vinyl alcohol, because vinyl alcohol does not exist in significant quantities.

H H C=C H OH ------C—C—C—C—C—C------ (H H H H H H / H OH H OH H OH) or —(C—C)n— (H H / H OH)

vinyl alcohol poly(vinyl alcohol)

Your turn 26.10. Predict why vinyl alcohol is unfavored thermodynamically and isomerizes to a different product.

To prepare PVA, chemical plants begin with the synthesis of poly(vinyl acetate) from vinyl acetate:

vinyl acetate → poly(vinyl acetate)

$$CH_2{=}CH{-}O{-}C(=O){-}CH_3 \longrightarrow \cdots{-}CH_2{-}CH(OC(=O)CH_3){-}CH_2{-}CH(OC(=O)CH_3){-}CH_2{-}CH(OC(=O)CH_3){-}\cdots \text{ or } {-}[CH_2{-}CH(OC(=O)CH_3)]_n{-} \qquad (26\text{-}27)$$

Poly(vinyl acetate) can then undergo transesterification to produce PVA:

$$-[CH_2{-}CH(OC(=O)CH_3)]_n- \xrightarrow[CH_3OH,\ \Delta]{NaOCH_3} -[CH_2{-}CH(OH)]_n- \qquad (26\text{-}28)$$

Your turn 26.11. What is the other product of the reaction in eqn. 26-28? Provide the mechanism for the reaction that occurs.

The properties of PVA depend upon the degree of hydrolysis. At a minimum, eighty percent of the acetate groups are removed; the amount can be as high as 99.3%.

***26.4a2. De-*tert*-butylation of PEEK*.** One property that chemists have tried to introduce into polymers is thermal stability; that is, polymers that can experience high temperatures without degrading. Most linear polymers undergo oxidation at high temperatures and effectively burn up.

Oxidation, like other chemical reactions, requires collisions between oxygen and the reacting molecules. One way to prevent oxidation of polymers is to create rigid polymers which do not rotate readily. These **rigid-rod polymers** are highly crystalline and maintain their shape until they are subjected to extremely high temperatures. An example is **poly(aryl ether ether ketone)**, or **PEEK**. This polymer is stable to temperatures above 500°C; a more flexible polymer such as poly(ethylene terephthalate) decomposes at 300°C.

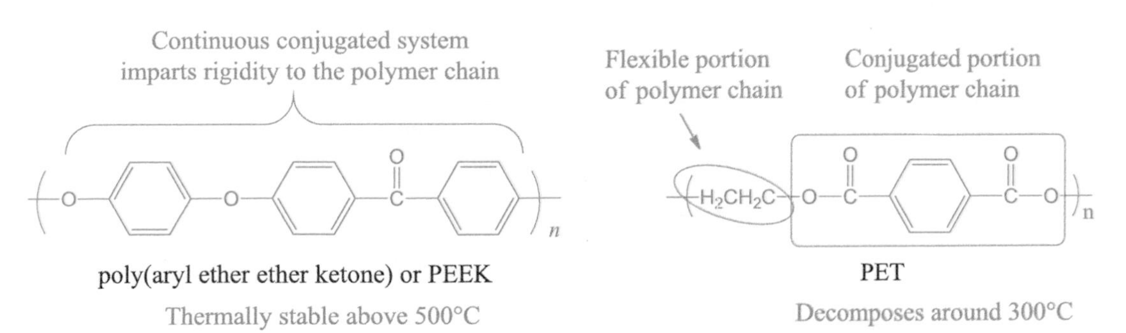

The poly(aryl ether ether ketone) is rigid because the highly conjugated main chain does not undergo rotation readily. In addition, because the chains are long and rigid, they can organize and pack readily in to crystals:

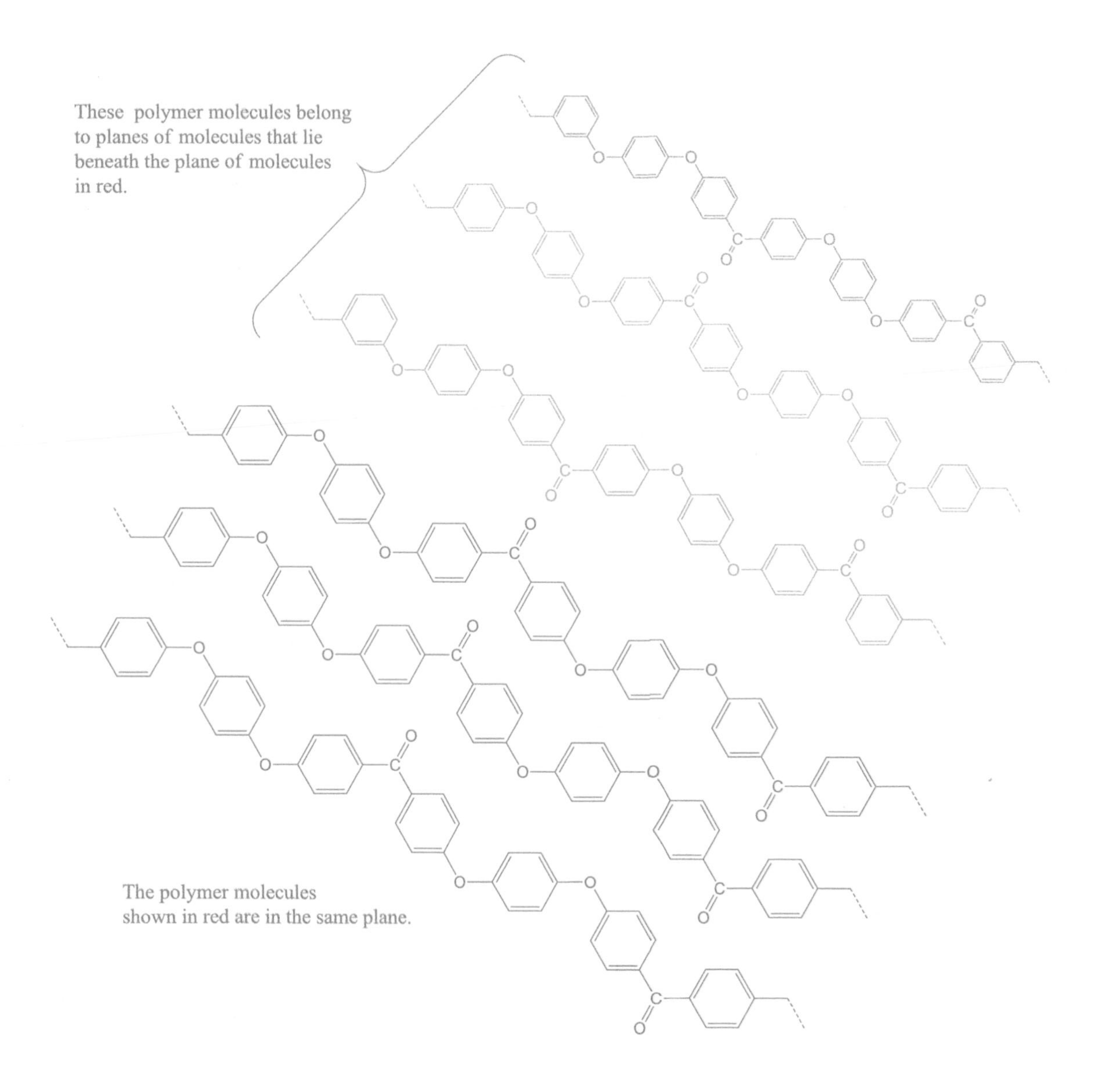
These polymer molecules belong to planes of molecules that lie beneath the plane of molecules in red.
The polymer molecules shown in red are in the same plane.

Figure 26-11. A crystal of a poly(aryl ether ketone) or PEEK

These crystals are stable, and a large amount of energy (available only at high temperatures) is required to separate the chains and make them available for chemical reactions.

Problem 26.7. All the bond angles in PEEK are approximately 120°. Explain why the C—O—C bonds between the phenyl rings have a bond angle closer 120° than to 109.5°.

However, the advantages of PEEK are also its disadvantages. When chemists began to synthesize poly(aryl ether ether ketone), they found that the polymer chains would crystallize out of solution before reaching a substantial length. That is, the formation of the crystalline polymer is thermodynamically favored over the polymer in solution, where it could continue to react.

To address this problem, the chemists incorporated a monomer with a *tert*-butyl group off the aryl ring:

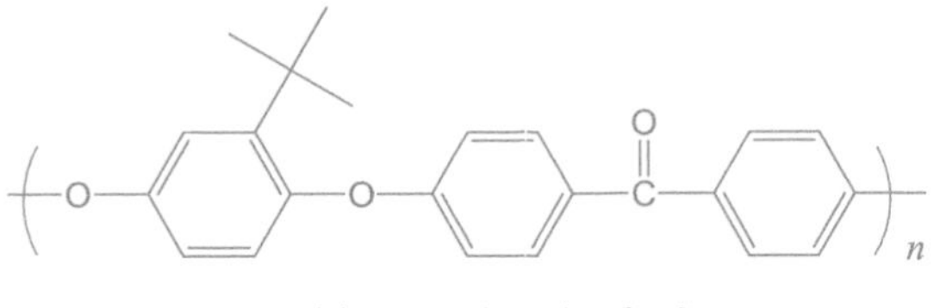

PEEK with a *tert*-butyl substituent

Because the *tert*-butyl groups prevent crystallization of the polymer as it forms, the reaction is able to proceed to a higher degree of polymerization.

To isolate the PEEK, the tert-butyl groups must be removed. The reverse reaction of Friedel-Crafts alkylation allows this to occur. When the reaction occurs in toluene, the solvent acts as a substrate for Friedel-Crafts alkylation. The overall reaction is then a trans-*tert*-butylation, in which the tert-butyl group moves from the polymer to the solvent:

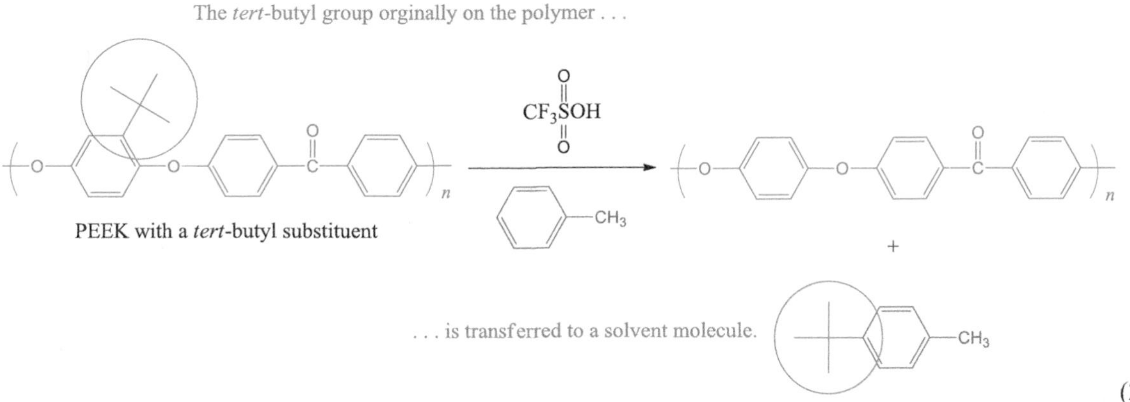

The *tert*-butyl group orginally on the polymer . . .

CF_3SO_2OH

CH_3

PEEK with a *tert*-butyl substituent

. . . is transferred to a solvent molecule.

CH_3

(26-29)

Problem 26.8. Propose a mechanism for the reaction that occurs in Equation 26-29.

26.4b. Crosslinking

In the previous section, linear polymers underwent chemical reactions that changed their structure and properties; the chains, however, remained linear. Many polymers undergo reactions that connect linear polymer chains to create networks.

We examined the structures and uses of PVA in Section 26.4a2, and noted that PVA is extremely water-soluble. To lessen the solubility of PVA, one can crosslink the hydroxyl groups. An interesting example of this is the creation of "slime" from PVA and borax. You can see a video of slime made from PVA and borax at http://www.sciencebob.com/experiments/videos/video-slime3.php. The reaction that occurs is:

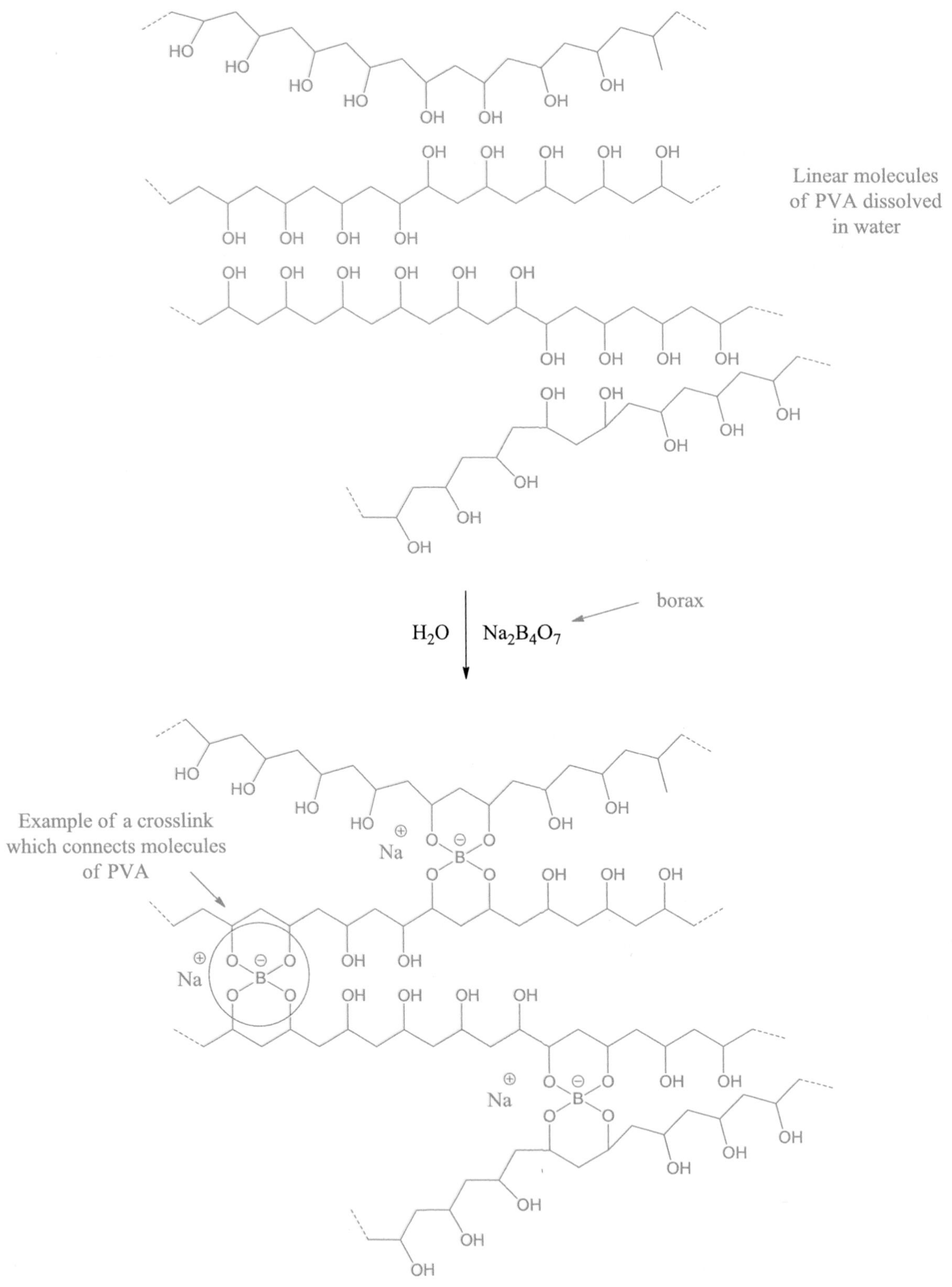

Linear molecules of PVA dissolved in water

borax

H_2O | $Na_2B_4O_7$

Example of a crosslink which connects molecules of PVA

(26-30)

The crosslinking decreases the solubility of the PVA, and also traps water molecules in the polymer, creating a **gel**.

PVA can also be cross-linked with formaldehyde, through formation of an acetal:

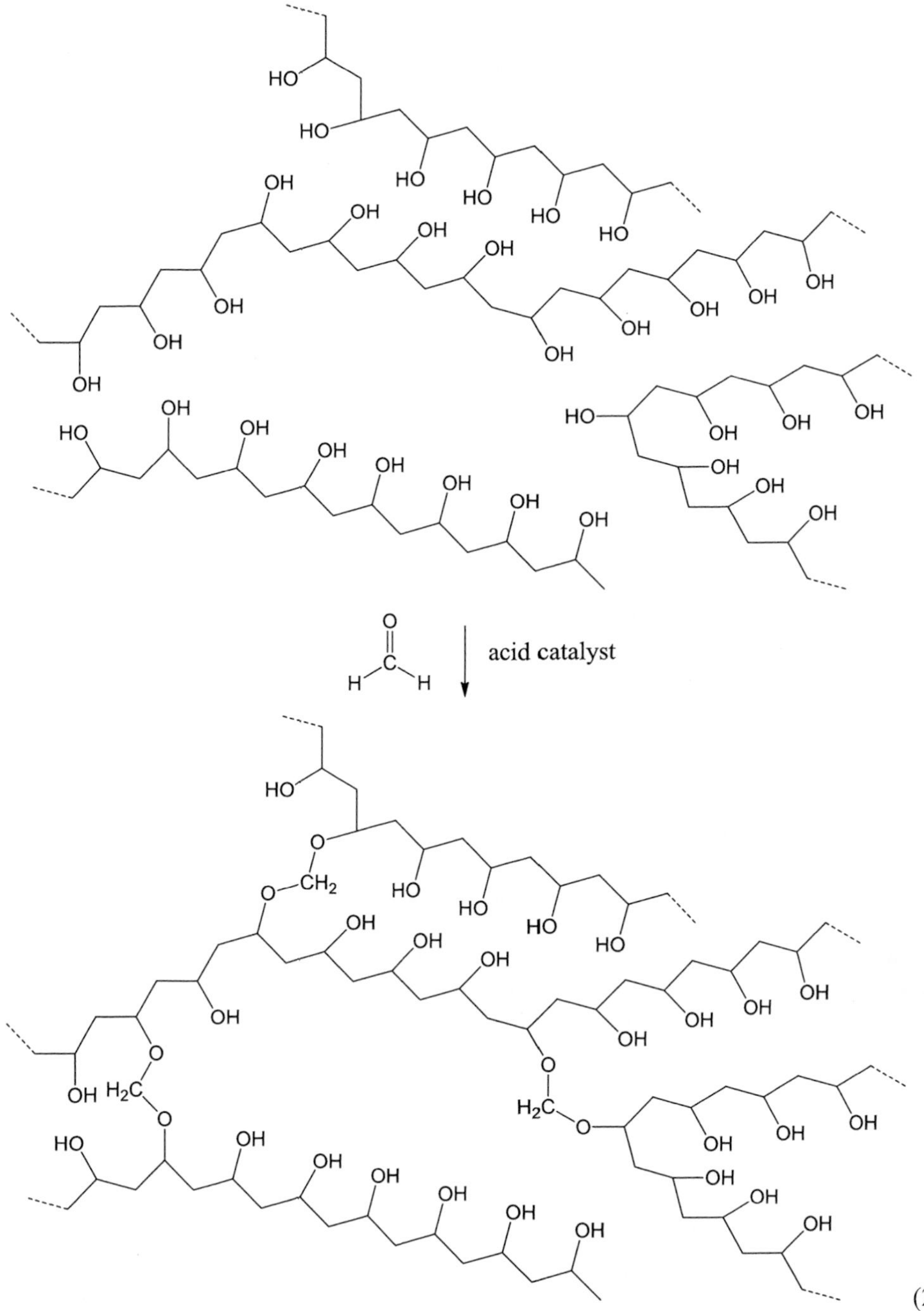

acid catalyst

(26-31)

Problem 26.9. Provide the mechanism for the reaction of two PVA molecules with formaldehyde. Assume some acid is present to catalyze the reaction. (Only the reactive portions of the PVA molecules are shown in detail.)

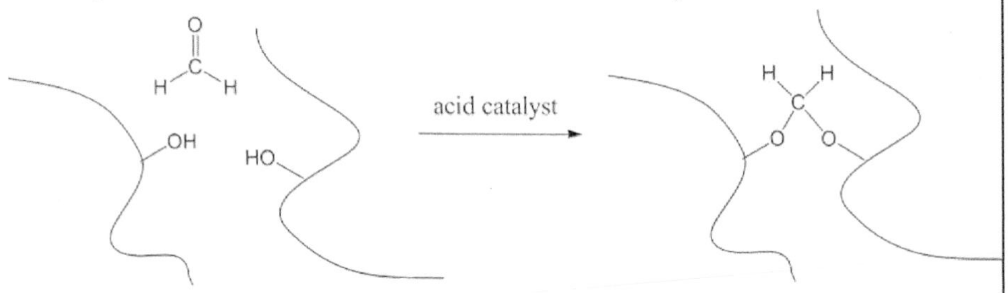

26.5. PROPERTIES OF POLYMERS

You will have noticed that the final properties of a polymer are important, and polymers are frequently "designed," as are drugs and other molecules, to perform a specific function. We will consider several properties in terms of structural properties you studied earlier in the course: intermolecular forces and conformational isomerism. First, however, we have to consider thermal transitions in polymers.

26.5a. Thermal transitions in polymers

You are familiar with organic compounds which are liquids, in which the molecules can flow readily past one another. You are also familiar with solids, in which the molecules are in fixed positions relative to each other. One aspect of organic solids that we have not discussed is their **crystallinity**. Crystalline solids are ones in which the molecules arrange themselves in a regular pattern which repeats throughout the solid. This pattern is referred to as the **crystal lattice**, a term which may be familiar to you from general chemistry. Given the opportunity, organic molecules will arrange themselves in a crystalline structure in which there is regular, repeating pattern of molecules in a crystal lattice. An example of the crystal lattice of solid benzene is shown in Figure 26.11, with four different representations of the benzene molecule.

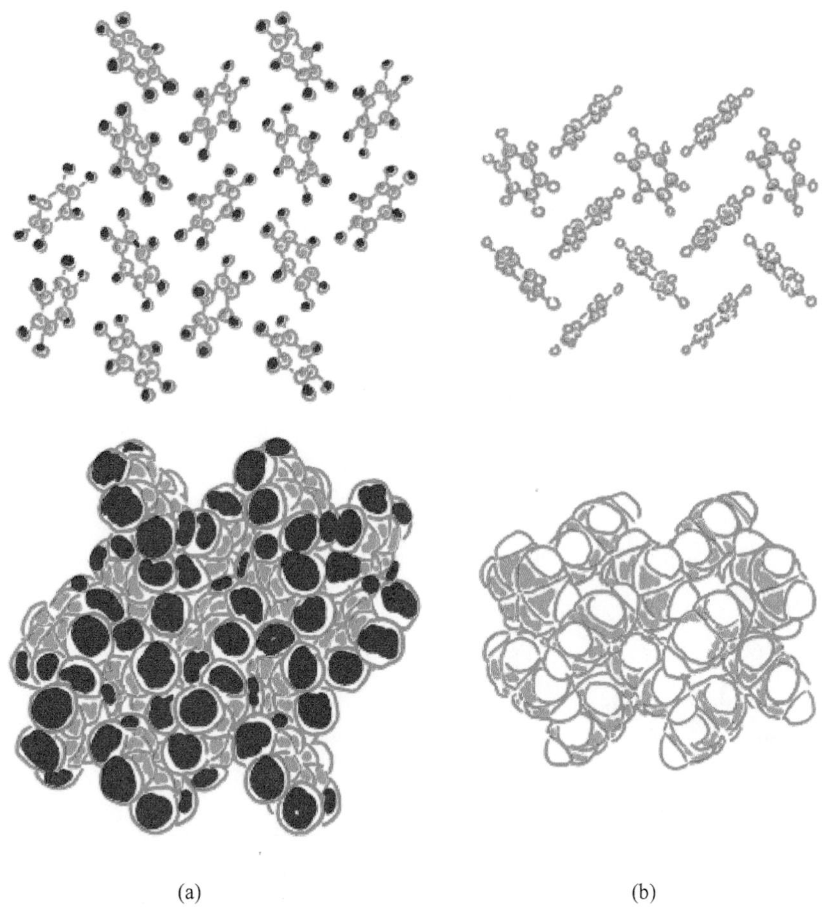

(a) (b)

Figure 26-11. Crystal lattice of solid benzene.

In contrast to crystalline solids, some solids are **amorphous**. In amorphous solids, there is no long range order. The most common example of an amorphous solid is glass, which is composed primarily of silicon dioxide, SiO_2. Figure 26.12 shows a representation of the arrangement of atoms in SiO_2.

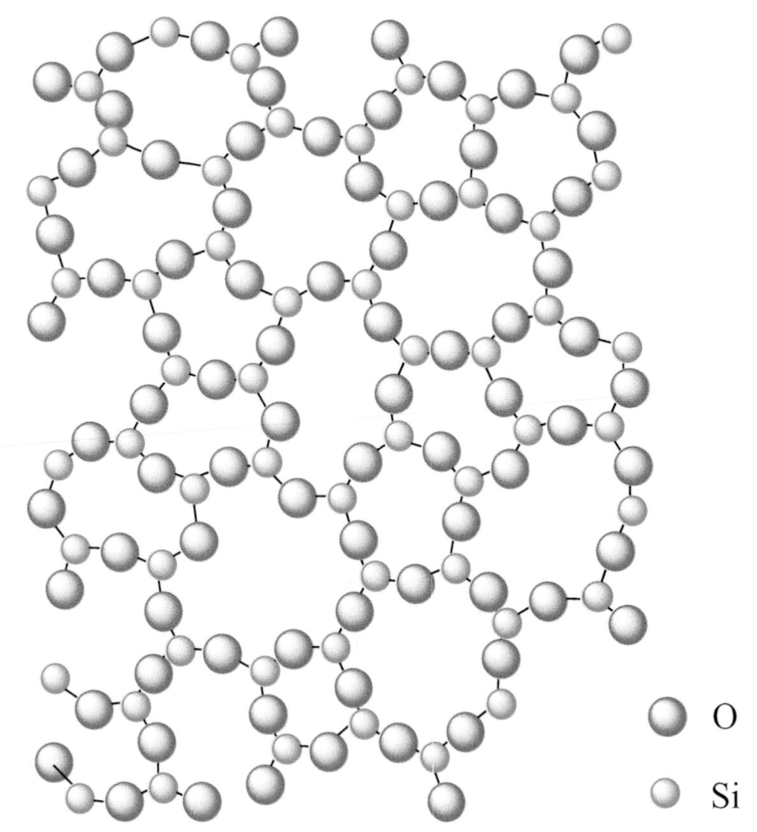

Figure 26-12. Structure of silicon dioxide, an amorphous solid

Crystalline solids have a clearly defined **melting point, T_m**. In polymers, this is the temperature at which the polymer chains have sufficient kinetic energy to leave the crystal lattice and flow as a liquid. As you may have learned in your laboratory course, a pure, crystalline solid has a narrow, well-defined melting point. Incorporation of impurities into the solid lowers the melting point and broadens the range.

Amorphous solids, on the other hand, do not have a defined melting point. There is, however, a temperature at which the atoms in the solid have sufficient kinetic energy that they can move past each other and flow. This temperature is called the **glass transition temperature**. In polymers, the glass transition temperature, T_g, is the temperature at which the molecules begin to display significant molecular motion and exhibit a loss in mechanical strength.

Note that the energy required to change a crystalline solid to a liquid is greater than the energy required for a glass transition. If you compared two samples of the same substance, one in an amorphous state and one in a crystalline state, you would find that the glass transition for the first sample would take place at a lower temperature than the melting point of the second sample. Figure 26-13 depicts the difference between two such solids, and briefly explains the difference in the kinetic energy required by each sample for the molecules to be able to flow past each other.

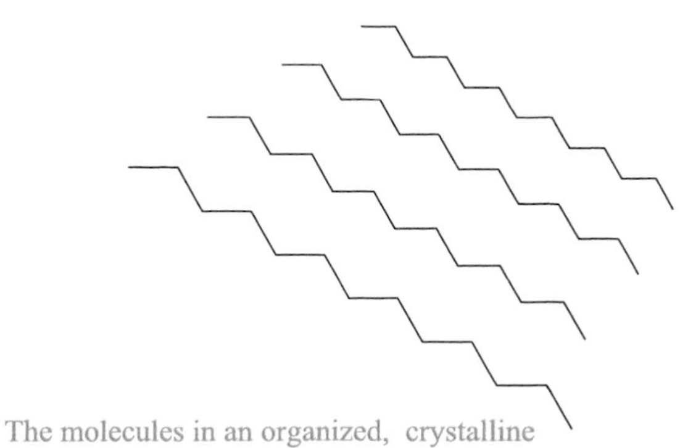

The molecules in an organized, crystalline solid will require significant kinetic energy to overcome intermolecular forces and to increase the entropy of the system as it enters the liquid phase.

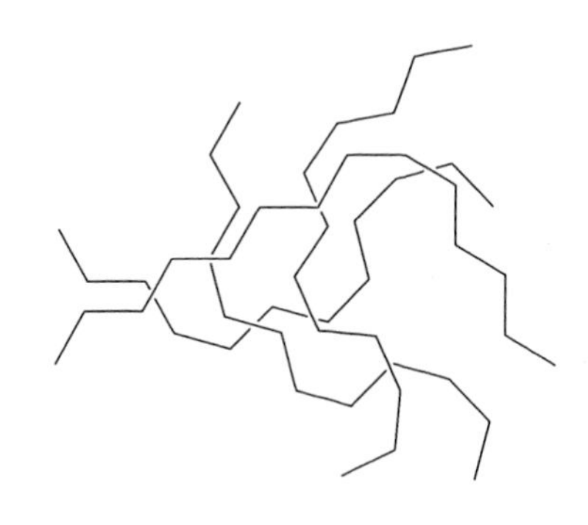

The molecules in an amorphous solid are already at higher entropy; they will require less kinetic energy for molecules to act as a liquid and flow past each other. In addition, the intermolecular forces are not maximized, as in a crystalline solid.

Figure 26.13. A comparison of a sample in crystalline and amorphous forms.

The melting points and the glass transition temperatures of polymers are important because polymers are generally heated and formed into a particular shape. In addition, these temperatures determine the range of temperature in which the polymer can function without losing its shape. Note that applying the word "melting" to a polymer is somewhat misleading. When a polymer melts, it softens and the molecules flow, but rarely to the degree that you observe in solids with smaller molar masses. Polymers "in the melt," as they are called, have a high viscosity. **Viscosity** is the measure of flow of molecules, and the large molecules in polymers flow with more difficulty than smaller molecules.

Polymers range from being completely amorphous to being highly crystalline. Polymers are rarely entirely crystalline for several reasons. First, polymers are mixtures of long chains that vary in length. This variation in length makes the creation of a regular, repeating crystal lattice difficult. In addition, the length of the chains makes it difficult for a single molecule to arrange itself entirely in a regular, orderly fashion.

Polymers can have both crystalline regions and amorphous regions. The crystalline regions are more organized, reflect the order found in crystalline solids, and have a melting point. The amorphous regions lack regular order and undergo a glass transition. Note that the glass transition temperature of a polymer can vary and depends on how the polymer was processed and the conditions under which it was cooled. In addition, the amount of crystallinity affects the glass transition temperature; the crystalline regions "anchor" the amorphous regions and impede movement of the chains in the amorphous regions. Consequently, the more crystalline a polymer, the higher its T_g. Figure 26.14 illustrates this point.

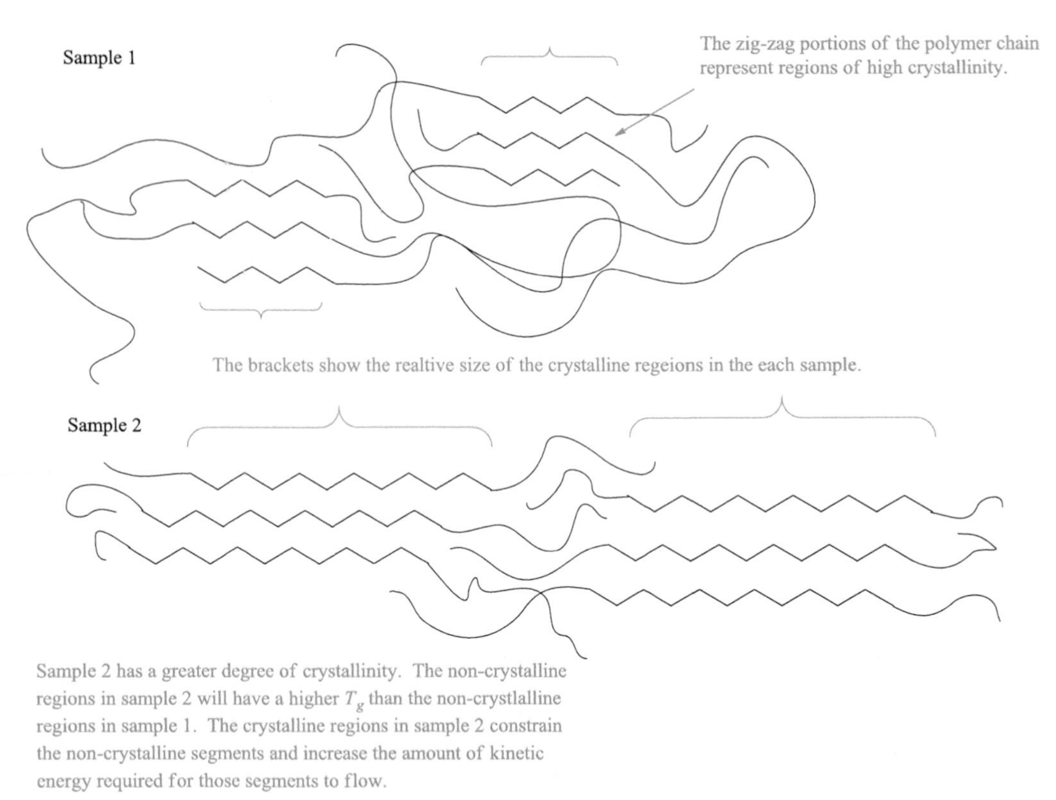

Sample 1
The zig-zag portions of the polymer chain represent regions of high crystallinity.
The brackets show the realtive size of the crystalline regeions in the each sample.
Sample 2
Sample 2 has a greater degree of crystallinity. The non-crystalline regions in sample 2 will have a higher T_g than the non-crystlalline regions in sample 1. The crystalline regions in sample 2 constrain the non-crystalline segments and increase the amount of kinetic energy required for those segments to flow.

Figure 26.14. A comparison of two samples with different degree of crystallinity and the effect of crystallinity on T_g.

Note that both changes in polymers are endothermic. However, crystallization of a polymer is exothermic. That is, when polymer molecules arrange themselves in an organized crystal lattice, they release energy as they go from a higher energy state to a lower energy state. This lower energy is due to the maximization of intermolecular forces, the minimization of steric repulsions, and the minimization of entropy.

A detailed discussion of the glass transition temperature is beyond the scope of this book. The critical ideas are (1) to recognize that polymers can have one or both type of thermal transitions; (2) above the glass transition temperature or melting, polymer molecules have significant mobility; and (3) the melting point, T_m, occurs at a higher temperature than the glass transition, T_g.

Consider the rubber in a rubber band or a racquetball. At room temperature, the rubber is considered an **elastomer** because it can experience mechanical stress yet return to its original shape. For example, a rubber band can be stretched and snap back to its original shape. A racquetball can be deformed by the impact of a racquet or a wall, yet resume its shape and, in the process, force itself away from the racquet or the wall. The rubber can do this because its glass transition temperature is well below room temperature. Consequently, at room temperature, the molecules are not particular constrained and can be deformed readily.

However, if you cool a racquetball in liquid nitrogen (77 K) to a temperature below its T_g, the rubber is in a glassy, amorphous state and the molecules cannot flow past each other. If you throw a frozen racquetball against the wall, it will shatter like glass because the molecules no longer have the mobility they had at room temperature. However, if you warm the broken pieces to room temperature, the rubber will pass through its glass transition state and regain its elasticity.

Second, consider the curve below for a poly(etheretherketone), obtained by differential scanning calorimetry (DSC). DSC essentially measures the heat that flows into or out of a sample.

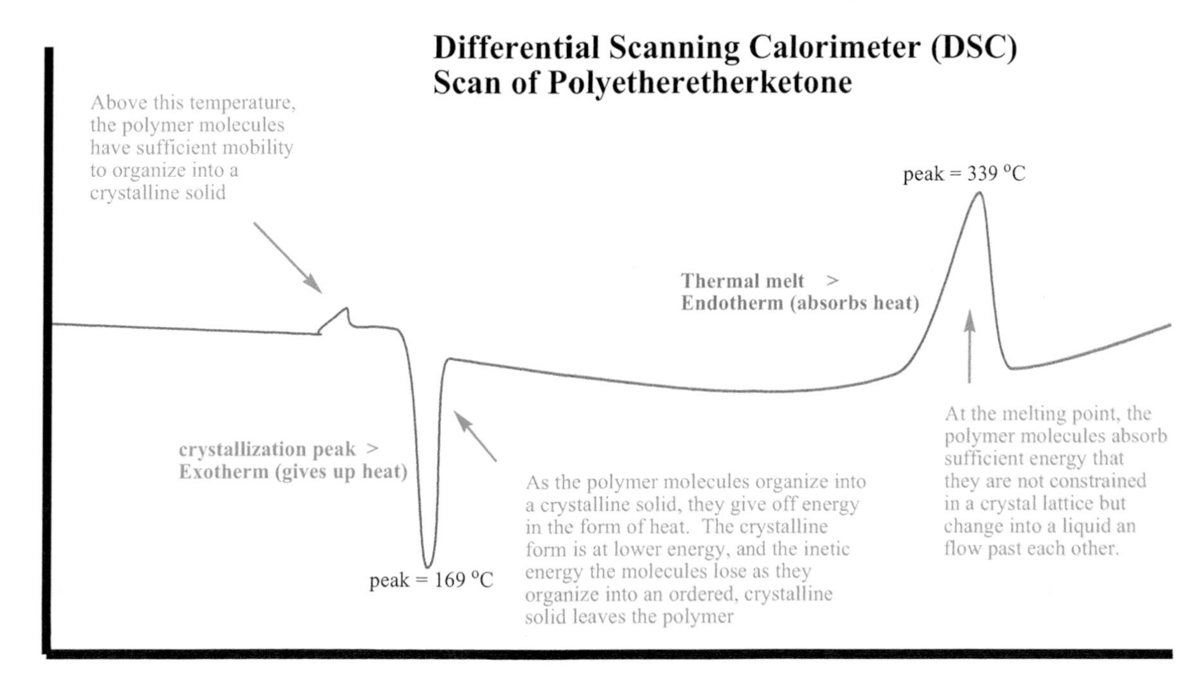

Differential Scanning Calorimeter (DSC)
Scan of Polyetheretherketone
Above this temperature, the polymer molecules have sufficient mobility to organize into a crystalline solid
peak = 339 °C
Thermal melt > Endotherm (absorbs heat)
crystallization peak > Exotherm (gives up heat)
As the polymer molecules organize into a crystalline solid, they give off energy in the form of heat. The crystalline form is at lower energy, and the inetic energy the molecules lose as they organize into an ordered, crystalline solid leaves the polymer
At the melting point, the polymer molecules absorb sufficient energy that they are not constrained in a crystal lattice but change into a liquid an flow past each other.
peak = 169 °C

Figure 26.13. Differential scanning calorimetry scan of a polymer

You can see that around 140°C, the polymer absorbs heat and goes through its glass transition. This gives the polymer chains enough mobility to crystallize. When they do this, heat is given off, as they go from a higher energy state to a lower, more stable crystalline form. At a higher temperature, the crystalline form melts and the polymer molecules are capable of flow.

Figure 26.13 illustrates an important point. When the polymer chains crystallize, they give off energy and attain a more stable state. Note that this stability accounts for the high melting point of the polymer. Keep this in mind as we proceed to the next section.

Also note that polymers range from those that are highly amorphous to those that are highly crystalline. Most polymers have a glass transition state; not all have an actual melting point. Figure 26.14 contains a generic DSC diagram, showing the three possible thermal transitions. Note that, as the diagram shows, the endotherm for melting is much greater for that of the glass transition. For amorphous polymers, the peaks associated with crystallization and melting will be small or non-existent; for highly crystalline polymers, these peaks will be significant and may make the glass transition appear insignificant as in Figure 26.13.

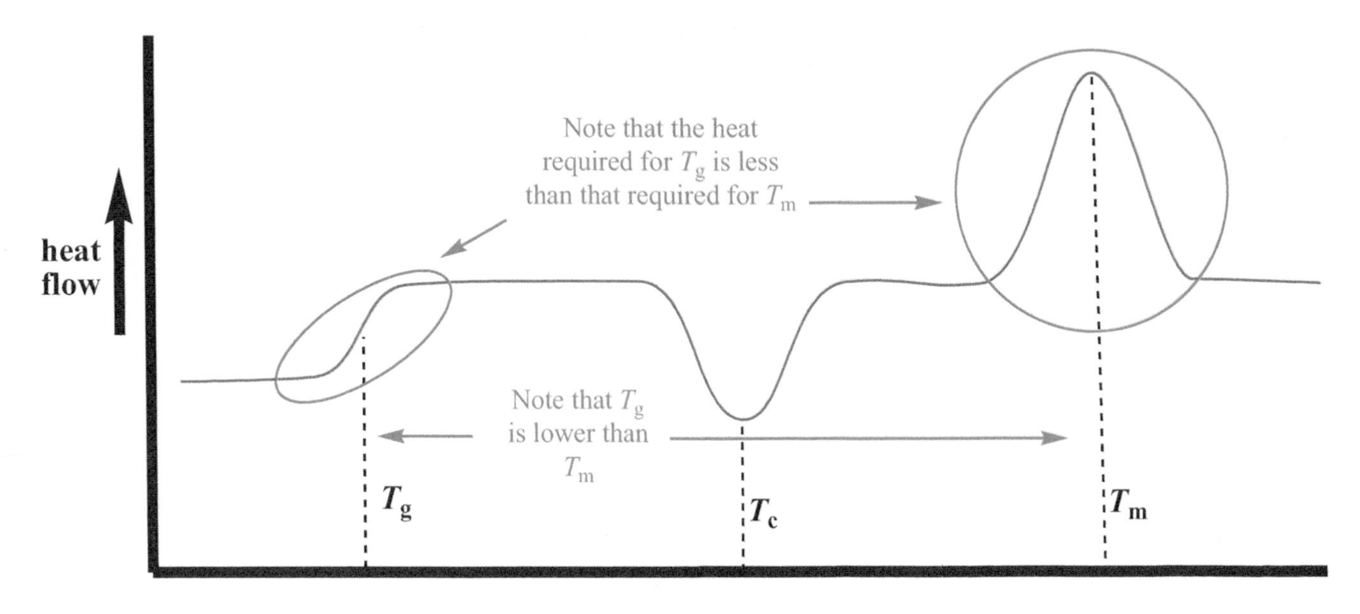

Figure 26-14. A generic DSC scan of a polymer

> Amorphous polymers experience a glass transition at a temperature represented by T_g. Crystalline polymers melt at a temperature represented by T_m. The glass transition requires less energy than melting, and, consequently, T_g is less than T_m for polymers with both amorphous and crystalline regions.

26.5b. Factors affecting thermal transitions in polymers

Synthetic polymers are useful because they can be molded into useful objects. **Thermoplastic** polymers can be heated above their glass transition temperature or melting point and then forced into molds, pushed through slots to form films or threads. This is the origin of the term **plastic** to describe polymers.

In Chapter 2, we examined intermolecular forces, and observed that the stronger the IMF, the higher the temperature required for a phase transition, either from solid to liquid or liquid to gas. This is also true for polymers: the stronger the IMF, the higher the glass transition temperature or melting point.

In general, strong IMF will lead to a more stable crystal lattice, one with an arrangement of molecules that will maximize attractions between the molecules and minimize steric repulsions and other unfavorable arrangements. In order for the molecules in a solid to move past each other and flow, the solid must absorb sufficient heat to overcome the attractions between molecules and provide the molecules with kinetic energy for movement away from the crystal lattice. We will examine the factors that affect the amount of heat required for this change.

1. An increase in chain length of linear molecules raises the melting point.

As we saw in Section 2.6d, the longer a hydrocarbon chain, the more energy (or higher temperature) to melt the solid. As the linear molecules increase in length, the dispersion forces experienced by each molecule increase, the stronger IMF stabilize the solid and require a higher temperature for melting. Similarly, as the molecular mass or degree of polymerization increases for a linear polymer, the melting point increases.

2. Structural features or functional groups that increase intermolecular forces will increase melting point.

In general, polar molecules will have higher melting points than similar, nonpolar molecules. For example, polypropylene and poly(vinyl chloride) have significantly different T_g's:

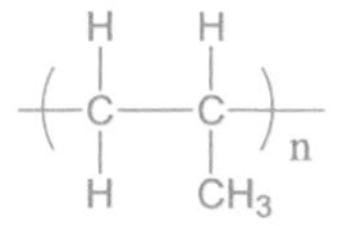

polypropylene

$T_g = -18°C$

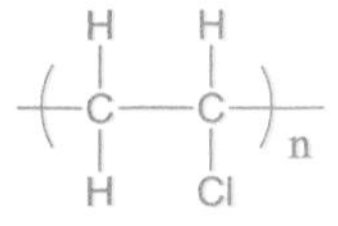

poly(vinyl chloride)

$T_g = 87°C$

3. Periodic or random branching will decrease melting point.

You may recall that branched alkanes have lower melting points or boiling points than straight-chain alkanes. Polymers follow this same trend. In addition to reducing surface area for induced-dipole/induced-dipole attractions, branching interferes with the molecules' ability to organize into a regular crystal lattice. There is no longer a simple, regular pattern for organizing the molecules into the solid. Moreover, in the solid form, branches push the neighboring molecules away from the main chain, decreasing the dispersion forces between them. For example, branched polyethylene has a melting point of 112°C while linear polyethylene has a melting point of 135°C.

4. The regular branching of side groups increases the melting point.

If the polymer has side groups that occur regularly, then the melting point will increase because these groups increase the barrier to rotation about single bonds. For example, vinyl polymers with side-groups generally have higher melting points than polyethylene. Consider polyethylene and polypropylene:

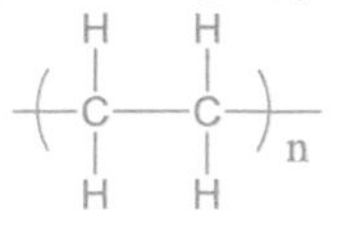

polyethylene

$T_m = 135°C$

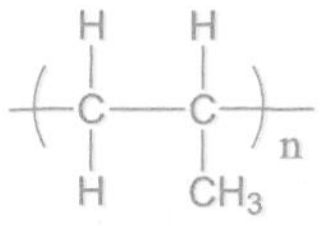

polypropylene

$T_m = 160$ to $185°C$

If we look at the Newman projection for the two carbons in the repeating unit of each of these polymers, we see the methyl group presents a barrier to rotation that is not present when there are only hydrogens attached to the carbons:

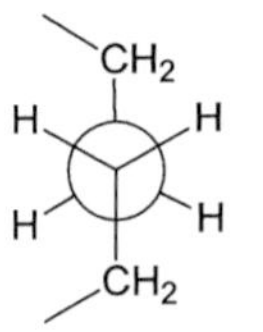

Newman projection for polyethylene

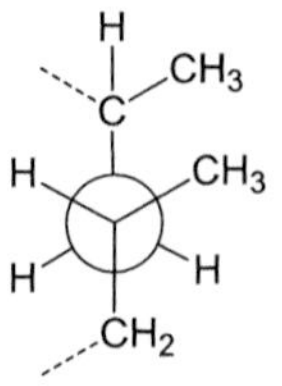

Newman projection for polypropylene

The cumulative effect of the methyl groups is significant; as a result, the polypropylene chain requires a much higher melting temperature.

However, if the side groups get long, they push the polymer molecules apart, decrease intermolecular attractions, and decrease the melting point or glass transition temperature. Consider the following two polymers:

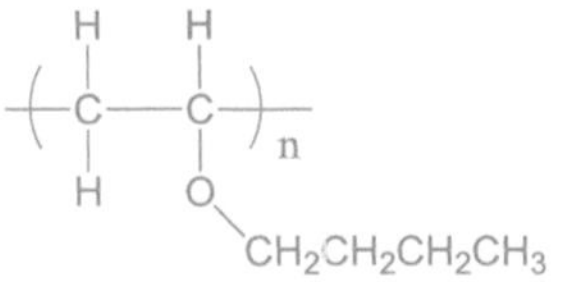

poly(vinyl *n*-butyl ether)
T_g = -52°

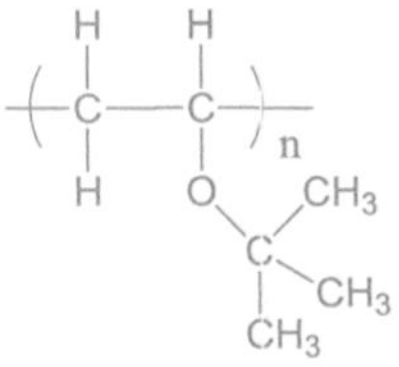

poly(vinyl *tert*-butyl ether)
T_g = 88°

The bulky *tert*-butyl group greatly hinders rotation around the single bonds in the polymer chain. The *n*-butyl group does not have as dramatic effect and, in addition, is slightly longer and pushes the neighboring chains away. Consequently, the polymer with the *tert*-butyl group has a higher glass transition temperature.

5. Rigid chains have higher melting points than flexible chains.

If rotation about single bonds is not possible, then more energy is required for the molecule to move away from the crystal structure. We have already seen this effect in Section 26.4a2, in the comparison of PEEK and PET. PEEK, with its more rigid chain, has the higher melting point.

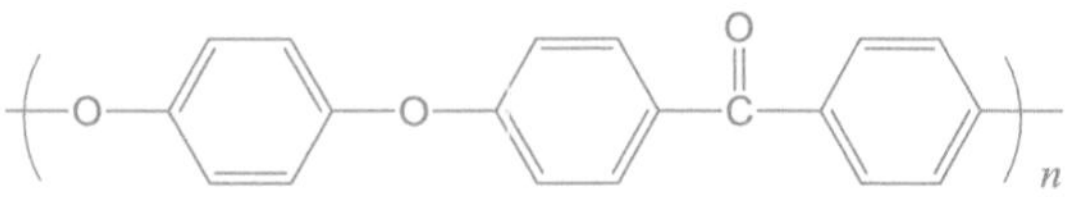

poly(aryl ether ether ketone) or PEEK

T_m = 365 °C

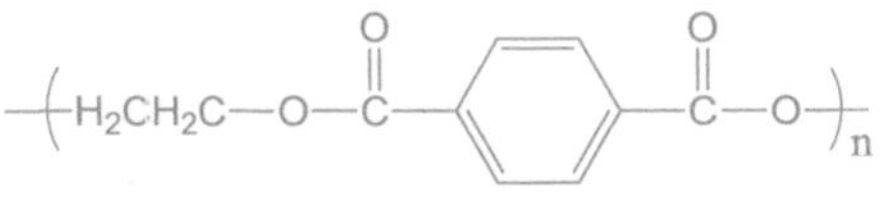

PET

T_m = 270 °C

6. In general, factors that allow molecules to pack into an orderly crystal structure will increase melting point.

Highly symmetric molecules, which have an inherently lower entropy than less symmetric molecules, have higher melting points. Consider pentane and neopentane:

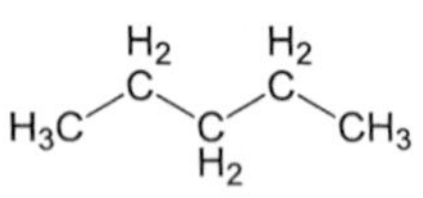

pentane
m.p = -129.7°C
b.p = 36.1°C

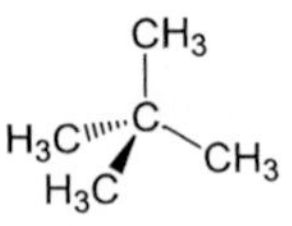

neopentane
m.p = -19.8°C
b.p. = 9.5°C

Both compounds have the same molar mass and a comparison of the boiling points indicate that neopentane has weaker intermolecular forces. We expect this, because of its smaller surface area.

However, the high symmetry of neopentane contributes to its higher melting point. The symmetry of the molecules of neopentane allow them to pack easily into a crystal lattice. Pentane, on the other hand, has to go to a lower temperature (at which the molecules have less kinetic energy) before they organize themselves into a crystal lattice.

7. Electrostatic attractions from ionic groups in organic molecules dramatically increase T_g and T_m.

The attraction between cations and anions is extremely strong. In fact, some organic compounds with ionic groups decompose before they melt. The energy required to overcome the electrostatic forces is greater than that required to break the covalent bonds. Polymers with ionic side groups frequently decompose before they melt. For example, poly(acrylic acid) has a glass transition temperature of 106°C. Poly(sodium acrylate), however, does not soften when heated and decomposes at temperature above 260°C.

Hydrogen bonds between molecules of poly(acrylic acid) give it a relatively high T_g.

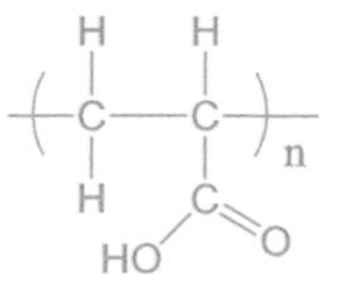

The electrostatic forces between molecules of poly(sodium acrylate), however, prevent the polymer from softening before it reaches a temperature at which it decomposes.

poly(acrylic acid)

$T_g = 106°C$

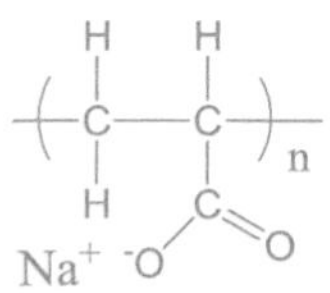

poly(sodium acrylate)

Decomposes at T > 260°C

8. Crosslinking polymer chains increases melting point.

As we noted in Section 26.4b, crosslinking increases the rigidity of a polymer system and restricts movement of the polymer chains. This results in an increase in melting point. For example, the use of natural rubber was a disaster in the nineteenth century. Raincoats made of cotton treated with rubber became gooey messes in the summer, because rubber has a melting point around 28°C. Natural rubber was also poorly suited for use in automobile tires because the rubber softened under the friction of use. The introduction of vulcanization, in which the polymer chains were cross-linked by sulfur, raised the melting point of the rubber and eliminated these problems. (See Section 26.2c.)

26.5c. Solubility

In general, the solubility of polymers follows the same patterns that we discussed in Chapter 2. When the intermolecular forces of the solvent and polymer are similar, the polymer will dissolve. For example, polystyrene readily dissolves in toluene, an aromatic solvent that readily solvates the aromatic side groups in polystyrene. Poly(vinyl alcohol) dissolves in water, due to the ability of the hydroxyl groups to hydrogen bond with water. Polymers with ionic sides groups, such as poly(sodium acrylate), dissolve even more readily in water because of ion-dipole interactions.

However, any factors that limit solvent molecules' interactions with the polymer will decrease solubility. For example, network polymers are rarely soluble, because the crosslinks prevent sufficient solvent/polymer interactions. For example, linear poly(vinyl alcohol) (see Section 26.4b) is soluble in water, and is used in water-based glues. However, when PVA is crosslinked, it can be used as a sponge. The PVA retains its ability to hydrogen bond with water, but is no longer soluble in water.

Highly crystalline polymers also have lower solubilities. Solvent-polymer interactions may not be strong enough to overcome polymer-polymer interactions. Again, we saw this in the discussion of PEEK in 26.4a2.

26.6. USES OF POLYMERS: THE RELATIONSHIP BETWEEN STRUCTURE AND FUNCTION

In the previous sections, we have studied the effect of structure on the properties of polymers. This allows us to evaluate polymers and understand their suitability for certain uses.

26.6a. Food storage: Polyethylene, polystyrene and PET

Historically, food products were shipped in containers made of glass, metal, or ceramic. In an effort to improve shelf life, lower costs, and expand the range of foods that can be packaged, industry has turned to polymers for food packaging. Note that one property of materials for food storage is a lack of chemical reactivity: you don't want to store food in a material that will react with it and affect its taste. Consequently, polyolefins such as polyethylene and polypropylene, which are essentially alkanes, are logical choices for food storage. Also note that food storage requires materials that are essentially water-insoluble, because you do not want the material to dissolve on the surface of the food. Again, polyolefins are a good choice for this application.

Polyethylene, the simplest polyolefin, comes in three types: low-density polyethylene (LDPE), linear low-density polyethylene (LLDPE), and high-density polyethylene (HDPE).

LDPE is a flexible polymer that is used for packaging foods. It has a low T_g (-25°C) and fairly low T_m (around 112°C). As noted in Section 26.5b, it has substantial branching, which contributes to its low glass transition temperature. This is because of hydrogen atom abstraction (see Section 25.4b) during free-radical polymerization:

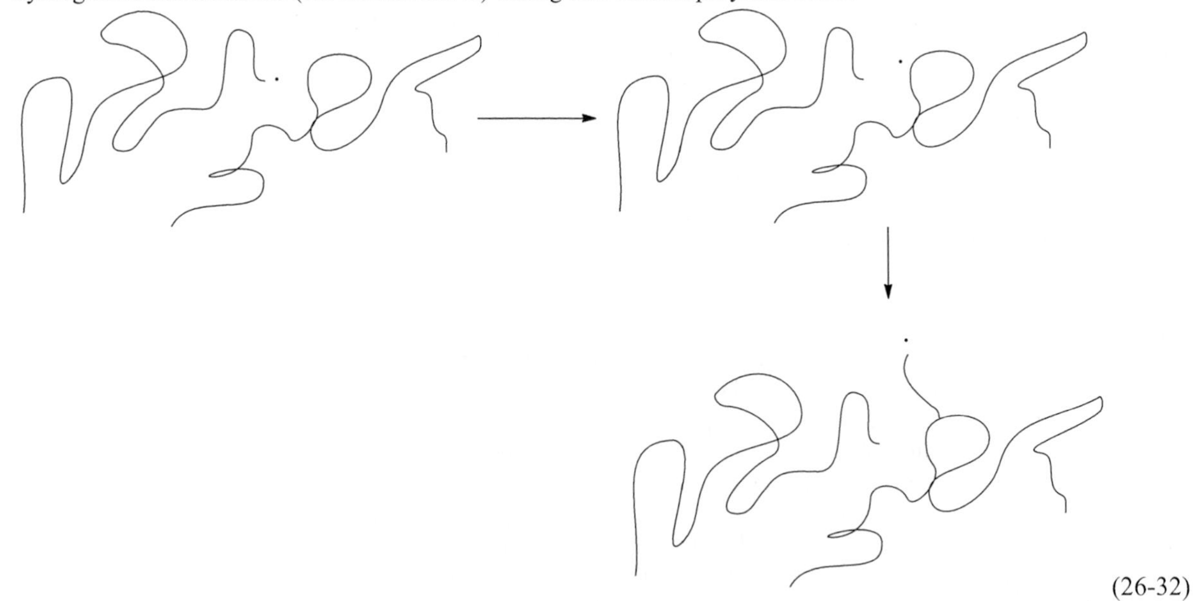

(26-32)

Your turn 26.12. Below are representations of the reaction in Equation 26-27), showing the details of the atoms involved. Use curved arrows to show the movement of electrons, and provide the product of the second reaction.

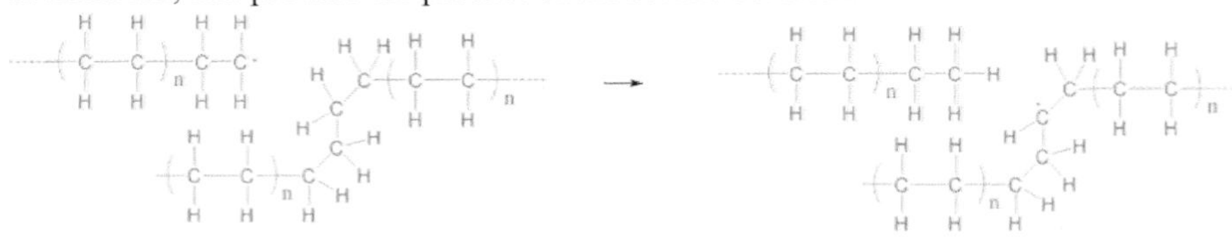

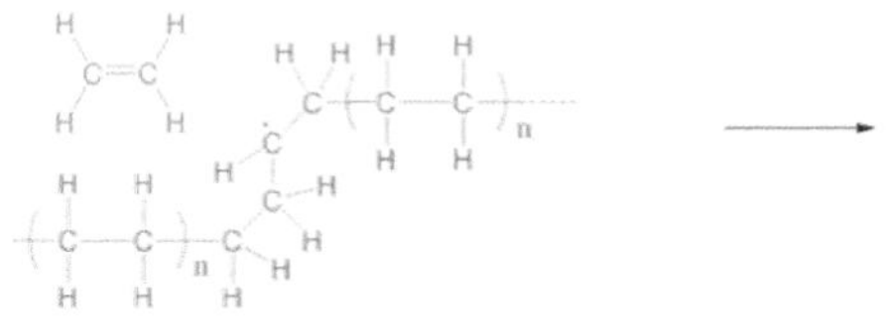

In contrast to LDPE, HDPE is synthesized using a catalytic system that prevents branching, and only a linear polymer is produced. Due to its increased crystallinity, HDPE has a higher melting point (135°C) and higher tensile strength. This makes HDPE suitable for applications in which LDPE would fail. For example, one of the major uses of HDPE is to make milk jugs and other containers for liquids.

Note that polyethylene molecules are essentially extremely large alkane molecules. Because alkanes are relatively unreactive, polyethylene makes an excellent material for food-contact applications such as film and bottles.

Linear low-density polyethylene, LLDPE, is a compromise between the LDPED and HDPE. LLDPE is made by copolymerization of ethylene and a small percentage of 1-alkenes. The copolymerization takes place with a catalyst that produces a linear polymer. The linearity of the polymer increases intermolecular forces, leading to a higher melting point (T_m = 125°C) and greater strength than that of LDPE. LLDPE is used extensively in the manufacture of garbage bags, where the plastic bag needs flexibility, but also needs high tensile strength to prevent rips in the bag.

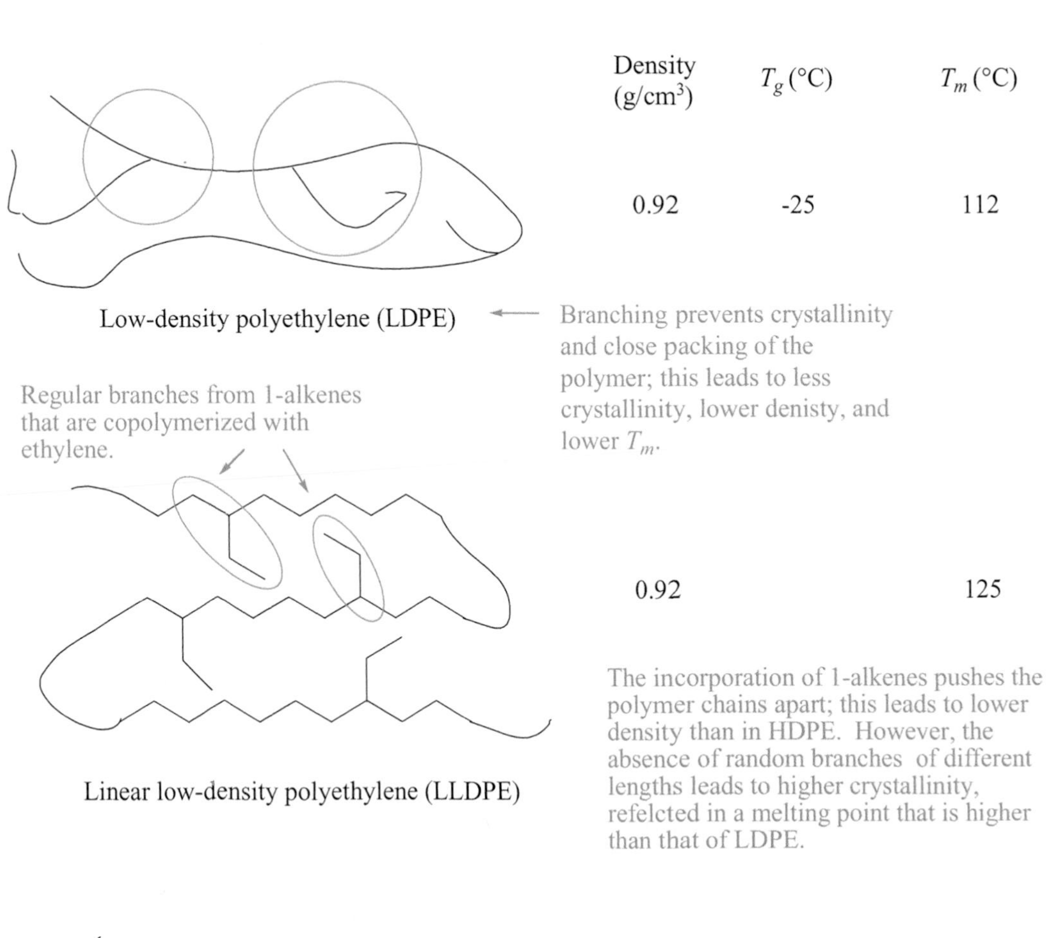

Density (g/cm3)
Tg (°C)
Tm (°C)
0.92
-25
112
Low-density polyethylene (LDPE)
Branching prevents crystallinity and close packing of the polymer; this leads to less crystallinity, lower denisty, and lower Tm.
Regular branches from 1-alkenes that are copolymerized with ethylene.
0.92
125
The incorporation of 1-alkenes pushes the polymer chains apart; this leads to lower density than in HDPE. However, the absence of random branches of different lengths leads to higher crystallinity, refelcted in a melting point that is higher than that of LDPE.
Linear low-density polyethylene (LLDPE)

0.95
135
High-density polyethylene (HDPE)
Highly linear polymer chains result in maximum crystallinity, maximum density, and the highest melting point. The polymer is about 94% crystalline, and, consequently, more rigid than LDPE or LLDPE.

Figure 26.15. A comparison of three grades of polyethylene

In contrast to PE, which is extremely flexible, a common plastic is polystyrene (PS). PS, with phenyl rings which increase the barrier to rotation around the main chain, has less flexibility than PE. Consequently, the T_g of PS (87–97°C) is much higher than that of PE. Note that commercial polystyrene is completely amorphous due to the random arrangement of the phenyl rings on either side of the main chain.

The presence of the phenyl groups makes the material denser (1.05 g/cm^3 vs. 0.94 g/cm^3 for HDPE). The rigidity and low cost of PS make it a choice for a variety of applications; the most familiar to you may be the "jewel" cases for compact discs. It is also used in foams (styrofoam) for insulation and for insulated food packaging such as coffee cups and "to-go boxes."

> **Problem 26.10.** Why would HDPE be an inappropriate material for a CD case? Why is is PS an inappropriate material for a milk jug?

Poly(ethylene terephthalate), or PET, is the material used in two-liter bottles for carbonated beverages. Faced with the shipping costs of relatively heavy glass bottles and loss from breakage, manufacturers of carbonated beverages have found PET to be an effective replacement. However, the important requirement for a pop bottle is impermeability: the carbon dioxide in carbonated beverages must be contained in the bottle and not seep through the plastic bottle over time.

Plastics manufacturers have maximized the impermeability and strength of PET by maximizing its crystallinity. When crystallinity is imposed on PET mechanically, the density of the plastic rises from 1.33 g/cm^3 to 1.39 g/cm^3. This compares to 0.94 for HDPE and 1.07 for PS. The high melting point of PET, 260 to 265°C, reflects its strength. PET has four times the tensile strength of HDPE and more than twice the tensile strength of PS.

26.6b. Textile fibers and Spandex

Replacement of natural fibers with synthetic ones has been an economic motivation for the development of several polymers. Nylon has been used to replace silk, due to its strength. PET, in addition to being used in pop bottles, is also the polyester used in textiles (and is the primary use of PET). PET's stiffness makes it resistant to wrinkling and has led to its use in cotton/polyester blends.

Spandex, however, is unlike natural fiber or nylon: it has elastic properties unlike these fibers. Designed by DuPont in 1959, Lycra, or spandex, is a copolymer that contains polyether segments. These are flexible, and can stretch up to 600% and then recover their shape. The other portion of the copolymer, usually a urethane, is rigid and imparts strength to the fiber. These portions also act to anchor the elastic segments and help the fibers keep their shape. Lycra is always blended with other fibers. Its overall weight is less than rubber and it is less prone to reaction with perspiration.

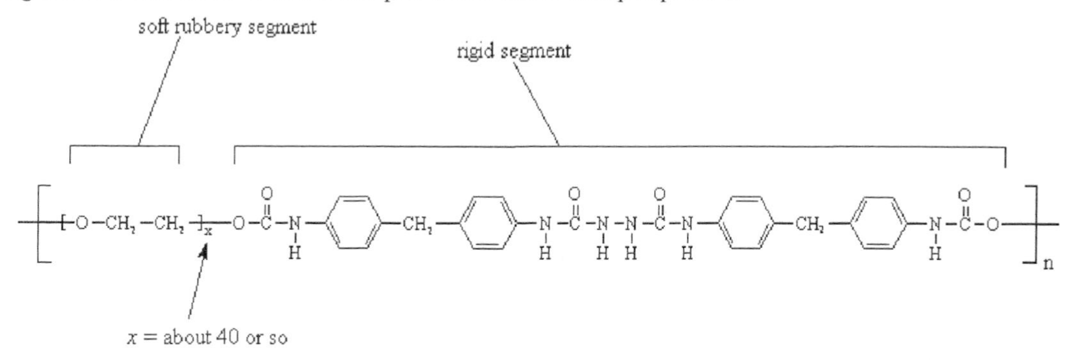
soft rubbery segment
rigid segment
x = about 40 or so
Spandex has a complicated structure, with both
urea and urethane linkages in the backbone chain.

Figure 26-15. The structure of Spandex

26.6c. Ion-exchange resins

In the previous examples, the application of the polymer depended primarily on physical properties. Some polymers are used for chemical reactions. **Ion-exchange resins** are polymer-based systems that allow the exchange of one ion for another. They are the basis for treatment of hard water in homes; that is, they are the chemistry behind water softeners.

Many water sources contain significant amounts of calcium ion, Ca^{2+}. This ion precipitates easily with soap molecules. This precipitation cuts down on the effectiveness of the soap and creates soap scum.

Recall that soaps are the sodium or potassium salts of fatty acids. The sodium and potassium salts are much more soluble than the calcium salts. Consequently, one way to treat hard water containing calcium ion is to replace the calcium ion with sodium ion. This minimizes the precipitation of soap; it also minimizes the precipitation of calcium salts (e.g., calcium carbonate) which can clog pipes.

To do this, chemists have created ion-exchange resins. The resin part of name refers to the polymeric material, usually cross-linked polystyrene, which is the solid phase on which the reaction takes place. The polystyrene is first sulfonated (see Section 22.7) and then neutralized with sodium hydroxide:

$$\left[\text{CH}_2\text{–CH(C}_6\text{H}_5)\right]_n \xrightarrow{H_2SO_4} \left[\text{CH}_2\text{–CH(C}_6\text{H}_4\text{SO}_3\text{H)}\right]_n \xrightarrow{NaOH} \left[\text{CH}_2\text{–CH(C}_6\text{H}_4\text{SO}_3^{\ominus}\ \text{Na}^{\oplus})\right]_n \qquad (26\text{-}33)$$

The resin now contains numerous ionic sites with sodium ions associated with the sulfonate groups.

When water begins to pass through a column of this resin, there is significant difference in the concentrations of the cations in the two systems:

Table 26-1. Changes in concentration of Ca^{2+} and Na^+ during different stages of use of an ion-exchange column.

	$[Ca^{2+}]$	$[Na^+]$
Initially	High concentration in hard water Low concentration in ion-exchange resin	Moderate to low concentration in hard water High concentration in ion-exchange resin
During treatment in water softener	Calcium ions migrate from hard water to sulfonate groups, increasing $[Ca^{2+}]$ in the resin and decreasing $[Ca^{2+}]$ in the water	Sodium ions are "exchanged" for calcium ions, with $[Na^+]$ increasing in water and decreasing in the resin.
After treatment	The majority of calcium ions are now in the resin	Sodium ions from the resin have replaced calcium ions that were in the water

The exchange is an example of Le Châtelier's principle in operation: the calcium ions move from a phase with a high concentration to one with a low concentration; the same is true for the sodium ions.

After repeated use, the ion-exchange resin becomes less effective because the sodium concentration in the resin has decreased and the calcium ion concentration has increased. There is less difference in the concentrations between the two phases (the resin and the water passing through) and the ion-exchange process becomes less effective. After repeated uses, the resin is ineffective.

To keep the resin active, it must be recharged. Homeowners use bags of salt to maintain their water softeners because the softener is programmed to flush the ion-exchange resin with a strong sodium chloride solution periodically. In this case, the situation is the reverse of the one above: the salt solution is high in sodium while the resin is high in calcium. The reverse movement takes place, and a salt solution with calcium ions from the resin is discharged from the softener.

26.7 DEGRADATION AND DEPOLYMERIZATION

Frequently, organic chemists have the need to reverse a reaction. The ability to form bonds between a large number of small molecules to create a polymer is useful. Under different circumstances, however, the ability to break a polymer into smaller units is also useful or, under certain conditions, unavoidable. A reaction which breaks a molecule into smaller molecules is generally referred to as a **degradation reaction**. A reaction which causes polymer molecules to revert to monomer molecules is called a **depolymerization**.

The retro Diels-Alder reaction (see Section 24.3a) is analogous to depolymerization: the Diels-Alder adduct is a dimer which reverts to the monomer. Recall that the reverse Diels-Alder reaction is entropy-driven and occurs at high temperatures. Consequently, dicyclopentadiene, which forms readily at room temperature, reverts to cyclopentadiene when heated to 200°C.

A dimer, a molecule of two parts, made from two dicyclopentadience molecules

200°C

Upon heating, the dimer reverts to the monomers from which it was made

(26-34)

Historically, a significant depolymerization was the isolation of isoprene from rubber. In 1860, Greville William heated rubber in the absence of oxygen. The volatile product that he isolated was identified as isoprene.

or

n

Δ

n

isoprene

(26-35)

Although poly(isoprene) has been synthesized from isoprene, note that the rubber plant does not use isoprene to biosynthesize rubber. Nevertheless, the isolation of isoprene from rubber is significant because many other natural products are built from the same building blocks that the rubber plant uses. Essential oils contain terpenes and terpenoids, most of which can be broken down into isoprene units (see Section 2.12c) or 2-methylbutane units.

In general, reactions in which the products have a higher entropy than the reactants are likely to occur at high temperatures. Elimination, for example, is favored at high temperatures because of the increase in entropy as the reactants form products (see Section 9.8). An analogous situation occurs in PVC, in which HCl can be eliminated to form double bonds:

Cl Cl Cl Cl Cl Cl —Δ→ Cl Cl Cl Cl Cl

↓

← ← ← Cl Cl Cl Cl

(26-36)

Once double bonds begin to form, subsequent eliminations of HCl from the polymer chain occur readily, and the molecule "unzips" to form a polyene and the equivalent of hydrogen chloride. Because of this problem, PVC poses a safety hazard when fires occur; the formation of hydrogen chloride can be dangerous. This danger is offset by the addition of metal salts which react with HCl.

Currently, chemists believe that the double bonds form via an E1 mechanism (see Chapters 8 and 9 for a review of this reaction).

Problem 26.11. Provide the mechanism for the reaction that forms the first double bond in the product in Equation 26-36.

Problem 26.12. In the series of reactions shown in Equation 26-36, the second and subsequent double bonds form more quickly than the first double bond. Explain this observation.

APPLICATIONS TO BIOLOGY AND BIOCHEMISTRY

26.8 APPLICATIONS TO BIOLOGY AND BIOCHEMISTRY: BIOLOGICAL MACROMOLECULES

In Section 1.12, we learned that proteins, carbohydrates (saccharides), and nucleic acids are constructed from relatively small molecular building blocks. Proteins are constructed from amino acids, carbohydrates are constructed from monosaccharides, and nucleic acids are constructed from nucleotides. Each of these molecular building blocks can therefore be viewed as a monomer, and when many such monomers link together to produce a large biomolecule, the result is a **biopolymer**. More specifically, a protein is also called a **polyamino acid** or **polypeptide** (due to the peptide bond that links together amino acids), a large carbohydrate is also called a **polysaccharide**, and a nucleic acid is also called a **polynucleotide**.

As we have seen throughout this chapter, the properties of a polymer are governed by the nature of the monomers from which they are constructed, as well as how the monomers link together. Biopolymers are no different. We will see examples of how this is so with polypeptides (Section 26.8a) and polysaccharides (Section 26.8b).

26.8a Polypeptides: Primary, Secondary, Tertiary, and Quaternary Structures

The specific function of a protein is governed by the location of all of the atoms of its amino acids in three-dimensional space. In turn, the complete specification of all locations of a protein's amino acids has four levels of structure, designated as *primary, secondary, tertiary*, and *quaternary structures.*

26.8a.1. Primary Structure

The **primary structure** of a protein specifies the *connectivity* of all of its amino acids. Thus, the specific sequence of amino acids is part of the primary structure.

> A protein is characterized by its primary structure; different proteins will have different primary structures.

In addition, some amino acids can be involved in *cross-linking*, whereby one portion of a protein's backbone is covalently bonded to another portion of the backbone (see Section 26.2c). This occurs when the thiol (RSH) groups of two cysteine amino acids are oxidized, creating a **disulfide bond** (also called a **disulfide bridge**), as shown below for a molecule of cysteine.

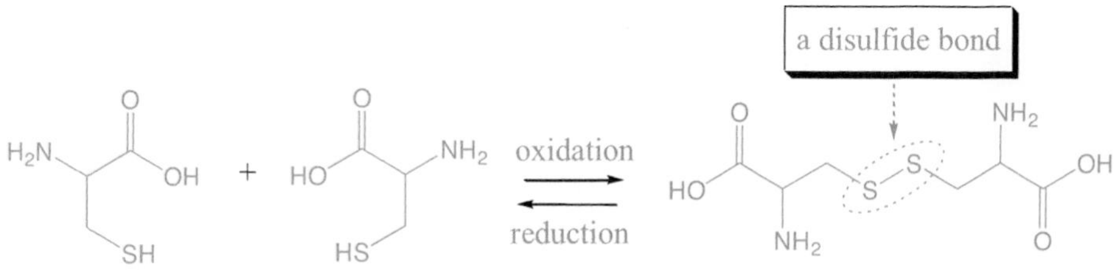

a disulfide bond

oxidation / reduction

cysteine + cysteine ⇌ cystine

An example where this takes place in a protein is vasopressin, a hormone that is responsible for the body's retention of water, and is involved in the "fight or flight" response of mammals. The sequence of amino acids that characterizes vasopressin is: Cys-Tyr-Phe-Gln-Asn-Cys-Pro-Arg-Gly-NH_2. When oxidized, the two cysteine amino acids form a disulfide bond, giving rise to the primary structure shown below.

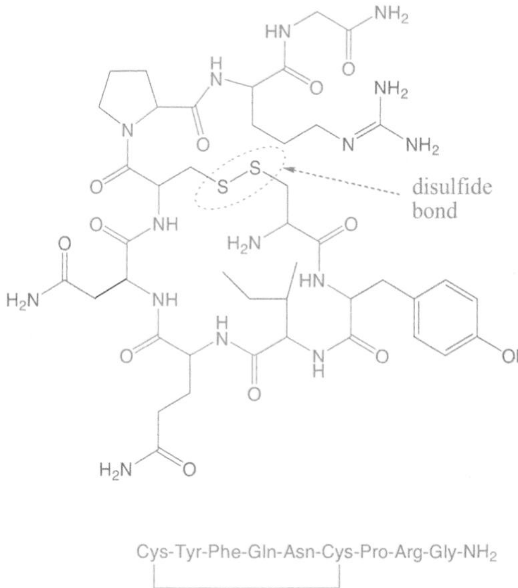

disulfide bond

Cys-Tyr-Phe-Gln-Asn-Cys-Pro-Arg-Gly-NH_2

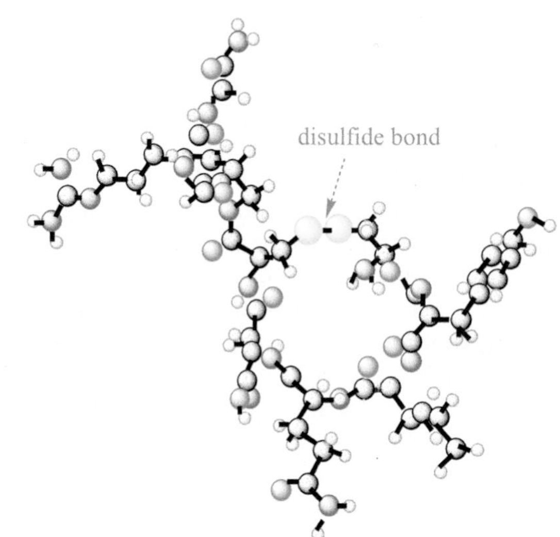

26.8a.2. Secondary Structures

A **secondary structure** of a protein describes a three-dimensional structural *pattern* involving specific portions of the protein's backbone. Two such secondary structures are the α-helix and the β-pleated sheet, shown in Figure 26-16a and 26-16b, respectively.

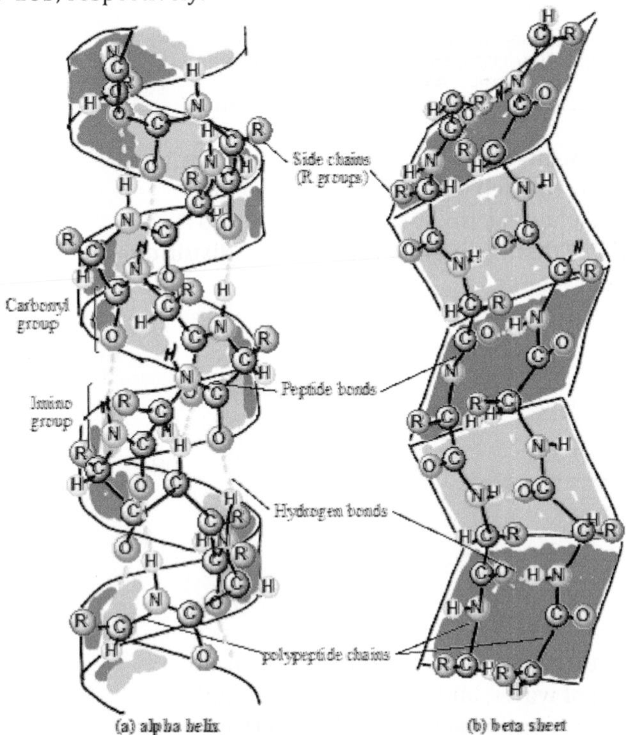

Figure 26-16. Secondary Structures Within a Protein
(a) An α-helix. Hydrogen bonds are established between the NH bonds and O atoms from different amino acids. Side groups project outward from the center of the helix. (b) A β-pleated sheet. Different portions of the protein's backbone align next to each other in the same region of space. Hydrogen bonds are established with NH bonds and O atoms from different amino acids.

As its name suggests, an α-helix has the protein's backbone wound tightly into a spiral. There are two factors that favor the formation of an α-helix. One is the large number hydrogen bonds produced, each involving the NH bond of an amino group from one amino acid, and the O atom of a carbonyl group from a nearby amino acid. The second factor is sterics. Notice that along an α-helix, the side groups of the amino acids project outward, maximizing the distances between them.

Whereas each α-helix involves a single portion of a protein's backbone, a **β-pleated sheet** is comprised of several portions of the backbone that align next to each other in the same region of space (Figure 26-16b)—these portions of the backbone can be many amino acids apart in the primary structure. As with the α-hexlix, a β-pleated sheet is stabilized by hydrogen bonds, each involving an NH amino bond and a carbonyl O atom from different amino acids. The β-pleated sheet is also favored by the planarity that each amide functional group is able to achieve. Recall from Section 13.5b that this planarity is an outcome of the contribution by a resonance structure that gives the C-N bond of an amide significant double bond character, as shown in Figure 26-17a. Adjacent amide planes, however, are slightly rotated relative to each other, giving the chain kinks that establish the pleats in the sheet (Figure 26-17b).

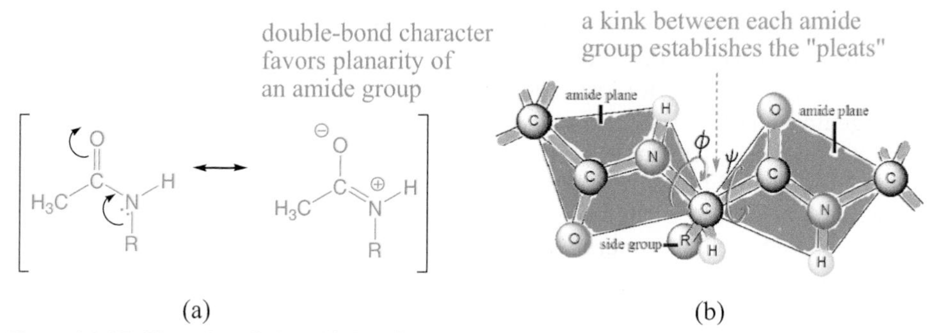

Figure 26-17. Planarity of a Peptide Bond
(a) Resonance structures of an amide group, showing the double bond character of the C-N bond. (b) In a β-pleated sheet, the planarity of each amide group is maintained, and the kink between each amide bond is what gives rise to the "pleats."

Although there is more extensive hydrogen bonding in a β-pleated sheet than in an α-helix, the nature of the side groups determines whether or not one of these secondary structures is favored. An α-helix tends to be disrupted when adjacent or nearby amino acids in a protein's sequence have side groups that are either bulky or carry the same charge (remember, like charges repel). Similarly, a β-pleated sheet tends to be disrupted if its side groups occupying similar locations in space are bulky or carry the same charge.

26.8a.3. Tertiary Structures

Even after a protein has been synthesized with a definite primary structure, and segments of the protein have adopted specific secondary structures, the protein can still lack proper biological activity. That's because the function of a protein depends critically on its **tertiary structure**, which is the location of all of its atoms in space. Achieving such a tertiary structure requires the protein to *fold* in a particular way.

A **ribbon structure** is typically used to depict the tertiary structure of a protein, as shown in Figure 26-18a for phosphotriose isomerase, an enzyme used in glycolysis to catalyze the isomerization of three-carbon sugars with an attached phosphate group (Section 7.9).

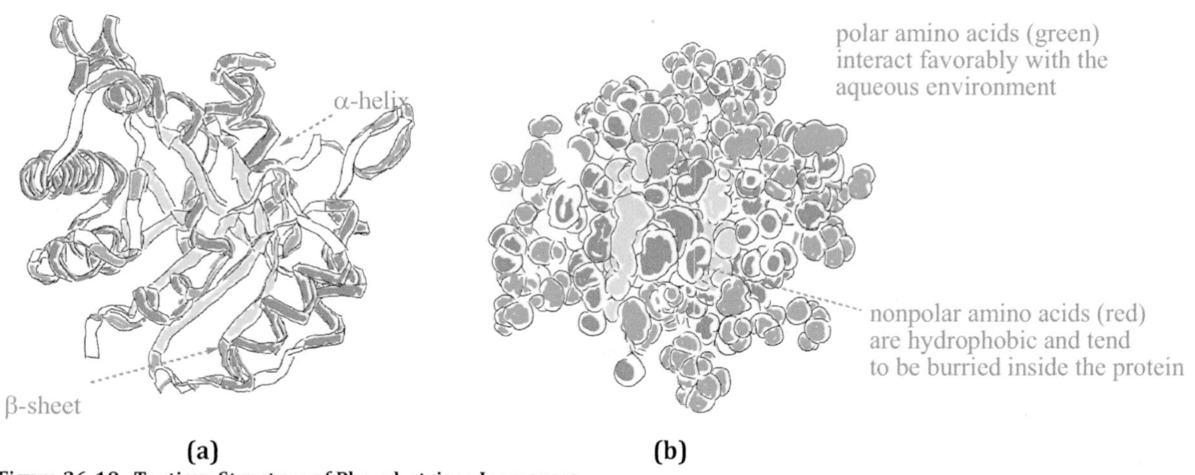

Figure 26-18. Tertiary Structure of Phosphotriose Isomerase
(a) Ribbon structure of phosphotriose isomerase. Magenta indicates an α-helix, and gold indicates a β-sheet. (b) Cross-section of a space-filling model of phosphotriose isomerase. Red indicates nonpolar amino acids, and green indicates polar amino acids.

In a ribbon structure, a trace of the backbone is shown explicitly, and the side groups are omitted. Secondary structures are usually easy to see, and are further highlighted using color schemes. In Figure 26-18a, for example, several different α-helices are indicated using magenta, and the β-sheet is indicated in gold. Additionally, portions of the backbone are depicted as arrows, which indicate the direction from the *N*-terminal amino acid to the *C*-terminal one.

The advantage of using a ribbon structure can be seen by examining Figure 26-18b, which is a cross section of phosphotriose isomerase, in which all atoms are shown explicitly by a space-filling model. In such a depiction, it is difficult to see any secondary structures.

In general, the tertiary structure of a protein tends to be the one that gives the lowest possible free energy, *G*. Certainly, factors such as intermolecular forces and steric crowding among amino acids contribute to a protein's overall free energy, similar to how they contribute to the stability of a secondary structure. Another important factor is the **hydrophobic effect**. Proteins typically reside in what is essentially an aqueous environment. Certain amino acids have polar side groups (see Section 1.12a) and therefore favor such an environment—they are *hydrophilic*. Others are nonpolar, and are thus *hydrophobic*. To maximize the favorable interactions among amino acids and the aqueous environment, and to minimize the unfavorable ones, a protein tends to fold in such a way as to place its polar amino acids on the exterior, and the nonpolar amino acids on the interior. This can be seen in Figure 26-18b.

26.8a.4. Quaternary Structures

Many proteins in living cells consist of multiple distinct peptide chains, not just one chain. **Quaternary structure** describes the way in which protein *subunits* combine to form an even larger structure. Subunits are individual polypeptide chains – each with a specific primary, secondary, and tertiary structure.

The pictures used to describe quaternary structure are typically less detailed than those used for tertiary structure. Sometimes only the general shape of a polypeptide chain will be drawn, with few of the finer structural details. Examples are shown in Figure 26-19.

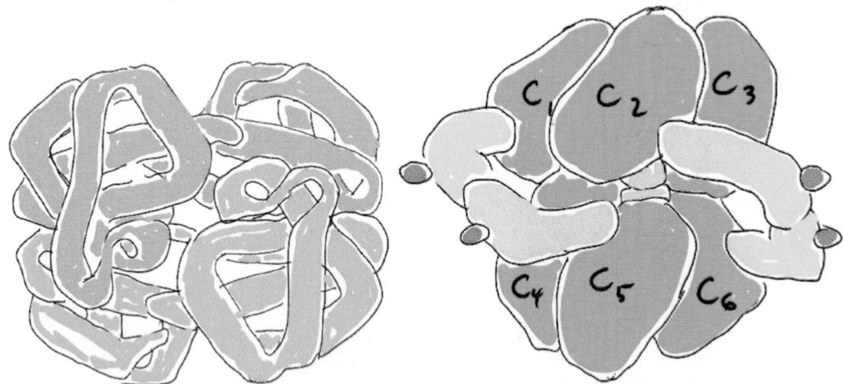

Figure 26-19. Quaternary Structures
The quaternary structure of hemoglobin (left) and aspartate transcarbamoylase (ATC). In hemoglobin, four distinct peptide chains have associated. ATC contains six peptide chains with a catalytic role, C_1 to C_6.

26.8b Polysaccharides

Polysaccharides have various biological roles. Some polysaccharides, such as *starch* and *glycogen*, are used to store energy, and are called **storage**

polysaccharides. Others, such as cellulose, are instrumental in establishing structural aspects of organisms, and are called **structural polysaccharides**.

Starch, a main component of foods such as rice, potatoes, corn, and wheat, is actually a mixture of two different polysaccharides—*amylose* makes up about 20%, and *amylopectin* makes up the remaining 80%. Amylose consists of unbranched chains of D-glucose, as shown below.

Importantly, the sugar units in amylose are connected by α-1,4'-glycosidic linkages (Section 9.14). That is, the glycosidic linkage involves C1 of one glucose unit and C4 of the next, and the substituent on C1 is axial. These glycosidic linkages are hydrolyzed readily by α-glucosidase, an enzyme that every mammal has. Hydrolysis of a glycosidic linkage releases a molecule of glucose, which is subsequently broken down further for energy.

The α configuration of the anomeric carbon also has implications on amylose's physical properties. Because of the α configuration, amylose favors a helical form, as shown in Figure 26.20a, which is reminiscent of an α-helix adopted by proteins. Looking at the cross section in Figure 26.20b, we can see that there are numerous hydroxyl groups on the exterior of the helix, available for extensive hydrogen-bonding with water. Thus, amylose is highly soluble in water.

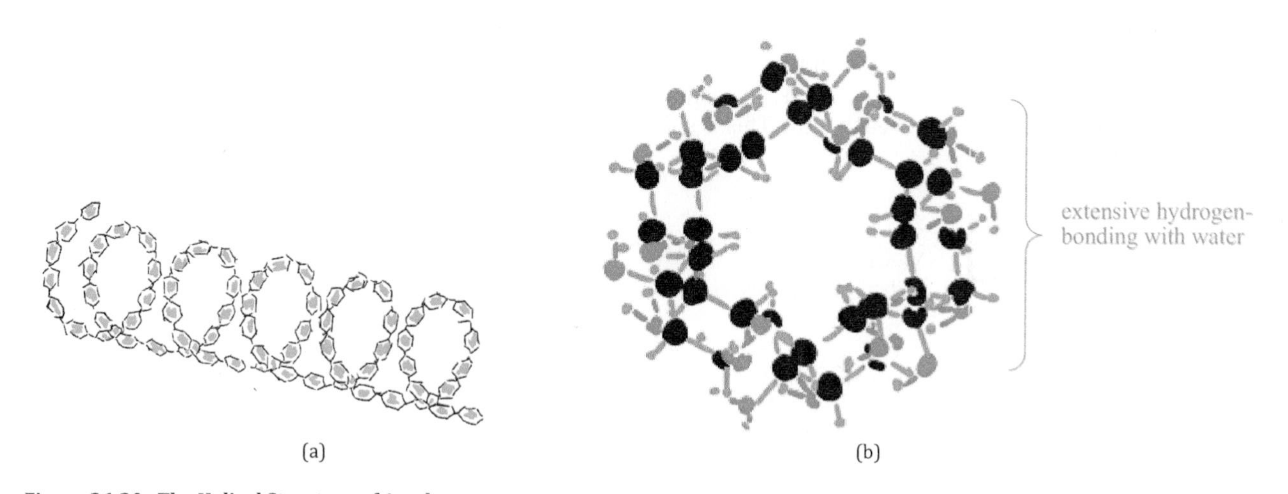

Figure 26.20. The Helical Structure of Amylose
(a) Lengthwise representation of amylose as a helix. (b) Cross section of amylose, showing that the exterior of the helix has numerous OH groups available for hydrogen-bonding with water.

Amylopectin is very similar to amylose, having a main chain that consists of glucose units joined by α-1,4'-glycosidic linkages. The essential difference between the two is that amylopectin's chain is relatively highly branched. Branching takes place via α-1,6'-glycosidic linkages, as shown below, which occur roughly every 25-30 glucose units. As a result of this branching, there are more terminal glycosidic linkages, so α-glucosidase is capable of releasing glucose units much faster. This is beneficial when faster energy use is necessary.

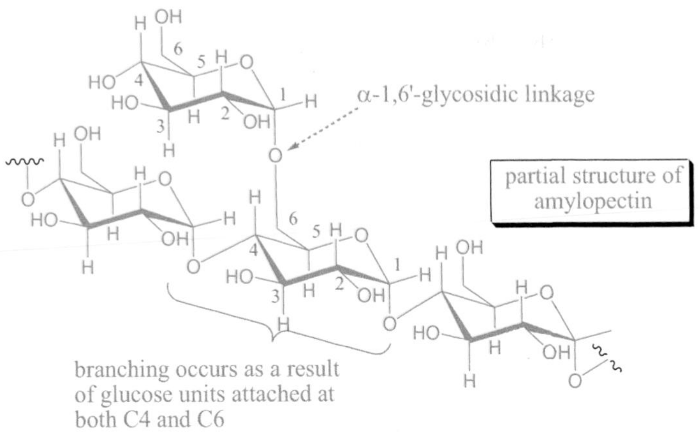

α-1,6'-glycosidic linkage

partial structure of amylopectin

branching occurs as a result of glucose units attached at both C4 and C6

In animals, excess glucose is stored in the form of *glycogen*, which is structurally very similar to amylopectin. The glucose units in glycogen are connected primarily by α-1,4'-glycosidic linkages to establish a main chain, and branching occurs via α-1,6'-glycosidic linkages. In glycogen, branching occurs even more frequently than in amylopectin—roughly every ten glucose units—allowing hydrolysis to take place even more quickly. This is important for organisms that need quick bursts of energy.

As mentioned previously, cellulose is a structural polysaccharide. It is the main structural component of plants' cell walls, comprising about one-third of all plant matter. The specific cellulose content of a plant, however, depends on the specific nature of the plant. Wood, for example, is about 50% cellulose, whereas cellulose comprises about 90% of cotton.

Cellulose consists of long, unbranched chains of D-glucose, and as such is very similar to amylose. The primary difference between the two is that whereas the glucose units in amylose are connected by α-1,4'-glycosidic linkages, the glucose units in cellulose are connected by β-1,4'-glycosidic linkages—i.e., the substituent attached to C1 is equatorial in each unit. This is shown in the partial structure of cellulose below.

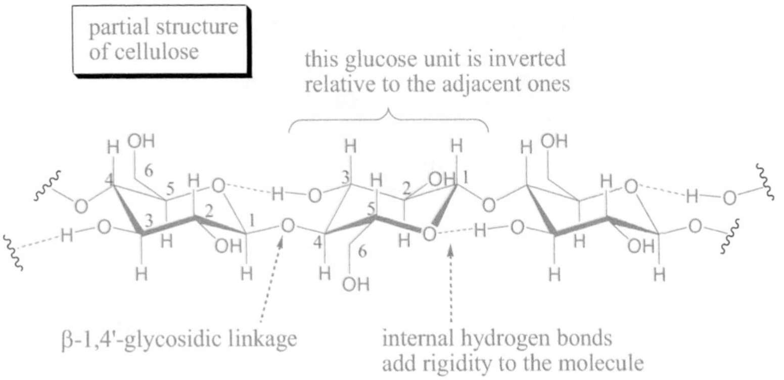

partial structure of cellulose

this glucose unit is inverted relative to the adjacent ones

β-1,4'-glycosidic linkage

internal hydrogen bonds add rigidity to the molecule

Although the difference the between an α- and β-linkage may seem slight on the small scale, the differences on the large scale are dramatic. For example, as shown above, the β-linkage allows for extensive intramolecular hydrogen-bonding, which makes cellulose more rigid than amylose. Further, the free OH groups are available for hydrogen-bonding with other cellulose chains to create a stable polymer network. This is what gives cellulose its structural attributes.

Another difference between cellulose and amylose is that whereas amylose is water-soluble, cellulose is not. Earlier, we saw that the helical shape of amylose allows the OH groups to remain free for hydrogen-bonding with water. By contrast, the OH groups in cellulose are tied up in hydrogen-bonding with adjacent glucose units of the same chain, or with OH groups from a separate chain. Without substantial hydrogen-bonding with water, there are not enough favorable interactions to make cellulose soluble.

Yet another difference is that mammals cannot digest cellulose directly. This is because mammals do not have β-glucosidase, the enzyme required for hydrolyzing the β-1,4'-glycosidic linkage. However, in the digestive tracts of some animals, such as horses and cows, there exist certain bacteria that do have the enzyme, and are therefore capable of breaking down cellulose. In this way, grazing animals can obtain glucose from grass and hay.

CHAPTER SUMMARY AND KEY TERMS

- **Polymers** are large molecules made from smaller molecules called **monomers**; they contain a **main chain** and **side groups**. Polymers are usually depicted in terms of their **repeating units**, since the chains are so large that a full structure is not practical. (Sections 26.1a and 26.2a)
- Numerous polymers are made by **free-radical polymerization**, which is a chain reaction with three steps: **initiation, propagation, and termination**. Termination can occur by combination or disproportionation. Most monomers add in a **head-to-tail** fashion during propagation. The length of the chains that is formed is determined by the **degree of polymerization**, or the number of monomer units that have been incorporated into the polymer chain. (Sections 26.1b and 26.1c)
- Polymers can be classified according to type of chain (**carbon-chain** or **heterochain** polymers), type of fuctional group in the chain, the type of monomer used to make the polymer, and by the number of monomers used to make the polymer (**homopolymers** versus **copolymers**). In addition, the polymers can be classified by the types of chain (**linear** versus **branched** polymers) and the degree of crosslinking (**crosslinked** and **network** polymers). (Sections 26.2b and 26.2c)
- Names for polymers can be derived from the repeating unit or from the monomer used to create the polymer. (Section 26.2d)
- Free-radical polymerization is an example of **chain-growth polymerization**, one general class of polymerization reactions. The other class of reactions is **step-growth polymerization**. In chain-growth polymerization, reaction occurs at the end of the growing chain, and each reaction results in an increase of a single repeating unit in the polymer chain. In step-growth polymerization, reaction occurs between ends of molecules, either monomers or polymer chains, and the increase in chain size depends on the size of the two molecules that react. (Sections 26.3a and 26.3b)
- Polymers can undergo chemical reactions after polymerizations. Most involve modifications to the side groups, and the most important of these is

crosslinking, in which polymer chains are joined together through the reaction of two side groups or a functional group within a chain with another reactant. (Sections 26.4a and 26.4b)

- Physical properties are critical to the use of polymers. The **melting point, T_m,** and **glass-transition temperature, T_g,** are examples of thermal properties which determine certain characteristics of the polymer. Thermal transitions and solubility depend upon several characteristics of the polymer: the length of molecules, branching, rigidity, symmetry, intermolecular forces, and crosslinking. (Section 26.5)
- The structure of a polymer determines how it can function; in other words, its properties dictate its uses. Polymers with flexible chains, reflected in their low glass-transition states, are flexible and can be used as packaging films; LDPE is an example. Polymers with more rigid chains, and consequently higher glass transition states, are more rigid and are used for objects that need to retain their shapes. The use of polystyrene for coffee cups and "to go" boxes is an example. Introduction of crystallinity increases rigidity and density but with retention of flexibility: consequently, HDPE is suitable for milk jugs and PET is suitable for bottles for carbonated beverages. Spandex, with a combination of rubbery segments and rigid, crystalline segments, is an example of a polymer with very specific properties that arise from its chemical structures. (Sections 26.6a and 26.6b)
- Polymers can be reactants in chemical reactions. Ion-exchange resins are an example. In these resins, sodium ions are available to exchange with calcium ions in hard water. (Section 26.6c)
- At high temperatures, depolymerization, the reverse reaction of a polymerization, and degradation, the loss of atoms from the polymer, are thermodynamically because of the higher entropy of the products. (Section 26.7)

PROBLEMS

1. Each monomer below can undergo free-radical polymerization.
i. Using benzoyl peroxide as the initiator, show the mechanism for the first two propagation steps.
ii. Draw the condensed formula for the polymer, showing the repeating unit.
iii. Provide a name for the polymer.

(a) $H_2C{=}CCl_2$ — vinylidene chloride

(b) $H_2C{=}CH{-}C({=}O)NH_2$ — acrylamide

(c) $H_2C{=}CH{-}OCH_3$ — methyl vinyl ether

2. For each polymer shown below:
i. Provide the condensed formula for the polymer.
ii. Propose a structure for the monomer from which the polymer was synthesized.
iii. Propose names for the monomer and the polymer.

(a)

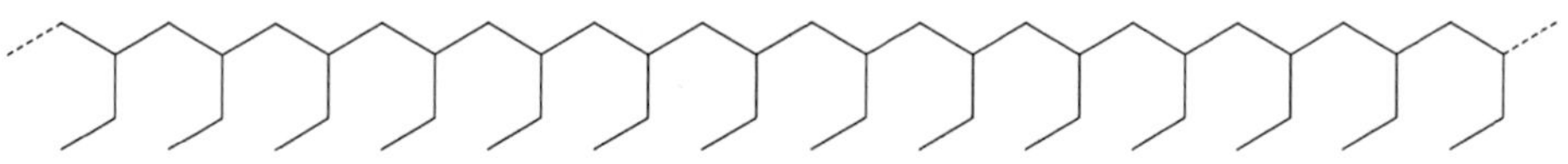

(b)

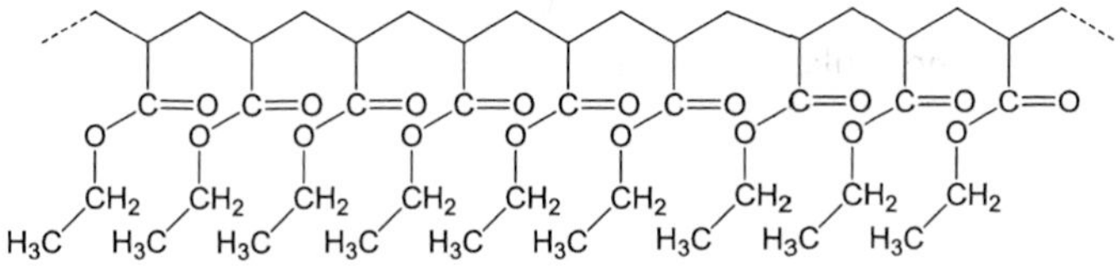

(c)

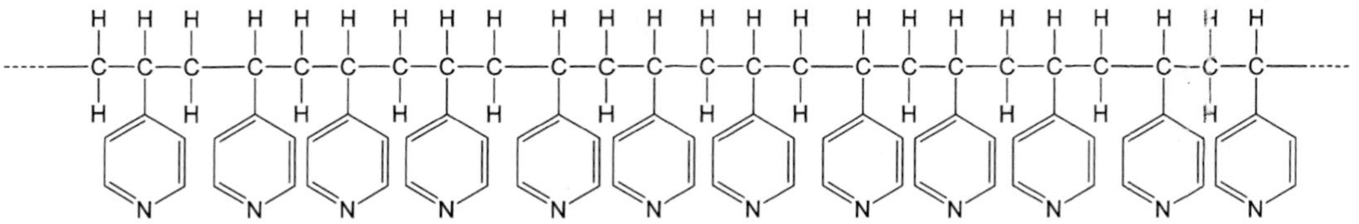

3. Which polymer in problem 1 will be most soluble in water? Justify your choice.
4. Which polymer in problem 2 will be most soluble in hexane? Justify your choice.
5. Identify the repeating unit in the following polymers and write the condensed formula for the polymer:

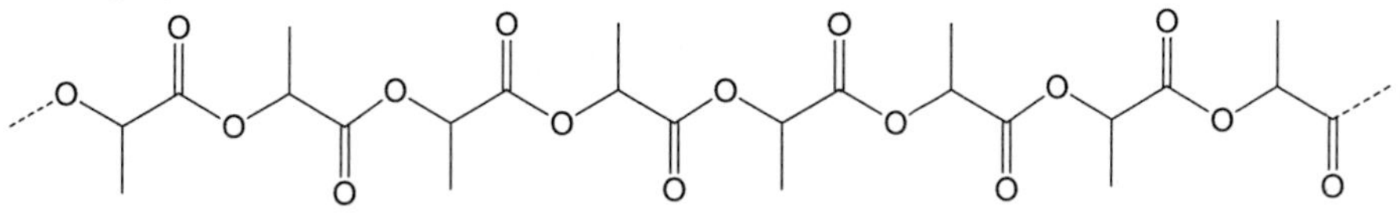

(a) poly(lactic acid) or polylactide

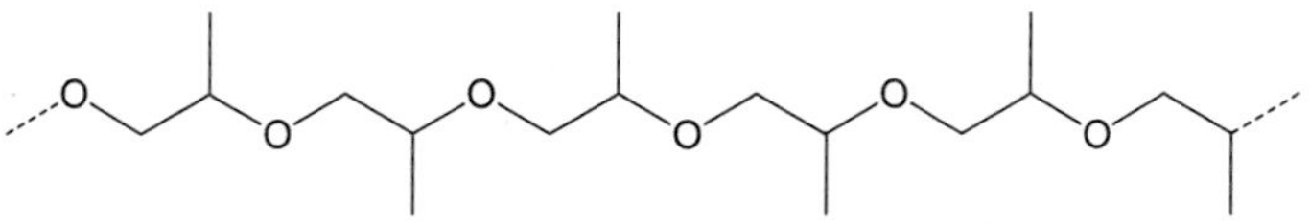

(b) poly(propylene oxide)

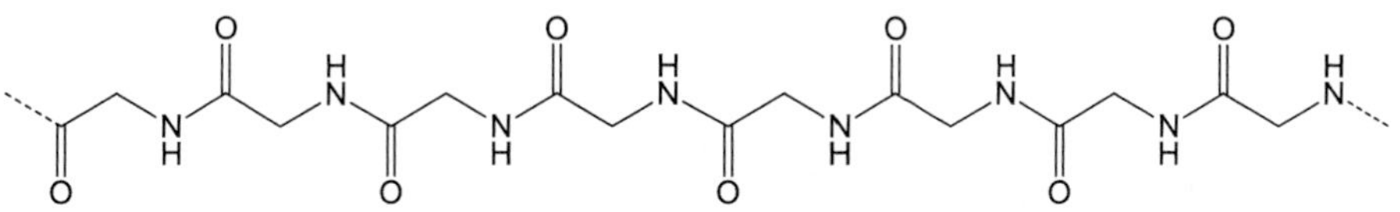

(c) polyglycine

6. Identify the class of polymer, based on functional groups, for the polymers in problem 5.
7. A polymer closely related to PET is PBT, which is made from terephthalic acid and 1,4-butanediol.
(a) Propose a structure for PBT and write the condensed formula for the structure.
(b) What does PBT stand for? That is, what do you expect the trivial name of PBT to be?

(c) Would you expect PBT to have a higher or lower melting point than PET? Justify you answer.
(d) PBT is used in molding rather than PET because it has a faster rate of crystallization. Explain why PBT will crystallize more quickly than PET.
8. Teflon can be made from tetrafluorethylene by means of free-radical polymerization. (See Figure 26.10) In the reaction, termination occurs only by combination and not by disproportionation. Explain this observation.
9. When polyethylene is made by free-radical polymerization, the resulting polymer has a significant amount of branching, resulting in low-density polyethylene. (See Section 26.6a) However, when styrene undergoes free-radical polymerization, very little branching occurs. Explain this phenomenon.
10. Polystyrene can **autoinitiate** free-radical polymerization and form polystyrene in the absence of an initiator. At temperatures above 100°C, radicals form due to homolysis of the double bond in the vinyl group. In the study of this reaction, researchers have found 1,2-diphenylcyclobutane in samples of heated styrene. The following mechanism for the formation of 1,2-diphenylcyclobutane has been proposed:
step 1: Homolysis of the vinyl double bond in a styrene molecule
step 2: Homolysis of the vinyl double bond in a second styrene molecule
step 3: Tail-to-tail addition of the radicals from steps 1 and 2
step 4: Radical coupling of the diradical formed in step 4

(a) Use curved-arrow notation to show the steps in this mechanism.
(b) Are the steps in this mechanism consistent with those for free-radical polymerization?
(c) Why is the use of an initiator such as benzoyl peroxide more efficient in the synthesis of polystyrene than autoinitiated polymerization?
11. Polyoxetane is a polyether similar to poly(ethylene oxide) and is made from oxetane, shown below, via a chain-growth polymerization. (See Section 26.3a.)

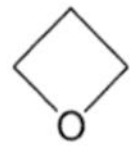

oxetane

(a) Propose a synthesis of polyoxetane and show the mechanism for the first propagation steps.
(b) Provide a condensed formula for polyoxetane.
(c) Do you expect polyoxetane to be more or less soluble in water than poly(ethylene oxide)? Justify your answer.
(d) Do you expect polyoxetane to have a higher or lower melting point than poly(ethylene oxide)? Justify your answer.
(e) Explain why furan, shown below, will react much more slowly if you attempt to use it to synthesize a polyether.

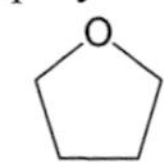

furan

12. As the number of hydroxyl groups increases in poly(vinyl alcohol), the solubility of the polymer in water decreases. How would you explain this behavior?
13. Dry-erase boards, or whiteboards, in classrooms are made of a network polymer similar to Bakelite that is made from formaldehyde and melamine, shown below.

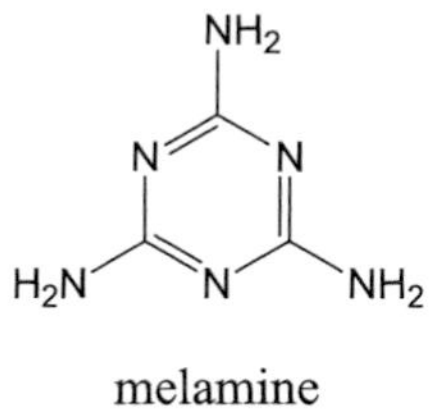

melamine

(a) Propose a structure for the polymer formed.
(b) Why is this type of polymer suitable for use in whiteboards?
14. Consider the series of poly(phenylene oxide) polymers shown below and their glass-transition temperatures. Explain how the change in structure can account for the change in T_g.

A: $T_g = 82°C$ B: $T_g = 211°C$ C: $T_g = 169°C$ D: $T_g = 99°C$

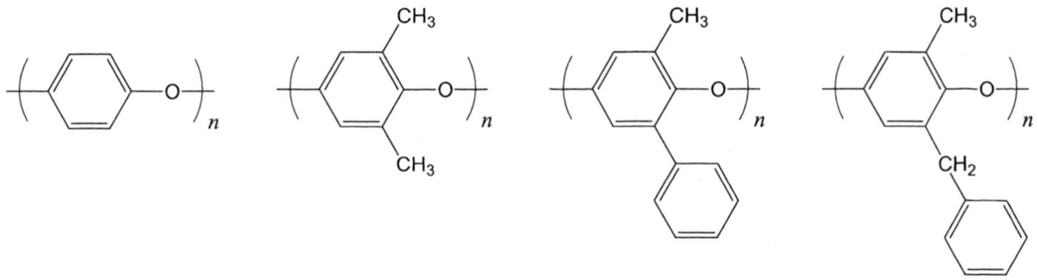

15. Consider the series of polycarbonate polymers shown below. Which one will have the highest glass transition temperature? Which will have the lowest glass transition temperature?

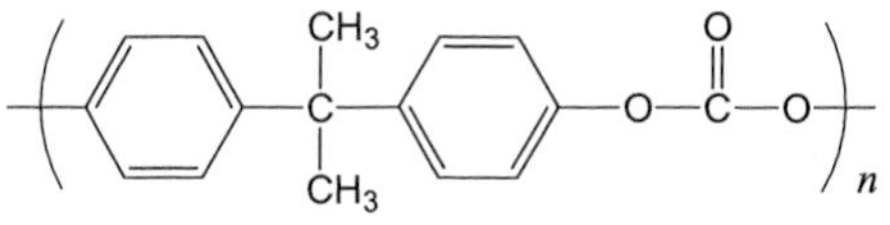

I 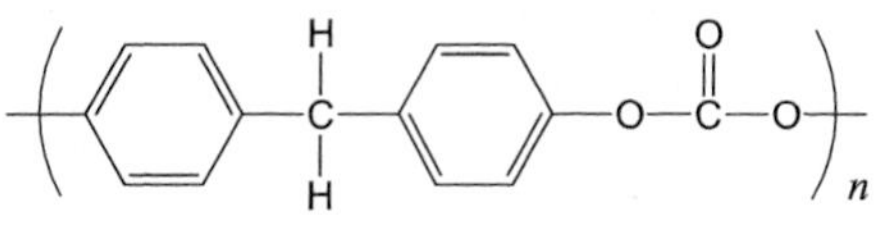 II 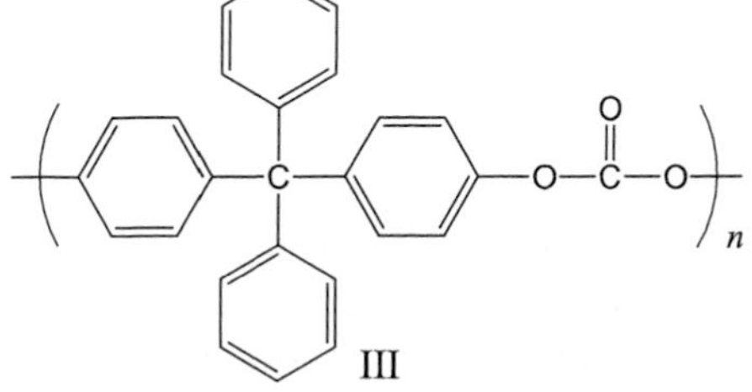 III

16. Two of the compounds will react with phosgene to form a polycarbonate, while the third one will not. Which compound will not form a polymer, and what will be the product of its reaction with phosgene?

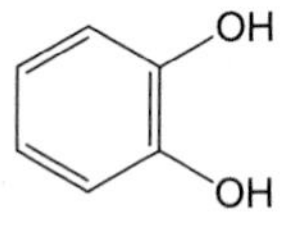

X 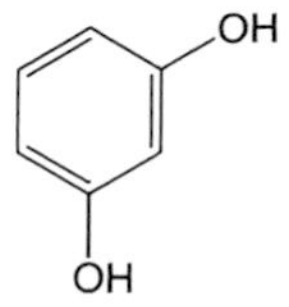 Y  Z 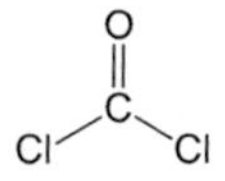 phosgene

17. One method for the purification of polystyrene samples is to dissolve the polymer in benzene and then add methanol slowly to cause precipitation of solid polystyrene. Explain why polystyrene precipitates under these conditions.
18. Polycarbophil is a dietary fiber supplement. It is the calcium salt of copolymer of acrylic acid and divinyl glycol (shown below), a crosslinking agent. In the stomach, the calcium ions exchange for hydrogen items and, in the higher pH of the intestine, the polymer absorbs 70 times its mass in water.

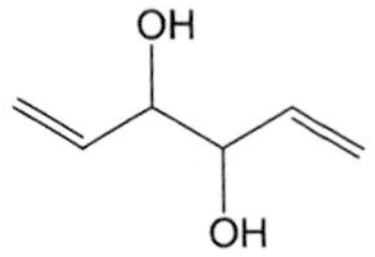

OH

OH

divinyl glycol

(a) Propose a structure for polycarbophil.
(b) Why is crosslinking of the polymer necessary for this application?
(c) Why is polycarbophil effective at providing bulk in the intestine? That is, what occurs on a molecular level to polycarbophil?
19. In the discussion of poly(ether ether ketone)s, or PEEK's, in 26.4a2, we observed that the addition of a *tert*-butyl group to the aromatic ring increased the solubility of PEEK's in organic solvents. However, when researchers added a second *tert*-butyl group, as shown below, they found that the solubility of PEEK's decreased. Explain this observation.

O

O O C

n

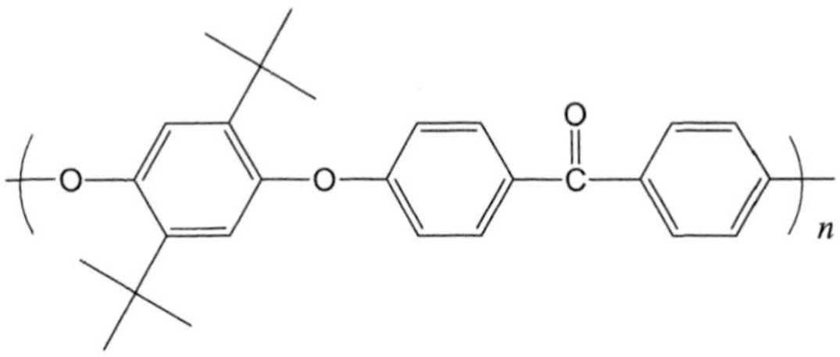

A PEEK with two tert-butyl groups per repeating unit

20. Urea has the structure below. Polyureas are used to make truck bed liners. Examine the synthesis of polyurethanes in 26.3b and (a) propose a synthesis of a polyurea and (b) provide the condensed formula for the polymer.

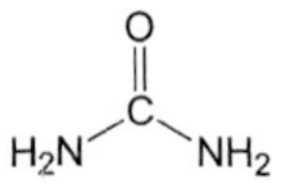

O
C
H_2N NH_2

urea

21. Research in the "unzipping" of poly(vinyl chloride) indicates that defects in the polymer contribute to the rate of unzipping. Such defects are arrangements of atoms that are different from the arrangements in the repeating unit shown in the condensed formula. Researchers have found that defects involving allylic chlorides and tertiary chlorides promote the reaction. Review the mechanism for unzipping and explain this observation.
22. PEEK (see Section 26.4a2) can be synthesized as shown below:

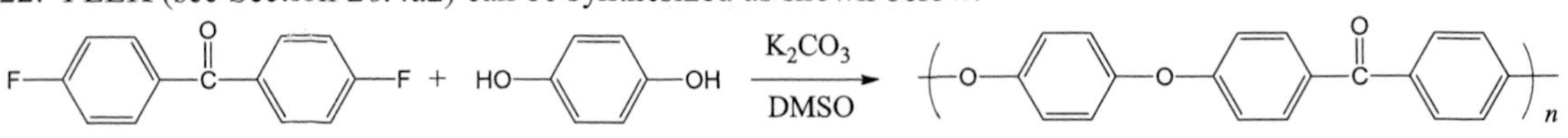

O O
F C F + HO OH $\xrightarrow[DMSO]{K_2CO_3}$ O O C n

poly(aryl ether ether ketone) or PEEK

Propose a mechanism for this reaction.
23. Explain how IR spectroscopy could be used to monitor the conversion of poly(vinyl acetate) to poly(vinyl alcohol). That is, how can a chemist use IR to tell if poly(vinyl acetate) has been converted to 99+% poly(vinyl alcohol)?
24. Methyl acrylate and methyl methacrylate are shown below. The difference in their reactivities in free-radical polymerizations is dramatic. For example, methyl acrylate is

less reactive with radicals than methyl methacrylate; however, free radicals formed from methyl acrylate are more reactive than those from methyl methacrylate. In other words, in the diagram below, C is more reactive than A and B is more reactive than D. Explain these observations.

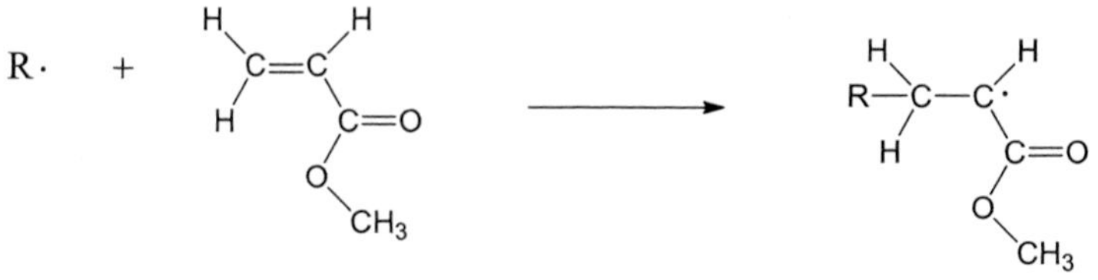

R· + methyl acrylate (A) ⟶ B

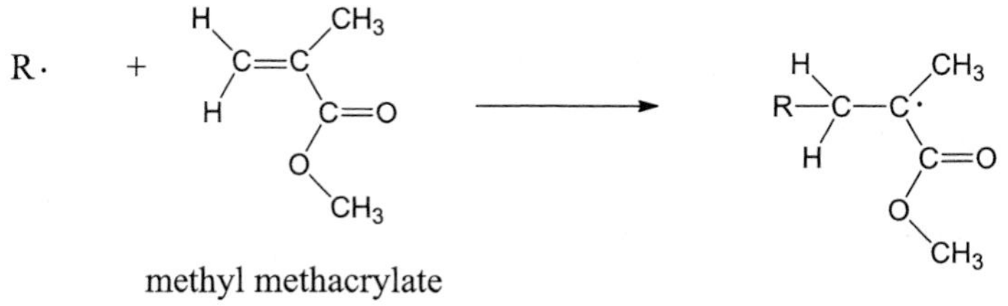

methyl acrylate
A

B

R· + methyl methacrylate (C) ⟶ D

methyl methacrylate

C

D

25. To introduce crosslinking in free-radical polymerizations, **divinyl monomers** are used. Two divinyl monomers which are used in the production of eyeglass lenses are tetra(ethylene glycol) diacrylate (TTEGDA) and hexanediol dimethacrylate(HDDMA), shown below.

[insert diagram]

(a) Draw structures of the polymers of TTEGDA and HDDMA, incorporating at least six monomer units and showing at least two crosslinks.

(b) Which monomer will produce the harder material? Explain your answer.

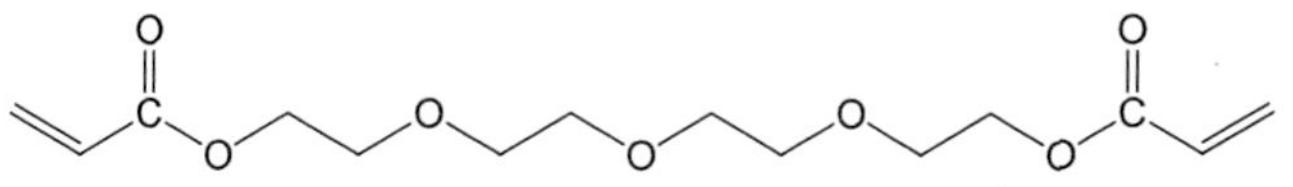

TTEGDA

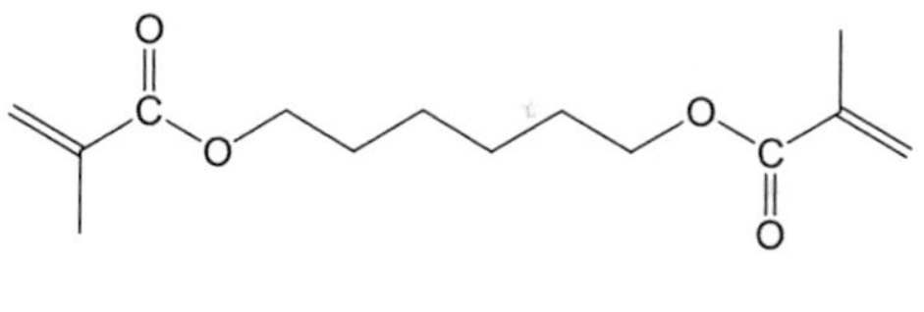

HDDMA

INDEX